SEARS, ROEBUCK AND CO.
INCORPORATED.

1909 CATALOG

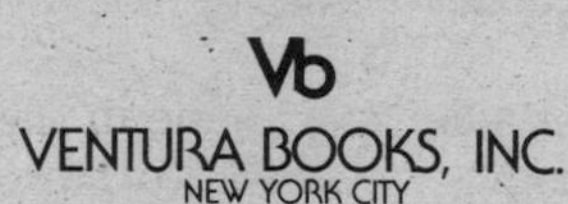

VENTURA BOOKS, INC./101 PARK AVENUE/NEW YORK 10017

INTRODUCTION

A look through the pages of this catalog is like a visit to early America. For what it mirrors is the dreams, hopes and goals of people at the turn of the century.

This early edition of the Sears catalog will have many different meanings. To young people it may simply be a fascinating view of different styles. To others it's an important document that chronicles these inflationary times, and to many it will simply be a nostalgic look at the "good old days."

Interestingly, these times were probably neither better nor worse than today. Although the prices are a fraction of today's, so was an individual's earning power. Ultimately, a true economist would only look at how many hours work does it take for a man to buy something rather than the actual selling price. It was every bit as much a dream to own a $20.00 gold-filled wrist watch as it is today to own a $500.00 gold-filled wrist watch. However, the fascination of this catalog is sure to bring joy to young and old alike.

Richard Warren Sears, the original founder of Sears, Roebuck & Company, is hailed as one of the pioneers of the mail order industry. In many ways the concept of delivering merchandise to far-reaching parts of this country at attractive prices is truly his idea. Today this billion dollar mail order industry owes much thanks to Richard Sears.

Richard Sears started part time in the mail order business. He sold watches, beginning in 1886, to supplement his income as a railroad station clerk. Because he needed to service the customers he sold, his great desire was to find a watch repairman. This led to his meeting a young watch tinkerer named Alvah Roebuck. The partnership grew by leaps and bounds. They soon realized they could sell much more than just watches. In 1891 they produced their first catalog of 32 pages. Soon the catalog was 100 pages and later thousands of pages.

Today the Sears Company still publishes a giant catalog and is considered the most important retailer in America. Even a man with the drive and energy of Richard Sears probably never imagined the future of his corporation. Today the firm sells over thirteen billion dollars in merchandise and employs more than 400,000 people.

Interestingly, many parts of the Sears story parallels mail order entrepreneurs, that is, many of today's giant mail order firms were started on kitchen tables. These part-time ventures grew to huge businesses. They were all part of the American dream of finding a need and filling it.

Today you can buy a whole house, and everything that's in it, by mail. Direct marketers bring to your easy chair the widest possible selection of merchandise. And mail order continues to grow as it allows one to easily and conveniently order merchandise without fighting crowds and traffic.

But enough about mail order today. Let's turn back the hands of time and revisit the original book of dreams. As your editor, I've selected some of the most interesting pages from the giant 1909 Sears catalog.

Jeffrey Feinman

Sears, Roebuck and Co.
Incorporated.

1909
CATALOG

6 CHAIRS FREE

WE ISSUE TO YOU

A PROFIT SHARING CERTIFICATE

for the full amount of every order you send us, and when the total **Profit Sharing Certificates** sent you amount to $50.00, meaning when all your purchases from us have amounted to $50.00, send your certificates to us and **we will send you free** the

SIX HANDSOME CANE SEATED DINING ROOM CHAIRS ILLUSTRATED HEREON

or your choice of many other equally valuable articles, shown in the last 16 pages in this book. **Save your Profit Sharing Certificates. If you already have profit sharing certificates, they, of course, are good;** save them and continue sending your orders to us and when your total orders sent us have amounted to $50.00 or more, send the certificates to us and select the article or articles you want free, from the last 16 pages in this book, which we will send you free as your share in our profits. **READ THE LAST 16 PAGES** in this book, telling of the many valuable articles we will send you free, when your total orders amount to $50.00 or more.

IT WILL PAY YOU HANDSOMELY to take orders from others. When about to order, it will pay you to find out what your neighbor wants and include his goods with yours. **Read all about it in the last 16 pages. DON'T BUY ANYTHING** anywhere (groceries, dry goods, or other goods) until after you have read the last 16 pages in this book and learn how you get part of your money back, how liberally you share in our profits.

READ THE LAST 16 PAGES IN THIS CATALOGUE, The Yellow Pages.

Read and learn all about our liberal method of sharing our profits with our customers, how we give you free as your share of the profit in this business, your choice of such valuable articles as upright grand pianos, organs, buggies, all kinds of furniture and household goods; your choice of hundreds of valuable articles that we send to you free of any cost, as your share of the profits in this business. **Read in the last 16 pages how a liberal part of all the money you send us for goods goes back to you,** in the shape of valuable articles of merchandise, how a big part of all the profit is returned to you. Understand, all this is done with the understanding and agreement on our part that anything you buy from us must be at a liberal saving in cost to you, quality for quality much lower in price than you can buy elsewhere.

PRICE AND QUALITY GUARANTEE.

While we now permit our customers to share liberally in the profits of this business, more liberally than ever before, a much larger share of all our profits now goes back to our customers than heretofore, articles that heretofore were furnished for $100.00 in profit sharing certificates, are now furnished for $50.00 in certificates; while our plan of dividing profits with our customers, as explained in the last 16 pages, is vastly more liberal than ever before, our prices on everything shown in this catalogue, market conditions of raw material and labor considered, are in many cases much lower than ever before, and far lower than you can buy elsewhere, and every order sent us is accepted with the understanding and agreement that we not only guarantee any goods you order from us to reach you in perfect condition, guarantee them to please you, guarantee them to be of the highest standard of quality, above the average sold by other catalogue houses and retail dealers generally, but we also guarantee our prices on every item in this catalogue, quality for quality, to be lower than you can buy from any other house, at home, in Chicago or elsewhere, and if you do not find this to be the case in every instance, if you ever send us an order, large or small, and you find we haven't saved you money on every item, you are at liberty and are invited to return the goods to us at our expense, and we will return your money. **We guarantee the quality of every article shown in this catalogue, we guarantee our prices to be lower than you can buy elsewhere.** Every order is accepted and filled by us subject to these conditions, the customers always having the privilege of returning the goods to us at our expense, and we will immediately return their money; but notwithstanding our prices are lower than ever before, though our prices are very much lower than you can find elsewhere, in spite of the fact that we guarantee our standard of quality much higher than that maintained by dealers generally, every time you send us an order you will receive from us, by mail, a profit sharing certificate for the full amount of your purchase, a certificate for every cent you have sent us, and these certificates can be exchanged, whenever you like, for any of the many valuable articles shown in the Profit Sharing Department, the last 16 pages.

READ OUR LIBERAL PROFIT SHARING TERMS as explained in the last 16 pages. Read how you can accumulate certificates rapidly and share liberally in the profits, by taking orders from your neighbors, friends and others. Don't fail to read the first of the 16 yellow pages in the back of this book.

DON'T BUY ANYTHING, ANYWHERE, until after you refer to this catalogue, and see how much money we can save you. Every time you need anything of any kind, anything in groceries, furniture, wearing apparel, anything to use in the home, in the shop, on the farm in the store or elsewhere, no matter how small the order, every time you are in need of anything, by all means consult this catalogue, see how much money we can save you, and then remember for every penny you send us you get a profit sharing certificate by return mail, for the full amount of your purchase, a certificate that entitles you to get back from us a big part of all the profit, a liberal return to you free for every dollar you sent us. All of this is fully explained in the last 16 pages of this book. Immediately your order is received, we will send you a customers' profit sharing certificate, for the full amount of your order, a certificate for every penny you sent us for goods. Preserve these certificates and when all the certificates you have received have amounted to $50.00 or more, then select any one or more of the articles you want, as illustrated and described in the last 16 pages, return to us the required number of customers' profit sharing certificates, and the article or articles you select, will be sent to you free of any cost to you as your share of our profit.

ALL CERTIFICATES ARE GOOD

If you already hold profit sharing certificates from us, they are good in exchange for any of the more valuable articles shown in the last 16 pages of this book. They will apply on any article of merchandise which we now list for certificates in amounts of $50.00 or upwards. Every customer holding certificates is entitled to exchange them according to the LATEST, BEST AND MOST LIBERAL TERMS WE HAVE EVER MADE, as shown in the last 16 pages. If you have sent to us for goods within the last 18 months, profit sharing certificates for every penny you sent us have been sent to you.

PRESERVE THESE CERTIFICATES,

CONTINUE SENDING YOUR ORDERS TO US,
SAVE EVERY CERTIFICATE CAREFULLY,

and when the total certificates you have received amount to $50.00 or more, you can then exchange them free of cost to you, for the six chairs illustrated hereon or for your choice of the many valuable articles shown in the last 16 pages.

READ FULL DESCRIPTION OF ALL OUR FREE DINING ROOM CHAIRS ON THE YELLOW PAGES.

FOR ORDERS AMOUNTING TO $50.00

FACTORIES THAT WE OWN OR CONTROL

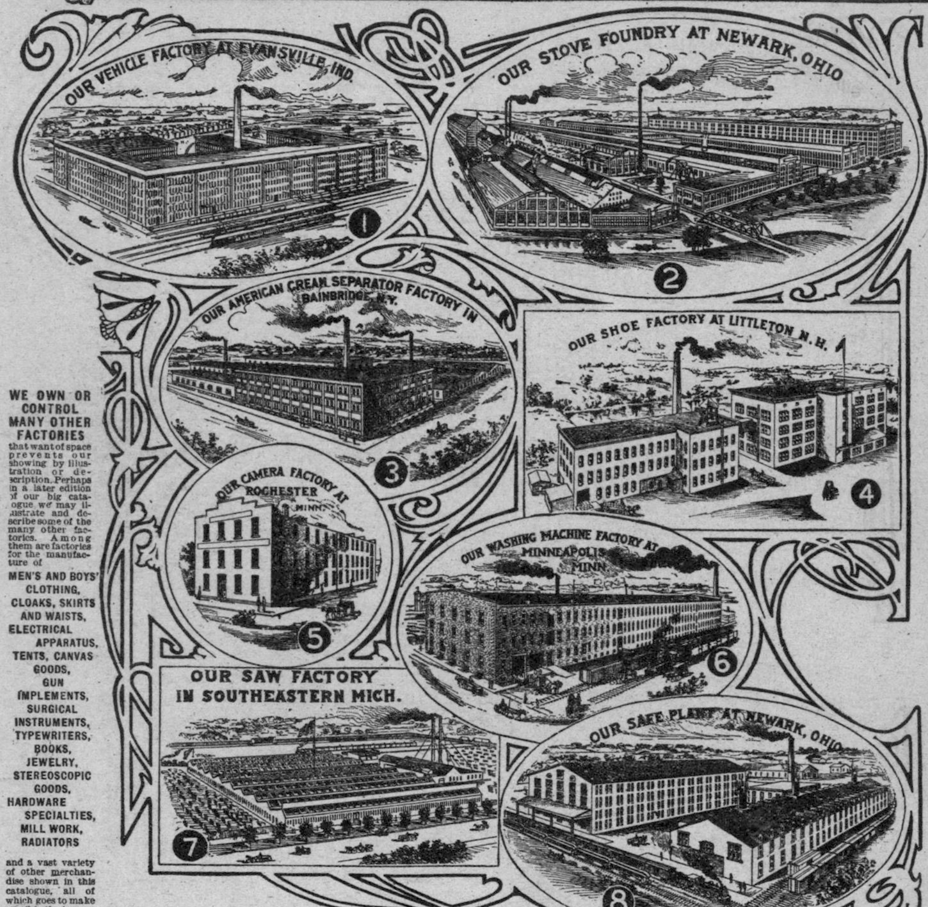

WE OWN OR CONTROL MANY OTHER FACTORIES that want of space prevents our showing by illustration or description. Perhaps in a later edition of our big catalogue we may illustrate and describe some of the many other factories. Among them are factories for the manufacture of

MEN'S AND BOYS' CLOTHING, CLOAKS, SKIRTS AND WAISTS, ELECTRICAL APPARATUS, TENTS, CANVAS GOODS, GUN IMPLEMENTS, SURGICAL INSTRUMENTS, TYPEWRITERS, BOOKS, JEWELRY, STEREOSCOPIC GOODS, HARDWARE SPECIALTIES, MILL WORK, RADIATORS

and a vast variety of other merchandise shown in this catalogue, all of which goes to make possible the incomparably low prices shown in this catalogue.

1—OUR VEHICLE FACTORY at Evansville, Ind., one of the largest vehicle factories in the world; capacity, 75,000 rigs (buggies and carriages) a year. With its unequaled hardwood lumber market, excellent skilled labor conditions, cheap fuel and other advantageous conditions, in this factory we produce buggies better in quality and at a lower cost than are produced in any other factory in the country, and we sell them at actual factory cost with only our one small profit added.

2—OUR STOVE FOUNDRY at Newark, Ohio, positively the largest stove foundry in the world, covering more than 30 acres, the only stove foundry in the world melting daily from eight cupolas at one time. Output amounting to four million dollars annually. With our many advantages, that is, enormous capacity, natural fuel and power gas, ideal labor conditions, wonderful mechanical equipment, unequaled design and pattern making facilities, from this foundry we turn out the best stoves made in this country and we sell them at about one-half the prices charged by others.

3—OUR CREAM SEPARATOR FACTORY at Bainbridge, N. Y., where we make the justly celebrated American Cream Separator. Before we secured control of this factory the American Cream Separator sold for $100.00. We now sell it for $29.00.

4—OUR SHOE FACTORY at Littleton, N. H. In this, our own shoe factory, we turn out daily more than twelve thousand pairs of high grade shoes. This is why we can sell you better wearing shoes than you can buy elsewhere, and at the same time, save you nearly one-half in cost.

5—OUR CAMERA FACTORY at Rochester, Minn. If we did not have this camera factory we would have to charge you nearly twice as much for poorer cameras

6—OUR WASHING MACHINE FACTORY at Minneapolis, Minn. Home of our celebrated Mississippi Washer, which we sell for $5.75, guaranteeing it better than machines others sell at $10.00 to $15.00.

7—OUR SAW FACTORY, where we make the highest grades of hand, circular and crosscut saws. Our catalogue prices on these goods speak for our wonderful facilities in this factory.

8—OUR FIREPROOF STEEL COMBINATION LOCK SAFE FACTORY at Newark, Ohio, where we make better safes, which we sell at $11.90 to $101.50, than you can buy elsewhere for double the money. Our Special Free Safe Catalogue tells of the wonders of this factory.

IN ADDITION TO OUR 40 ACRE PLANT

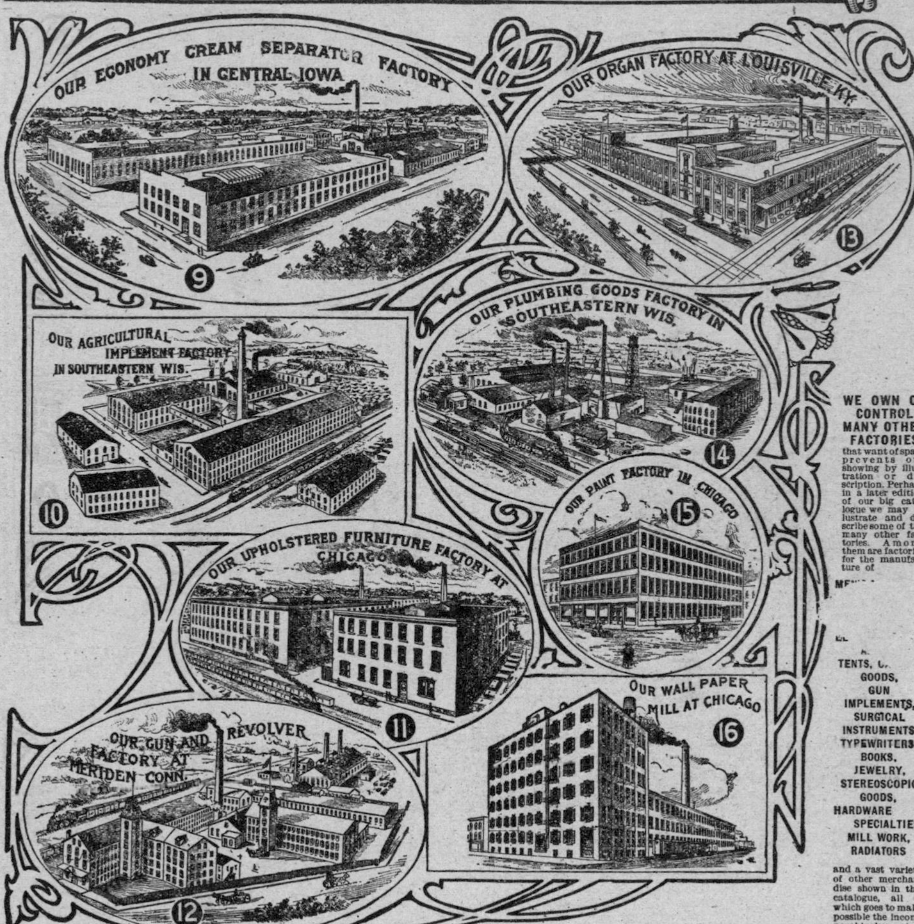

WE OWN OR CONTROL MANY OTHER FACTORIES that want of space prevents our showing by illustration or description. Perhaps in a later edition of our big catalogue we may illustrate and describe some of the many other factories. Among them are factories for the manufac ture of

TENTS, ... GOODS, GUN IMPLEMENTS, SURGICAL INSTRUMENTS, TYPEWRITERS, BOOKS, JEWELRY, STEREOSCOPIC GOODS, HARDWARE SPECIALTIES, MILL WORK, RADIATORS

and a vast variety of other merchandise shown in this catalogue, all of which goes to make possible the incomparably low prices shown in this catalogue.

9—THE ECONOMY CREAM SEPARATOR FACTORY; daily capacity, 300 separators. Guaranteed the best separators made in the world.

10—OUR AGRICULTURAL IMPLEMENT FACTORY, where we make plows, harrows, horse powers, corn shellers, power saws, etc., and our catalogue prices speak for the facilities of this modern plant.

11—OUR FURNITURE FACTORY in Chicago. Without this factory it would be impossible to give our customers such wonderful furniture values as this catalogue offers.

12—OUR GUN AND REVOLVER FACTORY at Meriden, Conn. In this factory we make more than 400 guns and revolvers daily. One of the largest fire arm factories in the United States. Since we own such wonderful manufacturing facilities, no one can think of meeting our prices on fire arms.

13—ORGAN FACTORY at Louisville, Ky. Home of the celebrated Beckwith instruments. With this enormous manufacturing facility, in conjunction with our sawmill at Lyons, Ky., for our hardwood lumber supply, we produce the highest grade instruments in the market, and can and do sell them at about one-half the prices charged by others.

14—IN THIS, OUR NEW BIG PLUMBING GOODS FACTORY, we make almost everything in bathtubs, lavatories, fixtures and plumbing supplies, and our catalogue will show you that this manufacturing facility enables us to sell these goods at but little more than one-half the prices charged by others.

15—OUR PAINT FACTORY. In this big factory we make the celebrated Seroco ready mixed paint, which we guarantee to cover double the surface and last twice as long as any other paint made, yet we sell it at about one-half the price per gallon charged by others. Here we can make 10,000 gallons daily. We also make our own barn, roof and fence paint, buggy paint, stains, varnishes, etc., which we sell at wonderfully low prices. Beautiful color sample book of everything in this line mailed free.

16—OUR OWN BIG SIX-MACHINE WALL PAPER MILL, with a capacity of 60,000 rolls per day. Making our own wall paper as we do from beginning to end, we can and do furnish wall paper at less than one-half the prices charged by others. Write for the free wall paper sample book and be convinced.

WILL BE SENT TO ANY ADDRESS
FREE
BY MAIL POSTPAID ON APPLICATION

WRITE A LETTER OR A POSTAL CARD
AND SAY
SEND ME YOUR BIG CATALOGUE
and it will be sent to you immediately free by mail, postpaid.

WRITE A LETTER OR A POSTAL CARD
AND SAY
SEND ME YOUR BIG CATALOGUE
and it will be sent to you immediately free by mail, postpaid.

SIMPLE RULES FOR ORDERING.

USE OUR ORDER BLANK IF YOU HAVE ONE. If you haven't one, use any plain paper.

TELL US IN YOUR OWN WAY WHAT YOU WANT, always giving the CATALOGUE NUMBER of each article. Enclose in the letter the amount of money, either a postoffice money order, which you get at the postoffice, an express ıoney order, which you get at the express office, or a draft, which you get at any bank; or put the money in the letter, take it to the postoffice and tell the postmaster you want it registered.

IF YOU LIVE ON A RURAL MAIL ROUTE, just give the letter and the money to the mail carrier and he will get the money order at the postoffice and mail it in the letter for you.

DON'T BE AFRAID YOU WILL MAKE A MISTAKE. We receive hundreds of orders every day from young and old who never before sent away for goods. We are accustomed to handling all kinds of orders.

TELL US WHAT YOU WANT IN YOUR OWN WAY, written in any language, no matter whether good or poor writing, and the goods will be promptly sent to you.

WE HAVE TRANSLATORS TO READ AND WRITE ALL LANGUAGES.

DON'T BE AFRAID OF THE FREIGHT OR EXPRESS CHARGES. You must pay them when you get the goods ı, but they never amount to much compared with what we save you in cost.

J FIND IT NECESSARY TO HAVE SOME SPECIAL INFORMATION you can undoubtedly obtain it by the matter contained within the first nineteen pages of this catalogue.

ENKLA REGLER ATT IAKTTAGA VID BESTÄLLNING.

Begagna vår beställningsblankett, om ni har en sådan. Om icke, begagna vanligt rent papper.

Säg oss på edert eget sätt hvad ni önskar, alltid uppgifvande katalognumret på hvarje sak. Inneslut beloppet i brefvet antingen i postoffice money order, hvilken köpes å postkontoret; express money order, hvilken köpes å expresskontoret, eller en vexel, hvilken kan köpas å hvilken bank som helst, eller också inneslut kontanta penningar i brefvet, tag det till postkontoret och säg postmästaren att ni önskar få det registrerat.

Var icke rädd för att ni gör ett misstag. Vi erhålla hundratals beställningar dagligen från unga och gamla hvilka aldrig förr sändt efter varor. Vi äro vana vid att expediera alla slags beställningar.

Säg oss på edert eget sätt hvad ni önskar. Skrif på hvilket språk som helst, bra eller dålig stafning, bra eller dålig handstil, och varorna skola blifva eder prompt tillsända.

Vi ha öfversättare som läsa och skrifva alla språk.

Det är icke nödvändigt för eder att genomläsa de första tio sidorna i denna katalog, såvida ni icke önskar någon speciell upplysning. Dessa tio sidor innehålla detaljerad upplysning, så att de som i alla delar önska göra sig förtrogna med sättet att beställa och sända varor, fraktkostnader o. s. v., o. s. v., icke behöfva skrifva till oss, utan helt enkelt kunna slå upp dessa sidor och finna den upplysning de önska.

Einfache Regeln zum Bestellen.

Gebraucht unsere Bestellungszettel wenn Sie welche haben, wenn nicht nehmen Sie gewöhnliches Papier.

Im Bestellen erwähnen Sie die Catalog Numero an allen Sachen. Die Bestellung soll das Geld enthalten, entweder eine „Postoffice Money Order," (welche man gewöhnlich an der Post bekommen kann), eine "Expreß Money Order," ein Bank Certificate, das man an jeder Bank bekommen kann, oder legen Sie das Geld in den Brief mit der Bestellung, in welchem Falle Sie den Brief **Eingeschrieben** schicken sollten. Der Brief wird in der Post Eingeschrieben (Registered.)

Wir erhalten jeden Tag eine große Anzahl von Bestellungen von allen Leuten (Jung und Alt).

Sie brauchen nicht furchtsam zu sein Sachen zu bestellen, wir werden Ihr Bestellung schon verstehen.

Schreiben Sie uns in Ihrer eigener Weise, und in Ihrer eigener Sprache, was Sie wollen, einerlei ob gut oder schlecht geschrieben, und die Waare wird Ihnen sofort zugeschickt.

Wir haben Leute die alle Sprachen schreiben und übersetzen.

Die ersten zehn Seiten in diesem Catalog beziehen sich hauptsächlich an die Frachtbetrage der verschiedenen Waare und hat nur Wichtigkeit für Sie im Falle Sie in diesen Einzelheiten interessiert sind.

DO NOT FAIL TO GIVE SIZE, COLOR, WEIGHT, ETC., IF REQUIRED WHEN WRITING YOUR ORDER

THE FIRST purchase for our new home was about 20 acres. We have since then increased it by another purchase, making in all nearly 40 acres. This enormous plant covers nearly 40 acres of ground, with miles of railroad tracks, with a group of large buildings, the main building being by far the largest mercantile building in the world. This entire plant is now devoted to the handling of our business alone.

Nearly 40 acres of our own ground in the very heart of one of the very best districts in Chicago, midway between Garfield and Douglas Parks, one-half mile long and two blocks wide. Bounded by Kedzie Avenue, Polk Street, Harvard Street, Spaulding Avenue, St. Louis Avenue and the Chicago Terminal Railroad tracks. Over 40 acres of floor space, with plans for nearly 200 acres of floor space as nay be required from time to time to meet any growing demands. Miles of our own railroad tracks, our own railroad yards, our own motive power, engines, crews, etc., all on our own property; our own railroad facilities to insure promptest possible shipment, lowest handling cost and the lowest possible freight rates.

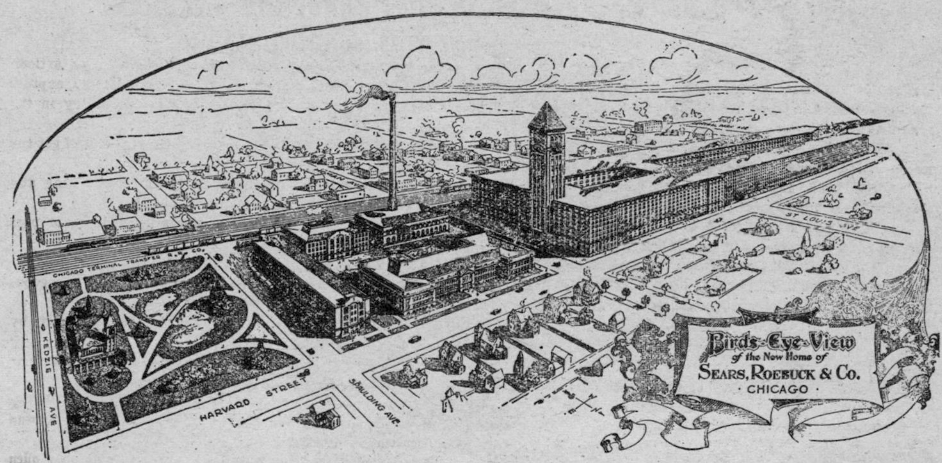

CHICAGO TERMINAL RAILROAD COMPANY.

Our own railroad connects directly with the Chicago Terminal Railroad, the great Chicago switching railroad, which in turn connects with all the different trunk line railroads entering Chicago, and under our contract, without one penny's cost to the customer for switching, transferring or hauling in Chicago, without one penny's cost being figured in the selling price of the goods or otherwise for teaming or handling, every order is now forwarded through our railroad, the Terminal Railroad, and the connecting main or trunk line railroads in Chicago with the greatest possible dispatch, and at the very lowest possible freight charge to the customer.

OUR MERCHANDISE BUILDING—THE WORKS.

The building in which we carry the merchandise is known by us as the **Works,** for in this building everything is work and everything working, the largest single building in the world devoted to the handling of merchandise, the one building being one-fourth of a mile long (over three blocks) and one block wide. Miles of raiload tracks run lengthwise through, in and around this building for e receiving, moving and forwarding of merchandise; elevators, chanical conveyers, endless chains, moving sidewalks, gravity chutes, apparatus and conveyers, pneumatic tubes and every known mechanical appliance for reducing labor, for the working out of economy and dispatch is utilized here in our great Works. In this building are employed thousands of people in the packing and filling of orders, in the packing, shipping and handling of merchandise.

With the facilities that we have in this enormous building, orders sent us are received, filled, put on to the cars and on their way to destination in an almost incredibly short time, and the saving in cost of doing all this goes to our customers in the shape of lower prices. In this building every express company in Chicago is represented by a local agent, delegated to handle our work and ours alone. The railroads and the postoffice are here specially represented for us. The Western Union Telegraph Company and the Postal Telegraph Company here have an office devoted exclusively to our use.

ADMINISTRATION BUILDING.

The building immediately opposite and across Homan Avenue from the Works is 450 feet long, 80 feet wide, three stories high and the highest type of fireproof construction, and is devoted entirely to the administration of our business. In this building are all the executive offices, the offices of the President, Vice-President, Secretary, Treasurer, offices of the General Manager and Superintendents, offices of the Customers' Profit Sharing and Banking Departments and of the traffic manager, auditor, comptroller and bookkeepers. In this building nearly 2,000 people are employed in opening the mail, writing the bills, answering letters and in attending to every little detail of the clerical work attached to every order that is received by us. From this building we communicate with the Works, or main building, by tunnels, pneumatic tubes, automatic carriers, telephone and telegraph, and your order opened in this building is dispatched to the works in a fraction of a minute, filled, conveyed to the railroad cars below and on the way to you in an incredibly short time.

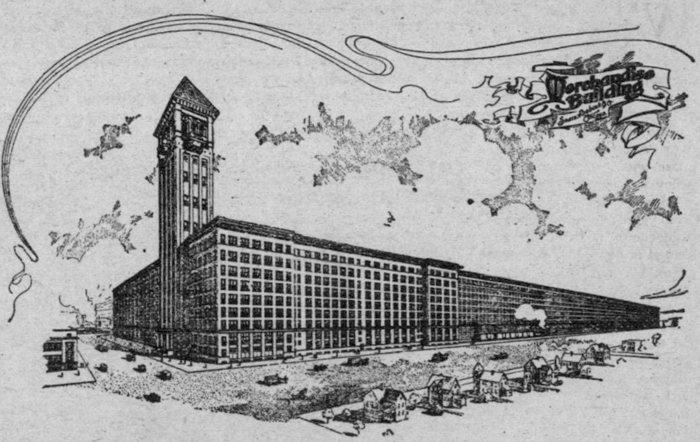

To promote health, efficiency and economy the building is equipped with the most modern hygienic and health giving apparatus, including filtered warm air in winter and filtered cold air in summer, light, space and ventilation, the most sanitary plumbing and pure water from a deep artesian well, etc.

OUR POWER PLANT.

In this building is an enormously large power plant, many boilers, large, medium and small engines for their various duties, many electric dynamos, etc. The equipment produces more than 12,000 horse power with room to later develop more than as much more. Here we generate the electricity to run 30,000 electric lights, which are required to light our plant by night. In this plant all heat and power is generated for the operating of the network of machinery necessary to the handling of our business.

PRINTING PLANT.

This building, about 50 feet to the south of the Administration Buildin, is given up in its entirety to the printing of our catalogues, big and small, and to the printing of the stationery used in our business. This building, constructed especially for our purpose, is 90 feet wide, 250 feet long and four stories high, and makes the most modern and model printing plant possible. With perfect light, everything built to our own measure and requirements, railroad tracks to carry the paper leading direct to the printing presses, we look for greater economy. This building is built to contain twenty special Cottrell rotary perfecting catalogue printing presses, each made to our order, made specially to make our big catalogues. Add to this a large number of large, medium and small flat bed, rotary and other printing presses, plate making machines, binding, covering, gathering, trimming and other machinery and equipment, and you can form some idea of the extensiveness of the plans necessary to take care of the printing branch of our business. All the printing done in this building will be exclusively for our own requirements. Our own printing plant is another economy that makes for lower prices.

BUILDING TO HANDLE OUR ADVERTISING MATTER.

This building, just west of the printing plant, will be a plant 90 feet wide, 160 feet long and four stories high, built expressly for the purpose, to suit our requirements in every way, and will be devoted in its entirety to the compiling, composition (type setting) and mailing of our catalogues, circulars and price lists of all kinds. In this building we will have a large photographic department for the making of cuts and engravings of all descriptions. Here we expect to send out as high as fifty tons of printed matter daily, consisting of large catalogues, special catalogues, sample books, price lists, circulars, notifications to our customers, etc. This building will also contain our supply department for stationery, entry tickets (bills), blank forms, ink, pens, pencils, etc., such as are used by our various clerical and merchandise departments.

OUR OWN PARK.

To the east and south of the Administration Building we have laid out a beautiful park, with gravel walks, beautiful shade trees, ornamental shrubs, flowers, green grass and a beautiful artificial lake. The artificial lake will serve the double purpose of holding millions of gallons of water as a reservoir for fire protection. Here our employes can breathe the fresh air, free from the dust and noise common to most parts of our city. All this is planned with a view to better serving our customers in every state and territory. Everything we can do in the way of bettering the surroundings and conveniences of our employes adds to their happiness and contentment, improves their efficiency and thus tends to improve our service, quickens the dispatch of order lessons cost of handling and makes for lower prices.

OUR CITY WITHIN A GREAT CITY AND HOW WE CAME TO BUILD

WE SAY, "cur city within a city" because it covers a tract of land one-half mile long, a fair size **farm plat within great Chicago.** On this land great buildings have been erected, now occupied and in full operation. More than 7,000 people are employed within our walls, and with the families of our employes, more than 40,000 people are now seeking new homes within convenient distances of our big plant.

Ten years ago this company was organized as **a house with a policy.** That policy was, is and ever shall be, **quality and price.** Ten years ago we offered our catalogue to the world. Then, located in a five story building on Adams street, we were in less than one year driven to seek larger quarters at Fulton and Desplaines streets, and the ten years past have been a history of build and enlarge. Covering the entire block at Fulton and Desplaines streets, we were soon driven to seek large buildings in other blocks, and one by one these buildings were added, until we occupied in their entirety, seven enormously large buildings in Chicago, in addition to the main big store, and the last move has been to our new 40-acre plant, illustrated and described on these pages.

The people's ability to judge quality and price has been shown in the unparalleled growth of our business. So accurately do they judge that they have left their accustomed places of supply and come to us, and they tell their friends and their friends' friends and then everyone tells everyone's friends until the orders are fairly flowing to our doors. **So general and so great** has been the demand from every section for the past few years, that we have been compelled at times to limit and restrict the circulation of our catalogue. Announcements of new catalogues have been withheld. The past year we have not been able to supply one catalogue where three catalogues were wanted, so thoroughly do the people appreciate **quality and price. We must supply the demand.** We are now in the hands of the people. It's really the people who are placing us on this broad expanse, **our city within a city.** It's the people that are causing all our factories to be enlarged. Our catalogues must go into the additional millions of hands that want them. **Our policy,** the Sears, Roebuck & Co. policy, the policy of Mr. Sears and every officer, manager and director of our organization is, **quality, price, satisfaction, every facility exhausted to serve the people.**

Mere money making is far from our greatest ambition. If the principle that shapes, develops and expands our policy was not influenced and directed by a principle much higher, much greater than hat of mere money making, we would have little hope for the future. the great success for the future of this business was only in money aking, it would not begin to pay the writer and his co-officers for directing the affairs of this institution. If the success of this institution was to be measured only by dollars gained, it would be a thousand times easier for the writer and his co-executives to retire from the multitudinous responsibilities of so great an organization and seek rest, recreation and pleasure the remainder of their lives. Dollars and cents enter into our business policy only so far as is actually necessary for the legitimate conduct and perpetuity of our business. Our ambition is to gain, merit and hold the confidence of as many of the citizens of the United States as can be made possible by the best service we can give. We have an ambition to, and we believe we will, within five years be selling more than one hundred million dollars worth of merchandise annually, and our ambition is to see how much more we can make your dollar buy than it has ever bought before. We would rather know that in five or ten years' time we had served at least a large percentage of all the people in the United States in a way that their dollars went further, that we brought them nearer to the source of supply, thus advancing their comfort and happiness; this accomplished, we would feel much more richly repaid for all our efforts than we would if we knew we were to be repaid only by mere dollars, even riches beyond that of the richest individual or corporation in land.

There is one policy in our house. The office boys know it as well as the officers, the managers, the assistant managers, the order pickers the freight handlers, the clerks up and down the line, one knows it as well as the other. It's infused in every act and every thought of every individual on our pay roll, and will ever be inculcated into the minds of every one that is added to our force, and that is, **consider our customers, don't consider us.** Give our customers every advantage that our facilities will permit, serve every customer as it becomes an honest lawyer to serve his client, namely, with all the talent, all the ability that he may possess. Give the customer the highest possible quality, give him the lowest possible cost. In questions of doubt give the customer the benefit of the doubt. If we can own better goods and own them cheaper by manufacturing them ourselves, we make them ourselves, not for our own gain but for our customers, for every penny of saving, every betterment of quality all goes to our customers. That's the policy of our house and our customers understand it. It's a policy for the people and by the people, organized and run for the people and not for mere gain alone. Our own factories are building and enlarging all over the United States, all the time getting closer to the raw material and all the time working toward lower prices, not for mere profit, not alone for money gained, but done through the people, by the people and for the people. If by building another factory, if by enlarging a present factory, we reduce the cost of any commodity by five per cent, you get it, not we. Our policy says it belongs to you, therefore we cannot take it. Our buyers know it and our sellers know it. Our policy is made, fixed and set for you.

Our work has hardly begun. You have encouraged us to do what we have and instilled us with an ambition to do more. With your support, which we already have in the fullest measure, we shall continue to seek the foundation of cost in every commodity. Many more factories will be erected, cost will be greatly reduced, you will yet be brought much nearer to the first cost of production. The day will come when your dollar will go much farther towards purchasing for you those things which you require. You have and are furnishing us the material with which to work, and we find our pleasure, our ambition and future in working for you, the spirit of which is not for mere dollar making, but for comfort, pleasure and luxury building, the building of a full equivalent for the dollars of a progressive and enlightened people. And when our work is done and the time comes to hand it over to the next set of generals in line, I promise you, reader or customer, from the bottom of my heart, that if the writer and his associates have been instrumental in bringing about a condition by which the people are served and get in exchange for the dollars they earn (whether their purchases are made from us or from others) a more liberal measure, a more just equivalent than would have been possible for them to have gotten had it not been for the inception, progress and development of this institution; this accomplished, if the remaining years of our application to this business do not add one penny to our present individual fortunes, I will feel abundantly repaid for all the responsibilities, all the care, all the work and effort that is yet to go into the guidance of this ship of commerce in my remaining years. This, reader, is the policy of the institution that calls your attention to the pages of this catalogue.

A MESSAGE OF GOOD CHEER.

With malice towards none and charity for all, we extend to all mankind our sincere wishes for greater prosperity, health and happiness.

To all those who buy, to all those who build and to all those who sell, we wish you **success.** Perchance you are a competitor, retail dealer, wholesale dealer, manufacturer or a mail order house, **great** or **small,** we wish you **well.** We believe we are all entering an era of more modern merchandising, **better values, fewer losses, greater economies,** a larger equivalent for the dollar and therefore have a right to look for greater and grander successes than have heretofore been attained. With the almost phenomenal growth of wealth and buying power of our country, many new and more modern methods in the selling of merchandise will surely develop. Retail dealers will buy closer and closer and will thus be able to give better and better values. Many manufacturers now selling to jobbers only will begin selling to the retail dealer direct, saving him at least a good portion of the jobbers' profit, while many manufacturers now selling to jobbers or retailers will offer their wares direct to the user. Jobbers will study and learn new economics so as to make for lower prices. Retail dealers will buy more and more for cash, growing constantly keener and keener in their buying and study of economy. Catalogue houses, general and special, will continue to grow, many of the small getting large and the large getting larger, and with very few exceptions all sellers of goods, regardless of place or method, will give honest goods with honest representations and an ever growing equivalent for the dollar.

Certainly this must be the method of every successful institution of every kind and place.

If every seller of merchandise in every station will constantly study how to economize in his business, carefully study values and markets with a view of buying to the best possible advantage, getting to as near a spot cash basis as possible and strive to give every customer the most value possible for his money, he will find plenty of room for growth and with it success.

The consumer today is buying from many catalogue houses, special and general; he is also buying from many factories direct, as well as from the many thousands of retail dealers, special stores, general stores, department stores, etc. He has a right to buy where he likes and every seller has the same equal right to solicit his trade. Let us all believe as we do, that every successful dealer, retailer, catalogue house or otherwise, is reliable. If a grocer or clothier, let us think as well of our neighbor grocer or clothier across the street as if he were our banker. Let us rise above the petty jealousies and differences that so often grow out of competition, so that in the evening of the day's work your competitor will be as welcome to break bread at your table as would be your doctor or your banker.

We have a high regard for every honorable and reliable dealer, and even though we may at times differ in our opinions, **we bear no ill will against any maker or seller in our land.**

We solicit trade from all, promising everyone the very best service which the very best facilities and organization can give. We can't do more and we will never do less.

SEARS, ROEBUCK & CO.,
By R. W. SEARS, President.

HOW WE MAKE EVERY TRANSACTION WITH US STRICTLY CONFIDENTIAL.

Why our name and address do not appear on any box, package, wrapper, tag, envelope or article of merchandise.

As many people, especially merchants, business houses, townspeople and others, do not care to have others know where or from whom they buy their goods, as many people object to having the name of the shipper spread across every box or package, so that when it is unloaded at the station or express office everyone can see what they are getting and where they buy it, to protect all those who care for this protection and make it possible for you to order your goods from us with no fear of anyone learning at the railroad station, express office or elsewhere what you bought or where you bought it, our name and address will not appear on any box, package, tag, envelope or article of merchandise.

For example: If you are a merchant and wish to buy goods to sell again, your customers will be unable to learn from any marks inside or outside where you bought the goods or what you paid for them.

If you are a professional man, or even in the employ of some merchant, who for personal reasons might object to your sending to us for goods, you need have no fear, our name will not appear on any goods or packages you get.

While we would be glad to have our name appear on every article of merchandise and on every box and package, as a valuable means of advertising, we have learned that thousands of our customers need the protection that the omitting of our name affords. This applies especially to townspeople.

NO ORDER WILL BE ACCEPTED FOR LESS THAN 50 CENTS.

PLEASE DO NOT SEND US ANY ORDER AMOUNTING TO LESS THAN 50 CENTS. If you want some article, the price of which is less than 50 cents, please include one or more other needed articles and make your order amount to 50 cents or more.

AS A MATTER OF ECONOMY, BOTH TO OUR CUSTOMERS AND OURSELVES, we do not fill orders for less than 50 cents. The postage or express charges especially make small orders under 50 cents unprofitable to the purchaser, or at least much more expensive than the orders amounting to 50 cents or more.

WE MAKE THIS EXCEPTION: In the case of needed repairs, attachments and supplies, such as needles for our sewing machines, parts of guns, etc., which can be secured only from us, we will fill the order no matter how small it may be.

TO MAKE ORDERING BY MAIL VERY PROFITABLE TO OUR CUSTOMERS we especially urge that you make your order as large as possible. Orders of from $2.00 to $5.00 or more are always very much more profitable to the purchaser than smaller orders, for the express or freight charges are in this way very greatly reduced. It always pays, even if you have to get some friend or neighbor to join with you, to make up an order of from $2.00 to $5.00 or more, and include enough heavy goods to make a profitable freight shipment of fifty to one hundred pounds. In this way you reduce the transportation charges on each item to next to nothing. You then pay the exact same freight charges that your storekeeper must pay on the goods he sells.

ON THE BASIS OF FAR GREATER VALUE FOR YOUR MONEY THAN YOU CAN POSSIBLY GET ELSEWHERE, lower prices than any other house does or can name, the best possible service, every item ordered guaranteed to reach you in perfect condition and give perfect satisfaction or your money to be immediately refunded to you; on our binding guarantee to please you in every way on every dollar sent us, wholly in your own interest we ask you to kindly conform to these terms.

OUR COMPLIMENTS TO THE RETAIL MERCHANT.

IT IS NOT OUR DESIRE TO ANTAGONIZE THE RETAIL MERCHANT (the storekeeper of the country). This is a big growing country and there is ample room for us all. Our prices are alike to all. Whether to the largest or the smallest merchant, farmer, mechanic or laborer, our price is exactly the same. Our goods are for sale at the prices plainly printed in this book, and occupation or position restricts no one from buying goods from us at our printed prices.

However, we number thousands of the best merchants of the United States among our valued customers. The prejudice which for a time existed because we would not sell to the dealer and refuse to sell to his customers, is dying out; for the shrewd, careful buying up to date merchant of today has broader business views. He buys his goods where he can get the best value for his money, and on the basis of more value for the money than is furnished by any other house we especially invite all classes of merchants to carefully compare our prices as printed in this book with the prices you have been in the habit of paying.

As explained on this page, we ship all our goods in plain boxes or packages, and our name appears on no package or article of merchandise. You can buy your goods from us at our selling prices, which are much lower than you can buy elsewhere, you can fix your profit to suit yourself and your customers will not know where you bought the goods or what you paid for them.

We want to correct the impression that may be in the minds of some merchants, that we sell exclusively to the consumer, the party who buys the goods to use. If you have this impression we are anxious to correct it. A goodly percentage of the goods we ship in all lines go direct to merchants, business houses who buy to sell again, and in some lines, especially materials and supplies, a large percentage of our goods go to manufacturers, which they use in the manufacture of their wares, which in turn they sell to dealers. Among our valued customers are the U. S. Government, state and city institutions, railroads and other large corporations, and also jobbers, brokers, retailers and consumers in all foreign lands.

WE ESPECIALLY SOLICIT THE TRADE OF THE SUCCESSFUL, SHREWD BUYING MERCHANT, who wishes to buy his wares where he can get the highest standard of quality at lower prices than he can get elsewhere.

OUR LIBERAL TERMS OF SHIPMENT.

WE HAVE NO DISCOUNTS. We sell for cash only, and the prices quoted in this catalogue are absolutely net, from which there is no discount whatever. Our prices are alike to one and all, regardless of the amount of the order, the same to the merchant as to the farmer, mechanic or laborer.

OUR TERMS OF SHIPMENT ARE VERY LIBERAL. Nearly all our customers send cash in full with their orders, thus saving the small charge the express companies always make for collecting a C. O. D. and returning the money to us, and we certainly advise sending cash in full with the order, to make this saving and as a more satisfactory way of ordering, always, of course, with the understanding that we will immediately refund your money for any goods that are not perfectly satisfactory to you.

WE ADVISE AGAINST ORDERING GOODS TO BE SHIPPED BY EXPRESS OR FREIGHT C. O. D., SUBJECT TO EXAMINATION. First, by reason of an extra express charge (as above mentioned), a charge which the express companies always make for collecting the money and returning it to us. This charge is always saved when cash in full is sent with the order. Second, where goods are shipped by freight C. O. D., subject to examination, a draft for the amount of the C. O. D. must be sent for collection either by express or to some bank in your town, and the goods must be shipped consigned to ourselves, with instructions for the railroad agent to notify you that the goods are there. The freight agent, as a rule, will allow you to examine the goods before paying for them. (Goods shipped by express, you can always examine before paying for). But on a freight shipment, before the goods can be delivered to you, you must first go to the express office or bank and pay the amount of the C. O. D. in order to have the bill of lading or order for the delivery of the goods to you. With this bill of lading or order for the goods you can then go to the railroad station and get the goods; on the other hand, if the full amount of cash is sent with your order the goods are shipped direct to you, and you only have to go to the railroad station or express office and pay the freight or express charges and take the goods; always, of course, with the understanding that if the goods are not perfectly satisfactory when received you can return them to us at our expense and we will immediately refund your money. However, to those who prefer to see and examine the goods they buy before paying for them, we offer to make shipment on C. O. D., subject to examination, pay after received liberal terms as follows:

OUR C. O. D. TERMS.

ANY GOODS QUOTED IN THIS CATALOGUE (unless otherwise specially stated, provided the order amounts to $5.00 or more), will be shipped to any address east of the Rocky Mountains by freight C. O. D., subject to examination, on receipt of a sufficient amount of cash with the order to pay all express or freight charges both ways. On receipt of such an order, the goods will go forward by express or freight C. O. D., subject to examination. You will be credited on the bill for the amount of money sent with your order. After the goods are received and examined at your nearest railroad station or express office, if they are found perfectly satisfactory you can then pay the balance of our price and freight or express charges, less the amount of money sent with the order. If, however, the goods are not perfectly satisfactory you can return them to us at our expense and we will immediately refund the cash deposit sent with your order. Our only object in requiring you to send a cash deposit sufficient to pay the freight or express charges both ways is to protect us against a class of people who might order out of curiosity, with no idea of accepting and paying for the goods when received, thus putting us to an unnecessary expense for transportation charges which our low selling prices will not warrant.

WHERE THE EXACT DEPOSIT REQUIRED IS NOT STATED, we advise that on all orders amounting to less than $10.00, one-fourth of the amoun of the order be sent with the order. On orders amounting to more thar $10.00 one-fifth of the amount should be sent with the order. For example: If you wish the goods shipped C. O. D., subject to examination, and your order amounts to $8.00, you should send at least $2.00 with your order. If your order amounts to $20.00, send $4.00 with your order, the balance payable after received.

NOTE—WHERE A VERY SMALL CASH DEPOSIT WILL BE ACCEPTED.

On receipt of 50 cents any watch or any item of jewelry amounting to $3.00 or more will be sent C. O. D.

On receipt of $1.00 any camera, telescope or field glass amounting to $3.00 or more will be shipped C. O. D.

On receipt of $1.00 any graphophone or talking machine will be shipped C. O. D.

On receipt of $1.00 any organ or piano will be shipped C. O. D., to any point east of the Rocky Mountains and north of the Ohio River, or will be shipped without a deposit where the money is deposited with a reliable party in your town, as fully explained under the heading of organs and pianos.

On receipt of $1.00 any violin, guitar, mandolin, banjo, autoharp, zither or band instrument amounting to $3.00 or more will be shipped C. O. D.

On receipt of $1.00 any bicycle, gun or revolver amounting to $3.00 or more will be shipped C. O. D.

On receipt of $5.00 any buggy or carriage will be shipped to any address east of the Rocky Mountains, C. O. D.

On receipt of $1.00 any harness or saddle will be shipped to any address east of the Rocky Mountains, C. O. D.

On receipt of $1.00 any sewing machine will be shipped to any address C.O.D.

On receipt of $1.00 any stove will be shipped to any address east of the Missouri River and north of Tennessee C. O. D., or if you live east of the Rocky Mountains and south of Kentucky we will ship any stove C. O. D. on receipt of $5.00 deposit.

On receipt of $1.00 any item of men's, boys' or children's clothing or ladies' wearing apparel amounting to $3.00 or more will be sent to any address in the United States by express C. O. D.

THE ABOVE NAMED GOODS WILL BE SENT to any address within the radius mentioned on receipt of the small cash deposit named, which deposit must accompany the order, the balance, together with the freight or express charges, to be paid after the goods are received, examined and found satisfactory. All other merchandise where deposit is not mentioned, as before stated, will, unless otherwise stated, be sent subject to examination either by freight or express where a sufficient deposit accompanies the order to pay transportation charges both ways.

IN THE INTEREST OF OUR CUSTOMERS, to save you the extra express charge for the collection and return of the money, and to save you the inconvenience attached to delivery of goods shipped by freight C. O. D., subject to examination, we specially urge that you send cash in full with your order, understanding of course that you take no risk and that we will immediately return your money if you are not perfectly satisfied. Yet, to those who prefer to see and examine the goods before they pay for them, when so requested we will make shipment C. O. D., subject to examination, to be paid for after received on the small deposit terms as above stated.

Paragraph A.

ABOUT OUR PRICES.

HOW WE CAN UNDERSELL ALL OTHER CONCERNS.

SECTION 1. BY REASON OF OUR ENORMOUS OUTPUT OF GOODS we are able to make contracts with representative manufacturers and importers for such large quantities of merchandise that we can secure the lowest possible prices, and in some lines our trade has been so large, as, for example, in vehicles, organs, stoves, cloaks, tailoring, guns, revolvers, upholstered furniture, etc., that we have been able to equip our own factories and foundries, thus saving you even the manufacturer's profit; but whether the goods are manufactured by ourselves or bought direct in large quantities, we add the smallest percentage of profit possible to the actual cost to us, and on this economic, one small profit plan, direct from manufacturer to consumer, you can buy a large percentage of the merchandise we handle, direct from us at less than your storekeeper at home can buy in quantities.

WE EMPLOY THE MOST COMPETENT BUYERS that money can obtain, men who are experts and have a life long experience in their particular lines. Our established reputation for buying everything in enormous quantities gives our buyers inside track with all the largest manufacturers, thereby giving us the benefit of first choice in the markets. Manufacturers who are overstocked often come to us and offer their goods at a big discount for cash, knowing that we have a larger outlet for merchandise than any other concern. For this reason many articles in this catalogue are quoted at less money than the actual cost to produce. No matter how cheap we buy, we give our customers the benefit, for we feel that our bargains are our customers' bargains.

SECTION 2. WE BUY AND SELL FOR CASH, and having no bad debts, no traveling men's expenses, no expenses for collecting, securing the manufacturers' lowest spot cash prices, we can sell goods at a smaller margin of profit than any other business house could do and still exist.

WE MAKE NO REDUCTIONS IN OUR PRICES. To those who are inclined to write us for a reduction from the prices quoted in this catalogue, we wish to state that we cannot make any reduction or concession, whether you order in large or small quantities. The price quoted on each and every article in this catalogue is as low as we can possibly make it, and it is out of the question to reduce these prices still further; and we earnestly believe a careful comparison of our prices with those of any other concern will convince you that we can furnish you better goods for less money than you can obtain from any other house in the United States.

ALL PRICES ARE SUBJECT TO THE FLUCTUATION OF THE MARKET. The prices quoted in this book are correct, according to market conditions at the date the catalogue is printed, and our wants have been anticipated as far as possible by contract, goods in stock, etc.; but when our stock on hand is sold or when a contract expires and the market conditions at that time are such that we are compelled to pay more money for the goods, we reserve the right to advance our prices without notice, charging you the difference the advance represents, only the difference in cost to us. The necessity for advancing prices very rarely happens, but as a protection to us, at the extremely low prices we are making, we must reserve this right, and this space is used to inform everyone of the right so reserved. If prices decline so that we are able to buy any goods to fill orders at lower prices than those printed in this catalogue, you will always get the benefit of such prices and the difference will be returned to you in cash.

AS THE TENDENCY IS FOR LARGER CONTRACTS, larger purchases, closer buying, the history of our house and our records show that **we reduce prices and return the difference in cash ten times** where we make an advance and ask more money once; but for our protection the right to recognize advances and declines must be and is reserved.

IN THIS CATALOGUE you will find only such goods listed as we can save you money on, goods that can be delivered anywhere in the United States for less money than they can be bought at your local dealer's. The amount of money that we can save you over the prices you pay at home varies from 15 to 50 per cent, according to the nature of the goods, but there is not an item quoted in this entire catalogue on which the saving is not worth taking into consideration, to say nothing of the fact that our goods are, as a rule, of a higher grade than those carried by the average storekeeper or catalogue house.

THE ILLUSTRATIONS AND DESCRIPTIONS IN THIS CATALOGUE can be depended upon. We aim to illustrate and describe every article with the strictest accuracy. Most all of the illustrations are made from photographs taken direct from the article. They are such as enable you to order intelligently; in fact, with our assortment, correct illustrations and accurate descriptions, you can order from this catalogue with the same ease, confidence and security as though you were personally in our store selecting the goods yourself.

Paragraph C.

HOW TO ORDER.

Use our regular order blank if you have one; if not use any plain paper.

Always keep well supplied with our order blanks, as it is more convenient for you to make out your order on our regular order blanks than in any other way. If out of them at any time, drop us a postal card and we will be pleased to send you some.

Whether you write your order on our regular order blank or letter paper instead, **be sure to observe the following instructions:**

Always sign your full name (Christian name and surname).

Write your name in full, clearly and distinctly.

Give your postoffice, county and state, and your shipping point, if different from the postoffice.

Always give catalogue number in full (write every figure and letter in the catalogue number), description and price of each article ordered.

Always try to mention the number or name of the catalogue or circular from which your order is taken, and be sure to give the size, color, weight and measurements when required.

We must have your correct size or measurements for such goods as hats, shoes, clothing, ladies' ready made dresses, cloaks, and the size and color of everything that has size and color.

Be sure to enclose your money with your order and state plainly in your order how much money you enclose and in what form. Sending us money in one envelope and your order in another causes delay and confusion in our office, as they become separated in the mails. For instructions on how to send money see **paragraph F.**

Be sure you have followed our rules carefully about enclosing the proper amount of money with the order, including enough to pay postage if the goods are to be sent by mail, and insurance fee if to be sent by insured mail.

Be sure your name and address is written plainly and in full, that your shipping directions are plainly stated, that the exact amount of money enclosed is plainly stated, that you have given us catalogue number, price, description, correct size and measurements and you will seldom if ever have any delay or inconvenience. By carefully observing these rules you will avoid errors and loss of time by our having to write you for further information.

AFTER WRITING AN ORDER, please compare it with these rules, check it over closely and see if you have written your order correctly.

IF YOU WISH TO REFER TO ANY MATTER not concerning the order, be sure to write it on a separate sheet. Do not write about it on your order sheet, though you may enclose it in the same envelope with your order. Our orders and letters are handled in separate and distinct departments, and we ask you therefore please do not fail to observe this rule.

ALWAYS TRY TO WRITE REMARKS CONCERNING YOUR ORDER on the same sheet with the order. This will prevent the possibility of such remarks or instructions being separated from the order. Should you have occasion to write us concerning an order which you have already sent us, do not fail to mention the date on which your letter was mailed, also state the nature and value of your remittance and the name and address as given in your order. This information will enable us to promptly locate the matter you refer to.

SHOULD YOU CHANGE YOUR ADDRESS, please notify us, being sure to give old as well as new address in full.

Paragraph D.

ABOUT OMISSIONS.

ALL ORDERS FOR MERCHANDISE are accepted by us with the understanding that we will use every reasonable effort to promptly ship every item exactly as ordered, and in order to make this possible we carry in stock, constantly, merchandise to the value of more than four million dollars, and if we do not have the goods in stock we invariably buy them in Chicago if we can, even if we are compelled to pay more than we get for them, rather than delay an order or withhold shipment of any part of an order. But it sometimes happens that on an order including several items of merchandise there may be one or two items that are not in stock and cannot be had in Chicago, usually for the reason that the manufacturers are behind with their orders, have met with some accident or there has been some unusual delay in transportation.

WE THEREFORE ACCEPT ALL ORDERS with the understanding that we reserve the right when unable to ship every item, to cancel that portion of the order which we cannot ship promptly, filling the balance of the order, and returning to the customer in cash the amount for the item or items cancelled. We make this explanation so that anyone ordering merchandise from us, and receiving the goods with one or more items missing, and receiving by mail his money returned for the omitted items, will understand that the reason for omitting is that the goods are not in stock and cannot be had in Chicago at that time. Where an omission for the above reason is necessary we usually send a letter telling when we expect to have a stock of the missing goods, so that the customer may renew his order if he so desires.

UNDERSTAND, it seldom happens that we are unable to fill an order complete and exactly as given, but out of the many thousands of orders we receive every day, there are always a few (a very small number) on which items must be cancelled, and we make this explanation in our catalogue so that none of our customers need misunderstand our position.

Paragraph E.

ABOUT SUBSTITUTION.

WE ARE BITTERLY OPPOSED TO SUBSTITUTING one article for another unless instructed to do so by the customer. We believe, except in rare cases, it is very presuming on the part of any house receiving an order for one kind of goods to send another, without first having the written consent of the customer to do so. There are, however, exceptions where we take upon ourselves the responsibility of substituting, and with reference to this we make the following explanation:

IF A PARTY SENDS US AN ORDER and there is some article in that order which we have not in stock and cannot get in Chicago, but we have the same kind of an article in a higher grade, we then take the liberty of sending the higher grade at the price of the lower grade, sacrificing our profit rather than to disappoint the customer. A customer ordering a watch may call for a 7-jeweled Elgin or Waltham movement and we may not have one in stock, and there may not be one in the Chicago market, in which case we wou'd consider ourselves justified in taking the liberty of substituting a higher grade in an 11 or 15-jeweled Elgin or Waltham movement, but always at the price of the cheaper one ordered, taking the loss ourselves for the differenc3 in price. This is an example. The same would apply on hundreds of items in our stock, but only in cases where in our judgment the customer can only be the better pleased by reason of such action on our part. However, even this kind of substitution we admit is presuming on our part, and when such substitution is made it must be understood it is done entirely at our risk, and with the understanding that if our action is not entirely satisfactory to the customer, he is at liberty to return the goods at our expense of transportation charges both ways and his money is to be immediately returned to him.

Paragraph F.

HOW TO SEND MONEY.

SEND US A POSTOFFICE MONEY ORDER, express money order, bank draft, cash or stamps. Should you send stamps, fold them in waxed paper. We receive many orders with stamps stuck together and worthless. We do not accept revenue stamps, foreign stamps and due stamps, as they are of no value to us. Do not send them.

IF YOU LIVE ON A RURAL ROUTE you can just give the letter and the money to the mail carrier and he will get the money order at the postoffice and mail it in the letter for you.

POSTAGE STAMPS in amounts exceeding $1.00 will be accepted only at a discount of five per cent (5%), or ninety-five cents on the dollar. If you order an article priced at $2.00 and send stamps you should send $2.10. If a $3.00 article you should send $3.15 in stamps. We are compelled to dispose of all surplus stamps at a discount of from 2 per cent to 5 per cent and besides there is an extra expense in handling stamps, and our very small profit will not admit of this expense. We advise remitting by postoffice or express money order, but will accept postage stamps in any amount at 95 cents on the dollar. As an accommodation to our customers we will accept postage stamps at the face value in amounts less than $1.00.

WE RECOMMEND THE POSTOFFICE AND EXPRESS MONEY ORDER SYSTEMS, because they are inexpensive, of less trouble and safe. Besides this, if the money order should get lost or miscarry, your loss will be made good.

DO NOT UNDER ANY CIRCUMSTANCES send money or stamps in a letter except by registered mail. If sent by open mail the letter may never reach us, and in such a case a great amount of trouble and inconvenience is caused, as well as the loss you sustain. **If you prefer to remit by registered mail, we advise the use of two envelopes, one inside the other,** and the outer one carefully and securely sealed. **Do not send gold or silver coin that is defaced,** as light weight coins are worth no more than bullion and bullion is less than the face value of the coin.

TO INSURE SAFETY always register a letter containing money. Be sure to state in your order plainly how much cash you enclose and in what form. You need not be afraid of sending too much as we always refund when too much money is sent.

Paragraph G.

METHODS OF SHIPMENT.

We can ship goods by mail (see paragraph H about mail shipments), by express (see paragraph I about express shipments), by freight (see paragraph K about freight shipments). If left to our judgment we will ship goods in the manner which will be the least expensive to our customers. **In all cases transportation charges are to be paid by the customer.**

Paragraph H.

MAIL SHIPMENTS.

The mail service affords a convenient method for the transportation of merchandise of small weight and considerable value to points that are distant from express or railroad offices. On all orders to be shipped by mail we require the full amount of cash with the order, together with sufficient money extra to pay postage and insurance or registration, when same is desired. There are three methods of shipping goods by mail:

SECTION 1. OPEN MAIL, which is so called because only the regular amount of postage, according to the classification of goods, is paid and the customer must assume all risk. We do not recommend sending goods by open mail, for if the package is lost or stolen, neither we or the customer have any recourse. In sending goods by open mail the customer must assume all risk.

SECTION 2. INSURED MAIL. This we consider the best, safest and cheapest method of shipping by mail. The following is the rate, in addition to the regular postage: For orders valued at $5.00 or under, 5 cents each. For orders valued at $10.00 or under, 10 cents each. For each additional $5.00 in value, 5 cents extra. In case of loss, we refill the order on receipt of statement certified to by your local postmaster that goods were not received. We advise insuring everything of value. Insurance is less than the cost of registering, because no matter how many packages the order consists of, our insurance charge would be only on the value of the order and not on the number of packages, as is the case when sent by registered mail. We guarantee for our charge the safe arrival of the entire order. If you want your mail package insured be sure to write **"Insure"** in your order, and in addition to your remittance for the order be sure to add enough money to pay postage and insurance fee. To secure adjustment it is necessary to make prompt notification of the failure to receive package.

SECTION 3. REGISTERED MAIL, so called because in such cases the postoffice authorities keep a record of the transaction and are thus enabled to trace your shipment. Registry fee per package is 8 cents in addition to the regular postage. We are not responsible for loss of registered mail.

A PACKAGE SHIPPED BY MAIL CANNOT EXCEED 4 POUNDS, but any number of packages may be sent at one time, each weighing four pounds or less. If you live at a great distance from the express office, it might be more convenient to send an order by mail in two or more packages, each weighing four pounds. **One book can be sent by mail, no matter what its weight. The rate is ½-cent per ounce.**

THE RATE ON MERCHANDISE BY MAIL IS 1 CENT PER OUNCE, on books and printed matter, ½ cent per ounce, and you should allow, in addition to the weight of an article, from one to five ounces for packing material, according to size of package shipped.

IF YOU ARE NOT SURE as to the weight of the article, be sure to enclose enough money for postage; if you send too much we will refund balance.

EXPLOSIVES, POISONOUS OR INFLAMMABLE ARTICLES cannot be mailed under any circumstances whatever.

LIQUIDS OVER 4 OUNCES CANNOT BE SENT BY MAIL, but liquids weighing 4 ounces and under can be safely shipped by mail when packed in special mailing cases. Always allow 5 cents extra for this special case.

SECTION 4. PROFITABLE MAIL SHIPMENTS. ARTICLES SUCH AS WATCHES, JEWELRY and other valuable merchandise of light weight, make profitable mail shipments. In all cases where other goods are not ordered at the same time, we advise that such articles can be sent by mail economically.

CERTAIN MEDIUM PRICED GOODS, which, being weighty, cost considerable postage for transportation, should, if possible, be ordered in connection with other needed articles, sufficient to make up express or freight shipment, thus reducing the transportation charges to one-quarter or one-eighth of the postage rate and effecting a far greater saving for you.

WITH THE EXCEPTION OF ARTICLES OF SMALL WEIGHT and of some value, sending goods by mail is by far the most expensive means of transportation, but even in cases where the postage may seem out of proportion to the value of the goods, the cost of the goods with the postage added is usually less than if purchased at the local dealer's and frequently the article wanted is not handled by them at all, while our immense stock of merchandise will supply your demands.

Paragraph I.

EXPRESS SHIPMENTS.

HOW TO FIGURE EXPRESS CHARGES. **See pages 14 to 18.**

SHIPPING GOODS BY EXPRESS is an absolutely safe method of transportation and offers the advantages of quick service. It is the most profitable method of shipping goods when the weight is less than 20 pounds. Frequently a customer is in a hurry for certain goods and is willing to pay the extra cost of express charges over freight, the money we save him making it profitable on such shipments instead of buying the goods at home.

WHERE LIGHT AND EXPENSIVE ARTICLES, such as watches, jewelry and high priced revolvers, are ordered shipped with a miscellaneous freight or express order, we make separate shipment of the expensive goods, sending them by sealed express for greater safety.

IF YOU HAVE NO AGENT at your station, all express shipments will be carried to the nearest town where there is an agent. If there is no agent at your station always state in your order at what station you prefer to receive your goods.

A RECOMMENDATION THAT WILL SAVE YOU MONEY: If you live at a far distant point and wish to order some article of merchandise which would weigh about 20 pounds and amount to $6.00 or less, on which the express charges would be from $1.25 to $2.75, and you require nothing further from our catalogue at the time, show the book to your friends, let them add articles they may be in need of and the shipment can go by freight at about the same cost per 100 pounds as by express for 20 pounds, your proportion of the transportation charges being then about 60 cents. We frequently find it greatly to a customer's advantage to ship by freight instead of by express, and when we can save them money by changing the shipping directions we will often do so, unless the goods are wanted in great haste.

ALWAYS RESPOND PROMPTLY TO THE NOTIFICATION OF THE EXPRESS AGENT AS TO THE ARRIVAL OF MERCHANDISE. We are constantly in receipt of requests from them for disposition of packages by reason of the fact that consignee does not reply to postal notices promptly.

Paragraph K.

FREIGHT SHIPMENTS.

FOR FREIGHT CLASSIFICATION and freight rates see pages 14 to 18. Heavy, bulky merchandise, such as agricultural implements, household goods, furniture, groceries, hardware, etc., can be shipped most profitably by freight. When a shipment weighs 100 pounds or more, the railroad companies will charge only for the actual number of pounds.

WHERE LIGHT AND EXPENSIVE ARTICLES, such as watches, jewelry and high priced revolvers, are ordered shipped with a miscellaneous freight or express order, we make separate shipment of the expensive goods, sending them by sealed express for greater safety.

HOW TO SAVE MONEY ON FREIGHT SHIPMENTS. Railroad companies usually charge no more for 100 pounds than they do for 20 pounds. While the extremely low prices at which we sell our merchandise would make even a small order by freight profitable, as you would certainly be getting the goods cheaper than you could possibly buy them through a dealer, at the same time it would be a considerable saving of money if you could make up a larger order, either of your own wants or club together with your neighbors, as the freight charges will amount to comparatively very little more. The saving that may be effected by anticipating your wants and sending one large order instead of five or six smaller orders at different times is quite an item, and therefore should be taken into consideration by our customers.

YOU MUST PAY THE FREIGHT OR EXPRESS CHARGES, but it will amount to very little as compared with what you will save in the price.

IF YOU HAVE NO AGENT AT YOUR SHIPPING POINT, freight charges must be prepaid. If you do not know what the freight charge will amount to be sure and allow liberally for same. If you send more than actual amount required we will immediately refund the difference. If you have an agent at your station it is not necessary to prepay charges, as they are the same whether paid by you or by us, as our system of checking rates insures for our customers almost absolute correctness in transportation charges.

WHEN WE MAKE A SHIPMENT to a railroad station where there is no agent, we guarantee safe delivery to the station. From the fact that there is no agent at the station to receive the goods the railroad company will not assume any responsibility if after they are put on the platform they are lost or damaged, and we consequently cannot hold them for such loss or damage.

CUSTOMERS WHO ORDER GOODS shipped to a station where there is no agent, must make careful arrangements for the care of the goods after they are put on the platform; otherwise, they are liable to be damaged or stolen. We would recommend that you have the goods shipped, if possible, to your nearest open station where there is an agent, thus making the railroad company entirely responsible for the goods until they are delivered to you.

OVERCHARGES IN TRANSPORTATION. Whenever a customer suspects an overcharge on the part of the transportation company, we will be pleased to give same our most prompt and careful attention in his behalf, if he will send us the expense bill received from the agent, after he has paid the charges. Complaints for overcharges are very few, as our system of checking the rates on freight and express shipments insures for our customers almost absolute correctness in transportation charges.

IF YOU HAVE REASON TO BELIEVE THAT AN ERROR HAS OCCURRED IN THE WEIGHTS, as shown on the freight expense bill, ask the agent to weigh the goods, and if it is found that the shipment is billed overweight he will correct the error and ask you to pay only for the correct weight.

Paragraph L.

INFORMATION ABOUT GOODS SHIPPED DIRECT FROM THE FACTORY.

IN ORDER TO GIVE OUR CUSTOMERS THE VERY LOW PRICES WE DO, prices based on the actual cost to manufacture, cost of material and labor only, with but our one small percentage of profit added, prices much lower than they could possibly get elsewhere, we find it necessary to ship many heavy goods direct from the factory where they are made, and in doing this we save the freight on the goods into our warehouse in Chicago, the cartage, handling and other expenses incident to merchandise passing through the store in Chicago, and we give our customers every particle of the benefit of this saving in our extremely low prices. Wherever the catalogue states the goods are shipped from the factory, the prices quoted are for these goods delivered on board the cars at the factory and the customer pays the transportation charges from the factory. In many cases, the freight from the factory will be less than from Chicago, the factory being nearer to the purchaser. In some cases the factory will be at a greater distance than Chicago, in which case there will be an additional freight beyond the Chicago rate; but even in such cases the saving to you is very great, for if we were to ship the goods to you ourselves we would be compelled to add the freight to Chicago to all the goods, and to this add the expense of handling to and from the railroad, in and out of our store and other expenses incident to general handling of merchandise in the city.

IT SOMETIMES HAPPENS that a customer orders several articles in one order that are shipped from different factories. For instance, he may order a buggy to be shipped from our factory in Southern Indiana, a stove to be shipped from our foundry in Central Ohio, a windmill that will be shipped from our factory in Southwestern Michigan. In this case we would be compelled to make three different shipments. The goods would go direct to our customer from the three different factories, but there would be no extra freight charge by reason of the three shipments, as each shipment would weigh more than 100 pounds and would therefore entitle the customer to the same freight per hundred pounds as if the shipments were all made together.

WHILE THE GREATER PART OF OUR GOODS ARE CARRIED IN STOCK IN OUR STORE AND WAREHOUSES IN CHICAGO, and this factory shipment information does not apply to small or general merchandise, we have found it necessary to make factory shipments on many heavy and bulky articles, purely in the interest of our customers, in order to give our customers the greatest possible value for their money, to enable us to deliver the goods to them at our one small percentage of profit direct from the manufacturer to the consumer, and your attention is called to the explanation that is always made in the catalogue regarding any article that is to be shipped from the factory, that you may understand that the freight is to be paid by the purchasers from the factory direct, and also that you will understand our reason for this method of handling certain merchandise.

WE FREQUENTLY RECEIVE ORDERS which include merchandise, a part of which is to be shipped direct from the factory and part direct from our store. For example: A man may order a buggy and a harness. The buggy will be shipped from the factory, the harness from the store. He may order a stove and some stove furniture, cooking utensils, etc. The stove would be shipped direct from the foundry and the cooking utensils from the store.

WHEN AN ORDER INCLUDES SUCH HEAVY GOODS as we ship direct from the factory (in order to make the low price), and other goods which we ship direct from our store, if that portion of the order which is to be shipped direct from our store is a profitable shipment (see Paragraph M about unprofitable shipments), we make two shipments; the stove, buggy or other heavy shipment going direct from the factory, the balance from our store. But it sometimes happens that that portion of the order to be shipped from our store would not be a profitable shipment. It may be for a few cooking utensils, amounting to $1.00 or $2.00, or a very low priced harness of $5.00 or $6.00, or $1.00 or $2.00 worth of miscellaneous merchandise, on which the freight charges would amount to more than the saving, or difference between our price and the price at which the customer could buy in his own town. In such cases of unprofitable shipment we use our very best judgment, and where we deem that portion of the order that is to go from our house a nunprofitable shipment, we cancel that portion of the order and return the amount to our customer in cash for the goods canceled.

AS A FURTHER EXAMPLE: The customer may order a parlor suite for $15.00 to $20.00, which we ship from the factory, and may include with his order one chair for 90 cents, which we ship from the house. This one chair (except to nearby points), would be considered an unprofitable shipment. On such an order we would take the liberty of cancelling the order for the chair, returning the 90 cents to the customer at once, and we would ship the parlor suite to him direct from the factory by freight, with a letter of full explanation for our action. This article is intended to explain our methods of treating special orders only in the interest of the customers.

Paragraph M.

ABOUT UNPROFITABLE SHIPMENTS.

WE FREQUENTLY RECEIVE ORDERS which we term "unprofitable" shipments, which means that the shipment would not be profitable to our customer. For example: A party living far distant may order a dollar's worth of sugar to go by express. The express charges would equal the cost of the sugar. We occasionally get an order for heavy hardware, the order amounting to perhaps less than $5.00. The goods weigh 100 pounds. We are asked to ship them by express. This is usually an "unprofitable" shipment. An order for a single pair of heavy cheap boots to go a great distance by express, or for very bulky woodenware or heavy and low priced merchandise, such as molasses, nails or cornmeal, might be what we term an "unprofitable" shipment for far distant points.

WE WOULD ADVISE OUR CUSTOMERS to study the freight and express rates, as given on the following pages, for we do not wish you to send us a dollar for anything unless we can save you money on the purchase.

ORDERS THAT WOULD BE UNPROFITABLE to ship by mail or express may be very profitable when sent by freight, but as one hundred pounds is usually carried by freight for the same charge as ten pounds, by adding other merchandise to your order, either for yourself or by getting your neighbors to join you in making up a large order, **you can make the shipment very profitable. Read Paragraph K before making up your order.**

Paragraph N.

CLUB ORDERS.

TO EQUALIZE OR REDUCE THE COST OF TRANSPORTATION, we advise the sending of club orders. Anyone can get up a club. Simply have your neighbors or friends send their orders in with yours and advise us to ship all to one person by freight. If each customer writes his order under his own name, it will be a very easy matter for us to keep each one's goods separate, and the freight charges will be next to nothing when shared by several persons.

IF YOU LIVE AT A FAR DISTANT POINT and wish to order some article or articles of merchandise, which, together, would weigh about twenty pounds, the value of which may be $5.00 or less, and you find that the express charges will be from $1.25 to $2.75, and there is nothing further in our catalogue that you require at the time, show this catalogue to your friends. Let your friends add twenty, thirty or forty pounds, even fifty or seventy-five pounds of goods, then the goods can go by freight and the one hundred pounds by freight will cost no more than twenty pounds by express.

Paragraph O.

HOW TO RETURN GOODS.

BEFORE RETURNING THE GOODS to us in any manner, we would ask that you communicate with us in regard to them, as we are frequently able to adjust matters in a manner that will avoid the delay occasioned by return of goods.

INVOICE NUMBER. Be sure to mention your invoice number under which goods were shipped to you by us.

NEVER RETURN GOODS BY EXPRESS if the weight is more than twenty-five pounds, as it is cheaper to send heavy packages by freight. **When you return goods by express or freight** be sure to enclose in the package your letter of instructions and particulars. **Don't forget** we must always have your invoice number. **Never write us** about a shipment and omit the invoice number. **Don't forget** that a letter containing full instructions should be in all express and freight shipments returned. **Don't forget** we must have your full name and address, exactly as given in the original shipment, in order to properly adjust any matter pertaining to an order returned.

WHEN RETURNING A PACKAGE BY MAIL, write your name, address and invoice number plainly in the upper left hand corner, providing you do not have one of the labels which we furnish when we know goods are to be returned. **Send us by separate mail** the particulars and instructions.

DO NOT ENCLOSE WRITTEN MATTER of any kind in mail packages, as by so doing you are liable to a fine of $10.00 and double letter rate postage.

DO NOT UNDER ANY CIRCUMSTANCES ENCLOSE MONEY WITH THE RETURNED GOODS.

THE UNITED STATES POSTAL LAWS AND REGULATIONS require that all packages of merchandise sent in the mails must be wrapped or enveloped in such a manner that their contents may be readily examined by the postmaster without destroying the wrapper. **Never seal packages returned by mail,** but tie them securely with twine.

DO NOT FAIL TO REGISTER MAIL PACKAGES WORTH $2.00 OR MORE. Merchandise is sometimes lost when sent by open mail. A package can be registered for 8 cents and if necessary can be traced. **Do not enclose money with returned merchandise.** We cannot be responsible for its loss.

Paragraph P.

ABOUT DELAYED SHIPMENTS.

IF YOU HAVE SENT US AN ORDER FOR GOODS and you think it is time they should have arrived, before writing us concerning the delay please consider the following:

While we are willing and glad to answer all kinds of inquiries, to make every possible kind of research, to quickly look up and trace any shipment said to have been delayed, we are daily in receipt of hundreds of letters claiming that goods have been delayed, when the orders have been filled by us with all possible promptness, and have been handled by the railroad or express companies with their usual dispatch. The investigation simply shows the customer is impatient and has not allowed sufficient time for the order to reach us, we to fill the order and the railroad or express company to deliver the goods.

WE FILL ALL ORDERS with the greatest possible dispatch consistent with proper care and safety. It requires from two to six days after your order is received for us to ship goods. Where goods are ordered that have to be made to order or finished after received, such as tailoring, upholstered furniture, vehicles, etc., additional time must be allowed. Goods shipped direct from our factory, such as stoves, sewing machines, furniture and a few other heavy items, require from five to ten days to make shipment, add to this the necessary time for the express company or railroad company to carry the goods to you and you will seldom, if ever, be disappointed in the arrival of your goods.

BEFORE WRITING us concerning goods ordered or before calling for them at your railroad station, first consider if you have allowed ample time for your order to reach Chicago, the required time for us to fill same, as above stated, and for the railroad or express company to carry it to you. If you will always do this, allowing liberal time, bearing in mind that express and railroad companies sometimes delay goods a few days after they receive them, you will seldom, if ever, have occasion to write us concerning a delay. If there is more than one freight or express agent in your town, always make inquiries at each office before writing us concerning non-arrival of goods, as it often happens that a shipment is at one office and the notification card has miscarried, while the customer has been making inquiries at another office.

IN CASE, HOWEVER, an order should be delayed beyond the time above referred to, and you write us, do not fail to mention the date on which you mailed your order, the name and address as given in the original order, the value and nature of the cash you sent, and, if possible, give us your invoice number, for if you received from us a postal card acknowledging the receipt of the order, you will find the invoice number on the card mailed you.

ABOUT MISTAKES. If we make a mistake in filling your order, kindly give us a chance to correct it. We try to fill every order absolutely correct, but errors sometimes creep in. They do in all business houses. You will always find us willing to correct ours. Do not fail to write us in case of an error; otherwise we may never know of it.

CHANGE OF ADDRESS. We would kindly request our customers to **immediately advise** us concerning any **change of address,** as we keep our records according to states and towns, and should you order from one town and then write from another, we would be compelled to send for further information before we could adjust the matter in question.

Paragraph Q.

ABOUT UNNECESSARY CORRESPONDENCE.

WHILE WE EMPLOY OVER ONE HUNDRED STENOGRAPHERS for the accommodation of our customers, and are willing and glad to answer all letters and furnish any special information that may be desired, we daily receive hundreds of letters of inquiry about things that are plainly answered in this catalogue, hundreds of letters which might be avoided, saving loss of time and unnecessary expense.

IT IS VERY SELDOM NECESSARY TO WRITE US, asking what the freight or express charge will be on any article to any point, for, from the weights given under each description and from the express and freight rates shown on pages 14 to 18, you can calculate very closely what the freight or express will amount to and save the time and trouble of writing for this information.

OUR OLD CUSTOMERS rarely ever have occasion to write us, asking what the freight or express will be on any article, and new customers will hardly ever have occasion to if they will refer to pages 14 to 18.

LETTERS CONCERNING SHIPMENTS CAN OFTEN BE AVOIDED. We receive hundreds of letters every day from parties who have ordered and have not allowed sufficient time for the order to reach us, the goods to be packed and shipped and for the goods to reach them. **(See paragraph P.)** **Never write about a shipment until ample time has been allowed for the goods to reach you.** We receive hundreds of letters asking for prices or special prices on articles on which the price is plainly printed in this catalogue. All such letters are unnecessary, for it only means an answer again referring you to the catalogue.

WE RECEIVE HUNDREDS OF LETTERS DAILY from people who ask us if we can't make changes in the goods as advertised, that they want the same thing or things with slight changes. This is all irregular and could not be furnished excepting at an advanced price, and we have found it impracticable to make any such changes, and to all such inquiries we can save you the time and trouble by saying that no changes can be made from those made plain in this catalogue. Since we answer as many as ten thousand letters a day, you will help us where a reply is necessary by answering on the back of our letter.

Paragraph R.

INSTALLMENT PLAN OR PARTIAL PAYMENT.

WE RECEIVE HUNDREDS OF LETTERS asking for prices on certain goods, especially on organs, pianos and other goods that run into money, from parties who wish to buy on the installment plan and to make settlement in notes. All these inquiries can be avoided for the reason that our only terms are cash, we never extend time, we open no accounts nor allow goods to be sold on the installment plan.

Paragraph S.

ABOUT CLAIMS FOR DAMAGE AND OVERCHARGE ON TRANSPORTATION.

WE CAREFULLY PACK AND DELIVER ALL OUR GOODS in good condition on board the cars, either in Chicago or at the factory, as made plain in this catalogue. We accept a receipt from the railroad company for the goods in good order, and it very rarely happens that any goods that we pack and ship reach their destination in bad order.

IF IT SHOULD EVER HAPPEN that any article reaches you marred, scratched, broken or in any way defective, be sure to have the railroad agent make a notation of such defect on the freight receipt (expense bill) he gives you. You can then present your claim for damage to the railroad agent from whom you received the goods, it being his duty at that end to take the matter up with the officials of that road and collect for you any damage that may have occurred.

WHILE THE PROPER PLACE FOR TAKING UP ANY CLAIMS FOR DAMAGE OR OVERCHARGE ON TRANSPORTATION on goods in transit, either by freight or express, is through the agent who delivers the goods, the trouble, delay and expense of writing us to do this can also be avoided. We, however, guarantee the goods we ship to reach you in the same perfect condition they leave us, and to be satisfactory to you in every way, and if you find them damaged in transit and you accept them and the agent hesitates to take and collect your claim for damage, you can write us enclosing your receipt (expense bill) for the freight charges paid the agent, with the agent's written notation on the expense bill, stating what the damage is, and we will take the matter up at this end, collect the damage and send the money to you. **It will be impossible for us to consider claims for damages to shipments unless the expense bill bears a notation to the effect that the shipment was received in bad condition.**

WHILE WE HAVE a large corps of stenographers and corresponding clerks in our employ, whose duty it is to promptly and courteously answer all inquiries and give all desired information, in order to maintain our extremely low prices the cost of conducting our business must be cut down to the very minimum, and to do this our customers are especially requested before writing us concerning freight rates, claims, delays, or before asking us for information of any kind, to carefully consult this catalogue, and if they will do this they will find in nine cases out of ten the information can be had or the adjustment of damage made, without going to the trouble of writing us or putting us to the expense of corresponding on the subject.

ON THE BASIS OF BETTER VALUE THAN YOU CAN POSSIBLY GET ELSEWHERE, the best possible service, every item you order guaranteed to reach you in perfect condition and to prove perfectly satisfactory or your money to be immediately returned to you; under our binding guarantee to please you in every way in your dealings with us, we respectfully solicit your orders.

FREIGHT AND EXPRESS RATES.

THE FOLLOWING TABLE IS TO VARIOUS POINTS IN EVERY STATE AND TERRITORY . . . .

IT IS NOT NECESSARY to write us for freight and express rates, as the following tables and the instructions we herewith give will show just what the freight and express rates are to different points in the United States. Take the nearest town to your own in the table below, and the freight rate to your town will be almost, if not exactly, the same for 100 pounds.

YOU MUST PAY THE FREIGHT OR EXPRESS CHARGES AT THE TIME YOU GET THE GOODS FROM THE STATION.

Don't be afraid of the freight or express charges; they never amount to much compared with what we can save you in cost. In fact we guarantee that you will save money on every purchase after you pay the freight or express charges and if you do not find it so, YOU CAN RETURN THE GOODS AND WE WILL REFUND ALL YOUR MONEY AND YOU WILL NOT BE OUT ONE CENT.

NO MATTER HOW FAR AWAY you may live, we can still save you money on your purchases. **DISTANCE IS NO DRAWBACK.** Remember, your local dealer must pay the exact same rate of freight that you pay on the goods, and this cost of freight he must add to the cost of the goods when he figures his selling price. But our prices on practically everything are so very much lower than the same quality of goods can be had from smaller concerns, that after you pay all transportation charges, even to very distant points, we can save you money.

HOW TO FIGURE FREIGHT CHARGES.

SEE PAGE 18 for list of articles and their class, then find the weight of the desired article (which we aim to give underneath its description in this catalogue), and if not given you can estimate the weight very closely. Find the rate in following table under its class, and multiply the rate by the weight, and you have the freight charges sufficiently correct for your information.

THE RAILROADS have what is called a **MINIMUM FREIGHT CHARGE**, meaning the least amount of money they will haul a freight shipment for, no matter how little it weighs. **In the first column we quote the minimum freight charge or explain how it is made up.**

Rule 1. THE MINIMUM CHARGE is for 100 pounds at the class to which the article belongs, but not less than 50 cents.

Rule 2. THE MINIMUM CHARGE is for 100 pounds at the class to which the article belongs.

***Rule 3. THE MINIMUM CHARGE** is for 100 pounds at the class to which the article belongs, but not less than 75 cents.

EXPRESS CHARGES.

In the following table are given the express rates for 100 pounds, but for shipments weighing less than that see page 17. Freight is the cheapest way to ship orders weighing 20 pounds or more. Make your order for 100 pounds, if possible, and get the benefit of the minimum charge, as shipments weighing from 20 to 100 pounds usually cost no more than 20 pounds. Where two express rates are shown, add them together to figure the charges on packages weighing 7 pounds or under. For packages weighing more that 7 pounds, figure the charges at each rate separately, and then add these amounts for the total.

	Min. freight charge	1st class freight per 100 lbs	2d class freight per 100 lbs	3rd class freight per 100 lbs	4th class freight per 100 lbs	5th class freight per 100 lbs	6th class freight per 100 lbs	Express per 100 lbs
ALABAMA—								
Birmingham	Rule 3	$1 19	$1 03	$0 83	$0 64	$0 55	$0 42	$ 3 75
Brewton	Rule 3	1 55	1 28	1 05	86	79	72	4 00
Dadeville	Rule 3	1 82	1 54	1 23	99	84	65	4 50
Decatur	Rule 3	1 19	1 03	83	64	55	42	3 25
Gadsden	Rule 3	1 47	1 26	1 06	85	71	58	3 75
Mobile	$1 10	1 10	90	75	58	47	41	4 00
Montgomery	Rule 3	1 38	1 26	1 03	80	67	53	3 75
Ozark	Rule 3	1 88	1 68	1 43	1 11	93	76	4 75
Randolph, Bibb Co	Rule 3	1 67	1 42	1 21	97	88	64	4 00
Tuscaloosa	Rule 3	1 48	1 28	1 04	81	70	54	4 00
ARIZONA—								
Benson	$1 51	3 44	3 01	2 66	2 10	......	......	10 75
Flagstaff	3 40	3 90	3 40	2 70	2 10	......	......	10 50
Holbrook	3 39	3 74	3 39	2 70	2 10	......	......	10 25
Phœnix	1 70	3 79	3 33	2 90	2 30	......	......	12 50
Prescott	1 70	3 79	3 33	2 90	2 30	......	......	12 00
Seligman	3 40	3 90	3 40	2 70	2 10	......	......	10 75
Solomanville	1 90	3 35	3 10	2 78	2 30	......	......	10 25
Tucson	1 45	3 59	3 13	2 70	2 10	......	......	11 00
Yucca	3 40	3 90	3 40	2 70	2 10	......	......	11 00
ARKANSAS—								
Daleville	Rule 2	1 30	1 09	90	66	......	......	3 75
Fort Smith	Rule 2	1 30	1 06	87	69	......	......	4 00
Fayetteville	Rule 2	1 45	1 22	1 01	75	......	......	3 75
Knobel	Rule 2	95	84	68	33	......	......	2 75
Little Rock	Rule 2	1 20	1 01	77	59	......	......	3 50
Morrillton	Rule 2	1 35	1 16	90	66	......	......	3 75
Newport, Jackson Co	Rule 2	1 00	83	67	55	......	......	3 25
Pine Bluff	Rule 2	1 20	1 01	77	59	......	......	3 50
Texarkana	Rule 2	1 37	1 23	1 08	94	......	......	4 00
Van Buren	Rule 2	1 30	1 06	87	69	......	......	4 00
CALIFORNIA—								
Bakerfield	$2 85	3 78	3 34	2 90	2 56	......	......	11 50
Fresno	2 85	3 50	3 08	2 65	2 32	......	......	11 50
Los Angeles	2 60	3 00	2 60	2 20	1 90	......	......	11 50
Needles	3 40	3 90	3 40	2 70	2 10	......	......	11 50
Redding	2 85	3 61	3 16	2 70	2 32	......	......	12 50
Sacramento	2 60	3 00	2 60	2 20	1 90	......	......	11 50
San Bernardino	2 85	3 34	2 90	2 46	2 13	......	......	11 50
San Diego	2 60	3 00	2 60	2 20	1 90	......	......	11 50
San Francisco	2 60	3 00	2 60	2 20	1 90	......	......	11 50
Santa Cruz	2 85	3 21	2 79	2 37	2 05	......	......	12 25
Termo	3 10	5 20	4 57	3 74	3 01	......	......	13 25
COLORADO—								
Alamosa	1 65	3 05	2 55	2 02	1 56	......	......	$6 00- 2 00
Cripple Creek	1 35	2 70	2 26	1 83	1 52	......	......	7 50
Denver	75	2 05	1 65	1 25	97	......	......	6 00
Eagle	1 97	3 37	2 87	2 29	1 75	......	......	6 00- 2 75
Grand Junction	2 15	3 60	3 05	2 45	1 82	......	......	8 00
Greeley	75	2 05	1 65	1 25	97	......	......	6 00
Gunnison	1 75	3 20	2 65	2 10	1 72	......	......	8 00
Kit Carson	50	1 99	1 65	1 25	97	......	......	5 50
La Junta	75	2 05	1 65	1 25	97	......	......	6 00
Mancos	2 60	4 10	3 50	2 85	2 17	......	......	6 00- 4 00
Montrose	2 00	3 45	2 90	2 30	1 77	......	......	6 00- 3 00
Pagosa Springs	2 39	3 80	3 29	2 61	2 09	......	......	
Pueblo	75	2 05	1 65	1 25	97	......	......	6 00
Sterling	75	1 81	1 58	1 25	97	......	......	5 50
Thatcher	75	2 05	1 65	1 25	97	......	......	6 00
CONNECTICUT—								
Bridgeport	82	82	71	55	39	33	......	3 00
Canaan	82	82	71	55	39	33	......	3 00
Hartford	82	82	71	55	39	33	......	3 00
New Haven	82	82	71	55	39	33	......	3 00
New London	82	82	71	55	39	33	......	3 00
New Milford	82	82	71	55	39	33	......	3 00
Putnam	82	82	71	55	39	33	......	3 00
DELAWARE—								
Dover	75	75	65	50	35	30	......	2 90
Farmington	75	75	65	50	35	30	......	3 00
Middletown	75	75	65	50	35	30	......	2 90
Newark	73	73	63	48	33	28	......	2 25
DIST. OF COLUMBIA—								
Langdon	72	72	62	47	32	27	......	2 25
Washington	72	72	62	47	32	27	......	2 25
FLORIDA—								
Carrabelle	Rule 3	2 31	2 00	1 79	1 51	1 31	1 09	5 75
Caryville	Rule 2	1 65	1 37	1 04	92	85	78	4 50
Gainesville	Rule 2	1 87	1 64	1 43	1 23	1 05	83	5 50
Jacksonville	Rule 2	1 35	1 14	1 40	87	73	58	5 00
Key West	Rule 2	1 93	1 64	1 48	1 23	93	86	.....
Pensacola	$1 10	1 10	90	75	58	47	41	4 25
Punta Gorda	Rule 2	2 37	2 05	1 75	1 56	1 34	1 09	6 50
Sebastian	Rule 2	2 29	1 98	1 68	1 49	1 28	1 08	6 50
Tallahassee	Rule 2	1 99	1 70	1 44	1 18	98	80	5 25
Tampa (all rail)	Rule 2	1 85	1 57	1 34	1 19	1 01	95	6 00
Tampa (rail and water; via Mobile)	$1 35	1 47	1 34	1 03	93	78	63	.....
GEORGIA—								
Albany	Rule 2	1 67	1 43	1 21	98	82	67	4 75
Atlanta	Rule 2	1 47	1 26	1 06	85	71	58	3 75
Brunswick	Rule 2	1 35	1 14	1 00	87	73	58	4 50
Cairo	Rule 2	1 95	1 61	1 26	1 11	1 00	86	5 25

	Min. freight charge	1st class freight per 100 lbs	2d class freight per 100 lbs	3d class freight per 100 lbs	4th class freight per 100 lbs	5th class freight per 100 lbs	6th class freight per 100 lbs	Express per 100 lbs.
GEORGIA—Continued								
Columbus	Rule 2	$1 47	$1 26	$1 06	$0 85	$0 71	$0 58	$4 50
Doerun	Rule 2	2 37	2 01	1 67	1 48	1 25	1 00	5 75
Folkston	Rule 2	1 74	1 49	1 32	1 16	96	76	5 25
Macon	Rule 2	1 47	1 26	1 06	85	71	58	4 25
Quitman	Rule 2	1 87	1 60	1 35	1 10	91	74	5 25
Rome	Rule 2	1 47	1 26	1 06	85	71	58	3 75
Savannah	Rule 2	1 35	1 14	1 00	87	73	58	5 00
Stillmore	Rule 2	1 90	1 63	1 43	1 25	1 02	81	5 00
Thomasville	Rule 2	1 87	1 60	1 35	1 10	91	74	5 00
Valdosta	Rule 2	1 87	1 60	1 35	1 10	91	74	5 50
Warrenton	Rule 2	1 77	1 53	1 31	1 07	85	71	4 50
IDAHO—								
American Falls	$2 40	3 30	2 80	2 20	1 82	......	......	8 75
Boise City	2 40	3 30	2 80	2 45	2 02	......	......	10 00
Gem	2 85	3 60	3 10	2 60	2 10	......	......	10 00
Idaho Falls	2 40	3 30	2 80	2 20	1 82	......	......	8 00
Ketchum	2 65	3 55	3 05	2 45	2 07	......	......	10 00
Moscow	2 85	3 60	3 10	2 60	2 10	......	......	10 00
Mountain Home	2 40	3 30	2 80	2 45	2 02	......	......	10 00
Pocatello	2 40	3 30	2 80	2 20	1 82	......	......	8 00
Spencer	2 40	3 30	2 80	2 20	1 82	......	......	8 00
ILLINOIS—								
Baldwin	50	77	62	49	37	......	......	2 00
Belvidere	25	35	29	24	17	......	......	75
Cairo	25	59	48	39	25	......	......	1 75
Danville	25	30	25	20	14	......	......	1 00
Freeport	25	39	32	24	18	......	......	1 00
Joliet	25	22	19	15	10	......	......	50
Litchfield	25	47	38	29	23	......	......	1 25
Milan, Rock Island Co	25	47	37	29	22	......	......	1 25
Mt. Vernon	25	50	40	30	25	......	......	1 50
Peoria	25	40	32	24	18	......	......	1 00
Quincy	25	47	38	29	22	......	......	1 25
Springfield	25	47	38	29	22	......	......	1.00
INDIANA—								
Bedford	37	37	32	24	16	13	......	1 25
Connersville	39	39	33	25	17	14	......	1 50
Elkhart	25	25	22	20	13	09	......	75
Evansville	40	40	34	25	17	15	......	1 75
Ft. Wayne	29	29	25	20	14	11	......	75
Goshen	25	25	22	20	13	09	......	75
Indianapolis	32	32	27	22	14	12	......	1 25
Lafayette	30	30	25	20	13	10	......	90
New Albany	40	40	34	25	17	15	......	1 50
Terre Haute	32	32	27	22	14	12	......	1 25
INDIAN TERRITORY—								
Atoka	Rule 2	1 50	1 29	1 07	93	......	......	3 75
Checotah	Rule 2	1 35	1 16	90	70	......	......	3 25
Eufaula	Rule 2	1 37	1 20	92	75	......	......	3 50
Kiowa	Rule 2	1 48	1 28	1 04	85	......	......	3 75
Red Fork	Rule 2	1 21	1 03	80	57	......	......	3 75
South McAllister	Rule 2	1 40	1 20	95	74	......	......	3 75
Vinita	Rule 2	1 25	1 03	83	60	......	......	3 25
Wagoner	Rule 2	1 30	1 10	85	64	......	......	3 25
Wewoka	Rule 2	1 50	1 29	1 07	89	......	......	4 00
IOWA—								
Alta	$0 25	80	65	45	32	......	......	2 00
Audubon	25	80	65	45	32	......	......	2 00
Bedford	25	80	65	45	32	......	......	2 00
Bode	25	75	63	44	31	......	......	1 75
Burlington	25	47	38	29	22	......	......	1 25
Carroll	25	79	62	44	31	......	......	2 00
Cedar Rapids	25	58	47	35	24	......	......	1 50
Centerville	25	68	57	40	29	......	......	1 75
Council Bluffs	25	80	65	45	32	......	......	2 00
Davenport	25	46	37	29	22	......	......	1 25
Des Moines	25	68	57	40	29	......	......	1 75
Hamburg	25	80	65	45	32	......	......	2 00
Ireton	25	83	67	46	33	......	......	2 40
Keokuk	25	47	38	29	22	......	......	1 25
Mason City	25	63	53	42	26	......	......	1 75
Muscatine	25	47	38	29	22	......	......	1 25
Ottumwa	25	61	50	36	26	......	......	1 75
Waterloo	25	60	50	40	25	......	......	1 75
Waukon	25	60	50	40	25	......	......	1 50
KANSAS—								
Atchison	25	80	65	45	32	......	......	2 00
Council Grove	50	1 29	1 05	80	60	......	......	3 25
Dodge City	50	1 67	1 43	1 16	92	......	......	4 50
Ft. Scott	50	97	81	55	37	......	......	2 75
Garnett	50	1 05	86	65	45	......	......	3 00
Great Bend	50	1 46	1 23	95	73	......	......	4 00
Hartland	50	1 74	1 49	1 22	97	......	......	5 00
Leavenworth	25	80	65	45	32	......	......	2 00
Leoti	50	1 70	1 46	1 18	92	......	......	4 75
Mankato	50	1 33	1 13	85	64	......	......	3 50
Meade	50	1 60	1 38	1 15	93	......	......	4 25
Norton	50	1 52	1 29	1 05	84	......	......	4 00
Sawyer	50	1 57	1 34	1 05	82	......	......	4 25
Topeka	50	1 09	89	64	47	......	......	2 75
Vesper	50	1 38	1 17	91	67	......	......	3 75
Wichita	50	1 40	1 18	91	70	......	......	3 75

	Min. freight charge	1st class freight per 100 lbs	2d class freight per 100 lbs	3d class freight per 100 lbs	4th class freight per 100 lbs	5th class freight per 100 lbs	6th class freight per 100 lbs	Express per 100 lbs
KENTUCKY—								
Alexander, Fulton Co.	Rule 1	$0 80	$0 66	$0 53	$0 43	$0 34	$0 29	$2 10
Ashland	$0 45	45	39	30	21	18	15	2 00
Burnside	Rule 1	93	78	66	48	43	37	2 75
Campbellsville	Rule 1	97	83	69	56	49	44	2 25
Frankfort	Rule 1	66	57	45	34	31	27	2 00
Henderson (Eastern Class.)	$0 48	48	41	30	22	18	......	2 00
Hickman	60	60	50	40	33	27	24	3 25
Louisville (East'n Class.)	41	41	35	26	18	15	......	1 50
Maysville (East'n Class.)	44	44	38	29	20	17	......	2 00
Owensboro (East'n Class.)	48	48	41	30	22	18	......	2 00
Paducah	60	60	50	40	25	22	18	1 75
Paris	Rule 1	68	59	36	32	29	25	2 00
***LOUISIANA—**								
Alexandria	Rule 2	1 30	1 10	92	78	......	......	4 75
Baton Rouge	$1 10	1 10	90	75	58	47	41	3 75
Crowley	Rule 2	1 43	1 22	98	82	......	......	5 00
Kentwood	Rule 2	1 39	1 13	95	78	65	57	3 75
Lake Charles	Rule 2	1 50	1 29	1.02	85	......	......	4 75
Many	Rule 2	1 50	1 29	1 09	1 00	......	......	5 00
Monroe	Rule 2	1 37	1 17	99	84	......	......	4 25
Morgan City	Rule 2	1 29	1 11	89	75	......	......	4 50
Moreauville	Rule 2	1 50	1 29	1 09	1 00	......	......	5 85
New Orleans	$1 10	1 10	90	75	58	47	41	3 75
Ponchatoula	Rule 2	1 40	1 13	95	78	65	57	3 75
Shreveport	Rule 2	1 37	1 07	99	84	......	......	4 25
MAINE—								
Augusta	$1 07	1 02	89	69	49	41	......	3 00
Alfred	82	82	71	55	39	33	......	2 90
Bangor	1 07	98	85	65	47	40	......	3 25
Brownville Junction	1 07	95	83	66	49	42	......	3 75
Caribou	1 58	1 58	1 27	99	82	55	......	4 35
Eastport	1 07	1 07	91	72	51	43	......	4 00
Kennebunk	1 07	89	77	61	44	38	......	2 75
Lowelltown	1 08	1 08	95	77	59	51	......	$3 50- 60
Ludlow	1 32	1 32	1 10	86	69	50	......	4 00
Portland and Lewiston	82	82	71	55	39	33	......	3 00
Rockland	82	82	71	55	39	33	......	3 25
MARYLAND—								
Annapolis	77	77	69	53	38	32	......	2 50
Baltimore	72	72	62	47	32	27	......	2 25
Brandywine	75	75	66	49	33	29	...	2 75
Elkton	73	73	63	48	47	28	......	2 75
Finksburg	72	72	62	47	32	27	......	2 75
Frederick	72	72	62	47	32	27	......	2 25
Germantown	72	72	62	47	32	27	......	2 25
Hagerstown	72	72	62	47	32	27	......	2 25
Port Tobacco	75	75	65	49	34	29	......	2 75
MASSACHUSETTS—								
Ashley Falls	82	82	71	55	39	33	......	3 00
Barnstable	82	82	71	55	39	33	......	2 50- 75
Bellingham Jct.	82	82	71	55	39	33	......	2 90
Boston	82	82	71	55	39	33	......	2 50
Graniteville	82	82	71	55	39	33	......	2 50
Hinsdale	82	82	71	55	39	33	......	2 50
Jefferson	82	82	71	55	39	33	......	2 75
Lakeville	82	82	71	55	39	33	......	2 50- 60
New Bedford	82	82	71	55	39	33	......	3 00
Provincetown	82	82	71	55	39	33	......	2 50- 75
Springfield	82	82	71	55	39	33	......	2 50
Templeton	82	82	71	55	39	33	......	2 75
***MICHIGAN—**								
Adrian	35	35	30	23	15	13	......	1 25
Alba	53	53	45	34	26	20	......	1 85
Alpena	56	56	50	38	26	22	......	2 40
Bay City	37	37	32	24	16	13	......	1 75
Boyne Falls	53	53	45	34	26	20	......	2 00
Cheboygan	55	55	45	35	26	20	......	2 50
Detroit	37	37	32	24	16	13	......	1 25
Emmett	37	37	32	24	16	13	......	1 50
Grand Rapids	33	33	29	22	15	12	......	1 25
Kalamazoo	30	30	26	21	14	11	......	75
Lansing	36	36	31	23	16	13	......	1 25
Lake Linden	50	85	71	57	37	......	......	2 25
Manistee	47	47	41	31	23	18	......	1 75
Munising	25	75	65	48	38	......	......	2 00
Ishpeming	25	60	50	40	28	......	......	1 75
Paris	42	42	36	27	19	16	......	1 50
Petoskey	53	53	45	34	26	20	......	2 00
MINNESOTA—								
Albert Lea	25	60	50	40	25	......	......	2 00
Audubon	50	1 30	1 10	85	60	......	......	3 75
Crookston	50	1 27	1 07	94	59	......	......	4 25
Duluth	25	65	55	44	28	......	......	2 25
Edgerton	25	86	70	49	38	......	......	2 50
Farris	50	1 22	1 03	81	56	......	......	2 00- 1 75
Hallock	50	1 45	1 22	96	68	......	......	2 00- 2 50
Mankato	25	65	55	43	27	......	......	2 00
Marshall	25	81	70	55	39	......	......	3 00
Menahga	50	1 16	98	77	53	......	......	2 00 1 75
Milan	25	90	77	64	43	......	......	2 75
Minneapolis	25	60	50	40	25	......	......	2 00
Moorhead	25	1 17	99	77	54	......	......	3 50
Redwood Falls	25	70	56	45	34	......	......	2 75
St. Vincent	50	1 51	1 27	1 00	71	......	......	2 00- 2 50
Tower	50	1 10	94	78	57	......	......	2 75
MISSISSIPPI—								
Ackerman	Rule 2	1 25	1 02	82	70	57	51	3 50
Hazlehurst	Rule 2	1 36	1 10	92	76	63	55	3 50
Holly Spring	Rule 1	1 09	93	77	64	51	44	2 85
Jackson	$1 18	1 18	99	80	67	56	49	3 50
Meridian	1 18	1 18	99	80	67	56	49	4 00
Mississippi City	Rule 1	1 67	1 40	1 13	90	77	68	4 25
Natchez	$1 10	1 10	90	75	58	47	41	3 75
Ocean Springs	Rule 2	1 55	1 31	1 06	84	71	62	4 25
Pocahontas	Rule 2	1 35	1 09	92	76	62	54	3 50
Port Gibson	$1 47	1 47	1 24	1 03	82	68	59	3 50
Roxie	Rule 2	1 57	1 26	1 06	84	71	62	3 75
State Line, Wayne Co.	Rule 2	1 54	1 32	1 13	94	76	65	4 00
Vicksburg	$1 10	1 10	90	75	58	47	41	3 50
MISSOURI—								
Charleston	60	84	69	54	42	......	......	2 40
Chicopee	50	1 41	1 18	89	73	......	......	4 00
Chillicothe	25	80	65	45	32	......	......	2 00
Clinton	50	82	72	50	37	......	......	2 50
MISSOURI—Continued.								
Hannibal	$0 25	$0 47	$0 38	$0 29	$0 22	......	......	$1 25
Independence	Rule 1	80	65	45	32	......	......	2 00
Jefferson City	$0 50	71	58	42	29	......	......	2 00
Kahoka	25	52	43	32	23	......	......	1 50
Kansas City	25	80	65	45	32	......	......	2 00
Kirkwood	60	66	55	43	37	......	......	1 90
Lincoln	75	1 01	79	57	43	......	......	2 50
Noel	50	1 12	91	68	49	......	......	3 50
Osceola	25	82	72	50	37	......	......	2 75
Paris	50	63	49	37	26	......	......	1 75
Poplar Bluff	60	1 03	86	69	58	......	......	2 50
Richards	50	97	81	55	37	......	......	2 75
Rolla	60	79	66	39	27	......	......	2 50
Springfield	50	90	72	50	37	......	......	3 00
St. Joseph	25	80	65	45	32	......	......	2 00
MONTANA—								
Big Timber	2 25	2 90	2 50	2 02	1 67	......	......	7 75
Billings	2 20	2 85	2 45	1 98	1 65	......	......	7 00
Butte	2 40	3 10	2 65	2 15	1 75	......	......	8 00
Chinook	1 98	2 54	2 23	1 79	1 53	......	......	$2 00- 5 25
Dillon	2 40	3 10	2 65	2 15	1 75	......	......	8 00
Glasgow	1 61	2 24	1 86	1 56	1 26	......	......	5 00- 2 00
Glendive	1 51	2 15	1 76	1 46	1 19	......	......	5 50
Great Falls	2 30	2 95	2 55	2 05	1 70	......	......	8 00
Helena	2 40	3 10	2 65	2 15	1 75	......	......	8 00
Iron Mountain	2 70	3 40	2 95	2 44	2 01	......	......	10 00
Kalispell	2 56	3 27	2 81	2 31	1 90	......	......	2 00- 7 00
Livingston	2 30	2 95	2 55	2 05	1 70	......	......	8 00
Missoula	2 50	3 20	2 75	2 25	1 85	......	......	9 00
NEBRASKA—								
Ainsworth	50	1 57	1 33	1 06	82	......	......	3 75
Alliance	50	1 81	1 58	1 25	97	......	......	5.00
Battle Creek	50	1 15	95	72	53	......	......	3 00
Beaver City	50	1 48	1 28	1 03	82	......	......	4 00
Chadron	50	1 90	1 64	1 34	1 03	......	......	4 75
Chappell	50	1 81	1 58	1 25	97	......	......	4 75
Cody	50	1 68	1 45	1 15	91	......	......	4 25
Crawford	50	2 02	1 76	1 43	1 17	......	......	4 75
Duncan	50	1 17	99	73	53	......	......	3 00
Grant	50	1 63	1 41	1 16	94	......	......	4 50
Hastings	50	1 31	1 11	83	62	......	......	3 50
Hemingford	50	1 85	1 62	1 31	1 01	......	......	5 00
Imperial	50	1 63	1 41	1 16	91	......	......	4 50
Lincoln	50	85	70	49	36	......	......	2 7[illegible]
Loup City	50	1 45	1 23	96	75	......	......	3 75
McCook	50	1 55	1 35	1 09	85	......	......	4 25
Morrill	50	2 17	1 85	1 43	1 15	......	......	4 25
Nelson	50	1 31	1 11	83	62	......	......	3 50
Ogallala	50	1 63	1 41	1 16	91	......	......	4 50
Omaha	25	80	65	45	32	......	......	2 00
O'Neill	50	1 30	1 08	88	66	......	......	3 25
Pawnee, Pawnee Co.	50	89	74	53	40	......	......	2 75
Sidney	50	1 81	1 58	1 25	97	......	......	5 00
Thedford	50	1 58	1 36	1 10	86	......	......	4 25
NEVADA—								
Austin	3 60	4 65	4 15	3 45	2 85	......	......	13 00
Carson	3 10	4 15	3 65	2 95	2 35	......	......	12 25
Elko	2 85	3 90	3 40	2 70	2 10	......	......	11 50
Eureka, Ormsby Co.	3 10	4 20	3 70	3 00	2 40	......	......	12 00
Hawthorne	3 35	4 90	4 40	3 70	3 10	......	......	13 50
Reno	2 85	3 90	3 40	2 70	2 10	......	......	11 50
Toana	2 85	3 90	3 40	2 70	2 10	......	......	11 50
NEW HAMPSHIRE—								
Berlin	82	82	71	55	39	$0 33	......	3 50
Colebrook	82	82	71	55	39	33	......	3 60
Conway	82	82	71	55	39	32	......	3 00
Dover	1 07	89	71	61	44	30	......	2 50
Enfield	82	82	71	55	39	33	......	3 00
Keene	82	82	71	55	39	33	......	2 75
Laconia	82	82	71	55	39	33	......	2 90
Manchester	82	82	71	55	39	33	......	2 50
Plymouth	82	82	71	55	39	33	......	3 25
Portsmouth	82	82	71	55	39	33	......	2 50
Suncook	82	82	71	55	39	33	......	2 75
NEW JERSEY—								
Bridgeton	80	80	70	55	40	35	......	2 50
Chatsworth	80	80	70	55	40	35	......	2 50
Lafayette	75	75	65	50	35	30	......	2 75
Middletown	80	80	70	55	40	35	......	2 75
Morristown	75	75	65	50	35	30	......	2 50
Mullica Hill	78	78	68	53	38	33	......	2 50
Newark	75	75	65	50	35	30	......	2 50
Oxford Furnace	75	75	65	50	35	30	......	2 50
Pleasantville	80	80	70	55	40	30	......	2 75
Pompton	75	75	65	50	35	30	......	2 75
NEW MEXICO—								
Albuquerque	1 72	2 32	2 10	1 80	1 52	......	......	7 25
Carlsbad	Rule 2	2 29	1 99	1 67	1 48	......	......	6 75
Clayton	$0 75	2 05	1 65	1 25	97	......	......	6 50
Las Vegas	1 65	2 32	2 10	1 80	1 52	......	......	7 25
Lordsburg	1 72	2 72	2 46	2 27	2 07	......	......	8 75
Raton	1 00	2 22	1 85	1 45	1 17	......	......	6 50
Roswell	Rule 2	2 29	1 90	1 67	1 48	......	......	6 75
Santa Fe	$1 72	2 32	2 10	1 80	1 52	......	......	7 25
Socorro	1 72	2 32	2 10	1 80	1 52	......	......	7 25
NEW YORK—								
Albany	72	72	63	48	34	29	......	2 25
Big Moose	82	82	71	55	39	33	......	3 00
Boston Corners	82	82	71	55	39	33	......	2 75
Buffalo	45	45	39	30	21	18	......	1 75
Canton, St. Lawrence Co.	82	82	71	55	39	33	......	3 00
Cortland	60	60	52	40	28	24	......	2 25
Delhi	73	73	63	48	33	28	......	3 00
Elmira	60	60	52	40	28	24	......	2 25
Fort Edward	82	82	71	55	39	33	......	2 75
Hastings, Oswego Co.	68	68	59	45	32	27	......	2 50
Lake Placid	1 52	1 52	1 34	1 05	78	63	......	3 50
Lyons, Wayne Co.	60	60	52	40	28	24	......	2 00
Malone	82	82	71	55	39	33	......	3 10
New York	75	75	65	50	35	30	......	2 50
North Creek	1 10	1 10	95	75	57	50	......	3 75
Nunda	56	56	48	37	26	22	......	2 35
Plattsburg	1 08	1 08	92	72	52	43	......	3 25
Poughkeepsie	75	75	65	50	35	30	......	2 50
Rochester	56	56	48	37	26	22	......	2 00
Saranac Lake	82	82	71	55	39	33	......	3 10
Warsaw	56	56	48	37	26	22	......	2 00
Watertown	75	75	65	50	35	30	......	2 75

***LOUISIANA**—Towns with four class rates are governed by Western classification. Towns with six class rates are governed by Southern classification.

***MICHIGAN**—Towns with four class rates are governed by Western classification. Towns with five class rates are governed by Eastern classification.

	Min. freight charge	1st class freight per 100 lbs	2nd class freight per 100 lbs	3d class freight per 100 lbs	4th class freight per 100 lbs	5th class freight per 100 lbs	6th class freight per 100 lbs	Express per 100 lbs
NORTH CAROLINA—								
Belhaven	$0 97	$1 17	$1 00	$0 80	$0 57	$0 47	$0 39	$3 50
Charlotte	Rule 3	1 40	1 20	95	70	60	47	4 00
Clinton	Rule 3	1 40	1 20	95	70	60	47	4 00
Culberson	Rule 3	1 82	1 55	1 33	1 10	97	72	4 50
Elk Park	Rule 3	1 84	1 62	1 37	1 10	95	80	....
Fayetteville	Rule 3	1 40	1 20	95	70	58	42	4 00
Goldsboro	Rule 3	1 33	1 13	89	64	55	42	3 75
Goldston	Rule 3	1 40	1 20	95	70	60	47	4 25
Greensboro	Rule 3	1 33	1 13	89	64	55	43	3 75
Halifax	Rule 3	1 32	1 12	89	64	55	43	3 50
Hertford	$0 97	1 02	87	67	47	39	32	3 25
Mount Airy	Rule 3	1 43	1 22	97	71	61	48	4 25
Newbern	Rule 3	1 10	93	72	54	45	36	4 25
Newport	Rule 3	1 35	1 15	90	65	56	44	4 50
Raleigh	Rule 3	1 33	1 13	89	64	55	43	4 00
Salisbury	Rule 3	1 40	1 20	95	70	60	47	3 75
Shelby	Rule 3	1 52	1 32	1 07	82	68	54	4 50
Wadesboro	Rule 3	1 40	1 20	95	70	60	47	4 50
Washington	Rule 3	1 10	93	74	56	48	39	3 50
Wilkesboro	Rule 3	1 43	1 22	97	71	61	48	4 00
NORTH DAKOTA—								
Aneta	$0 50	1 45	1 22	96	68	....	....	$2 00- 2 40
Bismarck	50	1 60	1 35	1 07	76	....	....	4 75
Bottineau	50	1 74	1 47	1 18	88	....	....	2 00- 3 00
Carrington	50	1 53	1 24	1 01	72	....	....	4 50
Cooperstown	50	1 44	1 21	95	67	....	....	4 50
Dickinson	50	1 87	1 58	1 28	98	....	....	5 25
Ellendale	25	1 19	1 03	77	56	....	....	3 25
Fargo	25	1 17	99	77	54	....	....	3 50
Grand Forks	50	1 27	1 07	84	59	....	....	4 25
Hannah	50	1 63	1 38	1 09	78	....	....	2 00- 3 00
Jamestown	50	1 46	1 23	97	68	....	....	4 25
Lakota	50	1 48	1 25	98	69	....	....	2 00- 2 75
Maddock	50	1 62	1 37	1 09	78	....	....	5 00
Medora	50	1 94	1 64	1 34	1 05	....	....	5 50
Minot	50	1 75	1 49	1 20	89	....	....	5 00
Pembina	50	1 51	1 27	1 00	71	....	....	4 50
Stanley	50	1 88	1 57	1 28	99	....	....	2 00- 4 00
St. John	50	1 70	1 43	1 14	84	....	....	2 00- 3 00
OHIO—								
Bellefontaine	37	37	32	24	16	13	....	1 50
Bucyrus	39	39	33	25	17	14	....	1 50
Caldwell	45	45	39	30	21	18	....	2 00
Canton	41	41	35	26	18	15	....	1 50
Chillicothe	44	44	38	29	19	17	....	1 75
Cincinnati	40	40	34	25	17	15	....	1 50
Cleveland	41	41	35	26	18	15	....	1 50
Columbus	41	41	35	26	18	15	....	1 50
Coshocton	44	44	35	29	19	17	....	1 75
Eayton	40	40	34	25	17	15	....	1 50
Defiance	33	33	29	22	15	12	....	1 00
Georgetown, Brown Co.	65	60	54	41	32	26	....	....
Greenville	39	39	33	25	17	14	....	1 25
Hillsboro	44	44	38	29	19	17	....	1 50
Jobs	45	45	39	29	21	18	....	2 00
Laura	39	39	33	25	17	14	....	1 50
Lima	37	37	32	24	16	13	....	1 25
Logan, Hocking Co	45	45	39	29	21	18	....	1 75
Marion	39	39	33	25	17	14	....	1 25
Ottawa, Putnam Co	37	37	32	24	16	13	....	1 25
Portsmouth	45	45	39	30	21	18	....	2 00
Steubenville	45	45	39	30	21	18	....	1 75
Toledo	37	37	32	24	16	13	....	1 25
Xenia	40	40	34	25	17	15	....	1 50
OKLAHOMA TER.—								
Alva	Rule 2	1 50	1 29	1 07	88	....	....	4 25
Calumet	Rule 2	1 50	1 29	1 07	95	....	....	4 25
El Reno	Rule 2	1 50	1 29	1 07	89	....	....	4 25
Guthrie	Rule 2	1 50	1 29	1 07	89	....	....	4 00
Kingfisher	Rule 2	1 50	1 29	1 07	89	....	....	4 25
Newkirk	Rule 2	1 46	1 24	98	77	....	....	4 00
Oklahoma	Rule 2	1 50	1 29	1 07	89	....	....	4 00
Tecumseh	Rule 2	1 50	1 29	1 07	89	....	....	4 00
OREGON—								
Arlington	$2 85	3 60	3 10	2 60	2 10	....	....	11 00
Baker City	2 85	3 60	3 10	2 60	2 10	....	....	10 00
Elgin	2 85	3 60	3 10	2 60	2 10	....	....	10 00
Eugene	2 85	3 50	3 02	2 59	2 26	....	....	12 25
Heppner	2 85	3 60	3 10	2 60	2 10	....	....	11 50
Huntington	2 85	3 60	3 10	2 60	2 10	....	....	10 00
La Grande	2 85	3 60	3 10	2 60	2 10	....	....	10 00
Lebanon	2 85	3 43	2 96	2 53	2 20	....	....	12 00
Leland	2 85	3 90	3 40	2 70	2 10	....	....	13 00
Medford	2 85	3 90	3 40	2 70	2 10	....	....	13 00
Monmouth	2 85	3 38	2 92	2 48	2 15	....	....	12 00
Natron	2 85	3 52	3 03	2 60	2 27	....	....	12 25
Pendleton	2 85	3 60	3 10	2 60	2 10	....	....	10 00
Portland	2 85	3 00	2 60	2 20	1 90	....	....	11 50
Roseburg	2 85	3 76	3 24	2 80	2 45	....	....	13 00
Salem	2 85	3 33	2 88	2 44	2 10	....	....	12 00
Sheridan, Yamhill Co	2 85	3 34	2 89	2 45	2 11	....	....	12 00
Troutdale	2 85	3 15	2 73	2 32	2 00	....	....	11 50
PENNSYLVANIA—								
Allentown, Lehigh Co.	73	73	63	48	33	28	....	2 50
Bedford	72	72	62	47	32	27	....	3 00
Blairsville	53	53	45	34	24	21	....	2 25
Driftwood	72	72	62	47	32	27	....	3 00
Erie	45	45	39	30	21	18	....	2 00
Gettysburg	72	72	62	47	32	27	....	2 25
Harrisburg	72	72	62	47	32	27	....	2 25
Huntingdon	72	72	62	47	32	27	....	2 75
Jackson Center	45	45	39	30	21	18	....	2 10
Larabee	56	56	48	37	26	22	....	2 25
Lewisburg	72	72	62	47	32	27	....	2 50
Nanticoke	73	73	63	48	33	28	....	2 50
New Castle	44	44	38	29	19	17	....	1 75
Philadelphia	73	73	63	48	33	28	....	2 25
Pittsburg	45	45	39	30	21	18	....	1 75
Pottsville	73	73	63	48	33	28	....	2 50
Reading, Berks Co	73	73	63	48	33	28	....	2 25
Scranton	73	73	63	48	33	28	....	2 50
Sharpsville	44	44	38	29	19	17	....	1 75
Tionesta	45	45	39	30	21	18	....	2 10
Towanda	73	73	63	48	33	28	....	2 25
Uniontown	50	50	43	33	23	20	....	2 00
RHODE ISLAND—								
Bristol	82	82	71	55	39	33	....	2 50- 40
Greene	82	82	71	55	39	33	....	3 00
RHODE ISLAND—Con.								
Pascoag	$0 82	$0 82	$0 71	$0 55	$0 39	$0 33	....	$3 00
Providence	82	82	71	55	39	33	....	2 50
Slocum	82	82	71	55	39	33	....	3 00
Westerly	82	82	71	55	39	33	....	3 00
SOUTH CAROLINA—								
Abbeville	Rule 3	1 56	1 41	1 11	84	70	$0 62	4 50
Aiken	Rule 3	1 56	1 41	1 11	84	70	59	5 00
Beaufort	Rule 3	1 35	1 14	1 00	87	73	58	5 50
Charleston	Rule 3	1 35	1 14	1 00	87	73	58	4 75
Columbia	Rule 3	1 47	1 26	1 06	82	68	56	4 50
Ehrhardt	Rule 3	1 95	1 65	1 45	1 26	1 03	83	6 00
Florence	Rule 3	1 57	1 37	1 09	82	67	54	4 50
Georgetown	Rule 3	1 32	1 14	93	67	55	43	5 25
Greenville	Rule 3	1 56	1 41	1 11	84	70	62	4 50
Greenwood	Rule 3	1 56	1 41	1 11	84	70	62	4 50
Hampton	Rule 3	1 75	1 49	1 29	1 14	94	76	5 50
Lancaster	Rule 3	1 52	1 32	1 07	82	68	54	4 50
Ridgeway	Rule 3	1 56	1 34	1 11	83	70	56	4 50
Spartanburg	Rule 3	1 56	1 41	1 11	84	70	62	4 50
SOUTH DAKOTA—								
Aberdeen	$0 25	1 14	95	67	50	....	....	3 25
Armour	25	1 10	95	74	50	....	....	2 75
Belle Fourche	75	2 35	2 05	1 63	1 32	....	....	5 75
Canton	25	83	68	47	34	....	....	2 25
Chamberlain	25	1 25	1 08	80	55	....	....	3 00
Deadwood	75	2 25	1 95	1 60	1 32	....	....	5 75
Edgemont	75	2 04	1 78	1 43	1 19	....	....	5 50
Eureka	25	1 27	1 04	85	65	....	....	3 50
Gettysburg	25	1 27	1 04	85	65	....	....	3 25
Huron	25	1 14	95	67	47	....	....	3 25
Milbank Junction	25	94	79	65	43	....	....	3 00
Mitchell	25	1 05	94	67	47	....	....	2 75
Pierre	25	1 22	1 04	80	60	....	....	3 25
Rapid City	75	2 16	1 90	1 55	1 28	....	....	5 50
Redfield	25	1 14	95	67	50	....	....	3 25
Sisseton	25	1 01	82	65	46	....	....	3 00
Spearfish	75	2 35	2 05	1 63	1 32	....	....	6 25
Vermilion	25	89	73	51	37	....	....	2 25
Watertown	25	1 00	85	65	46	....	....	3 25
Wolsey	25	1 14	95	67	47	....	....	3 25
TENNESSEE—								
Antioch	Rule 1	1 90	77	62	48	40	33	3 25
Allens Creek	Rule 2	1 23	1 07	88	71	60	54	3 75
Bristol (Eastern Class)	$0 84	84	72	55	39	33	....	3 75
Charlestown	Rule 3	1 50	1 29	1 08	86	75	57	3 50
Chattanooga	Rule 1	1 16	99	82	64	55	42	3 00
Clarksville	Rule 1	81	70	56	43	36	30	2 65
Clinton	Rule 1	1 32	1 14	95	74	63	49	3 50
Greenfield	Rule 1	91	75	60	49	37	34	2 50
Knoxville	Rule 1	1 16	99	82	64	55	42	3 50
Jackson	Rule 1	1 03	85	70	57	42	39	2 60
Manchester	Rule 2	1 23	1 07	89	71	62	53	3 50
Memphis	$0 85	85	65	55	43	37	31	2 75
Monteagle	Rule 3	1 43	1 24	1 03	85	75	67	3 50
Parson	Rule 1	1 00	83	68	56	44	38	3 25
TEXAS—								
Abilene	Rule 2	1 57	1 37	1 16	1 06	....	....	5 50
Amarillo	Rule 2	1 67	1 46	1 24	1 13	....	....	5 50
Austin	Rule 2	1 57	1 37	1 16	1 06	....	....	5 25
Beaumont	Rule 2	1 57	1 37	1 16	1 06	....	....	5 25
Canadian	Rule 2	1 62	1 42	1 20	1 10	....	....	5 25
Corpus Christi	Rule 2	1 57	1 37	1 16	1 06	....	....	6 50
Dallas	Rule 2	1 57	1 37	1 16	1 06	....	....	4 25
Denison	Rule 2	1 57	1 37	1 16	1 06	....	....	3 75
El Paso	Rule 2	1 69	1 50	1 34	1 26	....	....	7 00
Henrietta	Rule 2	1 57	1 37	1 16	1 06	....	....	4 50
Houston	Rule 2	1 57	1 37	1 16	1 06	....	....	5 25
Kerrville	Rule 2	1 64	1 44	1 22	1 09	....	....	6 50
Laredo	Rule 2	1 69	1 50	1 34	1 26	....	....	6 75
Llano	Rule 2	1 57	1 37	1 16	1 06	....	....	5 75
Lufkin	Rule 2	1 57	1 37	1 16	1 06	....	....	5 00
Palestine	Rule 2	1 57	1 37	1 16	1 06	....	....	5 00
Pecos	Rule 2	1 93	1 65	1 47	1 36	....	....	6 75
Port Lavaca	Rule 2	1 57	1 37	1 16	1 06	....	....	5 75
San Angelo	Rule 2	1 64	1 44	1 22	1 09	....	....	5 75
San Antonio	Rule 2	1 57	1 37	1 16	1 06	....	....	5 75
Sanderson	Rule 2	1 94	1 66	1 48	1 37	....	....	7 00
Seymour	Rule 2	1 57	1 37	1 16	1 06	....	....	5 25
Sierra Blanca	Rule 2	1 94	1 66	1 48	1 37	....	....	6 75
Spofford	Rule 2	1 69	1 49	1 30	1 21	....	....	6 75
Waco	Rule 2	1 57	1 37	1 16	1 06	....	....	4 75
UTAH—								
Belknap	$2 73	3 60	3 13	2 61	2 19	....	....	9 00
Bingham Jct	2 25	3 10	3 65	2 15	1 75	....	....	8 00
Cache Jct.	2 40	3 30	2 80	2 20	1 82	....	....	8 00
Colton	2 25	3 10	2 65	2 15	1 75	....	....	8 00
Dewey	2 39	3 25	2 79	2 20	1 82	....	....	8 00
Echo	2 25	3 10	2 65	2 15	1 75	....	....	8 00
Ephraim	2 50	3 30	2 83	2 31	1 89	....	....	8 25
Fairfield	2 50	3 35	2 89	2 37	1 95	....	....	8 50
Frisco	2 78	3 65	3 18	2 66	2 24	....	....	10 50
Heber	2 25	3 10	2 65	2 15	1 75	....	....	8 50
Kelton	2 85	3 90	3 40	2 70	2 10	....	....	9 25
Manti	2 50	3 30	2 83	2 31	1 89	....	....	8 25
Milford	2 73	3 60	3 13	2 61	2 19	....	....	10 25
Nephi	2 50	3 30	2 83	2 31	1 89	....	....	8 75
Ogden	2 25	3 10	2 65	2 15	1 75	....	....	8 00
Salt Lake City	2 25	3 10	2 65	2 15	1 75	....	....	8 00
Terminus	2 52	3 40	2 92	2 40	1 98	....	....	9 00
VERMONT—								
Bradford	82	82	71	55	39	33	....	3 25
Brattleboro	82	82	71	55	39	33	....	2 75
Burlington	82	82	71	55	39	33	....	3 25
Cavendish	82	82	71	55	39	33	....	3 00
Essex Jct.	82	82	71	55	39	33	....	3 25
Greensboro	82	82	71	55	39	33	....	3 25
Hartford	82	82	71	55	39	33	....	3 10
Leicester Jct.	82	82	71	55	39	33	....	3 25
Montpelier	82	82	71	55	39	33	....	3 25
North Bennington	82	82	71	55	39	33	....	2 75
Rutland	82	82	71	55	39	33	....	3 00
St. Albans	82	82	71	55	39	33	....	3 25
St. Johnsbury	82	82	71	55	39	33	....	3 25
***VIRGINIA—**								
Abingdon	84	84	72	55	39	33	....	3 75
Alexandria	72	72	62	47	32	27	....	2 25
Basic	72	72	62	47	32	27	....	3 00

	Min. freight charge	1st class freight per 100 lbs	2d class freight per 100 lbs	3d class freight per 100 lbs	4th class freight per 100 lbs	5th class freight per 100 lbs	6th class freight per 100 lbs	Express per 100 lbs
*** VIRGINIA—Continued.**								
Big Stone Gap	Rule 3	$1 20	$1 03	$0 83	$0 70	$0 63	$0 56	$3 25
Clarksville	Rule 1	1 27	1 08	83	56	48	39	3 50
Emporia	Rule 3	1 22	1 04	82	55	47	......	3 50
Farmville	$0 72	72	62	47	32	27	......	3 50
Fredericksburg	72	72	62	47	32	27	......	2 85
Harrisonburg	72	72	62	47	32	27	......	2 50
Lexington	72	72	62	47	32	27	......	2 75
Lynchburg	72	72	62	47	32	27	......	3 25
Martinsville	Rule 3	1 08	90	70	50	43	33	4 00
Morley	$0 75	75	65	50	35	30	......	3 00
New Castle	84	84	72	55	38	31	......	3 25
Old Point Comfort	72	72	62	47	32	27	......	2 75
Orange, Rockingham Co.	72	72	62	47	32	27	......	3 00
Pulaski City	84	84	72	55	39	33	......	3 25
Richmond	72	72	62	47	32	27	......	3 00
Riverton	72	72	62	47	32	27	......	2 75
Salem	72	72	62	47	32	27	......	3 25
Suffolk	72	72	62	47	32	27	......	3 00
Swordscreek	84	84	72	55	39	33	......	3 25
Virginia City	84	84	72	55	39	33	......	3 25
West Point	72	72	62	47	32	27	......	3 00
WASHINGTON—								
Anacortes	2 60	3 00	2 60	2 20	1 90	......	......	11 50
Chehalis	2 60	3 00	2 60	2 20	1 90	......	......	11 50
Colfax	3 10	3 60	3 10	2 60	2 10	......	......	10 00
Connell	3 10	3 60	3 10	2 60	2 10	......	......	10 00
Coulee City	3 10	3 60	3 10	2 60	2 10	......	......	10 00
Dayton	3 10	3 60	3 10	2 60	2 10	......	......	10 00
Easton	3 10	3 60	3 10	2 60	2 10	......	......	11 00
Hoquiam	2 60	3 00	2 60	2 20	1 90	......	......	11 50
Kalama	2 60	3 00	2 60	2 20	1 90	......	......	11 50
Meyers Falls	3 39	4 14	2 62	3 09	2 55	......	......	$2 00– 9 50
Monroe	2 85	3 25	2 80	2 37	2 05	......	......	2 00– 9 00
New Whatcom	2 60	3 00	2 60	2 20	1 90	......	......	11 50
Northport	3 52	4 27	3 70	3 13	2 59	......	......	2 00– 9 50
North Yakima	3 10	3 60	3 10	2 60	2 10	......	....	11 00
Olympia	2 60	3 00	2 60	2 20	1 90	......	......	11 50
Pasco	3 10	3 60	3 10	2 60	2 10			11 50
Snohomish	[illegible]	3 00	[illegible]	2 20	1 90	......	......	11 50
South Bend	2 60	3 00	2 60	2 20	1 90	......	......	11 50
Spokane	2 85	3 60	3 10	2 60	2 10	......	......	10 00
Tacoma	2 60	3 00	2 60	2 20	1 90	......	......	11 50
Walla Walla	3 10	3 60	3 10	2 60	2 10	......	......	10 00
Wallula	3 10	3 60	3 10	2 00	2 10	......	......	10 00
Wenatchee	3 10	3 60	3 10	2 60	2 10	......	....	2 00– 9 00
WEST VIRGINIA—								
Acme	84	84	72	55	38	$0 31	......	2 60
Beverly	97	85	72	56	40	34	......	3 25
Charleston	45	44	39	30	21	18	......	2 50
Clarksburg	57	57	49	38	26	21	......	2 00
Dingess	84	84	72	55	39	33	......	2 50
Grafton	57	57	49	38	26	21	......	2 00
WEST VIRGINIA—Con'd.								
Harpers Ferry	$0 72	$0 72	$0 62	$0 47	$0 32	$0 27	......	$2 25
Hinton	72	72	62	47	32	27	......	3 00
Martinsburg	72	72	62	47	32	27	......	2 25
Parkersburg	45	45	39	30	21	18	......	2 00
Parsons	97	90	76	60	41	53	......	3 25
Ripley Landing	45	45	39	30	21	18	......	2 25
Romney	77	77	66	50	34	29	......	2 25
Spencer	70	63	55	46	34	27	......	2 25
Wheeling	45	45	39	30	21	18	......	1 75
WISCONSIN—								
Ashland	25	65	55	44	28	......	......	2 00
Athens	25	55	46	36	24	......	......	2 00
Beloit	25	37	30	24	18	......	......	75
Cameron	25	65	55	44	28	......	......	1 75
Chelsea	25	60	50	40	25	......	......	2 00
Chippewa Falls	25	60	50	40	25	......	......	1 75
Fond du Lac	25	40	33	28	20	......	......	1 00
Grand Rapids	25	50	42	33	23	......	......	1 50
Green Bay	25	43	36	29	20	......	......	1 25
Hudson	25	60	50	40	25	......	......	1 75
Hurley	25	65	55	44	28	......	......	2 00
Lancaster	25	50	42	33	23	......	......	1 50
Madison	25	40	35	36	18	......	......	1 00
Manitowoc	25	30	25	21	16	......	......	1 10
Milwaukee	25	25	20	15	12	......	......	60
Mineral Pt	25	46	38	30	21	......	......	1 10
Mondovi	50	60	50	40	25	......	......	1 75
Oconto	25	43	36	29	23	......	......	1 50
Pembine	25	60	50	40	25	......	......	1 50
Prairie du Chien	25	50	42	33	23	......	......	1 50
Prentice	25	60	50	40	25	......	......	2 00
Richland Center	25	50	42	33	23	......	......	1 25
Rhinelander	25	60	50	40	25	......	......	1 75
Sparta	25	50	42	33	23	......	......	1 50
Spooner	25	65	55	44	28	......	......	2 00
Sturgeon Bay	50	43	36	29	23	......	......	1 50
Wabeno	25	60	50	40	25	......	......	1 75
Wausau	25	50	42	33	23	......	......	1 75
WYOMING—								
Casper	75	2 70	2 35	1 90	1 55	......	......	6 00
Cheyenne	75	2 05	1 65	1 25	97	......	......	6 00
Cokeville	2 40	3 30	2 80	2 20	1 82	......	......	8 00
Dana	1 50	2 95	2 43	1 87	1 49	......	......	7 75
Evanston	2 00	3 10	2 65	2 15	1 75	......	......	8 00
Gillette	75	2 70	2 35	1 90	1 55	......	......	6 75
Green River	1 75	3 10	2 65	2 15	1 75	......	......	8 00
Hanna	1 50	2 91	2 40	1 85	1 47	......	......	7 50
Lander	3 65	4 00	3 65	3 20	2 85	......	......	......
Laramie	1 25	2 56	2 10	1 64	1 29	......	......	6 75
Lusk	75	2 45	2 01	1 55	1 22	......	......	5 25
Medicine Bow	1 50	2 85	2 35	1 81	1 43	......	......	7 50
Rawlins	1 50	3 06	2 53	1 94	1 56	......	......	8 00
Sheridan	75	2 70	2 35	1 90	1 55	......	......	7 00
Wamsutter	2 25	3 10	2 65	2 06	1 68	......	......	8 00
Wheatland	1 16	2 45	2 01	1 55	1 22	......	......	6 50

* VIRGINIA—Towns with five class rates are governed by Eastern classification. Towns with six class rates are governed by Southern classification.

HOW TO FIGURE EXPRESS CHARGES.

When rate per 100 pounds is ☞	$0.40	$0.50	$0.60	$0.75	$1.00	$1.25	$1.50	$1.75	$2.00	$2.50	$3.00	$3.50	$4.00	$4.50
Packages not over	1 lb. $0 25	1 lb. $0 25	1 lb. $0 25	1 lb. $0 25	1 lb. $0 25	1 lb. $0 25	1 lb. $0 25	1 lb. $0 25	1 lb. $0 25	1 lb. $0 25	1 lb. $0 25	1 lb. $0 25	1 lb. $0 25	1 lb. $0 30
Over 1 pound to	2 " 25	2 " 25	2 " 25	2 " 30	2 " 30	2 " 30	2 " 30	2 " 30	2 " 35	2 " 35	2 " 35	2 " 35	2 " 35	2 " 35
" 2 " "	3 " 25	3 " 25	3 " 25	3 " 30	3 " 30	3 " 35	3 " 35	3 " 40	3 " 45	3 " 45	3 " 45	3 " 45	3 " 45	3 " 45
" 3 " "	4 " 25	4 " 25	4 " 30	4 " 30	4 " 35	4 " 35	4 " 40	4 " 45	4 " 50	4 " 55	4 " 60	4 " 60	4 " 60	4 " 60
" 4 " "	5 " 25	5 " 25	5 " 30	5 " 35	5 " 40	5 " 40	5 " 45	5 " 50	5 " 55	5 " 60	5 " 65	5 " 70	5 " 70	5 " 75
" 5 " "	7 " 30	7 " 30	7 " 35	7 " 35	7 " 40	7 " 45	7 " 50	7 " 55	7 " 60	7 " 70	7 " 75	7 " 80	7 " 85	7 " 90
" 7 " "	10 30	10 30	10 35	10 40	10 45	10 50	10 55	10 60	10 70	10 75	10 80	10 90	10 1 00	10 1 00
" 10 " "	15 30	15 30	15 35	15 40	15 45	15 55	15 60	15 65	15 75	15 85	15 90	15 1 00	15 1 11	15 1 15
" 15 " "	20 30	20 30	20 35	20 40	20 50	20 60	20 70	20 75	20 85	20 1 00	20 1 10	20 1 20	20 1 25	20 1 30
" 20 " "	25 35	25 35	25 40	25 45	25 55	25 65	25 75	25 85	25 1 00	25 1 10	25 1 20	25 1 30	25 1 40	25 1 50
" 25 " "	30 35	30 40	30 45	30 50	30 60	30 70	30 80	30 90	30 1 00	30 1 15	30 1 30	30 1 50	30 1 60	30 1 70
" 30 " "	35 40	35 40	35 45	35 50	35 65	35 75	35 85	35 1 00	35 1 00	35 1 25	35 1 40	35 1 60	35 1 70	35 1 90
" 35 " "	40 40	40 40	40 50	40 55	40 70	40 80	40 90	40 1 00	40 1 00	40 1 25	40 1 50	40 1 75	40 1 85	40 2 00
" 40 " "	45 40	45 40	45 50	45 60	45 75	45 90	45 1 00	45 1 00	45 1 00	45 1 25	45 1 50	45 1 75	45 2 00	45 2 25
" 45 " "	50 40	50 45	50 55	50 60	50 80	50 1 00	50 1 00	50 1 00	50 1 00	50 1 25	50 1 50	50 1 75	50 2 00	50 2 25
" 50 " "	55 40	55 50	55 60	55 65	55 85	55 1 00	55 1 10	55 1 10						
" 55 " "	60 40	60 50	60 60	60 70	60 90	60 1 10	60 1 20	60 1 20						
" 60 " "	65 40	65 50	65 60	65 75	65 90	65 1 15	65 1 30	65 1 30						
" 65 " "	70 40	70 50	70 60	70 75	70 1 00	70 1 25	70 1 40	70 1 40						
" 70 " "	75 40	75 50	75 60	75 75	75 1 00	75 1 25	75 1 50	75 1 50						
" 75 " "	80 40	80 50	80 60	80 75	80 1 00	80 1 25	80 1 50	80 1 60						
" 80 " "	85 40	85 50	85 60	85 75	85 1 00	85 1 25	85 1 50	85 1 70						
" 85 " "	100 40	100 50	100 60	100 75	100 1 00	100 1 25	100 1 50	100 1 75						

This scale is the same as used by all express companies and shows how they arrive at the charges on shipments at the rates given.

Where two rates are shown in the rate tables, charges on packages weighing over 7 pounds are arrived at by adding the rates of the two different amounts given.

Where weight is 7 pounds or less, add the two amounts together and take the rate shown under the sum of the two amounts.

When the rate per 100 pounds is $2.00 or more, and the weight of the shipment is greater than 50 pounds, the express companies charge at pound rates. For example: Rate per 100 pounds, $3.00; weight of shipment, 60 pounds; charges would be $1.80.

When rate per 100 pounds is ☞	$5.00	$6.00	$7.00	$8.00	$9.00	$10.00	$11.00	$12.00	$13.00	$14.00	$15.00	$16.00	$17.00	$18.00	$20.00
Packages not over	1 lb. $0 30	1 lb. $0 30	1 lb. $0 30	1 lb. $0 30	1 lb. $0 30	1 lb. $0 30	1 lb. $0 30	1 lb. $0 30	1 lb. $0 30	1 lb. $0 30	1 lb. $0 35	1 lb. $0 35	1 lb. $0 35	1 lb. $0 35	1 lb. $0 40
Over 1 pound to	2 " 35	2 " 35	2 " 35	2 " 35	2 " 35	2 " 35	2 " 35	2 " 35	2 " 35	2 " 35	2 " 40	2 " 40	2 " 45	2 " 45	2 " 50
" 2 " "	3 " 45	3 " 45	3 " 45	3 " 45	3 " 45	3 " 45	3 " 45	3 " 45	3 " 45	3 " 45	3 " 50	3 " 50	3 " 55	3 " 60	3 " 60
" 3 " "	4 " 60	4 " 60	4 " 60	4 " 60	4 " 60	4 " 60	4 " 60	4 " 60	4 " 60	4 " 60	4 " 65	4 " 65	4 " 75	4 " 75	4 " 80
" 4 " "	5 " 75	5 " 75	5 " 80	5 " 80	5 " 80	5 " 80	5 " 80	5 " 80	5 " 80	5 " 80	5 " 85	5 " 85	5 " 90	5 " 95	5 " 1 00
" 5 " "	7 1 00	7 1 00	7 1 00	7 1 00	7 1 00	7 1 00	7 1 00	7 1 00	7 1 00	7 1 10	7 1 15	7 1 15	7 1 25	7 1 40	7 1 50
" 7 " "	10 1 10	10 1 15	10 1 20	10 1 25	10 1 35	10 1 50	10 1 50	10 1 50	10 1 50	10 1 50	10 1 65	10 1 65	10 1 75	10 1 80	10 2 00
" 10 " "	15 1 25	15 1 35	15 1 50	15 1 60	15 1 75	15 2 00	15 2 00	15 2 15	15 2 15	15 2 15	15 2 35	15 2 50	15 2 60	15 2 75	15 3 00
" 15 " "	20 1 40	20 1 65	20 1 75	20 2 00	20 2 00	20 2 50	20 2 50	20 2 75	20 2 75	20 2 85	20 3 00	20 3 20	20 3 40	20 3 60	20 4 00
" 20 " "	25 1 60	25 1 85	25 2 00	25 2 25	25 2 50	25 3 00	25 3 25	25 3 50	25 3 50	25 3 50	25 3 75	25 4 00	25 4 25	25 4 50	25 5 00
" 25 " "	30 1 75	30 2 10	30 2 50	30 2 75	30 3 00	30 3 25	30 3 75	30 4 00	30 4 00	30 4 20	30 4 50	30 4 80	30 5 10	30 5 40	30 6 00
" 30 " "	35 2 00	35 2 50	35 2 75	35 3 25	35 3 50	35 3 75	35 4 25	35 4 75	35 4 75	35 4 90	35 5 25	35 5 60	35 5 95	35 6 30	35 7 00
" 35 " "	40 2 25	40 2 75	40 3 25	40 3 50	40 4 00	40 4 25	40 4 75	40 5 25	40 5 25	40 5 60	40 6 00	40 6 40	40 6 80	40 7 20	40 8 00
" 40 " "	45 2 50	45 3 00	45 3 50	45 4 00	45 4 50	45 4 75	45 5 25	45 5 75	45 5 85	45 6 30	45 6 75	45 7 20	45 7 65	45 8 10	45 9 00
" 45 " "	50 2 50	50 3 00	50 3 50	50 4 00	50 4 50	50 5 00	50 5 50	50 6 00	50 6 50	50 7 00	50 7 50	50 8 00	50 8 50	50 9 00	50 10 00

FREIGHT CLASSIFICATION.

1 stands for First Class.
2 stands for Second Class.
3 stands for Third Class.
4 stands for Fourth Class.
5 stands for Fifth Class.
6 stands for Sixth Class.
1¼ stands for 1¼ times First Class.
1½ stands for 1½ times First Class.
D1 stands for 2 times First Class.
2½ stands for 2½ times First Class.
3T1 stands for 3 times First Class.
4T1 stands for 4 times First Class.

THE RAILROADS CHARGE FOR FREIGHT according to its classification. For example: Stoves take 3d class rate. By referring to pages 14 to 17 you will find the 3rd class rate to the nearest town in your state. Multiply the weight of the article (which you can get from our catalogue or estimate pretty closely) by the rate, and you will be able to figure the freight charges almost to a cent. If the following list does not contain the article you want, you can, as a rule, use the rate on some article of a similar nature.

THE CLASSIFICATION ON SOME ARTICLES is different to different sections of the country. For example: Hardware takes 2nd class rate to the western and southern states, and 3rd class rate to the eastern states. Hay presses take 3rd class rate to the western states, 2nd class to the eastern states and 4th class to the southern states.

REMEMBER, We always pack and ship our goods in a manner that secures for you the LOWEST FREIGHT CHARGES.

WEST. The railroads running west, northwest and southwest from Chicago, use the western classification. Use the classification in column marked "WEST" if you live in any of the following states: Arizona, Arkansas, California, Colorado, Idaho, Illinois, Indian Territory, Iowa, Kansas, Louisiana, Minnesota, Missouri, Montana, Nebraska, Nevada, New Mexico, North Dakota, Oklahoma Territory, Oregon, South Dakota, Texas, Utah, Washington, Wisconsin, Wyoming.

EAST. The railroads running east and northeast from Chicago, use the eastern classification. Use the classification in column marked "EAST" if you live in any of the following states: Connecticut, Delaware, District of Columbia, Indiana, Maryland, Maine, Massachusetts, Michigan, New Hampshire, New Jersey, New York, Ohio, Pennsylvania, Rhode Island, Vermont, Virginia, West Virginia.

SOUTH. The railroads running south and southeast from Chicago, use the southern classification. Use the classification in column marked "SOUTH" if you live in any of the following states: Alabama, Florida, Georgia, Kentucky, Mississippi, North Carolina, South Carolina, Tennessee.

ARTICLES	CLASS WEST	CLASS EAST	CLASS SOUTH
Advertising Matter	1	1	2
Ammunition	1	2	1
Anvils	4	4	5
Asbestos Building Felt	3	3	3
Axes	2	3	3
Axles	3	4	5
Baby Carriages	1½	1½	1
Bamboo Book Racks	3T1	3T1	1½
Barb Wire	4	4	6
Bar Iron	4	4	5
Barn Door Rail	3	3	4
Baskets, Nested	D-1	D-1	1
Bath Tubs	1	1	1
Beans, Dried	3	4	2
Bed Lounges	1½	1½	1
Beds, Folding	1½	1½	1
Beds, Iron or Wood	2	2	2
Bed Slats	3	3	4
Bed Springs, Spiral	D-1	D-1	D-1
Bed Springs, Woven Wire	1	1½	1
Bedsteads, Iron or Wood	2	2	2
Bells, Iron	3	3	3
Bellows	1	1	1
Belting, Rubber, Leather or Canvas	1	2	2
Bicycles	D-1	1½	1½
Binding Twine	3	3	3
Bird Cages	3T1	3T1	D-1
Blankets	1	1	1
Blinds	3	1	4
Blowers, Rotary	1	2	2
Boards, Shoveling	3	1	
Boats, Row	4T1	4T1	4T1
Boats, Stone	2	3	
Bob Sleds	2	1	
Boilers, Steam	3	2	3
Bone, Ground	4	4	6
Bookcases	1½	1½	1½
Books	1	1	1
Boots and Shoes	1	1	1
Buggies (See Vehicles)			
Buggy Bodies, Finished	1½	2½	1½
Buggy Bodies, Unfinished	1½	1½	2
Buggy Tops	1½	1½	1½
Buggy Wheels, Finished	1½	1	2
Buggy Wheels, Unfinished	1	1	2
Building Felt	3	3	3
Building Paper	3	3	5
Bureaus	1	1	1
Cameras	D-1	1	1½
Candles	3	3	4
Candy in Pails	2	2	4
Canned Goods	4	2	2
Cans, Milk	1	1½	1
Cant Hooks	3	2	2
Carpets	1	1	1
Carriages (See Vehicles)			
Carts, Hand, K. D	1		1
Carts, Road	1½	D-1	
Cement, Building	4	4	5
Cereals	3	4	4
Chains	3	4	5
Chairs, Bamboo, Rattan, Reed or Willow	3T1	3T1	D-1
Chairs, Cane Seat	1½	1½	1
Chairs, Invalid's Rolling	D-1	1	D-1
Chairs, Upholstered	D-1	1½	1½
Chairs, Wood or Leather Seat	1½	1½	1
Cheese	2	3	3
Chiffoniers	1	1	2
China Closets	D-1	1½	1½
Churns, Hand	2	1	2
Cigars and Cigarettes	1	1	1
Cloaks	1	1	1
Clocks	1	1	1
Clothes Bars	1	2	3
Clothing	1	1	1
Cobbler's Outfit	2	3	2
Cod Fish	4	5	5
Coffee	4	5	5
Coffee Mills	2	2	2
Commodes	1	1	2
Condensed Milk	4	3	3
Conductors, Pipe, Iron, not nested	D-1	1	1
Corn Cribs	4	3	5
Corn Huskers	1	1	1
Corn Planters	2	2	2
Corn Shellers, Hand, K. D.	3	2	2
Corrugated Iron	4	4	6
Cots, Folding, Wood	3	1	2
Couches	1	1	1
Crackers	2	2	4
Cribs, Iron or Wood	2	2	2

ARTICLES	CLASS WEST	CLASS EAST	CLASS SOUTH
Crockery	2	3	4
Crowbars	4	4	6
Cultivators, Disc, Riding, K. D.	2	2	4
Cultivators, Hand, K. D., in bundles	1	2	4
Cultivators, Walking, K.D.	3	2	4
Cupboards	1½	1½	1½
Cutters, Bone, K. D.	2	2	2
Cutters, Feed and Ensilage, K. D.	3	2	1
Cutters, Food and Vegetable, K. D.	3	2	1
Cutters (Sleighs)	2½	3T1	
Decoy Ducks	2	1	1
Desks	1	1½	1
Disc Sharpeners	2	3	2
Dishes	2	3	4
Dog Powers	1	1	1
Door Hangers	3	3	4
Door Screens	1	1	2
Doors, Common	4	3	4
Doors, Common, Glazed	4	1	3
Doubletrees, Unfinished	3	3	4
Dressers	1	1	2
Dried Fruits	3	3	2
Drills, Blacksmiths' Post	2	2	2
Drills, Corn, S. U.	1	1	1
Drugs	1	1	1
Drums	4T1	3T1	3T1
Dry Goods	1	1	1
Dynamite	D-1	D-1	D-1
Earthenware	2	3	4
Eave Troughs, nested	2	2	2
Egg Carrier Cases	1	1	1
Electric Batteries	1	1	1
Electrical Goods	1	1	1
Emery Wheels	3	3	3
Engines, Steam or Gasoline	1	2	3
Evaporators, Fruit, S. U.	1½	1½	1
Evaporators, Sugar, K. D.	2	1	2
Explosives	D-1	D-1	D-1
Fanning Mills, K. D.	1	1	1
Feed Grinders, S. U.	2	2	4
Feed Mills, Sweep, K. D.	2	2	4
Felt, Building	3	3	3
Fence Wire, Barb and Smooth	4	4	6
Fencing	3	3	5
Fencing Machines, K. D.	1	2	2
Fertilizers	4	4	6
Firearms	1	1	1
Fish, Canned	4	3	3
Fish, Pickled or Salted	4	5	5
Flax Meal	4	5	3
Flour	4	5	6
Flower Stands, Wire	3T1	3T1	D-1
Food, Animal or Poultry	4	4	3
Food Cookers, viz.:			
Acme	3	1	1
Economy	3	1	1
Farmers' Friend	3	3	4
Handy	3	1	1
Hercules	3	2	3
Kenwood	3	1	1
Forges, Portable	2	1	2
Forks, Horse Hay	2	2	3
Freezers	1	1	2
Fruit, Canned	4	3	3
Fruit, Dried	3	3	2
Fruit Jars	3	2	3
Galvanized Iron	4	4	6
Game Traps	2	3	2
Gas Fixtures	1	2	2
Gas for Calcium Lights	1	3	1
Gas Machines	1	1½	2
Gasoline Stoves	1	1	1
Gears, Running	1½	1	
Generators, Gas	1	D-1	2
Glassware	2	2	2
Grain Drills, K. D.	3	2	2
Granite & Enameled Ware	2	2	2
Graphophones	1½	1	1
Grease, Axle	4	3	5
Grindstone Frames	3	3	3
Grindstones	4	3	4
Grist Mills, Hand, boxed	2	2	4
Grits	4	5	5
Gunpowder	D-1	D-1	D-1
Guns, Revolvers, etc	1	1	1
Hall Trees	D-1	D-1	1½
Hammocks	1	1	1
Hardware	2	3	2
Harness and Saddles	1	1	2
Harrows, N. O. S., K. D	3	2	4

ARTICLES	CLASS WEST	CLASS EAST	CLASS SOUTH
Harrows, Disc, K. D.	3	2	3
Hay Carriers	2	2	3
Hay Carrier Tracks	3	4	4
Hay Presses, Hand	3	2	4
Hay Presses, Power, loaded in box cars, actual weight	3	2	4
Hay Presses, S. U	1	1	1
Heaters, Tank	3	1	
High Explosives	D-1	D-1	D-1
Hinges, Iron	3	3	3
Hoes	2	2	3
Hollow Ware	3	3	3
Hominy	4	5	5
Horse and Mule Shoes	4	4	6
Horse Power Jacks	3	3	2
Horse Powers	3	3	2
Hullers, Pea, Hand	1	D-1	2
Ice Cream Freezers	1	1	2
Ice Plows	1	1	
Incubators	1	1	1
Iron Beds	2	2	2
Ironing Boards	1	3	3
Iron Pipe	4	4	6
Iron Tires	3	4	6
Iron Tuyeres	3	4	2
Iron Wagon Wheels	3	2	4
Kettles	3	3	3
Kitchen Sinks, Iron	2	3	3
Ladders	1	3	1
Lamps	1	1	1
Land Rollers, K. D.	3	2	3
Lard	4	3	5
Lasts	3	2	2
Laundry Tubs, Galvanized Iron	3	1	1
Lawn Mowers	1	2	2
Lead Pipe	4	3	4
Lime	4	3	6
Linseed Meal	4	5	3
Lounges	1	1	1
Lye	4	3	5
Magic Lanterns	D-1	1	1
Mandrels	4	3	5
Matting	1	1	2
Mattresses, Woven Wire	1	1½	1
Meats, Cured	4	3	6
Milk Cans	1	1½	1
Mills, Cane	3	2	4
Mills, Cider and Wine Presses	2	2	4
Mills, Cob	2	2	4
Millwork (See Sash, Doors and Blinds).			
Mirrors	1	1	1
Molasses in Barrels or Kegs	4	4	5
Molasses in Cans or Kits	4	2	5
Mowers, Lawn	1	2	2
Musical Instruments	D-1	1½	1
Music Cabinets	D-1	D-1	1½
Nails	4	4	6
Notions	1	1	1
Nuts, Edible	2	2	2
Oars	1	3	3
Oat Meal	4	4	4
Oil in Barrels	3	3	3
Oil Cake Meal	4	5	3
Oil Cloth, under 13 ft. long	2	2	2
Oil Stoves	1	1	2
Organs	1	1	1
Ovens, Sheet Iron	1	1	1
Oyster Shells	4	4	6
Pails	2	1	3
Paint, in Barrel	4	3	4
Paint, in Cans or Pails	4	3	4
Paper Hangings	1	2	2
Pea Hullers, Hand	1	1	2
Phonographs	1½	1	1
Pianos	1	1	1
Pictures	1	1	1
Pipe, Lead	4	3	4
Planters, Corn, K. D.	3	2	2
Planters, Hand Corn, Bean and Potato	1	1	3
Planters, Potato, K. D	1	2	2
Plows, Gang or Sulky, K. D	3	2	4
Plows, Ice	1	1	
Plow Points and Shares	3	3	4
Plows, Walking, K. D	3	2	4
Plumbing Material	2	2	2
Poles, Buggy, Carriage or Wagon. Finished	1½	1	1
Unfinished	3	3	
Potato Diggers, K. D	3	2	4
Poultry Netting	3	3	5
Press Screws	3	3	3
Pulleys, Iron or Wood	2	3	4
Pumps	3	2	3
Queensware	2	3	2
Racks, Grain, Hay or Stalk, K. D.	2	2	3
Rakes, Revolving, K. D., Teeth in	1	1	3
Rakes, Sulky, K. D.	3	2	3
Range, Boilers, Iron	3	3	3
Refrigerators	2	2	2
Rice	4	4	6
Road Carts	1½	D-1	
Road Scrapers, Drag	3	1	3
Road Scrapers, Wheeled, K. D.	3	1	3
Rolled Oats	4	5	4
Roofing Paper	3	3	5
Rope	3	3	3

ARTICLES	CLASS WEST	CLASS EAST	CLASS SOUTH
Rope, Wire	3	3	4
Rubber Goods	1	1	1
Rugs, Woolen	1	1	1
Saddlery	1	1	2
Sad Irons	4	3	4
Safes, Iron	3	3	3
Salt	4	4	6
Sash, Unglazed	3	1	4
Sash Weights, Iron	4	4	6
Saw Frames, Circular, K. D	2	2	2
Saws, on Board	1	1	1
Sawing Machines, Drag, K. D	2	1	1
Scales, Wagon	2	2	3
Scientific Instruments	D-1	1	1
Screens, Door or Window	1	1	2
Seats, Carriage and Buggy	2	1	2
Seeders, Broadcast, K. D	3	2	2
Seeders, Endgate	D-1	2	1
Seeders, Hand, Crated	1	2	1
Settees, Lawn	D-1	D-1	1
Sewing Machines	1	1	1
Sewing Machines, Drop Head	1	1	2
Shafts, Carriage and Buggy, Finished	1½	D-1	1
Shot, in Boxes or Kegs	3	3	5
Shovels	2	2	3
Sideboards	1	1	2
Singletrees	3	3	
Skeins	3	4	5
Sleds, Bob	2	1	
Sleighs	2½	3T1	
Soap	4	3	6
Soap Powder	4	3	6
Sofas or Sofa Beds	D-1	D-1	1½
Sporting Goods	1	1	1
Spring Wagons (See Vehicles)			
Stalk Cutters, K. D	1	2	1
Stanchions, Cattle	2	3	4
Staples	4	4	6
Starch	3	3	3
Stationery	1	1	1
Stereopticons	D-1	1	1½
Stove Furniture	3	3	3
Stove Pipe, Crated	1½	1½	1½
Stove Pipe, Iron	3	4	4
Stoves and Ranges	3	3	3
Stump Pullers, K. D	3	2	4
Sugar	4	3	5
Sulkies	3T1	D-1	
Surreys (See Vehicles)			
Swage Blocks	3	3	5
Syrup in Barrels or Kegs	4	4	5
Tables, Extension	3	2	2
Tables, Parlor	D-1	1½	1½
Tackle Blocks	3	3	5
Tanks, Galvanized Iron (Set Up)	D-1	D-1	D-1
Tanks Galvanized Iron (Knocked Down) Sides in Rolls	1	2	2
Tank Heaters	3	1	
Tea	1	1	1
Tents	1	1	1
Tent Poles	3	3	3
Tinware	2	2	2
Tire Benders	3	2	2
Tire Shrinkers	3	2	2
Tire Upsetters	3	2	2
Tobacco	1	1	1
Tombstones	3	3	4
Tools	2	3	2
Tools in Chest	1	3	2
Tops, Buggy	1½	1½	1½
Toys	1	1	1
Traps, Animal or Bird	2	1	2
Troughs, Galvanized Steel	1	2	3
Troughs, Pig, Cast Iron	4	3	3
Trunks	1	1½	1
Tubs, Wooden	1	1	3
Twine	2	3	3
Varnish in Cans	1	2	2
Varnish in Wood	2	3	3
Vehicles (such as Buggies, Carriages, Spring Wagons, Surreys), crated under 30 inches in height and 94 inches long	1½	1¼	1
Vehicles, crated under 50 inches in height and 94 inches long	1½	D 1	1½
Vehicles, crated under 30 inches in height and over 94 inches long	1½	D-1	1
Vinegar, in Wood	4	3	6
Vises	2	3	4
Wagon Jacks	2	2	3
Wagons, Farm	1	1	4
Wall Paper	1	2	2
Wardrobes, set up	D-1	D-1	1½
Wardrobes, taken apart	2	2	2
Washing Machines	1	1	2
Washstands	1	1	2
Water Closets	1	2	3
Water Heaters	3	2	3
Weeders, K. D., in bundles	1	1	3
Wheelbarrows, K. D	2	2	2
Wheels, Buggy, Finished	1½	1	2
Wheels, Buggy, Unfinished	1	1	2
Wheels, Wagon, Iron	3	2	4
Wheels, Wagon, Wooden	1	1	4
White Lead, in kegs or barrels	4	4	4
Windmills and Towers	3	2	2
Window Screens	1	1	2
Wine	1	1	1
Wire, Barb or Smooth	4	4	6
Wire Fencing	3	3	5
Wire Rope	3	3	4
Woodenware	2	1	3
Wringers	2	2	3

JAMES B. FORGAN,
President.
FRANK O. WETMORE
Cashier.
WM. H. MONROE,
Assistant Cashier.

CAPITAL $8,000,000
SURPLUS $5,000,000
First National Bank
OF CHICAGO.

Chicago, March 15, 1905.

TO WHOM IT MAY CONCERN:

It is with pleasure that we testify to our own good opinion of the integrity, responsibility and business ability of Sears, Roebuck & Company. They show a fully paid up capital and surplus of over Five Million Dollars ($5,000,000.00), and are one of the largest mercantile institutions in Chicago.

Anyone can, in our judgment, feel perfectly secure in sending money to them with their orders, as we understand that they ship their goods agreeing that anything not proving entirely satisfactory when received can be returned to them, and the money paid will be immediately returned to the purchaser.

The officers and stock holders of the company are well and favorably known to us, command our full confidence, and we believe can be relied upon to do exactly as they agree.

Yours very truly,

Jas B Forgan Prs

ERNEST A. HAMILL, PRESIDENT
CHARLES L. HUTCHINSON, VICE PRESIDENT
CHAUNCEY J. BLAIR, VICE PRESIDENT
D. A. MOULTON, VICE PRESIDENT

JOHN C. NEELY, SECRETARY
FRANK W. SMITH, CASHIER
B. G. SAMMONS, ASS'T CASHIER
J. EDWARD MAASS, ASS'T CASHIER

No. 5106

THE CORN EXCHANGE NATIONAL BANK

OF CHICAGO

CAPITAL $3,000,000
SURPLUS $2,000,000

CHICAGO, March 1, 1905.

TO WHOM IT MAY CONCERN:

We are pleased to testify to the responsibility of Sears, Roebuck & Company of Chicago. The firm has a paid up capital and surplus of over Five Million Dollars ($5,000,000.00) and enjoys the highest credit with their Chicago banks, of which this bank is one.

We believe anyone who has dealings with this company will be treated in the fairest manner possible. We confidently assure anyone who is thinking of placing an order with them, that, in our judgment, there is absolutely no risk in sending the money with the order.

Very truly yours,

Frank W. Smith

Cashier.

In writing to either of the above banks as to our reliability, be sure to enclose a 2-cent stamp for reply.

WATCH, DIAMOND AND JEWELRY DEPARTMENTS.

WHEN YOU BUY A GOLD FILLED CASE bear in mind that the **Sears gold filled case is recommended above all others**, being made of two extra heavy plates of solid gold over a hard composition metal. Will wear longer than any other gold filled case made and is the handsomest, best finished and best fitting gold filled watch case made. **If you select a Sears case you will have the best gold filled watch case ever made.**

IN SELECTING A MOVEMENT we would advise by all means that **you pick out as the best possible value, one of the Edgemere or one of the Plymouth Watch Co. movements** illustrated on pages 24 to 26 and quoted throughout the following pages in the various sizes and grades. For a gentleman's watch, the 21 jeweled Prince of Wales, in 16-size, both open face and hunting, and the 21 jeweled King Edward, in 18-size, open face or hunting, both movements manufactured by the Plymouth Watch Co., stand out pre-eminently the best values and the most accurate timekeepers in this entire department. No pains or expense were considered in their making. In everything that constitutes a fine watch, timekeeping, finish and size, these movements are undoubtedly the finest in the American market.

SPECIAL PRICE INDUCEMENTS TO LARGE QUANTITY BUYERS. **Please take notice that we make special prices on certain of our watches, clocks, jewelry, etc.,** when quantities are purchased, but please understand that this special inducement only applies on such articles as are mentioned on the various pages. Dealers and traders can select their lines from us, as our prices are even lower on single items than what your wholesaler or jobber asks you, and in many instances we are able to give a still lower price when quantities are purchased, a price that is even less than what your wholesaler or jobber pays for the same goods.

MAIL AND EXPRESS SHIPMENTS. **We recommend sending watches by express, as they do not receive the hard usage as when sent by mail. Our statistics show that 90 per cent of breakages in watches happen while in transit through the mails; therefore, we again advise you to have watches shipped by express, and all other small jewelry by mail, as it is perfectly safe and far the cheapest.** Postage is 1 cent per ounce. A watch packed for shipment weighs from 6 to 8 ounces; chains, rings and other small articles of jewelry about 2 ounces. Packages amounting to $1.00 or over should be registered, which costs 8 cents extra, as this is the safest method. **25 cents will carry any watch to any part of the United States by express.**

ENGRAVING. **Cash in full must accompany all orders when goods are marked with engraving. We charge for engraving in script on jewelry, watches, etc.,** 2½ cents per letter; in old English, small, 5 cents per letter.

Monograms on silverware and jewelry are all the rage. Prices for two or three-letter combination, script or ribbon style, as follows:

	Script	Ribbon
½-inch size	20c	25c
¾-inch size	30c	35c
1 -inch size	40c	47c
1¼-inch size	55c	65c

In writing orders when goods are to be engraved, write or draw plain letters, so as to avoid mistakes. **We cannot exchange goods after they have been engraved.**

REGARDING ENGRAVINGS ON WATCH CASES. **It sometimes happens that we are out of the exact engraving on watch case ordered, but we aim to carry exact designs.** When the exact engraving cannot be had, we always have a very similar one, which we will take the liberty of sending rather than delay your order, **it being understood you can return same if not perfectly satisfactory.**

WATCH REPAIRING. **We have a thoroughly equipped mechanical department, which is fitted with all of the latest tools and appliances** for the repairing of all kinds of watches. Our charges are about one-half what is usually charged by the retail dealers, and the work will be done in a very superior manner. We cannot give an accurate estimate of the cost of repairs without a thorough examination of the work. Our charges are merely enough to cover cost of material and labor. In sending a watch for repairing be sure to send it by registered mail; mark on the outside of the package your name and address, and write us at the same time that you have done so, giving full explanation regarding trouble with watch.

OUR BINDING GUARANTEES.

WATCH CASE GUARANTEE. **Where a watch case in this catalogue is described as guaranteed for life, 25, 20, 10, 5 or 2 years,** it applies to gold filled watch cases, and means that the case is covered by two plates of solid gold over an inner plate of hard composition metal, and the gold is guaranteed to wear and retain its perfect color for the time stated, and if the gold in any piece or part of the case wears through within the stipulated time mentioned in the description and in the guarantee, the case will be replaced by a new case free of cost to you.

OUR SEARS LIFE GUARANTEE.

Where we describe any gold filled case or articleof jewelry or silverware as carrying our SEARS LIFE GUARANTEE, we mean that should any of these articles fail in any part to be exactly as warranted, we will exchange same at any time within your natural life, whether you have owned the article five years, twenty years or fifty years. Return it to us, and we will upon receipt of it send another one of the same quality FREE OF CHARGE.

MOVEMENT GUARANTEE. **Where we guarantee a watch movement for five years,** the guarantee is absolute and binding upon us to replace or repair, free of cost to you, any piece or part of the watch movement that may become defective by reason of imperfect material or workmanship at any time within five years; and while this guarantee does not include removing dirt, cleaning of movement or repairing, free of cost, any piece or part that may be broken or damaged through careless or improper handling, it is the widest, longest and strongest watch movement guarantee ever issued, and if you buy any movement from us and on the last day of the fifth year the watch stops or fails to keep accurate time, and this failure is in any way due to imperfect material or workmanship, it will be repaired by us or replaced with a new movement free of any cost to you. **Our written guarantees which accompany every watch and movement** are so written over our own signature that there can be no question of your absolute security in the purchase of any watch case, watch movement or complete watch from us.

DIAMOND GUARANTEE. **Our Refund, Exchange and Guarantee Certificate. With every diamond we issue a written, binding guarantee,** with a further agreement that you can at any time return any diamond you may select, where weight and quality are quoted, and exchange it for any other diamond or other article of jewelry at the same or higher price.

We further agree on the return of any diamond purchased from us within 60 days of purchase, when so requested, to refund in cash your full purchase price, and we further agree at any time after 60 days, on return of any diamond to us, when requested to do so, to refund your full purchase price less 10 per cent.

JEWELRY GUARANTEE. **Where we describe any article of jewelry as solid gold, gold filled or gold plated,** where we describe it as 18, 14 or 10-karat or solid silver, silver filled or silver plated, the article of jewelry is covered by our binding guarantee, guaranteeing it to be in every way exactly as represented by us, and if after received, examined and put to any kind of test, acid or otherwise, it should prove any different, should fall short in the slightest degree of the representation made in this catalogue, we will replace the article purchased with a new article or refund your money, as you may direct.

TECHNICAL TERMS USED IN DESCRIBING JEWELRY AND SILVERWARE.

BRIGHT POLISH is a finish on silver and gold showing the bright polished surface of the metal itself without coloring, and always has a bright and shining surface.

SATIN FINISH. The finishing of jewelry and silverware by sand blasting or a scratch brush, which dulls the surface and gives it a peculiar satiny effect, and shows the dull color of the metal without any other coloring.

ROMAN COLOR is the absolutely pure color of virgin gold. It is pure gold plated upon a lower karat of gold and is of a rich, bright yellow or canary color, the same color as nuggets or pure 24-karat gold. Two methods are used in putting this color on, the electro plating process and the acid process. The acid process is used only on 14 and 18-karat jewelry. When Roman color is used, the article is generally satin finished after.

HAND ENGRAVING. When stated that the article is hand engraved, we mean that the article is beautified, as the illustration of the article shows, by bright cutting done by hand with an engraving tool.

GOLD FILLED STOCK. Gold filled stock is made of stock that is gold filled, the outside or visible surface being a sheet of solid gold of substantial thickness, hard soldered on a plate of base metal.

ROLLED GOLD PLATE. Rolled gold plate is made very similarly to gold filled stock, with the exception that the plate is rolled to a thinner degree and has not the wearing ability of gold filled stock.

ELECTRO PLATE. Electro plate is a process of gold plating by electricity. This is the cheapest and quickest method of gold plating. Electro plated jewelry cannot be guaranteed, and will wear but a short time. It is very difficult to recognize electro plated jewelry from rolled plate or gold filled. Only one well versed and educated in the jewelry business can recognize the difference.

TECHNICAL TERMS USED IN DESCRIBING WATCHES.

FULL ADJUSTMENT. A high grade watch is fully adjusted when it is adjusted to heat, cold, isochronism and to six positions.

Our 17 jeweled **Plymouth Watch Co.** special line of movements in 18, 16 and 6 size are all fully adjusted.

ADJUSTED TO TEMPERATURE. As a watch is only as perfect as the balance wheel and hairspring is perfect, and as these parts are made of metal, and metal contracts and expands with variations in temperature, a watch to be adjusted to temperature must have the balance wheel so constructed as to allow for extreme cold or extreme heat. In other words, the balance wheel must be so constructed that one metal will expand to such an amount as can be taken up by the other metal used in its make-up. When the balance wheel is so constructed that this variation does not affect it, it is known then to be adjusted to temperature.

ADJUSTED TO ISOCHRONISM is an adjustment of the hairspring by which it vibrates with the balance wheel in perfect uniformity; that is, when the long and short arcs of a balance wheel are caused to perform in the same time by means of the hairspring. This assures accuracy in time keeping.

ADJUSTED TO POSITION. This adjustment can only be brought about by having the balance wheel in perfect poise and absolutely trued. The watch is run and timed in six different positions and corrections are made from time to time until the watch runs in each position without any variation in time.

Our 15 jeweled **Plymouth Watch Co.** special line of movements in 18, 16 and 6 size, also the **Edgemere** line of movements made especially for us, are all adjusted to position.

BREGUET HAIRSPRINGS. This hairspring differs from the old style flat hairspring in having the outer coil adjusted above the other coil and tempered in this position. This arrangement insures a condition for perfect adjustment of the hairspring in all positions, thus obviating all chances of its becoming misplaced and entangled, as has always been the case with flat hairsprings. Our **Plymouth Watch Co.** special movements and the **Edgemere** line of movements made expressly for us all have Breguet hairsprings.

PATENT REGULATOR is a device for controlling the vibrations of the hairspring, and by its use a watch can be regulated to the smallest fraction of time. Our 17 and 15 jeweled **Plymouth Watch Co.** special full adjusted movements, also the **Edgemere** movements in 18 and 0 size, have patent regulators.

STEM WIND AND STEM SET. All watches that are set by turning the winding crown, whether they are set by pulling out a setting lever or by pressing in a push pin, are known as stem set and stem wind watches.

PENDANT SET. All watches that are set without setting lever or push pin are known as pendant set watches, being set by pulling out the winding crown which is located at top of pendant or neck, as it is sometimes called; the hands may be set by simply turning the crown, which is pushed back into place when hands are in desired position.

TIMING SCREWS. With the use of these screws a watch can be brought down to accurate time without in any way changing the position of the hairspring. Only a watchmaker can manipulate these screws. Care must be taken in the use of them in timing a watch, together with great skill, as a well poised balance wheel is very delicate and easily put out of true and is often spoiled by incompetent workmen.

Our **Plymouth Watch Co.** special movements and the **Edgemere** line of movements made expressly for us all have timing screws.

CUT BALANCE. The cut or expansion balance is the most reliable for accurate time. They are constructed so that there can be only a minimum amount of variation by any climatic change, whereas the solid balance wheel, by contraction or expansion, will vary when used where variations of temperature are met with. Our **Plymouth Watch Co.** special movements and the **Edgemere** line of movements made expressly for us all have cut balance.

RUBY JEWELS are used in the high priced, fine finished watches. By ruby jewels, we mean the jewels are of genuine ruby. **Garnet jewels** are mostly used in the average middle priced watches and are made of garnet, and cheap imported watches are sometimes fitted with glass jewels.

Our **Plymouth Watch Co.** special movements and the **Edgemere** line of movements made expressly for us all have ruby jewels.

DOUBLE SUNK DIALS are made of three pieces: The outer part on which the numerals are placed, the center or plain field, and the small circular disc for registering the seconds. This construction is a great advantage over the plain dials, as a preventive of the hands catching, thereby causing the watch to stop. Our **Plymouth Watch Co.** special movements in 18 and 16 size have double sunk dials.

SAFETY PINION is a patent device on the center wheel arbor of a watch, the purpose of which is to protect the train wheels and mainspring barrel from damage in cases where the mainspring breaks.

Our **Plymouth Watch Co.** special movements and the **Edgemere** line of movements made expressly for us all have patent pinions.

DON'T OVERLOOK OUR

PROFIT SHARING DEPARTMENT

ON THE LAST PAGES. THESE SHOW WHAT IS YOURS FREE OF COST, YOUR SHARE OF OUR PROFIT ON YOUR PURCHASES.

OUR TROPHY AND PRIZE BADGES ARE THE VERY LATEST DESIGNED.

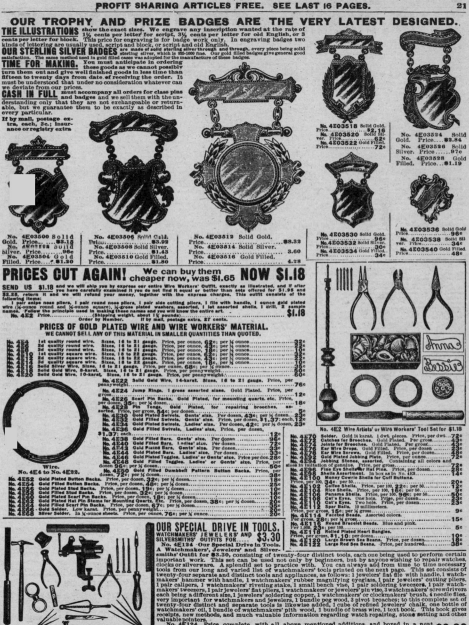

THE ILLUSTRATIONS show the exact sizes. We engrave any inscription wanted at the rate of 1½ cents per letter for script, 3½ cents per letter for old English, or 3 cents per letter for block. This price for engraving is for badge work only. In engraving badges two kinds of lettering are usually used, script and block, or script and old English.

OUR STERLING SILVER BADGES are made of solid sterling silver through and through, every piece being solid sterling silver, which is 925-1000 fine. Our gold filled badges give general good satisfaction. The same method used in gold filled cases was adopted for the manufacture of these badges.

TIME FOR MAKING. You must anticipate in ordering these goods as we cannot possibly turn them out and give well finished goods in less time than fifteen to twenty days from date of receiving the order. It must be understood that under no consideration whatever can we deviate from our prices.

CASH IN FULL must accompany all orders for class pins and badges and we sell them with the understanding only that they are not exchangeable or returnable, but we guarantee them to be exactly as described in every particular.

If by mail, postage extra, each, 3c.; insurance or registry extra

No. 4E03500 Solid Gold. Price......$3.15
No. 4E03502 Solid Silver. Price.........96c
No. 4E03504 Gold Filled. Price.........$1.20

No. 4E03506 Solid Gold. Price..........$3.92
No. 4E03508 Solid Silver. Price..........$1.43
No. 4E03510 Gold Filled. Price..........$1.80

No. 4E03512 Solid Gold. Price..........$8.32
No. 4E03514 Solid Silver. Price.......... 3.60
No. 4E03516 Gold Filled. Price.......... 4.28

No. 4E03518 Solid Gold. Price..........$2.16
No. 4E03520 Solid Silver. Price..........62c
No. 4E03522 Gold Filled. Price..........72c

No. 4E03524 Solid Gold. Price....$2.84
No. 4E03526 Solid Silver. Price......97c
No. 4E03528 Gold Filled. Price...$1.19

No. 4E03530 Solid Gold. Price..........96c
No. 4E03532 Solid Silver. Price..........30c
No. 4E03534 Gold Filled. Price..........34c

No. 4E03536 Solid Gold. Price..........96c
No. 4E03538 Solid Silver. Price..........34c
No. 4E03540 Gold Filled. Price..........48c

PRICES CUT AGAIN! We can buy them cheaper now, was $1.65 NOW $1.18

SEND US $1.18 and we will ship you by express our entire Wire Workers' Outfit, exactly as illustrated, and if after you have carefully examined it you do not find it equal or better than sets offered for $1.95 and $2.25, return it and we will refund your money, together with the express charges. This outfit consists of the following items:

1 pair snipe nose pliers, 1 pair round nose pliers, 1 pair side cutting pliers, 1 file with handle, 1 ounce gold plated wire (½-ounce round and ½-ounce square), ½-gross plated washers, assorted, 1 lot assorted shells, 1 drill, 2 sample names. Follow the principle used in making these names and you will know the entire art.

No. 4E2 Price..................(Shipping weight, about 1¼ pounds).................. **$1.18**

Order by Number. If by mail, postage extra, 27 cents.

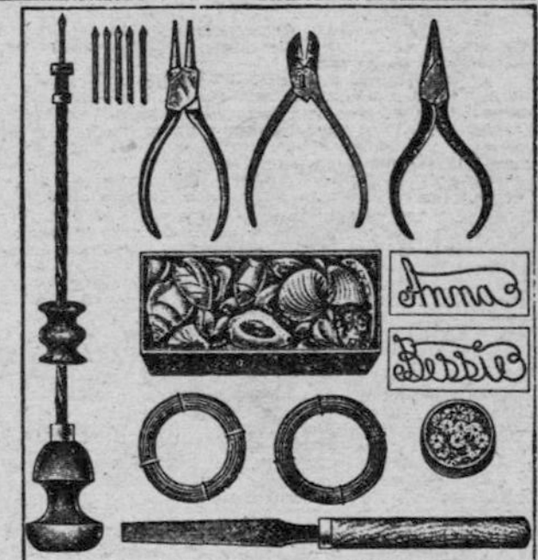

No. 4E2 Wire Artists' or Wire Workers' Tool Set for $1.18

PRICES OF GOLD PLATED WIRE AND WIRE WORKERS' MATERIAL.

WE CANNOT SELL ANY OF THIS MATERIAL IN SMALLER QUANTITIES THAN QUOTED.

No. 4E4 1st quality round wire. Sizes, 16 to 21 gauge. Price, per ounce, 62c; per ½ ounce..........32c
No. 4E6 2d quality round wire. Sizes, 16 to 21 gauge. Price, per ounce, 43c; per ½ ounce..........22c
No. 4E8 3d quality round wire. Sizes, 16 to 21 gauge. Price, per ounce, 18c; per ½ ounce..........10c
No. 4E10 1st quality square wire. Sizes, 18 to 22 gauge. Price, per ounce, 62c; per ½ ounce..........32c
No. 4E12 2d quality square wire. Sizes, 18 to 22 gauge. Price, per ounce, 43c: per ½ ounce..........22c
No. 4E14 3d quality square wire. Sizes, 18 to 22 gauge. Price, per ounce, 18c, per ½ ounce..........10c
No. 4E16 Solid Silver Wire, Sizes, 16 to 21 gauge. Price, per ounce, 68c; per ½ ounce..........35c
No. 4E18 Solid Gold Wire, 8-karat. Sizes, 16 to 21 gauge. Price, per pennyweight..........50c
No. 4E20 Solid Gold Wire, 10-karat. Sizes, 16 to 21 gauge. Price, per pennyweight..........60c
No. 4E22 Solid Gold Wire, 14-karat. Sizes, 16 to 21 gauge. Price, per pennyweight..........76c
No. 4E24 Jump Rings. 1 gross assorted sizes. Gold Plated. Price, per gross..........12c
No. 4E26 Scarf Pin Backs, Gold Plated, for mounting quartz, etc. Price, per dozen, 35c; per ½ dozen..........18c
No. 4E28 Pin Tongs, Gold Plated, for repairing brooches, assorted. Price, per gross, 54c; per dozen..........5c
No. 4E30 Gold Plated Swivels. Gents' size. Per dozen, 43c; per ½ dozen..........23c
No. 4E32 Gold Filled Swivels. Gents' size. Price, per dozen, $1.37; each, 12c
No. 4E34 Gold Plated Swivels. Ladies' size. Per dozen, 42c; per ½ dozen, 23c
No. 4E36 Gold Filled Swivels. Ladies' size. Price, per dozen, $1.37; each..........12c
No. 4E38 Gold Filled Bars. Gents' size. Per dozen..........96c
No. 4E40 Gold Filled Bars. Ladies' size. Per dozen..........72c
No. 4E42 Gold Plated Bars. Gents' size. Per dozen..........33c
No. 4E44 Gold Plated Bars. Ladies' size. Per dozen..........33c
No. 4E46 Gold Plated Toggles. Ladies' or Gents' size. Price per doz. 28c
No. 4E48 Gold Filled Toggles. Ladies' or Gents' size. Price, per dozen 96c; per ½ dozen..........50c
No. 4E50 Gold Filled Dumbbell Pattern Button Backs. Price, per dozen, 72c; per ½ dozen..........38c

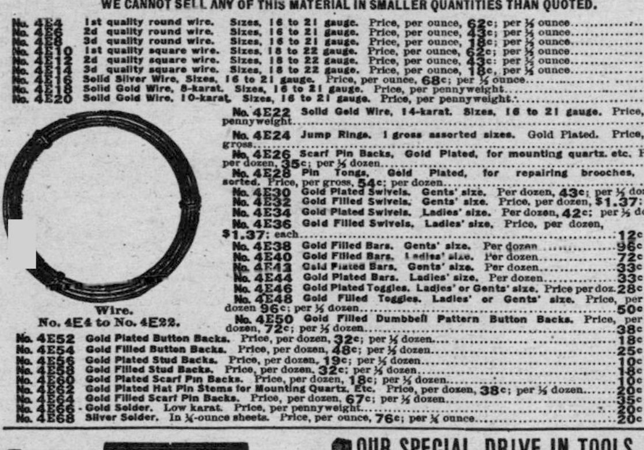

Wire.
No. 4E4 to No. 4E22.

No. 4E52 Gold Plated Button Backs. Price, per dozen, 32c; per ½ dozen..........18c
No. 4E54 Gold Filled Button Backs. Price, per dozen, 48c; per ½ dozen..........25c
No. 4E56 Gold Plated Stud Backs. Price, per dozen, 19c; per ½ dozen..........10c
No. 4E58 Gold Filled Stud Backs. Price, per dozen, 32c; per ½ dozen..........18c
No. 4E60 Gold Plated Scarf Pin Backs. Price, per dozen, 18c; per ½ dozen..........10c
No. 4E62 Gold Plated Hat Pin Stems for Mounting Quartz, Etc. Price, per dozen, 38c; per ½ dozen..........20c
No. 4E64 Gold Filled Scarf Pin Backs. Price, per dozen, 67c; per ½ dozen..........35c
No. 4E66 Gold Solder. Low karat. Price, per pennyweight..........20c
No. 4E68 Silver Solder. In ¼-ounce sheets. Price, per ounce, 76c; per ¼ ounce..........20c

No. 4E70 Solder. Gold 14 karat. 1 dwt. pieces. Price, per dwt...72c
No. 4E72 Catches for Brooches. Gold Plated. Per gross..........43c
No. 4E74 Joints for Brooches. Gold Plated. Per gross..........43c
No. 4E76 Ear Wire Drops. Gold Filled. Price, per dozen..........23c
No. 4E78 Ear Wire Screws. Gold Filled. Price, per dozen..........48c
No. 4E92 Gold Plated Jobbing Plate. Price, per ounce..........72c
No. 4E94 Jobbing Stones, assorted. Containing all colors and sizes in imitation of genuine. Price, per gross..........72c
No. 4E96 Fine Eye Shells for Hat Pins. Price, per dozen..........28c
No. 4E98 Shells Assortment. In box as in No. 4E2..........14c
No. 4E100 Money Cowrie Shells for Cuff Buttons. Price, per 100, 34c: per 50..........20c
No. 4E102 Coffee Shells. Price, per 100, 22c; per 50..........12c
No. 4E104 Rice Shells. Price, per 100, 16c; per 50.......... 9c
No. 4E106 Panama Shells. Price, per 100, 96c; per 50..........50c
No. 4E108 Cat's Eyes. One hole. Price, per dozen..........23c
No. 4E110 Cat's Eyes. Two hole. Price, per dozen..........23c
No. 4E112 Spar Balls. 10 millimeters. Price, per gross, 15c; per ½ gross.......... 9c
No. 4E114 Faceted Beads. Assorted colors. Per gross, 28c; per ½ gross..........15c
No. 4E116 Round Bracelet Beads. Blue and pink. Per 1,000, 23c; per 100.......... 5c
No. 4E118 Rolled Plated Heart Bangles. Price, per gross, $1.10; per dozen..........10c
No. 4E120 Large Brown Sea Beans. Price, per dozen..........18c
No. 4E122 Large Red Sea Beans. Price, per hundred..........38c

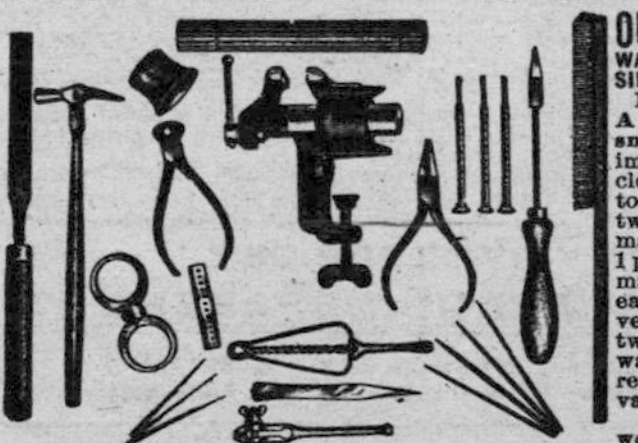

OUR SPECIAL DRIVE IN TOOLS.

WATCHMAKERS', JEWELERS' AND SILVERSMITHS' OUTFITS FOR..... $3.30

No. 4E124 Our Special Drive in Tools. A Watchmakers', Jewelers' and Silversmiths' Outfit for $3.30, consisting of twenty-four distinct tools, each one being used to perform certain important work. This set can be used not only by beginners, but by anyone wishing to repair watches, clocks or silverware. A splendid set to practice with. You can always add from time to time necessary tools from our long and varied list of watchmakers' tools printed on the next page. This set consists of twenty-four separate and distinct tools and appliances, as follows: 1 jewelers' flat file with handle, 1 watchmakers' hammer with handle, 1 watchmakers' rubber magnifying eyeglass, 1 pair jewelers' cutting pliers, 1 pair calipers, 1 watchmakers' riveting stake, 1 small bench vise, 1 pair soldering tweezers, 1 pair watchmakers' tweezers, 1 pair jewelers' flat pliers, 1 watchmakers' or jewelers' pin vise, 3 watchmakers' screwdrivers each being a different size, 1 jewelers' soldering copper, 1 watchmakers' or clockmakers' brush, 4 needle files, very important for watchmakers and jewelers, 1 bundle peg wood, 3 pivot broaches; to this complete set of twenty-four distinct and separate tools is likewise added, 1 cube of refined jewelers' chalk, one bottle of watchmakers' oil, 1 bundle of watchmakers' pith wood, 1 bundle of brass wire, 1 text book. This book gives receipts, new methods, and much valuable information regarding watch repairing, stone setting and other valuable pointers.

No. 4E124 Price, complete, with all above mentioned additions, and boxed in a neat wooden box..................(Weight, complete, about 5 pounds).......... **$3.30**

WATCHMAKERS' TOOLS AND MATERIALS.

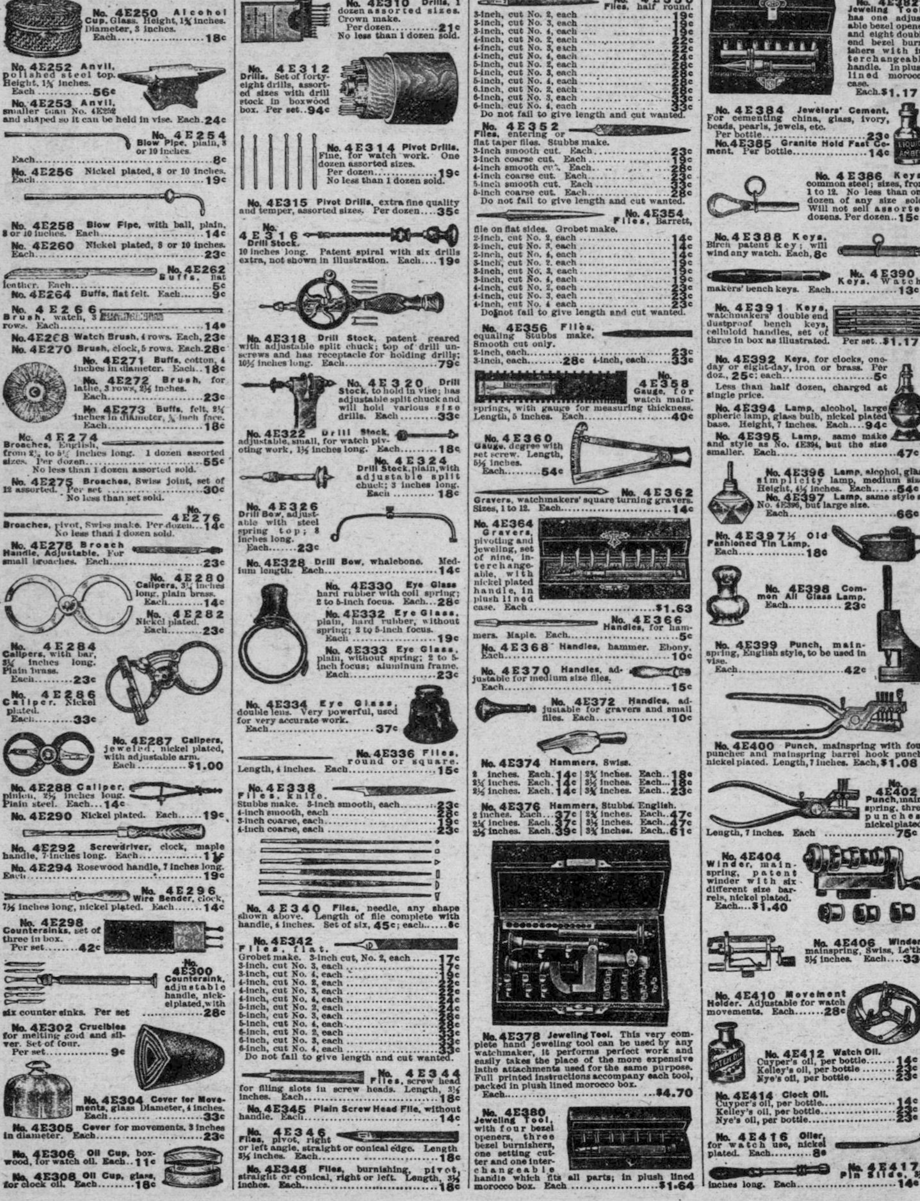

No. 4E250 Alcohol Cup. Glass. Height, 1⅜ inches. Diameter, 3 inches. Each........18c

No. 4E252 Anvil, polished steel top. Height, 1⅜ inches. Each........56c

No. 4E253 Anvil, smaller than No. 4E252 and shaped so it can be held in vise. Each..24c

No. 4E254 Blow Pipe, plain, 8 or 10 inches. Each........8c

No. 4E256 Nickel plated, 8 or 10 inches. Each........19c

No. 4E258 Blow Pipe, with ball, plain, 8 or 10 inches. Each........14c

No. 4E260 Nickel plated, 8 or 10 inches. Each........23c

No. 4E262 Buffs, flat leather. Each........5c

No. 4E264 Buffs, flat felt. Each........9c

No. 4E266 Brush, watch, 3 rows. Each........14c

No. 4E268 Watch Brush, 4 rows. Each, 23c

No. 4E270 Brush, clock, 5 rows. Each. 28c

No. 4E271 Buffs, cotton, 4 inches in diameter. Each..18c

No. 4E272 Brush, for lathe, 3 rows, 2½ inches. Each........23c

No. 4E273 Buffs, felt, 2¼ inches in diameter, ⅜-inch face. Each........18c

No. 4E274 Broaches, English, from 2½ to 5½ inches long. 1 dozen assorted sizes. Per dozen........55c
No less than 1 dozen assorted sold.

No. 4E275 Broaches, Swiss joint, set of 12 assorted. Per set........30c
No less than set sold.

No. 4E276 Broaches, pivot, Swiss make. Per dozen...14c
No less than 1 dozen sold.

No. 4E278 Broach Handle, Adjustable. For small broaches. Each........23c

No. 4E280 Callipers, 3¼ inches long, plain brass. Each........14c

No. 4E282 Nickel plated. Each........23c

No. 4E284 Callipers, with bar, 3¼ inches long. Plain brass. Each........23c

No. 4E286 Caliper. Nickel plated. Each........33c

No. 4E287 Callipers, jeweled, nickel plated, with adjustable arm. Each........$1.00

No. 4E288 Caliper, pinion, 2½ inches long. Plain steel. Each...14c

No. 4E290 Nickel plated. Each........19c

No. 4E292 Screwdriver, clock, maple handle, 7 inches long. Each........11c

No. 4E294 Rosewood handle, 7 inches long. Each........19c

No. 4E296 Wire Bender, clock, 7½ inches long, nickel plated. Each........14c

No. 4E298 Countersinks, set of three in box. Per set........42c

No. 4E300 Countersink, adjustable handle, nickel plated, with six counter sinks. Per set........28c

No. 4E302 Crucibles for melting gold and silver. Set of four. Per set........9c

No. 4E304 Cover for Movements, glass Diameter, 4 inches. Each........33c

No. 4E305 Cover for movements, 3 inches in diameter. Each........23c

No. 4E306 Oil Cup, boxwood, for watch oil. Each..11c

No. 4E308 Oil Cup, glass, for clock oil. Each........18c

No. 4E310 Drills, 1 dozen assorted sizes. Crown make. Per dozen........21c
No less than 1 dozen sold.

No. 4E312 Drills. Set of forty-eight drills, assorted sizes with drill stock in boxwood box. Per set..94c

No. 4E314 Pivot Drills. Fine, for watch work. One dozen assorted sizes. Per dozen........19c
No less than 1 dozen sold.

No. 4E315 Pivot Drills, extra fine quality and temper, assorted sizes. Per dozen....35c

No. 4E316 Drill Stock. 10 inches long. Patent spiral with six drills extra, not shown in illustration. Each....19c

No. 4E318 Drill Stock, patent geared with adjustable split chuck; top of drill unscrews and has receptacle for holding drills; 10½ inches long. Each........79c

No. 4E320 Drill Stock, to hold in vise; has adjustable split chuck and will hold various size drills. Each........33c

No. 4E322 Drill Stock, adjustable, small, for watch pivoting work, 1½ inches long. Each........18c

No. 4E324 Drill Stock, plain, with adjustable split chuck; 3 inches long. Each........18c

No. 4E326 Drill Bow, adjustable with steel spring top; 8 inches long. Each........23c

No. 4E328 Drill Bow, whalebone. Medium length. Each........14c

No. 4E330 Eye Glass hard rubber with coil spring; 2 to 5-inch focus. Each...28c

No. 4E332 Eye Glass, plain, hard rubber, without spring; 2 to 5-inch focus. Each........19c

No. 4E333 Eye Glass, plain, without spring; 2 to 5-inch focus; aluminum frame. Each........23c

No. 4E334 Eye Glass, double lens. Very powerful, used for very accurate work. Each........37c

No. 4E336 Files, round or square. Length, 4 inches. Each........15c

No. 4E338 Files, knife. Stubbs make. 3-inch smooth, each........23c
4-inch smooth, each........28c
3-inch coarse, each........19c
4-inch coarse, each........23c

No. 4E340 Files, needle, any shape shown above. Length of file complete with handle, 4 inches. Set of six, 45c; each........8c

No. 4E342 Files, flat. Grobet make. 3-inch cut, No. 2, each........17c
3-inch, cut No. 3, each........17c
3-inch, cut No. 4, each........19c
4-inch, cut No. 2, each........22c
4-inch, cut No. 3, each........22c
4-inch, cut No. 4, each........24c
5-inch, cut No. 2, each........24c
5-inch, cut No. 3, each........28c
5-inch, cut No. 4, each........28c
6-inch, cut No. 2, each........33c
6-inch, cut No. 3, each........33c
6-inch, cut No. 4, each........33c
Do not fail to give length and cut wanted.

No. 4E344 Files, screw head for filling slots in screw heads. Length, 3½ inches. Each........18c

No. 4E345 Plain Screw Head File, without handle. Each........14c

No. 4E346 Files, pivot, right or left angle, straight or conical edge. Length 3½ inches. Each........18c

No. 4E348 Files, burnishing, pivot, straight or conical, right or left. Length, 3½ inches. Each........18c

No. 4E350 Files, half round.
3-inch, cut No. 2, each........19c
3-inch, cut No. 3, each........19c
3-inch, cut No. 4, each........19c
4-inch, cut No. 2, each........22c
4-inch, cut No. 3, each........22c
4-inch, cut No. 4, each........24c
5-inch, cut No. 2, each........28c
5-inch, cut No. 3, each........28c
5-inch, cut No. 4, each........28c
6-inch, cut No. 2, each........28c
6-inch, cut No. 3, each........33c
6-inch, cut No. 4, each........33c
Do not fail to give length and cut wanted.

No. 4E352 Files, entering or flat taper files. Stubbs make.
3-inch smooth cut. Each........23c
3-inch coarse cut. Each........19c
4-inch smooth cut. Each........28c
4-inch coarse cut. Each........23c
5-inch smooth cut. Each........33c
5-inch coarse cut. Each........28c
Do not fail to give length and cut wanted.

No. 4E354 Files, Barrett, file on flat sides. Grobet make.
2-inch, cut No. 2, each........14c
2-inch, cut No. 3, each........14c
2-inch, cut No. 4, each........14c
3-inch, cut No. 2, each........19c
3-inch, cut No. 3, each........19c
3-inch, cut No. 4, each........19c
4-inch, cut No. 2, each........23c
4-inch, cut No. 3, each........23c
4-inch, cut No. 4 each........23c
Do not fail to give length and cut wanted.

No. 4E356 Files, equaling Stubbs make. Smooth cut only.
2-inch, each........23c
3-inch, each........28c 4-inch, each........33c

No. 4E358 Gauge, for watch mainsprings, with gauge for measuring thickness. Length, 5 inches. Each........40c

No. 4E360 Gauge, degree with set screw. Length, 5½ inches. Each........54c

No. 4E362 Gravers, watchmakers' square turning gravers. Sizes, 1 to 12. Each........14c

No. 4E364 Gravers, pivoting and jeweling, set of nine, interchangeable, with nickel plated handle, in plush lined case. Each........$1.63

No. 4E366 Handles, for hammers. Maple. Each........5c

No. 4E368 Handles, hammer. Ebony. Each........10c

No. 4E370 Handles, adjustable for medium size files. Each........15c

No. 4E372 Handles, adjustable for gravers and small files. Each........10c

No. 4E374 Hammers, Swiss.

2 inches.	Each. 14c	2¾ inches.	Each.. 18c
2¼ inches.	Each. 14c	3½ inches.	Each... 18c
2½ inches.	Each. 14c	3¾ inches.	Each.. 23c

No. 4E376 Hammers, Stubbs. English.

2 inches.	Each... 37c	2¾ inches.	Each.. 47c
2¼ inches.	Each. 37c	3¼ inches.	Each.. 47c
2½ inches.	Each. 39c	3¾ inches.	Each.. 61c

No. 4E378 Jeweling Tool. This very complete hand jeweling tool can be used by any watchmaker, it performs perfect work and easily takes the place of the more expensive lathe attachments used for the same purpose. Full printed instructions accompany each tool, packed in plush lined morocco box. Each........$4.70

No. 4E380 Jeweling Tool, with four bezel openers, three bezel burnishers, one setting cutter and one interchangeable handle which fits all parts; in plush lined morocco box. Each........$1.64

No. 4E382 Jeweling Tool, has one adjustable bezel opener and eight double end bezel burnishers with interchangeable handle. In plush lined morocco case. Each. $1.17

No. 4E384 Jewelers' Cement. For cementing china, glass, ivory, beads, pearls, jewels, etc. Per bottle........23c

No. 4E385 Granite Hold Fast Cement. Per bottle........14c

No. 4E386 Keys, common steel; sizes, from 1 to 12. No less than one dozen of any size sold. Will not sell assorted dozens. Per dozen..15c

No. 4E388 Keys. Birch patent key; will wind any watch. Each, 8c

No. 4E390 Keys. Watchmakers' bench keys. Each........13c

No. 4E391 Keys, watchmakers' double end dustproof bench keys, celluloid handles, set of three in box as illustrated. Per set..$1.17

No. 4E392 Keys, for clocks, one-day or eight-day, iron or brass. Per doz., 25c; each........5c
Less than half dozen, charged at single price.

No. 4E394 Lamp, alcohol, large spheric lamp, glass bulb, nickel plated base. Height, 7 inches. Each....94c

No. 4E395 Lamp, same make and style as No. 4E394, but the size smaller. Each........47c

No. 4E396 Lamp, alcohol, glass simplicity lamp, medium size. Height, 4½ inches. Each......54c

No. 4E397 Lamp, same style as No. 4E396, but large size. Each........66c

No. 4E397½ Old Fashioned Tin Lamp. Each........18c

No. 4E398 Common All Glass Lamp. Each........23c

No. 4E399 Punch, mainspring, English style, to be used in vise. Each........42c

No. 4E400 Punch, mainspring with four punches and mainspring barrel hook punch, nickel plated. Length, 7 inches. Each, $1.08

No. 4E402 Punch, mainspring, three punches, nickel plated. Length, 7 inches. Each........75c

No. 4E404 Winder, mainspring, patent winder with six different size barrels, nickel plated. Each....$1.40

No. 4E406 Winder, mainspring, Swiss, Le'th, 3½ inches. Each....33c

No. 4E410 Movement Holder. Adjustable for watch movements. Each........28c

No. 4E412 Watch Oil.
Cuyper's oil, per bottle........14c
Kelley's oil, per bottle........23c
Nye's oil, per bottle........23c

No. 4E414 Clock Oil.
Cuyper's oil, per bottle........14c
Kelley's oil, per bottle........23c
Nye's oil, per bottle........23c

No. 4E416 Oiler, for watch use, nickel plated. Each........8c

No. 4E417 Pin Slide, 3½ inches long. Each........14c

WATCHMAKERS' TOOLS AND MATERIALS—Continued.

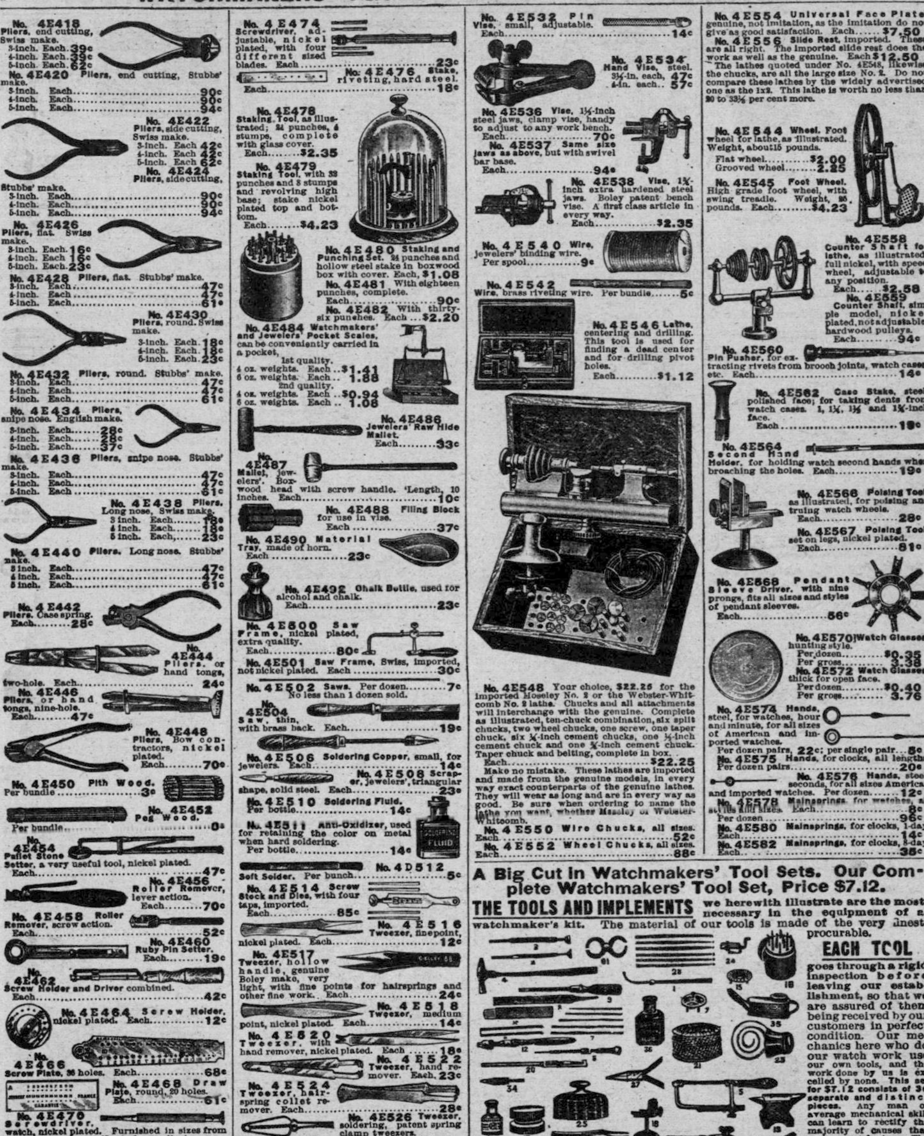

No. 4E418 Pliers, end cutting, Swiss make.
3-inch. Each. 39c
4-inch. Each. 39c
5-inch. Each. 62c

No. 4E420 Pliers, end cutting, Stubbs' make.
3-inch. Each. 90c
4-inch. Each. 90c
5-inch. Each. 94c

No. 4E422 Pliers, side cutting, Swiss make.
3-inch. Each 42c
4-inch. Each 42c
5-inch. Each 62c

No. 4E424 Pliers, side cutting, Stubbs' make.
3-inch. Each. 90c
4-inch. Each. 90c
5-inch. Each. 94c

No. 4E426 Pliers, flat. Swiss make.
3-inch. Each. 16c
4-inch. Each 16c
5-inch. Each. 23c

No. 4E428 Pliers, flat. Stubbs' make.
3-inch. Each. 47c
4-inch. Each. 47c
5-inch. Each. 61c

No. 4E430 Pliers, round. Swiss make.
3-inch. Each. 18c
4-inch. Each. 18c
5-inch. Each. 23c

No. 4E432 Pliers, round. Stubbs' make.
3-inch. Each. 47c
4-inch. Each. 47c
5-inch. Each. 61c

No. 4E434 Pliers, snipe nose. English make.
3-inch. Each. 28c
4-inch. Each. 28c
5-inch. Each. 37c

No. 4E436 Pliers, snipe nose. Stubbs' make.
3-inch. Each. 47c
4-inch. Each. 47c
5-inch. Each. 61c

No. 4E438 Pliers. Long nose, Swiss make.
3 inch. Each. 18c
4 inch. Each. 18c
5 inch. Each. 23c

No. 4E440 Pliers. Long nose. Stubbs' make.
3 inch. Each. 47c
4 inch. Each. 47c
5 inch. Each. 61c

No. 4E442 Pliers. Case spring. Each 28c

No. 4E444 Pliers, or hand tongs, two-hole. Each 24c

No. 4E446 Pliers, or hand tongs, nine-hole. Each 47c

No. 4E448 Pliers, Bow contractors, nickel plated. Each 70c

No. 4E450 Pith Wood. Per bundle 3c

No. 4E452 Peg Wood. Per bundle 8c

No. 4E454 Pallet Stone Setter, a very useful tool, nickel plated. Each 47c

No. 4E456 Roller Remover, lever action. Each 70c

No. 4E458 Roller Remover, screw action. Each 52c

No. 4E460 Ruby Pin Setter. Each 19c

No. 4E462 Screw Holder and Driver combined. Each 42c

No. 4E464 Screw Holder, nickel plated. Each 12c

No. 4E466 Screw Plate, 36 holes. Each 68c

No. 4E468 Draw Plate, round, 20 holes. Each 61c

No. 4E470 Screwdriver, watch, nickel plated. Furnished in sizes from No. 1, the largest, to No. 6, the smallest. Set of six, 45c; each 8c

No. 4E472 Screwdrivers, set of six, nickel plated, with colored celluloid heads; in pasteboard box. Set of six $1.00

No. 4E474 Screwdriver, adjustable, nickel plated, with four different sized blades. Each 23c

No. 4E476 Stake, riveting, hard steel. Each 18c

No. 4E478 Staking Tool, as illustrated; 24 punches, 4 stumps, complete with glass cover. Each $2.35

No. 4E479 Staking Tool, with 32 punches and 8 stumps and revolving high base; stake nickel plated top and bottom. Each $4.23

No. 4E480 Staking and Punching Set. 24 punches and hollow steel stake in boxwood box with cover. Each, $1.08

No. 4E481 With eighteen punches, complete. Each 90c

No. 4E482 With thirty-six punches. Each $2.20

No. 4E484 Watchmakers' and Jewelers' Pocket Scales, can be conveniently carried in a pocket.
1st quality.
4 oz. weights. Each $1.41
6 oz. weights. Each 1.88
2nd quality.
4 oz. weights. Each $0.94
6 oz. weights. Each 1.08

No. 4E486 Jewelers' Raw Hide Mallet. Each 33c

No. 4E487 Mallet, jewelers'. Boxwood head with screw handle. Length, 10 inches. Each 10c

No. 4E488 Filing Block for use in vise. Each 37c

No. 4E490 Material Tray, made of horn. Each 23c

No. 4E492 Chalk Bottle, used for alcohol and chalk. Each 23c

No. 4E500 Saw Frame, nickel plated, extra quality. Each 80c

No. 4E501 Saw Frame, Swiss, imported, not nickel plated. Each 30c

No. 4E502 Saws. Per dozen 7c
No less than 1 dozen sold.

No. 4E504 Saw, thin, with brass back. Each 19c

No. 4E506 Soldering Copper, small, for jewelers. Each 14c

No. 4E508 Scraper, jewelers', triangular shape, solid steel. Each 23c

No. 4E510 Soldering Fluid. Per bottle 14c

No. 4E511 Anti-Oxidizer, used for retaining the color on metal when hard soldering. Per bottle 14c

No. 4D512 Soft Solder. Per bunch 5c

No. 4E514 Screw Stock and Dies, with four taps, imported. Each 85c

No. 4E516 Tweezer, finepoint, nickel plated. Each 12c

No. 4E517 Tweezer, hollow handle, genuine Boley make, very light, with fine points for hairsprings and other fine work. Each 24c

No. 4E518 Tweezer, medium point, nickel plated. Each 14c

No. 4E520 Tweezer, with hand remover, nickel plated. Each 18c

No. 4E522 Tweezer, hand remover. Each 23c

No. 4E524 Tweezer, hairspring collet remover. Each 28c

No. 4E526 Tweezer, soldering, patent spring clamp tweezers. Each 8c

No. 4E528 Pin Vise, hollow handle. Extra quality. Each 45c

No. 4E530 Pin Vise, hollow handle, patent adjustable jaws. Genuine Lowell. Each 94c

No. 4E532 Pin Vise, small, adjustable. Each 14c

No. 4E534 Hand Vise, steel. 3½-in. each, 47c; 4-in. each 57c

No. 4E536 Vise, 1½-inch steel jaws, clamp vise, handy to adjust to any work bench. Each 70c

No. 4E537 Same size jaws as above, but with swivel bar base. Each 94c

No. 4E538 Vise, 1¾-inch extra hardened steel jaws. Boley patent bench vise. A first class article in every way. Each $2.35

No. 4E540 Wire, jewelers' binding wire. Per spool 9c

No. 4E542 Wire, brass riveting wire. Per bundle 5c

No. 4E546 Lathe, centering and drilling. This tool is used for finding a dead center and for drilling pivot holes. Each $1.12

No. 4E548 Your choice, $22.25 for the imported Moseley No. 2 or the Webster-Whitcomb No. 2 lathe. Chucks and all attachments will interchange with the genuine. Complete as illustrated, ten-chuck combination, six split chucks, two wheel chucks, one screw, one taper chuck, six ⅛-inch cement chucks, one ½-inch cement chuck and one ⅜-inch cement chuck. Taper chuck and belting, complete in box. Each $22.25

Make no mistake. These lathes are imported and made from the genuine models, in every way exact counterparts of the genuine lathes. They will wear as long and are in every way as good. Be sure when ordering to name the lathe you want, whether Moseley or Webster-Whitcomb.

No. 4E550 Wire Chucks, all sizes. Each 52c

No. 4E552 Wheel Chucks, all sizes. Each 88c

No. 4E554 Universal Face Plate, genuine, not imitation, as the imitation do not give as good satisfaction. Each $7.50

No. 4E556 Slide Rest, imported. These are all right. The imported slide rest does the work as well as the genuine. Each $12.50

The lathes quoted under No. 4E548, likewise the chucks, are all the large size No. 2. Do not compare these lathes by the widely advertised one as the 1x2. This lathe is worth no less than 20 to 33⅓ per cent more.

No. 4E544 Wheel. Foot wheel for lathe, as illustrated. Weight, about 15 pounds.
Flat wheel $2.00
Grooved wheel 2.25

No. 4E545 Foot Wheel. High grade foot wheel, with swing treadle. Weight, 25 pounds. Each $4.23

No. 4E558 Counter Shaft for lathe, as illustrated, full nickel, with speed wheel, adjustable to any position. Each $2.58

No. 4E559 Counter Shaft, simple model, nickel plated, not adjustable, hardwood pulleys. Each 94c

No. 4E560 Pin Pusher, for extracting rivets from brooch joints, watch cases, etc. Each 14c

No. 4E562 Case Stake, steel, polished face; for taking dents from watch cases. 1, 1¼, 1½ and 1¾-inch face. Each 19c

No. 4E564 Second Hand Holder, for holding watch second hands when broaching the holes. Each 19c

No. 4E566 Poising Tool, as illustrated, for poising and truing watch wheels. Each 28c

No. 4E567 Poising Tool, set on legs, nickel plated. Each 81c

No. 4E568 Pendant Sleeve Driver, with nine prongs, fits all sizes and styles of pendant sleeves. Each 56c

No. 4E570 Watch Glasses, hunting style.
Per dozen $0.35
Per gross 3.38

No. 4E572 Watch Glasses, thick for open face.
Per dozen $0.40
Per gross 3.76

No. 4E574 Hands, steel, for watches, hour and minute, for all sizes of American and imported watches. Per dozen pairs, 22c; per single pair 5c

No. 4E575 Hands, for clocks, all lengths. Per dozen pairs 20c

No. 4E576 Hands, steel, seconds, for all sizes American and imported watches. Per dozen 12c

No. 4E578 Mainsprings, for watches, all styles and sizes. Each 8c
Per dozen 96c

No. 4E580 Mainsprings, for clocks, 1-day. Each 14c

No. 4E582 Mainsprings, for clocks, 8-day. Each 35c

A Big Cut in Watchmakers' Tool Sets. Our Complete Watchmakers' Tool Set, Price $7.12.

THE TOOLS AND IMPLEMENTS we herewith illustrate are the most necessary in the equipment of a watchmaker's kit. The material of our tools is made of the very finest procurable.

EACH TOOL goes through a rigid inspection before leaving our establishment, so that we are assured of them being received by our customers in perfect condition. Our mechanics here who do our watch work use our own tools, and the work done by us is excelled by none. This set for $7.12 consists of 36 separate and distinct pieces. Any man of average mechanical skill can learn to rectify the majority of causes that make a watch stop. The set not alone includes tools necessary for watch repairing, but likewise includes a complete set of tools for silverware, jewelry and clock repairing. We know that you would not fail to be pleased with your purchase if you conclude to favor us with an order for one of these wonderful watchmakers' and jewelers' sets.

No. 4E584 Complete Tool Set, $7.12.

No. 4E584 Price for complete set, including text book $7.12

DESCRIPTION OF OUR OWN WATCH MOVEMENTS.

OUR OWN MOVEMENTS as listed through our Watch Department, complete with the various cases, movements that are made especially for us under contract and as illustrated and described on this and following pages, are recommended by us in preference to any other movement you can buy, for in these movements we can give you far greater value for your money than is possible for us or any other house to give you in any other watch movement made. Why you get almost double the watch movement value when you select one of our movements, illustrated and described on this page, as compared with any other movement made.

ALL WATCH MOVEMENTS bearing the manufacturer's name are sold by the manufacturer to the wholesaler at a fixed list price, subject to certain fixed discounts, and for these movements, no matter whether the wholesaler buys a dozen or a thousand at a time, the fixed list price and the fixed list discount is exactly the same, and as a result the very largest buyer pays the exact same price for an Elgin, Waltham, Hampden, Illinois, Hamilton or other factory made movement that the very smallest wholesale buyer pays. Everyone pays a price that means for the manufacturer a very handsome profit.

DETERMINED that we should give our customers far greater watch value for their money than any other house does or can give, that we should sell direct to our customer one movement, quality considered, at a much lower price than the largest wholesaler can buy from the regular manufacturer even in thousand lots, we took the matter up with one of the largest manufacturers of strictly high grade movements in America, with the idea of making a contract for so large a number of movements, for so large a part of the entire capacity of his factory as would induce this manufacturer to depart from the long established custom of one list price and one discount, and we succeeded to this extent:

THIS MANUFACTURER agreed that on condition that we would take one-half of all the movements they would produce in their factory they would agree with us on a plan by which we could own the movements at a cost to us approximately the very same as if we owned the factory ourselves, but as this meant that we could produce and offer for sale their movements at about one-half the price which they were getting from the largest wholesalers, the agreement made restricted us from using the manufacturer's name. For example, take the gents' 18-size, 17-jeweled, patent regulator Edgemere movement which the manufacturer sells to the largest wholesale dealers at $14.00, less 50 per cent (or $7.00), under his name. We sell the exact same movement, piece for piece and part for part, made in the same factory under our name, the Edgemere, complete with a 3-ounce silverine case for $4.95; in other words, we sell this movement complete with case and all, selling one single watch to any customer for $1.15 less than the manufacturer sells the identical same movement alone without the case, under his own name, to the largest wholesale watch dealers.

THE MANUFACTURER OF OUR MOVEMENTS takes this position, in which he is quite correct: If we were permitted to put these movements out under his name, mentioning his (the manufacturer's) grade, and sell them, including cases, at the price we do, it would ruin his business with every wholesale and retail watch dealer in America, since we sell the complete watch, movement, case and all, for less than the wholesale dealers buy the movement alone from the manufacturer, or the complete watch for about one-half the price the little retail dealer must pay the wholesale dealer for the movement alone.

THESE, OUR SPECIAL EDGEMERE AND PLYMOUTH WATCH CO.'S MOVEMENTS **as illustrated and described on this and following pages, and as priced complete with the different cases on the following pages, are made by one of the largest, most reliable and best known watch movement manufacturers in America,** a watch company whose name is almost a household word, a movement maker whose name appears on the dial and plate of hundreds of thousands of watches that are now in the pockets of users all over the world, and our contracts permit us to sell you the identical same movements, the same high grade work, everything exactly alike, piece for piece and part for part, under our own name, at about one-half the lowest price at which you can buy the identical same movement from almost any retail jeweler in the country; for this company's movements will be found in almost every jewelry store in the land.

OUR 7-JEWELED EDGEMERE.

NOTE THE ILLUSTRATION AND DESCRIPTION of our gents' 18-size 7-jeweled Edgemere movement as shown on this page, and note, especially, the very low prices at which we furnish this movement complete, with the various cases, as shown on the following pages. Remember, in spite of the low price, we guarantee this 7-jeweled Edgemere movement the equal of any 7-jeweled movement made, regardless of name, make or price.

DON'T COMPARE THIS, our 7-jeweled Edgemere movement, with any of the cheap 7-jeweled movements on the market. We have discontinued the sale of the Trenton, Standard and Century 7-jeweled movements, since our contract enables us to offer you one of the highest grade 7-jeweled movements made at a lower price than other houses can sell even the cheap grade of 7-jeweled movements. **Our 7-jeweled Edgemere is put out under our binding five years' guarantee as the equal of any 7-jeweled movement made in America,** and in running and lasting qualities worth more than double any of the cheap 7-jeweled movements, and if you order one and do not find it so, you may return it to us at our expense and we will immediately refund your money. Therefore, if you want a 7-jeweled movement you will get double the value in our Edgemere that you will get in any one of the cheap 7-jeweled movements, and we guarantee you will get all and more value than you will get in any of the 7-jeweled movements you can buy of any make at any price.

OUR 12-JEWELED, GENTS' 18-SIZE, PATENT REGULATOR EDGEMERE MOVEMENT.

WHILE OUR CONTRACTS FOR MOVEMENTS permit of our furnishing this high grade, full 12-jeweled, fancy nickel damaskeened, patent regulator, cut balance, Breguet hairspring movement for less money than we could sell you under the manufacturer's name even a 7-jeweled Elgin, Waltham, Hampden, Hamilton or Illinois movement, if you order a watch with one of our 12-jeweled Edgemere movements, and if after receiving it you are not satisfied that the movement intrinsically is worth double that of any 7-jeweled movement made, you can return the watch to us at our expense, we to refund your money.

OUR 17-JEWELED, PATENT REGULATOR, GENTS' 18-SIZE EDGEMERE MOVEMENT.

WHILE THIS MOVEMENT HAS FULL 17 JEWELS, solid nickel, fancy gold damaskeened, patent regulator, Breguet hairspring, cut balance, patent pendant, all jewels in screw settings, everything the highest grade, yet under our contract we own this movement at a price, and we can furnish you even this, our 17-jeweled Edgemere movement, fitted complete in any case shown on the following pages at from $3.00 to $5.00 less money than it would be possible to furnish you the exact same movement under the manufacturer's name, or any other movement of equal grade; in short, we can furnish you this movement for less than it is possible to furnish you the plain 15-jeweled non patent regulator Elgin, Waltham, Hampden or Illinois movement; in short, for a strictly high grade watch, by selecting this, our 17-jeweled patent regulator Edgemere movement, we can almost double the value we can give you in any watch with a movement bearing the manufacturer's name and therefore also bearing the manufacturer's long profit.

OUR OTHER SPECIAL MOVEMENTS.

THE OTHER SPECIAL MOVEMENTS **we furnish in the different sizes and grades illustrated and described on this page,** all movements that we own on the basis of the actual cost of material and labor, to which we add but our one small percentage of profit, and can therefore furnish you almost double the watch movement value in any one of these movements that we can possibly furnish you in any movement bearing the name of the manufacturer.

OUR FIVE YEARS' GUARANTEE.

EVERY ONE OF THESE MOVEMENTS **is covered by our binding five years' guarantee, covering every piece and part that enters into the movement,** and if any part should fail to perform its duty within five years, through defective material or workmanship, it will be replaced or repaired by us free of any charge.

WE WOULD ESPECIALLY RECOMMEND **in selecting a watch from the following pages, to get the greatest possible value for your money,** to avoid paying unnecessary profit to any manufacturer for name only, that you select one of our special movements fitted in any case you may choose. **Remember, the movement goes to you under our binding five years' guarantee** and with the understanding and agreement that if it isn't perfectly satisfactory to you, if you are not convinced you have made a big saving by buying one of our special movements rather than buying an Elgin, Waltham, Hampden or any other make of movement, you can return the watch to us at our expense and we will immediately refund your money.

Gents' 18-size, Open Face or Hunting Case, 7-Jeweled Edgemere Movement.

Gents' 18-size Edgemere, open face or hunting case, full nickel, 7-jeweled, neatly damaskeened, expansion balance, hairspring hardened and tempered, highly finished regulator, patent pinion, polished screws, marginal figures on dial, true timing screws, quick train, worth double any of the cheap 7-jeweled movements and guaranteed the equal of any 7-jeweled movement made.

NOTE—We sell this high grade 7-jeweled movement complete in any case for less than others sell the cheap grades of 7-jeweled movements.

Gents' 18-Size, Stem Wind, Open Face or Hunting Case, 12-Jeweled Edgemere Movement.

This movement is solid nickel, fancy gold damaskeened and ornamented, patent regulator, upper plate full jeweled, all jewels are set in screw settings, cut expansion balance, true timing screws, Breguet hairspring. You will note from the prices as shown on the following pages that we can furnish you a case fitted with this 12-jeweled patent regulator Edgemere movement complete for less than we can furnish the same case with a 7-jeweled movement bearing the manufacturer's name. If you order a watch with this 12-jeweled patent regulator Edgemere movement and do not consider the movement double the value of any 7-jeweled movement made, you can return it to us at our expense and we will immediately refund your money.

Gents' 18-Size, Open Face or Hunting Case, 17-Jeweled Edgemere Movement.

This movement is regular 18-size; it is solid nickeled, beautifully gold and nickel damaskeened and finished; it has 17 jewels, all set in screw settings, patent regulator, Breguet overstrung hairspring, cut expansion balance, true timing screws quick train, safety pinion, compensating balance, exposed winding wheel, fine sunk enamel dial.

You will note from the prices on the following pages that we furnish this 17-jeweled patent regulator movement at a few cents less than the plain 15-jeweled movement without patent regulator furnished under manufacturers' names, and at from $3.00 to $5.00 less than the identical same grade 17-jeweled patent regulator movement furnished under the manufacturer's name. Therefore, to get double the value for your money in a gent's 18-size watch, we especially recommend, in preference to all other movements, that you select a case and order us to fit in the case one of these 17-jeweled patent regulator movements.

This gents' 18-size, open face or hunting case, full 15-jeweled movement bears the name "Plymouth Watch Co." It is gotten out for us by the manufacturer with a view of making it in every way a higher grade 15-jeweled movement than is made by any other manufacturer, an improvement over any other 15-jeweled movement on the market; full plate, solid nickel, richly damaskeened, full 15-jeweled, jewels have screw settings, micrometer patent regulator, cut expansion balance, overstrung Breguet hairspring, patent pinion and escapement. In quality of material and fine mechanical lines, in workmanship, finish, in lasting qualities, in accurate time keeping, nothing is spared to make this positively the highest grade 15-jeweled movement on the market, and while, as shown in the following pages, we furnish it for less than we sell 15-jeweled movements bearing the manufacturer's name, if you buy this movement and after giving it a reasonable test as to time, if you do not consider it better than any other 15-jeweled movement on the market, you can return it to us at our expense and we will immediately refund your money.

NOTE, that different from any of the 15-jeweled movements of other makes, this, our 15-jeweled movement, is accurately adjusted to all positions, and you get in this the only accurately adjusted 15-jeweled movement made.

This is a Cheap Traveling Watch, Made to Look Like the Most Expensive 23-Jeweled Adjusted Railway Watch Made.

While it is in interior construction a plain 7-jeweled movement, to give to it all the appearance of the highest priced railway movement made, it is made of nickel, the upper plate is very showily gilt damaskeened, imitation of rich ruby jewels in imitation of solid gold screw settings have been set with the screws over the pinion places of the entire top of the plate, including all pinion spots, center, first, second and third wheels and balance; has a patent regulator; it is stamped "23-Jewels, adjusted;" it is also stamped with a locomotive on the plate and on the front or dial and is named "Trainmen's Special." It is essentially a trading watch. We have sold thousands of these movements to auctioneers, horse traders and other traders, peddlers, jewelers, publishers and scheme houses for premiums, etc., for while we sell it for just what it is, in interior construction a plain 7-jeweled American movement, it has all the appearance of a movement that you would pay $25.00 or more for. It is especially popular in our No. 4E1114 Alaska silver stem wind case, and all for $2.75, making an ideal trading watch or watch that really has the appearance of a $50.00 gold filled, 23-jeweled, adjusted watch, but you buy the complete watch for $2.75. Many of our customers among the traveling men carry them as a side line and sell them at from $5.00 to $20.00, adding from $5.00 to $25.00 a week to their net income. If you want a very showy watch for trading purposes there is nothing that will match this watch.

Gents' 18-Size, Open Face or Hunting Case, Stem Wind, 17-Jeweled, Adjusted Plymouth Watch Co. Movement.

This movement is marked "Plymouth Watch Co.," is solid nickel, richly damaskeened and finished, has 17 ruby jewels, raised gold settings with screws, accurately and especially adjusted to heat, cold, isochronism and all positions, the most accurate and complete adjustment lines on any watch made; quick train, hand finished escape wheel, compensating balance, Breguet overstrung tempered hairspring, new improved patent micrometer regulator barrel arbor pivots, double sunk glass enamel dial with marginal figures. This 17-jeweled, full adjusted, full plate movement is gotten out for us with a view to furnishing a higher grade adjusted movement than is made and sold by any watch company in America. While we furnish it at a much lower price than you can buy a 17-jeweled adjusted movement bearing the manufacturer's name, if you order this movement and do not find, after giving it a thorough trial, that it gives better satisfaction than any other 17-jeweled movement made, you can return it to us at our expense and we will immediately refund your money.

NOTE the difference between this 17-Jeweled Plymouth Watch Co. and our 17-Jeweled Edgemere. It is the very fine adjustment of this movement, the adjustment to all positions, temperature and isochronism, which accounts for the difference in cost to manufacture.

Gentlemen's 18-Size, Stem Wind, Lever Set, Open Face or Hunting Style, 21-Jeweled King Edward Movement, Manufactured by the Plymouth Watch Co.

This movement procured by us under a new deal and for an immense quantity, represents the highest perfection in watchmaking. It has 21 fine ruby jewels in gold settings, cut expansion balance, Breguet hairspring, patent safety pinion, patent regulator, adjusted to temperature and the positions, the most accurate and most modern watch on the market to day quoted throughout our catalogue, at less cost than the 17-jeweled adjusted movements bearing the makers' name. This watch we can recommend as being perfection in the watchmaking art, and is made with the idea not to equal any 21-jeweled watch on the market but to have something better than has been heretofore manufactured. By all means, if you want the best watch manufactured, we would advise either the Prince of Wales in the 16-size or the King Edward in 18-size.

Gentlemen's 16-Size, Open Face or Hunting Style, 7-Jeweled Nickel Edgemere Movement.

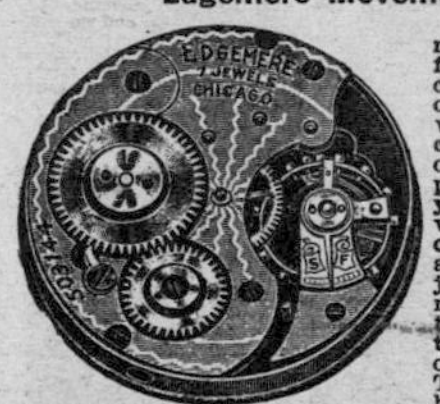

This movement is made for us under contract, and at our price fitted with any 16-size case as shown on the following pages, will give you double the value that you can get in any 16-size 7-jeweled movement bearing the manufacturer's name on the market. This movement has nickel plates, richly damaskeened, exposed high polished winding wheels, non-magnetic balance and hairspring, full polished pinions, handsome double pressed dial with red marginal figures, is stem wind and pendant set and positively gives the best satisfaction of any 7-jeweled cheap watch on the market. Its equal cannot be procured for twice what we ask for it.

Gentlemen's 16-Size, Open Face or Hunting Style, 15-Jeweled Patent Regulator Edgemere Movement.

This movement is made under our new arrangement, is highly finished and an accurate timekeeper, has full nickel plates, jewels in screw settings, high polished exposed winding apparatus, cut expansion balance, with Breguet hairspring, fine polished patent regulator, the equal of any 15-jeweled movement manufactured bearing the makers' name. By reason of our new contract, we are able to quote it in this catalogue on the various pages at less than we ask for 7-jeweled movements bearing the makers' name. If you want a good and accurate timekeeper, we would advise you to select this watch above all other 16-size movements with 7 jewels, stamped with the makers' name.

Gents' 16-Size, Open Face or Hunting Case, Stem Wind Plymouth Watch Co. Movement.

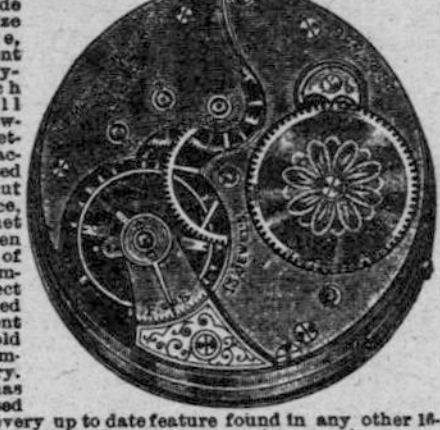

This is positively the highest grade 15-jeweled 16-size movement made, each movement stamped "Plymouth Watch Co." It is full 15-jeweled, all jewels in screwed settings and it is accurately adjusted to positions; has cut expansion balance, overstrung Breguet hairspring, gotten out with a view of giving our customers in every respect a better 15-jeweled 16-size movement than is made or sold by any watch company in the country. This movement has the latest exposed winding wheel, every up to date feature found in any other 16-size movement, and still we furnish it at as low a price as any other 16-size movement made.

Gents' 16-Size, Open Face or Hunting Case, 17-Jeweled Adjusted Plymouth Watch Co. Movement.

This is our gents' 17-jeweled adjusted 16-size movement, each movement stamped "Plymouth Watch Co." It is 17-jeweled, all jewels in screwed settings, accurately adjusted to heat, cold, position and isochronism; has the latest patent micrometer regulator, patent pinion and escapement, exposed winding wheel, has every new and up to date improvement, combines all the best in all the highest grade 17-jeweled 16 size movements made, and yet we offer it at a lower price than we can offer any other 17-jeweled movement.

Gentlemen's 16-Size, Open Face or Hunting, 21-Jeweled, Nickel, Patent Regulator Prince of Wales Movement, Manufactured by the Plymouth Watch Company.

This movement is a new addition to our exceptional value page and represents positively the highest grade watch in 21-jeweled manufactured. A new deal with a new company for an immense quantity enables us to sell this watch to you at less money than 17-jeweled named watches manufactured by others. This watch has full nickel plates, jewels all in settings, cut expansion balance, double sunk dial, in fact, all modern improvements, adjusted to temperature and positions, in fact, a watch such as cannot be compared with any other watch quoted or illustrated in our catalogue. If you purchase this watch you are making a saving of no less than $12.00 to $15.00 and are getting the best production of modern watch making.

Gents' 12-Size, Open Face or Hunting Case, Solid Nickel, 10-Jeweled, Stem Wind and Stem Set Movement.

These movements are stamped "Edgemere." They are 10-jeweled, exposed winding wheel, cut expansion balance, Breguet hairspring, true timing screws. This is a movement made especially for us. It is extra high grade, and under our contract we can furnish it for less money than we can furnish 7-jeweled 12-size movements of other makes, and in buying a 12-size gents' watch, we especially recommend that you select this movement.

Gents' 12-Size, 15-Jeweled, Open Face or Hunting Style, Stem Wind and Stem Set, Plymouth Watch Co. Movement.

These movements are stamped "Plymouth Watch Co." They have fifteen fine ruby jewels, patent regulator, exposed polished winding wheels, Breguet hairspring, accurately trued and timed and positively the finest 15-jeweled 12-size movement manufactured. We control the prices on account of an immense contract and while this watch is positively the finest 15-jeweled 12-size movement on the market, still we are able to offer it at less money than any of the 12-size stamped movements offered by such factories as the Elgin, Waltham, Hampden and other makers. If you want the latest extra thin model 12-size watch in 15-jeweled grade, we recommend, above any other, this movement fitted in any of the cases illustrated and described in our catalogue.

Gentlemen's 12-Size, 17-Jeweled, Open Face or Hunting Style, Stem Wind and Pendant Set, Plymouth Watch Co. Movement.

As positively the acme of perfection in 17-jeweled, 12-size movements, we offer this, our latest production from the factory. This movement is stamped "Plymouth Watch Co.," and represents the highest order in this grade above all other makes. This movement is adjusted, trued and timed before leaving the factory to the very closest possible degree. It has high polished exposed winding wheels, Breguet hairspring, true timing screws, patent safety pinion, handsomely damaskeened nickel plates and patent regulator, jewels in screw settings; in fact, every detail in watchmaking has been covered and perfected. While this movement stands pre-eminent for timekeeping and perfection of finish, still, by our new contract in placing our immense order, we are able to sell it at less than watches stamped with the maker's name throughout these pages. We would advise, if you are looking for a small size extra thin gents' watch in a high jeweled grade, to positively select this one to the exclusion of all other grades and makes.

Ladies' 6-Size Hunting Style Countess Janet.

This watch is made for a trading watch in ladies' size. Never before has a ladies' size watch been placed on the market for this purpose. It looks exactly like a high grade 17-jeweled or 19-jeweled watch; is richly nickeled; has 17 large imitation ruby jewels screwed on the plates, which, however, have no utility, but are made for show only. The movement itself is merely a 7-jeweled American made movement, manufactured for our express use by one of the big watch companies. It is for a trading watch only, but as a timekeeper will keep only fair time. It is richly damaskeened so as to make a beautiful appearance; is stem wind and stem set. Our 18-size cheap trading watch for travelers has met with exceptionally fine sale. The profit from a watch of this sort cannot be estimated. Never before have they been placed on the market. They have the appearance of a watch being worth twenty times more than what we ask. This watch is particularly attractive for the purposes of watch trading, for peddlers' use, publishing houses, scheme houses, partial payment houses, in fact, any one wanting a watch having the appearance of the very highest grade for next to nothing in cost.

Ladies' 6-Size, Hunting Case, Stem Wind and Stem Set, 7-Jeweled Edgemere Movement.

Like the gents' 18-size movement, we guarantee this 7-jeweled movement the equal of any 7-jeweled 6-size movement made, and worth two of any of the cheap 7-jeweled movements on the market. It is the highest grade 7-jeweled movement made, and in selecting a ladies' watch, we would especially recommend that you select our 7-jeweled, Edgemere; has gold damaskeening, cut expansion balance, sunk second enamel dial, a great improvement over any other 7-jeweled 6-size movement on the market.

Ladies' 6-Size, Hunting Case, Stem Wind and Stem Set, Solid Nickel, 12-Jeweled Edgemere Movement.

This is the highest grade 12-jeweled 6-size movement made. All jewels are in screwed settings. It is richly damaskeened in gold, cut expansion balance, finest overstrung Breguet hairspring, patent pinion and escapement, quick train, fine enameled dial with marginal figures. While this movement is worth double that of any 7-jeweled movement on the market, with our special arrangements we furnish this movement, as shown on the following pages, at even less than the regular grade 7-jeweled movements.

Ladies' 6-Size, Stem Wind and Stem Set, Hunting Style, 17-Jeweled Edgemere Movement.

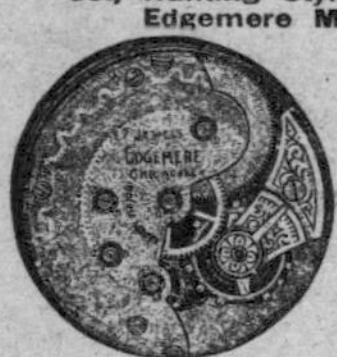

This movement is full 17-jeweled, all jewels in screwed settings, solid nickel, richly damaskeened and ornamented in gold, has cut expansion balance, true timing screws, finest overstrung Breguet hairspring, and yet, under our special arrangements, we can furnish this movement at about one-half the price charged by manufacturers for identically the same movement under their name. **Rather than buy a 7 or 15-jeweled movement of any other make we especially recommend that in selecting a ladies' 6-size watch you choose this, our 17-jeweled Edgemere.**

Ladies' 6-Size, Hunting Case, Stem Wind and Stem Set, Solid Nickel, Ruby Jeweled Plymouth Watch Co.

These movements are especially made for us, and they are gotten out with a view of giving our customers a higher grade 15-jeweled 6-size movement than is made by any watch company in America. This movement is accurately adjusted to position, the 15 jewels are the highest grade rubies, perfect settings, set with screws, has the latest compensating cut balance true, timing screws, has the finest overstrung Breguet hairspring, is richly damaskeened in gold, has sunk second dial, patent pinion and escapement, quick train, guaranteed the highest grade 6-size 15-jeweled movement on the market.

Ladies' 6-Size, Hunting Case, Stem Wind, 17-Jeweled Adjusted Movement.

These movements are marked "Plymouth Watch Co." They are positively the highest grade 17-jeweled 6-size movements made. Solid nickel, richly damaskeened in gold, full 17 jewels, finest ruby jewels in gold settings, settings set with screws, compensating cut balance, balance adjusted with true timing screws, finest overstrung patent Breguet hairspring, polished center wheel, quick train, patent pinion. Movement is accurately adjusted to heat, cold, position and isochronism, combining everything that you could get in any movement that you would pay three times the price for if sold by any manufacturer under the manufacturer's name and number, so in selecting the very finest thing in a ladies' 6-size watch, we would especially recommend that you select this movement, and we will furnish it to you, quality for quality, at one-half the price you could buy any other make.

Ladies' 0-Size, 7-Jeweled, Swiss, Stem Wind and Stem Set Movement.

This movement is made for us under contract. It is full nickel, quick train, 7 jewels patent pinion and patent lever escapement, and we guarantee it the highest grade 7-jewel, small 0-size movement made. You will find this movement will keep better time and last twice as long as any other 7-jeweled 0-size movement on the market, and yet, under our special arrangements with the manufacturer, we can furnish this in a much higher grade 7-jeweled movement than you could get elsewhere at less than the ordinary 7-jeweled movements are sold by others. In selecting a very small watch for a lady in an 0-size, unless you want to get our high grade Edgemere 0-size movement, we would especially advise that you select this in preference to any other 7-jeweled 0-size movement made.

Ladies' 0-Size, 15-Jeweled Patent Regulator Edgemere Movement.

This small 0-size ladies' movement is solid nickel, richly finished, full 15-jeweled, jewels in beautiful settings, full screwed. It is very elaborately finished, has the latest patent micrometer regulator, cut expansion balance, finest patent straight line lever escapement, quick train, patent pinion; in short, it is the highest grade 15-jeweled 0-size movement made and will outwear two of the ordinary 0-size 15-jeweled movements, and yet, under our special arrangements with the manufacturer, owning this movement as we do on the basis of the actual cost of material and labor, we can, after adding our one small percentage of profit, furnish it to you at a much lower price than we can furnish a 15-jeweled movement of other makes bearing the manufacturer's name and grade.

If you want a small watch for a lady, select this, our highest grade 15-jeweled Edgemere movement, fit it in any 0-size case, and if, after giving it a fair trial, you are not convinced that it is the highest grade 15-jeweled 0-size movement made, you can return the watch to us at our expense and we will immediately refund your money.

THESE SPECIAL MOVEMENTS

AS ILLUSTRATED AND DESCRIBED ON THIS AND THE PRECEDING PAGE, as before explained, we own under contract at the actual cost of material and labor with but our one small percentage of profit added. As a result they cost you very much less than any other movement we can offer, and if you will send us your order for any watch fitted with any one of our special movements it will go to you under our binding five years' guarantee, and with the understanding and agreement that if you do not find it, grade for grade, jeweling for jeweling, as good, if not better than any movement made by any maker in America, regardless of name, make or price, you can return the watch (movement and case) to us at our expense and we will refund your money.

JEWELED SERIES THE SMALLEST SIZE AMERICAN WATCH IN SOLID GOLD 14-KARAT CASES, FOR $21.70

IN ADDITION TO OUR ALREADY IMMENSE VARIETY OF WATCHES, WE HAVE THIS YEAR ADDED THE VERY LATEST PRODUCTION OF THE WALTHAM WATCH CO., THE NEW JEWELED SERIES MOVEMENTS, FITTED IN SOLID GOLD 14-KARAT CASES.

THE CASES are manufactured by the Western Watch Case Co. Their stamp appears in each case. The Jeweled Series is a new size, being nearly two sizes smaller than the smallest 0-size. We show No. 4E650 in open face. This gives you an idea of how the front of the open face watches appears. On the other numbers, the back of the cases will be exactly as the illustration shows. The movements fitted in these cases are all high jeweled and all stem wind and pendant set, the Ruby, being a 15-jeweled nickel movement, raised settings, exposed pallets, compensating balance, exposed winding wheels and patent Breguet hairspring.

THE RIVERSIDE IS A 17-JEWELED NICKEL MOVEMENT, with raised gold settings, red gold center wheels, exposed sapphire pallets, compensating balance, adjusted, Breguet hairspring and safety barrel. **THE DIAMOND MOVEMENT** being the highest grade, has 17 diamond and ruby jewels, both balance pivots running on genuine diamonds, raised gold settings, gold train, exposed sapphire pallets, compensating balance, adjusted, patent micrometric regulator, Breguet hairspring, hardened and tempered in form, tempered steel safety barrel; nothing finer manufactured in a ladies' watch.

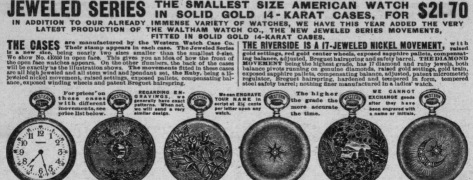

For prices on these cases with different movements, see price list below.
REGARDING ENGRAVINGS, we generally have exact patterns. When not, we will send a very similar design.
We can ENGRAVE YOUR NAME in script at 2½ cents per letter upon any watch.
The higher the grade the more accurate the time.
WE CANNOT EXCHANGE goods after they have been engraved with a name or initials.
WESTERN

Solid Gold, 14-karat, plain polished. No. 4E650 Open Face. No. 4E652 Hunting.

Solid Gold, 14-karat, hand engraved and engine turned. No. 4E654 Open Face. No. 4E656 Hunting.

Solid Gold, 14-karat, hand engraved, diagonal design. No. 4E658 Open Face. No. 4E660 Hunting.

Solid Gold, 14-karat, plain polished, with genuine cut diamond. No. 4E662 Open Face. No. 4E664 Hunting.

Solid Gold, 14-karat, full hand engraved. No. 4E666 Open Face. No. 4E668 Hunting.

Solid Gold, 14-karat, plain polished, set with 4 genuine cut diamonds. No. 4E670 Open Face. No. 4E672 Hunting.

WE FIT THE FOLLOWING WALTHAM JEWELED SERIES MOVEMENTS IN ALL OF THE ABOVE CASES. ORDER BY NUMBER.	No. 4E650	No. 4E652 4E654	No. 4E658	No. 4E656 4E662	No. 4E660 4E666	No. 4E664	No. 4E668	No. 4E670	No. 4E672
15 Jeweled RUBY Waltham Watch Co.	$21.70	$24.20	$24.70	$25.20	$26.20	$27.20	$28.70	$31.20	$33.20
17 Jeweled RIVERSIDE Waltham Watch Co.	26.95	29.45	29.95	30.45	31.45	32.45	33.95	36.45	38.45
17 Jeweled DIAMOND Waltham Watch Co.	31.12	33.62	34.12	34.62	35.62	36.62	38.12	40.62	42.62

WE WANT JEWELERS, GENERAL MERCHANTS WHO HANDLE WATCHES, AND EVERYBODY TO SEND US THEIR WATCH REPAIRS.

IT WILL PAY THE JEWELER better to send his repairs to us and have the work properly done, with new material of the right kind, than to patch up the job with old material, softsolder or material which does not fit, as is the custom where there is not a large stock of well selected material and a good outfit of tools at hand. Our prices being from one-half to one-fourth the regular prices, there is a large profit left for the dealer or an equal saving to those who send their watches to us direct.

REMEMBER, that a watch should not run longer than one and one-half years without having the oil cleaned off and fresh oil applied. An engine or sewing machine will be oiled several times per day, but we have known people to carry a watch for ten years without having it cleaned or fresh oil applied. Usually, a movement thus treated is of no value, being entirely worn out. Our charge for cleaning and oiling is 50 cents. The regular retail price is $1.50. We give below a list of charges for repairs which will be subject to change in some cases. For example: Old fusee watches, made some fifty or sixty years ago in England, the material of which is difficult to procure.

Balances, American Expansion	$1.50 to $2.75
Balances, Am. Steel or Nickel	.50
Balances, English, Steel or Composition	1.00
Balances, Swiss, Composition	.75
Balances, Swiss, with screw	1.25
Balances, Swiss, Expansion, cut	3.00
Cleaning, ordinary Swiss, Duplex or American	.50
Cleaning, ordinary English	1.00
Demagnetizing Watch Movements, ordinary	.75
Demagnetizing Watch Movements, finer grades	$1.00 to 2.00
Dials, Swiss, without seconds	1.00
Dials, Swiss, with seconds	1.50
Dust Bands, American	.25
Hairsprings, ordinary flat	.75
Hairsprings, Breguet	1.50
Hands, common, each	.10
Hands, fine, each	.20
Jewels, American, Cock or Foot (with settings)	.50
Jewels, American, 3d, 4th or 'Scape	50c to .75
Jewels, Endstone, in setting	.50
Jewels, Cap, Swiss (with plate)	.25
Jewels, Swiss, 3d, 4th, 'Scape or Balance, set in plate	.50
Jewels, Swiss, 3d, 4th, 'Scape or Balance, Fine Ruby	1.50
Jewels, Swiss, Center, Fine Ruby in Gold Set	3.00
Jewels, Roller	.35
Jewels, Pallet, Set in old Settings, American	.75
Mainsprings, Swiss	$0.50
Mainsprings, English, with hook	.75
Mainsprings, American	.50
Mainsprings, Repeaters, etc.	$1.00 to 1.50
Pallets, Fork and Arbor, complete, ordinary	3.00
Pallets, Fork and Arbor, complete, American	$1.25 to 2.50
Pinions, American, 3d, 4th or 'Scape	.75
Pinions, American, Center	1.00
Pinions, American, Center, Patent, complete with Wheel	2.00
Pinions, Cannon	.50
Pinions, Swiss, 3d, 4th or 'Scape, ordinary	1.00
Pinions, Swiss, 3d, 4th or 'Scape, fine	$1.75 to 2.00
Pinions, Swiss, Center, ordinary	1.50
Pinions, Swiss, Center, fine	2.00
Pinions, Swiss, Cannon	.50
Ratchets, English, Swiss or American	.50
Staffs Balance, American, 75c to	$1.25
Staffs Balance, Howard, etc.	2.50
Staffs Balance, English, ordinary	1.25
Staffs Balance, English, fine	$1.50 to 2.50
Staffs Balance, Swiss, ordinary	1.25
Staffs Balance, Swiss, fine	2.50

Changing Key Wind Cases to Stem Wind.

Silver Cases	$1.50
Gold Cases	2.50

Our New Swiss Imported 12-Size Thin Model 17 Jeweled Movement.

It has 17 fine ruby jewels, cut expansion balance wheel, patent high polished whip lash patent regulator, Breguet hairspring, plate jewels all in screw settings, has exposed winding wheels, full dust protecting side bands, is stem wind and pendant set. The dial has plain Arabic figures, with red marginal minute figures. Remember, this movement is not American make. However, it is offered and sold by many as a product of American manufacture. We sell them for what they are, a very fine Swiss imported movement, a movement that we can recommend and warrant to you for a term of five years. Each one carries our binding guarantee.

Prices in the various cases for the watch complete are as follows:

No. 4E700 Fitted in Alaska silver open face case, screw back and bezel....$ 8.75

No. 4E702 Fitted in solid silver Hunting case....11.00

No. 4E704 Fitted in a 20-year gold filled case, open face, screw back and bezel, beautifully engraved....$11.27

No. 4E706 Fitted in a 20-year gold filled case, Hunting style, beautifully engraved....$14.27

This Fine Watch Box for 20c.

No. 4E588 This picture, made from a photograph, shows one of our fine silk plush lined and covered watchboxes that we supply for 20 cents extra with any watch purchased of us. In ordering, state what size watch the case is intended for.

Price....20c

CUT PRICE, 18 CENTS.

The Ajax Watch Insulator or Protector protects your watch. It is made of a secret compounded metal, beautifully enameled and lined with velvet. Order by number. The maker guarantees that this insulator protects the watch case from wear and the movement from all ordinary magnetic influence. It fits all size watches, open face or hunting style of all makes. When ordering don't fail to give size and make of case and whether open face or hunting style is wanted.

No. 4E586 Price....18c

WHEN WATCHES are sent with instructions to put them in good order we will do everything necessary to put them in good running condition, but when the instructions are to repair a certain particular part of a watch, the repairs will be strictly confined only to the part or parts specified and we cannot hold ourselves responsible for anything further that may be necessary to insure correct running of the watch. In sending any part of a watch, if your intention is to fit same yourself, do not instruct us to fit same, but kindly use the word "select." This prevents misunderstanding your wishes.

If an idea of the cost of repairs cannot be obtained from the above list, send the watch to us and on receipt of same we will examine it, quote cost of repairing and hold for instructions. **SHIPPING DIRECTIONS**—When shipping watches or jewelry for repairs or exchange, mark plainly as follows: SEARS, ROEBUCK & CO., Watch Repair Dep't, Chicago, Ill., and in upper left hand corner put your own name and address, prefixing the word "From." Also inclose a card in the package with your name and address and state that the watch is for repairs. At the same time write us a letter stating that you have sent a watch (by mail or express) for repairs, what repairs you want made, or that you wish us to quote cost of repairing.

PACKING FOR SHIPMENT. Watches should be wrapped in some soft material (cotton batting is good), and packed in a strong box, about 2x3x3 inches. Do not try and ship more than one watch in a box of this size, as it requires considerable packing about each watch to insure safe shipment.

CASH WITH THE ORDER must be sent for all repair work. If you do not know what the cost will be, send what you think will more than cover it and we will refund the balance. If to be returned by mail, send 7 cents for each watch for postage and 8 cents extra for registry.

WE BUY OLD GOLD AND SILVER and pay the highest market price, namely, 18-karat gold, 72c; 14-karat gold, 56c, and 10-karat gold, 40c per pennyweight. Silver fluctuates in value, but at the present time is worth 50c per ounce. In all cases we hold old metal until we are advised by customers that estimate of value is satisfactory.

PRICES OF ELGIN AND WALTHAM MOVEMENTS WITHOUT CASES.

For the accommodation of our customers only, and so as to avoid inquiries for prices, we herewith quote our prices on Elgin and Waltham movements without cases. When ordering be sure to give the size and make of case, whether open face or hunting movement required, also keep in mind that only an open face movement will go in an open face case and the hunting style movement in the hunting style case, and that we can furnish only stem wind movements; stem wind movements cannot be fitted in key wind cases.

4E750	18-size, 7 jeweled Elgin or Waltham, gilded plates	$3.67
4E752	18-size, 7 jeweled Elgin or Waltham, nickel	4.20
4E754	18-size, 15 jeweled Elgin or Waltham, nickel plates	5.25
4E756	18-size, 17 jeweled Elgin or Waltham, nickel, not adjusted	6.30
4E758	18-size, 17 jeweled G. M. Wheeler, Elgin or P. S. Bartlett, Waltham	10.50
4E764	16-size, 7 jeweled Elgin or Waltham, nickel	5.25
4E766	16-size, 15 jeweled Elgin or Waltham	6.82
4E768	16-size, 17 jeweled Royal grade Waltham	14.43
4E770	16-size, 17 jeweled No. 243 Elgin	23.10
4E772	12-size, 7 jeweled Elgin or Waltham, nickel	6.56
4E774	12-size, 15 jeweled Elgin or Waltham, nickel	9.45
4E776	12-size, 17 jeweled No. 275 grade Elgin or Royal grade Waltham	14.44
4E778	6-size, 7 jeweled Elgin or Waltham, nickel	4.73
4E780	6-size, 15 jeweled Elgin or Waltham, nickel	5.78
4E782	0-size, 7 jeweled, Elgin or Waltham	6.82
4E784	0-size, 15 jeweled Elgin or Waltham	10.50
4E786	0-size, 17 jeweled Riverside Waltham	19.42

$14.10 $14.10

NEW THIN MODEL OPEN FACE AND HUNTING STYLE

DUEBER-HAMPDEN

16-SIZE 25-YEAR WARRANTED GOLD FILLED AND 14-KARAT SOLID GOLD COMPLETE WATCHES

These cases are made by the Dueber Watch Company. They are the correct thing, the right size and shape, hand engraved and in every respect perfect. The movements are all new models manufactured by the Hampden Watch Company, each one guaranteed an accurate time piece for five years. Note the prices and compare them with what others ask for the same watch. We fit these movements into case as number shows.

The engraving will be similar to the illustration.

No. 4E712 25-year gold filled open face, screw back and screw bezel.

No. 4E714 25-year gold filled hunting.

No. 4E716 14-karat solid gold, heavy weight, open face.

No. 4E718 14-karat solid gold, heavy weight, hunting.

	No. 4E712	No. 4E714	No. 4E716	No. 4E718
Full 17 jeweled General Stark movement	$14.10	$15.65	$30.50	$35.00
Full 17 jeweled William McKinley movement	15.85	17.55	32.20	36.70
Full 21 jeweled William McKinley movement	27.00	28.40	43.25	47.75

DEALERS AND ALL MERCHANTS WHO SELL WATCHES AND JEWELRY CAN MAKE MONEY by buying from us. We can furnish them any goods from our big Watch and Jewelry Department for much less than they can buy elsewhere. Our Watch and Jewelry Department offers a great opportunity for money making.

64c AND UPWARDS FOR AMERICAN WATCHES

Nickel, Metal, Electro Plate, Silver, Gold Filled and Solid Gold Watches at prices heretofore unknown. SWEEPING REDUCTIONS ON EVERYTHING IN THIS DEPARTMENT made possible by larger purchases and larger contracts than ever before, means lowest prices ever quoted by us or any other house. Our prices are prices unknown to others. A great saving to buyers. Remember, we are always ready to refund your money if our goods are not found at all times as represented.

No. 4E800
64c

CUT AGAIN
No. 4E800

64-CENT AMERICAN WATCH.

Far better than ever and yet only 64 cents.

A gentleman's stem wind watch for 64 cents.

This is a **nickel plated** metal watch, stem wind and pendant set, regular 18-size, **open face case. A patent lever** movement, and runs 30 to 36 hours with one winding.

Guaranteed American made and a very good timekeeper; movement is strong in construction, and will stand much rougher usage than a finer and higher priced watch. A one year guarantee signed by the maker goes with each watch.

Remember your boy with one of these 64-cent watches. Nothing will please him better. **64 cents** is little money and **far less money** than the watch can be bought for elsewhere.

No. 4E800 Price, each....... $0.64
No. 4E801 Price, per dozen.. 7.44

We will not sell less than one dozen at dozen price.

ALASKA SILVER ALL AMERICAN OPEN FACE WATCH

$1.90 FOR AN AMERICAN STEM WIND AND STEM SET nickel movement and American case.

With Every Watch Sold We Send Our Signed Five-year Written Binding GUARANTEE.

$1.90

ALASKA SILVER CASE. THIS HANDSOME CASE, AS ILLUSTRATED, is what is known as ALASKA SILVER. It is a composition of several metals, giving the watch the appearance of **coin silver**; and in fact, it is in appearance and in every way, except intrinsic value, the equal of coin silver. **It will wear and retain its coin silver color for a lifetime.** It is handsomely finished, as shown in illustration, in **a CORRUGATED PATTERN** with fancy heavy beaded edge. It is **open face, full 18-size, stem wind and stem set**, and is fitted **with a heavy bevel edge crystal.**

AT $1.90 WE FURNISH THIS CASE COMPLETE WITH MOVEMENT in what we call snap back and snap bezel. The front and back snap on.

MOVEMENT. WE FURNISH IN THIS WATCH AT OUR SPECIAL PRICE OF $1.90 a 7-jeweled solid nickel stem wind and stem set movement. These movements are made expressly for us by one of the largest makers of American watches.

No. 4E802 Snap back and snap bezel.

OUR SPECIAL AND HERETOFORE UNHEARD OF PRICE OF $1.90 COMMENDS THIS WATCH to all those who require a reliable timepiece and American case that will not tarnish, for very little money, and **$1.90** is a price based on the actual cost to produce, with but our one small profit added.

No. 4E802 Price.. $1.90
No. 4E804 Same case as No. 4E802, but fitted with a genuine 7 jeweled Elgin or Waltham movement. Price.............................. $3.38

No. 4E806 Same Watch as No. 4E802, with the case hinged in front and snap back, $2.05. We recommend this hinged or jointed front case at $2.05. The 15 cents additional which we charge you is the exact difference in the cost to us, and we believe the watch is well worth the difference. Price.......................... $2.05
No. 4E808 Same case as No. 4E806, but fitted with a genuine 7-jeweled Elgin or Waltham movement. Price.......... $4.03

No. 4E810
$1.23

NEW WONDER WATCH.

AT $1.23 THIS NEW ENGLAND WONDER. **A genuine American made watch.** It runs thirty to thirty-six hours with one winding and **keeps good time.** It is stem wind and stem set. If properly handled and cared for it will last for years. The case is **plain polished, nickel plated.** The movement is one of the most simple known. It comes in both nickel and gilt, has the duplex escapement, both pivots fitted with genuine jewels. While we do not guarantee this watch for the price, **$1.23, we know you will be entirely satisfied.**

No. 4E810 Price..... $1.23

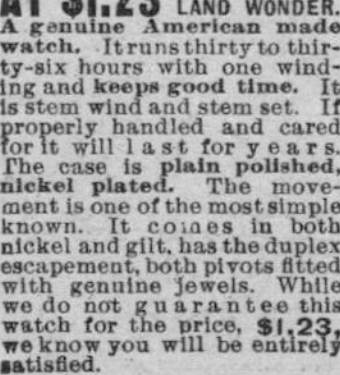

PRICES CUT ON 8-DAY WATCHES

No. 4E812
SILVER,
$9.25

No. 4E814
NICKEL,
$7.80

$9.25 for an 8-day, 15-jeweled solid silver open face watch.
$7.80 for an 8-day, 15-jeweled solid nickel open face watch.

An 8-Day Watch now perfected. Why be bothered winding your watch every night! Each one carries with it our written, binding, five-year guarantee, we warrant it to run accurately and give entire satisfaction for a term of five years. Remember, you need wind it but once every eight days. Never before, at anything like the price, has such a marvel of mechanical skill been offered; never before has an 8-day watch been successfully constructed. At **$9.25** we have to offer a solid silver, 8-day, full fifteen-jeweled Swiss lever, stem wind and stem set watch warranted for five years. The case is heavy solid silver, plain polished, open face, jointed front and back. The movement has fifteen fine ruby jewels, finely gilded plates, has lever escapement, cut balance wheel, true timing screws, polished safety pinions, breguet hair spring, and is manufactured by one of the largest and most reliable concerns in Switzerland.

No. 4E812 Fifteen-jeweled, solid silver, 8-day watch. Price... $9.25

At $7.80 we offer a fine solid nickel case, open face, plain polished, stem wind and set, fitted with a fine 8-day, fifteen-jeweled, gilded movement, made in Switzerland. This movement has fifteen fine ruby jewels, plates beautifully gilded, breguet hair spring, true timing screws, polished safety pinions and **is guaranteed for a term of five years.**

No. 4E814 Fifteen-jeweled, solid nickel, 8-day watch. Price $7.80

SWISS CALENDAR WATCH.

No. 4E816

If you own one of these watches you will not find it necessary to consult an almanac or ask anyone to tell you the day of the month. The case is nickel plated, and fitted with a heavy beveled edge glass. **The movement** is imported, stem wind and stem set, jeweled, cylinder escapement, hard enameled dial, and in addition to being complete in every respect as a timekeeper, it has **a complete calendar, which works automatically, always indicating correctly the day of the month.**

No. 4E816 Price...... $2.98

No. 4E816
$2.98

Solid Silver, Gold Filled and Gunmetal

MOON CALENDAR WATCHES

AT PRICES CUT AGAIN.

This watch is made in Switzerland and is a mechanical wonder, but at the same time is offered at a price which is within the reach of all. The case is **solid silver**, beautifully engraved, and fitted with heavy beveled edge glass.

No. 4E818
$5.88

The movement is stem wind and stem set, patent lever escapement, full jeweled, and in addition to being a complete timepiece, it is also a **COMPLETE CALENDAR, indicating the day of the week, day of the month, month of the year, and the changes of the moon.** At the same time it is so simple that it is not more liable to get out of order than an ordinary watch. **It is fully guaranteed by both the manufacturers and ourselves.**

We can furnish it in open face only.

No. 4E818 Price, solid silver, each.............................. $5.88
No. 4E820 Price, gunmetal, same as above.............................. $4.41
No. 4E822 Price, gold filled, 20 years guaranteed.......................... $12.20

12 of these Watches for **$23.40**

No. 4E824 **$2.06**

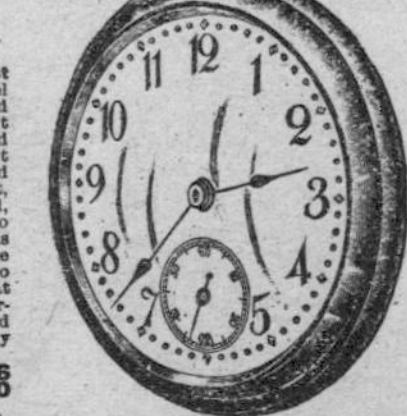

A BOY'S GOOD WATCH FOR $2.06.

This watch, as illustration shows, is the very latest twelve size, extra thin model. The case is snap bezel and back, dustproof, made of solid nickel, not plated as most of these watch cases on the market are, but solid nickel through and through. It looks like solid silver. It will never rust; it will never tarnish; it will always be bright. The movement will keep good time, it is jeweled, it is stem wind and pendant set, the balance wheel is compensated, plates frosted, in fact, a watch such as any boy would be proud to own, and one that will give good satisfaction. This watch is imported by us from Switzerland, the home of watchmaking. While we guarantee it to be the best $2.06 can buy, and sold by others for at least $5.00, we cannot warrant it, but we will guarantee it being received in perfect going order, and if properly taken care of, it should last as long as any other watch.

No. 4E824 Price.............................. $ 2.06
No. 4E825 Price, per dozen.............. 23.40

We will not sell less than one dozen at dozen price.

REMEMBER, YOU GET YOUR PROFIT SHARING CERTIFICATE FOR EVERY PURCHASE

GENTLEMEN'S 18-SIZE AND LADIES' 6-SIZE WATCHES.

OPEN FACE AND HUNTING STYLE, MADE IN ELECTRO PLATE, GOLD FILLED AND SOLID SILVER.

$2.00 In Open Face or Hunting Style.

DEALERS AND TRADERS TAKE NOTE.

THESE 10 WATCHES for $26.69. The entire assortment of gentlemen's watches illustrated on this page, one of each kind, comprising five open face 18-size and five hunting style, no two watches alike, exactly as illustrated and quoted here; ten complete watches in all, each one fitted with 7 jeweled Edgemere movement for **$26.69.** When ordering this assortment, ask for assortment **No. 4E2.**

We give with each watch sold our own guarantee, to substantiate and verify the manufacturers'.

Electro Plate, 18-Size.
No. 4E902 Open Face, Screw Back and Bezel.
No. 4E904 Hunting Style.

Gold Filled, 18-Size, Guaranteed for 2 years.
No. 4E906 Open Face, Screw Back and Bezel.
No. 4E908 Hunting Style.

OUR SOLID SILVER CASES

We guarantee to be pure coin silver through and through, and give our written guarantee to that effect.

We can furnish a fine Plush Presentation Case to fit any watch. See page 27.

ELECTRO PLATED CASES.

These cases are made by the electro plating process. This is the cheapest known process of plating and we do not guarantee the wearing ability of them. They may wear for one month or six. We offer these electro plated cases for just what they are.

For **90c** extra we can furnish a fancy dial and gold hands on any watch on this page.

These cases are often used by unscrupulous merchants and fake concerns and offered as "high grade gold filled and solid silver," but we tell you plainly just what they represent.

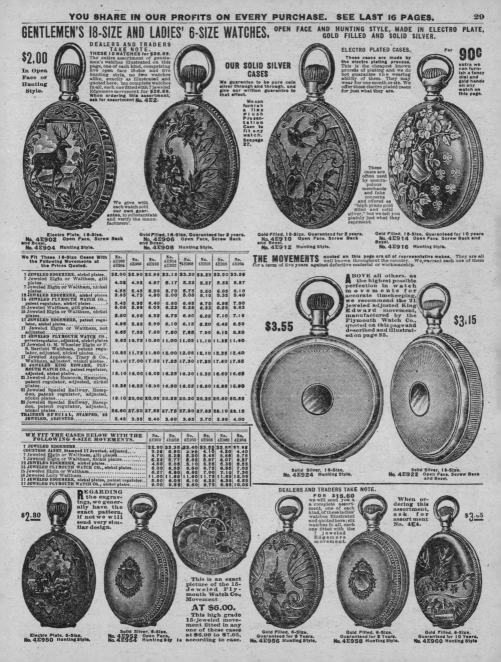

Gold Filled, 18-Size. Guaranteed for 5 years.
No. 4E910 Open Face, Screw Back and Bezel.
No. 4E912 Hunting Style.

Gold Filled, 18-Size. Guaranteed for 10 years
No. 4E914 Open Face, Screw Back and Bezel.
No. 4E916 Hunting Style.

We Fit These 18-Size Cases With the Following Movements at the Prices Quoted.	No. 4E902 4E904	No. 4E906	No. 4E910	No. 4E914 4E922	No. 4E908	No. 4E912	No. 4E916	No. 4E924
7 JEWELED EDGEMERE, nickel plates..	$2.00	$2.90	$2.95	$3.15	$3.20	$3.25	$3.50	$3.55
7 Jeweled Elgin or Waltham, gilt plates	4.02	4.92	4.97	5.17	5.22	5.27	5.52	5.57
7 Jeweled Elgin or Waltham, nickel plates	4.55	5.45	5.50	5.70	5.75	5.80	6.05	6.10
12 JEWELED EDGEMERE, nickel plates	3.85	4.75	4.80	5.00	5.05	5.10	5.35	5.40
15 JEWELED PLYMOUTH WATCH CO., patent regulator, nickel plates	5.45	6.35	6.40	6.60	6.65	6.70	6.95	7.00
15 Jeweled Waltham, gilt plates	5.08	5.98	6.03	6.23	6.28	6.33	6.55	6.63
15 Jeweled Elgin or Waltham, nickel plates	5.60	6.50	6.55	6.75	6.80	6.85	7.10	7.15
17 JEWELED EDGEMERE, patent regulator, nickel plates	4.95	5.85	5.90	6.10	6.15	6.20	6.45	6.50
17 Jeweled Elgin or Waltham, not adjusted	6.65	7.55	7.60	7.80	7.85	7.90	8.15	8.20
17 JEWELED PLYMOUTH WATCH CO., patent regulator, adjusted, nickel plates	9.85	10.75	10.80	11.00	11.05	11.10	11.35	11.40
17 Jeweled G. M. Wheeler Elgin or P. S. Bartlett Waltham, patent regulator, adjusted, nickel plates	10.85	11.75	11.80	12.00	12.05	12.10	12.35	12.40
17 Jeweled Appleton, Tracy & Co., Waltham, adjusted, nickel plates	16.10	17.00	17.05	17.25	17.30	17.35	17.60	17.65
21 JEWELED KING EDWARD, PLYMOUTH WATCH CO., patent regulator, adjusted, nickel plates	15.10	16.00	16.05	16.25	16.30	16.35	16.60	16.65
21 Jeweled John Hancock, Hampden, patent regulator, adjusted, nickel plates	15.35	16.25	16.30	16.50	16.55	16.60	16.85	16.90
21 Jeweled Special Railway, Hampden, patent regulator, adjusted, nickel plates	19.10	20.00	20.05	20.25	20.30	20.35	20.60	20.65
23 Jeweled Special Railway, Hampden, patent regulator, adjusted, nickel plates	26.60	27.50	27.55	27.75	27.80	27.85	28.10	28.15
TRAINMEN SPECIAL, STAMPED, 23 JEWELED, ADJUSTED	2.45	3.35	3.40	3.60	3.65	3.70	3.95	4.00

THE MOVEMENTS

quoted on this page are all of representative makes. They are all well known throughout the country. We warrant each one of them for a term of five years against defective material or workmanship.

ABOVE all others, as the highest possible perfection in watch movements for accurate timekeeping, we recommend the 21 jeweled adjusted King Edward movement, manufactured by the Plymouth Watch Co., quoted on this page and described and illustrated on page 25.

$3.55 **$3.15**

Solid Silver, 18-Size.
No. 4E924 Hunting Style.

Solid Silver, 18-Size.
No. 4E922 Open Face, Screw Back and Bezel.

WE FIT THE CASES BELOW WITH THE FOLLOWING 6-SIZE MOVEMENTS.	No. 4E950	No. 4E952	No. 4E958	No. 4E956	No. 4E960	No. 4E954
7 JEWELED EDGEMERE	$2.80	$3.35	$3.40	$3.55	$3.65	$3.85
COUNTESS JANET, Stamped 17 Jeweled, adjusted	3.25	3.80	3.95	4.10	4.20	4.40
7 Jeweled Elgin or Waltham, gilt plates	4.70	5.25	5.30	5.45	5.55	5.75
7 Jeweled Elgin or Waltham, nickel plates	5.22	5.77	5.82	5.97	6.07	6.27
12 JEWELED EDGEMERE, nickel plates	4.50	5.05	5.10	5.25	5.35	5.55
15 JEWELED PLYMOUTH WATCH CO., nickel plates	6.00	6.55	6.60	6.75	6.85	7.05
15 Jeweled Elgin or Waltham	6.27	6.80	6.85	7.00	7.10	7.30
16 Jeweled Lady Waltham	11.00	11.55	11.60	11.75	11.85	12.05
17 JEWELED EDGEMERE, nickel plates, patent regulator	5.50	6.05	6.10	6.25	6.35	6.55
17 JEWELED PLYMOUTH WATCH CO., nickel plates	9.00	9.55	9.60	9.75	9.85	10.05

$2.80

REGARDING the engravings, we generally have the exact pattern, if not we will send very similar design.

This is an exact picture of the 15-Jeweled Plymouth Watch Co., Movement

AT $6.00.

This high grade 15-jeweled movement fitted in any one of these cases at $6.00 to $7.05, according to case.

Electro Plate, 6-Size.
No. 4E950 Hunting Style.

Solid Silver, 6-Size.
No. 4E952 Open Face.
No. 4E954 Hunting Style.

DEALERS AND TRADERS TAKE NOTE.

FOR **$18.60** we will send you a complete assortment, one of each kind, of these ladies' watches illustrated and quoted here; six watches in all, each one fitted with the 7 jeweled Edgemere movement.

When ordering this assortment, ask for assortment No. 4E4.

$3.65

Gold Filled, 6-Size.
Guaranteed for 5 Years.
No. 4E956 Hunting Style.

Gold Filled, 6-Size.
Guaranteed for 2 Years.
No. 4E958 Hunting Style.

Gold Filled, 6-Size.
Guaranteed for 10 Years.
No. 4E960 Hunting Style

THE WORLD RENOWNED ALASKA SILVER, 18-SIZE WATCHES AT PRICES NEVER HEARD OF BEFORE.

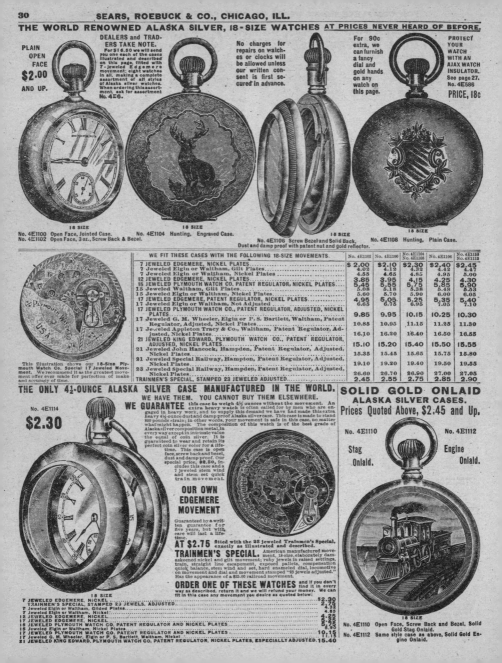

PLAIN OPEN FACE $2.00 AND UP.

DEALERS and TRADERS TAKE NOTE. For $16.50 we will send you one each of the cases illustrated and described on this page, fitted with 7-jeweled Edgemere movement; eight watches in all, making a complete assortment of all styles of Alaska silver watches. When ordering this assortment, ask for assortment No. 4E6.

No charges for repairs on watches or clocks will be allowed unless our written consent is first secured in advance.

For 90c extra, we can furnish a fancy dial and gold hands on any watch on this page.

PROTECT YOUR WATCH WITH AN AJAX WATCH INSULATOR. See page 27. No. 4E586 PRICE, 18c

18 SIZE

No. 4E1100 Open Face, Jointed Case.
No. 4E1102 Open Face, 3 oz., Screw Back & Bezel.

18 SIZE

No. 4E1104 Hunting, Engraved Case.

18 SIZE

No. 4E1106 Screw Bezel and Solid Back, Dust and damp proof with patent nut and gold reflector.

18 SIZE

No. 4E1108 Hunting, Plain Case.

This illustration shows our 18-Size Plymouth Watch Co. Special 17 Jeweled Movement. We recommend it as the greatest movement offer ever made for perfection of make and accuracy of time.

WE FIT THESE CASES WITH THE FOLLOWING 18-SIZE MOVEMENTS.	No. 4E1102	No. 4E1100	No. 4E1104 No. 4E1108	No. 4E1106	No. 4E1110 No. 4E1112
7 JEWELED EDGEMERE, NICKEL PLATES	$ 2.00	$2.10	$2.30	$2.40	$2.45
7 Jeweled Elgin or Waltham, Gilt Plates	4.02	4.12	4.32	4.42	4.47
7 Jeweled Elgin or Waltham, Nickel Plates	4.55	4.65	4.85	4.95	5.00
12 JEWELED EDGEMERE, NICKEL PLATES	3.85	3.95	4.15	4.25	4.30
15 JEWELED PLYMOUTH WATCH CO. PATENT REGULATOR, NICKEL PLATES	5.45	5.55	5.75	5.85	5.90
15 Jeweled Waltham, Gilt Plates	5.08	5.18	5.38	5.48	5.53
15 Jeweled Elgin or Waltham, Nickel Plates	5.60	5.70	5.90	6.00	6.05
17 JEWELED EDGEMERE, PATENT REGULATOR, NICKEL PLATES	4.95	5.05	5.25	5.35	5.40
17 Jeweled Elgin or Waltham, Not Adjusted	6.65	6.75	6.95	7.05	7.10
17 JEWELED PLYMOUTH WATCH CO., PATENT REGULATOR, ADJUSTED, NICKEL PLATES	9.85	9.95	10.15	10.25	10.30
17 Jeweled G. M. Wheeler, Elgin or P. S. Bartlett, Waltham, Patent Regulator, Adjusted, Nickel Plates	10.85	10.95	11.15	11.25	11.30
17 Jeweled Appleton Tracy & Co., Waltham, Patent Regulator, Adjusted, Nickel Plates	16.10	16.20	16.40	16.50	16.55
21 JEWELED KING EDWARD, PLYMOUTH WATCH CO., PATENT REGULATOR, ADJUSTED, NICKEL PLATES	15.10	15.20	15.40	15.50	15.55
21 Jeweled John Hancock, Hampden, Patent Regulator, Adjusted, Nickel Plates	15.35	15.45	15.65	15.75	15.80
21 Jeweled Special Railway, Hampton, Patent Regulator, Adjusted, Nickel Plates	19.10	19.20	19.40	19.50	19.55
23 Jeweled Special Railway, Hampden, Patent Regulator, Adjusted, Nickel Plates	26.60	26.70	26.90	27.00	27.05
TRAINMEN'S SPECIAL, STAMPED 23 JEWELED ADJUSTED	2.45	2.55	2.75	2.85	2.90

THE ONLY 4½-OUNCE ALASKA SILVER CASE MANUFACTURED IN THE WORLD.

WE HAVE THEM. YOU CANNOT BUY THEM ELSEWHERE.

No. 4E1114

$2.30

WE GUARANTEE this case to weigh 4½ ounces without the movement. An extra heavy watch is often called for by men who are engaged in heavy work, and to supply this demand we have had made this extra heavy 4½-ounce dust and damp proof Alaska silver case. This case is made to stand 800 pounds strain; in other words, your movement is safe in this case, no matter what might happen. The composition of this watch is of the best grade of Alaska silver composition metal, in every way except in intrinsic value the equal of coin silver. It is guaranteed to wear and retain its perfect coin silver color for a lifetime. This case is open face, screw back and bezel, dust and damp proof. Our special price, $2.30, includes this case and a 7 jeweled stem wind and stem set quick train movement.

OUR OWN EDGEMERE MOVEMENT

Guaranteed by a written guarantee for five years, but with care will last a lifetime.

AT $2.75 fitted with the 23 jeweled Trainmen's Special, exactly as illustrated and described.

TRAINMEN'S SPECIAL. American manufactured movement, 18-size, elaborately damaskeened nickel and gilt movement; ruby jewels in raised settings, train, straight line escapement, exposed pallets, compensation quick balance, stem wind and set, hard enameled dial, locomotive on movement and dial and movement stamped "23 jewels adjusted." Has the appearance of a $25.00 railroad movement.

ORDER ONE OF THESE WATCHES and if you don't find it in every way as described, return it and we will refund your money. We can fit in this case any movement you desire as quoted below:

18 SIZE

7 JEWELED EDGEMERE, NICKEL	$2.30
TRAINMEN'S SPECIAL, STAMPED 23 JEWELS, ADJUSTED	2.75
7 Jeweled Elgin or Waltham, Gilded Plates	4.32
7 Jeweled Elgin or Waltham, Nickel	4.85
12 JEWELED EDGEMERE, NICKEL	4.25
17 JEWELED EDGEMERE, NICKEL	5.25
15 JEWELED PLYMOUTH WATCH CO. PATENT REGULATOR AND NICKEL PLATES	5.75
15 Jeweled Elgin or Waltham, Nickel Plates	5.90
17 JEWELED PLYMOUTH WATCH CO. PATENT REGULATOR AND NICKEL PLATES	10.15
17 Jeweled G. M. Wheeler, Elgin or P. S. Bartlett, Waltham, Nickel	11.15
21 JEWELED KING EDWARD, PLYMOUTH WATCH CO. PATENT REGULATOR, NICKEL PLATES, ESPECIALLY ADJUSTED	15.40

SOLID GOLD ONLAID ALASKA SILVER CASES.

Prices Quoted Above, $2.45 and Up.

No. 4E1110 Stag Onlaid.

No. 4E1112 Engine Onlaid.

18 SIZE

No. 4E1110 Open Face, Screw Back and Bezel, Solid Gold Stag Onlaid.

No. 4E1112 Same style case as above, Solid Gold Engine Onlaid.

LADIES' 0-SIZE SOLID 14-KARAT GOLD WATCHES

Guaranteed Exactly as Represented and Described.

QUALITY. These cases are solid gold 14-karat fine. Warranted 14-karat. You are positively protected and need have no hesitancy in buying.

DEALERS AND TRADERS TAKE NOTE. We will send you for $28.90 three solid gold 0-size cases, illustrated on this page under Nos. 4E4805, 4E4807 and 4E4809, fitted with 7 Jeweled Swiss lever movements. When ordering this assortment, ask for assortment No. 4E48.

The illustrations of all watches in this catalogue show exact size of the watch.

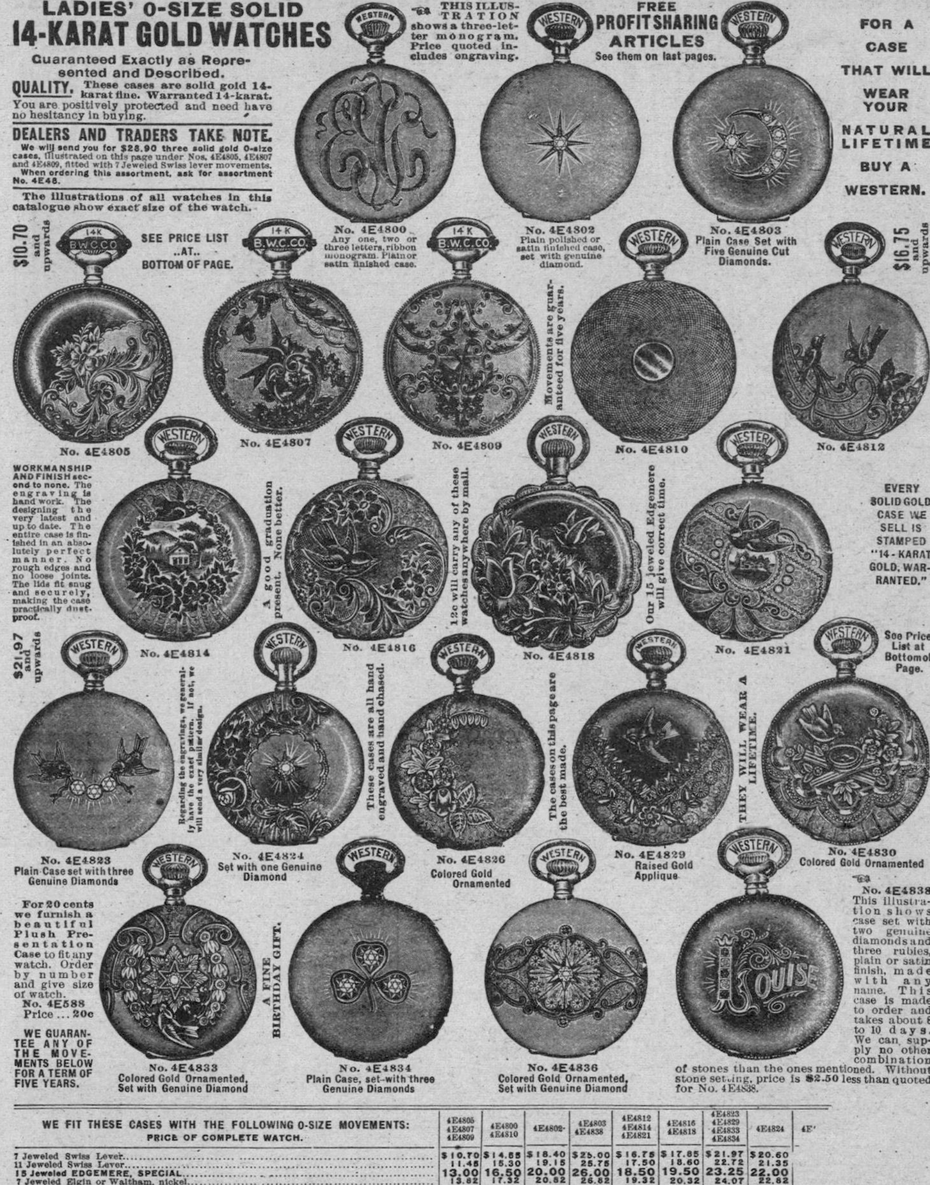

THIS ILLUSTRATION shows a three-letter monogram. Price quoted includes engraving.

FREE PROFIT SHARING ARTICLES See them on last pages.

FOR A CASE THAT WILL WEAR YOUR NATURAL LIFETIME BUY A WESTERN.

No. 4E4800 Any one, two or three letters, ribbon monogram. Plain or satin finished case.

No. 4E4802 Plain polished or satin finished case, set with genuine diamond.

No. 4E4803 Plain Case Set with Five Genuine Cut Diamonds.

$10.70 and upwards

SEE PRICE LIST ..AT.. BOTTOM OF PAGE.

$16.75 and upwards

Movements are guaranteed for five years.

No. 4E4805

No. 4E4807

No. 4E4809

No. 4E4810

No. 4E4812

WORKMANSHIP AND FINISH second to none. The engraving is hand work. The designing the very latest and up to date. The entire case is finished in an absolutely perfect manner. No rough edges and no loose joints. The lids fit snug and securely, making the case practically dust-proof.

A good graduation present. None better.

12c will carry any of these watches anywhere by mail.

Our 15 jeweled Edgemere will give correct time.

EVERY SOLID GOLD CASE WE SELL IS STAMPED "14-KARAT GOLD, WARRANTED."

No. 4E4814

No. 4E4816

No. 4E4818

No. 4E4821

$21.97 and upwards

See Price List at Bottom of Page.

Regarding the engravings, we generally have the exact pattern. If not, we will send a very similar design.

These cases are all hand engraved and hand chased.

The cases on this page are the best made.

THEY WILL WEAR A LIFETIME.

No. 4E4823 Plain Case set with three Genuine Diamonds

No. 4E4824 Set with one Genuine Diamond

No. 4E4826 Colored Gold Ornamented

No. 4E4829 Raised Gold Applique

No. 4E4830 Colored Gold Ornamented

For 20 cents we furnish a beautiful Plush Presentation Case to fit any watch. Order by number and give size of watch. No. 4E588 Price ... 20c

WE GUARANTEE ANY OF THE MOVEMENTS BELOW FOR A TERM OF FIVE YEARS.

A FINE BIRTHDAY GIFT.

No. 4E4833 Colored Gold Ornamented, Set with Genuine Diamond

No. 4E4834 Plain Case, set with three Genuine Diamonds

No. 4E4836 Colored Gold Ornamented, Set with Genuine Diamond

No. 4E4838 This illustration shows case set with two genuine diamonds and three rubies, plain or satin finish, made with any name. This case is made to order and takes about 8 to 10 days. We can supply no other combination of stones than the ones mentioned. Without stone setting, price is $2.50 less than quoted for No. 4E4838.

WE FIT THESE CASES WITH THE FOLLOWING 0-SIZE MOVEMENTS: PRICE OF COMPLETE WATCH.	4E4805 4E4807 4E4809	4E4800 4E4810	4E4802	4E4803 4E4838	4E4812 4E4814 4E4821	4E4816 4E4818	4E4823 4E4829 4E4833 4E4834	4E4824	4E'
7 Jeweled Swiss Lever	$10.70	$14.55	$18.40	$25.00	$16.75	$17.85	$21.97	$20.60	
11 Jeweled Swiss Lever	11.45	15.30	19.15	25.75	17.50	18.60	22.72	21.35	
15 Jeweled EDGEMERE, SPECIAL	**13.00**	**16.50**	**20.00**	**26.00**	**18.50**	**19.50**	**23.25**	**22.00**	
7 Jeweled Elgin or Waltham, nickel	13.82	17.32	20.82	26.82	19.32	20.32	24.07	22.82	
15 Jeweled Elgin or Waltham, nickel	17.50	21.00	24.50	30.50	23.00	24.00	27.75	26.50	
16 Jeweled Lady Waltham, nickel	20.13	23.63	27.13	33.13	25.63	26.63	30.38	29.13	
17 Jeweled Riverside Waltham, nickel	26.42	29.92	33.42	39.42	31.92	32.92	36.67	35.42	
19 Jeweled Riverside Maximus, or No. 201 grade Elgin	30.62	34.12	37.62	43.62	36.12	37.12	40.87	39.62	

Gentlemen's FINEST QUALITY GOLD FILLED, ROLLED GOLD PLATE, GOLD ELECTRO PLATE, WHITE METAL, NICKEL AND SOLID SILVER Vest Chains

WE GUARANTEE them to be exactly as described on this page. All chains come 12 inches long, and they have the regular bar, swivel and drop attachment for charm. Each chain is enclosed in a separate envelope, upon which is printed our binding guarantee, as described. Postage on gents' chains, 3 cents; registry, 8 cents extra.

No. 4E02 Gold filled, bright polish, extra strong, illustration shows exact size. Warranted 20 years. Price, 3 for $10.94; each.....$4.05

Pony Vest Chain, plain trace links, patent fastener; just the thing you can't drop your watch; chain is 8 inches long, warranted 6 years. Price, 3 for $2.87; each.....$1.06

No. 4E04 Solid nickel snake chain. Price, 3 for 76c; each......28c

No. 4E06 Two-strand soldered curb, solid sterling silver. No drop attachment. Price, 3 for $6.16; each......$2.28
No. 4E08 White metal, soldered, as above. Price, 3 for $1.03; ea. .38

No. 4E010 Curb chain, solid sterling silver. Price, 3 for $4.38; ea. $1.62
No. 4E012 Solid white metal. Price, 3 for 49c; each........ .18

No. 4E013 Fancy trace, soldered links, solid silver. Price, 3 for $3.87 Each........1.43
No. 4E014 Solid white metal, soldered. Price, 3 for 58c; each, .28

No. 4E016 Fancy soldered rope pattern, solid sterling silver. Price, 3 for $5.13; each........$1.90
No. 4E018 Solid white metal, soldered. Price, 3 for 90c; each .33

No. 4E020 Plain polish trace, links soldered, solid silver. Price. $1.58
No. 4E022 Solid nickel, soldered links. Price, 3 for 52c; each.. .19

No. 4E024 Fine gold gilt fancy pattern. Not warranted. Not soldered. Price, 3 for $1.19; each........44c

No. 4E025 Plain polish, soldered trace links, good rolled gold plate. Price, 3 for $1.52; each........56c

No. 4E026 Trace links, soldered, rolled gold plate. Warranted 6 years. Price, 3 for $2.43; each........90c

No. 4E030 Trace links, rolled gold plate, soldered links. Warranted 6 years. Price, 3 for $2.68; each........99c

No. 4E040 Pony vest chain, soldered links, plain trace links, patent fastener; just the thing for a boy. You can't drop your watch; chain is 8 inches long. Warranted 6 years. Price, 3 for $2.87; each........$1.06

No. 4E042 Fancy center Boston and square links, bright polish. Rolled gold plate, not soldered. Warranted 6 years. Price, 3 for $2.87; ea., $1.06

No. 4E044 Loose curb soldered links, rolled gold plate. Warranted 6 years. Price, 3 for $2.92; each........$1.08

No. 4E046 Plain soldered trace links, rolled gold plate. Warranted 6 years. Price, 3 for $2.92; each........$1.08

No. 4E048 Fancy rope, rolled gold plate, not soldered. Warranted 6 years. Price, 3 for $3.19; each........$1.18

No. 4E050 Trace links, soldered, rolled gold plate. Warranted 6 years. Price, 3 for $3.22; each........$1.19

No. 4E052 Chased soldered trace links, alternated with bright polish, rolled gold plate. Warranted 6 years. Price, 3 for $3.22; each......$1.19

No. 4E054 Boston square links, not soldered, rolled gold plate. Warranted 6 years. Price, 3 for $3.35; each........$1.24

No. 4E056 Fancy links, not soldered, rolled gold plate. Warranted 6 years. Price, 3 for $3.35; each........$1.24

No. 4E058 Plain soldered trace links, rolled gold plate. Warranted 6 years. Price, 3 for $4.24; each........$1.57

No. 4E060 Fancy chased trace links, extra heavy, soldered, rolled gold plate. Warranted 6 years. Price, 3 for $4.24; each........$1.57

No. 4E062 Fancy chased trace links, rolled gold plate, soldered. Warranted 6 years. Price, 3 for $4.59; each........$1.70

No. 4E064 Fancy chased soldered trace links, rolled gold plate. Warranted 6 years. Price, 3 for $4.76; each........$1.76

No. 4E066 Two-strand rolled gold plate, soldered. Warranted 6 years. Price, 3 for $4.76; each........$1.76

No. 4E068 Three-strand gold plate, soldered links. Warranted 3 years. Price, 3 for $5.89; each........$2.18

No. 4E070 Gold filled curb chain, soldered links, bright polish. Warranted 10 years. Price, 3 for $5.13; each........$1.90

No. 4E080 Gold filled, soldered, loose links. Warranted 10 years. Price, 3 for $5.54; each........$2.05

No. 4E082 Gold filled, soldered curb chain. Warranted 10 years. Price, 3 for $5.89; each........$2.18

No. 4E084 Fancy cable links, gold filled, soldered links. Warranted 10 years. Price, 3 for $5.89; each........$2.18

No. 4E086 Gold filled, extra strong Boston links, not soldered. Warranted 10 years. Price, 3 for $5.89; each........$2.18

No. 4E088 Gold filled, soldered trace links, very strong. Warranted 10 years. Price, 3 for $5.94; each........$2.20

No. 4E090 Gold filled, soldered rope chain. Warranted 10 years. Price, 3 for $5.94; each........$2.20

No. 4E092 Gold filled, soldered rope chain. Warranted 10 years. Price, 3 for $6.67; each........$2.47

No. 4E094 Fancy links, hand engraved, gold filled, not soldered. Warranted 10 years. Price, 3 for $7.43; each........$2.75

No. 4E096 Fancy chased, soldered links, gold filled. Warranted 10 years. Price, 3 for $7.70; each........$2.85

No. 4E098 Gold filled, small fancy curb, soldered. Warranted 20 years. Price, 3 for $3.24; each........$1.20

No. 4E0100 Boston square links, not soldered, rolled gold plate. Warranted 6 years. Price, 3 for $3.49; each........$1.29

No. 4E0102 Chased trace soldered links, rolled gold plate. Warranted 6 years. Price, 3 for $3.78; each........$1.40

No. 4E0104 Rolled plate, plain, soldered trace links. Warranted 6 years. Price, 3 for $3.87; each........$1.43

No. 4E0106 Fancy engraved trace links, soldered, rolled gold plate. Warranted 6 years. Price, 3 for $4.00; each........$1.48

GENTLEMEN'S GOLD FILLED CHAINS.

WARRANTED FOR 20 YEARS WEAR.

REGULATION LENGTH, 12 INCHES EXCEPT WHEN OTHERWISE STATED.

All these chains have the regular bar, swivel, and drop attachment for charm.

Postage on gentlemen's chains, 3 cents; registry 8 cents extra.

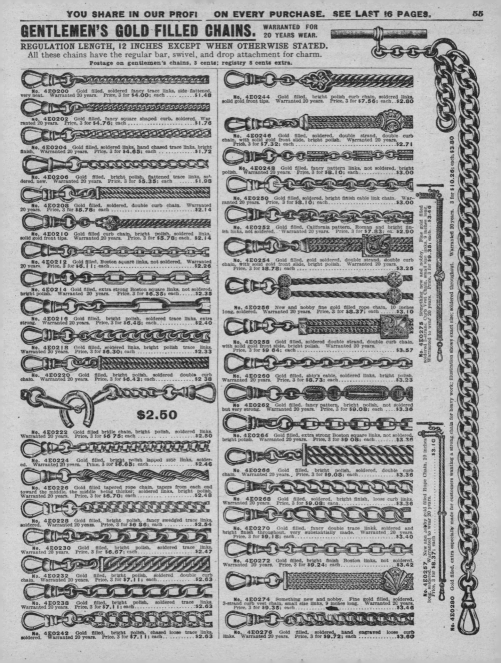

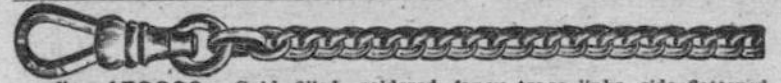

No. 4E0200 Gold filled, soldered fancy trace links, side flattened, very neat. Warranted 20 years. Price, 3 for $4.00; each $1.48

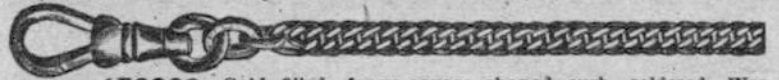

No. 4E0202 Gold filled, fancy square shaped curb, soldered. Warranted 20 years. Price, 3 for $4.76; each $1.76

No. 4E0204 Gold filled, soldered links, hand chased trace links, bright finish. Warranted 20 years. Price, 3 for $4.65; each $1.72

No. 4E0206 Gold filled, bright polish, flattened trace links, soldered, new. Warranted 20 years. Price, 3 for $5.35; each $1.98

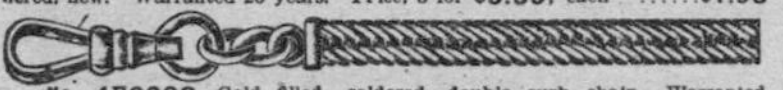

No. 4E0208 Gold filled, soldered, double curb chain. Warranted 20 years. Price, 3 for $5.78; each $2.14

No. 4E0210 Gold filled curb chain, bright polish, soldered links, solid gold front tips. Warranted 20 years. Price, 3 for $5.78; each. $2.14

No. 4E0212 Gold filled, Boston square links, not soldered. Warranted 20 years. Price, 3 for $6.11; each $2.26

No. 4E0214 Gold filled, extra strong Boston square links, not soldered, bright polish. Warranted 20 years. Price, 3 for $6.35; each $2.35

No. 4E0216 Gold filled, bright polish, soldered trace links, extra strong. Warranted 20 years. Price, 3 for $6.48; each $2.40

No. 4E0218 Gold filled, soldered links, bright polish trace links. Warranted 20 years. Price, 3 for $6.30; each $2.33

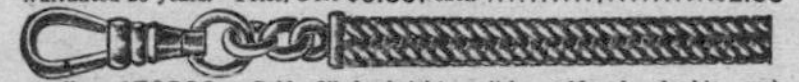

No. 4E0220 Gold filled, bright polish, soldered double curb chain. Warranted 20 years. Price, 3 for $6.43; each $2.38

$2.50

No. 4E0222 Gold filled bridle chain, bright polish, soldered links. Warranted 20 years. Price, 3 for $6.75; each $2.50

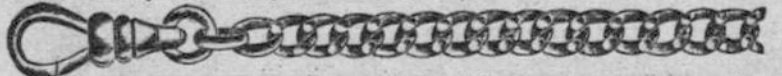

No. 4E0224 Gold filled, bright polish lapped side links, soldered. Warranted 20 years. Price, 3 for $6.65; each $2.46

No. 4E0226 Gold filled tapered rope chain, tapers from each end toward the middle, the middle being thicker; soldered links, bright polish. Warranted 20 years. Price, 3 for $6.70; each $2.48

No. 4E0228 Gold filled, bright polish, fancy swedged trace links, soldered. Warranted 20 years. Price, 3 for $6.86; each $2.54

No. 4E0230 Gold filled, bright polish, soldered trace links. Warranted 20 years. Price, 3 for $6.67; each $2.47

No. 4E0232 Gold filled, bright polish, soldered double curb chain. Warranted 20 years. Price, 3 for $7.11; each $2.63

No. 4E0238 Gold filled, bright polish, soldered trace links. Warranted 20 years. Price, 3 for $7.11; each $2.63

No. 4E0242 Gold filled, bright polish, chased loose trace links, soldered. Warranted 20 years. Price, 3 for $7.11; each $2.63

No. 4E0244 Gold filled, bright polish curb chain, soldered links, solid gold front tips. Warranted 20 years. Price, 3 for $7.56; each .. $2.80

No. 4E0246 Gold filled, soldered, double strand, double curb chain, with solid gold front slide, bright polish. Warranted 20 years. Price, 3 for $7.32; each $2.71

No. 4E0248 Gold filled, fancy pattern links, not soldered, bright polish. Warranted 20 years. Price, 3 for $8.10; each $3.00

No. 4E0250 Gold filled, soldered, bright finish cable link chain. Warranted 20 years. Price, 3 for $8.10; each $3.00

No. 4E0252 Gold filled, California pattern, Roman and bright finish links, not soldered. Warranted 20 years. Price, 3 for $7.83; ea. $2.90

No. 4E0254 Gold filled, gold soldered, double strand, double curb chain, with solid gold front slide, bright polish. Warranted 20 years. Price, 3 for $8.78; each $3.25

No. 4E0256 New and nobby fine gold filled rope chain, 10 inches long, soldered. Warranted 20 years. Price, 3 for $8.37; each $3.10

No. 4E0258 Gold filled, soldered double strand, double curb chain, with solid gold front slide, bright polish. Warranted 20 years. Price, 3 for $9.64; each $3.57

No. 4E0260 Gold filled, ship's cable, soldered links, bright polish. Warranted 20 years. Price, 3 for $8.73; each $3.23

No. 4E0262 Gold filled, fancy pattern, bright polish, not soldered but very strong. Warranted 20 years. Price, 3 for $9.08; each $3.36

No. 4E0264 Gold filled, extra strong Boston square links, not soldered, bright polish. Warranted 20 years. Price, 3 for $9.08; each $3.36

No. 4E0266 Gold filled, bright polish, soldered, double curb chain. Warranted 20 years. Price, 3 for $9.08; each $3.36

No. 4E0268 Gold filled, soldered, bright finish, loose curb links. Warranted 20 years. Price, 3 for $9.08; each $3.36

No. 4E0270 Gold filled, fancy double trace links, soldered and bright finish throughout, very substantially made. Warranted 20 years. Price, 3 for $9.18; each $3.40

No. 4E0272 Gold filled, bright finish Boston links, not soldered. Warranted 20 years. Price, 3 for $9.24; each $3.42

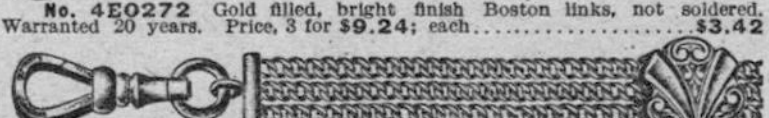

No. 4E0274 Something new and nobby. Fine gold filled, soldered, 3-strand curb vest chain, small size links, 9 inches long. Warranted 20 years. Price, 3 for $9.35; each $3.46

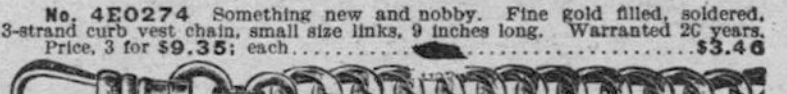

No. 4E0276 Gold filled, soldered, hand engraved loose curb links. Warranted 20 years. Price, 3 for $9.72; each $3.60

No. 4E0275 Something new and nobby. Fine gold filled soldered 3-strand Curb Vest Chain, small size links, 9 inches long. Warranted to wear 20 years. Price, 3 for $9.35; each $3.46

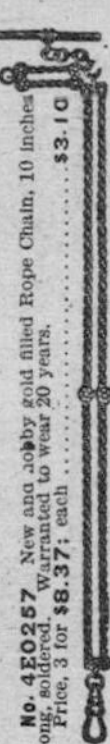

No. 4E0257 New and nobby gold filled Rope Chain, 10 inches long, soldered. Warranted to wear 20 years. Price, 3 for $8.37; each $3.10

No. 4E0280 Gold filled, extra especially made for customers wanting a strong chain for heavy work; illustration shows exact size; soldered throughout. Warranted 20 years. 3 for $10.26; each $3.80

SOMETHING NEW IN HIGH GRADE GOLD FILLED CHAINS.

OUR SEARS' LIFE GUARANTEE GOLD FILLED CHAINS.

On this page we show our very latest addition in the Chain Department. Our SEARS' LIFE GUARANTEE CHAIN is the highest grade gold filled chain on the market.

Postage on gents' chains, 3 cents. Registry, 8 cents extra.

WE GUARANTEE IT TO WEAR FOR THE TERM OF YOUR NATURAL LIFE.

By this we mean should any one of our Sears' Life Guarantee Gold Filled Chains wear down to the inner composition metal, although you owned it for 50 years, 25 years, 10 years, or any time within your natural life, you can return it to us, and upon its receipt, we will forward at once a brand new Sears' Life Guarantee Gold Filled Chain, free of all charge.

Every chain shown on this page, unless otherwise stated, has soldered links. They are all 12 inches long and have the bar, swivel and drop attachment for charm. The gold filled chains, warranted for 20 years, shown on this page, are all simple and practical in design and exact counterparts of solid gold chains. Each one carries our guarantee for time stated continuous wear.

REMEMBER, every purchase brings you that much nearer the FREE PROFIT SHARING ARTICLE you have picked out; see what you can get FREE, shown on the last pages.

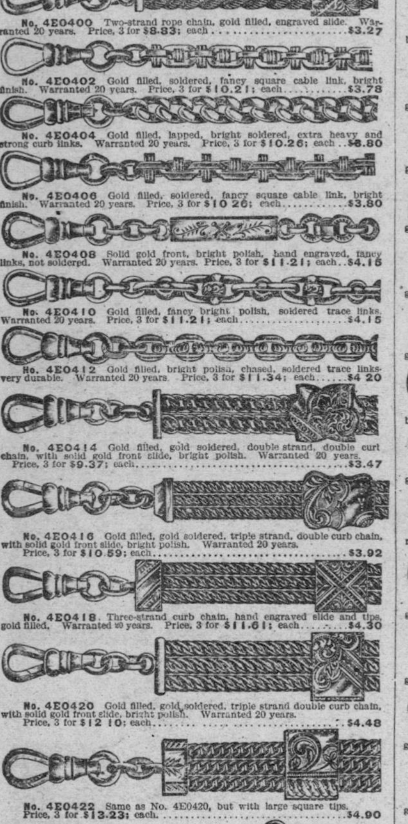

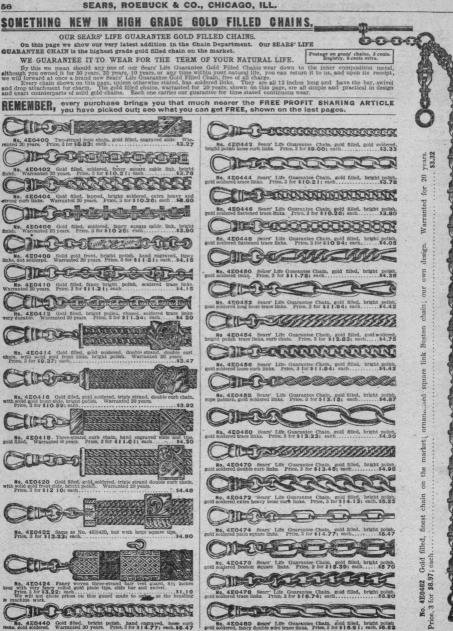

No. 4E0400 Two-strand rope chain, gold filled, engraved slide. Warranted 20 years. Price, 3 for $8.83; each $3.27

No. 4E0402 Gold filled, soldered, fancy square cable link, bright finish. Warranted 20 years. Price, 3 for $10.21; each $3.78

No. 4E0404 Gold filled, lapped, bright soldered, extra heavy and strong curb links. Warranted 20 years. Price, 3 for $10.26; each $3.80

No. 4E0406 Gold filled, soldered, fancy square cable link, bright finish. Warranted 20 years. Price, 3 for $10.26; each $3.80

No. 4E0408 Solid gold front, bright polish, hand engraved, fancy links, not soldered. Warranted 20 years. Price, 3 for $11.21; each $4.15

No. 4E0410 Gold filled, fancy bright polish, soldered trace links. Warranted 20 years. Price, 3 for $11.21; each $4.15

No. 4E0412 Gold filled, bright polish, chased, soldered trace links—very durable. Warranted 20 years. Price, 3 for $11.34; each $4.20

No. 4E0414 Gold filled, gold soldered, double strand, double curb chain, with solid gold front slide, bright polish. Warranted 20 years. Price, 3 for $9.37; each $3.47

No. 4E0416 Gold filled, gold soldered, triple strand, double curb chain, with solid gold front slide, bright polish. Warranted 20 years. Price, 3 for $10.59; each $3.92

No. 4E0418 Three-strand curb chain, hand engraved slide and tips, gold filled. Warranted 20 years. Price, 3 for $11.61; each $4.30

No. 4E0420 Gold filled, gold soldered, triple strand double curb chain, with solid gold front slide, bright polish. Warranted 20 years. Price, 3 for $12.10; each $4.48

No. 4E0422 Same as No. 4E0420, but with large square tips. Price, 3 for $13.23; each $4.90

No. 4E0424 Fancy woven three-strand hair vest guard, 8½ inches long with very fancy rolled gold plate tips, slide bar and swivel. Price, 3 for $3.22; each $1.19

We will not quote prices on this guard made to order, as the braiding is machine work.

No. 4E0440 Gold filled, bright polish, hand engraved, loose curb links, gold soldered. Warranted 20 years. Price, 3 for $14.77; each, $5.47

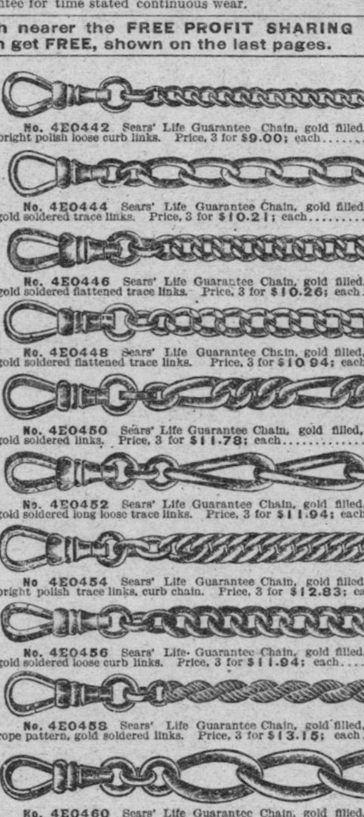

No. 4E0442 Sears' Life Guarantee Chain, gold filled, gold soldered, bright polish loose curb links. Price, 3 for $9.00; each $3.33

No. 4E0444 Sears' Life Guarantee Chain, gold filled, bright polish, gold soldered trace links. Price, 3 for $10.21; each $3.78

No. 4E0446 Sears' Life Guarantee Chain, gold filled, bright polish, gold soldered flattened trace links. Price, 3 for $10.26; each $3.80

No. 4E0448 Sears' Life Guarantee Chain, gold filled, bright polish, gold soldered flattened trace links. Price, 3 for $10.94; each $4.05

No. 4E0450 Sears' Life Guarantee Chain, gold filled, bright polish, gold soldered links. Price, 3 for $11.78; each $4.36

No. 4E0452 Sears' Life Guarantee Chain, gold filled, bright polish, gold soldered long loose trace links. Price, 3 for $11.94; each $4.42

No. 4E0454 Sears' Life Guarantee Chain, gold filled, gold soldered, bright polish trace links, curb chain. Price, 3 for $12.83; each $4.75

No. 4E0456 Sears' Life Guarantee Chain, gold filled, bright polish, gold soldered loose curb links. Price, 3 for $11.94; each $4.42

No. 4E0458 Sears' Life Guarantee Chain, gold filled, bright polish, rope pattern, gold soldered links. Price, 3 for $13.15; each $4.87

No. 4E0460 Sears' Life Guarantee Chain, gold filled, bright polish, gold soldered trace links. Price, 3 for $13.23; each $4.90

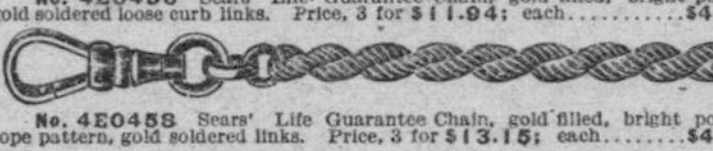

No. 4E0470 Sears' Life Guarantee Chain, gold filled, bright polish, gold soldered double curb links. Price, 3 for $13.45; each $4.98

No. 4E0472 Sears' Life Guarantee Chain, gold filled, bright polish, gold soldered extra heavy loose curb links. Price, 3 for $14.13; each, $5.23

No. 4E0474 Sears' Life Guarantee Chain, gold filled, bright polish, gold soldered plain square links. Price, 3 for $14.77; each $5.47

No. 4E0476 Sears' Life Guarantee Chain, gold filled, bright polish, gold soldered Boston square links. Price, 3 for $15.39; each $5.70

No. 4E0478 Sears' Life Guarantee Chain, gold filled, bright polish, gold soldered trace links. Price, 3 for $16.74; each $6.20

No. 4E0480 Sears' Life Guarantee Chain, gold filled, bright polish gold soldered, fancy double wire trace links. Price, 3 for $16.91; each, $6.62

No. 4E0482 Gold filled, finest chain on the market; ornamented square link Boston chain; our own design. Warranted for 20 years. Price, 3 for $8.97; each $3.32

CRYSTALLINE DIAMOND JEWELRY.

, Scarf Pins, Studs, Earrings and Brooches in Solid Gold, Solid Silver and Gold Filled untings, Set With Crystalline Diamonds. You Must See Them to Appreciate Them.

DON'T FAIL TO GIVE EXACT SIZE OF RING WANTED.

stalline Diamonds are worn by actors and actresses and those wanting the most perfect imitation diamond known. We have thousands of profes- people, actors and actresses throughout the United States, who buy our Crystalline diamonds to wear instead of using the genuine article. Postage extra ugs, earrings, studs and scarf pins, 2 cents; brooches, 4 cents; registration, 8 cents extra on any.

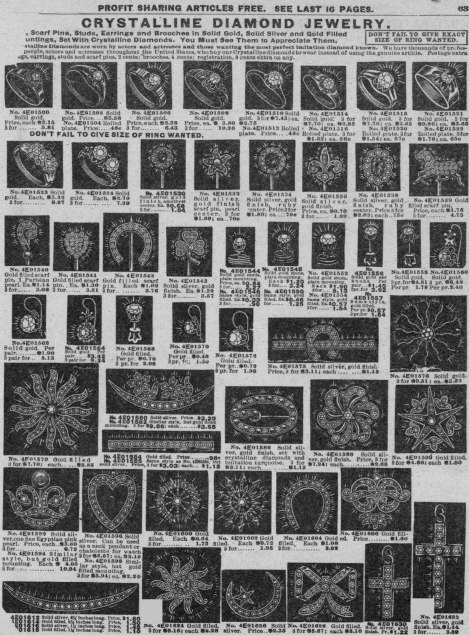

No. 4E01500 Solid gold. Price, each $2.15; 3 for....... 5.81

No. 4E01502 Solid gold. Price....$3.58
No. 4E01504 Rolled plate. Price:....48c

No. 4E01506 Solid gold. Price, each $2.38; 3 for........ 6.43

No. 4E01508 Solid gold. Price, ea. $ 3.80; 3 for...... 10.26

No. 4E01510 Solid gold. 3 for $7.43; ea. $2.75
No. 4E01512 Rolled plate. Price... .48c

No. 4E01514 Solid gold. 3 for $7.70; ea. $2.85
No. 4E01516 Rolled plate. 3 for $1.52; ea. 56c

No. 4E01518 Solid gold. 3 for $7.70; ea. $2.85
No. 4E01520 Rolled plate. 3 for $1.54; ea. 57c

No. 4E01521 Solid gold. 3 for $9.86; ea. $3.65
No. 4E01522 Rolled plate. 3 for $1.76; ea. 65c

DON'T FAIL TO GIVE SIZE OF RING WANTED.

No. 4E01523 Solid gold. Each, $3.32; 3 for.......... 8.97

No. 4E01524 Solid gold. Each, $2.70; 3 for....... .... 7.29

No. 4E01530 Solid silver, gold finish, amethyst center. Ea. $0.68; 3 for.......... 1.84

No. 4E01532 Solid silver, gold finish scarf pin, pearl center. 3 for $1.89; ea..70c

No. 4E01534 Solid silver, gold finish, ruby center. Price 3 for $1.89; ea.....70c

No. 4E01536 Solid silver, gold finish. Price, ea. $0.70; 3 for...... 1.89

No. 4E01538 Solid silver, gold finish, ruby center. Price 3 for $2.03; each..75c

No. 4E01539 Gold filled scarf pin, Price, each $1.75; 3 for........ 4.73

No. 4E01540 Gold filled scarf pin, 1 Parisian pearl. Ea. $1.14; 3 for...... 3.08

No. 4E01541 Gold filled scarf pin. Ea. $1.30; 3 for...... 3.51

No. 4E01542 Gold filled scarf pin. Each $1.02; 3 for.. .... 2.76

No. 4E01543 Solid silver, gold finish. Ea. $1.32; 3 for........ 3.57

No. 4E01544 Solid gold studs, plain mounting. Price, ea. $0.84; 3 for...... 2.27
No. 4E01546 Same style, gold filled. Ea. $0.33; 3 for....... .90

No. 4E01548 Solid gold studs, plain mounting. Each $1.20; 3 for.... 3.24
No. 4E01550 Same style, gold filled. Ea. $0.46; for...... 1.25

No. 4E01552 Solid gold studs, plain mounting. Each $1.90; 3 for.... 5.13
No. 4E01554 Same style, gold filled. Ea. $0.57; 3 for...... 1.54

No. 4E01556 Solid gold ear knobs. Per pair...$1.45; 3 pr. for 3.92
No. 4E01557 Same style, gold filled. Per pr. $0.57; 3 pr. for 1.54

No. 4E01558 Solid gold. 3 pr. for $4.81; Per pr 1.78

No. 4E01560 Solid gold. 3 pr. $6.43; Per pr. 2.40

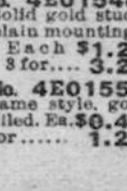

No. 4E01562 Solid gold. Per pair.........$1.90; 3 pair for.. 5.13

No. 4E01564 Solid gold. Per pair.......$3.42; 3 pair for 9.24

No. 4E01568 Gold filled. Per pr.. $0.76; 3 pr. for 2.06

No. 4E01570 Gold filled. Per pr.. $0.48; 3 pr. for 1.30

No. 4E01572 Gold filled. Per pr.. $0.72; 3 pr. for 1.95

No. 4E01575 Solid silver, gold finish. Price, 3 for $3.11; each $1.15

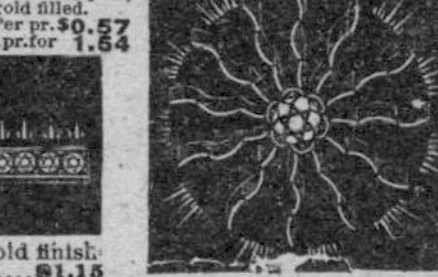
No. 4E01576 Solid gold. 3 for $9.51; ea..$3.52

No. 4E01578 Gold filled. 3 for $7.70; each.. ...$2.85

No. 4E01580 Solid silver. Price..$3.20
No. 4E01582 Similar style, but gold filled mounting. 3 for $9.86; each.... ....$3.65

No. 4E01584 Gold filled. Price.........98c
No. 4E01585 Same style as No. 4E01584, but solid silver. Price, 3 for $3.03; each... $1.12

No. 4E01586 Solid silver, gold finish, set with crystalline diamonds and imitation turquoise. 3 for $3.11; each.... ......$1.15

No. 4E01588 Solid silver, gold finish. Price, 3 for $7.24; each..........$2.68

No. 4E01590 Gold filled. 3 for $4.86; each $1.80

No. 4E01592 Solid silver, one fine Egyptian pink pearl. Price, each..$3.60; 3 for.... .... 9.72
No. 4E01594 Similar style, but gold filled mounting. Each $ 4.05; 3 for.... .... 10.94

No. 4E01596 Solid silver. Can be used as a neck pendant or chatelette for watch 3 for $5.67; ea. $2.10
No. 4E01598 Similar style, but gold filled mounting. 3 for $5.94; ea. $2.20

No. 4E01600 Gold filled. Each $0.64; 3 for......... .. 1.73

No. 4E01602 Gold filled. Each $0.72; 3 for....... 1.95

No. 4E01604 Gold filled. Each $1.08; 3 for............ 2.92

No. 4E01606 Gold filled. Price.........$1.80

4E01612 Solid silver, 2¼ inches long. Price, $1.80
4E01614 Gold filled, 2¼ inches long. Price, 1.50
01616 Solid silver, 1¼ inches long. Price, 1.45
01618 Gold filled, 1¼ inches long. Price, 1.10

No. 4E01624 Gold filled. 3 for $6.16; each $2.28

No. 4E01626 Solid silver. Price..$2.35

No. 4E01628 Gold filled. 3 for $5.67; each $2.10

No. 4E01630 Solid silver, gold finish. Pr..$1.22

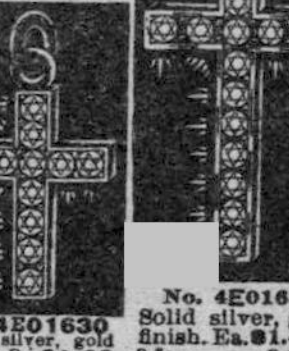
No. 4E01632 Solid silver, gold finish. Ea. $1.44; 3 for...... 3.89

GOLD FILLED, GOLD PLATED AND SOLID SILVER RINGS.

HOW GOLD FILLED RINGS ARE MADE.

WE offer you here a line of gold filled rings. It will be interesting to you and much more satisfactory before making a purchase of a gold filled ring to know just how they are made. The operation is very easy when it is understood. To start with, a piece of solid gold tube from 1¼ to 2 inches in diameter is taken and the hole on the inside made perfectly smooth, after which a piece of hard, fine composition metal is placed on the inside of the tube so as to fit the opening perfectly. Some fine gold solder is now placed in the crevice and the whole is inserted in the furnace. As soon as the two pieces are heated sufficiently the solder flows into the crevice, after which it is removed from the furnace, and after it is cold the two original pieces are one. One end of this piece is then hammered and drawn out, so as to make it a little smaller, after which it is inserted in what is called the draw plate, which is a long steel plate with a number of holes in it of such shape as the pieces which it is desired to make. These holes are graduated in size, at one end being very large and at the other end small. The piece of material to be worked on is inserted in the large hole first, and with a pair of tongs it is drawn through; this reduces the piece, when it is again hammered at the end to make it small enough to be inserted in the next smaller hole and in turn drawn through this.

THE edges of the holes are all polished so as not to scrape, but to press the metal. This drawing hardens the metal to such an extent that after drawing it through several times it would break easily. It is then annealed by inserting it in the fire and allowing it to cool gradually. After the piece has been drawn out to the required shape and size, one end is bent around a steel mandrel until it has formed a circle of the size the ring is to be made. It is then cut off at the proper place and both ends are carefully surfaced in order to bring them together and make a perfect joint, and on this joint is placed some fine gold solder and the ring inserted in a furnace sufficiently heated to cause the solder to flow into the joint. The ring is then polished carefully on a cotton buff wheel with tripoli and rouge, after which it is ready for the market. Solid gold rings are made in the same manner with the exception of the composition metal on inside.

The market is flooded with cheap brass rings which are electro gold plated, and are called rolled plate or rolled gold plate, and which are utterly worthless. In gold filled rings we handle nothing but the very best.

SEE OUR PRICES ON BEST QUALITY 14-KARAT GOLD FILLED RINGS.

WILL BE FURNISHED IN SIZES 5 TO 13.

If by mail, postage on rings, 2 cents.

For prices on engraving see page 20.

No. 4E01700 Plain oval band. Ea. $0.53 3 for.......... 1.44

No. 4E01702 Plain oval band. Ea. $0 85 3 for.......... 2.30

No. 4E01704 Plain oval band. Ea. $1.13 3 for.......... $3.06

No. 4E01706 Plain oval band. Ea. $1.50

No. 4E01708 Plain flat band. Ea. $1.10 3 for.......... 2.97

No. 4E01710 Plain flat band. Price $1.38

No. 4E01712 Flat band chased. Price..76c

No. 4E01714 Flat band chased. 3 for $1.62; ea. 60c

No. 4E01716 Flat band chased. 3 for $1.68; ea. 62c

No. 4E01718 Flat band, fancy engraved and embossed. Ea..........82c

No. 4E01720 Flat band, fancy engraved and embossed. Ea..........88c

No. 4E01722 Flat band, engraved and embossed. Each...$1.10 3 for.......... 2.97

No. 4E01724 Flat band, fancy engraved and embossed. Ea...$1.28

No. 4E01726 Flat band fancy engraved and embossed. Ea. $1.38

Don't fail to give size of ring wanted.

SECOND QUALITY GOLD FILLED RINGS.

FOR THE PRICE NOTHING BETTER ON THE MARKET.

No. 4E01728 Plain oval band. Ea. $0.40 3 for.......... 1.08

No. 4E01730 Plain oval band. Ea. $0.54 3 for.......... 1.46

No. 4E01732 Plain oval band. Price. 72c

No. 4E01733 Plain oval band. Ea.....90c

No. 4E01734 Plain flat band. Ea. $0.80 3 for.......... 2.16

No. 4E01736 Plain flat band. Price.......90c

No. 4E01738 Flat band chased. 3 for $1.08; ea. 40c

No. 4E01740 Flat band chased. 3 for 71c; each 26c

No. 4E01742 Flat band chased. 3 for $1.08; ea. 40c

No. 4E01744 Flat band chased. Ea. 38c

No. 4E01746 Flat band chased. 3 for $1.14; ea. 42c

No. 4E01748 Flat band chased. Ea. 60c

No. 4E01750 Flat band chased. Ea. 78c

No. 4E01752 Flat band chased. Ea. 80c

GOLD FILLED AND SOLID SILVER SET RINGS, GUARANTEED TO GIVE ENTIRE SATISFACTION.

No. 4E01760 Gold filled. 8 rhinestones, 1 turquoise. Each..........62c

No. 4E01762 Gold Filled. 1 rhinestone. Each....$0.58 3 for.......... 1.57

No. 4E01764 Gold Filled. 1 emerald. Each. 64c

No. 4E01766 Gold filled. 3 rubies. Ea....68c

No. 4E01768 Gold filled. 5 rhinestones. Each...$0.48 3 for.... 1.30

No. 4E01770 Gold filled. 1 almandine. Price.....23c

No. 4E01772 1 ruby. Price....23c

No. 4E01774 1 emerald. Each. 23c

No. 4E01778 1 fine brilliant. Price...42c

No. 4E01780 1 ruby 3 for $1.14; ea. 42c

No. 4E01782 1 emerald. Price......42c

No. 4E01784 Gold Filled. 1 rhinestone, extra fine. 3 for $1.30; ea. 48c

No. 4E01786 Gold Filled Seal Ring....62c Engraving, 5c per letter extra for Old English.

No. 4E01788 Gold Filled Seal Ring. Each.......... 28c 3 for.......... 76c Monogram 10c extra.

No. 4E01790 Gold filled. 1 fine imitation ruby. Each, 16c 3 for.......44c

No. 4E01792 Gold filled. Carbuncle. Each....$0.57, 3 for..... 1.54

No. 4E01793 Gold filled. Fine ruby doublet. Each....$0.38 3 for.... 1.03

No. 4E01794 Gold filled. Fine imitation ruby. Each.......$0.80 3 for....... 2.16

No. 4E01796 Gold filled. Carbuncle. Each..........$0.38 3 for.......... 1.03

No. 4E01798 Gold filled. 1 genuine tiger eye cameo. Price.....46c

No. 4E01800 Gold filled. Brilliant and 2 garnets. 3 for $1.54; each 57c

No. 4E01802 Solid silver, same style as No. 4E01800, but set with ruby and emerald. 3 for $2.27; each...84c

No. 4E01804 Gold filled. Fine imitation opal. Each ....$0.68 3 for.......... 1.84

No. 4E01810 Gold filled. Rubies and pearls Each. ..$0.38 3 for..... 1.03

No. 4E01806 Gold filled. 2 imitation rubies, 1 imitation diamond. 3 for $2.06; ea. 76c

No. 4E01812 Gold filled. Emerald set. Price.....36c 3 for..........98c

HOW TO DETERMINE THE SIZE OF RING WANTED. Cut a strip of thick paper so that the ends will exactly meet when drawn tightly around the second joint of the finger. Lay one end of slip on the diagram at O and order the size the other end indicates, also send slip so that we can verify size wanted.

RING SIZES.

0 1 2 3 4 5 6 7 8 9 10 11 12 13

Don't Fail to Give Exact Size Wanted.

SOLID SILVER RINGS.

No. 4E01808 Solid silver seal ring, gray finish, extra heavy. Price..........60c Two or three letter monogram, 20c extra.

No. 4E01813 Solid silver, bright polish, set with emerald doublets. Price 75c

No. 4E01814 Solid silver, extra heavy; set with ruby doublet. Price $1.38

No. 4E01816 Skull and cross bones, solid silver, gray finish. 3 for $1.89; ea. 70c

No. 4E01818 Solid silver seal ring. Price..........48c Monogram, 10c extra.

No. 4E01820 Solid silver, plain polish, set with imitation ruby. Price.....62c

No. 4E01822 Solid silver, engraved, set with imitation turquoise. Price.....65c

No. 4E01824 Horseshoe nail Solid silver, r doublet. Price,

SOLID GOLD AND SOLID SILVER SEAL AND ENGRAVED RINGS.

Don't Fail to Give Exact Size Wanted.

No. 4E01900 Seal Ring, bright polish. Price.....$1.43 Monogram 20 cents extra.

No. 4E01902 Ladies' Seal Ring, Roman yellow finish, light weight. Price....$1.53 Monogram 20 cents extra.

No. 4E01904 Misses' Seal Ring, bright polish, substantial weight, hand carved shank. Price..........$1.70 Monogram 15 cents extra.

No. 4E01906 Ladies' Seal Ring, hand carved, Roman yellow finish. Price.....$1.90 Monogram 20 cents extra.

No. 4E01908 Ladies' Seal Ring, hand carved fancy heads, Roman yellow finish. Price..........$2.06 Monogram 25 cents extra.

No. 4E01910 Ladies' Seal Ring, Roman yellow finish. Price.......$1.92 Monogram 25 cents extra.

No. 4E01911 Ladies' Seal Ring, Roman yellow finish. Price.......$2.54 Monogram 25 cents extra.

No. 4E01912 Ladies' Seal Ring, set with 6 pearls, Roman yellow finish. Price......$2.14 Monogram 20 cents extra.

No. 4E01914 Gentlemen's Seal Ring, hand carved, Roman yellow finish. Price.......$2.40 Monogram 25 cents extra.

No. 4E01916 Ladies' Seal Ring, very artistic, Roman yellow finish, hand carved. Price.......$2.32 Monogram 25 cents extra.

No. 4E01918 Seal Ring, ladies' or gentlemen's, hand carved, Roman yellow finish. Price......$2.45 Monogram 25 cents extra.

No. 4E01920 Seal Ring for young men, hand carved, Roman finish. Price...$2.60 Monogram 25c extra.

No. 4E01924 Young Men's Seal Ring, Roman yellow finish, hand carved. Price..$2.65 Monogram 25c extra.

No. 4E01926 Seal Ring, gentlemen's style, Roman yellow finish, hand carved. Price.......$2.70 Monogram 25c extra

No. 4E01928 Ladies' Seal Ring, hand carved, Roman yellow finish. Price........$2.70 Monogram 25 cents extra.

No. 4E01930 Seal Ring, bright polish. Price.....$2.82 Monogram 25 cents extra.

No. 4E01932 Gentlemen's hand carved seal ring, Roman yellow finish, very heavy. Price.........$3.75 Monogram 25c extra.

No. 4E01934 Seal Ring, Roman yellow finish. Price.....$3.90 Monogram 25c extra.

No. 4E01936 Seal Ring, Ladies' or Gentlemen's, Roman yellow finish. Hand carved. Price.......$4.20 Monogram 25 cents extra.

No. 4E01938 Seal Ring, Roman yellow finish. Price.....$4.50 Monogram 25c extra.

No. 4E01940 Seal Ring, Ladies' or Gentlemen's, Roman yellow finish, hand carved mermaids. Price........$4.65 Monogram 25 cents extra.

No. 4E01942 Seal ring, gentlemen's style, Roman yellow finish, hand carved, extra heavy. Price...$5.25 Monogram 25c extra.

No. 4E01944 Seal Ring, Gentlemen's. Roman yellow finish, very heavy, hand carved. Price..........$5.30 Monogram 25 cents extra.

No. 4E01946 Gentlemen's Seal Ring, hand carved, 4 emerald doublets. Roman yellow finish. Price........$6.22 Monogram 30c extra.

No. 4E01948 Gentlemen's Seal Ring, extra heavy, hand carved, Roman yellow finish. Price...........$7.60 Monogram 30c extra.

No. 4E01950 Seal Ring. Extra finely carved and extra heavy. Roman yellow finish. Price...........$7.60 Monogram 30c extra.

No. 4E01960 Extra Heavy Engraved, set with Ruby Doublet. Price.........$5.20

No. 4E01962 Gypsy Ring. Set with 3 Ruby Doublets. Price...................$3.78

No. 4E01963 Same style as No. 4E01962, set with Emerald Doublet. Price..........$3.78

No. 4E01964 Same style as No. 4E01962, but set with genuine Opals. Price........$5.68

No. 4E01965 Flat Belcher, set with Ruby Doublet. Price.......$3.30

No. 4E01966 Same as No. 4E01965, set with Emerald Doublet. Price.......$3.30

SOLID SILVER RINGS.

No. 4E01982 Solid Silver. Price..........57c

No. 4E01984 Gold Topped Shield..........76c

No. 4E01986 Solid Silver. Price..........48c

No. 4E01988 Gold Topped Hearts. Price..........68c

No. 4E01989 Solid Silver. Price.........38c

No. 4E01990 Solid Silver. Price.......................22c

No. 4E01968 Extra Heavy, Large Genuine Opal Set. Price........$5.72

No. 4E01970 Carbuncle. Price.....$2.68

No. 4E01972 Set with Ruby Doublet. Price.........$3.32

No. 4E01974 Same set with Emerald Doublet. Price.......$3.32

No. 4E01976 Tiger Eye Cameo. Price..$1.42

No. 4E01978 Onyx Intaglio. Price...$1.95

No. 4E01980 Tiger Eye Cameo. Price....$2.80

No. 4E01992 Solid Silver. Price..........36c

No. 4E01994 Solid Silver Price..........................42c

No. 4E01996 Solid Silver. Price..........62c

No. 4E01998 Solid silver, snake pattern, set with 1 fine ruby, 2 emerald eyes. Ea. 84c

No. 4E02000 Very Light Weight. Price..................90c

No. 4E02002 Very Light Weight. Price..........$1.05

No. 4E02004 Light Weight. Price...............$1.12

No. 4E02006 Light Weight. Price..............$1.16

No. 4E02008 Light Medium Weight. Price...............$1.24

No. 4E02010 Light Medium Weight Price...............$1.32

DON'T FAIL TO GIVE SIZE OF RING.

No. 4E02012 Light Medium Weight. Price..............$1.32

No. 4E02014 Light Medium Weight Price..............$1.32

No. 4E02016 Medium Weight. Price..............$1.40

No. 4E02018 Medium Weight. Price.......... $1.50

No. 4E02020 Medium Weight. Price...........$1.50

No. 4E02022 Medium Weight. Price...........$1.60

No. 4E02024 Medium Weight. Price...........$1.66

No. 4E02026 Heavy Medium Weight. Price...........$1.72

No. 4E02028 Heavy Medium Weight. Price...........$1.85

No. 4E02030 Heavy Medium Weight. Price...........$1.94

No. 4E02032 Heavy Medium Weight. Price...........$1.98

No. 4E02034 Heavy Weight. Price...........$2.10

No. 4E02036 Heavy Weight. Price...........$2.10

No. 4E02038 Heavy Weight. Price...........$2.14

No. 4E02040 Very Heavy Weight. Price..............$2.46

No. 4E02042 Very Heavy Weight. Price..............$2.50

No. 4E02044 Very Heavy Weight. Price..............$2.60

No. 4E02046 Extra Heavy Weight. Price..............$3.20

No. 4E02048 Extra Heavy Weight. Price..............$3.35

No. 4E02050 Heavy Medium Weight. Colored Gold Inlaid. Price, $2.40

No. 4E02052 Heavy Weight. Colored Gold Inlaid. Price........$2.[illegible]

FINEST QUALITY SOLID GOLD SEAMLESS AND SOLDERLESS 10, 14 AND 18-KARAT PLAIN BAND RINGS AT UNHEARD OF PRICES.

For Prices on Engraving See Page 20.

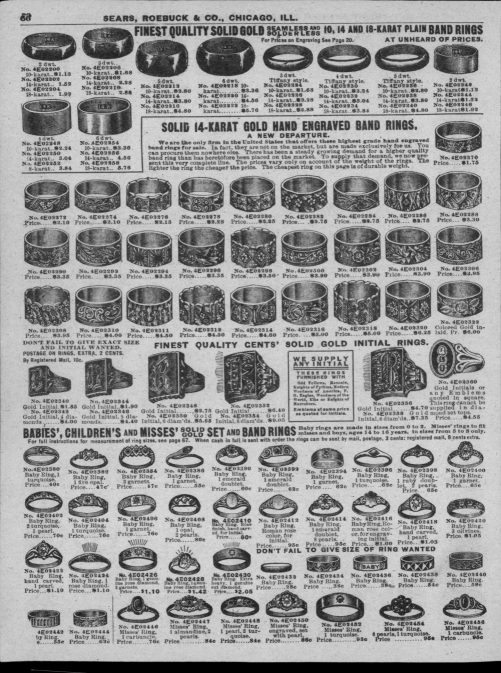

2 dwt.
No. 4E02200 10-karat..$1.12
No. 4E02202 14-karat.. 1.52
No. 4E02204 18-karat.. 1.92

3 dwt.
No. 4E02206 10-karat..$1.68
No. 4E02208 14-karat.. 2.28
No. 4E02210 18-karat.. 2.88

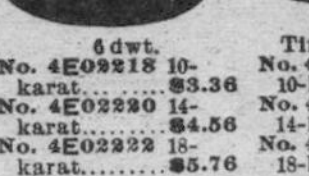

5 dwt.
No. 4E02212 10-karat..$2.80
No. 4E02214 14-karat..$3.80
No. 4E02216 18-karat..$4.80

6 dwt.
No. 4E02218 10-karat........$3.36
No. 4E02220 14-karat........$4.56
No. 4E02222 18-karat........$5.76

3 dwt. Tiffany style.
No. 4E02224 10-karat..$1.68
No. 4E02226 14-karat..$2.28
No. 4E02228 18-karat..$2.88

4 dwt. Tiffany style.
No. 4E02230 10-karat..$2.24
No. 4E02232 14-karat..$3.04
No. 4E02234 18-karat..$3.84

5 dwt. Tiffany style.
No. 4E02236 10-karat..$2.80
No. 4E02238 14-karat..$3.80
No. 4E02240 18-karat..$4.80

2 dwt.
No. 4E02242 10-karat$1.12
No. 4E02244 14-karat$1.52
No. 4E02246 18-karat$1.92

4 dwt.
No. 4E02248 10-karat..$2.24
No. 4E02250 14-karat.. 3.04
No. 4E02252 18-karat.. 3.84

6 dwt.
No. 4E02254 10-karat..$3.36
No. 4E02256 14-karat.. 4.56
No. 4E02258 18-karat.. 5.76

SOLID 14-KARAT GOLD HAND ENGRAVED BAND RINGS.

A NEW DEPARTURE.

We are the only firm in the United States that offers these highest grade hand engraved band rings for sale. In fact, they are not on the market, but are made exclusively for us. You can procure them nowhere else. There has been a steady growing demand for a higher quality band ring than has heretofore been placed on the market. To supply that demand, we now present this very complete line. The prices vary only on account of the weight of the rings. The lighter the ring the cheaper the price. The cheapest ring on this page is of durable weight.

No. 4E02270 Price.....$1.75

No. 4E02272 Price.....$2.10
No. 4E02274 Price.....$2.10
No. 4E02276 Price.....$2.15
No. 4E02278 Price.....$2.23
No. 4E02280 Price.....$2.25
No. 4E02282 Price.....$2.75
No. 4E02284 Price.....$2.75
No. 4E02286 Price.....$2.75
No. 4E02288 Price.....$3.30

No. 4E02290 Price.....$3.35
No. 4E02292 Price.....$3.35
No. 4E02294 Price.....$3.35
No. 4E02296 Price.....$3.35
No. 4E02298 Price.....$3.50
No. 4E02300 Price.....$3.90
No. 4E02302 Price.....$3.90
No. 4E02304 Price.....$3.90
No. 4E02306 Price.....$3.95

No. 4E02308 Price.....$3.95
No. 4E02310 Price.....$4.00
No. 4E02311 Price.....$4.50
No. 4E02312 Price.....$4.50
No. 4E02314 Price.....$4.60
No. 4E02316 Price.....$5.00
No. 4E02318 Price.....$5.00
No. 4E02320 Price.....$6.25
No. 4E02322 Colored Gold Inlaid. Pr. $6.00

DON'T FAIL TO GIVE EXACT SIZE AND INITIAL WANTED.
POSTAGE ON RINGS, EXTRA, 2 CENTS.
By Registered Mail, 10c.

FINEST QUALITY CENTS' SOLID GOLD INITIAL RINGS.

No. 4E02340 Gold Initial..$1.85
No. 4E02342 Gold Initial, 4 diamonds.......$4.00

No. 4E02344 Gold Initial..$1.90
No. 4E02346 Gold Initial, 5 diamonds.......$4.40

No. 4E02348 Gold Initial.......$2.75
No. 4E02350 Gold Initial, 6 diam'ds..$5.85

No. 4E02352 Gold Initial.......$6.40
No. 4E02354 Gold Initial, 6 diam'ds..$9.05

WE SUPPLY ANY INITIAL

THESE RINGS FURNISHED WITH Odd Fellows, Masonic, Knights of Pythias, Modern Woodmen of America, F. O. Eagles, Woodmen of the World, Elks or Knights of Maccabees.

Emblems at same price as quoted for initials.

No. 4E02356 Gold Initial.........$4.70
No. 4E02358 Gold Initial, 6 diam'ds..$7.35

No. 4E02360 Gold Initials or any Emblems quoted in square. This ring cannot be supplied in diamond set tops. Price.....$4.55

BABIES', CHILDREN'S AND MISSES' SOLID GOLD SET AND BAND RINGS

Baby rings are made in sizes from 0 to 2. Misses' rings to fit misses and boys, ages 14 to 16 years, in sizes from 5 to 8 only.

For full instructions for measurement of ring sizes, see page 67. When cash in full is sent with order the rings can be sent by mail, postage, 3 cents; registered mail, 8 cents extra.

No. 4E02380 Baby Ring, 1 turquoise. Price....40c
No. 4E02382 Baby Ring, 1 fire opal. Price....47c
No. 4E02384 Baby Ring, 3 garnets. Price......47c
No. 4E02386 Baby Ring, 1 garnet. Price......55c
No. 4E02390 Baby Ring, 1 emerald doublet. Price......60c
No. 4E02392 Baby Ring, 1 emerald doublet. Price......62c
No. 4E02394 Baby Ring, 1 garnet. Price.... 62c
No. 4E02396 Baby Ring, 1 turquoise. Price......62c
No. 4E02398 Baby Ring, 1 ruby doublet, 2 pearls. Price.... 65c
No. 4E02400 Baby Ring, 1 garnet. Price....65c

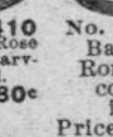

No. 4E02402 Baby Ring, 2 turquoise, 1 pearl. Price......70c
No. 4E02404 Baby Ring, 1 turquoise. Price......76c
No. 4E02406 Baby Ring, 1 garnet. Price......76c
No. 4E02408 Baby Ring, 1 opal, 2 pearls. Price......80c
No. 4E02410 Baby Ring. Rose finish, hand carved, for initial. Price......80c
No. 4E02412 Baby Ring, Roman rose color, for initial. Price......95c
No. 4E02414 Baby Ring, 1 emerald doublet, 8 pearls. Price.....
No. 4E02416 Baby Ring, Roman rose color, for engraving initial. Price....$1.00
No. 4E02418 Baby Ring, hand carved, 1 pearl. Price....$1.03
No. 4E02420 Baby Ring, 3 olivines. Price. $1.05

DON'T FAIL TO GIVE SIZE OF RING WANTED

No. 4E02422 Baby Ring, hand carved, 1 pearl. Price....$1.10
No. 4E02424 Baby Ring, 1 rose diamond. Price....$1.10
No. 4E02426 Baby Ring, 1 genuine rose diamond, 2 garnets. Price....$1.10
No. 4E02428 Baby Ring, 1 genuine rose diamond. Price....$1.42
No. 4E02430 Baby Ring. Extra heavy. 1 genuine cut diamond. Price....$2.05
No. 4E02432 Baby Ring. Price......28c
No. 4E02434 Baby Ring. Price......38c
No. 4E02436 Baby Ring. Price......38c
No. 4E02438 Baby Ring. Price......54c
No. 4E02440 Baby Ring. Price....58c

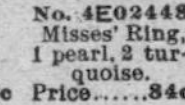

4E02442 by Ring. e......55c
No. 4E02444 Baby Ring. Price......62c
No. 4E02446 Misses' Ring, 1 carbuncle. Price......76c
No. 4E02447 Misses' Ring, 1 almandine, 2 pearls. Price......84c
No. 4E02448 Misses' Ring, 1 pearl, 2 turquoise. Price......84c
No. 4E02450 Misses' Ring, engraved, set with pearl. Price......86c
No. 4E02452 Misses' Ring, 1 turquoise. Price..........92c
No. 4E02454 Misses' Ring, 6 pearls, 1 turquoise. Price 95c
No. 4E02456 Misses' Ring, 1 carbuncle. Price 95c

MISSES' AND LADIES' FINE SOLID GOLD STONE SET AND BAND RINGS.

DO NOT FAIL TO GIVE EXACT SIZE WANTED.

Compare any ring illustrated on the following pages with any ring owned by your friends, or shown in your local store, and compare prices. If ours is not the best, and you are not saving money, don't buy. Remember, postage on rings is only 2 cents; insurance, 5 cents extra, up to $5.00 purchase. For prices on engraving, see page 20.

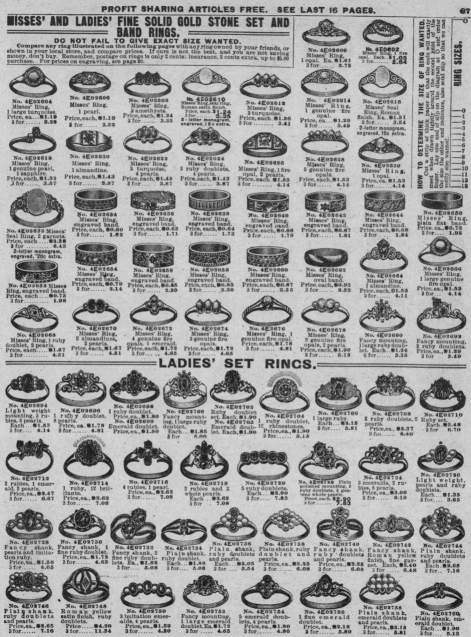

No. 4E02600 Misses' Ring, 1 opal. Ea. $1.01 3 for...... 2.73

No. 4E0602 Misses' Ring, 1 fire opal. Each.. $1.05 3 for........ 2.84

HOW TO DETERMINE THE SIZE OF RING WANTED. Cut a strip of thick paper so that the ends will exactly meet when drawn tightly around the second joint of the finger. Lay one end of slip on the diagram at O and order the size the other end indicates, also send slip so that we can verify size wanted.

RING SIZES.

0 1 2 3 4 5 6 7 8 9 10 11 12 13

No. 4E02604 Misses' Ring, 1 large turquoise. Price, ea... $1.19 3 for 3.22

No. 4E02606 Misses' Ring, 1 pearl. Price, each, $1.19 3 for...... 3.22

No. 4E02608 Misses' Ring, 3 amethysts. Price, each, $1.24 3 for...... 3.35

No. 4E02610 Misses' Ring, seal ring, Roman satin finish. Price, each. $1.24 3 for........ 3.35 2 - letter monogram, engraved, 15c extra.

No. 4E02612 Misses' Ring, 3 turquoise. Price, each. $1.26 3 for 3.41

No. 4E02614 Misses' Ring, 1 genuine fire opal. Price, ea... $1.29 3 for...... 3.49

No. 4E02616 Misses' Seal Ring, Roman finish. Ea.. $1.31 3 for...... 3.54 2-letter monogram, engraved, 15c extra.

No. 4E02618 Misses' Ring, 1 genuine pearl, 1 sapphire. Price, each, $1.32 3 for...... 3.57

No. 4E02620 Misses' Ring, 1 almandine. Price, each, $1.43 3 for...... 3.87

No. 4E02622 Misses' Ring, 3 turquoise, 4 pearls. Price, each, $1.43 3 for...... 3.87

No. 4E02624 Misses' Ring, 3 ruby doublets, 4 pearls. Price, each, $1.43 3 for...... 3.87

No. 4E02626 Misses' Ring, 1 fire opal, 2 pearls. Price, each. $1.53 3 for 4.14

No. 4E02628 Misses' Ring, 5 genuine fire opals. Price, each, $1.53 3 for...... 4.14

No. 4E02630 Misses' Ring, 1 opal. Price, ea. $1.53 3 for........ 4.14

No. 4E02632 Misses' Seal Ring, 2 garnets. Price, each .... $2.38 3 for .... 6.43 2-letter monogram, engraved, 20c extra.

No. 4E02634 Misses' Ring, engraved band. Price, each, $0.60 3 for...... 1.62

No. 4E02636 Misses' Ring, engraved band. Price, each, $0.63 3 for...... 1.71

No. 4E02638 Misses' Ring, engraved band. Price, each, $0.64 3 for...... 1.73

No. 4E02640 Misses' Ring, engraved band. Price, each, $0.66 3 for...... 1.79

No. 4E02642 Misses' Ring, engraved band. Price, each, $0.67 3 for...... 1.81

No. 4E02644 Misses' Ring, engraved band. Price, each, $0.68 3 for...... 1.84

No. 4E02650 Misses' Ring, plain flat band. Price. ea., $0.72 3 for...... 1.95

No. 4E02652 Misses Ring, engraved band. Price, each .... $0.73 3 for...... 1.98

No. 4E02654 Misses' Ring, engraved band. Price, each, $0.79 3 for...... 2.14

No. 4E02656 Misses' Ring, engraved band. Price, each, $0.85 3 for...... 2.30

No. 4E02658 Misses' Ring, engraved band. Price, each, $0.85 3 for...... 2.30

No. 4E02660 Misses' Ring, engraved band. Price, each, $0.87 3 for...... 2.35

No. 4E02662 Misses' Ring, oval band. Price. each, $0.93 3 for...... 2.52

No. 4E02664 Misses' Ring, 1 almandine. Price, each, $1.52 3 for...... 4.11

No. 4E02666 Misses' Ring, 1 large genuine fire opal. Price, ea., $1.53 3 for... 4.14

No. 4E02668 Misses' Ring, 1 ruby doublet, 2 pearls. Price, each..... $1.67 3 for.......... 4.51

No. 4E02670 Misses' Ring, 2 almandines, 2 pearls. Price, each, $1.67 3 for...... 4.51

No. 4E02672 Misses' Ring, 4 genuine fire opals, 1 emerald. Price, each, $1.72 3 for...... 4.65

No. 4E02674 Misses' Ring, 3 genuine fire opals. Price, each, $1.72 3 for...... 4.65

No. 4E2676 Misses' Ring, 1 genuine fire opal. Price, each, $1.78 3 for...... 4.81

No. 4E02678 Misses' Ring, 2 genuine fire opals, 2 pearls. Price, each, $1.90 3 for...... 5.13

No. 4E02690 Fancy mounting, 1 large ruby doublet. Each.. $1.24 3 for...... 3.35

No. 4E02692 Fancy mounting, 2 ruby doublets. Price, ea., $1.29 3 for . 3.49

LADIES' SET RINGS.

No. 4E02694 Light weight mounting, 3 rubies, 6 pearls. Each... $1.53 3 for.... 4.14

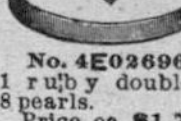

No. 4E02696 1 ruby doublet, 8 pearls. Price, ea. $1.78 3 for...... 4.81

No. 4E02698 1 ruby doublet. Price, ea., $1.80
No. 4E02699 Emerald doublet. Price, ea., $1.80

No. 4E02700 Fancy mounting, 1 large ruby doublet. Each... $1.85 3 for 5.00

No. 4E02702 Ruby doublet set. Each, $1.90
No. 4E02703 Emerald doublet. Each, $1.90

No. 4E02704 1 ruby doublet, 12 rhinestones. Price, ea., $1.90 3 for...... 5.13

No. 4E02706 1 large ruby. Each... $2.15 3 for.... 5.81

No. 4E02708 2 ruby doublets, 2 pearls. Price, ea., $2.37 3 for 6.40

No. 4E02710 Ruby set. Each. $2.48 3 for 6.70

No. 4E02712 2 rubies, 1 emerald, 2 pearls. Price, ea., $2.47 3 for...... 6.67

No. 4E02714 1 ruby, 12 brilliants. Price, ea., $2.62 3 for...... 7.08

No. 4E02716 4 rubies, 1 pearl. Price, ea., $2.62 3 for...... 7.08

No. 4E02718 2 rubies and 2 whole pearls. Each .. $2.62 3 for .. 7.08

No. 4E02720 5 ruby doublets. Each... $2.90 3 for...... 7.83

No. 4E02722 Plain polished mounting, 2 ruby doublets, 2 genuine whole pearls. Price, each. $2.90 3 for.......... 7.83

No. 4E02724 3 emeralds, 2 rubies, 8 pearls. Price, ea., $3.00 3 for...... 8.10

No. 4E02726 Light weight, pearls and ruby doublets. Each... $1.35 3 for.... 3.65

No. 4E02728 Fancy shank, pearls and imitation ruby. Price, ea., $1.50 3 for...... 4.05

No. 4E02730 Fancy shank, 1 fine ruby doublet. Price, ea.. $1.72 3 for...... 4.65

No. 4E02732 Fancy shank, 2 fine ruby doublets. Ea., $1.88 3 for...... 5.08

No. 4E02734 Plain shank, ruby doublet. Each... $1.88 3 for...... 5.08

No. 4E02736 Plain shank, ruby doublets and pearls. Each... $2.05 3 for...... 5.54

No. 4E02738 Plain shank, ruby doublet and pearls. Price, ea., $2.25 3 for...... 6.08

No. 4E02740 Fancy shank, ruby doublets and pearls. Price, ea., $2.25 3 for...... 6.08

No. 4E02742 Fancy shank, Roman yellow finish, fine garnet. Each, $2.40 3 for 6.48

No. 4E02744 Plain shank, ruby doublets and pearls. Each. $2.65 3 for.. 7.16

No. 4E02746 Plain shank, ruby doublets and pearls. Price, ea., $2.65 3 for...... 7.16

No. 4E02748 Roman yellow satin finish, ruby doublets. Price..... $4.20 3 for...... 11.34

No. 4E02750 3 imitation emeralds, 4 pearls. Price, ea., $1.59 3 for...... 4.30

No. 4E02752 Fancy mounting, 1 large emerald doublet. Ea. $1.72 3 for...... 4.65

No. 4E02754 5 emerald doublets, 4 pearls. Price, ea., $1.80 3 for...... 4.86

No. 4E02756 1 fine emerald doublet. Price, ea., $2.18 3 for...... 5.89

No. 4E02758 Plain shank, emerald doublets and pearls. Price, ea., $2.15 3 for...... 5.81

No. 4E02760 Plain shank, emerald doublet. Each... $1.90 3 for...... 5.13

DON'T FAIL TO GIVE EXACT SIZE WANTED.

LADIES' FINE SOLID GOLD SET RINGS.

Remember, postage on rings is only 2 cents; insurance 5 cents extra, up to $5.00 purchase.

GET A BIRTHDAY RING. We particularly direct your attention to ring No. 4E02988. This is the ideal birthday ring. Price, $1.46. The best value ever offered. The stones used according to month are as follows: January, garnet; February, amethyst; March, bloodstone; April, diamond doublet; May, emerald; June, agate; July, ruby; August, sardonyx; September, sapphire; October, opal; November, topaz; December, turquoise. **Don't fail to give exact size of ring wanted.** For prices on engraving see page 20.

No. 4E02900 Extra heavy, ruby set. Each...... $3.10 3 for...... 8.37

No. 4E02902 Plain polished mounting, 2 ruby doublets, 4 genuine whole pearls. Each...... $3.38 3 for...... 9.13

No. 4E02904 One ruby doublet. Each...... $3.47 3 for...... 9.37

No. 4E02906 12 rubies, 5 pearls. Each...... $3.58 3 for...... 9.67

No. 4E02908 1 ruby doublet, 4 genuine half pearls. Each.... $ 3.80 3 for.... 10.26

No. 4E02910 2 rubies, 2 genuine whole pearls. Each.... $ 3.80 3 for..... 10.26

No. 4E02912 Plain mounting, 3 large ruby doublets. Each, $2.52 3 for...... 6.81

No. 4E02914 Fancy mounting, 1 large ruby doublet. Each. $1.90 3 for...... 5.13

No. 4E02920 4 rubies, 5 whole pearls. Each.... $ 3.80 3 for..... 10.26

No. 4E02922 Fancy mounting, 6 ruby doublets, 1 genuine whole pearl. Each.... $ 3.86 3 for... 10.43

No. 4E02924 Fancy mounting, 2 ruby doublets, 5 genuine whole pearls. Ea... $3.86 3 for....... 10.43

No. 4E02926 Fancy mounting, 3 ruby doublets, 6 genuine whole pearls. Ea. $ 3.98 3 for...... 10.75

No. 4E02928 10 rubies, 5 real pearls. Each... $ 4.23 3 for..... 11.43

No. 4E02930 4 ruby doublets, 6 genuine pearls. Each.... $ 4.56 3 for..... 12.32

No. 4E02931 2 emerald sets. Ea. $1.28 3 for...... 3.46

No. 4E02932 Turquoise set. Ea. $1.28 3 for...... 3.46

No. 4E02933 Ruby set. Each.... $1.28 3 for..... 3.46

No. 4E02934 Emerald and ruby. Each.. $1.48 3 for...... 4.00

No. 4E02940 Plain shank, rhinestones and emerald doublets. Each.. $2.40 3 for...... 6.48

No. 4E02942 1 emerald, 6 pearls. Each...... $2.38 3 for...... 6.43

No. 4E02944 7 emerald doublets, 6 pearls. Each...... $2.38 3 for..... 6.43

No. 4E02946 5 emeralds, 8 pearls. Ea. $2.60 3 for...... 7.02

No. 4E02948 Fancy mounting, 1 large emerald doublet, 2 genuine pearls. Each..... $2.75 3 for...... 7.43

No. 4E02950 Fancy shank, emeralds and pearls. Each,.... $3.40 3 for..... 9.18

No. 4E02952 Roman yellow color, emeralds and ruby doublets. Ea.. $ 4.75 3 for..... 12.83

No. 4E02960 1 emerald, 12 pearls. Each.... $2.65 3 for...... 7.10

No. 4E02962 1 large emerald doublet, 2 genuine pearls. Each. ...$2.95 3 for...... 7.97

No. 4E02964 11 emeralds, 10 pearls. Each...... $3.15 3 for. 8.51

No. 4E02966 4 emerald doublets. Each. $3.40 3 for...... 9.18

No. 4E02968 Plain polished mounting, 4 emerald doublets, 10 genuine pearls. Each...... $3.46 3 for...... 9.35

No. 4E02970 6 fine emerald doublets. Each...... $3.40 3 for. ... 9.18

No. 4E02972 1 emerald doublet, 6 genuine pearls. Each..... $4.75 3 for..... 12.83

No. 4E02974 4 emeralds, 8 genuine pearls. Each.... $ 4.64 3 for..... 12.53

No. 4E02980 2 ruby doublets, 1 emerald doublet. Each.. $ 7.60 3 for.. 20.52

No. 4E02982 Light weight, 3 genuine opals, 4 pearls. Ea. $1.52 3 for...... 4.11

No. 4E02984 Light weight, 6 genuine opals, 3 pearls. Each...... $1.52 3 for..... 4.11

No. 4E02986 Light weight, 4 genuine opals, 5 pearls. Each..... $1.52 3 for...... 4.11

No. 4E02988 Special Bargain Birthday Ring, plain Tiffany. See description at top of page. Each...... $1.46 3 for...... 3.95

No. 4E02990 1 genuine opal, 2 pearls. Each..... $1.77 3 for 4.78

No. 4E02992 2 genuine opals, 4 pearls. Each. .... $1.80 3 for...... 4.86

No. 4E02994 2 genuine opals. Each...... $1.90 3 for. 5.13

No. 4E03000 1 genuine opal. Each.... $1.90 3 for... 5.13

No. 4E03002 1 large genuine opals, 2 pearls. Each...... $1.72 3 for...... 4.65

No. 4E03004 Tiffany mounting, 5 genuine opals. Each...... $2.10 3 for...... 5.67

No. 4E03006 3 genuine opals. Each...... $2.38 3 for...... 6.43

No. 4E03008 7 genuine opals. Each...... $2.55 3 for...... 6.89

No. 4E03010 1 large genuine opal. Each..... $2.64 3 for..... 7.13

No. 4E03012 3 genuine opals. Each..... $2.70 3 for...... 7.29

No. 4E03014 6 pearls and 3 turquoise. Each.. ..$2.75 3 for...... 7.43

No. 4E03020 5 genuine opals, 5 pearls. Each.... $2.98 3 for.... 8.05

No. 4E03022 opals, 1 olivine. Each...... $2.85 3 for. 7.70

No. 4E03024 1 large opal. Each...... $2.20 3 for...... 5.94

No. 4E03026 Large genuine opal. Each..... $2.98 3 for..... 8.05

No. 4E03028 2 genuine opals, 8 pearls. Each...... $3.40 3 for...... 9.18

No. 4E03030 1 opal, 1 almandine, 6 pearls. Each..... $3.48 3 for.... 9.40

No. 4E03032 4 genuine opals, 10 emerald doublets. Each...... $3.65 2 for..... 9.86

No. 4E03034 1 large genuine opal. Ea... $3.45 3 for...... 9.32

No. 4E03036 Fancy shank, large genuine opal. Each... $1.25 3 for...... 3.38

No. 4E03038 Light weight, genuine opals and pearls. Ea. $1.50 3 for...... 4.05

No. 4E03040 Fancy pearl encrusted shank, genuine opals and ruby doublets. Each.... $1.90 3 for..... 5.13

No. 4E03042 Plain shank, genuine opals and pearls. Each. ... $2.35 3 for...... 6.35

No. 4E03044 Plain shank, 2 genuine opals, 4 ruby doublets, 3 pearls. Each,..... $2.40 3 for 6.48

No. 4E03048 Fancy shank, opals and pearls. Each...... $2.60 3 for...... 7.02

No. 4E03050 Plain shank, large genuine opal, pearls and emerald doublets. Each..... $2.75 3 for...... 7.43

No. 4E03052 3 opals, 4 rubies. Each.... $ 3.78 3 for.... 10.21

No. 4E03054 3 genuine fire opals, 12 pearls. Each.. $ 3.90 3 for.. 10.53

No. 4E03056 6 genuine opals, 6 pearls, 1 ruby. Each.. $ 3.92 3 for..... 10.59

No. 4E03058 3 genuine opals. Each.... $ 3.80 3 for.... 10.26

No. 4E03060 4 genuine opals, 12 pearls. Each.... $ 4.05 3 for.... 10.94

No. 4E03062 3 genuine opals, 4 garnets, 16 pearls. Each.... $ 4.50 3 for.... 12.15

No. 4E03064 4 genuine opals and 20 olivines. Each.... $ 3.98 3 for..... 10.75

No. 4E03066 1 genuine opal. Each.... $ 4.20 3 for.. 11.34

No. 4E03068 1 genuine opal, 26 pearls. Each.... $ 4.60 3 for.... 12.42

No. 4E03070 Extra heavy, genuine opals. Each.. $ 4.98 3 for.. 13.45

Don't Fail To Give Exact Size Wanted.

LADIES' SOLID GOLD FANCY STONE SET RINGS.

For Prices on Engraving See Page 20.

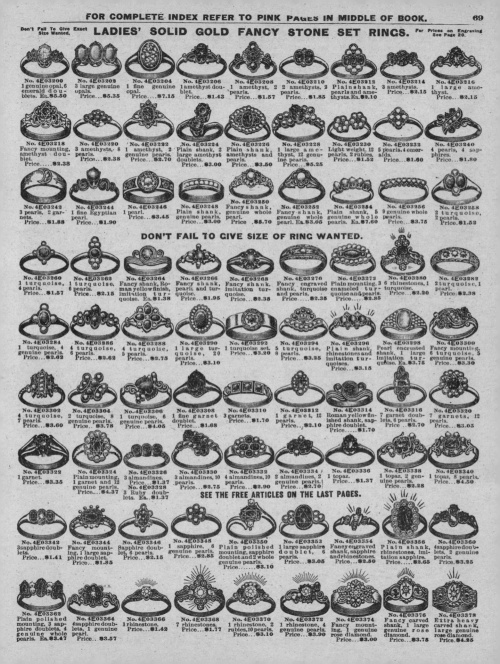

No. 4E03200 1 genuine opal, 6 emerald doublets. Ea. $5.50

No. 4E03202 3 large genuine opals. Price... $5.35

No. 4E03204 1 fine genuine opal. Price.... $7.15

No. 4E03206 1 amethyst doublet. Price... $1.43

No. 4E03208 1 amethyst, 2 pearls. Price... $1.57

No. 4E03210 2 amethysts, 2 pearls. Price... $1.85

No. 4E03212 Plain shank, pearls and amethysts. Ea. $2.10

No. 4E03214 3 amethysts. Price... $2.15

No. 4E03216 1 large amethyst. Price... $2.15

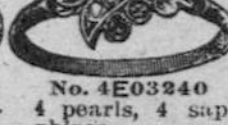

No. 4E03218 Fancy mounting, amethyst doublet. Price..... $2.38

No. 4E03220 3 amethysts, 8 pearls. Price... $2.38

No. 4E03222 1 amethyst, 2 genuine pearls. Price... $2.70

No. 4E03224 Plain shank, 2 large amethyst doublets. Price... $3.00

No. 4E03226 Plain shank, amethysts and pearls. Price... $3.50

No. 4E03228 1 large amethyst, 12 genuine pearls. Price... $5.25

No. 4E03230 Light weight, 12 pearls, 2 rubies. Price... $1.52

No. 4E03232 5 pearls, 4 emeralds. Price... $1.60

No. 4E03240 4 pearls, 4 sapphires. Price... $1.80

No. 4E03242 3 pearls, 2 garnets. Price... $1.88

No. 4E03244 1 fine Egyptian pearl. Price... $1.90

No. 4E03246 1 pearl. Price... $3.45

No. 4E03248 Plain shank, genuine pearls. Price... $3.00

No. 4E03250 Fancy shank, genuine whole pearl. Price $5.70

No. 4E03252 Fancy shank, genuine whole pearl. Ea. $3.05

No. 4E03254 Plain shank, 5 genuine whole pearls. Ea. $7.60

No. 4E03256 9 genuine whole pearls. Price... $3.75

No. 4E03258 2 turquoise, 2 pearls. Price. $1.52

DON'T FAIL TO GIVE SIZE OF RING WANTED.

No. 4E03260 1 turquoise, 4 pearls. Price... $1.57

No. 4E03262 1 turquoise, 6 pearls. Price... $2.15

No. 4E03264 Fancy shank, Roman yellow finish, imitation turquoise. Ea. $1.38

No. 4E03266 Fancy shank, pearls and turquoise. Price... $1.95

No. 4E03268 Fancy shank, imitation turquoise. Price... $2.35

No. 4E03270 Fancy engraved shank, turquoise and pearls. Price..... $2.35

No. 4E03272 Plain mounting, 3 enameled turquoise and pearls. Price..... $2.85

No. 4E03280 6 rhinestones, 1 turquoise. Price... $2.20

No. 4E03282 2 turquoise, 1 pearl. Price. $2.38

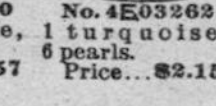

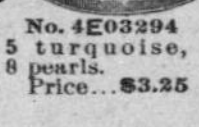

No. 4E03284 1 turquoise, 4 genuine pearls. Price... $2.62

No. 4E03286 4 turquoise, 6 pearls. Price... $2.62

No. 4E03288 4 turquoise, 5 pearls. Price... $2.75

No. 4E03290 1 large turquoise, 20 pearls. Price... $3.10

No. 4E03292 1 turquoise set. Price... $3.20

No. 4E03294 5 turquoise, 8 pearls. Price... $3.25

No. 4E03296 Plain shank, rhinestones and imitation turquoises. Price... $3.15

No. 4E03298 Pearl encrusted shank, 1 large imitation turquoise. Ea. $3.75

No. 4E03300 Fancy mounting, 6 turquoise, 5 genuine pearls. Price... $3.30

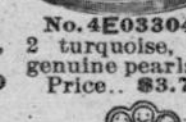

No. 4E03302 4 turquoise, 7 pearls. Price... $3.60

No. 4E03304 2 turquoise, 8 genuine pearls. Price.. $3.78

No. 4E03306 1 turquoise, 6 genuine pearls. Price... $4.05

No. 4E03308 1 fine garnet doublet. Price... $1.68

No. 4E03310 3 garnets. Price... $1.70

No. 4E03312 1 garnet, 12 pearls. Price... $2.10

No. 4E03314 Roman yellow finished shank, sapphire doublet. Price..... $1.70

No. 4E03316 7 garnet doublets, 6 pearls. Price .. $2.70

No. 4E03320 7 garnets, 12 pearls. Price... $3.05

No. 4E03322 1 garnet. Price... $3.35

No. 4E03324 Plain mounting, 1 garnet and 12 genuine pearls. Price.... $4.37

No. 4E03326 3 almandines. Price... $1.37

No. 4E03328 3 Ruby doublets. Ea.. $1.37

No. 4E03330 3 almandines, 10 pearls. Price... $2.75

No. 4E03332 4 almandines, 10 pearls. Price... $2.90

No. 4E03334 2 almandines, 2 genuine pearls. Price... $2.70

No. 4E03336 1 topaz. Price... $1.37

No. 4E03338 1 topaz, 2 genuine pearls. Price... $2.28

No. 4E03340 1 topaz, 8 pearls. Price... $4.50

SEE THE FREE ARTICLES ON THE LAST PAGES.

No. 4E03342 3 sapphire doublets. Price... $1.41

No. 4E03344 Fancy mounting, 1 large sapphire doublet. Price... $1.85

No. 4E03346 Sapphire doublet, 6 pearls. Price... $2.15

No. 4E03348 1 sapphire, 6 genuine pearls. Price... $2.85

No. 4E03350 Plain polished mounting, sapphire doublet and 2 whole genuine pearls. Price....... $3.10

No. 4E03352 1 large sapphire doublet, 6 pearls. Price... $3.05

No. 4E03354 Fancy engraved shank, sapphire and rhinestones. Price... $2.50

No. 4E03356 Plain shank, rhinestones, imitation sapphire. Price..... $2.65

No. 4E03360 4 sapphire doublets, 2 genuine pearls. Price. $3.25

No. 4E03362 Plain polished mounting, 3 sapphire doublets, 4 genuine whole pearls. Ea. $3.47

No. 4E03364 4 sapphire doublets, 1 genuine pearl. Price.. $3.57

No. 4E03366 1 rhinestone. Price... $1.42

No. 4E03368 7 rhinestones. Price... $1.77

No. 4E03370 1 rhinestone, 2 rubies, 10 pearls. Price... $3.10

No. 4E03372 1 rhinestone, 4 genuine pearls. Price... $3.90

No. 4E03374 Fancy mounting, 1 genuine rose diamond. Price... $3.00

No. 4E03376 Fancy carved shank, 1 large genuine rose diamond. Price... $3.75

No. 4E03378 Extra heavy carved shank, large genuine rose diamond. Price. $4.25

GENUINE DIAMONDS AND SOLID GOLD 14-KARAT MOUNTINGS.

WITH EVERY DIAMOND we issue a written, binding guarantee, with a further agreement that you can at any time return any diamond you may select from this catalogue, and exchange it for any other diamond or other article of jewelry at the same or a higher price.

WE FURTHER AGREE on the return of any diamond purchased from us within 60 days of purchase, when so requested, to refund in cash your full purchase price, and we further agree, at any time after 60 days, on return of any diamond to us, when requested to do so, to refund your full purchase price, less 10 per cent.

YOU CAN BUY A DIAMOND from us today at $3.66 to $276.00 and you can keep it for three months or three years or longer, and if you so desire return it to us and we will refund you in cash the full amount of money you paid us for it, less 10 per cent. But we must caution you that we positively will not exchange, refund, or allow credit for any diamond purchased from us unless it is in or with the original setting and is accompanied by our guarantee and refund certificate that was sent with the diamond.

EXCEPTIONS WHERE WE DO NOT GIVE OUR REFUND AND EXCHANGE CERTIFICATE WITH A PURCHASE. This ruling applies to such items plainly marked "no refund certificate," and is made necessary for the reason that where we allow a refund certificate, the cost of making the mounting is but a small item of cost and the gold value is the principal one. Where we do not give our refund certificate, the actual gold value amounts to but little and the principal cost is in the making and the cost of the pearls, fancy stones, etc., and as we melt up all returned mountings, our loss would be too great where the cost of making the article is the principal expense. However, we will allow for the diamond without the mounting. On most of our diamond mounted jewelry we quote quality and weight. Where quality and weight are not given we do not allow refunds or exchange after goods have been worn.

GRADES OF DIAMONDS.

FIRST QUALITY. These stones are perfect in color, proportion, brilliancy, shape and are free from all flaws.

SECOND QUALITY (sometimes called "Commercial White"). A second quality diamond is in every particular the same as a first, except for the color. The second quality has a slight shade of yellow. This yellow sometimes increases the brilliancy of the stone. At night it is often more fiery than the best grade in the first quality. To the inexperienced it is difficult to see the yellow tinge. This can be discovered by holding the diamond sidewise to the sunlight.

THIRD QUALITY. A third quality diamond is one that is brilliant and well cut, but has some imperfection or blemish, generally so small and so slight that it requires one high in the knowledge of diamonds to be able to detect the imperfection at all. Our own third quality diamonds are practically perfect in cut and shape. The color may be the same as in our first or second quality, but by close examination it is possible to detect a blemish of some sort. Our third quality diamonds never have cracks in them or large, unsightly chunks or pieces knocked out of them. The same quality that we sell for third quality is sold by some monthly payment houses and by small dealers as first quality stones. These people either buy and sell them as first quality because they are unable to judge diamonds, or they are fully aware of the imperfections and are simply misrepresenting the goods.

TIME PAYMENT CONCERNS sometimes sell diamonds to people who do not care what they pay for them. Some of their customers never pay. Still these concerns are making money. The selling price on any merchandise is based on the actual cost of the item with the expense of advertising, marketing and collecting, to which sum a regular profit is added. We, therefore, caution and point out to you the fact that marketing diamonds by the partial payment system is known to be the most costly of all.

WE ASK A CAREFUL COMPARISON of our goods with those shown by other concerns, which will do more toward showing the value we give than any other argument.

FINE SOLID GOLD FINGER RINGS. SET WITH FINE SELECTED GENUINE DIAMONDS.

Our binding guarantee and refund certificate goes with every ring.

Flat Belcher Mounting, set with ⅛-carat diamond.
No. 44E10002 Third quality diamond. Price...$8.88
No. 44E10004 Second quality diamond. Price, $11.38
No. 44E10006 First quality diamond. Price, $13.50
No. 44E10008 Mounting only, without stone. Ea. $2.25

Flat Belcher Mounting, set with ¼-carat diamond.
No. 44E10010 Third quality diamond. Price, $17.50
No. 44E10012 Second quality diamond. Price, $23.50
No. 44E10014 First quality diamond. Price, $27.50
No. 44E10016 Mounting only, without stone. Ea. $2.50

Flat Belcher Mounting, set with 3/16-carat diamond.
No. 44E10017 Third quality diamond. Price, $52.53
No. 44E10019 Second quality diamond. Price, $62.09
No. 44E10021 First quality diamond. Price, $74.46
No. 44E10023 Mounting only, without stone. Ea. $4.15

Flat Belcher Mounting, set with ¾-carat diamond.
No. 44E10025 Third quality diamond. Price, $75.75
No. 44E10027 Second quality diamond. Price, $87.75
No. 44E10029 First quality diamond. Price, $108.00
No. 44E10031 Mounting only, without stone. Ea. $4.50

Flat Belcher Mounting, set with ½-carat diamond.
No. 44E10026 Third quality diamond. Price, $47.00
No. 44E10028 Second quality diamond. Price, $55.50
No. 44E10030 First quality diamond. Price, $66.50
No. 44E10032 Mounting only, without stone. Ea. $4.00

Flat Belcher Mounting, set with ⅞-carat diamond.
No. 44E10034 Third quality diamond. Price, $87.88
No. 44E10036 Second quality diamond. Price, $101.87
No. 44E10038 First quality diamond. Price, $125.50
No. 44E10040 Mounting only, without stone. Ea. $4.75

Flat Belcher Mounting, set with 1¼-carat diamond.
No. 44E10042 Third quality diamond. Ea. $135.50
No. 44E10044 Second quality diamond. Ea. $155.50
No. 44E10046 First quality diamond. Ea. $193.00
No. 44E10048 Mounting only, without stone. Ea. $5.50

Round Belcher Mounting, set with ⅛-carat diamond.
No. 44E10051 Third quality diamond. Price, $47.00
No. 44E10053 Second quality diamond. Price, $55.50
No. 44E10055 First quality diamond. Price, $66.50
No. 44E10057 Mounting only, without stone. Ea. $4.00

Round Belcher Mounting, set with ¾-carat diamond.
No. 44E10074 Third quality diamond. Price, $75.25
No. 44E10076 Second quality diamond. Price, $87.25
No. 44E10078 First quality diamond. Price, $107.50
No. 44E10080 Mounting only, without stone. Ea. $4.00

Round Belcher Mounting, set with 1-carat diamond.
No. 44E10082 Third quality diamond. Price, $104.75
No. 44E10084 Second quality diamond. Price, $123.25
No. 44E10086 First quality diamond. Price, $147.75
No. 44E10088 Mounting only, without stone. Ea.. $4.75

Round Belcher Mounting, set with 1⅓-carat diamond.
No. 44E10090 Third quality diamond. Price, $122.25
No. 44E10092 Second quality diamond. Price, $138.06
No. 44E10094 First quality diamond. Price, $166.13
No. 44E10096 Mounting only, without stone. Ea. $5.25

Tiffany Belcher Mounting, set with 3/16-carat diamond.
No. 44E10106 Third quality diamond. Price, $12.34
No. 44E10108 Second quality diamond. Price, $16.09
No. 44E10110 First quality diamond. Price, $19.28
No. 44E10112 Mounting only, without stone. Ea. $2.40

Tiffany Belcher Mounting, set with ¼-carat diamond.
No. 44E10114 Third quality diamond. Price, $17.50
No. 44E10116 Second quality diamond. Price, $23.50
No. 44E10118 First quality diamond. Price, $27.50
No. 44E10120 Mounting only, without stone. Ea. $2.50

Tiffany Belcher Mounting, set with 5/16-carat diamond.
No. 44E10122 Third quality diamond. Ea.. $21.75
No. 44E10124 Second quality diamond. Ea.. $29.25
No. 44E10126 First quality diamond. Ea.. $34.25
No. 44E10128 Mounting only, without stone. Ea. $3.00

Six-Pronged Tooth Mounting, set with ¼-carat diamond.
No. 44E10146 Third quality diamond. Price, $18.25
No. 44E10148 Second quality diamond. Price, $24.25
No. 44E10150 First quality diamond. Price, $28.25
No. 44E10152 Mounting only, without stone. Ea. $3.25

Six-Pronged Tooth Mounting, set with ½-carat diamond.
No. 44E10162 Third quality diamond. Price, $47.50
No. 44E10164 Second quality diamond. Price, $56.00
No. 44E10166 First quality diamond. Price, $67.00
No. 44E10168 Mounting only, without stone. Ea. $4.50

Fancy Belcher Mounting, set with ½-carat diamonds.
No. 44E10169 Third quality diamond. Price, $47.00
No. 44E10171 Second quality diamond. Price, $55.50
No. 44E10173 Third quality diamond. Price, $66.50
No. 44E10175 Mounting only, without stone. Ea. $4.00

Six-Pronged Tooth Mounting, set with ¾-carat diamond.
No. 44E10178 Third quality diamond. Price, $76.75
No. 44E10180 Second quality diamond. Price, $88.75
No. 44E10182 First quality diamond. Ea... $109.00
No. 44E10184 Mounting only, without stone. Ea... $5.50

Tiffany Mounting, set with ⅛-carat diamond.
No. 44E10300 Third quality diamond. Price, $8.63
No. 44E10302 Second quality diamond. Price....... $11.13
No. 44E10304 First quality diamond. Price, $13.25
No. 44E10306 Mounting only, without stone. Ea. $2.00

Tiffany Mounting, set with ¼-carat diamond.
No. 44E10316 Third quality diamond. Price, $17.25
No. 44E10318 Second quality diamond. Price....... $23.25
No. 44E10320 First quality diamond. Price, $27.25
No. 44E10322 Mounting only, without stone. Ea. $2.25

Tiffany Mounting, set with ⅜-carat diamond.
No. 44E10326 Third quality diamond. Ea.. $27.48
No. 44E10328 Second quality diamond. Price..... $37.23
No. 44E10330 First quality diamond. Ea.. $43.60
No. 44E10332 Mounting only, without stone. Ea. $2.35

GENTS' DUMB BELL PATTERN CUFF LINKS

In Rolled Gold Plate, Solid Gold Front, and Gold Filled Stock. If by mail, postage on cuff links, extra, 3 cents.

No. 4E05300 Rolled gold plate, imitation gold front, set with three fancy stones. Per pair.....21c 3 pairs for.....57c

No. 4E05302 Rolled gold plate, bright polish, raised ornamentation, fancy stone sets. Price, per pair.....22c 3 pairs for..........60c

No. 4E05304 Rolled gold plate, imitation gold front, imitation hand engraved, bright polish. Price, per pair, 26c 3 pairs for..........71c

No. 4E05306 Rolled gold plate, bright polish, raised ornamentation, imitation diamond. Price per pair.....28c 3 pairs for..........76c

No. 4E05308 Rolled gold plate, bright polish, raised ornamentation. Per pair.....28c 3 pairs for..........76c

No. 4E05310 Rolled gold plate, bright polish, colored gold effect, fancy stone set. Price, per pair.....30c 3 pairs for..........81c

No. 4E05312 Rolled gold plate, raised ornamentation, fancy stone center. Pair.33c 3 pairs for..........90c

No. 4E05314 Rolled gold plate, imitation gold front. Price, per pair.....33c 3 pairs for. 90c

No. 4E05316 Rolled gold plate, bright polish, fancy gold color. Price, per pair.....36c 3 pairs for..........98c

No. 4E05318 Rolled gold plate, bright polish. Per pair.$0.38 3 pairs for..... 1.03

No. 4E05320 Rolled gold plate mountings, pearl button effect. Per pair.$0.38 3 pairs for...... 1.03

No. 4E05322 Rolled gold plate, bright polish, raised ornamentation. Per pair...$0.40 3 pairs for...... 1.08

No. 4E05324 Rolled gold plate, bright polish, raised bead ornamentation. Pair.$0.40 3 pairs for...... 1.08

No. 4E05326 Rolled gold plate, bright polish, raised ornamentation. Per pair..$0.43 3 pairs for.... 1.17

No. 4E05328 Rolled gold plate, bright polish, raised ornamentation, various colored gold. Per pair...$0.46 3 pairs for...... 1.25

No. 4E05330 Rolled gold plate, bright polish, raised ornamentation, three fine imitation diamonds. Price, per pair..$0.46 3 pairs for...... 1.25

No. 4E05332 Rolled gold plate, bright polish, raised ornamentation. Price, per pair. $0.46 3 pairs for....... 1.25

No. 4E05334 Gold filled dumb bell links. Price, per pair.$0.48 3 pairs for 1.30

No. 4E05336 Solid gold. Per pair...$2.15 3 pairs for..... 5.81

No. 4E05337 Solid silver. Per pair.$0.48 3 pairs for...... 1.30

No. 4E05338 Rolled gold plate, bright polish and Roman yellow finish; applied ornamentation. Pair..$0.48 3 pairs for...... 1.30

No. 4E05340 Rolled gold plate, imitation solid gold front, bright polish. Price, per pair..$0.54 3 pairs for...... 1.46

No. 4E05342 Rolled gold plate, bright polish, raised ornamentation, set with two fancy stones. Per pair..$0.56 3 pairs for...... 1.52

No. 4E05344 Rolled gold plate, Roman yellow satin finish, set with imitation opals. Per pair..$0.56 3 pairs for...... 1.52

No. 4E05346 Rolled gold plate, bright polish, fancy knot effect. Per pair....$0.58 3 pairs for...... 1.57

No. 4E05348 Gold filled, hand engraved, brilliant set. Price, per pair..$0.62 3 pairs for...... 1.68

No. 4E05350 Gold filled, bright polish, raised ornamentation. Per pair...$0.66 3 pairs for....... 1.79

No. 4E05352 Solid gold front, hand engraved, sun ray pattern. Per pair....$0.69 3 pairs for...... 1.87

No. 4E05354 Gold filled, bright polish, raised ornamentation. Per pair....$0.69 3 pairs for...... 1.87

No. 4E05356 Solid gold front, hand engraved, bright polish. Pair....$0.71 3 pairs for.... 1.92

No. 4E05360 Gold filled, Roman yellow satin finish, set with two imitation diamonds and two fancy stones. Price, per pair.$0.72 3 pairs for...... 1.95

No. 4E05362 Gold filled, Roman yellow satin finish, set with two rhinestones and one fancy stone. Pair.$0.77 3 pairs for...... 2.08

No. 4E05364 Solid gold front, hand engraved. Price, per pair.$0.82 3 pairs for....... 2.22

No. 4E05366 Gold filled, bright polish, raised ornamentation. Price, per pair.$0.82 3 pairs for...... 2.22

No. 4E05368 Gold filled, bright polish and Roman yellow color, very artistic. Price, per pair. $0.86 3 pairs for...... 2.33

No. 4E05370 Solid gold front, bright polish, hand engraved. Price, per pair. $0.88 3 pairs for...... 2.38

No. 4E05372 Gold filled, bright polish, fancy beaded border. Per pair......$0.93 3 pairs for..... 2.52 Two or three-letter monogram, 40 cents extra.

No. 4E05374 Solid gold front, bright finish, hand engraved. Price, per pair..$0.95 3 pairs for...... 2.57

No. 4E05376 Gold filled, bright polish and Roman yellow satin finish. Per pair. $0.95 3 pairs for..... 2.57

No. 4E05378 Gold filled, bright polish, fancy turquoise center. Price, per pair..$1.00 3 pairs for...... 2.70

No. 4E05380 Solid gold front, bright polish, hand engraved. Price, per pair..$1.07 3 pairs for 2.89

No. 4E05382 Solid gold front, Roman yellow satin finish, bright cut, hand engraved. Price, per pair..$1.10 3 pairs for...... 2.97

No. 4E05384 Solid gold front, bright polish, hand carved. Price, per pair..$1.14 3 pairs for 3.08

No. 4E05386 Gold filled, Roman yellow finish, set with very fine imitation diamonds. Price, per pair$1.19 3 pairs for.... 3.22

No. 4E05388 Solid gold front, hand engraved, bright polish, two imitation diamonds. Price, per pair..$1.28 3 pairs for...... 3.46

No. 4E05390 Solid gold front, hand engraved. Price, per pair..$0.98 3 pairs for...... 2.65

No. 4E05392 Solid gold front, bright polish, hand engraved. Price, per pair.. $0.98 3 pairs for....... 2.65

Note the 6 varieties of Emblem Buttons we carry.

Order by number, and state Emblem wanted.

No. 4E05394 Masonic.
No. 4E05396 Odd Fellows.
No. 4E05398 Knights of Pythias.
No. 4E05400 Redmen.
No. 4E05402 Woodmen of America.
No. 4E05404 Woodmen of the World.

Solid gold front, hand engraved, your choice. 3 pairs for. $3.08: Pair.$1.14

ORDER BY NUMBER.

No. 4E05406 Solid gold front, hand engraved, bright. Per pair.......$1.00 3 pairs for.... 2.70

BEST QUALITY STUDS, COLLAR BUTTONS AND LADIES' WATCH CHATELETTE PINS.

If by mail, postage extra, 2 cents.

No. 4E05510 Solid gold, genuine opal. Price..$1.52

No. 4E05518 Solid gold, Emerald doublet. Price....$1.18

No. 4E05520 Ruby doublet. Price....$1.18

No. 4E05522 Genuine opal. Price... $1.27

No. 4E05528 Pearl front, rolled plate back, separable. Price, per set.........10c

No. 4E05530 Gold front, gold filled back, separable. Price, per set..........48c

Separable. No. 4E05532 Gold filled. Price.... 8c

Separable. No. 4E05534 Solid g'ld fr'nt Price......22c

SOLID GOLD COLLAR BUTTONS.

If by mail, postage extra, per dozen, 6 cents.

No. 4E05536 Ball top, medium. Price...... .85c

No. 4E05538 Ball top, high. Price.......95c

No. 4E05540 Flat top, low. Price. 85c

No. 4E05542 Flat top, medium. Price...... 90c

No. 4E05544 Flat top, high. Price.. ....95c

No. 4E05546 Lever top, medium..........75c

No. 4E05548 Lever top, large..$1.05

No. 4E05550 Lever pointer. Price...$1.05

GOLD FILLED COLLAR BUTTONS.

If by mail, postage extra, per dozen, 6 cents.

Ball Top.	Flat Top.	Lever Pearl Back	Lever Medium.	Lever High.	Lever Pointer.
No. 4E05562 Rolled gold plate. Price..... 7c	No. 4E05568 Rolled gold plate. Price.. .. 7c	No. 4E05574 Rolled gold plate. Price.........9c	No. 4E05580 Rolled gold plate. Price.. .... 7c	No. 4E05584 Rolled gold plate. Price........ 7c	No. 4E05588 Rolled gold plate. Price....... 7c
No. 4E05564 Gold filled. Price......18c	No. 4E05570 Gold filled. Price ...18c	No. 4E05576 Gold filled. Price.........18c	No. 4E05582 Gold filled. Price.. ......18c	No. 4E05585 Gold filled. Price.. ......18c	No. 4E05590 Gold filled. Price.... 18c
No. 4E05566 Gold plate. Per dozen.36c	No. 4E05572 Gold plate. Per dozen.36c	No. 4E05578 Gold plate. Per dozen...36c	No. 4E05583 Gold plate. Per dozen...36c	No. 4E05586 Gold plate. Per dozen...36c	No. 4E05592 Gold plate. Per dozen...36c

No. 4E05603 Solid gold, plain polish. Price, each..$1.80 3 for... .... 4.86

No. 4E05605 Solid silver, same style as No. 4E05603. Price, 3 for $1.89; each...70c

No. 4E05604 Rolled gold plate, blue enameled, bright polish. Price, ea....36c 3 for.........98c

No. 4E05606 Gold filled, bright polish, hand chased and engraved. Price, 3 for $2.08; each...77c

No. 4E05608 Rolled gold plate, bright polish, set with 7 pearls. Price, ea..$0.38 3 for.. ..... 1.03

No. 4E05610 Gold filled, bright polish, set with six fine imitation diamonds and five rubies. Price, each..........$1.00 3 for.... .... 2.70

No. 4E05612 Solid gold front, bright polish, hand engraved. Price, ea..$0.48 3 for....... 1.30

No. 4E05622 Gold filled, bright polish, set with fine imitation diamond and 21 pearls. Price, ea.. $1.05 3 for...... 2.84

No. 4E05624 Solid gold front, hand engraved, bright polish. Price, ea., $0.58 3 for...... 1.57

No. 4E05626 Rolled gold plate, Roman color, hard enameled. Price, 3 for 87c; each...32c

No. 4E05627 Gold filled, extra quality. Price, 3 for $1.25; each. ..46c

No. 4E05628 Gold filled, bright finish, beaded edge. Price, each.$0.58 3 for........ 1.57

No. 4E05630 Gold filled, bright finish, set with four pearls. Price, 3 for $1.95; each....72c

No. 4E05632 Gold filled, rose finish, raised ornamentation, four amethysts. Price, 3 for $3.19; each...$1.18

No. 4E05634 Gold filled, bright finish, chased, beaded border. Price, 3 for $2.43; each .90c

No. 4E05638 Gold filled, rose finish, burnished, opal and seven emerald doublet sets. Price, 3 for $3.06; each. $1.13

No. 4E05640 Gold filled over sterling silver; set with 36 crystalline diamonds. 3 for $5.81; each. $2.15

No. 4E05642 Gold filled, bright polish, set with fine imitation diamonds. One of the most attractive chatelettes on the market. Price, 3 for $8.37; each... $3.10

No. 4E05644 Rolled gold plate, Roman finish. 3 for $1.08; each....40c

No. 4E05646 Solid silver, satin finish. Price, 3 for $1.52; each....56c

No. 4E05648 Gold filled, bright finish. Price, 3 for $1.52; each....56c

No. 4E05650 Gold filled, bright finish. Price, 3 for $1.84; each....68c

No. 4E05652 Gold filled, bright finish. Price, 3 for $2.03; each, 75c

IT-SO-EZIE.

No. 4E05560 It-So-Ezie Combination Button and Cuff Holder. The set consists of four heavy rolled gold plated buttons. The base of the button worn in the cuff is provided with a reliable and durable mechanism for engaging and disengaging the head of the button that is worn in the wrist band. The illustrations show the button attached and detached. To release them, tip the top button and they will separate.

ATTACHED / DETACHED

Price, per set	$0.19
Six sets	1.05
Twelve sets	1.90

LADIES' WATCH CHATELETTES.

You can improve the appearance of your costume by wearing one of our swell chatelettes to hang your watch on, or, if you desire, you can use one of these nobby pins as a brooch. Illustrations show the exact size. Each one comes with a swivel attached as on No. 4E05644. If by mail, postage extra, 8 cents.

No. 4E05594 Solid gold, bright polish, raised ornamentation. Price, ea. $1.65 3 for..... 4.46

No. 4E05595 Solid gold, bright polish, set with three genuine pearls. Price, each ..$2.60 3 for........... 7.02

No. 4E05596 Solid gold, plain polish, oval shape, extra strong. Price, ea. $2.65 3 for..... 7.16

No. 4E05597 Solid gold, bright polish, beaded edge, set with three turquoise. Price, ea..$2.70 3 for...... 7.29

No. 4E05598 Solid gold, plain polish, very heavy and durable. Price, ea..$3.25 3 for...... 8.78

No. 4E05600 Solid gold, Roman finish, set with 4 turquoise. Price, ea..$2.85 3 for...... 7.70

No. 4E05620 The very latest ladies' chatelaine fob, gold filled, bright polish and rose yellow satin finish. Illustration shows exact size. Price, 3 for $5.81; each..................$2.15

ROLLED GOLD PLATE, GOLD FILLED AND SOLID GOLD SCARF AND STICK PINS.

All scarf pins shown on this page have the regular 2-inch pin stems. Postage extra on scarf and stick pins 2c extra; 5c extra if by insured mail.

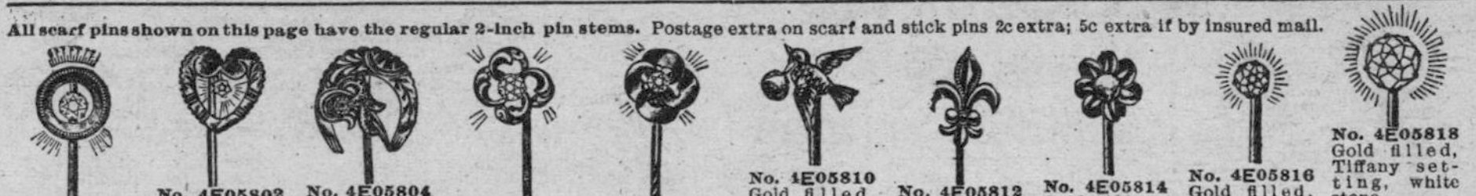

No. 4E05800 Rolled gold plate, 1 rhinestone. Ea. 14c 3 for ... .38c

No. 4E05802 Rolled gold plate, 1 rhinestone. Ea. 16c 3 for..... 44c

No. 4E05804 Rolled gold plate, 1 ruby doublet set. Each.... 18c 3 for..... 49c

No. 4E05806 Rolled gold plate, 1 rhinestone. Ea. 21c 3 for..... 57c

No. 4E05808 Rolled gold plate, 1 rhinestone set.. 23c 3 for..... 63c

No. 4E05810 Gold filled, bright finish, chased, opal set. Ea. $0.43 3 for.. 1.11

No. 4E05812 Rolled gold plate, 2 pearls and 1 turquoise. Ea. 19c 3 for..... 52c

No. 4E05814 Gold filled, bright finish, opal set. Each.. $0.38 3 for... 1.03

No. 4E05816 Gold filled, Tiffany setting, white stone. Ea. 24c 3 for..... 65c

No. 4E05818 Gold filled, Tiffany setting, white stone. Ea.. $0.38 3 for.. 1.03

No. 4E05820 Gold filled, 1 large imitation emerald. Each.... 25c 3 for..... 68c

No. 4E05825 Rolled plate, cluster, 4 rubies, 4 white stones, 1 pearl. Each.. $0.38 3 for.. 1.03

No. 4E05830 Gold filled, emerald doublet, 4 rhinestones. Ea 27c 3 for..... 73c

No. 4E05832 Gold filled, emerald set, 2 rhinestones and 3 pearls. Each.... 33c 3 for..... 90c

No. 4E05834 Gold filled head, 3 pearls, gold filled pin. Each.. $0.38 3 for... 1.03

No. 4E05836 Solid gold head, gold filled pin. Each.... 32c 3 for. ... 87c

No. 4E05838 Rolled plate, pearl, 2 brilliants. Each.... 23c 3 for..... 63c

No. 4E05840 Solid gold head, pearl set, gold filled pin. Ea... 36c 3 for..... 98c

No. 4E05842 Solid gold head, 1 pearl, gold filled pin. Each. .. 36c 3 for.... 98c

No. 4E05844 Rolled plate, fancy, 5 brilliants, 1 sapphire. Ea.. $0.48 3 for 1.30

No. 4E05846 Solid gold head, 3 pearls, gold filled pin. Each.. $0.38 3 for.. 1.03

No. 4E05848 Solid gold head, 1 large ruby doublet, gold filled pin. Each.. $0.43 3 for.. 1.17

No. 4E05850 Solid gold head, 1 ruby doublet set, gold filled pin. Each.. $0.43 3 for.. 1.17

No. 4E05852 Rolled plate, horseshoe, 9 brilliants. Each.... 36c 3 for..... 98c

No. 4E05854 Rolled plate, horseshoe, 7 rubies, 8 brilliants .. $0.58 3 for.. 1.57

No. 4E05856 Rolled plate, cluster, 14 brilliants, 8 rubies, 1 pearl Each.. $0.58 3 for.. 1.57

No. 4E05858 Solid gold head, 1 pearl set, gold filled pin. Ea. $0.48 3 for.. 1.30

No. 4E05860 Gold filled, horseshoe and arrow, 9 pearls. Each.. $0.38 3 for... 1.03

No. 4E05862 Solid gold head, 3 pearls, gold filled pin. Each.. $0.48 3 for.. 1.30

No. 4E05864 Solid gold, Roman, yellow finish, set with genuine pearl and ruby doublet. Ea.. $1.65 3 for 4.46

No. 4E05865 Solid gold, bright finish. Each, $0.55 3 for.. 1.49

No. 4E05866 Solid gold, bright finish. Each, $0.62 3 for.. 1.68

No. 4E05868 Solid gold, bright finish. Each, $0.70 3 for.. 1.89

No. 4E05872 Solid gold hearts. Each.. $0.72 3 for.. 1.95

No. 4E05874 Solid gold, bright polish, emerald setting. Each.. $0.82 3 for.. 2.22

No. 4E05876 Solid gold, hand eng'ved, genuine opal. Each.. $1.05 3 for.. 2.84

No. 4E05877 Solid gold, Roman yellow finish, set with ruby doublet. Each, $0.82 3 for.. 2.22

No. 4E05880 Solid gold head, 1 genuine opal. Each.. $0.58 3 for.. 1.57

No. 4E05882 Solid gold, fancy flower, 1 opal. Each.. $1.18 3 for.. 3.19

No. 4E05884 Solid gold, 13 brilliants, ruby center. Ea... $1.42 3 for 3.84

No. 4E05886 Solid gold, any initial. Each.. $0.95 3 for.. 2.57

No. 4E05890 Solid gold, Roman knot. Ea.... $0.73 3 for. 1.98

No. 4E05892 Solid gold, Roman color. Ea.. $0.67 3 for.. 1.81

No. 4E05895 Solid gold, bright finish, green gold leaves, set with genuine pearls. Each... $2.00 3 for ... 5.40

No. 4E05898 Solid gold, 2 genuine opals. Each... $1.16 3 for... 3.14

No. 4E05900 Solid gold, bright finish, knot, emerald set. Ea. $1.05 3 for.. 2.84

No. 4E05902 Solid gold, bright finish, Roman colored rope. Each.. $1.10 3 for.. 3.00

No. 4E05904 Solid gold, 1 large Egyptian pearl. Each.. $1.25 3 for 3.38

No. 4E05905 Solid gold, Roman yellow finish, set with genuine rose diamond. Each... $1.35 3 for... 3.65

No. 4E05907 Solid gold, rose finish, set with genuine garnet. Each. $1.50 3 for. 4.05

No. 4E05912 Solid gold, Bright polish, beaded ornamentation. Each . $0.78 3 for.. 2.11

No. 4E05914 Solid gold, bright finish, set with pearl. Each. $0.95 3 for.. 2.57

No. 4E05916 Solid gold, bright finish, beaded ornamentation. Each. $0.98 3 for.. 2.65

No. 4E05918 Solid gold, bright finish, beaded ornamentation, set with genuine opal. Ea. $1.15 3 for.. 3.11

No. 4E05920 Solid gold, bright finish, set with genuine opal. Each. $1.35 3 for.. 3.65

No. 4E05922 Solid gold, bright finish, set with pearls. Each . $1.55 3 for.. 4.19

No. 4E05924 Solid gold, bright finish, set with pearls. Each . $1.60 3 for.. 4.32

No. 4E05926 Solid gold, bright finish, set with pearls and ruby doublet. Each. $1.70 3 for.. 4.59

No. 4E05928 Solid gold, bright polish, set with pearl and genuine opal. Each. $1.88 3 for.. 5.08

No. 4E05930 Solid gold, bright finish, set with pearls. Each. $2.65 3 for 7.16

SILVER, GOLD FILLED AND SOLID GOLD THIMBLES.

If by mail, postage extra, 2 cents. DON'T FAIL TO GIVE SIZE OF THIMBLE WANTED.

Don't fail to give size of thimble wanted

No. 4E05950 Solid silver. Each........ 10c 3 for......... 27c

No. 4E05952 Solid silver, heavy. Each........ 20c 3 for......... 54c

No. 4E05954 Solid silver, beautifully engraved. Each....... $0.40 3 for...... 1.18

No. 4E05956 Solid silver, octagon shape, hand engraved. Ea.. 31c 3 for......... 84c

No. 4E05958 Solid silver, open top. Each......... 23c 3 for......... 63c

No. 4E05960 Gold filled, engraved, warranted. Each....... $0.90 3 for...... 2.43

No. 4E05962 Solid 10-karat gold. Each...... $1.78 3 for...... 4.81

No. 4E05964 Solid 14-karat gold. Each.. $3.52 3 for.... 9.51

LADIES' LACE PINS, CUFF PINS, BABY PINS AND PIN SETS.

MAIL CHARGES on Lace Pins, Brooches, Cuff Pins, Baby Pins and Sets, 2 cents extra; 8 cents extra by insured or registered mail.

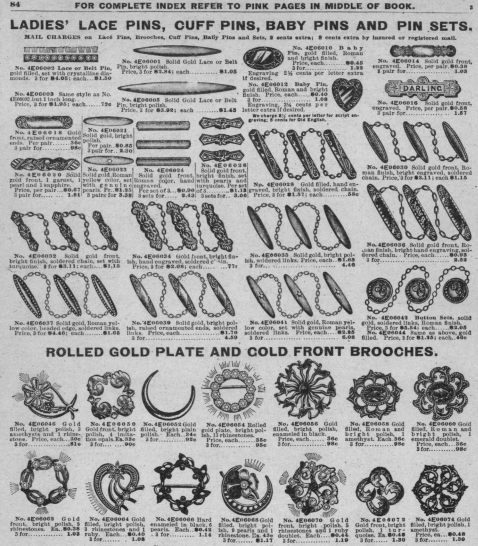

No. 4E06002 Lace or Belt Pin, gold filled, set with crystalline diamonds. 3 for $4.05; each...$1.50

No. 4E06003 Same style as No. 4E06002 but 1 inch long. Price, 3 for $1.95; each......72c

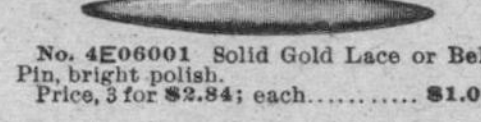

No. 4E06001 Solid Gold Lace or Belt Pin, bright polish. Price, 3 for $2.84; each.......... $1.05

No. 4E06005 Solid Gold Lace or Belt Pin, bright polish. Price, 3 for $3.92; each $1.45

No. 4E06010 Baby Pin, gold filled, Roman and bright finish. Price, each.........$0.45 3 for.................. 1.22

Engraving 2½ cents per letter extra if desired.

No. 4E06012 Baby Pin, gold filled, Roman and bright finish. Price, each.....$0.40 3 for.......... 1.08

Engraving, 2½ cents per letter extra if desired.

We charge 2½ cents per letter for script engraving; 5 cents for Old English.

No. 4E06014 Solid gold front, engraved. Price, per pair.$0.38 3 pair for................... 1.03

No. 4E06016 Solid gold front, engraved. Price, per pair.$0.58 3 pair for................ .. 1.57

No. 4E06018 Gold front, raised ornamented ends. Per pair.......36c 3 pair for...........98c

No. 4E06021 Solid gold, bright polish. Per pair..$0.85 3 pair for.. 2.30

No. 4E06020 Solid gold front, 1 garnet, 1 pearl and 1 sapphire. Price, per pair...$0.67 3 pair for..... ... 1.81

No. 4E06023 Solid gold, Roman yellow color, set with genuine pearls. Pr..$1.25 3 pairs for 3.38

No. 4E06024 Solid gold front, Roman color, hand engraved. Per set of 3...$0.90 3 sets for..... 2.43

No. 4E06026 Solid gold front, bright finish, set with pearls and turquoise. Per set of 3..........$1.13 3 sets for.. 3.06

No. 4E06028 Gold filled, hand engraved, bright finish, soldered chain. Price, 3 for $1.57; each..........58c

No. 4E06030 Solid gold front, Roman finish, bright engraved, soldered chain. Price, 3 for $3.11; each $1.15

No. 4E06032 Solid gold front, bright finish, soldered chain, set with turquoise. 3 for $3.11; each....$1.15

No. 4E06034 Gold front, bright finish, hand engraved, soldered chain. Price, 3 for $2.08; each..........77c

No. 4E06035 Solid gold, bright polish, soldered links. Price, each..$1.65 3 for.......................... 4.46

No. 4E06036 Solid gold front, Roman finish, bright hand engraving, soldered chain. Price, each......$0.93 3 for............................... 2.52

No. 4E06037 Solid gold, Roman yellow color, beaded edge, soldered links. Price, 3 for $4.46; each........$1.65

No. 4E06039 Solid gold, bright polish, raised ornamented ends, soldered links. Price, each...............$1.70 3 for............................ 4.59

No. 4E06041 Solid gold, Roman yellow color, set with genuine pearls, soldered links. Price, each....$2.25 3 for......................... 6.08

No. 4E06042 Button Sets, solid gold, soldered links, Roman finish. Price, 3 for $5.54; each......$2.05

No. 4E06044 Same as above, gold filled. Price, 3 for $1.25; each..46c

ROLLED GOLD PLATE AND GOLD FRONT BROOCHES.

No. 4E06046 Gold filled, bright polish, 3 amethysts and 1 rhinestone. Price, each...30c 3 for..................81c

No. 4E06050 Gold front, bright polish, 4 imitation opals. Ea. 33c 3 for.... ....90c

No. 4E06052 Gold filled, bright plain polish. Each..34c 3 for..........92c

No. 4E06054 Rolled gold plate, bright polish, 13 rhinestones. Price, each.......35c 3 for............ .95c

No. 4E06056 Gold filled, bright polish, enameled in black. Price, each...... 36c 3 for............ 98c

No. 4E06058 Gold filled, Roman and bright polish, 1 amethyst. Each 36c 3 for............98c

No. 4E06060 Gold filled, Roman and bright polish, 1 emerald doublet. Price, each...36c 3 for..........98c

No. 4E06062 Gold front, bright polish, 5 rhinestones. Ea..$0.38 3 for.............. 1.03

No. 4E06064 Gold filled, bright polish, 3 rhinestones and 1 ruby. Each...$0.40 3 for....... 1.08

No. 4E06066 Hard enameled in black, 6 pearls. Each..$0.42 3 for.......... 1.14

No. 4E06068 Gold filled, bright polish, 9 pearls and 1 rhinestone. Ea. 43c 3 for....... $1.17

No. 4E06070 Gold front, bright polish, 5 rhinestones and 1 ruby doublet. Each....$0.44 3 for............ 1.19

No. 4E06072 Gold front, bright polish, 1 turquoise. Ea. $0.48 3 for...... 1.30

No. 4E06074 Gold filled, bright polish, 1 amethyst. Price, ea...$0.48 3 for........ 1.30

No. 4E06076 Rolled gold plate, bright and Roman finish, one amethyst and 2 rhinestones. Price, 3 for 81c; each......30c

No. 4E06078 Gold front, bright polish, 7 rhinestones. Price, each.$0.38 3 for................ 1.03

No. 4E06080 Gold front, hand engraved, bright polish. Price, 3 for $1.17; each......43c

No. 4E06082 Gold front, bright polish and Roman finish, 1 ruby doublet. 3 for $1.44; ea. 53c

Extra for engraving 2½ cents per letter for script, 5c for Old English.

No. 4E06084 Gold filled, bright and Roman finish, for initial. Price, each.....$0.50 3 for........ .... 1.35

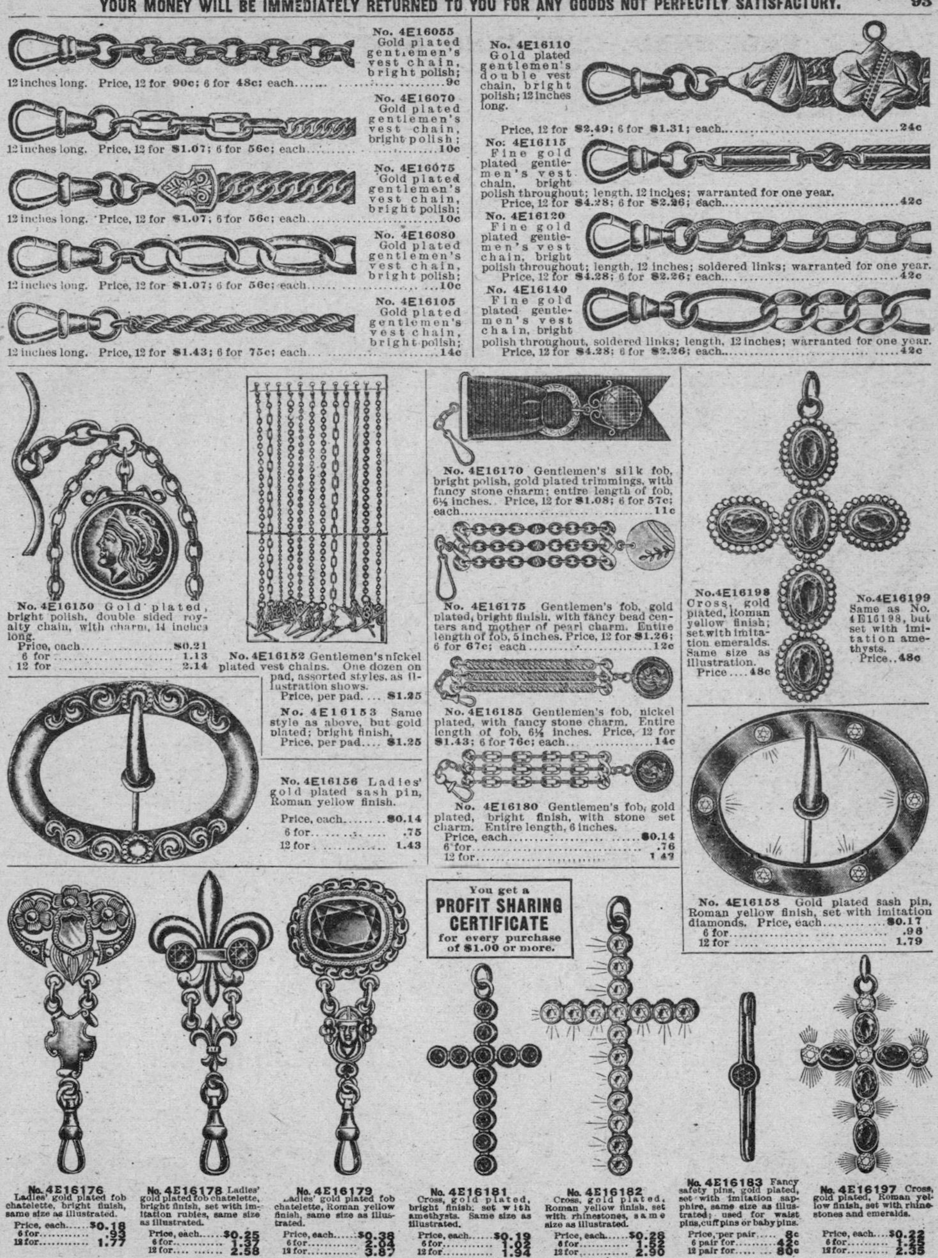

No. 4E16055 Gold plated gentlemen's vest chain, bright polish; 12 inches long. Price, 12 for 90c; 6 for 48c; each......9c

No. 4E16070 Gold plated gentlemen's vest chain, bright polish; 12 inches long. Price, 12 for $1.07; 6 for 56c; each......10c

No. 4E16075 Gold plated gentlemen's vest chain, bright polish; 12 inches long. Price, 12 for $1.07; 6 for 56c; each......10c

No. 4E16080 Gold plated gentlemen's vest chain, bright polish; 12 inches long. Price, 12 for $1.07; 6 for 56c; each......10c

No. 4E16105 Gold plated gentlemen's vest chain, bright polish; 12 inches long. Price, 12 for $1.43; 6 for 75c; each......14c

No. 4E16110 Gold plated gentlemen's double vest chain, bright polish; 12 inches long. Price, 12 for $2.49; 6 for $1.31; each......24c

No. 4E16115 Fine gold plated gentlemen's vest chain, bright polish throughout; length, 12 inches; warranted for one year. Price, 12 for $4.28; 6 for $2.26; each......42c

No. 4E16120 Fine gold plated gentlemen's vest chain, bright polish throughout; length, 12 inches; soldered links; warranted for one year. Price, 12 for $4.28; 6 for $2.26; each......42c

No. 4E16140 Fine gold plated gentlemen's vest chain, bright polish throughout, soldered links; length, 12 inches; warranted for one year. Price, 12 for $4.28; 6 for $2.26; each......42c

No. 4E16150 Gold plated, bright polish, double sided royalty chain, with charm, 14 inches long.
Price, each......$0.21
6 for......1.13
12 for......2.14

No. 4E16152 Gentlemen's nickel plated vest chains. One dozen on pad, assorted styles, as illustration shows. Price, per pad......$1.25

No. 4E16153 Same style as above, but gold plated; bright finish. Price, per pad......$1.25

No. 4E16156 Ladies' gold plated sash pin, Roman yellow finish.
Price, each......$0.14
6 for......75
12 for......1.43

No. 4E16170 Gentlemen's silk fob, bright polish, gold plated trimmings, with fancy stone charm; entire length of fob, 6¼ inches. Price, 12 for $1.08; 6 for 57c; each......11c

No. 4E16175 Gentlemen's fob, gold plated, bright finish, with fancy bead centers and mother of pearl charm. Entire length of fob, 5 inches. Price, 12 for $1.26; 6 for 67c; each......12c

No. 4E16185 Gentlemen's fob, nickel plated, with fancy stone charm. Entire length of fob, 6½ inches. Price, 12 for $1.43; 6 for 76c; each......14c

No. 4E16180 Gentlemen's fob, gold plated, bright finish, with stone set charm. Entire length, 6 inches.
Price, each......$0.14
6 for......76
12 for......1.47

No. 4E16198 Cross, gold plated, Roman yellow finish; set with imitation emeralds. Same size as illustration. Price......48c

No. 4E16199 Same as No. 4E16198, but set with imitation amethysts. Price......48c

No. 4E16158 Gold plated sash pin, Roman yellow finish, set with imitation diamonds. Price, each......$0.17
6 for......98
12 for......1.79

You get a
PROFIT SHARING CERTIFICATE
for every purchase of $1.00 or more.

No. 4E16176 Ladies' gold plated fob chatelette, bright finish, same size as illustrated.
Price, each......$0.18
6 for......93
12 for......1.77

No. 4E16178 Ladies' gold plated fob chatelette, bright finish, set with imitation rubies, same size as illustrated.
Price, each......$0.25
6 for......1.37
12 for......2.58

No. 4E16179 Ladies' gold plated fob chatelette, Roman yellow finish, same size as illustrated.
Price, each......$0.38
6 for......2.04
12 for......3.87

No. 4E16181 Cross, gold plated, bright finish; set with amethysts. Same size as illustrated.
Price, each......$0.19
6 for......1.02
12 for......1.94

No. 4E16182 Cross, gold plated, Roman yellow finish, set with rhinestones, same size as illustrated.
Price, each......$0.28
6 for......1.52
12 for......2.90

No. 4E16183 Fancy safety pins, gold plated, set with imitation sapphire, same size as illustrated; used for waist pins, cuff pins or baby pins.
Price, per pair......8c
6 pair for......42c
12 pair for......80c

No. 4E16197 Cross, gold plated, Roman yellow finish, set with rhinestones and emeralds.
Price, each......$0.22
6 for......1.25
12 for......2.35

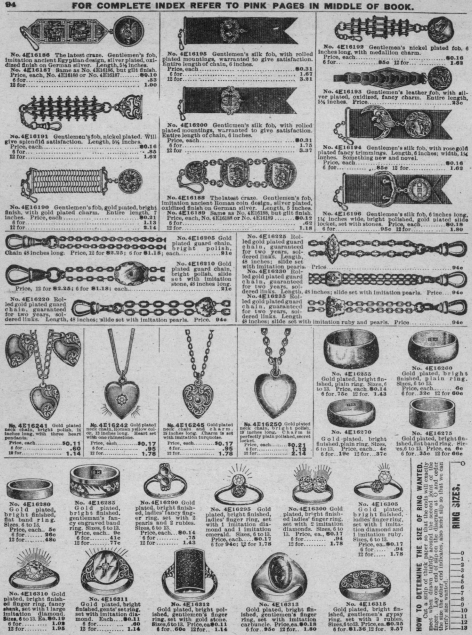

No. 4E16186 The latest craze. Gentlemen's fob, imitation ancient Egyptian design, silver plated, oxidized finish on German silver. Length, 5½ inches.

No. 4E16187 Same as No. 4E16186, but gilt finish.
Price, each, No. 4E16186 or No. 4E16187........$0.10
6 for.... .53
12 for.... 1.00

No. 4E16191 Gentlemen's fob, nickel plated. Will give splendid satisfaction. Length, 5½ inches.
Price, each.... $0.16
6 for.... .85
12 for.... 1.62

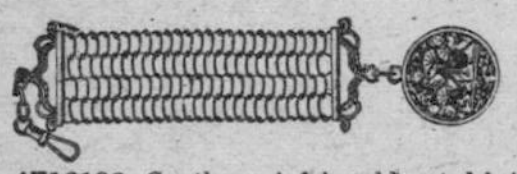

No. 4E16190 Gentlemen's fob, gold plated, bright finish, with gold plated charm. Entire length, 7 inches. Price, each.... $0.21
6 for.... 1.13
12 for.... 2.14

No. 4E16195 Gentlemen's silk fob, with rolled plated mountings, warranted to give satisfaction. Entire length of chain, 6 inches.
Price, each.... $0.31
6 for.... 1.67
12 for.... 3.21

No. 4E16200 Gentlemen's silk fob, with rolled plated mountings, warranted to give satisfaction. Entire length of chain, 6 inches.
Price, each.... $0.31
6 for.... 1.75
12 for.... 3.37

No. 4E16188 The latest craze. Gentlemen's fob, imitation ancient Roman coin design, silver plated, oxidized finish on German silver. Length, 5 inches.

No. 4E16189 Same as No. 4E16188, but gilt finish.
Price, each, No. 4E16188 or No. 4E16189........$0.12
6 for.... .62
12 for.... 1.18

No. 4E16192 Gentlemen's nickel plated fob, 6 inches long, with medallion charm.
Price, each.... $0.16
6 for.... 85c 12 for.... 1.62

No. 4E16193 Gentlemen's leather fob, with silver plated, oxidized, fancy charm. Entire length, 5½ inches. Price.... 23c

No. 4E16194 Gentlemen's silk fob, with rose gold plated fancy trimmings. Length, 6 inches; width, 1¼ inches. Something new and novel.
Price, each.... $0.16
6 for.... 85c 12 for.... 1.62

No. 4E16196 Gentlemen's silk fob, 6 inches long, 1¼ inches wide, bright polished, gold plated slide locket, set with stones. Price, each.... $0.18
6 for.... 95c 12 for.... 1.80

No. 4E16205 Gold plated guard chain, bright polish. Chain 48 inches long. Price, 12 for $2.25; 6 for $1.18; each.... 21c

No. 4E16210 Gold plated guard chain, bright polish, slide set with imitation stone, 48 inches long. Price, 12 for $2.25; 6 for $1.18; each.... 21c

No. 4E16220 Rolled gold plated guard chain, guaranteed for two years, soldered links. Length, 48 inches; slide set with imitation pearls. Price. 94c

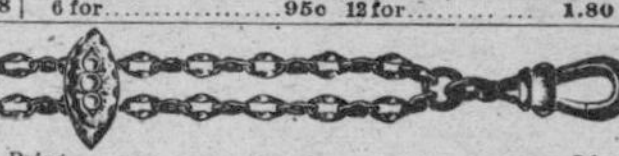

No. 4E16225 Rolled gold plated guard chain, guaranteed for two years, soldered links. Length, 48 inches; slide set with imitation pearls. Price.... 94c

No. 4E16230 Rolled gold plated guard chain, guaranteed for two years, soldered links. Length, 48 inches; slide set with imitation pearls. Price.... 94c

No. 4E16235 Rolled gold plated guard chain, guaranteed for two years, soldered links. Length 48 inches; slide set with imitation ruby and pearls. Price.... 94c

No. 4E16241 Gold plated neck chain, bright polish, 14 inches long, with three heart pendants.
Price, each.... $0.11
6 for.... .60
12 for.... 1.14

No. 4E16242 Gold plated neck chain, Roman yellow color, 13 inches long. Heart set with one rhinestone.
Price, each.... $0.17
6 for.... .95
12 for.... 1.78

No. 4E16245 Gold plated neck chain and charm, 19 inches long. Charm is set with imitation turquoise.
Price, each.... $0.17
6 for.... .95
12 for.... 1.78

No. 4E16250 Gold plated neck chain, bright polish, 19 inches long. Charm is perfectly plain polished, secret locket.
Price, each.... $0.21
6 for.... 1.13
12 for.... 2.14

No. 4E16255 Gold plated, bright finished, plain ring. Sizes, 6 to 13. Price, each. $0.14
6 for. 75c 12 for. 1.43

No. 4E16260 Gold plated, bright finished, plain ring. Sizes, 6 to 13.
Price, each.... 6c
6 for.. 32c 12 for 60c

No. 4E16270 Gold plated, bright finished, plain ring. Sizes, 6 to 13. Price, each.. 4c
6 for.. 19c 12 for.... 37c

No. 4E16275 Gold plated, bright finished, flat band ring. Sizes, 6 to 13. Price, ea 6c
6 for.. 35c 12 for 66c

No. 4E16280 Gold plated, bright finished, flat band ring. Sizes, 6 to 13.
Price, each.. 5c
6 for.... 26c
12 for.... 48c

No. 4E16285 Gold plated, bright finished, gentleman's fancy engraved band ring. Sizes, 6 to 13.
Price, each.. 9c
6 for.... 41c
12 for.... 77c

No. 4E16290 Gold plated, bright finished, ladies' fancy finger ring, set with 2 pearls and 2 rubies. Sizes, 6 to 13.
Price, each... $0.14
6 for.... .75
12 for.... 1.43

No. 4E16295 Gold plated, bright finished, ladies' finger ring, set with 1 imitation diamond and 1 imitation emerald. Sizes, 6 to 13.
Price, each.... $0.17
6 for 94c; 12 for 1.78

No. 4E16300 Gold plated, bright finished ladies' finger ring, set with 2 imitation diamonds. Sizes, 6 to 13. Price, ea., $0.17
6 for.... .94
12 for.... 1.78

No. 4E16305 Gold plated, bright finished, ladies' finger ring, set with 1 imitation diamond and 1 imitation ruby. Sizes, 6 to 13.
Price, ea.. $0.17
6 for.... .94
12 for.... 1.78

HOW TO DETERMINE THE SIZE OF RING WANTED. Cut a strip of thick paper so that the ends will exactly meet when drawn tightly around the second joint of the finger. Lay one end of slip on the diagram at O and order the size the other end indicates, also send slip so that we can verify size wanted.

RING SIZES.

O — 0 — 1 — 2 — 3 — 4 — 5 — 6 — 7 — 8 — 9 — 10 — 11 — 12 — 13

No. 4E16310 Gold plated, bright finished finger ring, fancy shank, set with 1 large imitation diamond. Sizes, 6 to 13. Ea. $0.19
6 for.... 1.02
12 for.... 1.95

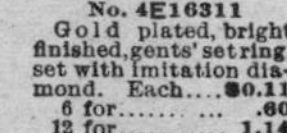

No. 4E16311 Gold plated, bright finished, gents' set ring, set with imitation diamond. Each.... $0.11
6 for.... .60
12 for.... 1.14

No. 4E16312 Gold plated, bright polished, gentlemen's finger ring, set with gold stone. Sizes, 6 to 13. Price, ea $0.11
6 for.. 60c 12 for.. 1.14

No. 4E16313 Gold plated, bright finished, gentlemen's finger ring, set with imitation carbuncle. Price, ea. $0.18
6 for.. 95c 12 for.. 1.80

No. 4E16315 Gold plated, bright finished, gentlemen's gypsy ring, set with 3 rubies. Sizes, 6 to 13. Price, ea. $0.25
6 for $1.36 12 for. 2.57

HEAVY SOLID SILVER NOVELTIES.

NOTHING MORE APPROPRIATE FOR A GIFT. EVERY NOVELTY ILLUSTRATED ON THIS PAGE IS OF SOLID SILVER AND HEAVIER THAN ANY OTHER LINE ON THE MARKET AT PRICES MORE THAN DOUBLE WHAT WE ASK.

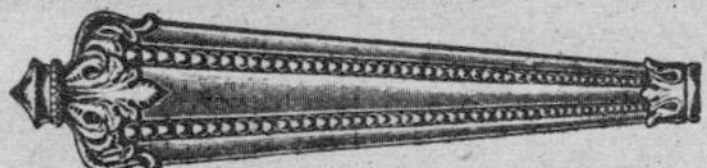

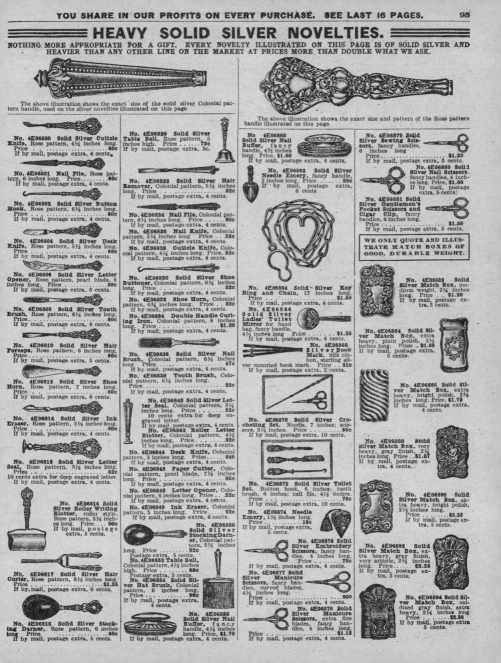

The above illustration shows the exact size of the solid silver Colonial pattern handle, used on the silver novelties illustrated on this page

No. 4E06800 Solid Silver Cuticle Knife, Rose pattern, 4½ inches long. Price 60c
If by mail, postage extra, 4 cents.

No. 4E06801 Nail File, Rose pattern, 6 inches long. Price 60c
If by mail, postage extra, 4 cents.

No. 4E06802 Solid Silver Button Hook, Rose pattern, 6½ inches long. Price 60c
If by mail, postage extra, 4 cents.

No. 4E06804 Solid Silver Desk Knife, Rose pattern, 5½ inches long. Price 60c
If by mail, postage extra, 4 cents.

No. 4E06806 Solid Silver Letter Opener, Rose pattern, pearl blade, 8 inches long. Price 80c
If by mail, postage extra, 5 cents.

No. 4E06808 Solid Silver Tooth Brush, Rose pattern, 6½ inches long. Price 60c
If by mail, postage extra, 4 cents.

No. 4E06810 Solid Silver Hair Forceps, Rose pattern, 6 inches long. Price 60c
If by mail, postage extra, 5 cents.

No. 4E06812 Solid Silver Shoe Horn, Rose pattern, 7 inches long. Price 60c
If by mail, postage extra, 6 cents.

No. 4E06814 Solid Silver Ink Eraser, Rose pattern, 5½ inches long. Price 60c
If by mail, postage extra, 4 cents.

No. 4E06815 Solid Silver Letter Seal, Rose pattern, 3¼ inches long. Price 62c
10 cents extra for deep engraved letter.
If by mail, postage extra, 4 cents.

No. 4E06816 Solid Silver Roller Writing Blotter, roller style, Rose pattern, 5½ inches long. Price 60c
If by mail, postage extra, 5 cents.

No. 4E06817 Solid Silver Hair Curler, Rose pattern, 8½ inches long. Price $1.35
If by mail, postage extra, 6 cents.

No. 4E06818 Solid Silver Stocking Darner, Rose pattern, 6 inches long Price 60c
If by mail, postage extra, 5 cents.

No. 4E06820 Solid Silver Table Bell, Rose pattern, 5 inches high. Price 75c
If by mail, postage extra, 5c.

No. 4E06822 Solid Silver Hair Remover, Colonial pattern, 5½ inches long. Price 52c
If by mail, postage extra, 4 cents.

No. 4E06824 Nail File, Colonial pattern, 6½ inches long. Price 80c
If by mail, postage extra, 4 cents.

No. 4E06826 Nail Knife, Colonial pattern, 5½ inches long Price .. 52c
If by mail, postage extra, 4 cents.

No. 4E06828 Cuticle Knife, Colonial pattern, 4¼ inches long. Price, 52c
If by mail, postage extra, 4 cents.

No. 4E06830 Solid Silver Shoe Buttoner, Colonial pattern, 6¼ inches long. Price 52c
If by mail, postage extra, 4 cents.

No. 4E06832 Shoe Horn, Colonial pattern, 6¾ inches long. Price .. 52c
If by mail, postage extra, 4 cents.

No. 4E06834 Double Handle Curling Iron, Colonial pattern, 8 inches long. Price $1.20
If by mail, postage extra, 4 cents.

No. 4E06836 Solid Silver Nail Brush, Colonial pattern, 6½ inches long Price 57c
If by mail, postage extra, 4 cents.

No. 4E06838 Tooth Brush, Colonial pattern, 6½ inches long. Price 52c
If by mail, postage extra, 4 cents.

No. 4E06840 Solid Silver Letter Seal, Colonial pattern, 3¼ inches long. Price 52c
10 cents extra for deep engraved letter.
If by mail, postage extra, 4 cents.

No. 4E06842 Roller Letter Blotter, Colonial pattern, 4½ inches long. Price 52c
If by mail, postage extra, 4 cents.

No. 4E06844 Desk Knife, Colonial pattern, 5 inches long. Price 52c
If by mail, postage extra, 4 cents.

No. 4E06846 Paper Cutter, Colonial pattern, pearl blade, 7½ inches long. Price 85c
If by mail, postage extra, 4 cents.

No. 4E06848 Letter Opener, Colonial pattern, 6 inches long. Price .. 52c
If by mail, postage extra, 4 cents.

No. 4E06849 Ink Eraser, Colonial pattern, 5 inches long. Price 52c
If by mail, postage extra, 4 cents.

No. 4E06850 Solid Silver Stocking Darner, Colonial pattern, 5½ inches long. Price 52c
Postage extra, 5 cents.

No. 4E06852 Table Bell, Colonial pattern, 4½ inches high. Price 68c
Postage extra, 5 cents.

No. 4E06854 Solid Silver Hat Brush, Colonial pattern, 6 inches long. Price 98c
If by mail, postage extra, 4 cents.

No. 4E06858 Solid Silver Nail Buffer, fancy handle, 4½ inches long. Price, $1.70
If by mail, postage extra, 4 cents.

The above illustration shows the exact size and pattern of the Rose pattern handle illustrated on this page

No 4E06860 Solid Silver Nail Buffer, fancy handle, 4½ inches long. Price. $1.60
If by mail, postage extra, 4 cents.

No. 4E06862 Solid Silver Needle Emery, fancy handle, 3 inches long. Price 38c
If by mail, postage extra, 6 cents

No. 4E06864 Solid Silver Key Ring and Chain, 17 inches long. Price $1.50
If by mail, postage extra, 4 cents.

No. 4E06866 Solid Silver Ladies' Toilet Mirror for hand bag, fancy handle, 4½ inches long Price $1.25
If by mail, postage extra, 4 cents.

No. 4E06868 Silver Book Mark. Silk ribbon, sterling silver mounted book mark. Price .. 21c
If by mail, postage extra, 2 cents.

No. 4E06870 Solid Silver Crocheting Set. Needle, 7 inches; scissors, 3½ inches. Price 95c
If by mail, postage extra, 10 cents.

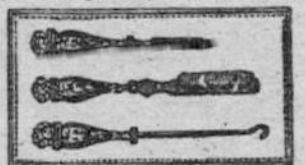

No. 4E06872 Solid Silver Toilet Set. Button hook, 6 inches; tooth brush, 6 inches; nail file, 4½ inches. Price 76c
If by mail, postage extra, 10 cents.

No. 4E06874 Needle Emery, 1½ inches long. Price 18c
If by mail, postage extra, 5 cents.

No. 4E06876 Solid Silver Embroidery Scissors, fancy handles, 4 inches long. Price 75c
If by mail, postage extra, 4 cents.

No. 4E06877 Solid Silver Manicure Scissors, fancy handles, curved blades, 4½ inches long. Price 90c
If by mail, postage extra, 4 cents.

No. 4E06878 Solid Silver Manicure Scissors, extra fine blades, fancy handles, 4 inches long. Price $1.15
If by mail, postage extra, 4 cents.

No. 4E06879 Solid Silver Sewing Scissors, fancy handles, 6 inches long Price $1.20
If by mail, postage extra, 5 cents.

No. 4E06880 Solid Silver Nail Scissors. fancy handles, 4 inches long. Price, $1.60
If by mail, postage extra, 5 cents.

No. 4E06881 Solid Silver Gentlemen's Pocket Scissors and Cigar Clip, fancy handles, 4 inches long. Price $1.60
If by mail, postage extra, 5 cents.

WE ONLY QUOTE AND ILLUSTRATE MATCH BOXES OF GOOD, DURABLE WEIGHT.

No. 4E06882 Solid Silver Match Box, medium weight, 2¼ inches long. Price .. $1.20
If by mail, postage extra, 3 cents.

No. 4E06884 Solid Silver Match Box, extra heavy, plain polish, 2½ inches long. Price .. $1.65
If by mail, postage extra, 5 cents.

No. 4E06886 Solid Silver Match Box, extra heavy, bright polish, 2⅝ inches long. Price, $1.75
If by mail, postage extra, 4 cents.

No. 4E06888 Solid Silver Match Box, very heavy, gray finish, 2¼ inches long. Price .. $1.87
If by mail, postage extra, 4 cents.

No. 4E06890 Solid Silver Match Box, extra heavy, bright polish, 2½ inches long. Price $2.25
If by mail, postage extra, 3 cents.

No. 4E06892 Solid Silver Match Box, extra heavy, gray finish, very artistic, 2½ inches long. Price...... $2.25
If by mail, postage extra, 5 cents.

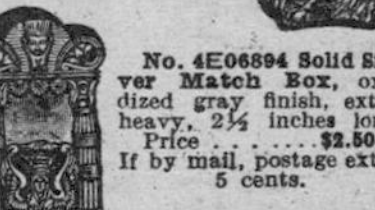

No. 4E06894 Solid Silver Match Box, oxidized gray finish, extra heavy, 2½ inches long Price $2.50
If by mail, postage extra 5 cents.

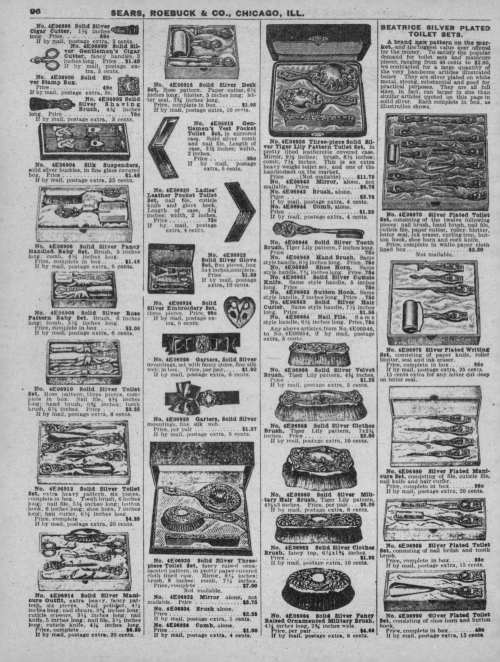

No. 4E06896 Solid Silver Cigar Cutter, 1½ inches long. Price........63c
If by mail, postage extra, 3 cents.

No. 4E06898 Solid Silver Gentlemen's Cigar Cutter, fancy handles, 3 inches long. Price..$1.48
If by mail, postage extra, 3 cents.

No. 4E06900 Solid Silver Stamp Box. Price........49c
If by mail, postage extra, 3c.

No. 4E06902 Solid Silver Shaving Brush, 4¼ inches long. Price........76c
If by mail, postage extra, 3 cents.

No. 4E06904 Silk Suspenders, solid silver buckles, in fine glass covered box. Price........$1.48
If by mail, postage extra, 25 cents.

No. 4E06906 Solid Silver Fancy Handled Baby Set. Brush, 5 inches long; comb, 4½ inches long.
Price, complete in box........$1.48
If by mail, postage extra, 6 cents.

No. 4E06908 Solid Silver Rose Pattern Baby Set. Brush, 6 inches long; comb, 5½ inches long.
Price, complete in box........$2.00
If by mail, postage extra, 6 cents.

No. 4E06910 Solid Silver Toilet Set, Rose pattern, three pieces, complete in box. Nail file, 4½ inches long; hand brush, 6¾ inches; tooth brush, 6½ inches. Price........$2.25
If by mail, postage extra, 8 cents.

No. 4E06912 Solid Silver Toilet Set, extra heavy pattern, six pieces, complete in box. Tooth brush, 6 inches long; nail file, 5½ inches long; button hook, 6 inches long; shoe horn, 7 inches long; hair curler, 6½ inches long.
Price, complete........$4.25
If by mail, postage extra, 20 cents.

No. 4E06914 Solid Silver Manicure Outfit, extra heavy, fancy pattern, six pieces. Nail polisher, 4½ inches long; nail shears, 3¾ inches long; cuticle scissors, 3½ inches long; nail knife, 5 inches long; nail file, 5½ inches long; cuticle knife, 4¾ inches long.
Price, complete........$6.50
If by mail, postage extra, 20 cents.

No. 4E06916 Solid Silver Desk Set, Rose pattern. Paper cutter, 6½ inches long; blotter, 5 inches long; letter seal, 3¼ inches long.
Price, complete in box........$1.95
If by mail, postage extra, 10 cents.

No. 4E06918 Gentlemen's Vest Pocket Toilet Set, in mirrored case. Solid silver comb and nail file. Length of case, 3½ inches; width, 2 inches.
Price........95c
If by mail, postage extra, 5 cents.

No. 4E06920 Ladies' Leather Pocket Toilet Set, nail file, cuticle knife and glove hook. Length of case, 3½ inches; width, 2 inches.
Price........75c
If by mail, postage extra, 4 cents.

No. 4E06922 Solid Silver Glove Set, five pieces, box 5x4 inches, complete.
Price........$1.58
If by mail, postage extra, 10 cents.

No. 4E06924 Solid Silver Embroidery Set, three pieces. Price, 98c
If by mail, postage extra, 6 cents.

No. 4E06926 Garters, Solid Silver mountings, set with fancy stone, fine silk web; in box. Price, per pair........$1.90
If by mail, postage extra, 6 cents.

No. 4E06928 Garters, Solid Silver mountings, fine silk web.
Price, per pair........$1.27
If by mail, postage extra, 6 cents.

No. 4E06930 Solid Silver Three-piece Toilet Set, fancy raised ornamented pattern, in pretty paper covered cloth lined case. Mirror, 8½ inches; brush, 8 inches; comb, 7½ inches.
Price, complete........$7.00
Not mailable.

No. 4E06932 Mirror alone, not mailable. Price........$3.75

No. 4E06934 Brush alone.
Price........$2.25
If by mail, postage extra, 5 cents.

No. 4E06936 Comb, alone.
Price........$1.00
If by mail, postage extra, 4 cents.

No. 4E06938 Three-piece Solid Silver Tiger Lily Pattern Toilet Set, in pretty lined leatherette covered case. Mirror, 9½ inches; brush, 8½ inches; comb, 7½ inches. This is an extra heavy weight toilet set, and one of the handsomest on the market.
Price.....(Not mailable).....$11.75

No. 4E06940 Mirror, alone, not mailable. Price........$6.75

No. 4E06942 Brush, alone.
Price........$3.75
If by mail, postage extra, 4 cents.

No. 4E06944 Comb, alone.
Price........$1.25
If by mail, postage extra, 4 cents.

No. 4E06946 Solid Silver Tooth Brush, Tiger Lily pattern, 7 inches long.
Price........75c

No. 4E06948 Hand Brush. Same style handle, 6½ inches long. Price..75c

No. 4E06950 Shoe Horn. Same style handle, 7¾ inches long. Price..75c

No. 4E06951 Solid Silver Cuticle Knife. Same style handle, 5 inches long. Price........75c

No. 4E06952 Button Hook. Same style handle, 7 inches long. Price..75c

No. 4E06953 Solid Silver Hair Curler. Same style handle, 7½ inches long. Price........$1.50

No. 4E06954 Nail File. Same style handle, 6½ inches long. Price, 75c

Any above articles, from No. 4E06946, to No. 4E06954, if by mail, postage extra, 5 cents.

No. 4E06956 Solid Silver Velvet Brush, Tiger Lily pattern, 4¾ inches.
Price........$1.35
If by mail, postage extra, 5 cents.

No. 4E06958 Solid Silver Clothes Brush, Tiger Lily pattern, 7x2¼ inches. Price........$3.00
If by mail, postage extra, 10 cents.

No. 4E06960 Solid Silver Military Hair Brush, Tiger Lily pattern, 4½x3 inches. Price, per pair....$6.00
If by mail, postage extra, 8 cents.

No. 4E06962 Solid Silver Clothes Brush, fancy top, 6½x1⅝ inches.
Price........$1.98
If by mail, postage extra, 10 cents.

No. 4E06964 Solid Silver Fancy Raised Ornamented Military Brush, 4½ inches long, 2¾ inches wide.
Price, per pair........$4.65
If by mail, postage extra, 8 cents.

BEATRICE SILVER PLATED TOILET SETS.

A brand new pattern on the market, and the biggest value ever offered for the money. To satisfy the popular demand for toilet sets and manicure pieces, ranging from 48 cents to $2.80, we contracted for a large quantity of the very handsome articles illustrated below. They are silver plated on white metal, strong, substantial and good for practical purposes. They are all full sizes, in fact, run larger in size than similar articles quoted on this page in solid silver. Each complete in box, as illustration shows.

No. 4E06970 Silver Plated Toilet Set, consisting of the twelve following pieces: nail brush, hand brush, nail file, cuticle file, paper cutter, roller blotter, letter seal, ink eraser, curling iron, button hook, shoe horn and corn knife.
Price, complete in white paper cloth lined box........$2.80
Not mailable.

No. 4E06975 Silver Plated Writing Set, consisting of paper knife, roller blotter, seal and ink eraser.
Price, complete in box........95c
If by mail, postage extra, 25 cents.
15 cents extra for any letter cut deep on letter seal.

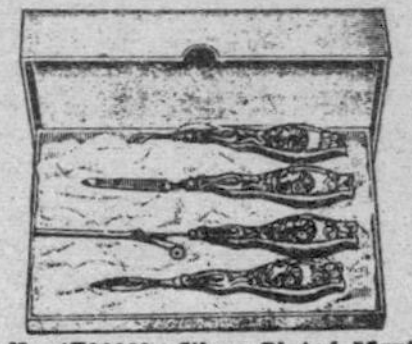

No. 4E06980 Silver Plated Manicure Set, consisting of file, cuticle file, nail knife and hair curler.
Price, complete in box........95c
If by mail, postage extra, 20 cents.

No. 4E06985 Silver Plated Toilet Set, consisting of nail brush and tooth brush.
Price, complete in box........58c
If by mail, postage extra, 15 cents.

No. 4E06990 Silver Plated Toilet Set, consisting of shoe horn and button hook.
Price, complete in box........48c
If by mail, postage extra, 15 cents

SOLID GOLD PENS AND PEARL HOLDERS.

MADE UNDER CONTRACT FOR US. THE SPECIFICATIONS ARE CARRIED OUT IN EVERY DETAIL.

OUR PENS AND HOLDERS.

THE BEST ON THE MARKET. The manufacturer, following the exact details of our contract, produces for us, at a price cheaper by 25 per cent, pens that are worth 50 per cent more than the best pen sold by others. We have them made of solid gold through and through, heavy and well tempered. The points of every one of them are tipped with genuine iridium (sometimes called diamond pointed). Iridium, a very hard metal, being applied at the writing point of a pen, gives it a wearing period of practically a lifetime. The pearl sticks, gold filled holders and noses are made and selected from the best stock to be purchased. Illustrations are reduced size. The actual size of pens and holders are from 6 to 7¾ inches long. No. 1 pen and holder is 6 inches long, balance of sizes in proportion.

Don't be misled by fancy prices asked by others. We warrant our pens and holders the equal of any and better than the most.

AT 12 OR 19 CENTS EXTRA WE WILL FURNISH A FINE PEN BOX.

No. 4E07140 Moroccoine covered............................12c
No. 4E07142 Genuine silk plush covered, plush lined....19c

With any pen you select.

BEST QUALITY SOLID GOLD PEN IN GOLD FILLED AND EBONY DESK HOLDER.

		No. 1 Pen.	No. 2 Pen.	No. 3 Pen.	No. 4 Pen.	No. 5 Pen.	No. 6 Pen.	No. 7 Pen.
No. 4E07100	10-karat gold Pen with Holder.	$0.57	$0.62	$0.67	$0.72	$0.86	$0.95	$1.14
No. 4E07102	16-karat gold Pen with Holder.	.67	.72	.86	.95	1.10	1.19	1.43

BEST QUALITY SOLID GOLD PEN IN GOLD PLATED AND EBONY SLIDE HOLDER.

		No. 1 Pen.	No. 2 Pen.	No. 3 Pen.	No. 4 Pen.	No. 5 Pen.	No. 6 Pen.	No. 7 Pen.
No. 4E07104	10-karat gold Pen with Holder.	$0.80	$0.85	$0.95	$1.00	$1.15	$1.35	$1.50
No. 4E07106	16-karat gold Pen with Holder.	.90	.95	1.15	1.25	1.40	1.60	1.80

BEST QUALITY GOLD PEN IN GOLD FILLED AND PLAIN PEARL DESK HOLDER.

		No. 1 Pen.	No. 2 Pen.	No. 3 Pen.	No. 4 Pen.	No. 5 Pen.	No. 6 Pen.
No. 4E07108	10-karat gold Pen with Holder.	$0.59	$0.86	$0.91	$1.05	$1.28	$1.48
No. 4E07110	16-karat gold Pen with Holder.	.81	.95	1.10	1.29	1.52	1.71

SOLID GOLD PEN IN BEST QUALITY GOLD FILLED AND PLAIN PEARL SLIDE HOLDER.

		No. 1 Pen.	No. 2 Pen.	No. 3 Pen	No. 4 Pen.	No. 5 Pen.	No. 6 Pen.
No. 4E07112	10-karat gold Pen with Holder.	$0.95	$1.10	$1.14	$1.33	$1.43	$1.62
No. 4E07114	16-karat gold Pen with Holder.	1.05	1.19	1.37	1.57	1.67	1.90

SOLID GOLD PEN IN BEST QUALITY GOLD FILLED AND FANCY FULL TWIST PEARL DESK HOLDER.

		No. 1 Pen.	No. 2 Pen.	No. 3 Pen.	No. 4 Pen.	No. 5 Pen.	No. 6 Pen.
No. 4E07116	10-karat gold Pen with Holder.	$0.95	$1.10	$1.25	$1.40	$1.60	$1.80
No. 4E07118	16-karat gold Pen with Holder.	1.05	1.25	1.45	1.65	1.85	2.05

SOLID GOLD PEN IN BEST QUALITY GOLD FILLED AND FANCY THREE-QUARTER TWIST CUT PEARL DESK HOLDER.

		No. 1 Pen.	No. 2 Pen.	No. 3 Pen.	No. 4 Pen.	No. 5 Pen.	No. 6 Pen.
No. 4E07120	10-karat gold Pen with Holder.	$0.95	$1.10	$1.25	$1.40	$1.60	$1.80
No. 4E07122	16-karat gold Pen with Holder.	1.05	1.25	1.45	1.65	1.85	2.05

SOLID GOLD PEN IN BEST QUALITY GOLD FILLED AND FANCY HAND TURNED PEARL DESK HOLDER.

		No. 1 Pen.	No. 2 Pen.	No. 3 Pen.	No. 4 Pen.	No. 5 Pen.	No. 6 Pen.
No. 4E07124	10-karat gold Pen with Holder.	$1.00	$1.15	$1.30	$1.45	$1.65	$1.85
No. 4E07126	16-karat gold Pen with Holder.	1.10	1.30	1.50	1.70	1.90	2.10

SOLID GOLD PEN IN BEST QUALITY GOLD FILLED AND TWIST PEARL SLIDE HOLDER.

		No. 1 Pen.	No. 2 Pen.	No. 3 Pen.	No. 4 Pen.	No. 5 Pen.	No. 6 Pen.
No. 4E07128	10-karat gold Pen with Holder.	$1.20	$1.40	$1.50	$1.60	$1.85	$1.95
No. 4E07130	16-karat gold Pen with Holder.	1.30	1.50	1.75	1.85	2.10	2.20

SOLID GOLD PEN IN BEST QUALITY GOLD FILLED AND RUSTIC CUT PEARL DESK HOLDER.

		No. 1 Pen.	No. 2 Pen.	No. 3 Pen.	No. 4 Pen.	No. 5 Pen.	No. 6 Pen.
No. 4E07132	10-karat gold Pen with Holder.	$0.90	$1.05	$1.19	$1.38	$1.52	$1.72
No. 4E07134	16-karat gold Pen with Holder.	1.00	1.19	1.38	1.57	1.76	1.95

If by mail, postage extra, 3 cents; registry or insurance extra. Be sure to state how much is inclosed for postage, and follow instructions in front of book.

Sterling Silver Desk Set.

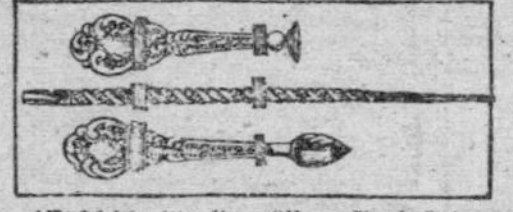

No. 4E07144 Sterling Silver Desk Set on card. Set consists of silver penholder, 6 inches long; silver handled ink eraser, 3¾ inches long; silver handled letter seal, 3 inches long.

Price, complete set..$1.19

If by mail, postage extra, 6 cents.

Combination Desk Set.

No. 4E07146 Combination Desk Set, consisting of one solid silver penholder, 6¼ inches long, and one solid silver lead pencil holder with rubber eraser attached, 2¾ inches long; entire length, with pencil, 5 inches. Complete in hardwood polished oak box, silk plush lined. Price, per set.....................$1.88

If by mail, postage extra, 6 cents.

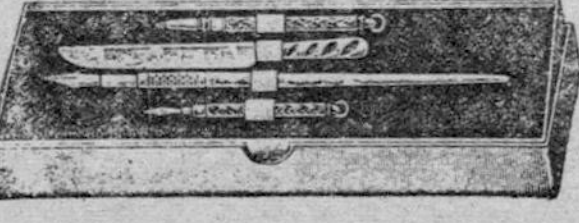

Our $1.77 Desk Set.

No. 4E07148 Combination Desk Set, with the best gold filled mountings, consisting of one pearl letter opener, 4¼ inches long; one pen and penholder, pen, solid gold; entire length, 6¼ inches; one fancy screw toothpick, full extended length, 2¾ inches; and one screw pencil, full extended length, 3 inches.

Price, complete in enameled paper velvet lined box..$1.77

If by mail, postage extra, 4 cents.

Sig. 7—1st Ed.

Combination Desk Sets.

No. 4E07150 Desk Set, consisting of pearl paper cutter and pearl handled penholder and solid gold 16-K No. 1 pen. Cutter and penholder made to match, ornamented with gold filled wire work.

Price, with box complete $1.90

If by mail, postage extra, 3 cents.

No. 4E07152 Sterling Silver Desk Set, in fine silk lined paper box. Set consists of silver covered fluted square ink well, 1½x1½x1½ inches; silver handled letter seal, 2¼ inches long; pearl penholder with solid No. 1 gold pen, 5 inches long; silver handled ink eraser, 3½ inches long.

Price, for complete set..............................$1.85

If by mail, postage extra, 20 cents.

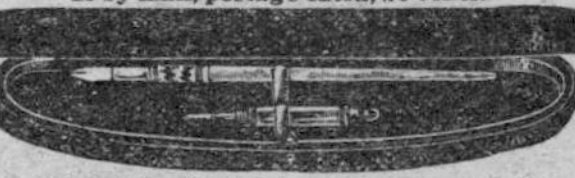

No. 4E07154 Desk Set, consisting of pearl pen and pearl pencil and plush covered and lined box. Pen is solid gold, 16-karat, No. 1 size; pencil is pearl with gold filled trimmings.

Price, for complete set..............................$2.42

If by mail, postage extra, 4 cents.

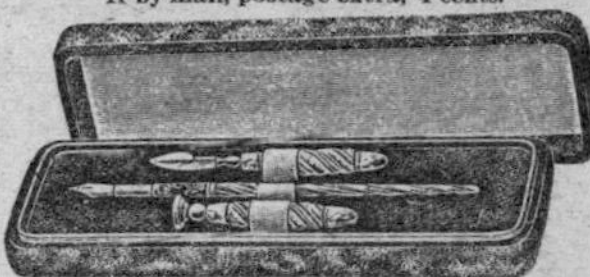

No. 4E07156 The Ideal Desk Set, consisting of one fine pearl letter seal, 2½ inches long; one fine pearl hand turned penholder with solid silver nose, fitted with a solid gold pen; full length of penholder and pen, 6¼ inches, and one pearl handled steel eraser; full length, 3¾ inches. Price, complete in beautiful silk plush box, velvet lined..........$3.06

If by mail, postage extra, 4 cents.

No. 4E07158 Combination Desk Set, consisting of one gold filled magic pencil, full extended length, 5 inches; one pearl penholder with gold filled nose, fitted with large size solid gold pen; full length of pen holder, including pen, 7¼ inches. Price, complete in beautiful silk plush box, velvet lined..........$3.12

If by mail, postage extra, 4 cents.

Screw Pencils.

No. 4E07160 Rolled Gold Plate Screw Pencil; full extended length, 2¾ inches. Price..........17c

If by mail, postage extra, 2 cents.

No. 4E07162 Rolled Gold Plate Screw Pencil, handsomely engraved; full extended length, 4 inches. Price...52c

If by mail, postage extra, 2 cents.

No. 4E07164 Rolled Gold Plate, Bright Polish, Fancy Screw Pencil; full extended length, 4 inches. Price...54c

If by mail, postage extra, 2 cents.

No. 4E07166 Gold Filled, Bright Polish, Handsomely Engraved Magic Pencil; full extended length, 3¾ inches. Price.............. ......72c

If by mail, postage extra, 2 cents.

No. 4E07200 Rolled Gold Plate, Bright Polish, Handsomely Engraved Magic Pencil; full extended length, 4¾ inches. Price....................76c
If by mail, postage extra, 3 cents.

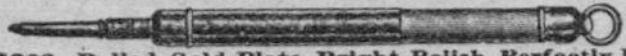

No. 4E07202 Rolled Gold Plate, Bright Polish, Perfectly Plain Magic Pencil; full extended length, 4¾ inches. Price....................86c
If by mail, postage extra, 3 cents.

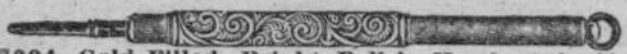

No. 4E07204 Gold Filled, Bright Polish, Handsomely Chased Magic Pencil; full extended length, 4¾ inches. Price....................$1.12
If by mail, postage extra, 3 cents.

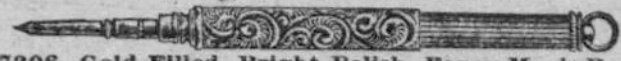

No. 4E07206 Gold Filled, Bright Polish, Fancy Magic Pencil; full extended length, 6 inches. Price....................$1.44
If by mail, postage extra, 3 cents.

PAUL E. WIRT FOUNTAIN PENS AND OUR OWN SPECIAL MAKE, THE NEW WABASH MADE ONLY FOR US.

BEFORE LISTING A LINE OF FOUNTAIN PENS we have thoroughly investigated the mechanism of all makes, and have spared no pains to place at the disposal of our customers, the finest fountain pens manufactured. The construction of these pens is of such a simple and practical kind that it is utterly impossible for one of them to become out of order, and cause more trouble to the writer and destroy more copy than the entire thing is worth, instead of being a convenience, making it in reality an absolute inconvenience.

THE PAUL E. WIRT FOUNTAIN PEN stands at the head without a peer. It is most simple and practical in construction as to operation and beauty of workmanship. Their popularity rests upon the fact that their ink feed device is the most perfect and simplest ever discovered. Do not buy inferior imitations, but get the original, genuine article. They are elegant, simple, clean and durable; every fountain is fitted with a 14-karat solid gold pen. Each one is warranted by the manufacturers and we guarantee them to you personally to be the finest and most practical pen made.

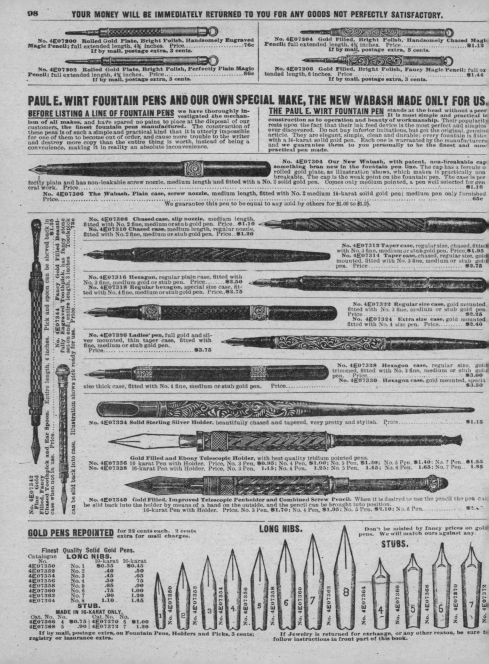

No. 4E07304 Our New Wabash, with patent, non-breakable cap, something bran new in the fountain pen line. The cap has a ferrule of rolled gold plate, as illustration shows, which makes it practically non breakable. The cap is the weak point on the fountain pen. The case is perfectly plain and has non-leakable screw nozzle, medium length and fitted with a No. 2 solid gold pen. Comes only medium pointed, a pen well selected for general work. Price....................$1.16

No. 4E07306 The Wabash. Plain case, screw nozzle, medium length, fitted with No. 2 medium 14-karat solid gold pen; medium pen only furnished. Price....................65c

We guarantee this pen to be equal to any sold by others for $1.00 to $1.25.

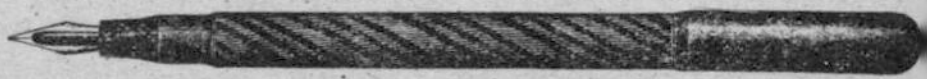

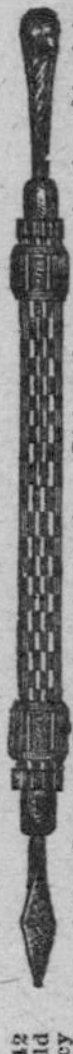

No. 4E07342 Fine Gold Filled, Fancy Chased Toothpick and Ear Spoon. Entire length, 4 inches. Pick and spoon can be shoved back in case when not in use. Price....................$1.25

No. 4E07344 Fancy Gold Filled Beautifully Engraved Toothpick, has fancy stone set on end; entire length, 3 inches. Price.................... Toothpick 72c can be slid back into case. Illustration shows pick ready for use.

No. 4E07308 Chased case, slip nozzle, medium length, fitted with No. 2 fine, medium or stub gold pen. Price..$1.10
No. 4E07310 Chased case, medium length, regular nozzle, fitted with No. 2 fine, medium or stub gold pen. Price..$1.20

No. 4E07312 Taper case, regular size, chased, fitted with No. 3 fine, medium or stub gold pen. Price..$1.95
No. 4E07314 Taper case, chased, regular size, gold mounted, fitted with No. 3 fine, medium or stub gold pen. Price....................$2.75

No. 4E07316 Hexagon, regular plain case, fitted with No. 3 fine, medium gold or stub pen. Price........$2.50
No. 4E07318 Regular hexagon, special size case, fitted with No. 4 fine, medium or stub gold pen. Price..$2.75

No. 4E07322 Regular size case, gold mounted, fitted with No. 3 fine, medium or stub gold pen. Price....................$2.25
No. 4E07324 Extra size case, gold mounted, fitted with No. 4 size pen. Price..........$2.40

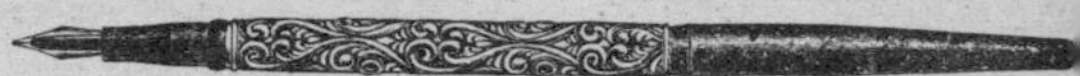

No. 4E07326 Ladies' pen, full gold and silver mounted, thin taper case, fitted with fine, medium or stub gold pen. Price....................$3.75

No. 4E07328 Hexagon case, regular size, gold trimmed, fitted with No. 3 fine, medium or stub gold pen. Price....................$3.00
No. 4E07330 Hexagon case, gold mounted, special size thick case, fitted with No. 4 fine, medium or stub gold pen. Price....................$3.50

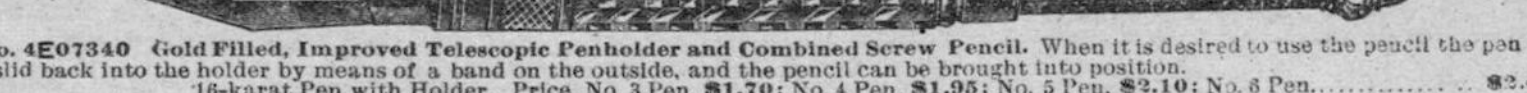

No. 4E07334 Solid Sterling Silver Holder, beautifully chased and tapered, very pretty and stylish. Price....................$1.15

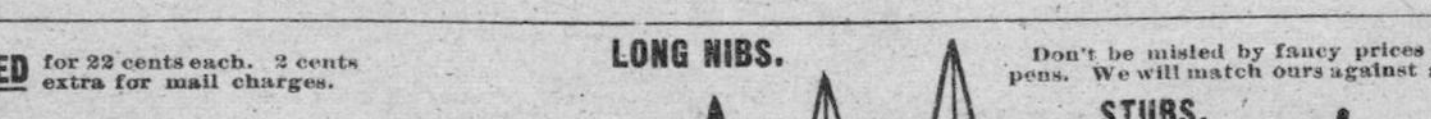

Gold Filled and Ebony Telescopic Holder, with best quality iridium pointed pens.
No. 4E07336 10 karat Pen with Holder. Price, No. 3 Pen, $0.95; No. 4 Pen, $1.00; No. 5 Pen, $1.20; No. 6 Pen, $1.40; No. 7 Pen..$1.55
No. 4E07338 16-karat Pen with Holder. Price, No. 3 Pen, 1.15; No. 4 Pen, 1.25; No. 5 Pen, 1.45; No. 6 Pen, 1.65; No. 7 Pen..1.85

No. 4E07340 Gold Filled, Improved Telescopic Penholder and Combined Screw Pencil. When it is desired to use the pencil the pen can be slid back into the holder by means of a band on the outside, and the pencil can be brought into position.
16-karat Pen with Holder. Price, No. 3 Pen, $1.70; No. 4 Pen, $1.95; No. 5 Pen, $2.10; No. 6 Pen....................$2.[illegible]

GOLD PENS REPOINTED for 22 cents each. 2 cents extra for mail charges.

Finest Quality Solid Gold Pens.

LONG NIBS.

Catalogue No.		10-karat	16-karat
4E07350	No. 1	$0.35	$0.45
4E07352	No. 2	.40	.50
4E07354	No. 3	.45	.65
4E07356	No. 4	.50	75
4E07358	No. 5	.65	.90
4E07360	No. 6	.75	1.00
4E07362	No. 7	.90	1.20
4E07364	No. 8	1.10	1.45

STUB.

MADE IN 16-KARAT ONLY.

Cat. No.	No.		Cat. No.	No.	
4E07366	4	$0.75	4E07370	6	$1.00
4E07368	5	.90	4E07372	7	1.20

If by mail, postage extra, on Fountain Pens, Holders and Picks, 3 cents; registry or insurance extra.

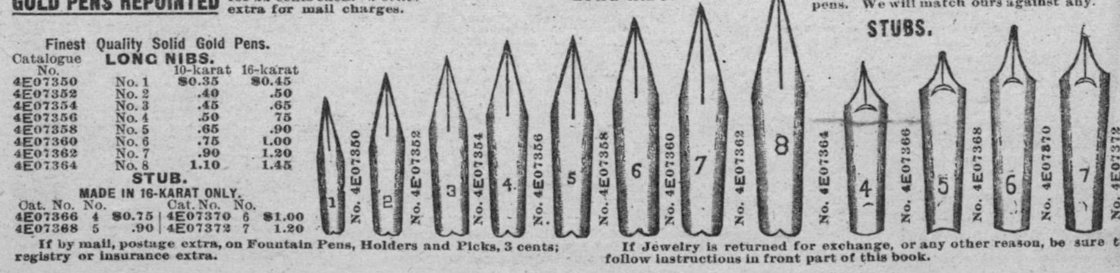

Don't be misled by fancy prices on gold pens. We will match ours against any.

If Jewelry is returned for exchange, or any other reason, be sure to follow instructions in front part of this book.

OUR SILVERWARE DEPARTMENT.

THE REASON WHY WE ARE SUCCESSFUL. We have only carried such makes as we know to be of such honest material and workmanship that there could be no question as to its wearing ability. When we sold an item, we sold it on honor, and we knew that it was going to give entire satisfaction in every particular.

OUR SEARS, ROEBUCK & CO.'S FLAT WARE, stamped "Paragon" and the Seroco Brand Silver Plated Cutlery (Sears, Roebuck & Co.'s name does not appear on it) is made under special contract. We can recommend them above all other makes. A full description and prices are quoted on page 101. We can not engrave knives as they are made of steel.

THE SEROCO BRAND KNIVES AND FORKS, another brand of our own, the equal of all other brands offered by others as being the best. This brand equals any manufactured, with the exception of our Paragon brand, which positively has no equals. See the prices on knives and forks below. You can not buy the equal of our 16-dwt. knives and forks anywhere. They positively are the best manufactured.

Mail Charges on Knives and Forks, About 48 Cents Per Dozen. | All Medium Knives are 9¼ inches long. Forks are 7½ inches long.

Sears, Roebuck & Co.'s Special Brand 12 and 16-dwt. Knives and Forks.—Stamped Paragon.

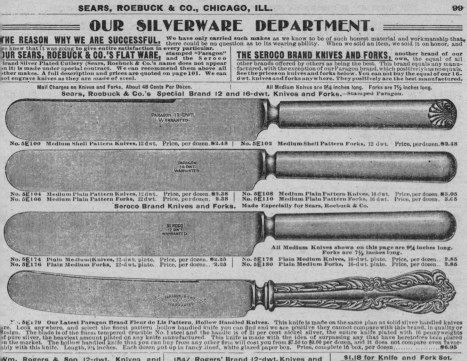

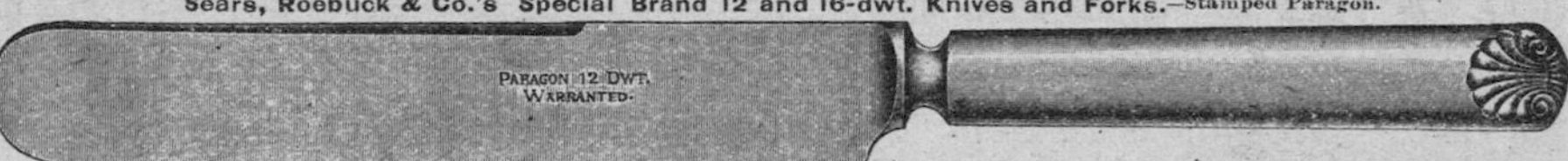

No. 5E100 Medium Shell Pattern Knives, 12 dwt. Price, per dozen. $2.48 | No. 5E102 Medium Shell Pattern Forks, 12 dwt. Price, per dozen. $2.48

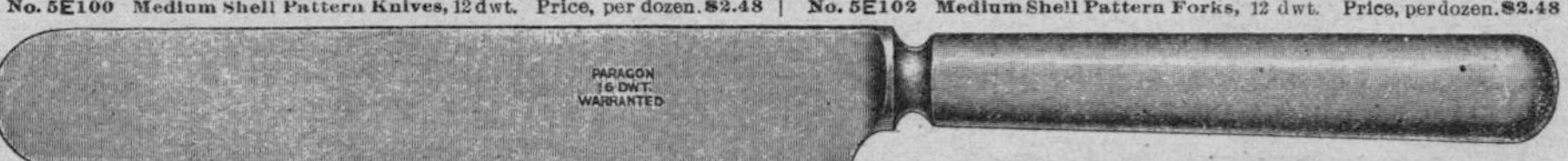

No. 5E104 Medium Plain Pattern Knives, 12 dwt. Price, per dozen. $2.38
No. 5E106 Medium Plain Pattern Forks, 12 dwt. Price, per dozen. 2.38
No. 5E108 Medium Plain Pattern Knives, 16 dwt. Price, per dozen. $3.05
No. 5E110 Medium Plain Pattern Forks, 16 dwt. Price, per dozen. 3.05

Seroco Brand Knives and Forks. Made Especially for Sears, Roebuck & Co.

All Medium Knives shown on this page are 9¼ inches long. Forks are 7½ inches long.

No. 5E174 Plain Medium Knives, 12-dwt. plate. Price, per dozen. $2.25
No. 5E176 Plain Medium Forks, 12-dwt. plate. Price, per dozen.. 2.25
No. 5E178 Plain Medium Knives, 16-dwt. plate. Price, per dozen.. 2.85
No. 5E180 Plain Medium Forks, 16-dwt. plate. Price, per dozen.. 2.85

No. 5E179 Our Latest Paragon Brand Fleur de Lis Pattern, Hollow Handled Knives. This knife is made on the same plan as solid silver handled knives are. Look anywhere, and select the finest pattern hollow handled knife you can find and we are positive they cannot compare with this brand, in quality or design. The blade is of the finest tempered crucible No. 1 steel and the handle is of 21 per cent nickel silver, the entire knife plated with 16 pennyweights of pure silver, the heaviest amount plated on any knife manufactured. This knife is made with the idea of surpassing any that have heretofore been placed on the market. The hollow handled knife that you can buy from any other firm will cost you from $7.50 to $9.00 per dozen, and it does not compare even favorably with this knife. Length, 9¼ inches. Each dozen put up in fancy lined, white glazed paper box. Price, complete in box, per dozen........ $6.95

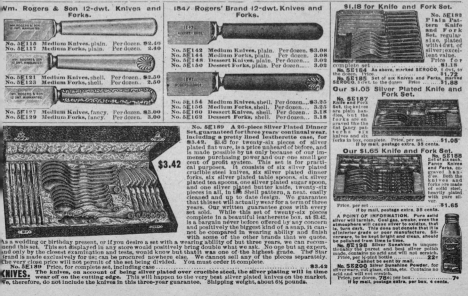

Wm. Rogers & Son 12-dwt. Knives and Forks.

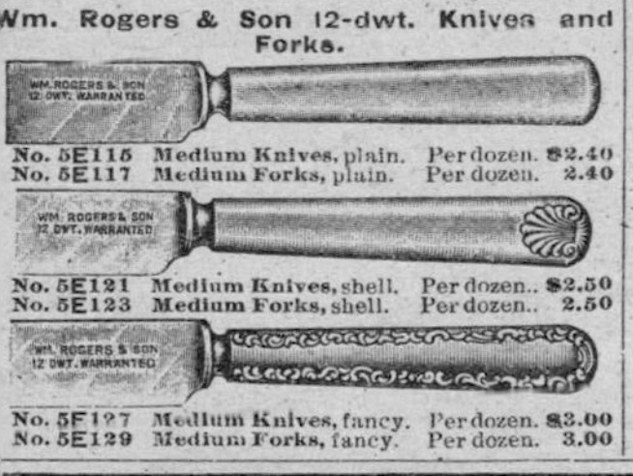

No. 5E115 Medium Knives, plain. Per dozen. $2.40
No. 5E117 Medium Forks, plain. Per dozen. 2.40

No. 5E121 Medium Knives, shell. Per dozen.. $2.50
No. 5E123 Medium Forks, shell. Per dozen.. 2.50

No. 5E127 Medium Knives, fancy. Per dozen. $3.00
No. 5E129 Medium Forks, fancy. Per dozen. 3.00

1847 Rogers' Brand 12-dwt. Knives and Forks.

No. 5E142 Medium Knives, plain. Per dozen. $3.08
No. 5E144 Medium Forks, plain. Per dozen. 3.08
No. 5E148 Dessert Knives, plain. Per dozen.... 3.02
No. 5E150 Dessert Forks, plain. Per dozen..... 3.02

No. 5E154 Medium Knives, shell. Per dozen.... $3.25
No. 5E156 Medium Forks, shell. Per dozen... 3.25
No. 5E160 Dessert Knives, shell. Per dozen.. 3.18
No. 5E162 Dessert Forks, shell. Per dozen... 3.18

$1.18 for Knife and Fork Set.

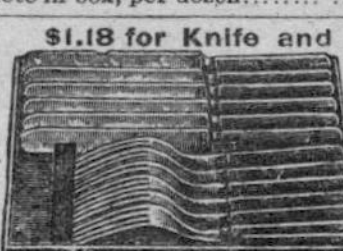

No. 5E182 Plain Pattern Knife and Fork Set, regular size, plated with 4 dwt. of silver; excellent value. Price for complete set........ $1.18

No. 5E184 As above, marked SEROCO, 6 dwt. to the dozen. Price........ $1.72

No. 5E185 Set of six Knives and Forks, marked SEROCO, 8 dwt. to the dozen. Price........ $1.88

Our $1.05 Silver Plated Knife and Fork Set.

No. 5E187 Knife and Fork Set, the knives are plain handles, but the forks are engraved like the flat fancy patterns; six knives and six forks in box, complete. Price, per set........ $1.05
If by mail, postage extra, 35 cents.

Our $1.65 Knife and Fork Set.

No. 5E188 Set of six each, Fancy Knives and Forks, engraved handles. Both the knives and forks are made of solid steel, heavily plated with pure silver.

Price, per set........ $1.65
If by mail, postage extra, 35 cents.

A POINT OF INFORMATION. Pure solid silver will tarnish. Coal gas, smoke, even the atmosphere will cause silver to oxidize, that is, turn dark. This does not denote that it is of inferior grade or poor manufacture. Silverware, to be kept bright and clean, should be polished from time to time.

No. 5E198 Silver Sunshine is unquestionably the purest and best silver polish made, contains no acid and will not scratch. Price, per ½-pint bottle........ 22c
Cannot be sent by mail.

No. 5E200 Silver Sunshine Powder, for silverware, cut glass, china, etc. Contains no acid and will not scratch.
Price, per dozen, 78c; per box........ 7c
If by mail, postage extra, per box, 4 cents.

$3.42

No. 5E189 A 26-piece Silver Plated Dinner Set, guaranteed for three years' continual wear, including a pretty lined leatherette case, for $3.42. $3.42 for twenty-six pieces of silver plated flat ware, is a price unheard of before, and is made possible by us only because of our immense purchasing power and our one small per cent of profit system. This set is for practical purposes. It consists of six silver plated crucible steel knives, six silver plated dinner forks, six silver plated table spoons, six silver plated tea spoons, one silver plated sugar spoon, and one silver plated butter knife, twenty-six pieces in all, in the Shell pattern, a neat, easily cleaned and up to date design. We guarantee that this set will actually wear for a term of three years. Our written guarantee goes with every set sold. While this set of twenty-six pieces complete in a beautiful leatherette box, at $3.42, is a bargain never before offered by any concern and positively the biggest kind of a snap, it cannot be compared in wearing ability and finish with some of the other brands that we quote. As a wedding or birthday present, or if you desire a set with a wearing ability of but three years, we can recommend this set. This set displayed in any store would positively bring double what we ask. No one but an expert, and only by the closest examination and tests, would know but that it was one of the highest grade. The Star Brand is made exclusively for us; can be procured nowhere else. We cannot sell any of the pieces separately. The very close price will not permit of the set being divided. You must order it complete.

No. 5E189 Price, for complete set, including case........ $3.42

KNIVES. The knives, on account of being silver plated over crucible steel, the silver plating will in time wear off on the cutting edge. This will happen to the very best silver plated knives on the market. We, therefore, do not include the knives in this three-year guarantee. Shipping weight, about 6½ pounds.

ALASKA SILVERWARE—A NEW DISCOVERY

THE CHEAPEST AND BEST FLAT WARE MADE The Alaska silverware is not plated, but is the same solid metal through and through, and will hold the same color as long as there is any portion of the goods left. Do not be deceived by any dealer who undertakes to sell you any of the numerous imitations of this ware, that are sold on the market for more money than we ask for the genuine. **The genuine Alaska Silverware can be had only of us.**

BEFORE TAKING HOLD OF THIS NEW DISCOVERY we left nothing undone to thoroughly investigate the properties of this metal, and to test the same in every conceivable manner, to satisfy ourselves that it was all that it was represented to be. After having made all sorts of experiments, **and it stood all tests,** we made a contract with the factory to handle the goods. It has now been about seven years since we began to handle this line, and it has not only proved from experiment to be as represented, but with seven years of actual service in the hands of many thousands of our customers, who send us the most flattering recommendations in praise of these goods, and with the rapidly increasing sales, we feel that we cannot recommend it too highly.

THE METAL IS VERY DENSE AND TOUGH, is almost as white as genuine silver, takes a beautiful polish and requires much less care than does silver plated ware.

OUR GUARANTEE.

ALASKA SILVERWARE KNIVES are not plated. They are the same metal and color through and through. They are proof against all table and fruit acids. They will not rust. They will not tarnish. They will cut and cut well. They can be ground and sharpened like a steel knife, and we guarantee them for the term of your natural lifetime.

Relative Lengths of Alaska Silverware: Tea spoons, 5¾ inches; dessert spoons, 7¼ inches; table spoons, 8¼ inches; dessert forks, 7 inches; medium forks, 7¼ inches; medium knives, 9 inches; sugar shells, 5⅝ inches; butter knives, 7 inches.

SEE WHAT YOU GET FOR
PROFIT SHARING CERTIFICATES
On the last pages.

THE FANCY PATTERN is equal in appearance and artistic finish to any of the best silver plated or solid silver goods on the market. The immense quantities of these goods we handle, and the conditions of our contract direct with the factory, puts us in a position to furnish this genuine Alaska Silverware at a slight advance over cost to manufacture.

ALASKA SILVERWARE SET.

26-piece Set of Alaska Silverware in fancy lined leatherette case, consisting of six medium size knives, six medium size forks, six table spoons, six tea spoons, one butter knife, one sugar shell; a complete dinner set.

No. 5E352 Tipped pattern, 26-piece set. Price...........**$3.14**
No. 5E354 Shell pattern, 26-piece set, plain knives. Price.**$3.14**
No. 5E356 Fancy pattern, 26-piece set plain knives. Price..**$3.36**
No. 5E358 Beaded pattern, 26-piece set, plain knives. Price.**$3.36**
Knives have plain handles as shown in illustration.

No. 5E332 Medium Alaska Silverware Knife.

SIX TEA SPOONS FOR **38c**

Tipped Pattern Tea Spoon.

We can supply leatherette cases, fancy lined, to hold twelve tea spoons for 25 cents, to hold six knives and six forks, for 25 cents; to hold twelve tea spoons, butter knife, sugar shell and pickle fork, at 25 cents; to hold twelve tea spoons and six table spoons, at 38 cents; to hold one dozen table spoons, at 25 cents. Cases only supplied when goods are ordered to fill same from us.

SIX TEA SPOONS FOR **42c**

Fancy Pattern Tea Spoon.

SIX TEA SPOONS FOR **38c**

Shell Pattern Tea Spoon.

SIX TEA SPOONS FOR **42c**

Beaded Pattern Tea Spoon.

Silverware and Jewelry Cleaning Outfits.

No. 5E300 Our Silverware and Jewelry Cleaning Outfit, consisting of one cleaning brush, one box of fine sifted drying sawdust, one fine India sponge, one piece chamois skin, one box Silver Sunshine powder, with full directions; one ½-pint bottle Silver Sunshine polish, with full directions. This complete cleaning outfit in wooden case, made especially for the purpose.
Price..........................**72c**
Weight, packed for shipment, 2½ pounds.

No. 5E302 Our Cleaning Outfit, similar to above described outfit, but consisting of one cleaning brush, drying sawdust, sponge, chamois, and Silver Sunshine in powder form, in fine pasteboard leatherette case made for the purpose, durable and strong. Price.....**44c**
If by mail, postage extra, 16 cents.

OUR SPECIAL PRICES.

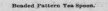

Any of these goods can be sent by mail on receipt of price and additional amount named to pay postage.

Postage on the silverware, if to go by mail, will be extra per half dozen as follows: On tea spoons, 6 cents; dessert spoons or forks, 12 cents; table spoons or medium forks, 15 cents; medium knives, 24 cents; and sugar shells or butter knives, 2 cents each. It is cheaper to send them by express, if you have an express office near by.

No.	Article		Tipped or Shell Pattern, per Set of Six	Tipped or Shell Pattern, per Gross	Fancy or Beaded Pattern, per Set of Six	Fancy or Beaded Pattern, per Gross
No. 5E326	Tea Spoons	set of ½ dozen,	$0.38	$ 8.66	$0.42	$ 9.58
No. 5E327	Dessert Spoons	set of ½ dozen,	.60	13.68	.74	16.88
No. 5E328	Table Spoons	set of ½ dozen,	.76	17.32	.84	19.16
No. 5E329	Medium Forks (regular size)	set of ½ dozen,	.76	17.32	.84	19.16
No. 5E330	Dessert Forks	set of ½ dozen,	.60	13.68	.74	16.88
No. 5E332	Knives, plain handle only, as illustration shows.	set of ½ dozen,	1.00	22.80	Not made	Not made
No. 5E333	Sugar Shells	each,	.12	pr doz. 1.36	each, .13	pr doz. 1.48
No. 5E334	Butter Knives	each,	.12	pr doz. 1.36	each, .13	pr doz. 1.48

The standard of quality and finish of the above goods **are guaranteed** by the manufacturer to us, and we guarantee them to our customers. You run no **risk** whatever in purchasing this ware, for if you do not find them to be exactly as represented, they can be returned to us and your money will be refunded. **Be** sure to state catalogue number and pattern wanted when you order.

WE DO NOT MAKE ANY OTHER PIECES OF ALASKA SILVERWARE THAN THOSE MENTIONED ABOVE.

No. 5E10360 Holy Water Fount, Faith, Hope and Charity. French imported china, tinted in red, blue and gold. Shipping weight, about 3 pounds. Height, 8 inches.
Price, each **$0.25**
Per dozen.. **2.85**

Adoring Angel Holy Water Fount. White imported china, decorated in gold. Shipping weight, about 3 pounds.

No. 5E10370 Height, 5¾ inches.
Price, each... **$0.14**
Per dozen.... **1.55**

No. 5E10380 Height, 7 inches.
Price, each... **$0.32**
Per dozen... **3.65**

Solid Silver, Gold Filled and Solid Gold Crosses.

Illustrations Show Exact Sizes.

No. 5E10422 Solid silver. Price, each.. **$0.45** Doz. **5.12**

No. 5E10424 Gold filled, bright burnished.
Price, each... **$0.45**
Per dozen.... **5.12**

No. 5E10432 Gold Filled Pin, bright burnished, set with French pearls. Ea. **$0.25** Per dozen. **2.85**

No. 5E10402 Solid silver. Each.. **$0.32** Per dozen... **3.65**

No. 5E10404 Gold filled, bright burnished. Ea. **$0.32** Per dozen... **3.65**

No. 5E10406 Solid gold. Ea. **$ 1.75** Per dozen **19.95**

If by mail, postage extra, on crosses, 2 cents.

No. 5E10412 Solid silver.
Each... **$0.40**
Per doz. **4.56**

No. 5E10414 Gold filled, bright burnished. Ea. **$0.40**
Per doz. **4.56**

No. 5E10416 Solid gold.
Price, per dozen. **$18.85**; each, **$1.65**

No. 5E10620 Rosary. Silver filled connections, mother of pearl cross and beads. Length, 14 ins. Price, each.. **$0.50** Doz. **5.70**

If by mail, postage extra, 3 cents.

No. 5E10630 Rosary. Solid silver connections, cross and heart, fine cut imitation amethyst beads; 14 inches long. Each one comes in a fine silk lined box.
Price, **$1.25**

No. 5E10640 Same as above, ruby beads. Price, **$1.25**

No. 5E10650 Same as above, jet beads.
Price, per dozen, **$14.75**; each.... **$1.25**

No. 5E10652 Amethyst beads, gold filled chain. Guaranteed for 5 years.
Price, per dozen, **$15.95**; each..... **$1.40**

No. 5E10654 Amethyst beads, gold filled chain. Guaranteed for 10 years.
Price, per dozen, **$21.08**; each..... **$1.85**

If by mail, postage extra, 4 cents.

No. 5E10660 Rosary. Silver filled cross and connections, imitation amethyst beads. Length, 14 inches. Price.......................**42c**

No. 5E10670 Same as above jet beads, Price.......................**42c**

No. 5E10680 Same as above, imitation ruby beads. Dozen, **$4.78**; each........**42c**

If by mail, postage extra, 3 cents.

No. 5E10760 Rosary Beads. Made from wood from the forests of Lebanon. Silver filled link connections. Length, 18 inches.
Price, per dozen, **$3.46**; each..........**30c**

If by mail, postage extra, 3 cents.

No. 5E10770 Rosary Beads. Black wood, steel link connections. Length, 14½ in.
Price, per dozen, **75c**; each..................**7c**

If by mail, postage extra, 3 cents.

No less than one dozen quantities sold at the dozen price.

No. 5E10928 Silver Statuette. Immaculate conception. This beautiful statuette is 5¾ inches high. Is heavily plated with pure silver and perfectly finished. Ea.. **$0.42**
Per dozen.. **4.78**

No. 5E198 Silver Sunshine Paste is unquestionably the purest and best silver polish made, contains no acid and will not scratch.
Price, per ½-pint.......... **22c**

No. 5E200 Silver Sunshine Powder, for silverware, cut glass, china, etc. Contains no acid and will not scratch.
Price, per dozen boxes, **78c**; per box.....**7c**

If by mail, postage extra, 8 cents.

ONLY $3.55 FOR THIS VIATICUM CABINET OR SICK CALL OUTFIT.

Guaranteed the Finest Silver Plated on Genuine Hard White Britannia Metal.

No. 5E10942 This Viaticum Cabinet or Sick Call Outfit is the official and rubrical household sacramental service, recommended and approved by the highest in the church. It is adaptable to many religious uses, and is always ready for use in the home during the administration of the sacrament. It is made to satisfy and comfort the aged and infirm, and to serve as a family altar, around which the members of the domestic circle may gather at the appropriate time. **In the cabinet, each having a special place to receive it,** are the following articles: Combination silver crucifix, holy water fount and candelabrum. The holy water fount is gold lined; the crucifix is detachable. A silver handled holy water sprinkler, a glass bottle with screw top and rubber washer for holy water; two hand cast beeswax candles. These candles are positively rubrical and can be blessed. A linen napkin and a linen communion cloth; a supply of cotton used by the priest; a silver, gold lined spoon cup, for administering the water to the communicant; two silver plates. The cabinet itself is a gem of the woodmaker's art. It is constructed of highly polished wood, the inside being beautifully upholstered in purple cloth. Has double swinging doors, each door ornamented with a metal cross. Weight of set, packed for shipment, 10 to 12 lbs. Price, **$3.55**

No. 5E10943 Same style as No. 5E10942, but not so heavily plated, sold by others at $3.55 and $4.00. Our price is figured on our one small percentage of profit above cost of manufacturing. Price............................ **$3.10**

BEST QUALITY CRUCIFIXES, CANDLESTICKS AND CANDELABRUMS.

No. 5E10904 Crucifix, silver plated on white metal. Height, 7½ inches. Weight, about 3 lbs. Each. **$0.40**
Per dozen. **4.56**

No. 5E10908 Crucifix, silver plated. Height, 9¾ inches. Wgt., about 3 pounds.
Price, ea. **$0.60**
Per dozen. **6.85**

No. 5E10980 Hanging Crucifix. White celluloid, to imitate ivory; indestructible; can be kept clean by washing in soap and water. Length, 11 inches.
Price, each.... **$0.82**
Per dozen...... **9.34**

No. 5E10985 Same style as No. 5E10980, 6½ inches long.
Price, each.... **$0.42**
Per dozen...... **4.78**

No. 5E10990 Same style as No. 5E10980, 5½ inches long.
Price, each. **34c**
Per dozen. **$3.88**

Crucifix of white metal, 10 inches high. Weight, about 3 pounds.

No. 5E10916
Price, silver plated, ea.. **$0.62**
Per dozen. **7.06**

No. 5E10918
Price, gold plated, ea.... **$ 1.12**
Doz...... **12.76**

No. 5E10920 Crucifix, silver plated on white metal, 10¼ inches high. Weight, about 3 pounds.
Price, ea. **$0.88**
Per dozen. **9.98**

Crucifix. white metal, heavily plated with pure silver. Is well made and finished in the best manner. Height, 7¾ inches.

No. 5E10922
Price, silver plated, each........... **$0.40**
Per dozen... **4.56**

No. 5E10924
Price, gold plated, each........... **$0.60**
Per dozen.. **6.85**
Shipping weight, 2 pounds.

No. 5E10926 Candlestick. Quadruple silver plated candlestick. This is not a cheap importation, but is made in the best manner by skilled workmen. Height, 8¾ inches.
Price, ea.. **$0.65**
Per dozen **7.40**
Shipping weight, 2 pounds.

No. 5E10940 Crucifix, Candelabrum and Holy Water Fount all combined. Silver plated on genuine white metal. 13 inches high. Weight, about 6 pounds.
Price, each................. **$ 1.76**
Per dozen........ ..... **20.00**

No. 5E10992 Finest Quality Quadruple Silver Plated Candlesticks, Colonial pattern, bright burnished. Height, 8¼ inches. Shipping weight, about 4½ pounds.
Price, each. **$1.50**

No. 5E10994 Finest Quality Quadruple Silver Plated Candlesticks. Beaded edges, fluted pattern. Height, 7½ inches. Shipping weight, about 4½ pounds.
Price, each.. **95c**

IN OUR CLOCK DEPARTMENT

THE BEST CLOCK MAKERS IN THE UNITED STATES ARE REPRESENTED. They are the oldest and most reliable makers. The Waterbury Clock Co., the Seth Thomas Clock Co., the New Haven Clock Co., and the Ansonia Clock Co., stand preeminent. Every clock we sell is guaranteed by the manufacturers, and we personally warrant every clock sold to give entire and absolute satisfaction; for the biggest value for the money, for clocks that we can and do give our written binding guarantee with every one sold, we would direct your attention to the following clocks: Each one is made under special contract for us. They are manufactured by one of the makers named, but on account of the very low price, we cannot print the maker's name. However, each one of these clocks carries our 5-year binding guarantee. For an alarm clock we recommend The Reliable Alarm, No. 5E2916, at 69 cents; our new Luminous Radium at 85 cents; or our New Continuous Long Alarm, No. 5E2921, price, $1.89. For a cabinet clock, we would recommend our No. 5E3096, price, $2.20, or if this design does not suit you and you wish a calendar attachment together with a thermometer and barometer, we would direct your attention to our No. 5E3099, price, $2.64, or the Prophet, price, $3.24. If you want a mantel clock, something very fine, the greatest value for the money, you can surely make a selection from the following clocks: The movements are of the highest standard. It is only a question of design in the case. Conqueror at $4.70, No. 5E3290; our Prince Elias, No. 5E3302; our Queen Clyde, No. 5E3305; Our American Lady, No. 5E3917, price, $3.98; our Countess Janet, No. 5E3711, price, $3.62; or the Empress, No. 5E3901, price, $4.45.

No. 5E2900 Nickel Alarm Clock, 4-inch dial. Height, 6¼ inches; width, 4¼ inches. Price....44c
If by mail, postage extra, 20 cents.

Shows the Time in the Dark. Luminous Dial.

No. 5E2907 Our New Luminous Radium Alarm Clock. You can see the time at night if you own one of these clocks. This clock has a 4-inch dial, being large enough to see the numerals from any part of the room. It is an improvement over all others. This clock carries with it our two-year guarantee. Directions enclosed with each clock, printed on back of guarantee. Price..(Postage, 20c)...85c
No. 5E2962 In case lots of 25.
Price, each....80c
We cannot sell less than 25 clocks at this price.

No. 5E2908 Luminous Pirate Alarm Clock, made by the Ansonia Clock Company, height, 6½ inches; width, 4¼ inches; dial, 4 inches. This dial is luminous. You can tell the time in the darkest night, the darker it is, the brighter it glows. Price........80c
If by mail, postage extra, 27 cents.
No. 5E2966 In case lots of 25.
Price, each....75c
We cannot sell less than 25 clocks at this price.

No. 5E2910 "Must Get Up" Nickel Alarm Clock. Height, 5⅝ inches; dial, 4½ inches; made by the Waterbury Clock Co. This clock has very large bell on the back of the clock; the alarm runs five minutes with one winding; can be made to run a short, medium, long, or extra long time, and can be stopped at pleasure. Price, $1.16
If by mail, postage extra, 29 cents.

No. 5E2911 Our New Interval Alarm Clock. Height, 6 inches; dial, 4½ inches; bell on back of clock. It is one of our new clocks, being guaranteed for a term of two years. It rings at intervals for a duration of fifteen minutes. You cannot oversleep yourself with one of these clocks. It is made for us under contract at a special price, with the idea of producing a better clock than any on the market. Our guarantee goes with every clock sold. Price......$1.20
If by mail, postage extra, 28 cents.

No. 5E2914 The Fly Alarm Calendar Clock. Height, about 6⅛ inches; dial, 4 inches; one-day clock with calendar and alarm, manufactured by the New Haven Clock Company. Movement, very fine grade lever; clock that we know will give entire satisfaction in every respect, has fine large nickel alarm bell on top, entire clock beautifully burnished, and thoroughly inspected before leaving our establishment. Has extra long alarm ring or can be regulated by winding apparatus for short ring. Price..........86c
If by mail, postage extra, 24 cents.
No. 5E2968 In case lots of 25.
Price, each....80c
We cannot sell less than 25 clocks at this price.

The Reliable Alarm, 69 Cents.

No. 5E2916

Nickel Alarm Clock. Height, 6¼ inches; dial, 4 inches; made expressly for us by one of the largest clock companies in the United States. It goes through a thorough inspection before leaving our establishment by one of our expert watchmakers; a clock we can conscientiously recommend to you as being everything an alarm clock should be. Price.....69c
If by mail, postage extra, 20 cents.
No. 5E2972 In case lots of 25.
Price, each....64c
We cannot sell less than 25 clocks at this price.

No. 5E2919 The Racket Strike Alarm Clock, made by the Ansonia Clock Co. Height, 6½ inches; width, 4¾ inches, dial, 4¼ inches. Strikes the hours and half hours on bell. A good timekeeper, guaranteed to give entire satisfaction.
Price....$1.36
If by mail, postage extra, 36 cents.

No. 5E2929 The Repeater Intermitting Alarm Clock, manufactured by the Ansonia Clock Co.; runs thirty-six hours with one winding; dial, 5 inches in diameter. Alarms for twenty-five minutes at intervals; twenty seconds of alarm, then fifteen seconds of silence.
Price....$1.12
If by mail, postage extra, 36 cents.

No. 5E2931 Wasp Alarm Clock, lever escapement, runs one day with one winding; stands 3¼ inches high; dial, 2 inches in diameter; is manufactured by the Waterbury Clock Company and is guaranteed to keep correct time.
Price....$1.06
If by mail, postage extra, 10 cents.

No. 5E2933 Same as No. 5E2931, but without alarm, time only. Price. 78c

No. 5E2921 Our New Continuous Long Alarm Clock. Rings from seven to ten minutes, but can be switched off when desired by throwing lever on the back of the clock. We have had this clock manufactured especially for us, our purpose being to procure for our customers' benefit, a clock that is superior to all others on the market. With our Continuous Long Alarm Clock, you will need no batteries or any other troublesome device to get results. The case is finished in oxidized copper, beautiful in design and in execution, handsome enough for any parlor or mantel. Dial of clock is 4¼ inches in diameter. The movement is manufactured by the celebrated Waterbury Clock Company, of Waterbury, Conn., one of the greatest American clock manufacturers in the United States and is positively guaranteed to give absolute and entire satisfaction. We give our unconditional two-year guarantee with it. Clock runs thirty to thirty-six hours with one winding. The steel parts are all oil hardened, brass parts wrought by hand, full complement of conical pivots, patent pinions, agate drawn hairspring, agate drawn mainspring; thoroughly timed and adjusted for accurate time keeping. Entire height of clock, 12½ inches. Price. $1.89
Shipping weight, 9 pounds.

SAVE YOUR VALUABLE PROFIT SHARING CERTIFICATES.

Our $2.20 Cabinet Clock.

No. 5E3096 THE AMSTERDAM Cabinet Clock. This clock stands 22 inches high and is 15 inches wide. Made exclusively for us by one of the four big clock manufacturers. The case is made of solid oak only, not veneered, or grained to imitate oak but solid oak through and through. The illustration shows you, but in a very faint way, the beautiful floral design worked out in the wood. The movement is manufactured by one of the most representative clock companies and carries with it our own special written binding guarantee for a term of five years. It runs eight days with one winding, strikes the hours and half hours. Dial, 6 inches in diameter. We would particularly advise purchasing this clock, as we know that it is without the shadow of a doubt, the greatest clock value ever offered. You positively will be more than pleased with your purchase should you favor us. Weight of clock, boxed ready for shipment, about 15 pounds. Price....$2.20
No. 5D3098 With alarm attachment. Price........ 2.40

This 8-Day Clock for $1.85.

THE ALDRICH is made by the Waterbury Clock Co., in either oak or walnut, as desired. It runs eight days with one winding, it stands 22 inches high, has 6-inch dial, strikes the hours and half hours on a wire bell. Case is beautifully carved and perfectly made in every detail. Weight, boxed ready for shipment, about 15 lbs.

No. 5E3102 Price...$1.85
No. 5E3104 With alarm. Price..........$2.20
No. 5E3106 With cathedral gong, no alarm. Price....$2.10
No. 5E3108 With cathedral gong and alarm. Price...$2.35

The Netherlands, $2.64.

No. 5E3099 THE NETHERLANDS. We cannot tell you the maker's name on account of the special cut price, but we can tell you that it is manufactured by one of the four big clock companies in the United States, and we guarantee it to give entire and absolute satisfaction. Our written, binding guarantee goes with every clock sold. This clock is made of solid oak only, guaranteed not veneered or stained to represent oak, but is solid oak through and through. The clock stands 22 inches high and is 15 inches wide. The illustration does not, by any means, give you any idea of the beautiful effect this clock has. The movement runs 8 days with one winding, strikes the hours and half hours, and has calendar attachment, showing the days of the month, likewise has barometer and thermometer, indicating at all times the temperature and enabling you to anticipate the changes in the weather. Dial, 6 inches in diameter. Our price for this specially made clock is $2.64. Don't think that because we have named such a wonderfully low price on this clock that it is not the best on the market. Money cannot buy a better clock, no matter what price you pay for this style of clock. This price is possible only for the reason that we maintain our one small per cent profit policy and on account of a special arrangement with the factory for an immense quantity at a remarkably low price, as always, we give you the benefit of this remarkable purchase. Weight of clock boxed ready for shipment, 15 pounds.
Price..........$2.64

Nothing Finer for $4.00. Our Price, $2.10.

No. 5E3115 THE LAYTON. Fancy Cabinet Clock; 22½ inches high; dial, 6 inches; made in oak only; beautifully carved and ornamented; fine eight-day movement; made by the Ansonia Clock Company; strikes the hours and half hours on wire bell. Weight, boxed ready for shipment, about 18 lbs.
No. 5E3115 Price...... $2.10
No. 5E3117 With alarm. Price $2.38
No. 5E3119 With gong. Price. $2.30

Our $2.55 Cabinet Clock.

No. 5E3144 THE DABNEY. One of the most complete clocks ever offered to the public. It has an eight-day movement, guaranteed by the Waterbury Clock Company. Oak or walnut case, beautifully carved and decorated, glass door. Strikes the hours and half hours on a wire bell. It also has thermometer and barometer attachment. The pendulum is ornamented and very fancy. Entire clock stands 22 inches high and has a 6-inch fancy rococo dial. Weight, boxed ready for shipment, about 16 pounds.

No. 5E3144 Price.......$2.55
No. 5E3146 With alarm. Price......... 2.85
No. 5E3148 With cathedral gong. Price, 2.75

Our 44-Cent Miniature Cuckoo Clock.

No. 5E3552 A Miniature Cuckoo Clock, imported from Switzerland, imitating a genuine cuckoo clock. It does not cuckoo or strike; runs 24 hours with one winding; is 7¼ inches high. Made of dark wood. We examine and test each one before shipping; we do not warrant this clock, but if it is not in good going order when received, return same at once and we will ship another. Shipping weight, 6 pounds.

Price........................44c

$2.20 Buys this Eight-Day Clock.

No. 5E3132 THE CHAPMAN Cabinet Clock, made by the Waterbury Clock Co., in either oak or walnut. It runs eight days with one winding, it strikes the hours and half hours on a wire bell. The case stands 22 inches high, is beautifully carved and ornamented. Has a fancy rococo dial. Warranted to give entire satisfaction. Weight, boxed ready for shipment, about 15 lbs.

No. 5E3132 Price.........$2.20
No. 5E3134 With cathedral gong $2.35
No. 5E3136 With alarm attachment...........$2.50

A Bargain for $3.45.

No. 5E3151 THE ROCHESTER. Fancy Cabinet Clock in solid black walnut only; very fancy ornamented and **carved** case; height, 26⅜ inches; dial, 8 inches; fitted with eight-day movement; made by the Waterbury Clock Company; strikes hours and halfhours on wire bell; with calendar attachment. Weight, boxed ready for shipment, about 20 pounds.

No. 5E3151 Price.....$3.45
No. 5E3153 With cathedral gong. Price, $3.75

$2.65 Buys a Calendar Clock with Barometer and Thermometer.

No. 5E3166 THE GIBSON Calendar 8-Day Clock with thermometer and barometer. This clock is one of the greatest bargains that we have ever been able to offer to our customers. It can be furnished in black walnut or antique oak case, as desired. The height is 24 inches, dial, 6 inches. The movement is one of the **best made** by the Waterbury Clock Co. Runs eight days with one winding and strikes the hours and half hours. **It is warranted to be an accurate timekeeper.** Has a complete calendar attachment which works automatically and always indicates correctly the day of the month. It has a perfect thermometer on one side and on the other a barometer. We cannot furnish it with alarm. Weight of clock, boxed ready for shipment, 17 pounds.

Price..........................$2.65

The Stanton, $2.40.

A new pattern eight-day clock, made by the Waterbury Clock Company and is guaranteed to give entire satisfaction. The case is made of solid oak, stands 22 inches high, embellished with beautiful gilt ornaments, which lend a beauty to this style of clock, unequaled by any other style of ornamentation. The dial is 6 inches in diameter. The pendulum is of corrugated brass. The clock runs 8 days at one winding, strikes the hours and half hours on a wire bell. Weight, boxed ready for shipment, about 15 pounds.

No. 5E3121 Price..........................$2.40
No. 5E3123 With alarm. Price.............. 2.65
No. 5E3125 With gong and alarm. Price... 2.85

The Prophet, only $3.24.

No. 5E3136 8-day clock with calendar, thermometer and barometer attached, called the Prophet. A new addition to our extensive line of guaranteed clocks, made under special contract for us by one of the four great clock companies. Our guarantee for a term of five years goes with every one sold. The manufacturers' name does not appear on it. It was made for us not with the idea of matching similar clocks on the market, but rather to improve on any heretofore manufactured. The idea being not how cheap a clock could be produced, but rather how fine a one for the price. Clock stands 44 inches high, width, 13 inches; has 6-inch dial. The case is handsome carved oak. We do not supply in walnut nor can it be had with alarm attachment. This clock is especially adapted as a wall clock, having a shelf attachment. Runs eight days with one winding and strikes the hours and half hours on a wire bell, likewise shows day of the month, temperature, and changes of the weather, having calendar attachment and supplied with barometer and thermometer on either side of case, as illustration shows. The movement is of oil tempered hand rolled steel and brass, pinions, pivots and all friction gear being well polished to avoid friction, thereby increasing its ability as a timekeeper. Weight, boxed ready for shipment, 16 pounds.

Price..........................$3.24

A Special Value for $2.32.

THE FELIX Eight-Day Clock, suitable for the office, workshop or the house. It has a complete calendar attachment, showing the days of the month. It strikes the hours and half hours on a wire bell. Stands 22 inches high, has 6-in. dial, beautifully embossed, made in oak or walnut by the Waterbury Clock Co., guaranteed an accurate timepiece. Weight, boxed ready for shipment, about 15 pounds.

No. 5E3128 Price.........$2.32
No. 5E3130 Same with cathedral gong. Price.........$2.55

Office, Church and School Room Clocks.

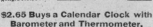

DROP OCTAGON. Has solid oak or fine veneered case. Made by the Waterbury Clock Company and is thoroughly reliable. Is designed for offices, schools or churches. Weight, boxed, 25 pounds.

No. 5E3518 Eight-day, 10-in. dial, time only. Price..........$2.75
No. 5E3520 Eight-day, 10-in. dial; time only, with calendar. Price......$3.10
No. 5E3522 Eight-day, 10-in. dial; strikes hours and halves. Price..........$3.28
No. 5E3524 Eight-day, 12-in. dial; time only. Price....$3.05
No. 5E3526 Eight-day 12-in. dial; strikes hours and half hours. Price..........$3.45
No. 5E3528 Eight-day, 12-in. dial; time only, with calendar. Price..........$3.30

The Conqueror.

Price, as illustrated, **$4.70**

$4.70 for a genuine Waterbury hard enameled eight-day bronze ornamented large size mantel clock with solid bronze figure.

This is our special offer, $4.70 for this grand clock, and we challenge any manufacturer, jobber or retailer to duplicate it.

We ask for comparison. We want you to investigate. Read the descriptions of clocks in any catalogue issued by any concern, examine the clocks shown by any jeweler, write for prices from any firm in the United States, and if you buy this clock from us, you will find our price actually gives you $2.50 to $4.00 as a profit. Never before has such a value in a clock, marked with the name of one of the greatest clock manufacturers been offered. The Conqueror, so named because it beats any clock on the market. Height, including figure, 23 inches; the width at base is 17½ inches; depth, 8 inches; height of clock alone, 11 inches. It is durably made of hard seasoned wood, guaranteed not to warp or crack, beautifully hard black enameled to imitate black marble, and trimmed in colors to imitate the lighter Mexican onyx.

A special feature of this clock is the secret process of enameling. It is guaranteed not to peel or chip off. A rag slightly moistened with oil keeps it as new for a lifetime. This clock is magnificent in its bronze metal ornamentation, which includes the heavy one-inch border all around the clock just above the base, massive bronze feet and massive side bronze scroll ornaments. The dial is plain but still beautiful, with bright finished gilded sash.

The Waterbury Clock Co. guarantees the movement in this clock to give perfect satisfaction. It runs eight days with one winding, strikes the hours on a cathedral gong and the half hours on a cup bell. Each piece and part is perfectly inspected at the factory before it is assembled, and again timed and tested after the clock has been put together. No clock but what is absolutely perfect in going and time keeping is allowed to leave this splendidly organized factory. Our Conqueror is an example of the possibility of our buying powers. The manufacturer, by reason of a big contract, reduced his profits to a mere fraction compared to what he generally makes, and we, following out our accustomed rule and method, have added only our one small percentage of profit. $4.70, after all the figuring, was the wonderfully low price arrived at and the price we are able to sell it to you.

You will get your PROFIT SHARING CERTIFICATE and can soon get a couch, bed, parlor table or other article entirely FREE, as explained on the last pages.

Weight of clock, boxed ready for shipment, 20 pounds.

No. 5E3290 Price, including figure $4.70
No 5E3292 Price of figure alone.......... .88
No. 5E3294 Price of clock alone, without bronze figure.............. 3.82

Regular Eight-Day Clock with Perpetual Calendar Attachment for $5.80.

No. 5E3310 This clock is manufactured by the Waterbury Clock Company in either oak or walnut. Stands 28¼ inches high. It runs 8 days with one winding, strikes the hours and half hours on a cathedral gong. **It has the calendar attachment,** as shown on the lower dial, which is a perpetual one, marking even the leap years without having to be reset. The dials are 8 inches in diameter. This clock is particularly adapted for dining rooms, libraries and offices. We warrant it to be an accurate timekeeper. The parts are made of finely wrought brass and oil tempered steel, most accurate for timekeeping, and giving it great durability. **The case is beautifully hand engraved and embossed.** The glass in the door is decorated in black and gold. See our price, **$5.80. We absolutely guarantee it to give satisfaction.** Weight, boxed for shipment, about 25 pounds.

Price..........................$5.80

$3.65 for Our Prince Elias.

OUR PRINCE ELIAS, the newest clock out of the factory, exactly in every particular as illustration shows, for $3.65. Don't think that you will not get or cannot buy from us a fine clock for this price. In fact, this price is no criterion. The clock is really worth twice as much. Your local dealer or the jobber he buys it from would pay 25 to 45 per cent more than we ask you for it, in other words, you would have to pay your local dealer for a clock as good as this and as handsome as this one, from $5.00 to $6.00. This clock is made expressly for us by the Waterbury Clock Co., of Waterbury, Conn. Each one of them is thoroughly guaranteed and we warrant them to give entire satisfaction.

DESCRIPTION OF CASE. The case is made of wood, covered with a secret prepared enamel, imitating black marble. It is guaranteed not to chip or wear off and always retains its deep black marble-like appearance. It has handsome gilt feet, marbleized gilt metal capped and gilt metal based columns, beautiful gilt scroll metal work at top and base. The sides are also ornamented by two gilt metal designs, exactly as the illustration shows. The dial is very pretentious, made of metal fancy work and is 5 inches in diameter.

DESCRIPTION OF MOVEMENT. The movement fitted in this case is one of the Waterbury guaranteed movements, runs eight days with one winding. It is made of the finest tempered steel and hand wrought brass; it strikes the hours on a cathedral gong and the half hours on a brass bell. You can always know the time without seeing the clock. The hands are very fine hand sawed blue steel of the fleur de lis pattern. Shipping weight, 16 pounds.

No. 5E3302 Price **$3.65**

Our Queen Clyde Mantel Clock, for $2.48.

Never before in the history of the clock business was ever such a fine clock offered for this price, $2.48.

Description of case. The clock case is of wood, well seasoned and guaranteed not to warp or crack, it is enameled in black, then polished to a high gloss.

The ornamentation. A beautiful gilt border of the rococo pattern made of metal sets off the top. This is entirely a new idea in clock ornamentation, no other clock has it. The front of the clock on the base is ornamented by three beautiful gilt metal scrolls, two fine columns, one on each side of the dial, made in exact imitation of marble, lend a rich appearance to the clock; the dial is 5½ inches in diameter with ornamented sash.

This clock stands 10½ inches high and is 12½ inches wide at the base.

The movement is manufactured by one of the most representative clock makers in the United States. On account of the cut price we cannot give name. It runs eight days with one winding, strikes the hours and half hours on a soft toned gong. Weight, packed ready for shipment, about 14 pounds.

You will not alone get a clock at a great bargain price, but you will get a PROFIT SHARING CERTIFICATE for the full amount of your purchase, and can soon get one of the valuable articles FREE, shown on the last pages.

No. 5E3305 Price **$2.48**

Our $3.62 Mantel Clock.

No. 5E3711 · OUR COUNTESS JANET Mantel Clock. The most wonderful bargain ever offered in the United States. This mantel clock is made of wood, then hard enameled in black with marbleized ornamentation, exactly as illustration shows. Stands 10¾ inches high, 7⅛ inches deep, 16¼ inches wide. Has gilt metal feet, side ornaments and tops and bases of the two columns on front of clock. It has an eight-day movement, strikes the half-hours on a bell, and the hours on a gong. The dial is 5½ inches in diameter, with plain numerals; the dial sash is the latest Parisian pattern. This is one of the most wonderful values offered. It was made especially for us, and carries our five-year binding guarantee. We cannot divulge the maker's name on account of the low price quoted. The movement will give particularly good satisfaction, it is of hard rolled brass and oil tempered steel parts. All friction in the train and delicate running parts has been reduced to a minimum, thereby giving it a life of accurate time keeping not possible in other clocks. Weight, 18 pounds. Price **$3.62**

No. 5E3301 Handsome Bronze Figure, representing a cowboy on horseback, throwing a lariat. This figure placed on top of the Countess Janet Clock makes a most beautiful parlor ornament.

Price, figure only 65c

No. 5E3542 THE DORIS Eight-Day Calendar, Barometer and Thermometer Wall Clock, for $2.44. Stands 24 inches high, and is 14 inches wide. Comes in walnut only. Dial, 5½ inches in diameter. By owning this clock, you will not only have accurate time for eight days, with one winding, but likewise perpetual calendar and barometer and thermometer; the thermometer showing the temperature and the barometer prognosticating climatic changes. The movement is a very good one, manufactured by the Ansonia Clock Co., and is warranted to give entire satisfaction. $2.44 may seem little or nothing for a clock such as we describe, and this $2.44 price is only made possible by a new deal with the Ansonia Clock Co. It is made especially for us by them and sold to no one else but to us. The purchase of an immense quantity was the only way to make this deal possible. Remember, this clock is not just a show clock but a clock that runs eight days with one winding, strikes the hours and half hours on a wire bell, in every way timed and accurately adjusted, so as to give satisfaction. Weight, boxed for shipment, 17 pounds Price **$2.44**

Second to None at the Price, $4.08

No. 5E3555 CUCKOO CLOCK. Case is made of German oak or walnut ornamented with inlaid ash, ebony and mahogany. Beautifully hand carved throughout, strikes the hours and half hours on a wire bell, the cuckoo appears and calls at the same time. Height of clock, 21 inches; width, 14 inches. The movement is made in the Black Forest, Germany, of the finest tempered steel and polished brass, finely finished and adjusted guaranteed to be a good timekeeper. One of the most artistic ornaments for a parlor ever made. Weight, boxed, 20 pounds.

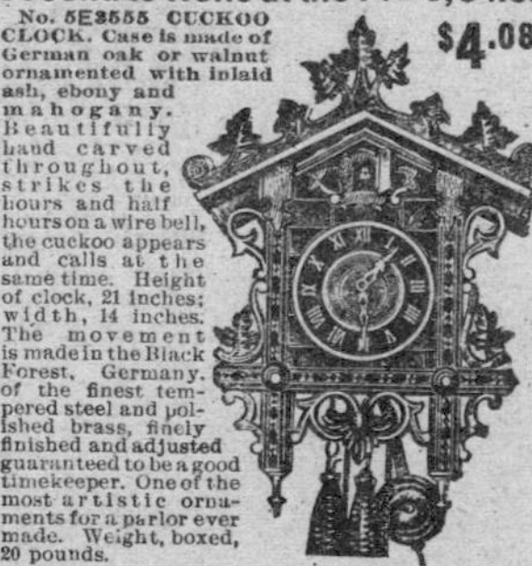

Price **$4.08**

German Cuckoo Clock, $6.65.

It strikes the hours and half hours on a wire bell, a cuckoo appears and calls at the same time.

No. 5E3557 CUCKOO. Case made of German oak or walnut, hand carved bird top, hand carved oak leaves. The entire carving on this clock is done by hand by the natives of the Schwarzwald, Germany, and is especially fine and artistic. The figures are accurate and lifelike. **The movement is made of the very finest tempered steel and highly wrought brass.** It is finely finished and perfectly adjusted. Height, 18 inches; width, 14 inches. Weight, boxed, 20 lbs. Price **$6.65**

$6.65

Quail and Cuckoo Clock.

Price, $10.78.

No. 5E3561 The quail whistles the quarter hours and the cuckoo calls the full hours. The latest improved and genuine Black Forest masterpiece, imported especially for us from Germany. It is new, novel and practical. The case is hand carved German walnut or oak, as desired. Height of clock, 21 inches; width, 16 inches. The movement is of fine polished brass and steel. Each one is carefully examined and adjusted before shipment. It strikes the hours and quarter hours on a fine toned gong. The quail whistles the quarter hours and the cuckoo calls the full hours. Every detail in this clock is finished to perfection. Weight, boxed ready for shipment, about 32 pounds.

We guarantee this clock to satisfy you.

Price **$10.78**

Hand Carved Cuckoo Clock, $5.10.

$5.10

No. 5E3558 Our New Triple Bird Hand Carved Cuckoo Clock. This clock is made of black walnut with three beautiful hand carved birds and sprays of grape leaves. Height from head of bird to base of clock, 18 inches; extreme width, 14 inches. The movement is built of tempered steel and brass. We guarantee the clock to give entire and absolute satisfaction. Runs 30 hours with one winding and the cuckoo calls the hours and half hours. Winds up by pulling chain, as illustration shows. The movement is imported from Germany. The case is carved and made in the United States. Dial is 5 inches in diameter with white celluloid figures and genuine white bone hands. Full directions how to hang and regulate clock printed on back of case. While it is not the equal of other cuckoo clocks, which we illustrate, in finish or quality, and the movement not as fully adjusted, considering the price, it will give excellent satisfaction. Weight, packed for shipment, 22 pounds.

Price **$5.10**

A Beautiful Gilt Mantel, Desk or Bureau Clock, 98c.

No. 5E3705 Runs 36 hours with one winding. Has 2-inch dial, with fine French beveled glass. Clock stands 6 inches high, and is manufactured by the Waterbury Clock Co. We guarantee this clock to give entire satisfaction.

Price **98c**

If by mail, postage extra, 27 cents.

$3.98 Buys an $8.00 Clock.

No. 5E3722 The Dawson. A polished wood, eight-day clock, strikes the hours on a gong and the half-hours on a cup bell. Clock stands 11 inches high; width, 16⅝ inches; dial, 5¼ inches. The combination of two colors, black and marble, together with the gilt front, side ornaments and gilt feet, lends a beauty to this clock that cannot be described. You must see the clock to appreciate it. Remember, this clock is not made by a cheap manufacturer, but is the creation of the celebrated Waterbury Clock Co., Waterbury, Conn., and warranted in every respect. Weight, boxed ready for shipment, about 18 pounds. Price........................$3.98

Beautiful Mantel Clock for $4.87.

No. 5E3723 THE PATMOS. A very handsome mantel clock, a most excellent imitation of Mexican onyx, and unless it is examined very closely no one would believe that it was not a real onyx clock. **It holds a beautiful polish and with proper care will last a lifetime.** If the case gets soiled or dirty it can be wiped off with a damp cloth. Has fancy bronze feet in artistic design and side dragon head metal **ornaments.** Length of clock, 17 inches; height, 11½ inches. **Has an eight-day movement,** made by **Seth Thomas Clock Company.** Strikes hours on a cathedral gong and half hours on a cup bell. Weight, boxed, about 16 pounds. Price............$4.87

Our Empress Mantel Clock, $4.45.

No. 5E3901 OUR EMPRESS MANTEL CLOCK, exactly as illustration shows in every detail. It stands 10¾ inches high, 7 inches deep, 17⅛ inches wide. It has solid gilt bronze feet, gilt bronze ornaments on the front of the clock. Clock is made of wood, enameled in black, with marbleized trimmings. This enameling is guaranteed not to warp or chip off. A woolen cloth, slightly sprinkled with sweet oil, lightly rubbed over this clock, will keep it in perfect condition for a lifetime. The dial is 5¾ inches in diameter. The sash which surrounds it is the very latest rococo design. The movement runs for eight days with one winding, strikes the half hours on a metal bell and the hours on a sweet toned gong. It is manufactured by one of the most celebrated clock companies in the United States, on account of the low price quoted here, we cannot print the maker's name. The movement, as in all of our own special clocks, is made of hardened rolled brass and oil tempered steel parts. The bearings and all intricate and delicate parts, where friction reduces the wearing ability, are so constructed that it is reduced to a minimum, therefore we know our special line of clocks will outwear any on the market and give accurate time. **This clock is the most massive and most pretentious and biggest value for the money ever before offered.** Clocks sold by the makers of this clock, of similar design but not so massive or elaborate, bring from the retail jewelers and from the jobbers from 25 to 30 per cent more than the price we ask. Just compare this clock with others, and we are satisfied that we will get your order. Weight, boxed for shipment, 18 pounds. Price........................$4.45

The Hollis. Rare Value for $4.48.

No. 5E3905 THE HOLLIS. Adamantine finished clock, manufactured by The Seth Thomas Clock Co. The movement fitted in this case we guarantee to give entire satisfaction. **The enamel is guaranteed not to wear or chip off. A beautiful head of a lion in solid bronze ornaments** the sides. Handsome bronze feet. **Hand engraved scrolls of various designs ornament the front.** The dial is 5 inches, with Roman figures. This clock stands 11 inches high and 14 inches long, **goes eight days with one winding; strikes the hours and half hours upon a cathedral gong.** Warranted to keep accurate time, with care will last a natural lifetime. Weight of clock when boxed is about 15 pounds. Price........................$4.48

The Beauty Mantel Clock and Ornament for $5.85.

$5.85 as Illustrated.

No. 5E3908 THE BEAUTY. One of the finest and most artistic clocks ever manufactured. We contracted with the factory to use an immense quantity at an unheard of price. **We quote a selling price unheard of before for a clock of this high standard of make.** Height, without ornament, 11 inches; base, 17 inches; with ornament, clock stands 19 inches high. **The movement is manufactured by the Seth Thomas Clock Company,** and is guaranteed to keep accurate time. It runs for eight days with one winding. The parts are made of fine wrought polished brass and oil tempered steel. It strikes the half hours on a cup bell and the hours on a cathedral gong that is toned with the church bells. **The case is adamantine finished and highly polished,** therefore can be cleaned without injury with a damp cloth. **Foot and side ornaments are of highly burnished bronze.** It is a clock such as you have never seen before for the price. Clock and ornament, boxed ready for shipment, weighs 25 pounds.

No. 5E3908 Price, complete with figure........$5.85

No. 5E3910 Price, without figure............$4.95

No. 5E3912 Figure alone. Price....................90c

Our Edgemere Queen Mantel Clock at $5.15.

No. 5E3915 OUR EDGEMERE QUEEN MANTEL CLOCK. The latest and newest design in clocks. This is one of the Seth Thomas Clock Co.'s latest productions. **The case is mahogany, covered with a transparent material called adamantine, guaranteed impervious to dust, damp and age.** A damp cloth keeps it new and polished forever. **It is always glossy, always new** and one of the richest appearing clocks ever placed on the market. **Dimensions of clock**—Height, 11½ inches; length, 16¼ inches; depth, 6¼ inches. **The movement is one of the latest improved Seth Thomas clock movements.** It runs eight days with one winding, the parts are guaranteed fine wrought polished brass and oil tempered steel. It strikes the hours on a cathedral gong and half hours on a cup bell. **The case** is ornamented with two gilt lion heads, one on each end. The front is ornamented by four columns, topped and based with fine gilded metal ornaments. The entire clock rests upon four gilded feet, exactly as shown in illustration. **The dial is one of the latest Parisian patterns,** gilded and beautifully executed; the design is brought out most elaborately. Dial is 5¾ inches in diameter, making it possible for you to see the time from quite a distance. We consider this one of the most artistic and one of the most beautiful clocks on the market. It embodies the perfections of all and the faults of none. Weight, boxed for shipment, about 17 pounds. Price........................$5.15

Our American Lady Mantel Clock, $3.98.

$3.98

No. 5E3917 OUR AMERICAN LADY MANTEL CLOCK, manufactured by one of the biggest and most representative makers in the United States, but on account of the very low price quoted, we dare not print the maker's name. However, it carries our five-year written binding guarantee, and we know you will be entirely satisfied with it. This clock stands 10¾ inches high, 7 inches deep and 17 inches wide. It has solid gilt bronze feet and side ornaments, also metal top and base on the four columns, as illustration shows. The dial is 5¾ inches in diameter, the very latest pattern of fancy fret work, with a beautiful rococo sash. The case is of wood, black enameled, warranted not to peel, chip or crack off. A soft woolen cloth, sprinkled with sweet oil, will keep it as new, practically, for a lifetime. The movement runs eight days with one winding; strikes the half hours on a metal bell and the hours on a soft toned gong. **This our American Lady mantel clock, is one of the special bargains we have referred you to in our description on page 112.** If this clock suits your taste, we refer to the design, we know that a better clock or a greater value for the money cannot be had for twice what we ask. We are particularly proud of the movement used in this clock, as it is made of solid hardened rolled brass and oil tempered steel parts. The bearings and other delicate parts are so constructed that the friction is reduced to a minimum, therefore the life of the clock is greater than any other. Weight, boxed for shipment, 18 pounds. Price........................$3.98

REMEMBER YOU SHARE IN OUR PROFIT.

Every purchase means not only money saved on the purchase, but you help yourself to get some valuable article absolutely FREE of cost to you, as explained on the last pages.

OUR CROCKERY AND GLASSWARE DEPARTMENT.

DINNER AND TOILET SETS herein shown consist of only the best goods made by the world's foremost potters, and include French, German, Austrian, English and American ware, in the latest and most handsome patterns, which include the following celebrated makers' wares, which for years have been acknowledged by china experts to be the best:

- Theo. Haviland, Limoges, France.
- Elite China Company, Bavaria.
- Hapsburg China Company, Germany.
- Victoria China Company, Austria.
- Johnson Bros., England.
- Grindley & Co., England.
- Jno. Maddock & Sons, England.
- Wood & Sons, England.
- Hulm Pottery Company, England.
- Homer Laughlin China Company, America.
- Edwin M. Knowles China Company, America.
- Smith Phillips China Company, America.
- Mayer Pottery Company, America.

The above potters comprise the world's best makers of high grade dinner ware, who for many years have enjoyed the reputation of producing goods **absolutely perfect in body, finish and glaze**, having wearing qualities that are unsurpassed.

THE LATEST PATTERNS. Being in close touch with the largest and best potteries in the world we are in a position to contract for the newest and best patterns at all times, and are, therefore, able to not only offer the best goods, but are in a position to offer the very latest patterns long before they are offered to the regular crockery dealer.

COMPARE OUR PRICES with those asked by your local dealer and you will readily appreciate that every dinner set herein offered represents a saving of from $2.50 to $10.00. **DO NOT BE DECEIVED** by allowing your dealer to lead you to believe that our goods are second quality, which is the only excuse he could offer for our low prices.

WE SELL NO SECONDS in any of these wares, and only handle the finest and most carefully selected goods the market affords.

WE GUARANTEE OUR WARE to please you in every respect, not only in wearing quality, but we also guarantee the decoration will meet with your entire approval and please you in every way, or it may be returned at our expense and we will immediately refund the price of the set, together with all transportation charges and extra expense you may have been put to. With this binding guarantee you take no risk whatever in sending us your order.

ABOUT FREIGHT CHARGES. Nearly all railroad companies carry crockery and glassware at second class rate, and sometimes as low as third class, depending on the section of the United States to which it is shipped. The second class rate averages from 40 to 50 cents per 100 pounds for 500 miles. The weights of different dinner sets and glassware sets are all plainly given in the catalogue, and by referring to the freight rates in the front of this book you can get the freight rate to your railroad station and thus figure very close to what your freight will amount to, and you will find that it will amount to next to nothing as compared to what you will save in price.

OUR BINDING GUARANTEE. We guarantee that if you order one of our sets of dinnerware or glassware, and do not find it in every respect better in quality and lower in price than what you could procure the same grade of ware for from any other dealer, upon return of goods we will refund your money in full. We furthermore guarantee that our dinnerware will not craze, and will agree to replace, free of charge, any piece that may prove defective in material or workmanship. All the glassware listed is of the best grade it is possible to procure, and will, with ordinary care, stand the test of a lifetime.

FOR 5 CENTS each we send, postpaid, an individual butter plate of any dinner set. This sample, though small, will show the quality of the ware and give a fair idea of the decoration of the set. It is impossible to show a dinner set to the best advantage by submitting so small a piece, as all pieces are decorated with sprigs best adapted to its respective size, and therefore the sprigs used on individual butters are quite small and will give you simply an idea of the colors and a general idea of the flower or decoration used.

NOTE—ALL PLATTERS ARE MEASURED FROM EDGE TO EDGE.

UNDER THE ILLUSTRATION AND DESCRIPTION OF EACH STYLE OF DINNERWARE

will be shown the combination which can be furnished of that kind, and in every case it would be advisable for the customer to **REFER TO THIS PAGE** to see exactly what pieces are contained in each set.

100-Piece Dinner Set.

- 12 Tea Cups
- 12 Tea Saucers
- 12 Dinner Plates
- 12 Tea Plates
- 12 Pie Plates
- 12 Sauce Dishes
- 12 Butter Plates
- 1 Platter, 12 inch
- 1 Platter, 14-inch
- 1 Oval Open Vegetable Dish
- 1 Round Open Vegetable Dish
- 1 Covered Vegetable Dish (2 pieces)
- 1 Covered Sugar Bowl (2 pieces)
- 1 Sauce Boat
- 1 Pickle Dish
- 1 Covered Butter Dish (3 pieces)
- 1 Bowl
- 1 Cream Pitcher
- 1 Pitcher, quart size

Shipping weight, 90 pounds.

101-Piece Dinner Set.

- 12 Tea Cups
- 12 Tea Saucers
- 12 Dinner Plates
- 12 Tea Plates
- 12 Soup Plates
- 12 Sauce Dishes
- 12 Butter Plates
- 1 Oval Open Vegetable Dish
- 1 Round Open Vegetable Dish
- 2 Covered Vegetable Dishes (4 pieces)
- 1 Platter, 12-inch
- 1 Platter, 14-inch
- 1 Covered Sugar Bowl (2 pieces)
- 1 Cream Pitcher
- 1 Pickle Dish
- 1 Bowl
- 1 Covered Butter Dish (3 pieces)
- 1 Sauce Boat

Shipping weight, 90 pounds.

56-Piece Dinner Set.

- 6 Tea Cups
- 6 Tea Saucers
- 6 Dinner Plates
- 6 Tea Plates
- 6 Pie Plates
- 6 Sauce Dishes
- 6 Butter Plates
- 1 Platter, 10-inch
- 1 Platter, 12-inch
- 1 Oval Baker
- 1 Covered Vegetable Dish (2 pieces)
- 1 Sauce Boat
- 1 Pickle Dish
- 1 Covered Butter Dish (3 pieces)
- 1 Sugar Bowl (2 pieces)
- 1 Cream Pitcher
- 1 Bowl

Shipping weight, 50 pounds.

80-Piece Dinner Set.

- 12 Tea Cups
- 12 Tea Saucers
- 12 Dinner Plates
- 12 Pie Plates
- 12 Sauce Dishes
- 12 Butter Plates
- 1 Platter, 12-inch
- 1 Platter, 14-inch
- 1 Round Open Vegetable Dish
- 1 Oval Open Vegetable Dish
- 1 Covered Vegetable Dish (2 pieces)
- 1 Sauce Boat
- 1 Pickle Dish

Shipping weight, 65 pounds.

SEVEN OF OUR MOST POPULAR AND UP TO DATE DINNERWARE PATTERNS are listed as open stock patterns (each article quoted separately), on pages 120, 122 and 125. **THE PRICES** in many instances are less than regular wholesale prices.

OUR LEADER, 100-PIECE DINNER SET.

$3.98

REMEMBER you will get a valuable **PROFIT SHARING CERTIFICATE** and can soon get something FREE, shown on the last pages.

AT $3.98 we offer a complete 100-piece Plain White Dinner Set, which we guarantee to be the best value ever offered. It is made of plain white stone china (white granite), pure white in color with smooth white glaze. **This set is absolutely first quality in every respect,** and contains no crooked or chipped pieces, found in sets offered by many other dealers, who sacrifice quality in order to make an attractive price. While this set is the greatest value ever offered, we call special attention to our **semi-vitreous set,** illustrated and described below, at $4.98, the equal of the best grade of genuine imported English dinnerware, usually sold at from $7.00 to $10.00 for a 100-piece set, and not equaled in quality nor price by any other dealer. Each set is carefully packed in a barrel and shipped from the pottery in East Liverpool, Ohio, from which point the customer pays the freight.

When ordered with dinner set, we can furnish the following pieces:

Coffee Cups and Saucers, per doz.. 85c	Ind. Vegetable or Side Dishes, per doz. 75c
New shape Coupe Soups, per dozen 75c	Bone Dishes, per dozen 65c

No. 2E195 100-piece Plain White Dinner Set. Shipping weight, 80 pounds. Price.................................... **$3.98**

For number and style of pieces included in above set, see top of this page.

100-PIECE SEMI-VITREOUS CHINA.

$4.98

FINEST QUALITY OF AMERICAN PORCELAIN.

THE FINEST GRADE OF SEMI-VITREOUS CHINA DINNERWARE made in America, and is considered the most up to date and best modeled dinner service on the market. It is made by the celebrated Laughlin China Company, who enjoys the reputation of making only the finest ware. Its wearing qualities are unsurpassed, as the body is composed of the finest grades of clay, fired to a flinty hardness and covered by a deep, glossy, milk white glaze heretofore to be found only in the most expensive sets. As the illustration shows, this set is extremely handsome, as it is **very light and thin** and most gracefully modeled and neatly embossed. **We positively guarantee the ware** to be the finest selection, perfect in every way, without misshapes or small impractical sizes.

Each set is carefully packed by expert packers and shipped direct from the pottery in East Liverpool, Ohio, from which point the customer pays the freight. We will furnish the set in our regular 100-piece combination, as shown above, or **in open stock at prices quoted below.**

No. 2E200 100-piece Dinner Set. Price.......................(Shipping weight, 70 pounds)......................... **$4.98**

	Actual Size	Per Dozen
Tea Cups and Saucers...	8¼ oz.	$0.85
Coffee Cups and Saucers	10¼ oz.	1.00
Pie Plates..................	7½ in.	.48
Tea Plates	8⅜ in.	.58
Dinner Plates	9⅜ in.	.69
Dinner Plates, ex. large	10¼ in.	.85
Coupe Soup Plates........	8 in.	.70
Sauce Dishes.............	5¼ in.	.32
Oatmeal Dishes	6¼ in.	.59
Individual Butters........	2¾ in.	.21

	Actual Size	Per Dozen
Bone Dishes	6x3 in.	$0.65
Oyster Bowls..............	1¼ pt.	.85
Indv. Vegetable Dishes..	5½ in.	.75
		Each
Pitchers	1 qt.	$0.15
Pitchers....................	2 qt.	.25
Pitchers....................	3 qt.	.43
Tea Pots	3 pt.	.35
Gravy or Sauce Boats....	¾ pt.	.15
Sauce Tureens and Stands	9¾ in.	.55

	Actual Size	Price, each
Pickle Dishes..............	9½ in.	$0.12
Round Bakers or Vegetable Dishes..................	8½ in.	.12
Round Bakers or Vegetable Dishes..................	9½ in.	.18
Cake Plates................	9⅝ in.	.18
Oval Bakers	9¼ in.	.14
Oval Bakers	10¼ in.	.18
Platters	10¾ in.	.08
Platters	11½ in.	.15

	Actual Size	Price, each
Platters.....	13½ in.	$0.28
Platters.......	15¼ in.	.39
Platters.....................	18 in.	.69
Covered Dishes...........	9¾ in.	.45
Covered Casseroles	9¼ in.	.55
Soup Tureens and Stands	15¼ in.	1.98
Creamers.....	⅞ pt.	.12
Sugar Bowls, covered....	¾ qt.	.25
Covered Butter Dishes...	5½ in.	.33
Bowls........................	1¼ pt.	.07

The above **open stock dinnerware** shipped from Chicago to our customers living in the West, and from the pottery in East Liverpool, Ohio, to our Eastern and Southern trade.

HAMPSHIRE DINNER SET, $4.40.

MOST WONDERFUL VALUE.

NEW THIS SEASON. Our Hampshire Dinner Set is made of high grade semi-porcelain, pure white in color, with a rich heavy glaze. It has a new and attractive shape which has never before been offered in a dinner set so low in price. The decoration consists of neat floral sprays with the background of dainty ferns arranged in a most effective manner, as illustration shows. The decoration is applied by the stencil process over the glaze and then thoroughly baked in, and therefore will not fade or wear off. It is made by the Laughlin China Co., whose reputation stands for only first class ware. Furnished in three decorations, green, blue or brown. Mention the color desired when ordering.

No. 2E205 Hampshire Dinner Sets furnished in two combinations as follows:

56-piece Dinner Set. Shipping weight, 50 pounds. Price............**$4.40**
100-piece Dinner Set. Shipping weight, 70 pounds. Price............ **5.98**

For number and style of pieces, see list on page 120.

We also furnish our Hampshire dinner set decorated as described above, but with **hand gold tracing added on all handles and knobs, at the prices** mentioned below:

No. 2E206 Hampshire Sets, with gold decorated knobs and handles.
56-piece Dinner Set. Shipping weight, 50 pounds. Price..........**$4.98**
100-piece Dinner Set. Shipping weight, 70 pounds. Price.......... **6.75**

Each set is carefully packed and shipped from the pottery in East Liverpool, Ohio, from which point the customer pays the freight.

ARBUTUS DINNER SET, $4.69.

OUR ARBUTUS FLORAL PATTERN

is one of the best medium priced patterns in our line. The decoration is entirely new and exceptionally handsome, as it consists of dainty clusters and sprays of arbutus flowers and foliage, delicately shaded and artistically applied by the French decalcomania process, which heretofore has only been used on the highest priced ware. The decoration is furnished in two colors, a rich shade of green or a rich deep pink. Either is exceptionally handsome and is sure to harmonize with the finest table decorations. The ware is made of the finest grade of semi-porcelain by the famous Dresden Pottery, one of America's best potteries. The ware is light and thin and is most carefully selected, and has a deep, glossy, milk white glaze. All pieces are handsomely modeled and embossed in such a manner as to form a neat border encircling each piece. Without doubt, this is the finest set ever offered at so low a price.

These sets are shipped direct to our customers from East Liverpool, Ohio, and are carefully packed by expert packers, which insures safe delivery.

No. 2E214 Our Arbutus Semi-Porcelain Dinner Set.

56-piece Dinner Set. Shipping weight, 50 pounds Price...............**$4.69**
80-piece Dinner Set. Shipping weight, 60 pounds. Price............. **4.98**
100-piece Dinner Set. Shipping weight, 70 pounds. Price.............**$6.49**
101-piece Dinner Set. Shipping weight, 70 pounds. Price............ **7.48**

For number and style of pieces quoted above, see page 120. In ordering, please mention number of pieces desired.

THE ROSELYN DINNER SET, $5.49.

WONDERFUL VALUE.

The most attractive, popular priced dinner set made. The decoration, which consists of pink roses entwined with dainty little forget-me-nots and green leaves, makes one of the handsomest patterns we offer. **All handles and knobs on the platters, covered dishes, butter dishes, sugar bowls, creamers, pickle dishes, sauce boats, cups, etc., are neatly hand traced with bright coin gold, fully burnt on.**

THE SHAPE IS ENTIRELY NEW

and is very light and thin. One of the prettiest and most practical shapes made in American dinnerware. Every piece is perfectly modeled, and has rich embossings, in lace effect as illustration shows. It is made by the Smith-Phillips China Co., one of the best potters in America. We guarantee the ware to be perfect in every respect and not to craze. Each set is carefully packed in a barrel and shipped direct from the pottery in East Liverpool, Ohio, from which point the customer pays the freight.

When ordered with regular sets quoted above we furnish the following pieces:

Coffee Cups and Saucers. Price, per dozen.................................**$1.49**
Coupe Soup Plates. Price, per dozen....................................... **1.20**
Individual Side Dishes. Price, per dozen.................................. **1.39**

For number and style of pieces included in the dinner sets quoted above, see list on page 120.

No. 2E241 Roselyn Dinner Sets.

56-piece Dinner Set. Shipping weight, 50 pounds. Price..........**$5.49**
80-piece Dinner Set. Shipping weight, 60 pounds. Price........... **6.45**
100-piece Dinner Set. Shipping weight, 70 pounds. Price.......... **7.89**
101-piece Dinner Set. Shipping weight, 70 pounds. Price.......... **9.35**

100-PIECE FLORAL BORDER DINNER SET, $6.98.

MADE IN ENGLAND.

FURNISHED IN CANTON BLUE OR RICH SAGE GREEN.

OUR FLORAL BORDER DINNER SET

is the best value ever offered in good quality English ware. It is made by the celebrated W. Hulm Pottery, Burslem, Eng., and is guaranteed never to craze. **The body of the ware is thin and light** in weight and has a deep glossy milk white glaze. This set is superior in every respect to the average makes of medium priced English dinnerware and must be seen to be fully appreciated. **The shape is new and attractive,** having fancy scalloped edges, all covered pieces, including covered dishes, sugar, creamer, butter dish, etc., are very gracefully embossed. **This is one of the best underglazed print decorations.** It consists of a border of flowers and foliage, as shown in illustration, and can be furnished in **CANTON BLUE or RICH SAGE GREEN.**

The set consists of 100 pieces as follows:

12 Tea Cups	12 Individual Butters	1 Covered Sugar Bowl
12 Saucers	1 Platter, 10-inch	1 Creamer
12 Dinner Plates	1 Platter, 14-inch	1 Pickle Dish
12 Tea Plates	1 Baker, 8-inch	1 Sauce Boat
12 Pie Plates	2 Covered Dishes, 10-inch	1 Covered Butter Dish
12 Sauce Dishes	1 Bowl	

Each set is carefully packed in a barrel and is shipped from Chicago to our customers in the Central and Western States, and from our warehouse in Boston, Mass., to eastern customers, thus assuring the lowest freight charges.

No. 2E243 100-piece Dinner Set. Price.................................**$6.98**

Shipping weight, 70 pounds. In ordering, please mention the color you desire.

FLORENCE ROSE DINNER SET, $4.95.

Made by the
E. M. KNOWLES CHINA CO.

THIS BEAUTIFUL PATTERN sold in open stock and complete dinner sets. **Our Florence Rose Ware** is one of the prettiest and most dainty patterns on the market. The decoration is applied by the new decalcomania process and is an exact reproduction of one of the most popular Haviland china patterns. The decoration consists of a delicate spray border of pink roses, with background of small white daisies with pink tinted petals and green foliage, with small clusters of roses artistically arranged to form a border. It is made by the celebrated Edwin M. Knowles China Company, one of the best known potteries in America. The ware is made from the best quality of semi-porcelain, being handsomely modeled and embossed and covered with a heavy milk white glaze. We fully guarantee the ware to be of the finest selection, perfect in every respect.

No. 2E217 Our Florence Rose Dinner Set.
56-piece Dinner Set. Shipping weight, 50 pounds. Price........ **$4.95**
80-piece Dinner Set. Shipping weight, 60 pounds. Price........ **5.85**
100-piece Dinner Set. Shipping weight, 70 pounds. Price........ **$7.48**
101-piece Dinner Set. Shipping weight, 70 pounds. Price........ **8.85**
For number and style of pieces quoted above, see page 120.

No. 2E217 Open Stock. **Our Florence Rose Dinner Ware,** as above illustrated and described, is also quoted in **open stock** at prices mentioned below, giving our customers the advantage of making their own selections of pieces at exceptionally low prices. No order for less than $3.00 will be accepted.

Each dinner set or order for open stock is very carefully packed in a barrel and shipped direct from the pottery in East Liverpool, Ohio, to customers in the east, and from Chicago to our western trade.

	Actual Size	Per Dozen
Tea Cups and Saucers	½ pt.	$1.39
Coffee Cups and Saucers	⅝ pt.	1.69
Bread and Butter Plates	6½ in.	.69
Pie Plates	7⅜ in.	.89
Tea Plates	8¼ in.	1.10
Dinner Plates	9 in.	1.28
Dinner Plates, extra large	9¾ in.	1.39
Coupe Soup Plates	8⅜ in.	1.29
Sauce Dishes	5¼ in.	.59
Oatmeal Dishes	6½ in.	.95
Individual Butters	3⅜ in.	.38

	Actual Size	Per Dozen
Bone Dishes		$1.20
Oyster Bowls	1½ pts.	1.59
Individual Vegetable Dishes	5½ in.	1.39
		Price, each
Pitchers	1¼ pts.	$0.17
Pitchers	2⅛ pts.	.19
Pitchers	3½ pts.	.23
Pitchers	4½ pts.	.38
Pitchers	6 pts.	.59
Tea Pots	3 pts.	.59

	Actual Size	Price, each
Sauce or Gravy Boats		$0.29
Sauce Tureens and Stands		.98
Pickle Dishes		.19
Round Nappies	8 in.	.19
Round Nappies	9 in.	.29
Cake Plates	10 in.	.25
Oval Bakers	9 in.	.19
Oval Bakers	9⅞ in.	.29
Platters, small	10 in.	.17
Platters, medium	11¾ in.	.29
Platters, medium large	14 in.	.48

	Actual Size	Price, each
Platters, large	16 in.	$0.69
Platters, extra large	17⅜ in.	.98
Oval Covered Dishes	9¼ in.	.69
Oval Covered Dishes	9¾ in.	.79
Covered Casseroles	8½ in.	.79
Soup Tureens	10 in.	1.98
Creamers	¾ pt.	.19
Covered Sugar Bowls	¾ qt.	.39
Covered Butter Dishes		.59
Bowls	1¾ pt.	.12

ENGLISH SEMI-PORCELAIN DINNER SET, $4.98.

Made by
JOHNSON BROTHERS.
ENGLAND.

ENTIRELY NEW PLAIN WHITE

Johnson Bros.' Genuine English Semi-Porcelain is recognized as the best in the world. The shape, as illustration shows, is far superior to any heretofore offered by this famous pottery. Every piece is gracefully modeled and handsomely embossed. The ware is pure white with a deep glossy glaze and is exactly the same quality and perfect selection as found in Johnsons' highest priced decorated sets. The ware is light and thin and closely resembles the highest priced Haviland china. We highly recommend this ware and fully guarantee it to be absolutely the best English semi-porcelain made, regardless of price.

We furnish this pattern in open stock and complete dinner sets. The dinner sets are carefully packed by expert packers, shipped direct to our customers in the Eastern and Southern States from our warehouse in Cleveland, Ohio, and to our customers in the West from Chicago, thus insuring the lowest freight charges on each shipment.

No. 2E245 Johnson Bros.' English Semi-Porcelain Dinner Set.
56-piece Dinner Set. Shipping weight, 50 pounds Price........ **$4.98**
80-piece Dinner Set. Shipping weight, 60 pounds. Price........ **5.98**
100-piece Dinner Set. Shipping weight, 70 pounds. Price........ **$7.65**
101-piece Dinner Set. Shipping weight, 70 pounds. Price........ **8.95**
In ordering, state the number of pieces desired.
For number and style of pieces quoted above, see page 120.

No. 2E245 Johnson Bros.' Silver Shape White Semi-Porcelain Ware sold in open stock. For the convenience of our customers we also offer this fine ware (as described above) as an open stock pattern. Choose the number of pieces you desire at the prices mentioned below. No orders will be accepted amounting to less than $2.00. Open stock shipped from Chicago only.

	Actual Size	Per Doz.
Tea Cups and Saucers	½ pt.	$1.10
Coffee Cups and Saucers	⅝ pt.	1.32
Bread and Butter Plates	6⅜ in.	.60
Pie Plates	6¾ in.	.64
Tea Plates	7¾ in.	.78
Dinner Plates	8¾ in.	.92
Dinner Plates, extra large	9¾ in.	1.08
New Coupe Soup Plates	8 in.	.96
Soup Plates	8¾ in.	.92
Sauce Dishes	5¼ in.	.42
Oatmeal Dishes	6¼ in.	.75
Individual Butters	3 in.	.28
Bone Dishes		.95

	Actual Size	Per Doz.
Individual Vegetable Dishes or Bakers	5¼ in.	$0.95
Oyster Bowls	1 pt.	1.09
		Each
Oval Covered Dishes	8½ in.	.48
Oval Covered Dishes	9½ in	.58
Round Covered Casseroles	8½ in.	.65
Sauce Tureens with Ladle and Stand	6½x5½ in.	.72
Sauce Tureens without Ladle and Stand		.53
Gravy and Sauce Boats	1 pt.	.19
Soup Tureens with Ladle and Stand	10x8 in.	2.65

	Actual Size	Price, each
Round Open Nappies	8½ in.	$0.20
Round Open Nappies	9½ in.	.24
Oval Open Vegetable Dishes	9 in.	.14
Oval Open Vegetable Dishes	10½ in.	.22
Platters, small	9⅞ in.	.11
Platters, medium	13½ in.	.21
Platters, medium large	14 in.	.33
Platters, large	14⅞ in.	.50
Platters, extra large	16⅞ in.	.78
Pitchers	½ pt.	.11
Pitchers	1 pt.	.15

	Actual Size	Price, each
Pitchers	1 qt.	$0.17
Pitchers	2 qts.	.27
Pitchers	2½ qts.	.42
Bowls	½ pt.	.07
Bowls	1 pt.	.09
Bowls	1 qt.	.11
Creamers	⅞ pt.	.15
Covered Sugar Bowls	¾ qt.	.33
Covered Butter Dishes		.43
Tea Pots	1 qt.	.38
Cake Plates	10 in.	.20
Pickle Dishes		15

GOLD WREATH DINNER SET, $6.95.

Made by
LAUGHLIN CHINA CO.

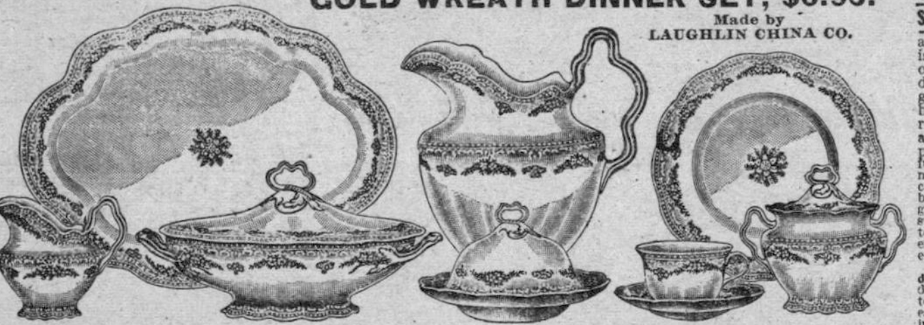

THIS WHITE AND GOLD DINNER SET is made by the Homer Laughlin China Company, and is a dainty and most beautiful dinner set which is exceedingly low in price. Lovers of dainty china will most appreciate this rich dinner service, as the decoration consists of gold floral wreaths which form a complete border pattern encircling all pieces and has rich gold lace medallion centers. All handles and knobs are hand traced in gold. Your particular attention is drawn to the beautiful shape known as the Angelus pattern, which is much thinner than the ordinary dinner ware and closely resembles Haviland china. It is richly embossed and equal in appearance to the best grade of English porcelain ware. In fact, this is of such a superior quality that we positively guarantee every piece against crazing even when put to extremely hard use. Being carefully packed by expert packers, we guarantee safe delivery.

We quote below four special sets at greatly reduced prices, but will also furnish white and gold dinner ware in open stock. Shipped from the pottery in Eastern Ohio to our customers living in the east and from Chicago to our western trade, thus insuring lowest freight rates.

No. 2E273 White and Gold Dinner Set.
56-piece Dinner Set. Shipping weight, 50 pounds. Price........ **$6.95**
80-piece Dinner Set. Shipping weight, 60 pounds. Price........ **7.95**
100-piece Dinner Set. Shipping weight, 70 pounds. Price........ **$8.98**
101-piece Dinner Set. Shipping weight, 70 pounds. Price........ **9.85**
In ordering, please mention the number of pieces desired.
For number and style of pieces included in the dinner sets quoted above, see page 120.

No. 2E273 Open Stock. **Our White and Gold Dinner Ware,** as above illustrated and described, is also quoted in **open stock** at prices mentioned below, giving our customers the advantage of making their own selections of pieces at exceptionally low prices. No order for less than $3.00 will be accepted.

	Actual Size	Per Doz.
Tea Cups and Saucers	8¼ oz.	$1.33
Coffee Cups and Saucers	10½ oz.	1.58
Pie Plates	7½ in.	.85
Tea Plates	8⅜ in.	.94
Dinner Plates	9⅜ in.	1.15
Dinner Plates, extra large	10¼ in.	1.33
Coupe Soup Plates	8 in.	1.15
Sauce Dishes	5¼ in.	.60
Oatmeal Dishes	6¼ in.	1.35
Individual Butters	2¾ in.	.36

	Actual Size	Per Doz.
Bone Dishes	6x3 in.	$1.10
Oyster Bowls	1¼ pt.	1.39
Individual Veg. Dishes	5½ in.	1.23
		Each
Pitchers	1 qt.	.23
Pitchers	2 qt.	.28
Pitchers	3 qt.	.35
Tea Pots	3 pt.	.63
Gravy or Sauce Boats	¾ pt.	.26
Sauce Tureens and Stands	9¾ in.	.65

	Actual Size	Price, each
Pickle Dishes	9½ in.	$0.19
Round Bakers Vegetable Dishes	8½ in.	.21
Round Bakers Vegetable Dishes	9½ in.	.28
Cake Plates	9⅞ in.	.23
Oval Bakers	9¼ in.	.21
Oval Bakers	10¼ in.	.28
Platters	10¾ in.	.12
Platters	11½ in.	17

	Actual Size	Price, each
Platters	13½ in.	$0.29
Platters	15¼ in.	.55
Platters	18 in.	.69
Covered Dishes	9¾ in.	.79
Covered Casseroles	9½ in.	.89
Soup Tureens and Stands	15¼ in.	2.95
Creamers	⅞ pt.	.17
Sugar Bowls, Covered	¾ pt.	.39
Covered Butter Dishes	5½ in.	.55
Bowls	1¼ pt.	12

KENSINGTON DINNER SET, $5.49.

Made by the MAYER POTTERY CO.

YOU WILL GET A PROFIT SHARING CERTIFICATE ALSO.

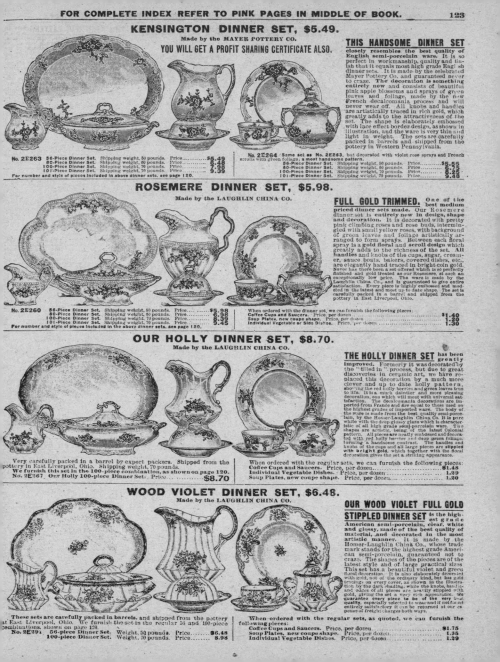

THIS HANDSOME DINNER SET closely resembles the best quality of English semi-porcelain ware. It is so perfect in workmanship, quality and finish that it equals most high grade English dinner sets. It is made by the celebrated Mayer Pottery Co. and guaranteed never to craze. **The decoration is something entirely new and consists of beautiful pink apple blossoms and sprays of green leaves and foliage, made by the new French decalcomania process and will never wear off.** All knobs and handles are artistically traced in rich gold, which greatly adds to the attractiveness of the set. The shape is elaborately embossed with lace effect border design, as shown in illustration, and the ware is very thin and light in weight. The sets are carefully packed in barrels and shipped from the pottery in Western Pennsylvania.

No. 2E263 **56-Piece Dinner Set.** Shipping weight, 50 pounds. Price............$5.49
80-Piece Dinner Set. Shipping weight, 60 pounds. Price............ 6.48
100-Piece Dinner Set. Shipping weight, 70 pounds. Price............ 7.98
101-Piece Dinner Set. Shipping weight, 70 pounds. Price............ 9.39

For number and style of pieces included in above dinner sets, see page 120.

No. 2E264 **Same set as No. 2E263**, but decorated with violet rose sprays and French scrolls with green foliage; **a most handsome pattern.**

56-Piece Dinner Set. Shipping weight, 50 pounds. Price............$5.55
80-Piece Dinner Set. Shipping weight, 60 pounds. Price............ 6.75
100-Piece Dinner Set. Shipping weight, 70 pounds. Price............ 8.25
101-Piece Dinner Set. Shipping weight, 70 pounds. Price............ 9.48

ROSEMERE DINNER SET, $5.98.

Made by the LAUGHLIN CHINA CO.

FULL GOLD TRIMMED. **One of the best medium priced dinner sets made.** Our Rosemere dinner set **is entirely new in design, shape and decoration.** It is decorated with pretty pink climbing roses and rose buds, intermingled with small yellow roses, with background of green leaves and foliage artistically arranged to form sprays. Between each floral spray is a **gold floral** and **scroll design** which greatly adds to the richness of the set. **All handles** and knobs of the cups, sugar, creamer, sauce boats, bakers, covered dishes, etc., are elegantly hand traced in bright coin gold. Never has there been a set offered which is so perfectly finished and gold treated as our Rosemere, at such an exceptionally low price. The ware is made by the Laughlin China Co., and is guaranteed to give entire satisfaction. Every piece is highly embossed and modeled in the latest and most up to date shape. The set is carefully packed in a barrel and shipped from the pottery in East Liverpool, Ohio.

No. 2E260 **56-Piece Dinner Set.** Shipping weight, 50 pounds. Price............$5.98
80-Piece Dinner Set. Shipping weight, 60 pounds. Price............ 6.98
100-Piece Dinner Set. Shipping weight, 70 pounds. Price............ 8.39
101-Piece Dinner Set. Shipping weight, 70 pounds. Price............ 9.45

For number and style of pieces included in the above dinner sets, see page 120.

When ordered with the dinner set, we can furnish the following pieces:

Coffee Cups and Saucers. Price, per dozen............$1.40
Soup Plates, new coupe shape. Price, per dozen............ 1.20
Individual Vegetable or Side Dishes. Price, per dozen............ 1.30

OUR HOLLY DINNER SET, $8.70.

Made by the LAUGHLIN CHINA CO.

THE HOLLY DINNER SET **has been greatly improved.** Formerly it was decorated by the "filled in" process, but due to great discoveries in ceramic art, we have replaced this decoration by a much more clever and up to date holly pattern, showing the red holly berries and green leaves true to life. It is a much daintier and more pleasing decoration, one which will meet with universal satisfaction. The decalcomania decorations are imported from France and are equal to those used on the highest grades of imported ware. The body of the ware is made from the best quality semi-porcelain, by the Homer-Laughlin China Co. It is pure white with the deep glossy glaze which is characteristic of all high grade semi-porcelain ware. The shapes are artistic, being of the latest Colonial pattern. All pieces are neatly embossed and decorated with red holly berries and deep green foliage, forming a handsome contrast. The handles and knobs of the cups and all large pieces are stippled **with bright gold**, which together with the floral decoration gives the set a striking appearance.

Very carefully packed in a barrel by expert packers. Shipped from the pottery in East Liverpool, Ohio. Shipping weight, 70 pounds.

We furnish this set in the 100-piece combination, as shown on page 120.

No. 2E267 **Our Holly 100-piece Dinner Set.** Price............**$8.70**

When ordered with the regular sets, we can furnish the following pieces:

Coffee Cups and Saucers. Price, per dozen............$1.48
Individual Vegetable Dishes. Price, per dozen............ 1.29
Soup Plates, new coupe shape. Price, per dozen............ 1.20

WOOD VIOLET DINNER SET, $6.48.

Made by the LAUGHLIN CHINA CO.

OUR WOOD VIOLET FULL GOLD STIPPLED DINNER SET **is the highest grade American semi-porcelain, clear, white and glossy, made of the best quality of material, and decorated in the most artistic manner.** It is made by the Homer-Laughlin China Co., whose trade mark stands for the highest grade American semi-porcelain, guaranteed not to craze. The shapes of the pieces are of the latest style and of large practical sizes. This set has a beautiful violet and green floral decoration. It is also elaborately decorated with gold, not of the ordinary kind, but has gold tracings on every cover, as shown in the illustration by the dark shading, while the knobs, handles and edges of all pieces are heavily stippled with gold, giving the set a very rich appearance. **We guarantee every piece to be of the very best quality**, especially selected to wear and if not found entirely satisfactory it can be returned at our expense of freight charges both ways.

These sets are carefully packed in barrels, and shipped from the pottery at East Liverpool, Ohio. We furnish the set in the regular 56 and 100-piece combinations, shown on page 120.

No. 2E291 **56-piece Dinner Set.** Weight, 50 pounds. Price............$6.48
100-piece Dinner Set. Weight, 70 pounds. Price............ 8.98

When ordered with the regular sets, as quoted, we can furnish the following pieces:

Coffee Cups and Saucers. Price, per dozen............$1.75
Soup Plates, new coupe shape. Price, per dozen............ 1.35
Individual Vegetable Dishes. Price, per dozen............ 1.29

OUR HASTINGS ROSE DINNER SET, $7.20.

MADE BY W. H. GRINDLEY & CO., ENGLAND.

OUR HASTINGS ROSE DINNER SET presents Grindley & Co.'s latest pattern. It is considered by china experts to be one of the most clever and dainty English rose patterns ever produced and is sure to please. The famous Grindley's semi-porcelain ware is noted for its fine pure milk white body and its pure deep white glaze, and is fully guaranteed never to craze.

THE WARE IS LIGHT AND THIN AND HANDSOMELY MODELED, being one of the very latest shapes made by this well known pottery. The decoration consists of dainty little pink rose scrolls on green foliage, forming a very pretty as well as attractive design, which is difficult to properly illustrate and which must be seen to be appreciated. Each set is carefully packed in a strong barrel, packed by experienced packers, which insures safe delivery, and is shipped from Chicago to customers living in Central and Western States, and from our warehouse in Boston, Mass., to our eastern trade.

No. 2E309 Our Hastings Rose Dinner Set.

56-piece Dinner Set.	Shipping weight, 50 pounds. Price	$7.20
80-piece Dinner Set.	Shipping weight, 60 pounds. Price	8.25
100-piece Dinner Set.	Shipping weight, 70 pounds. Price	$10.70
101-piece Dinner Set.	Shipping weight, 70 pounds. Price	11.98

For number and style of pieces, see page 120. In ordering, please mention the number of pieces desired.

LORRAINE WHITE AND GOLD DINNER SET, $7.75.

MADE BY JOHNSON BROS., ENGLAND.

THIS DINNER SET is one of the most handsome white and gold dinner sets ever produced by any pottery. You will observe by the illustration that the shape of this set is something entirely new; one which no one can fail to admire. Every piece is modeled in a most artistic manner. The handsome embossings are very gracefully planned, and the gold is hand traced in such a manner as to outline the edges of embossment. Great care has been taken to full trace all edges, handles and knobs, giving you a full hand traced white and gold dinner set which is hard to equal at double the price. Johnson Bros. are reputed as producing the best grade of semi-porcelain ware in the world. The cups and saucers, the plates, in fact, every piece contained in this high grade set is nearly as thin as the finest grades of fine china. The ware is clear and white and has deep heavy glaze. We fully guarantee the wearing qualities of this dinner set in every respect and with ordinary care it will last a lifetime. This set is very carefully packed by experienced packers and shipped from Cleveland, Ohio.

No. 2E326 Lorraine White and Gold English Semi-Porcelain Dinner Set.

56-piece Dinner Set.	Shipping weight, 50 pounds. Price	$7.75
80-piece Dinner Set.	Shipping weight, 60 pounds. Price	8.75
100-piece Dinner Set.	Shipping weight, 70 pounds. Price	$11.75
101-piece Dinner Set.	Shipping weight, 70 pounds. Price	12.48

For number and style of pieces quoted above, see page 120. In ordering, state number of pieces you desire.

NARCISSUS DINNER SET, $7.85.

MADE BY W. H. GRINDLEY & CO.

THIS SET is the daintiest ever produced by W. H. Grindley & Co. This pottery is especially noted for the thinness of their wares, the rich elegant glaze, and the artistic models and elegant decorations. The Narcissus is their newest creation, and is the prettiest set we have ever shown. The decoration consists of dainty clusters of pink Narcissus with background of delicate green ferns arranged in graceful festoons. The body of the ware is finished with a beautiful embossed edge, which adds considerably to the appearance of this set. Every piece is trimmed with a heavy gold line, which adds the crowning feature to this beautiful set. As rich in appearance as the best grades of French china at a fraction of the cost. We cannot recommend this set too highly.

REMEMBER, you get a PROFIT SHARING CERTIFICATE as well as saving on the price of the dinner set.

Shipped from Chicago to our customers living in Southern and Western states, and from our warehouse in Boston to our eastern customers, thereby insuring lowest freight charges on every shipment.

If ordered with the regular sets, we can furnish the following pieces:

Coffee Cups and Saucers. Price, per dozen	$2.25
Individual Vegetable Dishes. Price, per dozen	1.69
Soup Plates, new coupe shape. Price, per dozen	1.65

No. 2E349 Narcissus English Semi-Porcelain Dinner Set.

56-piece Dinner Set.	Shipping weight, 50 pounds. Price	$7.85
80-piece Dinner Set.	Shipping weight, 60 pounds. Price	9.28
100-piece Dinner Set.	Shipping weight, 70 pounds. Price	11.90
101-piece Dinner Set.	Shipping weight, 70 pounds. Price	13.40

For number and style of pieces in sets quoted above, see page 120. When ordering, mention number of pieces desired.

CARLSBAD CHINA DINNER SET.

MADE BY THE FAMOUS VICTORIA POTTERY, CARLSBAD GERMANY.

AT $12.95 we offer our customers a fine Carlsbad china set, which we consider the greatest china dinner set ever offered by any house at so low a price. Do not judge this high grade ware by the low price we quote, as sets of this quality usually sell for double the price we ask. This set is made of a very fine quality of translucent china, which is thinner than Haviland china. The shape used in this set is entirely new, being beautifully embossed and gracefully outlined. The cups, sugars, creamers, etc., modeled so light and thin in shape that they are termed egg shell china, yet are very strong and durable. The decoration is something entirely new and consists of dainty pink floral spray with green leaves and vines which form a background which greatly adds to the beauty of the set. The decoration is put on by the new decalcomania process, which produces the beautiful flowers and foliage in their natural colors and is guaranteed never to wear off. Besides this beautiful decoration, pieces are full gold traced on knobs and handles. This 100-piece set is carefully packed in a box and shipped direct from Chicago. Shipping weight, 75 pounds.

No. 2E371 100-piece Dinner Set, complete. (This set is furnished in the following composition:) Price **$12.95**

12 Tea Cups and Saucers	12 Sauce Dishes	1 14-inch Platter	1 Round Casserole
12 Pie or Tea Plates	12 Individual Butters	1 16-inch Platter	1 Baker
12 Large Dinner Plates	1 Covered Sugar Bowl	1 Gravy Boat	1 Covored Butter Dish and Drainer
12 New Coupe Soup Plates	1 Cream Pitcher	1 Covered Vegetable Dish	1 Pickle Dish

DIANA DINNER SET, $6.98.

OUR DIANA ENGLISH DINNER WARE PATTERN

OUR DIANA ENGLISH DINNER WARE PATTERN represents the latest and best pattern made by the celebrated John Maddock & Sons, one of the oldest and most reliable English potteries. The decoration is one of the prettiest ever created, consisting of dainty sprays of blue and white forget-me-nots, artistically entwined with green leaves and ferns and is applied by the French decalcomania process, which produces the flowers in their natural colors, true to life. **All knobs and handles are elaborately traced in bright gold.** As illustration shows, this is one of the most artistic shapes ever offered. Every piece is handsomely embossed and has fancy rococco edges. The body of the ware is made from the finest English china clays and is covered with a deep milk white glaze and is fully guaranteed not to craze.

No. 2E315 Diana English Dinner Set.
56-piece Dinner Set. Shipping weight, 50 pounds. Price.............. **$6.98**
80-piece Dinner Set. Shipping weight, 60 pounds. Price.............. **8.25**
100-piece Dinner Set. Shipping weight, 70 pounds. Price.............. **$10.60**
101-piece Dinner Set. Shipping weight, 70 pounds. Price.............. **11.95**
For number and style of pieces quoted above, see page 120.

Each dinner set or order of open stock is carefully packed in a barrel and shipped from Chicago, Illinois.

No. 2E315 Open Stock. Our Diana Dinner Ware, as above illustrated and described, is also quoted in **open stock** at prices mentioned below, giving our customers the advantage of making their own selections of pieces at exceptionally low prices. No order for less than $3.00 will be accepted.

	Actual Size	Per Dozen
Tea Cups and Saucers	½ pt.	$1.60
Coffee Cups and Saucers	⅝ pt.	1.80
Bread and Butter Plates	6⅛ in.	1.20
Pie Plates	6¾ in.	1.25
Tea Plates	7¾ in.	1.35
Dinner Plates	8¾ in.	1.45
Dinner Plates, extra large	9¾ in.	1.55
New Coupe Soup Plates	8 in.	1.45
Sauce Dishes	5¼ in.	.65
Oatmeal Dishes	6¼ in.	1.03
Individual Butters	3 in.	.40

	Actual Size	Per Dozen
Bone Dishes		$1.35
Individual Vegetable Dishes or Bakers	5¼ in.	1.45
Oyster Bowls	1 pt.	1.94
		Each.
Oval Covered Dishes	8½ in.	.85
Oval Covered Dishes	9½ in.	.98
Round Covered Casseroles	8½ in.	.98
Sauce Tureens with Ladle and Stand	6½x5½ in.	1.20
Gravy and Sauce Boats	1pt.	.29

	Actual Size	Price, Each
Soup Tureens with Ladle and Stand	10x8 in.	$3.48
Round Open Nappies	8½ in.	.32
Round Open Nappies	9½ in.	.35
Oval Open Vegetable Dishes	9 in	.32
Oval Open Vegetable Dishes	10½ in.	.35
Platters, small	9⅜ in.	.18
Platters, medium	13½ in.	.34
Platters, medium large	14 in.	.58
Platters, large	14⅞ in.	.79
Platters, extra large	16⅞ in.	1.25

	Actual Size	Price, Each
Pitchers, 36's	1¼ pt.	$0 22
Pitchers, 30's	1¾ qt.	30
Pitchers, 12's	2½ qt.	.48
Pitchers, 6's	3½ qt.	.68
Bowls	1½ pt.	.14
Creamers	⅞ pt.	.23
Covered Sugar Bowls	¾ qt.	.48
Covered Butter Dishes		.53
Covered Tea Pots	1 qt.	.65
Cake Plates	10 in.	.2[illegible]
Pickle Dishes		.20

THE ST. REGIS DINNER SET, $7.59.

MADE BY JOHNSON BROS., ENGLAND.

THE HANDSOMEST ENGLISH DINNER PATTERN MADE.

THE HANDSOMEST ENGLISH DINNER PATTERN MADE. Sold in open stock and complete dinner sets. It is made by the famous Johnson Bros., the world's best potters. The decoration is strikingly beautiful, yet very delicate and dainty, as it consists of dainty little border sprays of pink roses artistically entwined with forget-me-nots on a background of delicately shaded green leaves and foliage, producing a most pleasing effect which must be seen to be appreciated. The shape, known as the silver shape, is recognized as the most clever modeling ever attempted by any pottery. The outlines, embossings and graceful shapes of each piece can be readily recognized by the illustration.

THE BODY OF THE WARE is absolutely the best made in England, consisting of only the finest grade of semi-porcelain covered with a deep, glossy white glaze, which, when combined with the beautiful decoration, produces the most handsome set ever offered, regardless of price. This set is very carefully packed in a barrel by experienced packers and shipped from Cleveland, Ohio to eastern trade and from Chicago to customers living in the west.

No. 2E320 The St. Regis Dinner Set.
56-Piece Dinner Set. Shipping weight, 50 pounds. Price.............. $ **7.59**
80-Piece Dinner Set. Shipping weight, 60 pounds. Price.............. **8.59**
100-Piece Dinner Set. Shipping weight, 70 pounds. Price.............. **10.98**
101-Piece Dinner Set. Shipping weight, 70 pounds. Price.............. **11.98**
For number and style of pieces quoted above, see page 120.

No. 2E320 Johnson Bros.' St. Regis Semi-Porcelain Dinner Ware in open stock. For the convenience of our customers we also offer this fine ware (as described above) as an open stock pattern. Choose the number of pieces you desire at prices mentioned below. No orders will be accepted amounting to less than $2.00 **Open stock dinner ware shipped from Chicago only.**

	Actual Size	Per Dozen
Tea Cups and Saucers	½ pt.	$1.98
Coffee Cups and Saucers	⅝ pt.	2.23
Bread and Butter Plates	6⅛ in.	1.10
Pie Plates	6¾ in.	1.18
Tea Plates	7¾ in.	1.48
Dinner Plates	8¾ in.	1.68
Dinner Plates, extra large	9¾ in.	1.88
New Coupe Soup Plates	8 in.	1.69
Soup Plates	8¾ in.	1.64
Sauce Dishes	5¼ in.	.79
Oatmeal Dishes	6¼ in.	1.29

	Actual Size	Per Dozen
Individual Butters	3 in.	$0.48
Bone Dishes		1.48
Individual Vegetable Dishes or Bakers	5¼ in.	1.68
Oyster Bowls	1 pt.	2.12
		Price, each
Oval Covered Dishes	8½ in.	.88
Oval Covered Dishes	9½ in.	.96
Round Covered Casseroles	8½ in.	.98
Sauce Tureens with Ladle and Stand	6½x5½in.	1.29

	Actual Size	Price, each
Gravy and Sauce Boats	1 pt.	$0.32
Soup Tureens with Ladle	10x8 in.	3.39
Round Open Nappies	8½ in.	.29
Round Open Nappies	9½ in.	.39
Oval Open Vegetable Dishes	9 in.	.29
Oval Open Vegetable Dishes	10½ in.	.35
Platters, small	9⅜ in.	.22
Platters, medium	13½ in.	.39
Platters, medium large	14 in.	.69
Platters, large	14⅞ in.	.93
Platters, extra large	16⅞ in.	1.39

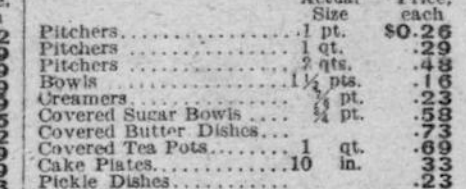

	Actual Size	Price, each
Pitchers	1 pt.	$0.26
Pitchers	1 qt.	.29
Pitchers	2 qts.	.48
Bowls	1½ pts.	.16
Creamers	½ pt.	.23
Covered Sugar Bowls	¾ pt.	.58
Covered Butter Dishes		.73
Covered Tea Pots	1 qt.	.69
Cake Plates	10 in.	33
Pickle Dishes		.23

THE ELITE BAVARIAN CHINA DINNER SET, $16.85.

COMPARE THIS $16.85 GENUINE BAVARIAN

COMPARE THIS $16.85 GENUINE BAVARIAN China Dinner Set with those offered at $25.00 and you will fully appreciate that this is the greatest value ever offered in high grade dinner ware. It is made from the finest quality of thin translucent china, which is lighter and equally as finely selected as the best grades of Haviland china, and is made by the most celebrated factory in Europe. The shape, you will note, is most cleverly modeled, each piece being finely embossed, as the illustration shows. No expense has been spared to elaborately hand trace all pieces with double gold lines on each side of the Grecian border, and all covered pieces, including sugar bowls, covered dishes and cups and saucers, have hand traced gold handles. The decoration consists of dainty little garlands of pink roses and green foliage, forming a neat border design much sought for by lovers of beautiful china. The covered dishes, cups and saucers are decorated both in and outside and all flat pieces have a floral wreath in the center, producing a most artistic effect.

100-piece Dinner Sets furnished in combination as follows:

12 Tea Cups	12 Tea or Pie Plates	1 Platter, 15½ inches	1 Sauce Boat and Stand (2 pieces)
12 Saucers	12 Sauce Dishes	2 Open Vegetable Dishes	1 Covered Butter Dish (3 pieces)
12 Dinner Plates	12 Individual Butters.	1 Covered Vegetable Dish (2 pieces)	1 Cream Pitcher
12 Breakfast Plates	1 Platter, 11½ inches	1 Covered Sugar Bowl (2 pieces)	1 Pickle Dish
			1 Large Salad Bowl

Shipping from Chicago Shipping weight, 90 pounds.

No. 2E378 100-piece Dinner Set, complete. Price.............................. **$16.85**

No. 2E378 The Elite Bavarian China Dinner Ware. For those desiring to make their own selection of pieces, we quote this beautiful china pattern in open stock, giving you the advantage of selecting every conceivable piece made which goes to make up a complete dinner service, at the following prices: Shipped from Chicago only.

	Actual Size	Per Dozen
Tea Cups and Saucers	6 oz.	$2.39
Coffee Cups and Saucers	8 oz.	3.25
Chocolate Cups and Saucers.	4 oz.	2.75
After Dinner Cups and Saucers	3 oz.	2.39
Bread and Butter Plates	5⅞ in.	1.48
Pie Plates	7½ in.	1.73
Tea Plates	8¼ in.	2.23
Dinner Plates	9½ in.	2.59
Soup Plates, Coupe Shape	7½ in.	2 28
Sauce Dishes	4½ in.	1.35
Oatmeal Dishes	5⅝ in.	1.65

	Actual Size	Per Dozen
Individual Butters	3¼ in.	$0.73
Bone Dishes	7 in.	2.10
Egg Cups	5 oz.	1.75
Bouillon Cups and Saucers	7 oz.	3.25
		Price, each
Cake Plates	10 in.	$0.48
Chop Dishes	11½ in.	.[illegible]8
Cream Pitchers	½ pt.	.23
Sugar Bowls	1 pt.	.48
Covered Butter Dishes	7 pts.	.55
Spoon Holders		.15
Tea Pots	3¼ pts.	.98

	Actual Size	Price, each
Chocolate Pots	3 pts.	$0.98
Pickle Dishes	8¾ in.	.35
Bowls	1½ pts.	.45
Celery Trays	12¾ in.	.48
Toothpick Holders		.10
Salt and Pepper Shakers (each)		.15
Platters, small size	11½ in.	.45
Platters, medium size	13½ in.	.73
Platters, large size	15½ in.	.98
Platters, extra size	17½ in.	1.95
Open Vegetable Dishes	8 in.	.43
Open Vegetable Dishes	9 in.	.49

	Actual Size	Price, each
Round Salad Bowls	9⅞ in.	$0.69
Oval Covered Dishes	9 in.	1.68
Round Casseroles (covered)	9 in.	1.75
Sauce Boats with Stands	9 in.	.95
Soup Tureens	11 in.	2.95
Covered Sauce Tureens	11 in.	1.75
Mustard Pots with Spoons		.23
Large Pitchers, No. 3	1 qt.	.89
Syrup Pitchers with Plates	3 oz.	.48
Tea Pot Stands	6 in.	.15
Pudding Sets with Lining and Stands		1.98

IMPERIAL AUSTRIAN CHINA DINNER SET,

$13.95

THE HIGHEST GRADE OF CHINA made in Austria. Very light in weight and very translucent, so much so that the light will readily pass through even the larger pieces, such as covered dishes and platters, thus showing it to be the equal of any of the French makes. It is sold at one-third less. This pattern is one of the choicest made by this noted factory. The shape is considered by china critics to be the best modeled and most graceful ever made. The decoration is an elegant transfer of dainty pink flowers with green leaves, and is gracefully arranged in dainty sprays.

Shipped from Chicago to customers living in the Central and Western States, and from our warehouse in Boston, Mass., to eastern customers, thereby insuring the lowest freight charges. Shipping weight, 90 pounds.

It is sold only in our 100-piece combination, as follows:
12 Dinner Plates
12 Breakfast Plates
12 Tea Plates
12 Sauce Dishes
12 Tea Cups
12 Tea Saucers
12 Individual Butters
1 Covered Sugar (2 pcs.)
1 Cream Pitcher
1 Sauce Bowl with Stand
1 Covered Butter Dish and Drainer (3 pieces)
1 Oval Covered Vegetable Dish (2 pieces)
1 Platter, 10 inches
1 Platter, 14 inches
1 Open Vegetable Dish
1 Pickle Dish
1 Round Covered Vegetable Dish (2pcs)

Soup plates when ordered with set. Price, per dozen.................$2.49

No. 2E374 100-piece Dinner Set, complete. Price.................. **$13.95**

OUR GENUINE HAVILAND FRENCH CHINA DINNER SETS.

THE EXTREMELY LOW PRICES which we quote for these three latest patterns of genuine Haviland French China Dinner Sets are made possible by reason of the very large contract we placed with Theodore Haviland, at an especially low price, to which we have added only our usual one small margin of profit. It is impossible for other dealers to purchase these sets, even at wholesale, at the extremely low price which we quote. On account of our low price a great many dealers try to convince our customers that our sets are not the genuine Haviland China; but do not allow yourself to be misled by what anyone may say of these sets, for we guarantee them to be made by Theodore Haviland, Limoges, France, with his trade mark stamped on the back of each piece. We will furnish sample individual butters, postpaid, of any of our Haviland sets on receipt of 10 cents.

The combination of each of the three dinner sets listed below consists of the following 100 pieces:

12 Coupe Soupe Plates 7¾ in.
12 Plates, 10-inch
12 Plates, 8½-inch
12 Cups
12 Saucers
12 Individual Butters
12 Fruit Plates
1 Platter, 11 inch
1 Platter, 16-inch
1 Baker
1 Round Covered Dish (2 pieces)
1 Oval Covered Dish (2 pieces)
1 Pickle Dish
1 Covered Butter Dish (3 pcs.)
1 Sugar Bowl (2 pieces)
1 Cream Pitcher
1 Sauce Boat (2 pieces)

Each set is carefully packed by expert packers and shipped direct to our customers in the west from Chicago and from our bonded warehouse in Boston to our eastern customers, thus insuring lowest rate of freight.

100-PIECE HAVILAND DINNER SET.

$19.98

THIS GENUINE HAVILAND SET is of a new and handsome shape, in that pure translucent white, delicately decorated, and made only by Theodore Haviland of Limoges, France. Haviland china is always very thin, light in weight, perfect in color, great in strength, perfect in finish and beautiful in decoration. The decoration of the above set consists of a very delicate pink wild crab apple blossom with light green moss fern background. It has the genuine coin gold knobs and handles, adding richness to the set. The above illustration will give you some idea of the beautiful shape, but no picture can do justice to a Haviland French China Dinner Set, as it does not show the delicate decorations nor the thinness of the ware. This kind of ware must be seen to be appreciated. Very carefully packed in small imported casks. Shipping weight, 100 pounds.

No. 2E380 100-piece Haviland Dinner Set, as listed above. Price........ **$19.98**

OUR HAVILAND ROSE 100-PIECE DINNER SET.

$24.95

OUR HAVILAND ROSE PATTERN. This is the most popular dinner set ever offered by this famous manufacturer. The decoration consists of dainty sprays of pink roses, artistically arranged on all pieces with faint green foliage and French scrolls. This decoration has heretofore only been displayed on sets sold at double the price we ask. This set is sure to please the most critical china buyer, as the decoration is not loud or gaudy, but very delicate and neat, yet strikingly beautiful. **Pure coin gold adorns all pieces,** such as cups, covered dishes, platters, bakers, etc., greatly adding to the richness of the set. The shape is known as the **Vincennes shape,** Haviland's newest and best pattern. Each piece is neatly embossed, as illustration shows, being a fancy festoon shape. **The ware is the finest made. It is light and thin, made from the choicest translucent china body, only obtainable in Limoges, France.** Very carefully packed in small imported casks. Shipping weight, 100 pounds.

YOUR PROFIT SHARING CERTIFICATE on your order for this set will help you get one of the valuable **FREE ARTICLES** shown on the last pages.

No. 2E384 100-piece Haviland Dinner Set. Price.................. **$24.95**

100-PIECE ROSE WREATH HAVILAND.

$27.50

THE DECORATION consists of dainty little climbing roses, entwined with very faint and delicate green foliage and leaves, gracefully arranged, forming one complete border, encircling the edges of each piece. All pieces are adorned with beautiful jewel center with four rose sprays. This decoration appeals to the most refined taste as it is very delicate and dainty. **Pure coin gold adorns all pieces,** such as cups, covered dishes, platters, bakers, etc., greatly adding to the beauty of the set. This set usually retails for $40.00.

The shape, known as Lambelle pattern, is the newest creation of Haviland. Each piece is artistically embossed with festoons of bow knot design, and bottom edges of each piece are embossed in rich lace effect.

The ware is the finest made, being very light and thin, and made from the very best quality white translucent china, only to be found in Limoges, France. Very carefully packed in small imported casks. Shipping weight, 100 pounds.

No. 2E386 100-piece Haviland Dinner Set. Price.................. **$27.50**

THIS IS THE PRETTIEST HAVILAND ROSE BORDER PATTERN MADE, REGARDLESS OF PRICE. THE BEAUTY OF THIS SET IS BEYOND DESCRIPTION.

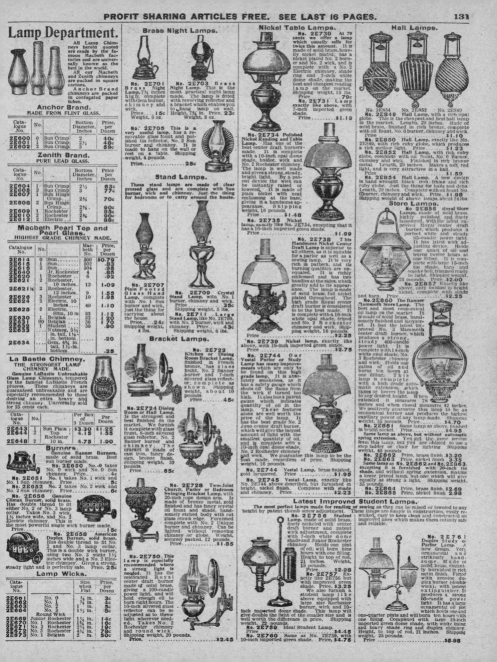

Lamp Department.

All Lamp Chimneys herein quoted are made by the famous Macbeth factories and are universally known as the best in the world.

All our Macbeth and Zenith chimneys are packed in square cartons.

Anchor Brand chimneys are packed in corrugated paper tubes.

Anchor Brand.

MADE FROM FLINT GLASS.

Catalogue No.	No.		Bottom Diameter, Inches	Price, per Dozen
2E600	0	Sun Crimp	2	40c
2E601	1	Sun Crimp	2½	48c
2E602	2	Sun Crimp	3	59c

Zenith Brand.

PURE LEAD GLASS.

Catalogue No.	No.		Bottom Diameter, Inches	Price per Dozen
2E604	1	Sun Crimp	2½	63c
2E605	2	Sun Crimp	3	77c
2E607	1	Sun Hinge Crimp...	2⅜	70c
2E608	2	Sun Hinge Crimp...	2⅜	90c
2E609	1	Rochester	2	85c
2E610	2	Rochester	2⅜	90c
2E612	2	Electric...	3	88c

Macbeth Pearl Top and Pearl Glass.

HIGHEST GRADE CHIMNEY MADE.

Catalogue No.	No.		Macbeth No.	Price, per Dozen
2E614	0	Sun........	500	$0.79
2E615	1	Sun........	502	.83
2E616	2	Sun........	504	.95
2E640		Jr. Rochester	4	.85
2E620	1	Rochester	6	.92
2E621	2	Rochester, 10 inches..	12	1.09
2E621½	2	Rochester, 12 inches..	9	1.55
2E626	3	Rochester	10	1.95
2E624	2	Electric, 10 inches....	40	1.10
2E625	2	Electric, Stm. 10 in	63	1.12
2E630	1	Belgian	32	1.20
2E631	00	Belgian	36	1.70
2E632	1	Student	50	.90
2E633	....	Nutmeg, 3½ in. tall, 1⅛ in. bottom..	.....	.20
2E634	....	Gem, 4⅜ in. tall, 1½-in. bottom....		.25

La Bastie Chimney.

THE STRONGEST LAMP CHIMNEY MADE.

Genuine LaBastie Unbreakable Glass Lamp Chimneys, tempered by the famous LaBastie French process. These chimneys are guaranteed unbreakable and are especially recommended to those desiring an extra heavy and strong chimney. Universally sold for 25 cents each.

Catalogue No.	No.		Per Box of 3 Dozen	Per Dozen
2E643	1	Sun Plain Top	$3.30	$1.25
2E644	2		4.15	1.55
2E648	2	Rochester 10 in.	4.75	1.90

Burners.

Genuine Banner Burners, made of solid brass. Best sun burner made.

No. 2E650 No. 0 takes No. 0 wick and No. 0 Sun chimney. Price.........4c

No. 2E651 No. 1 takes No. 1 wick and No. 1 Sun chimney. Price.........5c

No. 2E652 No. 2 takes No. 2 wick and No. 2 Sun chimney. Price.........6c

No. 2E656 Genuine Climax Burner, solid brass. Has double thread to fit either No. 2 or No. 3 lamp collar. Takes No. 3 wick, 1½ inches wide, and No. 2 Electric chimney. This is the most powerful single wick burner made. Price.........15c

No. 2E658 American Duplex Burner, solid brass. Has double thread to fit No. 2 and No. 3 lamp collar. This is a double wick burner, using two No. 3 wicks 1½ inches wide and a No. 2 Electric chimney. Gives a strong, steady light and is perfectly safe. Price, 25c

Lamp Wicks.

Catalogue No.		Size when Flat	Price, per Dozen
2E661	No. 0	⅝ in.	3c
2E662	No. 1	⅞ in.	4c
2E663	No. 2	1 in.	5c
2E664	No. 3	1½ in.	8c
	Round Wick		
2E669	Junior Rochester	1⅛ in.	14c
2E670	No. 1 Rochester	1¾ in.	16c
2E671	No. 2 Rochester	2½ in.	19c
2E672	No. 3 Rochester	4½ in.	78c
2E673	No. 1 Belgian	2 in.	50c

Brass Night Lamps.

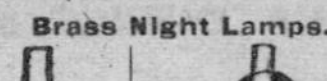

No. 2E701 Brass Night Lamp, 7¾ inches high, complete with Gem burner, chimney and wick. Price.....15c Weight, 6 oz.

No. 2E703 Brass Night Lamp. This is the most practical night lamp made. The lamp is fitted with revolving reflector and a bracket which enables you to hang lamp on wall. Height, 7¾ in. Price, 23c Weight, 8 oz.

No. 2E705 This is a very useful lamp, has a removable glass fount and polished tin reflector, No. 2 Sun burner and chimney. It is made to hang on the wall or rest on a table. Shipping weight, 4 pounds. Price.................25c

Stand Lamps.

These stand lamps are made of clear pressed glass and are complete with Sun burner, wick and chimney. Just the thing for bedrooms or to carry around the house.

No. 2E707 Plain Footed Glass Hand Lamp, complete with No. 1 Sun burner and wick, just the thing for carrying about the house. Price.......24c Shipping weight, 4 lbs.

No. 2E709 Crystal Stand Lamp, with No. 1 burner, chimney and wick. Price..............35c Shipping weight, 5 lbs.

No. 2E711 Large Stand Lamp, like No. 2E709, with No. 2 burner, wick and chimney. Price........43c Shipping weight, 6 lbs.

Bracket Lamps.

No. 2E722 Kitchen or Dining Room Bracket Lamp, finished in French bronze, has glass fount, No. 2 Banner burner and 7-inch silvered glass reflector; complete as shown. Shipping weight, about 10 pounds. Price........45c

No. 2E724 Dining Room or Hall Lamp. Is the strongest and best finished on the market. We furnish it complete with glass fount, 8-inch silvered glass reflector, No. 2 Banner burner and chimney. The bracket is made of cast iron, fancy design, bronze finish. Shipping weight, 10 pounds. Price........65c

No. 2E728 Two-Joint Church, Parlor or Bedroom Swinging Bracket Lamp, with 20-inch rope design arm. Is made of bronze metal, gold finished and has fancy crystal oil fount and shade, handsomely etched body with cut glass crown edge. Furnished complete with No. 2 Unique burner and chimney. Can be lighted without removing chimney or globe. Weight, securely packed, 12 pounds. Price..........$1.85

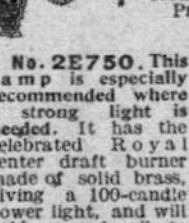

No. 2E750. This lamp is especially recommended where a strong light is needed. It has the celebrated Royal center draft burner made of solid brass, giving a 100-candle power light, and will hold enough oil to burn eight hours. The 10-inch silvered glass reflector can be so adjusted as to throw light wherever needed. Takes No. 2 Rochester chimney and round wick. Shipping weight, 20 pounds. Price..........................$2.45

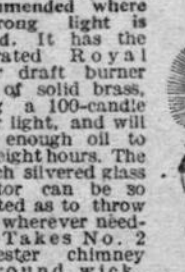

Nickel Table Lamps.

No. 2E730 At 79 cents we offer a lamp which usually sells for twice this amount. It is made of solid brass, heavily nickel plated; has a nickel plated No. 2 burner and No. 2 wick, and is complete with a No. 2 Electric chimney, shade ring and 7-inch white dome shade, making the best and cheapest reading lamp on the market. Shipping weight, 15 lbs. Price..........79c

No. 2E731 Lamp exactly like above, with 7-inch imported green shade. Price.........$1.19

No. 2E734 Polished Nickel Reading and Table Lamp. Has one of the best center draft burners made. It is complete with a 10-inch opal dome shade, holder, wick and No. 2 Rochester chimney. The lamp is well made and gives a strong, steady, bright light. By a patent device the wick can be instantly raised or lowered. It is made of plain nickel with neat embossing at the base, giving it a handsome appearance. Shipping weight, 16 pounds. Price.........$1.48

No. 2E735 Nickel lamp, exactly like No. 2E734, excepting that it has a 10-inch imported green shade. Price..........................$1.99

No. 2E738 This Handsome Nickel Center Draft Lamp is superior to all others, as it is suitable for a parlor as well as a sewing lamp. It's very rich in pattern, and its burning qualities are unequaled. It is richly embossed and has two handles at the sides, which greatly add to its appearance. The lamp is made of solid brass, full nickel plated throughout. The high grade Royal center draft burner is considered to be the best made. It is complete with a 10-inch white opal shade, tripod and No. 2 Rochester chimney and wick. Shipping weight, 16 pounds. Price..........................$2.25

No. 2E739 Nickel lamp, exactly like above, with 10-inch imported green shade. Price..........................$2.75

No. 2E744 Our Vestal Parlor or Study Lamp has many improvements which are only to be found on this high grade lamp. It is absolutely smokeless, as it has a safety gauge which shuts off the flame from the wick if turned too high. It also has a patent gauge which indicates quantity of oil in the lamp. These features alone are well worth the price of the lamp. It has the best grade No. 2 Juno center draft burner, which will give the largest amount of light with the smallest quantity of oil, and is complete with a 10-inch opal dome shade, No. 2 Rochester chimney and wick. We guarantee this lamp to be the best made, regardless of price. Shipping weight, 16 pounds.

No. 2E744 Vestal Lamp, brass finished, gold lacquered. Price $1.95

No. 2E745 Vestal Lamp, exactly like No. 2E744 above described, but furnished in bright, nickel finish. Complete with shade and chimney. Price..............$2.23

Hall Lamps.

No. 2E854 No. 2E852 No. 2E849

No. 2E849 Hall Lamp, with a rich opal globe. This is the cheapest and best hall lamp in the market. Length, 29 inches. Made of solid brass, finished in rich bronze, complete with oil fount, No. 0 burner, chimney and wick. Price..........................$1.10

No. 2E850 Hall Lamp, exactly like No. 2E849, with rich ruby globe, which produces a rich mellow light. Price.........$1.23

No. 2E852 Hall Lamp, with rich ruby globe, complete with oil fount, No. 0 burner, chimney and wick. Finished in rich bronze metal. Length, 29 inches. Makes a soft red light, and is very attractive in a hall. Price..........................$1.59

No. 2E854 Hall Lamp. A new design in hand wrought black iron frame and rich ruby globe. Just the thing for halls and dens. Length, 29 inches. Complete with oil fount No. 0 burner, chimney and wick. Price...$1.98 Shipping weight of above lamps, about 14 lbs.

Store Lamps.

No 2E856 Royal Store Lamps, made of solid brass, highly polished and finely lacquered, with the latest improved Royal center draft burner, which produces a perfect white and steady 85-candle power light. It has latest wick adjusting device. Holds one quart of oil and burns twelve hours at one filling. It is complete with large 15-inch tin shade, harp and smoke bell, trimmed ready to light. Shipping weight, 25 pounds. Price...$2.00

No. 2E857 Exactly like above, only finished in bright nickel, complete with shade and harp. Price.........................$2.25

No. 2E860 The Banner Mammoth Store Lamp. The best and most economical oil lamp on the market. It is made of solid brass, handsomely finished and lacquered. It has the latest improved No. 3 Mammoth center draft burner, which produces a strong, steady 400-candle power light. It is complete with 14-inch white opal shade, No. 3 Rochester chimney and wick. Holds one gallon of oil and burns ten hours at one filling. This lamp is complete with a high grade automatic extension, which raises or lowers the lamp to any desired height. When extended it measures 78 inches and when closed measures 42 inches. We positively guarantee this lamp to be an economical burner and produces the highest capillary power of any lamp made. Shipping weight, 35 pounds. Price.........$4.70

No. 2E861 Same lamp as above, finished in bright nickel. Price.................$4.95

Same lamp as above, but without automatic spring extension. You get the same service from this lamp, but you are obliged to use a step ladder or chair for lighting. Shipping weight, 40 pounds.

No. 2E862 Price, brass finish .$3.20
No. 2E863 Price, nickel finish 3.35

Same lamp as No. 2E862 and No. 2E863, excepting it is furnished with 20-inch tin shade, and without spring extension, making a lower priced lamp, but one which will give equally as strong a light. Shipping weight, 35 pounds.

No. 2E864 Price, brass finish..$2.69
No. 2E865 Price, nickel finish 2.98

Latest Improved Student Lamps.

The most perfect lamps made for reading or sewing as they can be raised or lowered to any height by patent thumb screw adjustment. These lamps are simple in construction, easily rewicked, easy to keep clean and constructed on improved lines which makes them entirely safe and reliable.

No. 2E756 Student Lamp, made of solid brass, finely nickeled with center draft burner and patent wick adjustment, complete with 7-inch white dome shade and Junior Rochester chimney. Holds one pint of oil; will burn nine hours with one filling. Height to top of rod, 21 inches. Weight, 18 pounds. Price..........$2.98

No. 2E757 Exactly like 2E756 but with improved green shade. Price, $3.25

We also furnish a student lamp like above equipped with large size Rochester burner, wick and 10-inch imported dome shade. This lamp will give double the light of the smaller size and is well worth the difference in price. Shipping weight, 22 pounds.

No. 2E759 Ideal Student Lamp. Price..........................$4.45

No. 2E760 Same as No. 2E759, with 10-inch imported green shade. Price, $4.75

No. 2E761 Duplex Study or Parlor Lamp. A new design. Very ornamental and strikingly handsome. Made of solid brass, elegantly burnished in rich satin finish. Fitted with genuine duplex burner (double wick), with patent extinguisher. It produces a strong 60-candle power light. It has a large ornamental oil pot which holds one and one-quarter pints and will burn ten hours with one filling. Completed with large 10-inch imported green dome shade, with white lining and heavy shade ring and duplex chimney. Height, to top of rod, 21 inches. Shipping weight, 25 pounds. Price $5.98

All Metal Parts of Our Lamps are Made of Solid Brass,

With Handsome Lacquered Bronze Finish.

A great many dealers advertise library lamps which in appearance are similar to ours, but are made of bronze metal, which is oftentimes mistaken for brass when the lamps are new, but will not stand the wear and retain the handsome appearance of a solid brass lamp. **We guarantee every one of our lamps to stand the wear of a lifetime, and guarantee them not to tarnish.** Each lamp carefully packed to insure safe delivery.

No. 2E785 This handsome lamp is equal in every respect to lamps generally sold at $3.50. It has a 14-inch plain white shade, No. 3 Climax burner, No. 2 Electric chimney, and 1½-inch wick. It has a solid brass frame and patent automatic spring extension. Length, closed, 27 inches; extended, 63 inches.

Price, with plain white shade...............**$1.79**

No. 2E786 Lamp as described above, with a beautiful 14-inch hand decorated dome shade. Shipping weight, 30 pounds. Price........**$2.21**

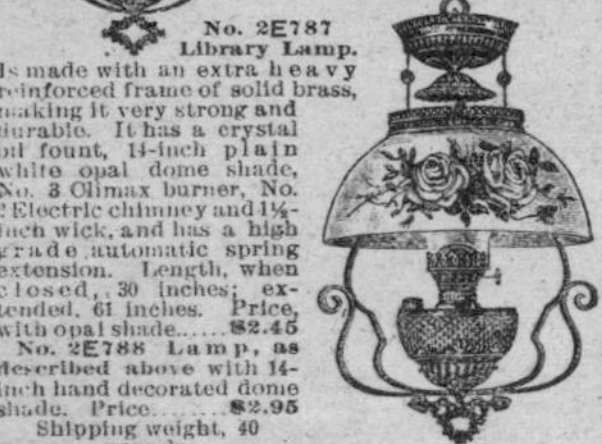

No. 2E787 Library Lamp. Is made with an extra heavy reinforced frame of solid brass, making it very strong and durable. It has a crystal oil fount, 14-inch plain white opal dome shade, No. 3 Climax burner, No. 2 Electric chimney and 1½-inch wick, and has a high grade automatic spring extension. Length, when closed, 30 inches; extended, 61 inches. Price, with opal shade.....**$2.45**

No. 2E788 Lamp, as described above with 14-inch hand decorated dome shade. Price........**$2.95**

Shipping weight, 40 pounds.

No. 2E789

No. 2E789 Solid Brass Library Lamp with No. 2 Juno center draft fount, 85-candle power. Fount removable for filling and cleaning. Automatic spring extension. Length, closed, 33 inches; extended, 69 inches. The base of the lamp is beautifully embossed and finished in rich bronze to match the frame. Complete with 14-inch white dome shade, No. 2 Rochester chimney and wick. Weight, 40 pounds. Price....**$3.48**

No. 2E793 Library Lamp with automatic spring extension. Plain white 14-inch shade, crystal oil fount, No. 3 Climax burner, No. 3 Electric chimney and 1½-inch wick. **Solid brass frame.** Has 39 cut glass pendants suspended from shade band. Length, closed, 30 inches; extended, 66 inches. Weight, about 40 lbs. Price **$3.49**

No. 2E794 Lamp as above, with beautifully decorated dome shade. Weight, about 46 pounds.

Price..............**$3.95**

No. 2E794

No. 2E798

No. 2E797 Library Lamp. Has elaborate frame of solid brass. The frame is extra heavy and reinforced, ornamented with fancy castings of solid brass. Has 14-inch dome shade with 30 cut glass pendants suspended from the shade band. Fancy crystal fount, No. 3 Banner burner takes 1½ inch wick. No. 2 Electric chimney. Weight, 40 pounds. Price, **$4.25**

No. 2E798 Lamp as described above, excepting that the dome shade is handsomely decorated with floral design on tinted background.

Price........**$4.48**

Extension Lamps.

No. 2E799 Parlor Extension Lamp, fitted with No. 2 center draft burner, 85-candle power; takes No. 2 round wick, No. 2 Rochester chimney. Fount can be removed from vase for filling. Automatic extension. Length, closed, 40 inches; extended, 76 inches. Can be used in room with either high or low ceiling. All metal parts are solid brass. Fancy collar at top of fount holder. Vase and globe are beautifully decorated with hand painted floral decorations on rich tinted background. Shipping weight, about 40 lbs. Price......**$4.86**

dome with 30 cut glass prisms suspended from dome band, make this one of the most attractive lamps in our line. Shipping weight, about 40 lbs.

Price........................**$5.75**

Polka Dot Cerise Lamp

No. 2E802 Library Lamp. This is the latest style in a Library or Parlor Lamp. It has a fancy ruby metal vase with gold plated cupid ornaments and solid brass embossed frame, and a beautiful 14-inch ruby polka dot dome. It is constructed so as to cast a rich ruby glow in the upper part of the room, and at the same time produces a bright steady light beneath for sewing or reading purposes. It has the latest improved No. 2 center draft burner, chimney and wick and produces 100-candle power light. It is one of the most ornamental lamps made, and is trimmed with 30 cut glass prisms or pendants which greatly add to the striking beauty of the lamp. Securely packed in a barrel and shipped to eastern customers from our factory in Connecticut, and to western customers from Chicago. Weight, 40 pounds.

Price..................**$5.98**

No. 2E799

No. 2E801 Library Lamp with automatic spring extension. Length, closed, 30 inches; extended, 73 inches. The celebrated No. 2 Juno fount and center draft burner giving 85-candle power light. Fount can be removed for filling and cleaning. No. 2 round wick, No. 2 Rochester chimney. Extra heavy collar at top of oil fount holder. Heavy reinforced solid brass frame and beautifully decorated and tinted fount and

No 2E802

No. 2E803 Library Lamp. Has solid brass frame of most beautiful design with ornamental heavy castings. Has automatic spring extension; length, closed, 30 inches; extended, 73 inches. The part of the frame on which the lamp is suspended is made of twisted brass instead of chains. Has No. 2 Juno fount and center draft burner, giving 85-candle power light; can be removed for filling and cleaning. Has No. 2 round wick and No. 2 Rochester chimney. The fount and dome are beautifully decorated with hand painted carnations. A heavy brass collar strengthens the top of oil fount holder. Thirty cut glass pendants are suspended from the dome band. Shipping weight, 40 lbs. Price........**$6.85**

ALL METAL PARTS OF OUR CHANDELIERS

ARE OF SOLID BRASS (NOT BRONZE METAL), WITH A HANDSOME BRONZE FINISH.

A great many dealers advertise chandeliers which, in appearance, are similar to ours, but are made of bronze metal or plated steel, which is often mistaken for brass when the lamps are new, but will not stand the wear and retain the handsome appearance of solid brass. **We GUARANTEE every one of our chandeliers to stand the wear of a lifetime and warrant them not to tarnish.**

Two-Light Chandelier for only $6.89.

This Beautiful Chandelier is made of solid brass, finished in rich gold bronze, complete with fancy glass oil founts, etched globes of very popular shape. The No. 2 Unique burner is of a new design that can be lighted and filled without removing chimney or globe, thus avoiding all possibility of breakage in handling them. Takes 1-inch wick and No. 2 hinge chimney. It has the best patent automatic extension for raising and lowering so that it can be used with high or low ceilings. Packed complete in box to insure safe delivery. Shipping weight, 50 to 75 pounds.

No. 2E810 Price, two lights complete...**$ 6.89**
No. 2E811 Price, three lights complete.. **8.65**
No. 2E812 Price, four lights complete.. **10.85**

Patent Extension Chandelier.

This Beautiful Chandelier has patent automatic extension for raising and lowering. It is made of solid brass, finished in rich gold bronze, with a center band studded with 12 beautifully colored cut glass jewels and 30 cut glass prisms suspended from same. This gives a very brilliant effect when lighted. Has fancy glass founts, best grade of No. 2 Unique burners and handsomely etched shades. The burners can be lighted without removing chimneys or shades, which is a great convenience. Takes 1-inch wick and No. 2 hinge chimney. The fancy rope shaped arms and standard make it very neat and attractive and it is an ornament as well as a fixture. Shipping weight, 70 to 100 pounds.

No. 2E826 Chandelier with two lights complete. Price..............................**$9.45**
No. 2E827 Chandelier with three lights complete. Price..............................**$10.65**
No. 2E828 Chandelier with four lights complete. Price..............................**$13.95**

Three and Four-Light Chandeliers for Church, Hall or Dwelling Use.

Patent Extension Chandelier. Extended 57 inches. This chandelier is solid brass, elegantly finished in rich gold, with large ball and cast ornaments in bright silver finish. The No. 2 Unique burners can be trimmed and lighted without removing the chimney or globe. Takes 1-inch wick and No. 2 hinge chimney. Furnished with fancy glass oil founts and etched crystal globes. Shipping weight of three lights, about 75 lbs.; four lights, about 90 lbs.

No. 2E841 Chandelier with three lights complete. Price..............................**$11.35**
No. 2E842 Chandelier with four lights complete. Price..............................**$13.95**

Church or Hall Chandelier. Same chandelier as above except founts. This fixture is trimmed with celebrated No. 1 Miller fount, with center draft 55-candle power burner, making a very strong light for church or hall use.

No. 2E843 Chandelier with three lights complete. Price..............................**$13.45**
No. 2E844 Chandelier with four lights complete. Price..............................**$16.85**

Banquet Lamps.

We take pleasure in presenting an entirely new and complete line of Banquet Lamps and Globes, which were selected with the greatest care after long and careful investigation.

We feel confident we are offering the best line of lamps made, as every lamp is carefully tinted and decorated by the most skilled artists. Every lamp is equipped with the best quality burners, wicks and chimneys. **Our prices are from 33 to 50 per cent less than quoted by the regular crockery dealers.**

Each lamp is carefully packed in box or barrel to insure safe delivery.

No. 2E950 Rustic Lamp, 89c. This banquet lamp is neat and attractive. It is heavily embossed, as shown in illustration, and richly tinted with rich green and pink, producing a most handsome effect. It is 17 inches high and is complete with an 8-inch globe, No. 2 Sun burner and wick and No. 2 Electric chimney. Shipping weight, 15 pounds.
Price **89c**

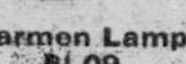

Carmen Lamp, $1.09.

No. 2E955 This banquet lamp has handsome decorations, consisting of large red flowers with dark green foliage on a tinted pink and white background. It is 19 inches high and has an 8-inch globe. The metal foot is of cast brass, highly polished and lacquered. It is furnished with a No. 2 brass Banner burner and takes a No. 2 chimney and 1-inch wick. Shipping weight, 18 pounds.
Price **$1.09**

Pansy Lamp, $1.79.

No. 2E958 Our Pansy Lamp is one of the prettiest medium priced lamps made, decorated with hand painted pansies and green leaves on a maroon and yellow tinted background, forming a very rich contrast. Complete with large 9-inch globe, No. 3 Climax burner, shade ring, No. 2 Electric chimney and 1½-inch wick and stands 22 inches high. All metal parts are made of heavy brass, highly polished and lacquered. Shipping weight, 20 pounds.
Price.........**$1.79**

Victor Lamp, $1.89.

No. 2E965 The embossings of this handsome lamp are dark green, designed to form four rich panels of white, which have beautiful floral centers consisting of wild roses and foliage. It has a removable oil fount made of solid brass and is complete with a large 8 inch globe, No. 3 Climax burner and wick and No. 2 Electric chimney. Height, 21 inches. This is one of the best values we offer. Shipping weight, 20 pounds.
Price **$1.89**

Poppy Lamp, $1.98.

No. 2E967 This beautiful parlor lamp is exceptionally large and attractive. It is complete with 9-inch globe and vase, and measures 21 inches high. The decoration consists of large hand painted poppies in pink, purple and white. The globe and also the vase are delicately tinted at the top in light green and the bottom in pink. It has a heavy brass plated metal foot of scroll design. It is equipped with No. 3 Climax burner, No. 3 wick and No. 2 Electric chimney, and produces 60-candle power light. Shipping weight, 20 pounds.
Price.......**$1.98**

Customers living in the Central and Eastern states who order one of our lamps only, will receive it shipped direct from our factory in Pennsylvania, thus effecting a saving in transportation charges.

No. 2E969 Our Princeton Lamp. This is a fine lamp at a very low price. It is decorated with large red poppies and green leaves on a brown and yellow tinted background. It is complete with a 9-inch globe, No. 2 Royal center draft burner, which produces a strong steady light, removable oil fount, No. 2 Rochester wick and chimney, and stands 22½ inches high. This lamp has a massive brass base, finely plated and lacquered. Shipping weight, 20 pounds.
Price **$2.78**

No. 2E971 Art Nouveau Lamp, $2.89. This beautiful lamp is a reproduction of a celebrated piece of French art. It is delicately tinted in purple and embossing is decorated in dark green with beautiful hand painted art figures on both sides of lamp and globe. It has the latest improved Success central draft burner (100-candle power) with large removable brass oil fount. All metal parts are made from satin finished brass. Shipping weight, 30 pounds.
Price **$2.89**

No. 2E973 Cerise Beauty, $2.95. This banquet lamp is made from ruby glass, and when lighted produces a rich ruby light, one of the most cheerful and charming illuminations, which casts a soft ruby glow on all of its surroundings. The handsome embossed satin finished cerise glass and bright gold trimmings go to make up a very striking and artistic lamp. It is fitted with the very best No. 2 Royal center draft burner and a No. 2 Rochester round wick and chimney and has a solid brass removable oil fount. This lamp stands 26 inches high and has a large 10-inch globe. Shipping weight, 25 pounds.
Price.........**$2.95**

No. 2E976 The American Beauty Lamp, $2.98. This is one of the prettiest lamps shown this season. The globe measures 10½ inches in diameter; the vase or cylinder to match is of equal size. The lamp measures 26 inches high. The hand painted decorations consist of beautiful American Beauty roses and foliage on a blue tinted background. It has the improved Success central draft burner, and takes No. 1 Belgium chimney and round wick. It produces a strong and steady 80-candle power light. This lamp compares favorably with those sold by crockery dealers at $4.50 and $5.00. Shipping weight, 25 pounds.
Price **$2.98**

No. 2E980 This beautiful lamp is particularly attractive owing to the beautiful dark American Beauty roses which form the floral decorations. These roses with the green foliage are printed on the tinted green background before the last firing of the lamp in the kiln and then the large roses are put on by hand in the deep red color, making the flowers stand out distinct from the lamp. The base is of solid cast brass and the fount holder has a solid brass drawn ring. The removable oil fount is of brass and has the No. 2 100-candle power center draft burner, taking No. 2 Rochester chimney and round wick. Shipping weight, 30 pounds. Price..........**$3.20**

No. 2E979 Lucile Lamp, $2.95. Compare this lamp with those offered by your local dealer at $5.00 or $6.00, and you will appreciate this wonderful value. This lamp is strictly the highest grade made. The beautiful pansies and green leaves are very carefully painted by hand by high class artists, every minor detail being brought out true to life. The entire lamp is magnificently tinted in an iridescent luster of light green, forming a deep contrast with the hand painted flowers. This lamp is extremely large, measuring 27 inches high and is complete with a 10½-inch globe, No. 2 Rochester chimney and wick. The highest grade center draft burner is used, which produces a strong steady light. Shipping weight, about 25 pounds. Price **$2.95**

No. 2E986 Romeo Lamp, $3.48, is one of the prettiest lamps made in a snow ball design. It is large and shapely throughout. The decoration consists of large hand painted snowballs, highly enameled, with light green leaves. The lamp and globe are richly tinted in a dark green and when lighted, the beautiful snowballs appear true to life. A decoration of this kind appeals to the most critical and is sure to meet with favor everywhere. The burner, which is the highest grade central draft type, produces a 100-candle power light and is complete with No. 2 Rochester chimney and wick. This lamp stands 27½ inches high and has a large 10-inch globe and is adorned with heavy brass crown and base which is finely gold lacquered. Securely packed in a box. Shipping weight, 30 pounds. Price......**$3.48**

No. 2E998 Excel Lamp, $3.89. This is an exceptionally large and handsome lamp at a very low price. It stands 31½ inches high and has an extra large globe 11½ inches in diameter. The decoration consists of large wreaths of delicate pink shaded water lilies and green lily leaves on a light yellow and green tinted background and produces a very pleasing effect when lighted. It is trimmed with a large and massive brass crown and base which greatly adds to the attractiveness of the lamp. It is equipped with the best grade No. 2 Royal center draft burner and removable oil fount made of solid brass, No. 2 Rochester chimney and round wick. This is the largest lamp ever offered at so low a price. Securely packed in a barrel. Shipping weight, 35 pounds. Price..............**$3.89**

No. 2E1010 The Brown Lion, $3.98. The body of this lamp is shaded from a dark seal brown to a light tan. The eight lions' heads stand out prominently from the lamp, and, together with the embossing, form the eight panels which contain the oriental landscapes, which are far beyond description or illustration. The mountings of this lamp are of brass and the removable brass oil fount has the highest grade center draft burner, which takes No. 2 Rochester chimney and round wick. It is 26 inches in height and has a 10-inch globe. Shipping weight, 30 pounds. Price..............**$3.98**

Our lamps are equipped with only the **best grades of burners and are fully guaranteed** to produce a strong, steady light. We will return your money if you are not perfectly satisfied.

No. 2E1016 Klondike Lamp, $4.98. Beautifully decorated by hand. This lamp is the work of high class artists, the decoration consisting of large white and pink chrysanthemums and light green leaves, very cleverly painted by hand and in such a manner that the beautiful flowers are true to life. The entire lamp is most handsomely tinted in pink and light green, forming a fine background for the flowers. No lamp has ever been made that can surpass it in beauty. It is extra large, measuring 26½ inches high and 11½-inch globe and 13-inch base. It has the best grade central draft burner, which produces 100-candle power light, and removable oil fount made of solid brass and is complete with No. 2 Rochester chimney and round wick. All metal parts, including the fancy cast crown and large base, are made of brass, gold plated and lacquered and will not tarnish. No better lamp made at any price. Securely packed in a barrel. Shipping weight, 40 pounds.
Price.........................**$4.98**

No. 2E1019 Iris Lily, $5.95. This lamp represents the largest and best lamp we offer. It measures 31½ inches high and has a large 11½-inch globe. The decoration, which consists of large purple and red iris lilies and green leaves on a beautifully tinted pale pink and maroon background, is beautiful to behold. The shape is the newest offered this season. It has a large massive brass crown and elaborate brass feet, which form a base, gold plated and fully protected from wear and tarnishing by a heavy coat of lacquer. Its burning and illuminating powers are unsurpassed and it is equipped with the very best grade of a Central draft burner, No. 2 Rochester round wick and No. 2 Rochester chimney. Lamps of this class usually sell at from $8.00 to $10.00. It is securely packed in a barrel. Shipping weight, 45 pounds. Price.........**$5.95**

Decorated Globes.

Decorated Globes for banquet or vase lamps, will fit any 4-inch globe ring.

These globes are beautifully decorated by hand with large pink wild roses and green leaves on a tinted background. Furnished in three tints, pink, yellow or green. Be sure to mention color of tint and size desired.

	Diameter	Price
No. 2E1201	8 inches	55c
No. 2E1202	9 inches	73c
No. 2E1203	10 inches	98c

Shipping weight from 8 to 12 pounds.

Crystal Etched Globes for banquet or vase lamps, made of etched crystal glass, beautifully figured like illustration. Will fit any 4-inch globe ring.

No. 2E1255 Diameter, 8 inches. Price.......**57c**

No. 2E1256 Diameter, 9 inches. Price.......**68c**

No. 2E1257 Diameter, 10 inches. Price..........................**99c**

No. 2E1258 Diameter, 10 inches, made of satin ruby glass. Price.........**$1.79**

Shipping weight from 8 to 12 pounds.

Banquet Lamp Globes beautifully decorated by hand with large white and pink chrysanthemums and dark green leaves on background, richly tinted in pink or light green. An exceptionally fine globe at an extremely low price. Be sure to mention the color of tinting and size desired.

	Diameter	Price
No. 2E1264	8 inches	$0.75
No. 2E1265	9 inches	.95
No. 2E1266	10 inches	1.39
No. 2E1267	11 inches	1.69

Shipping weight from 8 to 12 pounds.

MUSICAL GOODS DEPARTMENT—PIANOS AND ORGANS.

OUR NEW AND REMARKABLE OFFER No. 1

SEND NO MONEY. So well convinced are we that our pianos and organs are among the very finest manufactured and sold anywhere that we are now making our customers an astonishing, new and liberal offer. If you wish to try one of our pianos or organs and will send us your order, it will not be necessary for you to send us one cent or deposit any money until the instrument arrives at your town. Full particulars of this remarkably liberal proposition are more fully stated below.

WE DO NOT ASK YOU TO SEND US ANY MONEY when ordering a Beckwith piano or organ. Just send us your order with the name of the bank with which you expect to deposit the money for the instrument, and we will make immediate shipment and notify you. We will send the instrument to you freight prepaid, so that it will not be necessary for you to send us a cent either for the price of the instrument or freight charges. When you are notified that the instrument has arrived in your town you can deposit the price, together with freight charges, with your banker and take the instrument to your home for a thorough trial and examination. You can have it in your home full 30 days from the date you receive it, during which time you can call in your friends or any musical expert that you may desire and make a thorough test of the instrument, and if you are not fully satisfied with it in every particular, and fully convinced that you have made a great saving in purchasing from us you can box the instrument up and return it to us, and the banker will refund you every cent you have deposited.

SEARS, ROEBUCK AND CO.
CHICAGO.
CAPITAL AND SURPLUS OVER FIVE MILLION DOLLARS.

Certificate of Deposit

Town________ State________ Date________
Received from Mr.________________
________________ Dollars
in payment of Sears, Roebuck & Co.'s________

We agree to hold this money until the instrument has been received by Mr.________ residin in________ and has 30 days' trial, when we shall forward the amount to Sears, Roebuck & Co., Chicago, Ill.

If Mr.________ is not perfectly satisfied with the instrument, we will refund money on surrender to us of a bill of lading showing instrument has been reconsigned to Sears, Roebuck & Co.

____
Name of bank.

____
Your banker should sign his name here.

Above is shown a facsimile copy of the certificate of deposit which your banker will sign when the instrument arrives in your town and you deposit the money with him.

SEARS, ROEBUCK AND CO.
CHICAGO.
CAPITAL AND SURPLUS OVER FIVE MILLION DOLLARS.

Certificate No.

Certificate of Guaranty

This certifies that the ________ (the number and name of which has been registered), is made by skilled mechanics. Only thoroughly air and kiln dried lumber and other materials, specially selected and prepared, enter into this instrument and with fair usage we hereby agree to make good at our expense any defect in material or workmanship for a period of twenty-five years.

Dated at Chicago this________ day of________ A. D.____
SEARS, ROEBUCK & CO.,
R. W. SEARS, Pres't.

WHEN ORDERING AN INSTRUMENT from us under this plan, be sure to send us the name of the bank where you expect to deposit the money for the instrument. We then send the certificate of deposit and bill of lading to this bank, and when the instrument arrives in your town you can deposit the price, together with the freight charges, get your receipt for your money, take the bill of lading to the freight agent, get the instrument and take it to your home. Under this plan of shipment you run absolutely no risk in ordering an instrument from us, and should you return it for any reason whatever, you do not have to wait one hour for the return of your money, as both the money and the instrument remain in your town during the entire time of trial.

OUR OFFER NO. 2, should you wish to send the money for the instrument direct to us, or if there is no banker in your town you can send us the price of the instrument to be deposited in the Profit Sharing Department of our banking section. In many ways this is the preferable way to buy an instrument, because it makes your transactions with us absolutely confidential, and it gives you the same advantages as our Offer No. 1, because should the instrument prove unsatisfactory for any reason you can return it to us, our Banking Department will refund you the amount deposited with interest at the rate of 7 per cent per annum, and we will also return you the amount you have paid for freight. Our standing in the business world, and our financial responsibility (which you can ascertain from any bank or express company) makes us entirely responsible and fully guarantees that we will live up to every agreement and promise which we make. Customers who have dealt with us in the past and know us do not hesitate to send us any amount of money for any goods they may desire to purchase. We are reproducing below a facsimile of the certificate of deposit which we issue to customers who send us cash in advance. By reading the terms of this certificate you will see at once that we are entirely responsible for the return of the money in case the instrument should prove unsatisfactory for any reason whatever.

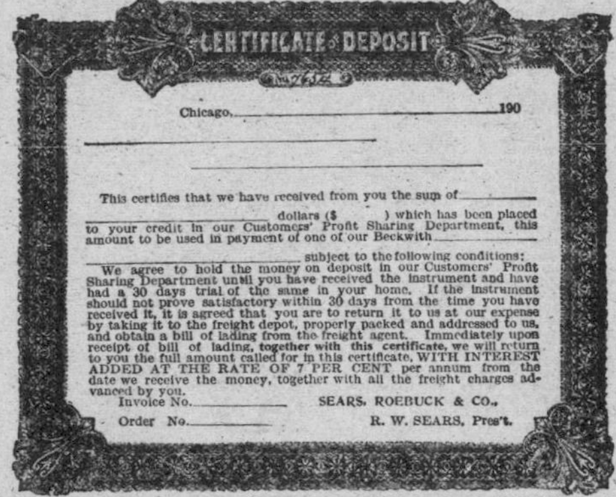
CERTIFICATE OF DEPOSIT

No. 7652

Chicago,________________ 190

____

____

This certifies that we have received from you the sum of________ ________ dollars ($) which has been placed to your credit in our Customers' Profit Sharing Department, this amount to be used in payment of one of our Beckwith________ ________ subject to the following conditions:

We agree to hold the money on deposit in our Customers' Profit Sharing Department until you have received the instrument and have had a 30 days trial of the same in your home. If the instrument should not prove satisfactory within 30 days from the time you have received it, it is agreed that you are to return it to us at our expense by taking it to the freight depot, properly packed and addressed to us, and obtain a bill of lading from the freight agent. Immediately upon receipt of bill of lading, **together with this certificate**, we will return to you the full amount called for in this certificate, WITH INTEREST ADDED AT THE RATE OF 7 PER CENT per annum from the date we receive the money, together with all the freight charges advanced by you.

Invoice No.________ SEARS, ROEBUCK & CO.,
Order No.________ R. W. SEARS, Pres't.

OUR 25 YEARS BINDING GUARANTEE. In order to remove all doubts in regard to the high quality of our instruments, with each instrument sold we issue a written, binding guarantee, a copy of which we show hereon. We could not afford to do this if we did not have the greatest faith in the quality of our instruments.

OUR 1-YEAR TRIAL OFFER. Not only do we allow you to try the instrument in your home for a full period of 30 days, giving it a thorough test, trial and examination, but we also allow you to return it to us at any time within one year should you not be perfectly satisfied with it in every particular. In such case we will return you every cent you have paid, together with charges for freight and cartage.

OUR SPECIAL PIANO CATALOGUE. We especially recommend that you select and purchase a piano from us as illustrated and described in this big catalogue, rather than to cause a delay by writing for our free Special Piano Catalogue, since we guarantee that any piano which you may order from these pages will reach you in perfect condition, prove in every way satisfactory, and that you will find it a much better piano than you can buy elsewhere at anything like the price we offer. We also guarantee that you will make a big saving in the cost, and if you do not find this to be so, you can return the piano to us any time within thirty days and we will immediately and cheerfully refund your money and pay the freight charges both ways. If, however, you are unable to make a selection from the illustrations and descriptions shown in this catalogue, and you feel that you would like to have better illustrations and more complete descriptions, then we will be glad to send you a copy of our Special Piano Catalogue. This catalogue will be sent to you, upon request, postage prepaid, and it will only be necessary for you to send us a postal card in order to obtain it. Simply say "Please send me your Piano Catalogue," and it will be sent by return mail.

The Beckwith Piano represents the very Highest Attainment in Piano Manufacture.

Read this Letter.

THEO. A. SALVO,
Practical
Piano and Organ Tuner and Repairer,
Formerly of Chickerings.

HICKORY, N. C. Sept. 19, 1905.

Sears, Roebuck & Co.,
Chicago, Ill.

Gentlemen:-

I was called upon the other day to look at a piano that you sold to Mr. J. Triplett at Coshen, N. C. The piano needed tuning and after I tuned it I must say I never was more surprised in my life. How can you make and sell such a piano as that at that extremely low price? The mechanism and material are excellent and I know if all who wish to purchase pianos could only see a Beckwith there would be lots of them sold. I have been in the business 54 years and have worked at three of the largest high grade piano factories. My knowledge of pianos and piano construction prompts me to write this unsolicited letter of praise for the Beckwith which I have just examined the second time. Again I say I am surprised that you can sell such a piano at such a low price. As I am on the road all the time following my vocation, I can and will speak to all I find who are about to purchase a piano, and advise them to give the Beckwith the first trial.

Wishing you success in this branch of business, I remain

Very respectfully,
Theo. A. Salvo.

The Beckwith Organs secured the Highest Award at the St. Louis Exposition. See page 158.

BUYING FROM THE DEALER.

IF A DEALER OFFERS YOU A PIANO which he claims is as good as the Beckwith and attempts to offer it to you at prices anywhere near as low as we are making, you can very easily ascertain what the quality of the piano is by a few judicious questions. The case of his piano may look very fine and may be highly finished, but you should always remember that in a piano, at least, a little veneer covers a multitude of sins. Ask him if the case of his piano is veneered with genuine sawed veneer. Ask him if it is cross banded and veneered both inside and out. In case he evades these questions you can easily ascertain for yourself by examining the bottom edge of the music desk or the lower front panel of the piano. If you do not find two layers of veneer plainly shown, you can make up your mind that they are not there.

Ask him if he is willing to place such a piano beside ours for a 30 days trial in your own home and will agree to keep away from you all of this time, allowing you and your musical friends to judge the instrument and test it without prejudice. Remember that we make you this offer only we go further We ask you to get your agent to take his best piano, one that he sells for at least twice what we ask, and have it placed beside ours in your parlor when we are perfectly willing and glad to rest the matter entirely in your hands

Ask him how many pianos he sells each year; ask him what his expenses are for store rent; how much he loses for bad debts on the installment plan, and what his losses are in taking various articles in exchange as part payment; figure what his honest living expenses are and you can easily determine how much he must make on each piano he sells to pay these expenses, how much he must make just to make both ends meet besides allowing a profit to be put aside for a rainy day.

Remember that where a dealer buys four or five pianos on consignment, or where he pays for them by turning in the notes received on other pianos sold on time at a very large discount, we contract for from two to three thousand pianos on a spot cash basis, therefore, at the lowest possible cost, making a great saving, all of which goes to you in the lower prices quoted.

Ask him if his piano is a full size concert grand, and up to the musical standard in every way. Then ask him if he will put it in your home for a full thirty days trial and allow you to return it at any time within one year and receive your money back with all freight charges paid in case it should prove unsatisfactory for any reason. If he agrees to this, then ask him if he will give you a written, binding 25 years guarantee to protect you against any defect in material or workmanship which may appear in the piano at any time within that period. If he refuses to give you this guarantee or to allow you the thirty days trial or to give you permission to return the piano at any time within one year, you may be sure that he has no faith in the instrument, and as he certainly knows more about the piano than you do, you cannot afford to purchase it. If he will not guarantee the instrument, he has no right to ask you to take any chances.

If he agrees to give you the 25 years guarantee and the thirty days trial on a piano he ordinarily asks from $450.00 to $500.00 for, then ask him if he will sell it to you for $195.00 cash. If he refuses to sell you the piano at this figure he is simply asking you to pay him not only his large profit, but also the profits and selling expenses of the different dealers through whose hands the piano passed before it came to him. We have had many instances where dealers have offered to sell pianos to our customers at from $165.00 to $200.00 which they claimed were equal to the Beckwith, but in every instance we have found that the piano was lacking in many of the essentials which go to make up a fine instrument. As a matter of fact it is absolutely impossible for a local dealer to sell a piano of the same high grade as the Beckwith for less than from $450.00 to $500.00. The local dealer cannot purchase a piano of this grade from his jobber or manufacturer at as low a price as we can sell it to you. No concern in this country possesses so great an advantage in buying as we do, and we are thus able to purchase these pianos at prices away below what any other concern can obtain. We give our customers all of this great advantage, as we base our prices upon the manufacturing cost with but one small margin of profit added.

A WORD ABOUT FREIGHT CHARGES.

Many of our friends hesitate to purchase pianos from us, because they believe that the freight charges will be so very high that it will make the piano too expensive. This is certainly a great mistake. In the first place the local dealer has to pay the freight upon any piano which he ships to your town, and in making up the price on the piano he has to include the freight charges which he has paid, and when you purchase the piano you not only pay the freight charges, but you pay his large profit as well. By comparing our prices on pianos with those asked you by local dealers, and then comparing the freight charges which you will have to pay with the amount which we can save you on your purchase, you will see at once that the freight charge is but a very small amount in comparison with the amount you will save on your purchase. Another advantage is, that in purchasing a piano from us you know exactly what the instrument costs you at the factory, and you know exactly what you pay in freight charges, while on the other hand, in purchasing from the local dealer you know what the piano costs you, but do not know how much of it is his profit and how much the freight charge. As a general thing the railroad companies are very reasonable in freight charges, and when you consider the fact that you have to pay the freight charges whether you buy from us or from the local dealer, we believe that you should not hesitate in giving us an opportunity to send you one of our splendid instruments under our great Thirty Days Free Trial Offer. We are always willing to tell our customers the exact cost of freight on a piano laid down at their town, and where parties wish us to do so, gladly prepay the freight where the amount of the charges is enclosed with the order. This guarantees that the freight charges will not be over the figures quoted by us. Do not let the small amount of freight charges which you will have to pay prove any obstacle to your purchasing one of these pianos, as we ship each one under our express promise to save you from $50.00 to $200.00, according to the grade of piano which you purchase.

A NEW PIANO LAMP.

We are giving an illustration of a new idea in a piano lamp, which we are sure will be welcomed by all performers on the piano. This piano lamp is so constructed that the base can be set upon the top of the instrument and the lamp regulated by thumb screws and rods so that it throws the light in any direction. The illustration shows the method of placing it on the instrument. The base is weighted so as to sustain the weight of the lamp. It has adjustable shades which not only throw the light squarely upon the music page, but also screen it from the eyes of the performer. The lamp can be detached from the frame, to be filled or cleaned, and the entire outfit can be removed from the piano by simply lifting it with the hand. It is handsomely nickel plated throughout, is very ornamental and carefully and substantially made. It is fitted with a circular wick and throws a strong brilliant light.

No. 2E102 Price, complete..**$3.25**

Weight, boxed and packed for shipment, 15 pounds.

The Profit Sharing Certificate we will send you on your purchase of a Piano will help you get valuable merchandise entirely free of charge. **See last pages in this book for full explanation.**

WHAT OUR FRIENDS SAY ABOUT THE MAGNIFICENT VALUES WHICH WE ARE GIVING IN PIANOS.

Voluntary Testimonials From Just a Few of Those Who Have Purchased Pianos From Us in the Last Year. What Our Customers Say About Our Pianos is the Best Evidence of Their Splendid Finish and Magnificent Tone.

EQUAL TO A KNABE AT $600.00.

We give below a testimonial from one of our enthusiastic customers, who is a business man in Columbus, Ohio, and not given to exaggeration in any way. We desire to call the attention of our customers to the difference in the two prices which the dealers made on the Knabe piano. $495.00 for cash and $600.00 on payments, being a difference of $105.00, which proves our assertion that dealers who sell instruments upon the installment plan must necessarily have their prices much higher than those who sell for cash. We do not know that we can add anything to this testimonial as it is complete in every respect. It is simply one of many which we receive from time to time.

Sears, Roebuck & Co., Chicago, Ill. Columbus, Ohio.

Dear Sirs:—I have already written you how well I like the Acme Cabinet Grand Piano, recently bought from you, but I would like again to state that according to my opinion the case is made and finished in the highest type of art. The tone is excellent and exquisite. I do not believe that I could have secured a better piano no matter how much I paid or what I bought. That was my opinion the first day I received it, and it is still my opinion. In fact, the better know the piano the better I like it. I would also add that the gentleman wh selected the piano for me surely thoroughly understands pianos and piano co struction. I do not believe that anyone else could have selected a piano me that would suit me any better, and I thank him sincerely for the troubl which he has gone. Miss Rose Lange, a young lady who is a fine pianist, tried our piano very thoroughly. Last evening she told me that she like piano every bit as well as her own. She has a Knabe, which sells here for a $600.00 on payments, and for which she paid $495.00 spot cash. She say case of my piano is much finer and more artistic than hers and that the ac[illegible]s easier and more responsive and the tone every bit as good as in her own piano. If you wish a recommendation at any time, refer any one to me, I will gladly tell them how much money they can save in buying a piano from you and how honorably you have treated me and of your very liberal terms of shipment. I will certainly recommend any one to get one of your pianos and thoroughly try it, knowing that you can suit them so well and save them so much money.

Respectfully yours, HENRY W. MUELLER.
662 Briggs St.

AS GOOD AS HIS NEIGHBOR'S PIANO WHICH COST $450.00.

The customer whose testimonial appears below, took advantage of our great 30 Days Free Trial Offer, which gave him a splendid opportunity to compare his piano with the $450.00 instrument owned by his neighbor, and by reading the testimonial you will see that he found his piano in every way equal to the one purchased by his neighbor at $450.00.

Sears, Roebuck & Co., Chicago, Ill. Sterling, Nebraska.

Dear Sirs:—The Beckwith piano I received of you in January has given good satisfaction so far. We are well pleased with the same. We cannot see but what it is as good as our neighbor's, that cost $450.00. We are well pleased with the mandolin attachment. My neighbor's has no attachments. C. B. SMITH.

EQUAL TO PIANOS SOLD BY AGENTS AT FROM $350.00 TO $400.00.

Below we give a testimonial from another party, who after comparison and trial of our piano is willing to say that the piano we sold him is equal to those generally sold by agents at from $350.00 to $400.00. Such testimonials as these ought to convince any unprejudiced person that what we say in regard to the great saving which we can make is absolutely true in every respect.

Sears, Roebuck & Co., Chicago, Ill. Elco, Penn.

Dear Sirs:—The piano which I purchased from you reached me on June 16th, and after giving it a thorough test, both myself and friends, I am pleased to inform you that it gives satisfaction in every respect and is equal to pianos sold here by agents at $350.00 and $400.00. I would recommend it to anyone as being all that you say it is and would be pleased to have anyone who is going to purchase a piano refer to me either by letter or personally and I will gladly do what I can to aid you in making a sale. Thanking you for your past favors,

I remain, yours truly, JAMES L. MOMETAIN.

EQUAL TO PIANOS SOLD BY DEALERS AT $350.00 AND BETTER TONED.

Below we give another testimonial from a customer who says that the piano we shipped him is equal to pianos sold by dealers at $350.00 and is much better in tone. Bear in mind, that the customer writes this letter entirely of his own accord and without any dictation from us in any respect. We would be glad to have you write to the writer of any one of these testimonials and get his opinion of the merits of our instruments.

Sears, Roebuck & Co., Chicago, Ill. Three Rivers, Mich.

Dear Sirs:—I received the piano April 6th, all O. K. In appearance it is equal to a $350.00 Wellington, sold by a dealer here and better toned.

Yours respectfully, G. W. BARTO.

WOULD NOT PART WITH IT FOR ANY $300.00 PIANO IN TOWN.

It is the universal verdict of our customers as gleaned from the numerous voluntary letters which we receive that, they would not exchange the pianos which we have sold them for other pianos in the neighborhood which have cost much more in price.

Sears, Roebuck & Co., Chicago, Ill. St. Cloud, Minn.

Dear Sirs:—We received our piano and must say that we are more than pleased with it. I would not part with it for any $300.00 piano in town. In fact, we are well pleased with all our goods. I wish to thank you very much. I'll advise everybody to get their goods from Sears, Roebuck & Co.

Yours very truly, MISS M. STUCKE.

OWING TO LACK OF SPACE, WE ARE UNABLE TO SHOW ANY ILLUSTRATION OF THIS PIANO.

$79.45 OUR BECKWITH BOUDOIR 6-OCTAVE PIANO

No. 46E3

Particularly suitable for small houses, summer cottages and other places where a large piano is not desirable. The tone is full and sweet, of a very pleasing quality and all that could be desired or expected in a piano of this size.

$79.45 REPRESENTS THE BARE COST to manufacture the instrument, with our usual small margin of profit added. It is the finest and most satisfactory small piano ever offered. It is built upon what is known as the F scale, beginning with the lower F and ending on the high F. Remember that the keyboard **only contains 6 octaves.** The keyboard is, therefore, one and one-third octaves shorter than the keyboard of all other Beckwith pianos. The compass is the same as in all other 6-octave pianos and is quite practical. We recommend it as the best 6-octave piano ever attempted.

THE CASE is double veneered in genuine mahogany, with a beautiful panel effect in the upper and lower front. The trusses are square; in keeping with the balance of the case. All pilasters, trusses and mouldings are solid wood, highly polished. The piano is furnished in mahogany veneer only.

THE ACTION, 6-octave, is of a very fine grade, responsive and repeats very nicely. The material and workmanship are of the best. **THE SCALE** is not overstrung. This piano has a straight stringing; in other words, it is strung straight up and down like a harp, and is not overstrung as is our Home Favorite Piano. There is not room enough in any 6-octave piano for the usual Beckwith overstringing. **THE PIN BLOCK** is built up in an approved manner, and cannot warp, crack or split. This construction holds the pin firmly. **THE SOUNDING BOARD** is very finely constructed of Canadian spruce pine, scientifically ribbed. **THE KEYS** are of highly polished **ivory and ebony, and not celluloid.** **THE PEDAL ACTION** is complete, having a loud and soft pedal and a practice pedal as well. This piano is not furnished with the mandolin attachment.

The price includes a handsome solid wood stool and complete instruction book.

THIS PIANO, THE BECKWITH BOUDOIR, in 6 octaves, is offered under our great 30 days free trial plan, as explained on page 138. All money refunded in full, together with the freight charges both ways, if you are not entirely satisfied. **We guarantee this piano for five years only.** Owing to its size and the peculiar manner of construction in all 6-octave pianos, we could not well afford to guarantee it for a longer period. If you contemplate the purchase of a 6-octave piano, you will find this the finest, the best, the most serviceable and attractive 6-octave piano ever offered.

No. 46E3 OUR BECKWITH BOUDOIR PIANO. Price....................$79.45

YOUR PARTICULAR ATTENTION IS INVITED

to the fact that this instrument is not a full size, upright piano. It is only 48 inches high, 4 feet long and 20 inches wide. It has not the usual 7⅓ octaves. It has 6 octaves only. The tone, however, and the volume of tone is all that you could possibly expect in a piano of this size. Remember, this is a Beckwith piano, and as such is sent out under our binding guarantee for quality and under the provisions of our great 30-day free trial offer.

With every purchase of this piano, we give, free, a scholarship certificate in one of the largest music schools in the United States, which entitles the holder to a course of fifty complete lessons on the piano, as fully explained on page 139.

$89.00 THE BECKWITH HOME FAVORITE PIANO

A Regular 7⅓ Octave Piano, With Overstrung Scale. A Full Size Parlor Piano, 4 Feet 6 Inches High, 5 Feet 1 Inch Long, and 2 Feet 2 Inches Deep. Weight, Boxed for Shipment, 750 Pounds.

A GUARANTEED PIANO, FULL PARLOR SIZE, FOR $89.00.

THE PRICE INCLUDES THE PIANO, a handsome solid wood stool and complete instruction book. To every purchaser of this piano we give, free, a scholarship certificate in one of the largest music schools in the United States, which entitles the holder to a course of fifty complete lessons on the piano, as explained on page 139.

FULL DESCRIPTION.

Our HOME FAVORITE PIANO is a full size instrument, very substantially built, and is a most remarkable value at the price named.

THE CASE is of a handsome design, as the illustration, taken direct from the photograph, will show. The panel in the duet or continuous music desk is ornamented with a handsome scroll and extends the full length of the piano. It is furnished in either mahogany or walnut finish, but is not veneered, therefore we can only guarantee it for five years. This piano is fitted with the latest style of rolling fall board.

THE SCALE is a regular full 7⅓ overstrung scale, the same as will be found in any piano offered by others at $200.00. It is not harp strung as is our Boudoir Piano, above described, but is overstrung in the regular manner, thus giving the latest possible length to the string.

THE PIN BLOCK is built up of several pieces of rock maple, which holds the tuning pin firmly.

THE STRINGS are of a very fine quality, thoroughly tested, and piano is fitted with overstrung, wound bass strings.

THE KEYS are genuine ivory and ebony, very finely polished.

THE SOUNDING BOARD is made of selected Canadian spruce, scientifically braced.

THE METAL FRAME is as strong as it is possible to have in a piano of this size, and is large enough to withstand the strain in this piano when it is tuned to pitch.

THE TONE is very full, sweet and melodious and of ample power for all ordinary requirements.

THE SIZE. Height, 4 feet 6 inches; length, 5 feet 1 inch; depth, 2 feet 2 inches. Weight, boxed for shipment, 750 pounds.

WITH THIS PIANO we will include, without any extra charge, either the mandolin attachment or the practice pedal, which is fully described on page 143. It will be necessary for you to advise us which attachment you desire, but we advise you to order the practice pedal. The price includes a substantial stool and complete instruction book.

REMEMBER, that this piano has full 7⅓ octaves, overstrung scale, ivory and ebony keys, and is the most marvelous value ever offered at this price. Owing to the size of the piano, however, the strings are not so long nor as heavy, the action is not so strong or as large as in our better grades, the case is not double veneered but is only finished, hence, we are compelled to guarantee this piano for five years only.

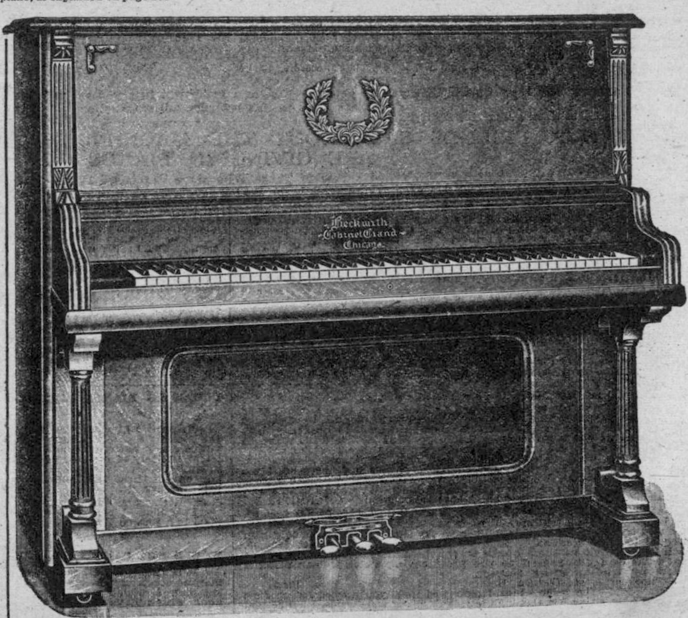

No. 46E1 Our Home Favorite Beckwith Piano. Price, $89.00.

YOU SHARE IN THE PROFITS OF OUR BUSINESS IF YOU PURCHASE THIS PIANO, AS EXPLAINED IN THE LAST PAGES OF THIS CATALOGUE. SOLD UNDER OUR LIBERAL 30 DAYS FREE TRIAL OFFER, AS EXPLAINED ON PAGE 138.

$115.00 THE BECKWITH PALACE GRAND PIANO.

A VERY HANDSOME PIANO WITH A FINE TONE.

MADE OF SELECTED MATERIAL AND SOLD TO YOU AT $115.00, which represents only the bare cost at the factory, with but our one margin of profit added, the equal of any piano sold through other channels for $250.00, and offered to you for a 30 days trial in your own home under our great "send no money with order" plan. Sold under our guarantee for quality running 25 years.

PIN BLOCK is built up of rock map[illegible] and holds pin firmly, thus preventing it from turning.

METAL FRAME is the same as used in all Beckwith pianos, but is not quite so large as in those instrument sold at a higher price, but it is just as scientifically cast.

SOUNDING BOARD is the genuine Beckwith sounding board, made of Canadian spruce of the best quality, specially prepared for this purpose, and it is ribbed in the most approved manner, which is a guarantee that the sounding board will never crack, split or warp.

FINISH. This piano can be furnished in either English quarter sawed oak, French burled walnut or richly figured mahogany veneer, very highly polished and hand rubbed. When ordering please state the veneer desired.

SIZE, 4 feet 7 inches high, 2 feet 3 inches deep, 5 feet 1 inch long. Weight, boxed for shipment, 780 pounds.

CASE is double veneered inside and outside, with cross banded, sawed veneer, and fitted with very handsome one-leg trusses, finished and polished in a beautiful manner. All mouldings, pilasters and trusses are of solid wood; a continuous music desk with handsomely raised panel in an artistic design; latest style of Boston rolling fall board. The hinges, pedals, pedal guards and metal parts are heavily nickel plated.

SCALE, full 7⅓ octaves, overstrung. Three-string unison in treble and two-string unison in bass register. Best quality Poehlmann piano wire strings. Keys of the best ivory with ebony sharps.

ACTION, very responsive, and adjusted in a most thorough manner, so that it responds to every call made upon it. All wool piano felt in the hammers and all bearings in the action properly bushed.

TONE is a full, rich Beckwith tone in all its beauty, but owing to the size of the instrument, the tone is not so full as in our Artists' Cabinet Grand Piano, but it is full and rich enough for all ordinary requirements.

THE PRICE INCLUDES a handsome stool with adjustable seat, complete instruction book, and a certificate, which entitles you to ninety-six weekly lessons on the piano, covering a period of two years, as thoroughly explained on page 139.

A Profit Sharing Certificate, as explained on the last pages, will be yours if you purchase this piano.

WE ARE OFFERING A FINE PIANO LAMP on page 141 of this catalogue, and we would like the privilege of sending you one, as we know it will fill a long felt want in your home. The piano lamps which are now on the market are very costly, and so far as lighting up the music on a piano is concerned, they are distinct failures. This lamp will set
on the top
your piano,
l throw a
ect light up-
the music
ore you.
only ask
5 for it, and
ill not only
e of great
ice to light
the music
ut will
ike a
orna-
your

Beckwith Cabinet Grand Chicago.

$115.00 DEALERS ASK $250.00 FOR THE EQUAL OF THIS INSTRUMENT.

Order by Number **No. 46E7**

No. 46E7 The Beckwith Palace Grand Piano, $115.00.

SEND US NO MONEY. DEPOSIT NOTHING IN ADVANCE.

We will ship this piano, freight charges prepaid, for a full 30 days free trial, as explained on page 138. Just send your trial order and write us the name of the bank where you wish to deposit the price of the piano with the freight charges **after it is received** at your local station and we will ship promptly. If the piano does not please you, send it back at our expense and the bank will refund your money. Remember that there will be no delay, because every dollar of **your money will be at your own bank waiting for you.**

PRICE. **At $115.00** we furnish this piano carefully boxed, including stool and instruction book, all delivered on board cars at Chicago.

THE MANDOLIN ATTACHMENT and the Muffler or Practice Pedal. We furnish with all of our pianos, without any extra charge, a mandolin attachment which is the best and most practical device yet invented for imitating the tones of the harp or mandolin. While this is unquestionably the best device of its character yet offered to the public, we do not advise our customers to order it in connection with their instruments. We find it necessary to furnish this mandolin attachment, as we frequently have calls for it, but in every case we advise the purchaser to substitute the practice pedal, as it is of much more practical value than the mandolin attachment. While the practice pedal muffles the tone of the instrument during practice, its use also preserves the hammers from wear and injury, while the constant use of the mandolin attachment is certain to injure the hammers to a greater or less degree, and impair the tone of the instrument in the same proportion. While we will gladly furnish the mandolin attachment to anyone desiring it, still we expressly recommend that the practice pedal be substituted for it. Teacher, pupil and the inmates of the home where music lessons are practiced will all testify to the practical value of the muffler, or practice pedal.

No. 46E7 The Beckwith Palace Grand Piano. Price..**$115.00**

$138.00 THE BECKWITH ARTISTS' CABINET GRAND PIANO.

A PARLOR UPRIGHT PIANO OF STERLING QUALITY, excellent workmanship, neat and attractive case, offered under our "from factory to customer direct" plan. Guaranteed to be the equal of pianos which regularly retail at $300.00.

IT IS A PIANO OF SPLENDID QUALITY AND IS WARRANTED BY US FOR TWENTY-FIVE YEARS.

The material and workmanship are of an excellent grade and we are perfectly willing to ship it to you with the understanding that you will find it the equal of any piano regularly sold at $300.00 or it must be returned at our expense.

SEND NO MONEY. DEPOSIT NOTHING IN ADVANCE. We will ship the piano, freight charges prepaid, for a full 30 days free trial, as explained on page 138. Just send us your trial order and write us the name of the bank where you wish to deposit the price of the piano with the freight charges **after it is received** at your local station, and we will ship promptly. If the piano does not please you, send it back at our expense and the bank will refund your money. Remember that there will be no delay, because every dollar of **your money will be at your own bank waiting for you.**

CASE is made of the very best seasoned hardwood lumber, double cross band sawed veneers inside and outside. It is beautifully finished and decorated with carved pilasters and trusses; all mouldings and trusses in solid wood.

MUSIC DESK is of the continuous or duet style, extending from side to side of the piano and is very handsomely ornamented with raised design on the panel.

SIZE. 4 feet 8½ inches high, 5 feet 2½ inches wide and 2 feet 3 inches deep, and will weigh, when boxed for shipment, 800 pounds.

SOUNDING BOARD is made of the very best thoroughly seasoned Canadian spruce pine especially prepared for this purpose and universally used in only the best pianos. It is thoroughly braced by bars of the same wood. Ribs are sc entifically plac making the tc full, rich and sw

KEYS are tu ivory, w ebony sharps, hi polished.

SOLD UNDER GREAT 30-DAY TRIAL FREIG' PAID OFFER T ED ON PAGE

46

Orde. by Number.

The Profit Sharing Certificate we send you will help you get valuable articles free, as explained on the last pages of this book.

FINISH. We furnish this piano either in English quarter sawed oak veneer, elegant burled walnut veneer, or richly figured mahogany veneer, as desired. The price is the same, and in ordering be sure to mention the veneer wanted.

ACTION responds instantly. It is a repeating action, built of selected materials and adjusted to a nicety. All bearings are carefully bushed with bushing felt. All hammers are genuine all wool piano felt; nickel plated action rail and brackets.

THE TONE is very full and sweet, pleasing to a wonderful degree. It is a Beckwith tone in all its purity and must be heard to be fully appreciated.

PIN BLOCK, to which the composition steel frame is bolted, has four thicknesses of maple veneers, the grain of each running in opposite directions, making it impossible to warp or split.

FALL BOARD is of the Boston rolling pattern, the same as used on the highest grade pianos made.

SCALE is full size, 7⅓ octaves, overstrung bass, three strings to each note except wound bass strings, full length metal frame, and is so constructed as to produce a remarkably even quality of tone throughout.

WITH EVERY PURCHASE of this piano we give, free, a scholarship, certificate in one of the largest music schools in the United States, which entitles the holder to ninety-six complete lessons on the piano, covering a period of two years, as fully explained on page 139.

PIANO LAMP. We have succeeded in procuring a piano lamp which fills a long felt want. You will find this lamp illustrated on page 141 of this catalogue, to which we call your attention. We only ask $3.25 for this splendid lamp, and at this price you cannot afford to be without one. Not only does it throw a direct stream of light upon the music, but is also so arranged as to shade the light from the eyes of the performer. It is a great improvement upon the old style costly piano lamp, and we recommend it to your consideration.

MANDOLIN ATTACHMENT. We furnish the mandolin attachment with this piano absolutely free of charge; or if the customer desires, we will furnish, as a substitute for this attachment, the Beckwith practice pedal, which muffles the tone of the instrument while the student is practicing. See what we have to say in regard to this mandolin attachment on page 143.

No. 46E9 The Beckwith Artists' Cabinet Grand Piano. Price.. **$138.00**

BECKWITH HOME QUEEN PIANO-ORGAN,

SHIPPED ONLY FROM CENTRAL OHIO. No. 46E15 **$69.00** ORDER BY NUMBER. AS ILLUSTRATED ON OPPOSITE PAGE.

This Organ is unquestionably the finest instrument of its kind ever placed on the market, and at the price we offer it, $69.00, it represents a saving to the purchaser of at least $50.00 or $75.00 on the purchase.

THIS INSTRUMENT HAS BEEN STEADILY REDUCED IN PRICE

Owing to the improving and cheapening of manufacturing processes and the reduction of selling expenses, until we are able, at the present time, to offer it at this exceedingly low price. It is made in response to a demand for a reed organ which will exactly resemble a grand piano, and the engraving will show you that we have succeeded in producing an instrument which the casual observer will not be able to distinguish from a $400.00 grand piano. In making this organ we have avoided the deadening and muffling of the tone, which is so common a fault with the ordinary piano-organ. Indeed, we have taken advantage of the shape of the case to produce in the instrument a large tone qualifying chamber, which amplifies and increases the tone volume of the instrument.

BY EXAMINING THE ENGRAVING YOU WILL NOTICE THAT WE HAVE AVOIDED THE NECESSITY OF PLACING KNEE SWELLS ON THIS INSTRUMENT AND THEIR PLACE IS TAKEN BY OUR GRAND PNEUMATIC SWELL.

CASE.

The case of this organ is in every way equal to the case on an ordinary piano and can be furnished in San Domingo mahogany only. It is veneered like any piano case and given the same high finish. The wood of this case is so treated by the finisher as to show the beautiful grain through the different coats of transparent varnish with which it is covered. The carving and ornamentations are the finest ever placed on an organ case of this variety, and the design is modeled after the most approved piano design. We have been very successful in selling this instrument as it has given such universal satisfaction. It has a full duet music desk which can be pulled forward as shown in the engraving and is fitted with a regular piano fall cover. This instrument is fitted with regular piano pedals and pedal guard of regular piano design, handsomely nickel plated and polished. While the engraving gives a very good idea of the design and ornamentations of the case it falls far short of giving you an idea of its handsome appearance and beautiful finish.

CAPACITY.

The tone, quality and power of this organ is far superior to the ordinary reed organ and it is fitted with three full sets of reeds and has a 7½-octave key board. It has 238 reeds in all and these can be formed into an immense number of harmonious combinations by the aid of the stops which can be seen in the engravings directly over the name of the organ. These stops are so arranged as not to be noticeable by the casual observer and do not detract from the piano effect in any way. The reeds are all the celebrated Newell reeds, are made of solid brass of the highest grade and the tongues are double riveted to the reed block. They are all tuned and bent especially for this instrument and we can guarantee their volume and sweetness of tone. The peculiar shape of the inside of the case adds to the singing quality and tone power of these reeds, and when the full power of the bellows is turned on, the effect of their different combinations is startling in its beauty.

GRAND PNEUMATIC SWELL.

This organ contains several improvements not found on any other instrument, among which is the grand pneumatic swell. This swell is placed on the organ to avoid incumbering it with knee swells. It is automatically opened by air pressure when the pedals are pumped hard and closes automatically when they are pumped lightly. When the performer desires to get more power out of the organ he naturally pumps the instrument harder and this opens the swell, allowing the full power of the organ to be heard, and when he does not desire such a volume of tone he naturally pumps the pedals with less violence and the swell closes, reducing the power of the instrument. This swell does not open suddenly, or all at once, but is opened gradually according to the power exerted on the pedals. This simple improvement will be recognized at once as being something especially fine in connection with the piano-organ, and it is not found in any other instrument on the market.

NEW PATENT OCTAVE COUPLER.

Another feature of this instrument is the new patent octave coupler operated by the middle pedal of the organ. This avoids the necessity of placing two extra stops on the organ, which would only detract from the piano effect of the case. It is an attachment whereby the tones of the instrument are coupled in both the treble and bass by pressing down the middle pedal. In order to release it, it is only necessary to press it a second time, when the coupler releases automatically. This will be recognized as a valuable addition to the instrument and will not be found on any other piano-organ on the market. The third pedal on this instrument gives the effect of a practice pedal on a grand piano, and adds to the magnificent appearance of the organ.

BELLOWS.

This organ is fitted with the celebrated Beckwith bellows and reservoir which produces a powerful and well balanced tone. These bellows are constructed of three-ply built-up stock which cannot warp or split, and covered with fine rubber cloth which guarantees them against leaking. They are so arranged that the bellows exhausts the air in the reservoir, forming a vacuum, into which the air rushes through the reeds causing them to sound. The reservoir is fitted with our Patent Automatic Pressure Valve, which relieves the surplus air pressure and prevents the bellows being over strained by violent pumping. While these bellows have an extra large capacity the pedals are so arranged that the greatest amount of leverage is taken advantage of and the smallest child can sustain the full power of the instrument for an indefinite length of time without any great effort. By the bellows and reservoir combination which we place in this instrument, and in fact, all of our organs, we insure an easy and steady supply of air to the reeds and this avoids that jerky, spasmodic effect which is so noticeable in other organs when the pedals are pumped violently.

PIPE SWELL ATTACHMENT.

This instrument has fitted over the reeds a patent pipe swell attachment which so qualifies their tone as to make them a close imitation of the pipes on the grand pipe organ. This is an improvement much sought after by organ builders, but so far it is the only invention of its kind that has ever proven successful. It has caused the sale of a good many hundreds of these organs, and has never failed to call forth the highest praise of the performer.

ACTION.

The action which we place in this organ is the very finest that can be obtained, and every bit of the material is thoroughly tested and examined before being used. Every bit of wood which enters into this action is thoroughly kiln and air dried before being worked up into the different parts for the action and so well are these things taken care of that we can guarantee our actions against defects in workmanship and material for a period of 25 years. All the different connecting parts are thoroughly felted with the best quality of wool felt, and all parts of the action intended to be air tight are covered by felt and sheepskin. In most organs the connecting parts are not felted and after they have been used for awhile they become loose and rattle. This is never found in the Beckwith organs. Every part of the action which we place in this organ is thoroughly and substantially built, so that the chances of it getting out of order are reduced to a minimum.

THE STOPS.

All of the different sets of reeds which we place in this instrument are at all times under the control of the performer and can be worked into all sorts of harmonious combinations so as to bring out the real beauty of the instrument. These stops, or rather buttons, are easily within the reach of the player's hands and enable him to change the tone combinations of the instrument at will.

OUR REDUCED PRICES.

This splendid instrument is shipped from our factory in Central Ohio directly to you. When you purchase it, you merely pay the manufacturer's price and the one small profit which we add to pay us for handling and selling the instrument. This fully explains how you can purchase this splendid organ for the extremely low price of $69.00. If this instrument was sold in the usual way through dealers it would cost you between $90.00 and $100.00 at the very lowest. We have steadily reduced the prices on our instruments and every reduction we have made in price has been the result of the improvement and cheapening of manufacturing processes, a reduction in selling expenses and not a deterioration in the quality of the goods.

OUR 25 YEARS GUARANTEE.

We are willing to stand behind our organs, and we do not ask our customers to take any chances whatever when they purchase from us. We will ship you one of these organs with the understanding and agreement that if you should discover any defect in the workmanship or material within 25 years from the time you receive it we stand ready to make the defect good and satisfy you perfectly.

OUR 30 DAYS FREE TRIAL OFFER.

We send this organ out upon the same terms that we ship all our other organs and can place it in your home for 30 days, allow you to try it thoroughly and get the opinions of your friends before finally accepting it. How you can take advantage of this trial offer is fully explained on page 138, which we trust you will read carefully. Should you take advantage of our 30 days free trial offer, and the organ proves satisfactory within that length of time, we will then allow you one year in which time you can return the instrument at our expense and have your money refunded in case it should prove unsatisfactory. This is known as **our one-year trial offer.**

FREE.

We furnish absolutely free with this instrument a splendid stool, manufactured of wood to match the case of the organ, with handsome turned legs, brass claws and glass balls on the feet. We also furnish a handsome piano scarf, and a splendid instruction book by the aid of which anyone can learn how to play the instrument without the aid of a teacher.

YOUR $69.00 PROFIT SHARING CERTIFICATE WOULD ENTITLE YOU IMMEDIATELY TO A FINE CHAIR, FINE COUCH, OR SOME ARTICLE ABSOLUTELY FREE OF FURTHER COST TO YOU.

$24.35 BUYS THE NEW BECKWITH COTTAGE HOME ORGAN

THE LATEST PRODUCTION OF THE CELEBRATED BECKWITH ORGAN COMPANY.

This Large, Handsome Golden Oak Case Organ stands 75 inches high, 44½ inches long and 23 inches deep. This same grade of organ is being sold at wholesale for from $25.00 to $35.00.

YOUR $24.35 PROFIT SHARING CERTIFICATE Would go far towards getting you something FREE SHOWN ON THE LAST PAGES OF THIS BOOK

Read our new and remarkable offer No. 1, on page 138.

CASE. **The case of this organ is made of solid oak, handsomely finished and polished.** From the bottom to the top it is beautifully ornamented with hand carvings and moulding. It has a tasty canopy top gracefully designed and ornamented. It is fitted with two lamp stands and has an extra wide music desk and large music cabinet. The design is one of the very prettiest that has ever been shown in a low priced organ, and we know that it will appeal to every person of taste and good judgment. It is fitted with handles, casters, and the pedals are furnished with tasty metallic guards and covered with Brussels carpet. The pedals are also fitted with the Beckwith device for preventing the pedal straps from wearing out and breaking. The illustration will give you a very good idea of the design of the case and general appearance of the instrument, but it utterly fails to convey to you any just idea of the immense value which we are offering in this organ at the extraordinary low price of $24.35.

ACTION. **This organ is fitted with 10 stops, 122 reeds, and has five octaves of keys.** It is also fitted with two knee swells for operating the swell organ and grand organ. It is fitted with the celebrated Newell reeds, with the tongues double riveted to extra heavy brass reed blocks. It is furnished with the celebrated Beckwith bellows, which guarantees a steady supply of air to the reeds. The names of the stops on this organ are as follows: Diapason, Principal, Celeste, Cremona, Diapason Forte, Principal Forte, Treble Coupler, Bass Coupler, Dulciana and Melodia. It has four sets of reeds, as follows: One set of Principal reeds, 24 notes; one set of Melodia reeds, 37 notes; one set of Diapason reeds, 24 notes; one set of Celeste reeds, 37 notes. Every piece and part of this action is thoroughly finished and durably constructed so as to come under our great 25-year guarantee.

THE TONE. **We are prepared to guarantee the tone quality of this instrument because it is fitted throughout with the very highest quality reeds and the most thoroughly constructed action.** The reeds are manipulated, bent, tuned and voiced by the same men who handle the reeds on all of our highest priced organs, men who have spent a lifetime in learning this art, the most competent men that can be secured. The stop and reed combinations are those which time and experience have proved to be the very best for an organ of this character. Every stop on the organ can be used for controlling and shading the tone in some way, and **there are no dummy stops whatever.** We know that many dealers are selling organs throughout the country and furnishing them with dummy stops, but you will not find an organ in our entire line fitted in this way.

WITH THIS ORGAN **we give a certificate which entitles the holder to a full course of musical instruction on the instrument,** consisting of fifty weekly lessons, covering a period of one year. We do not charge you one cent for this, and we do not add one penny extra to the price on this instrument, but give the certificate to you absolutely free. You will find our different courses of free instruction fully outlined and described on page 139 of this catalogue.

WE ALWAYS ADVISE **our customers to purchase the very best organ of which their financial circumstances will admit.** While this organ is the very best instrument that can possibly be made and sold for $24.35, and is in every way superior to organs now being sold by other dealers at a much higher price, still it is not reasonable to suppose that this organ is equal to our Royal Grand Organ at $36.75 or our magnificent Imperial Grand Organ at $39.95. If you are not so situated that you could purchase one of these higher priced organs and are looking for an organ at about the price of our Cottage Home, an instrument which will give you the greatest amount of satisfaction at this price, we will unhesitatingly recommend this instrument to you as being the very best reed parlor organ to be purchased anywhere in the country for less than double this price.

OUR TERMS OF SHIPMENT **are so liberal that if you have any doubts about the quality of this instrument or about any other organ in our line, you are given the fullest opportunity to thoroughly test and try it before finally deciding to accept it.** You will find these liberal terms of shipment fully outlined on page 138 of this catalogue, to which we call your attention. **This organ weighs, boxed and packed for shipment, about 400 pounds.**

NOTE—We Furnish this Organ in Oak Case Only.

No. 46E21 New Beckwith Cottage Home Organ. Five Octaves, Ten Stops. Price............... **$24.35**

$27.65 BUYS THE COTTAGE FAVORITE ORGAN

YOU WILL SHARE IN OUR PROFIT IF YOU SEND US AN ORDER FOR THIS ORGAN. We send you a profit sharing certificate showing the amount of your purchase for every order and when these certificates amount to certain sums you can get various kinds of goods, entirely free of charge, as fully explained in the last pages of this book.

THIS IS THE LATEST PRODUCTION OF THE CELEBRATED BECKWITH ORGAN COMPANY, AND IS ONE OF THE PRETTIEST DESIGNS ON THE MARKET.

IT IS BUILT of the same excellent material and with the same skill as all the other famous Beckwith Organs. It is offered in response to a demand for an organ with a very handsome case and artistic finish at a very moderate price. The reason why we are able to quote such an extremely low price upon it, is that our immense manufacturing facilities and enormous sales make it profitable for us to sell it at a very small increase over the manufacturing cost. We have gradually reduced the prices on our other organs, as we gained the knowledge and experience which enabled us to make and sell them at the least possible expense. We are giving our customers the advantage of this experience by quoting very low prices on this splendid new instrument.

REMEMBER, that this organ is covered by our celebrated 25 years guarantee and sold under our great 30 days and one years trial offers, which you will find fully explained on page 138 of this catalogue. We are prepared to ship you this instrument under our distinct promise to save you at least $25.00 on your purchase, and if you do not find that you have saved this amount, that it is the greatest bargain you ever saw in an organ, perfectly satisfactory in every particular and equal and in many points superior to other organs sold in your neighborhood at double the price, you can return it to us, we will refund your money and pay the entire cost of transportation both ways. So confident are we of the high quality of this instrument that we are prepared to guarantee that you cannot purchase one of the same grade from your dealer for less than $60.00.

A SPECIAL FEATURE of this instrument is the Vox Humana stop, which gives an exact imitation of the human voice in singing. You will not find any other organ on the market at anywhere near this price, which is fitted with the Vox Humana stop. This organ is also fitted with ten additional stops, which together with the 122 reeds, will form innumerable harmonious combinations. We also furnish this instrument with fifteen stops and 184 reeds at prices given below. For a description of all of these stops and reeds, see page 148. We also fit this instrument with knee swells, which place the entire power of the organ under immediate control of the performer. The pedals are so arranged as to take advantage of the greatest amount of leverage so that the immense bellows with which the organ is fitted, can be worked with perfect ease.

CASE. The case of this organ is of an absolutely new design, very handsome, massive and artistic in every respect. It is furnished in solid oak, handsomely and durably finished and is so designed as to provide for lamp stands, bric-a-brac shelves, etc. It is decorated with handsome hand carvings which are much more durable and artistic than the cheap pressed carvings usually found on organs for which your dealer charges you a much higher price. It has a handsome canopy top tastefully ornamented in keeping with the rest of the case. It is fitted with a music cabinet of new design which pulls down from the top and rests on the music desk. The front of this music cabinet is fitted with a handsome oval shape bevel French mirror. The music desk is made extra wide and will hold several pieces of music at one time. The entire front of the organ below the knee swells is so arranged that it can be taken out, thus exposing the entire front of the bellows and making it easy to remedy any defect which might appear in the valves. The entire design is original in every particular, has an appearance of quiet elegance, and an air of finish and completeness found in very few organs on the market at the present time. The case is built so as to provide for an extra large tone qualifying chamber, which increases the quality and volume of tone. The pedals are covered with handsome Brussels carpet, have neat metal frames finely nickel plated and are fitted with our patent device which prevents the pedal straps from wearing out and breaking.

THE TONE. The tone is the most important feature of any organ and this has been well provided for in the Cottage Favorite. It is fitted with the genuine Newell reeds, double riveted and of the very highest quality. These reeds are controlled at all times by the numerous stops with which the organ is fitted, thus insuring innumerable melodious combinations. It has great bellows capacity and is fitted with the **Celebrated Beckwith Bellows,** built on strictly scientific principles and durably constructed. The bellows is fitted with a large reservoir which forms the vacuum for the organ and guarantees a steady stream of air to the reeds, thus avoiding the jerky spasmodic effect noticed in other reed organs when the pedals are pumped violently.

WITH EVERY COTTAGE FAVORITE ORGAN we give a certificate entitling the holder to a complete course of musical instruction on the instrument, consisting of 50 weekly lessons covering a period of one year. See page 139.

YOU take no chances when you order this organ, because if it is not perfectly satisfactory in every particular, entirely suited to your wants, up to your expectations in every way and a great bargain in every respect, you can return it to us and we will send you back your money.

THIS IS A LARGE FULL SIZE PARLOR ORGAN.

The instrument is standard in every way. It stands 6 feet high, 42 inches long and 23 inches deep. It weighs, boxed and packed for shipment, 400 pounds.

No. 46E23 ALWAYS ORDER BY NUMBER.

No. 46E23	Action A, 5 octaves, 11 stops..	$27.65
No. 46E24	Action C, 5 octaves, 15 stops..	30.55

See page 148 for description of actions.

THIS ORGAN can be furnished in walnut finish without extra cost. Please note that walnut finish does not mean solid walnut, but that the case is made of hardwood and stained in a close imitation of walnut.

$32.85 OUR NEW PARLOR GEM ORGAN

No. 46E28

THE FINEST LOW PRICE, SIX-OCTAVE COTTAGE ORGAN EVER PLACED ON THE MARKET.

AN ENTIRELY ORIGINAL DESIGN CONTAINING THE VERY LATEST IDEAS IN ORGAN CONSTRUCTION.

YOU WOULD QUICKLY SHARE IN OUR PROFIT IF YOU BOUGHT THIS ORGAN.

BEFORE DESCRIBING THIS ORGAN **we wish to say that no organ dealer or manufacturer in the country can sell you an organ which is anywhere near its equal in beauty and appearance,** durability of construction and sweetness of tone for less than double the price we are asking. The immense increase in our organ sales has made it possible for our factories to install the very best up to date labor saving machinery and given them an opportunity to purchase their material in such immense quantities that they are in a position to produce an organ of this grade at a price which enables us to sell it to you for considerable less than one-half the price which other manufacturers and dealers are able to offer you. If you desire an instrument which will prove perfectly satisfactory under all conditions, be an ornament in your parlor and a never ending source of delight to yourself and family, you cannot do better than purchase this splendid

NEW PARLOR GEM ORGAN.

CASE. **We can furnish this organ either in solid walnut or handsome figured oak.** The case is beautifully decorated throughout with tasty hand carvings and given a very high finish such as is found upon all high priced organs. It has a beautiful canopy top supported by two gracefully turned pillars and ornamented with scroll work and carvings. The top is fitted with a large French bevel plate mirror, making it extremely attractive. The case is also fitted with three music cabinets, one on each side and one below the music desk. The music cabinets on the side are fitted with very pretty octagon mirrors and the cabinet beneath the music desk is so arranged that it is accessible by simply raising up the bottom of the desk. The key slip is ornamented with very pretty designs in scroll work backed by dustproof cloth. The engraving gives but a very faint idea of the real beauty of this instrument and nothing but a trial and examination will reveal to you its many fine qualities. The entire front of the organ below the knee swells is arranged like the front of a piano and can be removed instantly in case the purchaser desires to examine the bellows or repair in case of accident.

ACTION. **The instrument is fitted with our action A, six octaves, which has 11 stops and 146 reeds.** These reeds and stops are all so arranged that they are at all times under the control of the performer and can be combined in many different ways so as to produce pleasing and harmonious combinations.

TONE. **Great attention and study has been given to the tone quality of this instrument,** and, as this depends a great deal upon the bending and placing of the reeds, our factories have gone to great expense to secure the services of the very best reed benders in the country. To be a good reed bender requires a special talent, which very few men possess, and the magnificent tone quality of all our organs is due to the fact that our factories have spared no expense in this direction. As different styles of organs require different manipulation of the reeds, it is highly important that the men who handle this branch of manufacture must thoroughly understand their business. It is a common practice among organ manufacturers to place the same kind of reeds in each organ that they make regardless of its style or musical capacity. This is the reason why so many of the so called standard organs have a thin piping tone instead of the broad rich tone quality which they ought to possess, and which you will find in the Beckwith organ, regardless of style or price. As the tone quality of an organ depends also upon the evenness and strength of the air current which vibrates the reeds, we have placed in this organ our celebrated Beckwith bellows which insures a steady current of air and avoids the jerky spasmodic effect noticed in most organs when they are pumped violently. This bellows is fitted with pressure valves which relieves the bellows from any strain that might be caused by an over supply of air. This instrument is also fitted with the Vox Humana stop, which imparts a singing quality to the reeds and never found upon other instruments at the price.

Every purchaser of our New Parlor Gem Organ is given a certificate entitling him to a complete course of 96 weekly lessons. See page 139.

FREE. **We furnish free with every one of these organs a handsome stool made in wood to match the instrument and a complete instruction book, which will be of great assistance to the pupil in studying the instrument.**

DIMENSIONS. **This organ is a standard organ in every way, being 72 inches high, 49 inches wide and 23 inches deep.**

WEIGHT. **Boxed and packed for shipment, 425 pounds.**

No. 46E28 Action A, six octaves. Price, in oak..........**$32.85**

If you desire the organ in walnut you must add $2.00 to the above price. Be sure to specify in your order whether you desire oak or walnut.

See page 148 for detailed description of actions. Please examine the pictures of the Beckwith organ factory and our beautiful St. Louis World's Fair exhibit on page 158.

OUR HIGHEST GRADE ...THE... BECKWITH CATHEDRAL CHAPEL ORGAN

Catalogue No. 46E98 **FOR $49.25**

WONDERFUL VALUE.

WE PRESENT THIS as one of the finest instruments we are able to offer, and recommend it especially for SUNDAY SCHOOL, CHURCH, LODGE, SCHOOL or PARLOR; in fact, for all audience purposes.

THIS IS AN ENTIRELY NEW DESIGN. Fitted with our patent dust-proof action, 5 octaves, 9 sets of beautifully pipe toned reeds, 257 in all, double octave couplers, 18 necessary stops, 2 knee swells; all the very latest improvements. THIS IS ONE OF THE MOST POWERFUL PUBLIC SERVICE ORGANS EVER PRODUCED.

ON THE HIGH QUALITY OF OUR INSTRUMENTS, ON THE MONEY WE CAN SAVE YOU, ON OUR ESTABLISHED REPUTATION EVERYWHERE FOR FAIR AND HONORABLE DEALING, **WE BASE OUR CLAIM FOR YOUR ORDER.**

THESE ORGANS ARE COVERED BY A WRITTEN, BINDING TWENTY-FIVE YEARS' GUARANTEE, by the terms and conditions of which, if any piece or part gives out by reason of defect in material or workmanship, we will replace it free of charge. This is the longest, strongest and most binding guarantee issued by any concern on an organ.

DESCRIPTION OF CASE. The case is 55 inches high, 58 inches long, 24 inches wide, made of the very best selected quarter sawed oak, finished golden, very elaborately carved, decorated, ornamented, finished and polished, as shown in the back and front view illustrations. It is oil finished and hand rubbed over three coats of varnish. It is finished front and back and exactly as shown in illustrations. Has lamp stand, music desk receptacle, sliding fall cover with lock, rollers for moving, and in fact has every modern improvement.

WE CAN FURNISH walnut case if desired, but recommend our quarter sawed oak, golden finish, which is a dark color, as the handsomest organ case ever made, and one which will prove more universally satisfactory than walnut. Be sure to state finish desired when ordering.

Order by Number. No. 46E98
The above picture, engraved from a photograph, shows the front of our Cathedral Chapel Organ.

IF YOU ARE THINKING of purchasing a church organ, you cannot afford to make your purchase elsewhere without giving us an opportunity to send you one of these splendid instruments on approval. We do not ask you to take any chances or to assume any risks, because we will send you the organ for trial and approval, entirely at our own expense. We ship out these organs on our great thirty days free trial offer, and if they do not prove entirely satisfactory, they can be returned to us, we will refund the entire purchase price and pay the freight charges both ways. Why should you purchase an organ in the usual way and pay the extremely high prices which are always made up of intermediate dealers' profits, when you can purchase this splendid organ from us for about one-half the price you would have to pay the ordinary music dealer? We let you share in our profit also. Don't fail to read the last pages in this book. With every one of these organs we issue a binding twenty-five year guarantee, which fully protects you from loss.

WE WILL GIVE with this organ, a full course of 96 lessons by one of the best musical colleges in the country. If you were to obtain these lessons in any other way they would cost you from $45.00 to $50.00, but we give them to you absolutely free when you purchase a Cathedral Chapel Organ. See page 139.

No. 46E98
ACTION E; FIVE OCTAVES.
18 Stops.
Price **$49.25**

No. 46E100
ACTION E; SIX OCTAVES.
18 Stops.
Price **$57.25**

If desired in walnut, add $2.00 to the above prices.
See page 148 for description of actions.

NAMES OF STOPS: Diapason, Principal, Dulciana, Melodia, Bourdon, Clarionet, Cornet, Cornet Echo, Cremona, Flute, Viola, Celeste, Sub-Bass, Bass Coupler, Treble Coupler, Diapason Forte, Principal Forte, Vox Humana, Grand Organ and Knee Swell.

THE TONE. The action is the finest constructed. Built especially for the highest grade of church organ, and is peculiarly rich and full in tone and expression, and in the hands of the skilled organist, orchestral and pipe organ effects can be beautifully imitated. The voicing and peculiar arrangement of the reeds and the careful attention to the tuning have enabled us to place before our friends and the general public an action that we can pronounce to be absolutely perfect. It is practically dustproof and especially prepared and adapted to withstand all climatic changes. The organ weighs, boxed for shipment, about 500 pounds.

KINDLY REFER TO PAGE 158, on which you will find an illustration and description of the splendid exhibit of BECKWITH ORGANS at the St. Louis World's Fair. The Cathedral Chapel Organ shown on this page received honorable mention from the judges and was awarded a diploma of merit and medal of honor for superiority in construction and finish. We ask you to read carefully what we have to say in regard to this exhibit and the Beckwith Organ factories.

FREE. We send free with every one of these organs a fine organ bench, as shown in the illustration, and a complete instruction book, by the aid of which any one can learn to play the instrument without the assistance of a teacher.

BACK VIEW OF OUR CATHEDRAL CHAPEL ORGAN.

$1.95
VIOLINS
$22.45
AT $1.95 TO $22.45
WE OFFER GREAT BARGAINS IN VIOLINS,
EACH AND EVERY INSTRUMENT CAREFULLY
TESTED AND APPROVED BY OUR VIOLIN EXPERT.

OUR LINE OF VIOLINS **was never so complete and of such high grade as at the present time.** Our prices were never so low and we were never in a position to offer greater values in these popular instruments than we are at the present time. Some dealers are offering violins as low in price as 79 cents, but we feel that in offering a violin at **$1.95** we are striking the very lowest limit at which a violin can be offered containing any qualities of real merit. We could sell to our customers violins lower in price than any other dealer can offer, but we could not afford to sell and recommend to our customers violins which we know will not give satisfaction. From the very lowest to the very highest priced violin in our line each instrument is the very best value that can possibly be offered for the money. We will be glad to have you compare any instrument in our line with any violin offered by others at double the prices we are asking.

THE VALUE OF A VIOLIN **depends upon two things—workmanship and material.** The grade of workmanship and the quality of the material which enter into a violin can be fully judged by an expert only. The manager of our musical department has made a life study of violins and violin values, and has selected from among the hundreds of samples submitted, the following violins, which represent the very greatest values which can possibly be given at the prices asked. The purchase of a violin from us guarantees your receiving an instrument which cannot be duplicated for less than double the prices we are asking. The expert knowledge of the manager of this department and our great purchasing power are both entirely at the service of our customers. Should you desire a personal selection to be made for you, the manager will be glad to comply with your wishes, and select a violin for you which will represent full value and more for the price you pay. No instruments are so susceptible of false valuations, but our knowledge and experience of violin values fully protect you against any danger of loss in this respect.

OUR LIBERAL TERMS OF SHIPMENT **make it possible for you to order any violin from us for examination and comparison without entering into any obligations or making any promise to accept it** until you satisfy yourself by examination that it is the very best value that can be obtained anywhere for less than double the price we ask.

THE FITTINGS **which we send with all of our violins are in every way equal in value to the instrument itself,** and the bow which we give, free, with each instrument is not the usual cheap thrashy affair sent out with the violins sold by other dealers, but is in every way on a par with the violins themselves. **The bow** is a very important part of the outfit, and as it is good or bad, so will be the tone produced on the instrument. These are all things which you should take into consideration when figuring on the purchase of a violin. Do not be misled by the apparently lower prices offered by other dealers, as our great buying advantage and our inexpensive method of sale make it possible for us to sell our goods at lower prices than any other dealer can make. It is impossible for other dealers to undersell us on any goods without sacrificing quality to price.

FREE FURNITURE, FREE CLOTHING, Etc.

You get a PROFIT SHARING CERTIFICATE for every purchase and these entitle you to valuable articles FREE, as explained on the last pages of this book.

OUR $3.85 CONSERVATORY VIOLIN.

$3.85 FRONT VIEW

$3.85 BACK VIEW

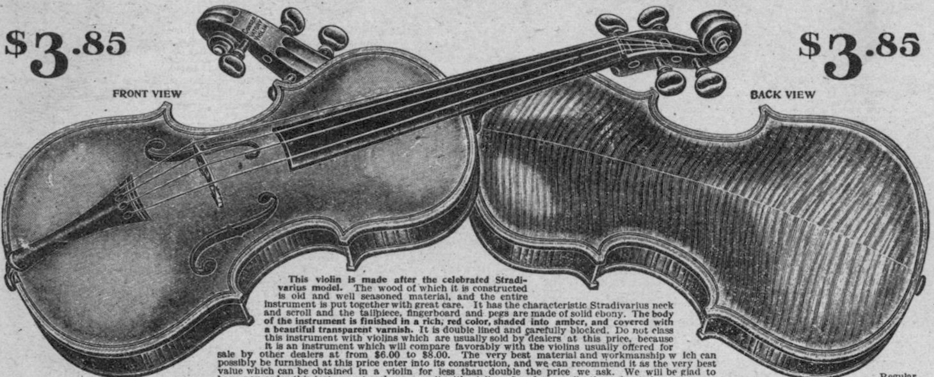

This violin is made after the celebrated Stradivarius model. The wood of which it is constructed is old and well seasoned material, and the entire instrument is put together with great care. It has the characteristic Stradivarius neck and scroll and the tailpiece, fingerboard and pegs are made of solid ebony. **The body of the instrument is finished in a rich, red color, shaded into amber, and covered with a beautiful transparent varnish.** It is double lined and carefully blocked. Do not class this instrument with violins which are usually sold by dealers at this price, because it is an instrument which will compare favorably with the violins usually offered for sale by other dealers at from $6.00 to $8.00. The very best material and workmanship w ich can possibly be furnished at this price enter into its construction, and we can recommend it as the very best value which can be obtained in a violin for less than double the price we ask. We will be glad to have you order this instrument and compare it with violins offered generally throughout the country at more than double the price, and we know you will find it superior in every way. Shipping weight, 10 pounds.

With this violin we furnish the following outfit:

	Regular Retail Price.
Our Conservatory Violin, as described above	$10.00
One Genuine Brazilwood Bow	1.00
One Case of Solid Wood, handsomely lined and finished	1.50
One Extra Set of Glendon Strings	.25
One Piece of Rosin, good quality	.05
One Winner's New American School Instruction Book	$0.50
One Fingerboard Chart, adjustable to any violin	.25
One Tuning Pipe	.10
Total Value of Outfit	$13.65

We also give a certificate which entitles the holder to a complete course of instruction on the instrument, to be given by one of the best musical colleges in the country.

No. 12E215 Our Special Outfit Price $3.85

OUR $1.95 STRADIVARIUS MODEL VIOLIN.

$1.95 FRONT VIEW

$1.95 BACK VIEW

No. 12E210 In this violin we are furnishing a genuine Stradivarius model at an extremely low price. While we always recommend that our customers buy the very best violin their circumstances will permit, still we believe you will find no instrument at this price which will give equal satisfaction. This violin is modeled very carefully after the celebrated violins of Stradivarius. It is made of selected wood, has very neat maple back and sides with top of resonant spruce. The tailpiece, fingerboard and pegs are of very fine imitation ebony and the body of the violin is finished in a brownish red color shaded into yellow. The purfling is very neatly and evenly inlaid and the entire instrument **has the appearance of the $4.00 violin ordinarily sold by music dealers.** Do not make the mistake of comparing it with the violins usually sold by dealers at $1.95, as it will be found far superior in every respect. With this violin we give a certificate, entitling the holder to a course of ten weekly lessons on the instrument.

Price, STRADIVARIUS MODEL........ $1.95

$4.35 OUR GENUINE MAGGINI MODEL VIOLIN. $4.35

FRONT VIEW — BACK VIEW

AN EXACT COPY OF THE CELEBRATED MAGGINI VIOLIN.

No. 12E216 **This violin is one of the neatest violins we have to offer in our cheaper line.** It is an exact copy of the celebrated Maggini violins and the characteristic Maggini double purfling gives it a very trim, graceful appearance. The back is made of two pieces of beautiful flamed maple, and the sides of the same material. The top is made of old, well seasoned spruce and the soundholes are evenly and gracefully cut. The tailpiece, fingerboard and pegs are of **solid ebony** and the scroll is the characteristic neat Maggini model. The body of the instrument is finished in golden red, blending into the natural color of the wood. The varnish is transparent and highly polished, bringing out the grain of the wood in a very effective manner. This is one of the very best values that we have to offer in a moderate priced violin and in beauty of appearance, excellence of tone and durability of construction it cannot be equaled by any violin on the market at anywhere near this price.

WE FURNISH WITH THIS VIOLIN **a very nicely finished serviceable bow,** which is in every way as good a value as the violin itself, a box of rosin, an extra set of strings, a complete instruction book, fingerboard chart and a marbleized pasteboard case. We also give a certificate which entitles the holder to a course of fifty weekly lessons on the instrument.
Price........ $4.35

$5.15 OUR STAINER MODEL VIOLIN. $5.15

FRONT VIEW — BACK VIEW

REMEMBER you not only save money on your violin purchase, but you get one of our valuable Profit Sharing Certificates also.

No. 12E218 **This violin is an exact copy of the famous Stainer violins, a characteristic of which is the bulging top and back and a long flat scroll.** The original Stainer violins are today much sought after by artists on account of their exceedingly beautiful tone. Great care has been used to pattern this instrument exactly after this celebrated model. The back of the instrument is made of two pieces of very highly flamed, well seasoned maple, the sides being of the same material. The top is made of well seasoned resonant silver spruce, the soundholes are graceful and very sharply and neatly cut and the purfling is accurately and evenly inlaid. The body of the violin is a deep red color blending into the natural color of the wood. The tailpiece, fingerboard and pegs are of solid ebony. If you will compare it with the violins usually sold by dealers throughout the country you will find that you cannot purchase an instrument of this grade elsewhere for less than $10.00 to $12.00.

THIS VIOLIN GOES COMPLETE **with well made, durable bow of good pattern and finely finished,** a complete instruction book, a box of rosin, an extra set of strings, a fingerboard chart and a very nice marbleized pasteboard case. Also a certificate which entitles the holder to a course of fifty weekly lessons on the instrument.
Price........ $5.15

$5.45 OUR PAGANINI GUARNERIUS MODEL VIOLIN. $5.45

FRONT VIEW — BACK VIEW

AN EXACT COPY OF THE VIOLIN USED BY THAT MARVELOUS PLAYER.

No. 12E219 **This violin is accurately patterned after the celebrated violins made by Joseph Guarnerius and has all the characteristics of the violins of that celebrated maker.** The model is not quite as flat as the well known Stradivarius model, but all of its lines are graceful and handsome in appearance. The back is made of beautifully flamed maple in two pieces, and is stamped with the name "Paganini." The sides are made of the same material and the top is made of old, well seasoned spruce. The soundholes have the characteristic Guarnerius turn, and the purfling is accurately and carefully inlaid. The body of the instrument is finished in a deep, rich red shaded into the beautiful natural wood color. The tailpiece and fingerboard are made of solid ebony and the entire instrument is highly polished and finished. The price which we ask for this violin represents but a very small part of its real value, and if you will compare it with other violins on the market at anywhere near this price, you will soon find that you cannot purchase an instrument of this model, grade and finish for less than from $10.00 to $12.00. All of our violins are strictly handmade, being made by workmen who have been trained from childhood in this profession. From the lowest to the highest grade in our line we absolutely guarantee every violin to be strictly handmade.

THIS INSTRUMENT GOES TO THE CUSTOMER COMPLETE with Brazilwood bow, **equal in grade to the violin and fully as highly finished and serviceable as the violin itself.** We also send one extra set of strings, complete instruction book, a box of rosin, fingerboard chart, and a very nice marbleized pasteboard case. We also give a certificate to the purchaser which entitles the holder to a full course of fifty weekly lessons on the instrument.
Price........ $5.45

$6.10 OUR STRADIVARIUS MODEL VIOLIN. $6.10

FRONT VIEW — BACK VIEW

WE SHARE our profit with you. Your PROFIT SHARING CERTIFICATE will help you get something for nothing from us.

No. 12E222 **This violin is a very accurate copy of the celebrated Stradivarius violin, and is the characteristic flat pattern of this maker.** The Stradivarius violins are the most gracefully made instruments of all the celebrated makes. Antonious Stradivarius unquestionably carried the art of violin making to its very highest perfection and today his violins are the most highly prized of any of the works of the great violin makers. Our $6.10 Stradivarius model violin has a two-piece back of fine grained, well flamed maple, the sides being of the same material. The top is made of old, well seasoned resonant silver spruce, and the soundholes are of the graceful Stradivarius pattern. The body of the violin is finished in rich, deep red color, shaded into a light yellowish red, and the transparent varnish brings out the grain of the wood and the color of the finish in a beautiful manner. The tailpiece, fingerboard and pegs are made of solid ebony. The edges of the top, back and scroll are finished in the natural color of the wood, giving the violin a rich, graceful appearance.

We ship this instrument complete with a durable and well finished Brazilwood bow, a complete instruction book, an extra set of strings, a box of rosin, fingerboard chart and a nicely marbleized pasteboard case. We also give free a certificate which entitles the holder to a full course of fifty weekly lessons on the instrument. Price.... $6.10

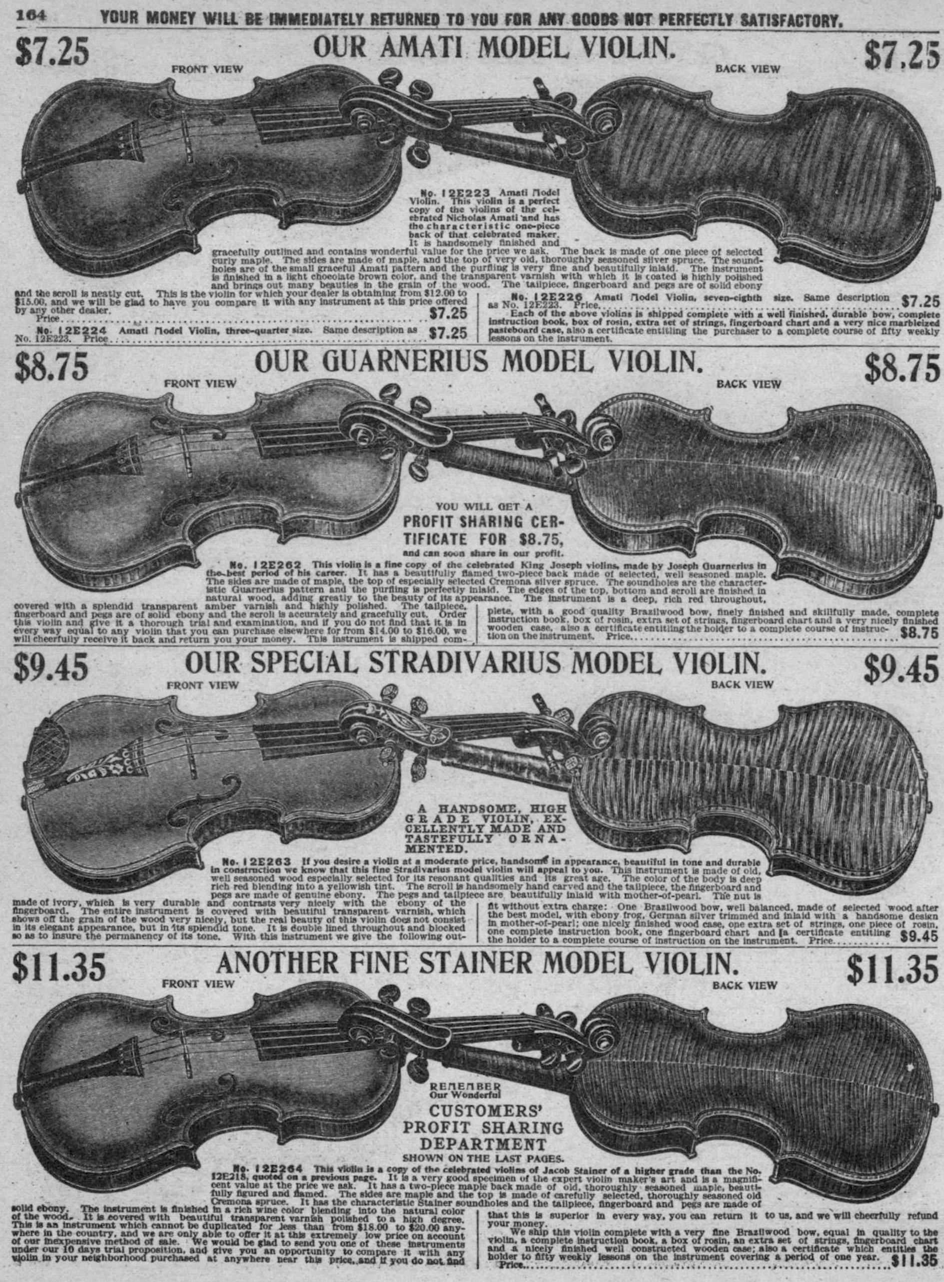

$7.25 OUR AMATI MODEL VIOLIN. $7.25

FRONT VIEW BACK VIEW

No. 12E223 Amati Model Violin. This violin is a perfect copy of the violins of the celebrated Nicholas Amati and has the characteristic one-piece back of that celebrated maker. It is handsomely finished and gracefully outlined and contains wonderful value for the price we ask. The back is made of one piece of selected curly maple. The sides are made of maple, and the top of very old, thoroughly seasoned silver spruce. The soundholes are of the small graceful Amati pattern and the purfling is very fine and beautifully inlaid. The instrument is finished in a light chocolate brown color, and the transparent varnish with which it is coated is highly polished and brings out many beauties in the grain of the wood. The tailpiece, fingerboard and pegs are of solid ebony and the scroll is neatly cut. This is the violin for which your dealer is obtaining from $12.00 to $15.00, and we will be glad to have you compare it with any instrument at this price offered by any other dealer.
Price.......... **$7.25**

No. 12E224 Amati Model Violin, three-quarter size. Same description as No. 12E223. Price.......... **$7.25**

No. 12E226 Amati Model Violin, seven-eighth size. Same description as No. 12E223. Price.......... **$7.25**

Each of the above violins is shipped complete with a well finished, durable bow, complete instruction book, box of rosin, extra set of strings, fingerboard chart and a very nice marbleized pasteboard case, also a certificate entitling the purchaser to a complete course of fifty weekly lessons on the instrument.

$8.75 OUR GUARNERIUS MODEL VIOLIN. $8.75

FRONT VIEW BACK VIEW

YOU WILL GET A
PROFIT SHARING CERTIFICATE FOR $8.75,
and can soon share in our profit.

No. 12E262 This violin is a fine copy of the celebrated King Joseph violins, made by Joseph Guarnerius in the best period of his career. It has a beautifully flamed two-piece back made of selected, well seasoned maple. The sides are made of maple, the top of especially selected Cremona silver spruce. The soundholes are the characteristic Guarnerius pattern and the purfling is perfectly inlaid. The edges of the top, bottom and scroll are finished in natural wood, adding greatly to the beauty of its appearance. The instrument is a deep, rich red throughout, covered with a splendid transparent amber varnish and highly polished. The tailpiece, fingerboard and pegs are of solid ebony and the scroll is accurately and gracefully cut. Order this violin and give it a thorough trial and examination, and if you do not find that it is in every way equal to any violin that you can purchase elsewhere for from $14.00 to $16.00, we will cheerfully receive it back and return you your money. This instrument is shipped complete, with a good quality Brazilwood bow, finely finished and skillfully made, complete instruction book, box of rosin, extra set of strings, fingerboard chart and a very nicely finished wooden case, also a certificate entitling the holder to a complete course of instruction on the instrument. Price.......... **$8.75**

$9.45 OUR SPECIAL STRADIVARIUS MODEL VIOLIN. $9.45

FRONT VIEW BACK VIEW

A HANDSOME, HIGH GRADE VIOLIN, EXCELLENTLY MADE AND TASTEFULLY ORNAMENTED.

No. 12E263 If you desire a violin at a moderate price, handsome in appearance, beautiful in tone and durable in construction we know that this fine Stradivarius model violin will appeal to you. This instrument is made of old, well seasoned wood especially selected for its resonant qualities and its great age. The color of the body is deep rich red blending into a yellowish tint. The scroll is handsomely hand carved and the tailpiece, the fingerboard and pegs are made of genuine ebony. The pegs and tailpiece are beautifully inlaid with mother-of-pearl. The nut is made of ivory, which is very durable and contrasts very nicely with the ebony of the fingerboard. The entire instrument is covered with beautiful transparent varnish, which shows off the grain of the wood very nicely, but the real beauty of this violin does not consist in its elegant appearance, but in its splendid tone. It is double lined throughout and blocked so as to insure the permanency of its tone. With this instrument we give the following outfit without extra charge: One Brazilwood bow, well balanced, made of selected wood after the best model, with ebony frog, German silver trimmed and inlaid with a handsome design in mother-of-pearl; one nicely finished wood case, one extra set of strings, one piece of rosin, one complete instruction book, one fingerboard chart and a certificate entitling the holder to a complete course of instruction on the instrument. Price.......... **$9.45**

$11.35 ANOTHER FINE STAINER MODEL VIOLIN. $11.35

FRONT VIEW BACK VIEW

REMEMBER
Our Wonderful
CUSTOMERS' PROFIT SHARING DEPARTMENT
SHOWN ON THE LAST PAGES.

No. 12E264 This violin is a copy of the celebrated violins of Jacob Stainer of a higher grade than the No. 12E218, quoted on a previous page. It is a very good specimen of the expert violin maker's art and is a magnificent value at the price we ask. It has a two-piece maple back made of old, thoroughly seasoned maple, beautifully figured and flamed. The sides are maple and the top is made of carefully selected, thoroughly seasoned old Cremona spruce. It has the characteristic Stainer soundholes and the tailpiece, fingerboard and pegs are made of solid ebony. The instrument is finished in a rich wine color blending into the natural color of the wood. It is covered with beautiful transparent varnish polished to a high degree. This is an instrument which cannot be duplicated for less than from $18.00 to $20.00 anywhere in the country, and we are only able to offer it at this extremely low price on account of our inexpensive method of sale. We would be glad to send you one of these instruments under our 10 days trial proposition, and give you an opportunity to compare it with any violin in your neighborhood purchased at anywhere near this price, and if you do not find that this is superior in every way, you can return it to us, and we will cheerfully refund your money.

We ship this violin complete with a very fine Brazilwood bow, equal in quality to the violin, a complete instruction book, a box of rosin, an extra set of strings, fingerboard chart and a nicely finished well constructed wooden case; also a certificate which entitles the holder to fifty weekly lessons on the instrument covering a period of one year.
Price.......... **$11.35**

$13.85 GENUINE DA SALO MODEL VIOLIN. $13.85

A $25.00 Violin for $13.85 and a PROFIT SHARING CERTIFICATE for $13.85 to help you get your share of our profit, as explained on the last pages.

No. 12E266 This violin is an elegant copy of the violins of Caspar da Salo, who was born in Lombardy, in 1558. The illustration given above will give you a very good idea of the characteristic ornamentation of the violins of this maker. These violins have the double purfling, the same as the Maggini, but the bulge of the top and back is not so marked, and the soundholes differ in shape. The back of this violin is made of two pieces of beautifully marked and flamed maple. The sides are made of maple, and the top of very close grain, thoroughly seasoned Cremona spruce. The purfling is beautifully and accurately set, and the model is one of the finest ever conceived. The instrument is a deep, rich red, softened by a tinge of yellow, giving the instrument a very elegant appearance. The instrument is very highly polished and covered with a coat of transparent varnish. The tailpiece, fingerboard and pegs are made of genuine ebony, and the outlines of the scroll are graceful in the extreme.

We ship this violin complete with a high quality, well balanced, Brazilwood bow, a complete instruction book, an extra set of strings, a box of rosin, a figerboard chart and a well finished and constructed case. We also give a complete course of fifty lessons on the instrument. Price.......................... **$13.85**

$16.25 OUR PERUGINI VIRTUOSO VIOLIN. $16.25

$16.25 is the lowest possible price we can make on this violin, and we share our profit with you by sending you a PROFIT SHARING CERTIFICATE for your purchase.

No 12E271 This violin is an excellent copy of some of the very rarest of the violins of Antonious Stradivarius, which were made with one-piece back. It will be necessary for you to see this violin and examine it before its real beauty will become apparent. Its beautiful outlines show the handiwork of the violin maker who loves his profession for its own sake. The back is made of one piece of especially selected beautifully figured maple. The sides are of the same material, and the top is made of very rare old Cremona spruce. The violin gets its delicate appearance from the manner in which the purfling is inlaid, it being set very close to the outside edge of the top and bottom of the instrument. The instrument is finished in a beautiful shade of reddish brown and polished to the last degree of completion. The tailpiece and fingerboard are made of genuine ebony and the pegs of rosewood. It is double lined throughout and carefully blocked. The scroll is beautifully carved and has the word "Virtuoso" stamped upon it. This is a violin such as you will very seldom find for sale by local music dealers.

We ship this instrument complete with an exceptionally high grade Pernambuco bow with frog German silver trimmed, complete instruction book, extra set of strings, box of rosin, fingerboard chart and a well finished wooden case. Please notice that the label in each one of these violins is carefully signed with the autograph of its maker. We give with this violin a complete course of instruction on the instrument, consisting of fifty weekly lessons. Price.......................... **$16.25**

$19.95 OUR GENUINE HEBERLIN. $19.95

No. 12E278 This violin is an exact copy of the violins made by Nicholas Amati, one of the chief characteristics of which was a one-piece back. It would be an extremely difficult matter to find a violin more beautiful in appearance than this exquisite instrument. The one-piece back is made of especially selected curled and flamed maple. The sides are made of the same material, and the top is made of very rare, old Cremona spruce. The model of the violin is very dignified and beautiful, and the body of the violin is finished in natural wood, tinged with golden yellow, blending off into a beautiful yellowish red. The instrument is double lined, carefully blocked, and the tailpiece, fingerboard and pegs are made of polished ebony. The pegs and tailpiece are ornamented with gold plated tips, which add much to the beauty of the instrument. This is an instrument which has been extensively imitated throughout the country, and we desire to caution our customers against purchasing a so called Heberlin violin, unless fully satisfied that it is genuine. We send a certificate of guarantee with each violin, signed by the maker, and each instrument has the autograph of the maker written across the label on the inside of the violin, and should anyone offer to sell you a Heberlin violin, you can easily detect the fraud by examining the label. The illustration given above will give you but a very poor idea of the real beauty of this instrument. We ship this violin complete with a very high quality Pernambuco Tourte model bow, with full German silver trimmed frog complete instruction book, extra set of strings, box of rosin, fingerboard chart and a finely finished wooden case. We give to each purchaser of this violin a certificate which entitles the holder to a course of instruction, consisting of fifty weekly lessons. Price...... **$19.95**

$22.45 OUR LUDWIG CONCERT VIOLIN. $22.45

Your $22.45 PROFIT SHARING CERTIFICATE will go a long way towards helping you get something valuable, absolutely FREE, as explained on last pages.

No. 12E280 This violin is a copy of the celebrated Guarnerius violin, beautifully worked out by the maker, L. Ludwig. It has a two-piece back of carefully selected, well seasoned maple, beautifully figured and flamed. The sides are maple and the top is made of carefully selected, close grained, thoroughly seasoned silver spruce. The soundholes are accurately and delicatel cut, and the entire general appearance of the instrument is very handsome. The body is finished in brownish red color covered with especially prepared varnish. It is double lined throughout and carefully blocked, and the tailpiece, fingerboard and pegs are made of solid ebony The tailpiece and fingerboard are very highly polished and the pegs and tailpiece are furnished with gold plated ornaments. Should you desire an instrument for orchestra or solo work where a powerful and sweet tone is desired we would unhesitatingly recommend this violin. Each violin bears the autograph of the maker across the label on the inside. Do not allow yourself to be deceived by imitations. This is a violin which cannot be duplicated anywhere in the country for less than $35.00 to $40.00, it will improve with age, and prove in the end a very profitable investment. We ship this violin complete with an extra quality Pernambuco wood bow, Tourte model, complete instruction book, extra set of strings, box of rosin, fingerboard chart and well finished wooden case. We also give with this violin a complete course of instruction, consisting of fifty weekly lessons. Price.......... **$22.45**

$2.95 VIOLIN OUTFITS $23.45

AT $2.95 TO $23.45 WE OFFER A COMPLETE LINE OF HIGH GRADE VIOLIN OUTFITS

These outfits are put up for the purpose of furnishing to the customer everything necessary in connection with the violin. Every article that appears in these outfits is the very best that can be obtained, considering the price that we ask for the outfit. Each article is selected from our own stock, which is a guarantee of quality, and each violin is selected for its peculiar fitness according to the price asked.

IN ORDER TO SHOW YOU COMPARISONS between our prices and the prices generally asked for these articles, under each outfit we give the usual retail price and then quote our special bargain price for the entire outfit. Each one of these outfits is put up under the special supervision of the manager of our musical department, who is fully acquainted with the articles necessary to violin outfits, for amateur and professional alike.

WE OFFER the same liberal terms of shipment on these outfits that we are offering upon all our other violins. Each one of these violins is strictly hand made.

$2.95 BUYS A REGULAR $10.20 OUTFIT.

THIS OUTFIT IS THE BEST VALUE ever offered for the money. Anyone desiring a complete outfit for general use should not fail to examine this famous bargain. This outfit must not be compared with the outfits offered generally by dealers at this price, because an outfit of this grade is sold by dealers generally at from $10.00 to $12.00. We furnish the following articles with this outfit: One genuine Stradivarius model violin, with two-piece curly maple back, sides of the same material and top of silver spruce. Tailpiece, fingerboard and pegs are solid ebony, the body of the instrument is finished in brown shaded to yellow. The violin is double lined and blocked throughout.

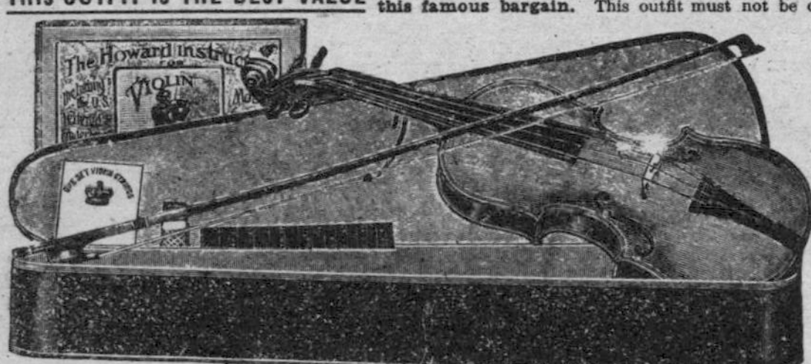

Regular retail price of this violin	**$8.00**
One Brazilwood bow with ebony frog inlaid with dots	.75
One marbleized pasteboard case	.40
One full set of strings	.25
One piece of rosin good quality	.05
One instructor. Simplest and most complete published	.50
One lettered fingerboard chart	.25
Total value of outfit	$10.20
No. 12E300 Price, for complete outfit	**$2.95**

Shipping weight, 7 pounds.

SEND $2.95 with your order and we will send you this outfit by express, and if you do not find it the greatest bargain you ever saw or heard of and perfectly satisfactory to you in every respect, you can return it to us at our expense and we will cheerfully refund your money. With this outfit we give a certificate which entitles the holder to a complete course of musical instruction.

OUR CHALLENGE $13.10 VIOLIN OUTFIT, $5.50.

THIS IS THE GREATEST VALUE OFFERED in a violin outfit at this price, and that this is true will be recognized at once by all who are familiar with violin values. We send this entire outfit complete, consisting of **one Maggini model violin, instruction book, bow, rosin, case, set of strings and fingerboard chart for $5.50. The most wonderful bargain ever offered in a violin outfit.**

THE VIOLIN which we offer with this outfit is modeled after the celebrated Maggini violin, and is very skillfully and durably made. It has the characteristic double purfling of the well known Maggini model and is the very best violin ever offered in an outfit at this price. The back is made of two pieces of very nicely flamed maple and the sides are constructed of the same material. The top is made of a carefully selected piece of thoroughly seasoned silver spruce, and the tailpiece, fingerboard and pegs are made of solid ebony. The body of the instrument is finished in a dark reddish brown, blending into the natural color of the wood. You will find this a very handsome violin and a very great bargain at this price. The neck is curly maple, very finely finished, and the scroll is neatly and gracefully cut.

One regular Maggini model violin	$10.00
One genuine Brazilwood bow	1.00
One canvas, fleece lined, leather bound case	1.00
One extra set of strings	.25
One piece of rosin	.10
One complete instruction book	.50
One fingerboard chart	.25
Total regular price of outfit	$13.10
No. 12E306 Our great bargain price for outfit	**$5.50**

Shipping weight, 7 pounds.

WE SHIP THIS OUTFIT to the customer with the assurance that it cannot be purchased in the regular way for less than $13.00 to $14.00. We are willing to have the purchaser compare it with anything his local dealer has to offer at these prices, and if he does not find that it is equal, and in many points superior, he can return the entire outfit to us, we will refund the money paid and pay the express charge both ways.

WITH THIS OUTFIT we give a certificate which entitles the holder to a complete course of musical instructions.

OUR HIGH GRADE CHALLENGE OUTFIT FOR $7.25.

THIS OUTFIT IS OFFERED to those who desire to invest a little more money in an outfit than we ask for the above. Every article which it contains is the very best which can possibly be supplied for the price we ask, the entire outfit has been gotten up with great care so as to insure the customer receiving something which will be perfectly satisfactory to him and fully supply his needs. **Remember, also, that you will get a Profit Sharing Certificate, and in this way you can quickly share in our profit and get something entirely free, as explained on the last pages.**

WITH THIS OUTFIT we send a certificate which entitles the customer to a full course of instructions on the instrument, consisting of fifty weekly lessons, covering a period of one year. This certificate costs you absolutely nothing, and the lessons are given by one of the best musical colleges in the country. You will find full particulars of this splendid offer fully outlined and explained on page 139 of this catalogue.

THIS OUTFIT is made up of one genuine Stradivarius model violin, one Brazilwood bow, case, extra set of strings, rosin, instruction book, fingerboard chart and a tuning pipe.

THE VIOLIN which we give with this outfit is a genuine Stradivarius model, very handsomely and durably made. The back is made of two pieces of beautifully curled and flamed maple. The sides are made of a very pretty piece of maple and the top of a well selected piece of close grained silver spruce. The tailpiece, fingerboard and pegs are made of solid ebony, the scroll is very nicely cut and the body of the instrument is finished a yellowish brown color very nicely blending into yellow.

Regular retail price	$12.00
The bow which we furnish with this outfit is made of Brazilwood, with ebony frog, German silver trimmed and has German silver buttons	1.50
The case is of solid wood, handsomely lined and has lock, handle and hook	1.50
One extra set of Acme strings	.75
One piece of rosin	.10
One instruction book	.50
One fingerboard chart	.25
One tuning pipe	.25
Total value of outfit	$16.85
No. 12E308 Our great bargain price	**$7.25**

Shipping weight, 12 pounds.

OUR SPECIAL CONSERVATORY OUTFIT FOR $9.85.

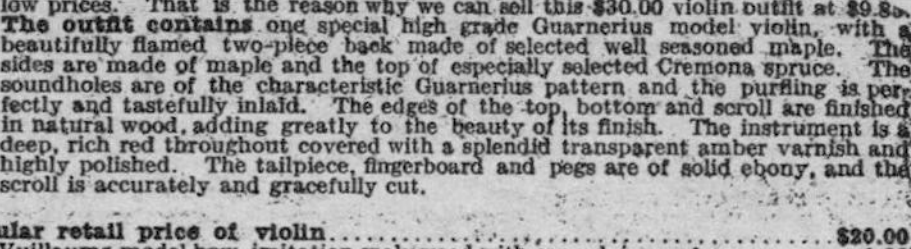

THIS OUTFIT is a little higher in price than those preceding it and is fully as great a bargain as any in our line. Each article which goes to make it up is carefully selected and is of the very best considering the price of the outfit. Do not make the mistake of comparing this outfit with the outfits sold generally by dealers throughout the country at this price, as this is a regular $30.00 outfit, and cannot be purchased for less than that amount from any dealer in the country. Our buying advantage is so great that we are in a position to get the very lowest possible prices upon all classes of goods, and as we import all of these goods from Europe we are able to quote the actual importing price with but our one small percentage of profit added. Every bit of advantage we can gain, either in buying or selling, we give to our customers in low prices. That is the reason why we can sell this $30.00 violin outfit at $9.85. **The outfit contains** one special high grade Guarnerius model violin, with a beautifully flamed two-piece back made of selected well seasoned maple. The sides are made of maple and the top of especially selected Cremona spruce. The soundholes are of the characteristic Guarnerius pattern and the purfling is perfectly and tastefully inlaid. The edges of the top, bottom and scroll are finished in natural wood, adding greatly to the beauty of its finish. The instrument is a deep, rich red throughout covered with a splendid transparent amber varnish and highly polished. The tailpiece, fingerboard and pegs are of solid ebony, and the scroll is accurately and gracefully cut.

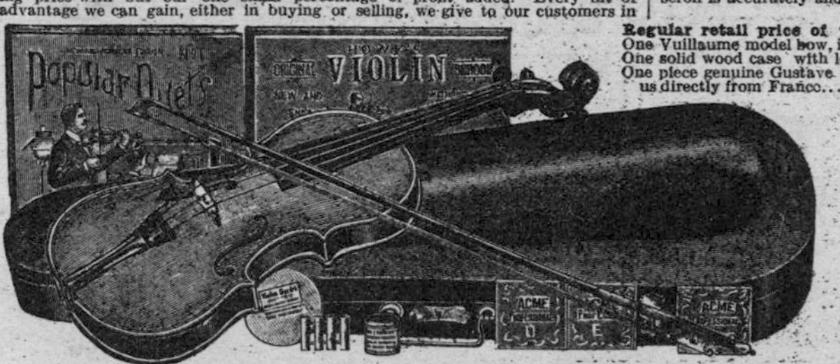

Regular retail price of violin	$20.00
One Vuillaume model bow, imitation snakewood with carved ivory frog	4.00
One solid wood case with lock, handle and spring clasps, lined with red flannel	2.75
One piece genuine Gustave Bernadel rosin, the best manufactured imported by us directly from France	.25
One Howe's Original Violin School, complete in every respect	.75
One extra set of Acme Professional strings, imported from Europe	.85
One fingerboard chart	.25
One set of violin tuning pipes	.65
One book of choice violin music	.50
Total value of outfit	$30.00
No. 12E314 Our great bargain price	**$9.85**

Shipping weight, 10 pounds.

WITH THIS OUTFIT WE GIVE A CERTIFICATE

Which entitles the holder to a full course of fifty weekly lessons in violin instruction, covering a period of one year. This certificate is absolutely free.

You also get your PROFIT SHARING CERTIFICATE, which entitles you to valuable articles, entirely FREE

OUR SPECIAL PROFESSIONAL VIOLIN OUTFIT, $13.95.

THIS OUTFIT is regularly sold by dealers throughout the country for from $45.00 to $55.00. We have been furnishing this outfit for the past five years, and it has given the greatest satisfaction to every purchaser. **We send with each outfit a certificate which entitles the holder to a complete course of instruction on the violin consisting of fifty weekly lessons covering a period of one year.** These lessons are given by one of the best music school in the country and we charge you absolutely nothing for the certificate.

WE ARE OFFERING This outfit in response to a demand from professionals who desire an outfit for general work and do not desire to pay the usual high prices asked by dealers generally for outfits of this grade. We furnish with this outfit one special high grade Stradivarius model violin, one bow, case, rosin, instruction book, extra set of strings, fingerboard chart, tuning pipes, violin and collection of violin music. All of these articles are of the very best that can possibly be purchased at the price.

THE VIOLIN which we furnish with this outfit is a genuine Stradivarius model and is very elegant in appearance. It has two-piece back of highly flamed well seasoned maple. The sides are made of a very nice quality of maple, and the top is made of a carefully selected piece of close grain Cremona spruce. The tailpiece, fingerboard and pegs are of solid ebony, the neck is of curly maple and the scroll is carefully and tastefully cut. The body of the instrument is finished in a very rich, brownish red color. It is the most elegant violin ever offered at this price.

Regular retail price of violin	$30.00
One Tourte model bow with full German silver trimming and best quality of Brazilwood stick	5.00
One solid wood case, Exposition shape, full flannel lined, provided with lock and spring clasp	3.00
One piece of genuine Gustave Bernadel rosin, the best manufactured and imported by us direct from Europe	.25
One instruction book, complete in every respect	1.00
One extra set of Acme Professional strings, our own importation	.85
One latest patent chin rest	1.50
One fingerboard chart	.25
One set of tuning pipes	.50
One violin mute	.15
One choice collection of violin music	.50
Total value of outfit	$43.00
No. 12E317 Our great bargain price	**$13.95**

Shipping weight, 10 pounds.

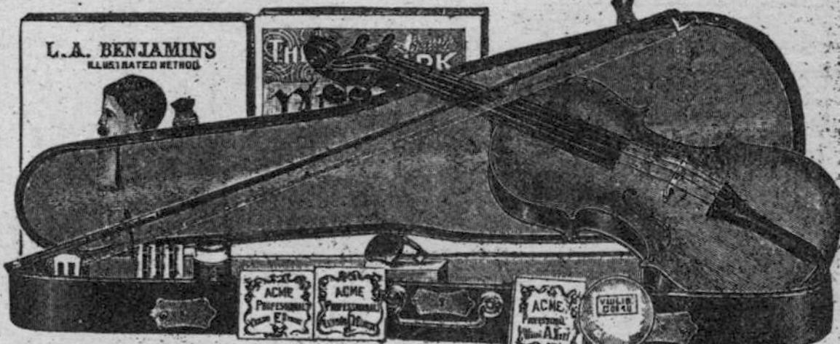

A GENUINE HEBERLIN VIOLIN OUTFIT, $17.65.

THIS OUTFIT is high grade in every respect, and every article in it is fully guaranteed by us. The maker of the violin which we send with this outfit is among the best known violin makers of Europe and we have been able to arrange with him to furnish us with a limited number of these instruments, which we can supply in an outfit at this exceptionally low price. The violin is guaranteed to be perfect in every respect and is accompanied by a numbered certificate countersigned with the autograph of the maker. Should anyone attempt to sell you a Heberlin violin you can easily detect the fraud by asking for the certificate. We are showing herewith a facsimile of the certificate which goes with every one of these violins.

THE VIOLIN is a genuine Stradivarius model, has two-piece, highly flamed maple back, nicely figured maple sides and top of old, well seasoned Cremona silver spruce. The edges of the top, bottom and scroll are finished in natural wood, adding greatly to the instrument's appearance. The fingerboard and tailpiece are of solid ebony and the pegs of rosewood. The violin is double lined throughout and carefully blocked. The body is a very deep, rich brown. An elegant instrument in every respect, and one which will please amateur and professional alike. We show below the comparison in price between this outfit at retail and our bargain price.

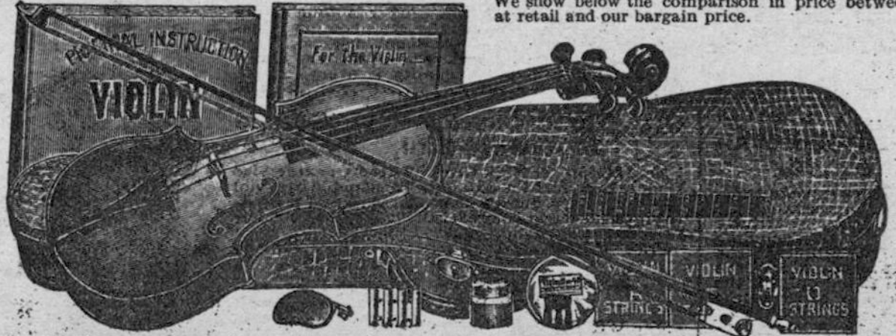

Regular retail price of violin	$40.00
One genuine snakewood Vuillaume model bow with handsomely carved genuine ivory frog, double pearl eye, German silver lining and ivory buttons	5.00
One violin case, covered with a durable waterproof material, made in perfect imitation of alligator skin, full lined with velvet, leather handles, nickel link clasps and nickel spring lock	5.00
One piece genuine Gustave Bernadel rosin	.25
One Henning's School for the Violin, one of the most complete instruction books published. 101 pages printed on fine paper, bound in boards	1.50
One mammoth collection of violin music with 350 selections	.75
One extra set of Acme Professional strings	.85
One latest patent violin chin rest	1.00
One violin mute	.15
One fingerboard chart	.25
One set tuning pipes	.50
Total value of outfit	$55.25
No. 12E321 Our great bargain price	**$17.65**

Shipping weight, 12 pounds.

WITH THIS OUTFIT we give a certificate which entitles the holder to a complete course of instruction on the violin, consisting of fifty weekly lessons, covering a period of one year. See page 139 for full particulars.

THE PROFIT SHARING CERTIFICATE FOR $17.65 which we will send you if you buy this outfit, will enable you to share in our profit, as explained on the last pages.

OUR GENUINE L. LUDWIG OUTFIT, $18.95.

BY A SPECIAL ARRANGEMENT with this celebrated maker we are able to offer a limited number of these fine violins in these outfits. We guarantee absolutely that each one of these outfits is genuine and the maker's autograph will be found plainly written across the label on the inside of the instrument. This entire outfit is of exceptionally high hrade and one which will satisfy anyone who desires an outfit which will prove satisfactory under all conditions. If any dealer should offer to sell you an L. Ludwig violin be sure to examine the label on the inside, and if you do not find the maker's signature written across it you will know at once that it is an imitation.

Regular retail price of violin	$35.00
One Tourte model bow with full German silver trimming and best quality Brazilwood stick	5.00
One leather case, Exposition shape, full velvet lined, nickel trimmed, spring clasps, lock, key and leather handle	5.00
One piece of genuine Gustave Bernadel rosin	.25
One "Wichtl's Young Violinist," containing 100 exercises and celebrated violin duets	1.00
One extra set of Acme Professional strings	.85
One latest patent chin rest	1.00
One fingerboard chart	.25
One set of violin tuning pipes	.50
One violin mute	.15
One Gigantic collection violin music	.50
Total value of outfit	$49.50

No. 12E325 Our great bargain price $18.95
Shipping weight, 12 pounds.

TO EVERY PURCHASER of this violin outfit we give a certificate entitling the holder to a full course of instruction on the violin, consisting of 50 weekly lessons, covering a period of one year. These lessons will be given by one of the best known and thorough musical colleges in the country.

THE VIOLIN is of the well known Stradivarius model, gracefully and carefully worked out by the maker. It is an exceptionally large instrument, and especially desirable for orchestra work, where a broad and powerful tone is desired. It has a two-piece beautifully figured and flamed maple back, and the sides are made of a fine piece of the same material. The top is made of a rare piece of genuine Cremona silver spruce, guaranteeing a deep, rich tone to the instrument. The tailpiece and fingerboard are made of solid ebony, highly polished, and the pegs of genuine rosewood. The body and scroll of the instrument are finished in rich cherry red, the edges of the top and bottom being finished in natural wood. This violin is one that we can highly recommend for its elegant appearance and beautiful tone.

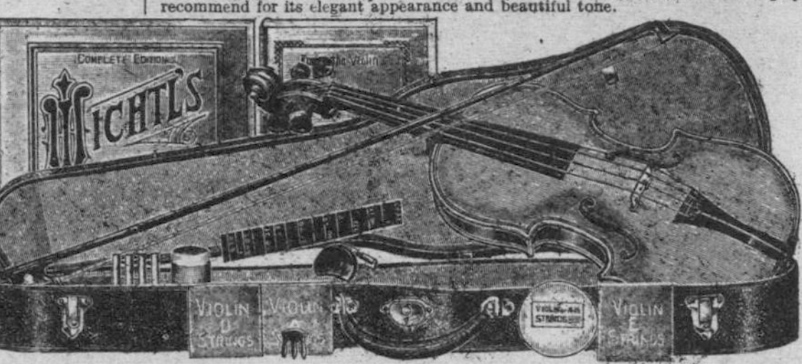

OUR GENUINE CHADWICK (LONDON) VIOLIN OUTFIT, $23.45.

THIS IS AN EXTREMELY HIGH GRADE VIOLIN OUTFIT which we have made up for the use of professionals and high class amateurs, and which we are prepared to furnish at the present time at a price never before heard of. This is one of the very best outfits we have ever offered to our customers, and its sale up to the present time proves that it is destined to become as popular as any of our other high grade outfits. If you are looking for a violin outfit which will be strictly high class in every respect and in which every article will be of the very best, you will make no mistake in purchasing this. You will not find an outfit of this grade offered for sale by any of your local dealers. The violin which we furnish with this outfit is made under the direct supervision of Chadwick, the famous London violin maker, and we guarantee its beauty of appearance, the durability of its workmanship and the quality of its tone. If you could purchase an outfit of this high grade from your local dealer it would cost you as follows: One high grade Chadwick violin, Stradivarius model, beautifully worked out by the maker. We cannot begin to describe the elegant and graceful appearance of this instrument, as it must be seen to be appreciated. The back is made of two pieces of very close grain, finely flamed maple. The sides are made of the same material and the top is made of a rare old piece of Cremona silver spruce. It is double lined throughout and carefully blocked. The tailpiece, fingerboard and pegs are made of solid ebony, and the body of the instrument is finished in deep orange yellow. This is undoubtedly the most elegant violin which we furnish with any outfit shown in our catalogue. It has the words, "The Chadwick London Violin" stamped on the back of the scroll.

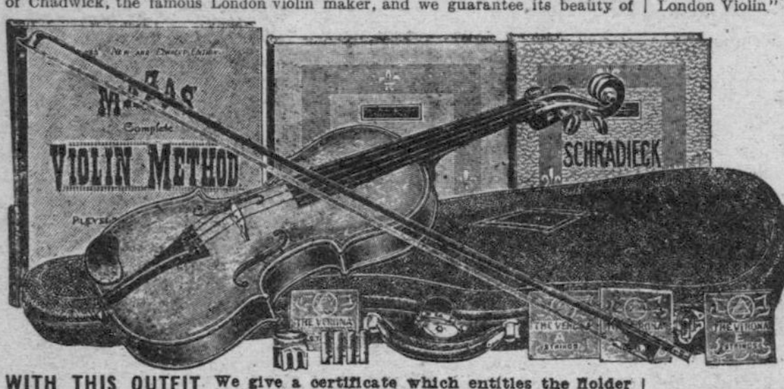

Regular retail price of violin	$40.00
One Tourte model bow, full German silver trimmed, and of the very best quality Pernambuco wood	12.00
One pulp case; covered throughout with a fine grade of leather, velvet lined and nickel trimmed	8.00
One genuine Quinn telescope music stand	2.00
One genuine piece Gustave Bernadel rosin	.25
One Mazas complete violin instructor	1.00
Two volumes of Schradieck's violin studies	1.00
One extra set of Verona strings	.85
One latest pattern chin rest	1.00
One set of tuning pipes	.50
One violin mute	.15
Total value of outfit	$66.75

No. 12E330 Our great bargain price $23.45
Shipping weight, 14 pounds.

WITH THIS OUTFIT We give a certificate which entitles the holder to a full course of instruction on the violin, consisting of 50 weekly lessons, covering a period of one year. These lessons will be given by one of the best known and most thorough musical colleges in the country, and we give you this certificate absolutely free

VIOLONCELLOS.

WEIGHT, PACKED FOR SHIPMENT, ABOUT 45 POUNDS.

Our $9.25 Violoncello with Patent Head.

No. 12E400 We furnish it complete with perfect fitting canvas bag, violoncello bow, a piece of fine rosin in pasteboard case, one fingerboard chart, and a complete instruction book, and the instrument is ready to play as soon as received by you. Price $9.25

No. 12E406 This instrument is of excellent quality and has handsome inlaid edges which add greatly to its general appearance. It has patent head as shown in illustration. It is fitted with a complete set of the best strings.

And with it are furnished FREE.
A Perfect Fitting Canvas Bag.
A Handsome Violoncello Bow.
An Extra Large Piece of fine Rosin and
A Valuable Instructor.

Price $11.20

Our Highest Grade Violoncello with Peg or Patent Head, $15.45.

No. 12E420 This is an instrument which must be seen, examined and tested in order to fully appreciate all its merits. This violoncello is extra fine quality, beautifully polished. Solid ebony trimmings throughout, including the solid ebony fingerboard and solid ebony tailpiece. The peg head is the very best which is manufactured and the material used in the body is such as is found only in the highest grade instruments. It is made by expert workmen, and the construction is such that it produces a tone such as you would naturally expect only from instruments which retailers sell at from $25.00 to $30.00. We include a perfect fitting canvas bag, valuable instruction book, a violoncello bow and a large piece of our best rosin in a pasteboard box, so that the instrument is ready to play as soon as received. Price $15.45

No. 12E422 Same description as our No. 12E420, but fitted with best quality patent head on brass plates. Price $17.85

DOUBLE BASS VIOLS.

EACH INSTRUMENT IS PACKED WITH GREAT CARE, AND WHEN READY TO SHIP WEIGHS 125 POUNDS.

Our $18.95 One-Half Size Double Bass Viol.

No. 12E450 At $18.95 we offer a four string Double Bass Viol, one-half size, with bow, and complete instruction book. This double bass viol is of the very best model, is dark red shaded, very highly polished, and is superior quality in every respect. Best patent head. Price $18.95

Our Three-Quarter Size Double Bass Viol.

No. 12E462 A High Grade Three-Quarter Size Double Bass Viol for $19.50. This double bass viol has four strings, finest iron patent head and is beautifully shaded and colored. In finish it is wonderfully fine, being highly polished throughout. Price $19.50

$22.85 Double Bass Viol.

Three-Quarter Size.

No. 12E466 This Double Bass Viol has four strings, high grade iron patent head, solid ebony fingerboard. The inlaid purfling is very handsome and adds greatly to the attractiveness of the instrument, giving it the appearance of the most expensive and highest priced viols on the market. We furnish free with each instrument a good double bass bow and complete instruction book. Price... $22.85

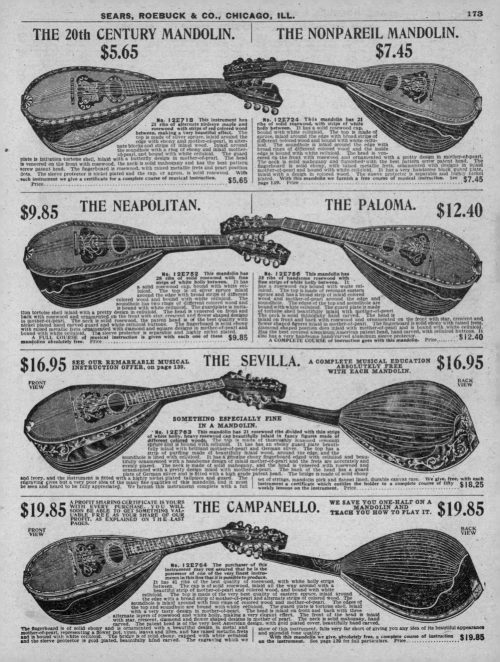

THE 20th CENTURY MANDOLIN.

$5.65

No. 12E718 This instrument has 21 ribs of alternate birdseye maple and rosewood with strips of red colored wood between, making a very beautiful effect. The top is made of silver spruce, inlaid around the edge with ebony and mother-of-pearl, in alternate blocks and strips of inlaid wood. Inlaid around the soundhole with a ring of ebony and inlaid mother-of-pearl, and bound with white celluloid. The guard plate is imitation tortoise shell, inlaid with a butterfly design in mother-of-pearl. The head is veneered on the front with rosewood, the neck is solid mahogany and has the best pattern screw patent head. The fingerboard is rosewood, with raised metallic frets and pearl position dots. The sleeve protector is nickel plated and the cap, or apron, is solid rosewood. **With each instrument we give a certificate for a complete course of musical instruction.**

Price.. $5.65

THE NONPAREIL MANDOLIN.

$7.45

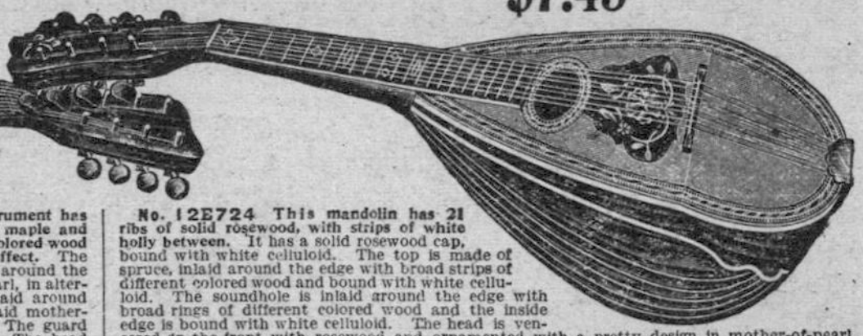

No. 12E724 This mandolin has 21 ribs of solid rosewood, with strips of white holly between. It has a solid rosewood cap, bound with white celluloid. The top is made of spruce, inlaid around the edge with broad strips of different colored wood and bound with white celluloid. The soundhole is inlaid around the edge with broad rings of different colored wood and the inside edge is bound with white celluloid. The head is veneered on the front with rosewood and ornamented with a pretty design in mother-of-pearl. The neck is solid mahogany and furnished with the best pattern screw patent head. The fingerboard is solid ebony, with raised metallic frets, ornamented with designs in inlaid mother-of-pearl and bound with white celluloid. It has a very handsome black guard plate, inlaid with a design in colored wood. The sleeve protector is separable and highly nickel plated. **With this mandolin we furnish a free course of musical instruction.** See page 139. Price.. $7.45

$9.85 THE NEAPOLITAN.

No. 12E752 This mandolin has 28 ribs of solid rosewood with fine strips of white holly between. It has a solid rosewood cap, bound with white celluloid. The top is of silver spruce inlaid around the edge with broad strips of different colored wood and bound with white celluloid. The soundhole has two rings of different colored wood and is bound with white celluloid. The guardplate is imitation tortoise shell inlaid with a pretty design in celluloid. The head is veneered on front and back with rosewood and ornamented on the front with star, crescent and flower shaped designs in mother-of-pearl. The neck is solid rosewood, the patent head is of the best quality with nickel plated hand carved guard and white celluloid buttons. The fingerboard is solid ebony with raised metallic frets ornamented with diamond and square designs in mother-of-pearl and bound with white celluloid. The sleeve protector is separable and highly nickel plated.

A FULL COURSE of musical instruction is given with each one of these mandolins absolutely free. Price.. $9.85

THE PALOMA. $12.40

No. 12E756 This mandolin has 35 ribs of handsome rosewood with fine strips of white holly between. It has a rosewood cap bound with white celluloid. The top is made of resonant eastern spruce and has a broad strip of inlaid colored wood and mother-of-pearl around the edge and soundhole. The edges of the top and soundhole are bound with white celluloid. The guard plate is made of tortoise shell beautifully inlaid with mother-of-pearl The neck is solid mahogany hand carved. The head is inlaid on front and back with rosewood and ornamented on the front with star, crescent and flower shaped figures inlaid in mother-of-pearl. The fingerboard is solid ebony with raised frets, diamond shaped position dots inlaid with mother-of-pearl and is bound with white celluloid. Has the best covered aluminum American patent head, hand carved, with celluloid buttons. It also has a very handsome hand carved aluminum sleeve protector.

A COMPLETE COURSE of instruction goes with this mandolin. Price........ $12.40

$16.95 THE SEVILLA. $16.95

SEE OUR REMARKABLE MUSICAL INSTRUCTION OFFER, on page 139.

A COMPLETE MUSICAL EDUCATION ABSOLUTELY FREE WITH EACH MANDOLIN.

FRONT VIEW

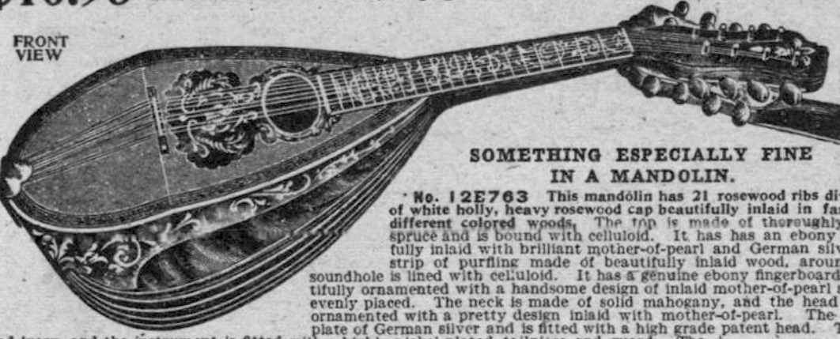

BACK VIEW

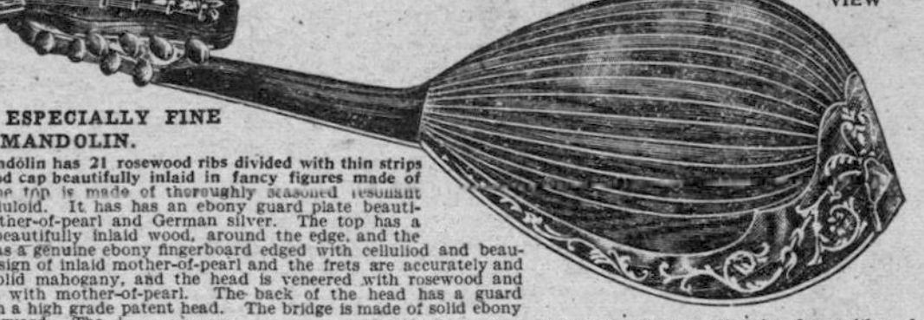

SOMETHING ESPECIALLY FINE IN A MANDOLIN.

No. 12E763 This mandolin has 21 rosewood ribs divided with thin strips of white holly, heavy rosewood cap beautifully inlaid in fancy figures made of different colored woods. The top is made of thoroughly seasoned resonant spruce and is bound with celluloid. It has has an ebony guard plate beautifully inlaid with brilliant mother-of-pearl and German silver. The top has a strip of purfling made of beautifully inlaid wood, around the edge, and the soundhole is lined with celluloid. It has a genuine ebony fingerboard edged with celluliod and beautifully ornamented with a handsome design of inlaid mother-of-pearl and the frets are accurately and evenly placed. The neck is made of solid mahogany, and the head is veneered with rosewood and ornamented with a pretty design inlaid with mother-of-pearl. The back of the head has a guard plate of German silver and is fitted with a high grade patent head. The bridge is made of solid ebony and ivory, and the instrument is fitted with a highly nickel plated tailpiece and guard. The engraving gives but a very poor idea of the many fine qualities of this mandolin, and it must be seen and heard to be fully appreciated. We furnish this instrument complete with a full set of strings, mandolin pick and flannel lined, durable canvas case. We give, free, with each instrument a certificate which entitles the holder to a complete course of fifty weekly lessons on the instrument. Price.. $18.25

$19.85 THE CAMPANELLO. $19.85

A PROFIT SHARING CERTIFICATE IS YOURS WITH EVERY PURCHASE. YOU WILL SOON BE ABLE TO GET SOMETHING VALUABLE FREE AS YOUR SHARE OF OUR PROFIT, AS EXPLAINED ON THE LAST PAGES.

WE SAVE YOU ONE-HALF ON A MANDOLIN AND TEACH YOU HOW TO PLAY IT.

FRONT VIEW

BACK VIEW

No. 12E764 The purchaser of this instrument may rest assured that he is the possessor of one of the very finest instruments in this line that it is possible to produce. It has 41 ribs of the best quality of rosewood, with white holly strips between. The cap is of solid rosewood, inlaid all the way around with a beautiful strip of mother-of-pearl and colored wood, and bound with white celluloid. The top is made of the very best quality of eastern spruce, inlaid around the edge with a broad strip of mother-of-pearl and alternate strips of colored wood. The soundhole is inlaid around with four rings of colored wood and mother-of-pearl. The edges of the top and soundhole are bound with white celluloid. The guard plate is tortoise shell, inlaid with a very tasty design in mother-of-pearl. The head is inlaid on front and back with three alternate layers of rosewood and white holly, making a very elegant effect. The front of the head is inlaid with star, crescent, diamond and flower shaped designs in mother of pearl. The neck is solid mahogany, hand carved. The patent head is of the very best American design, with gold plated cover, beautifully hand carved. The fingerboard is of solid ebony and is ornamented with a beautiful design in metal and mother-of-pearl, representing a flower pot, vines, leaves and lilies, and has raised metallic frets and is bound with white celluloid. The bridge is of solid ebony, capped with white celluloid and the sleeve protector is gold plated, beautifully hand carved. The engraving which we show of this instrument, falls very far short of giving you any idea of its beautiful appearance and splendid tone quality.

With this mandolin we give, absolutely free, a complete course of instruction on the instrument. See page 139 for full particulars. Price.. $19.85

$2.45 BANJOS $19.65

AT $2.45 TO $19.65 WE SHOW A SPLENDID LINE OF BANJOS, THE GREATEST VALUES EVER OFFERED.

WE WANT YOU TO MAKE A CAREFUL COMPARISON between the instruments which we are offering in this line and those offered by any other house. Such a comparison will convince you at once that no dealer can sell banjos which are in any way equal to ours at anywhere near the price we are quoting. It is not a question with us how cheap we can sell our banjos, but rather how good we can make them at the prices we quote. We could sell banjos at much lower prices than we are offering, but they could not possibly prove satisfactory to our customers, and they would prove very poor advertisements for our line of musical goods. From the highest to the lowest priced banjos in this line, each one contains the very best workmanship and material which it is possible to put into it at the price.

OUR TERMS OF SHIPMENT upon these banjos are as liberal as those which we make upon all of our other musical goods. We will ship any banjo C. O. D. upon receipt of $1.00 as an evidence of good faith. We will also allow each banjo to be tried for a period of ten days, and if it is not found satisfactory, we will receive it back and cheerfully return the money.

A PROFIT SHARING CERTIFICATE will be sent to you when you order, and you can soon get something valuable entirely FREE.

WE FURNISH, FREE, WITH EACH BANJO one set of Glendon strings, one instruction book of chords, one lettered fingerboard chart, and a complete course of instruction on the instrument.

OUR CHALLENGE BANJO OUTFIT.

$5.75 $5.75

You share in our profit when you buy from us, as well as saving a great deal on your purchase. See the last pages.

FRONT VIEW BACK VIEW

This is one of the best and most complete banjo outfits ever placed on the market at this price. Every article that goes to make up this outfit is the very best that possibly can be procured for the price asked. The banjo has an 11-inch head, with nickel shell, strainer hoop and wood lined. It has 39 nickel plated hexagon brackets, a well made neck, finished in mahogany. The front of the head is veneered with wood finished in ebony, the fingerboard is ebony, fitted with raised metallic frets, and inlaid pearl position dots. It is a very acceptable instrument and cannot be duplicated anywhere in the country for less than double the price we are asking. We would be glad to have you order this banjo and outfit and compare it with anything your dealer has to offer at from $10.00 to $12.00, and if you do not find it to be superior in every respect, it can be returned to us, and we will cheerfully refund your money.

This outfit consists of the following:	Regular Retail Price
One Challenge Banjo	$10.00
One Extra Set of Glendon Strings	.50
One Book of Guckert's Chords	.50
One Lettered Fingerboard Chart	.25
Total Value of Outfit	$11.25
No. 12E822 Our Great Bargain Price	5.75

We give, free, with this outfit a complete course of musical instructions, given by one of the very best musical colleges in the country. This course consists of fifty weekly lessons, covering a period of one year, and will be thorough and complete. Remember, that this outfit goes to you strictly on trial, and if you are not fully satisfied that it is a great bargain in every respect, we will gladly receive it back and refund every cent you have paid, including transportation charges. Shipping weight, about 12 pounds.

$2.45 OUR STUDENTS' BANJO.

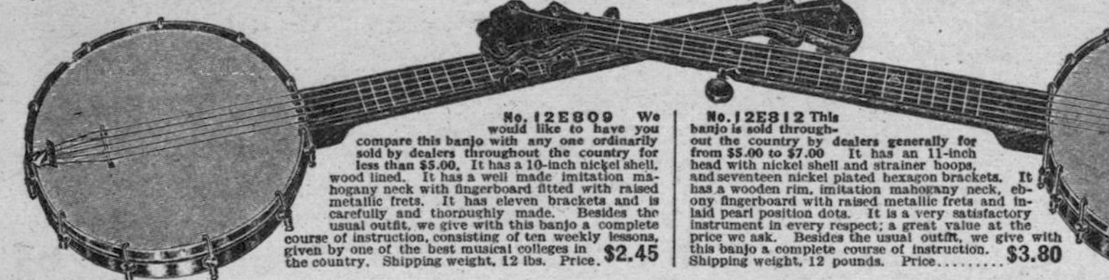

No. 12E809 We would like to have you compare this banjo with any one ordinarily sold by dealers throughout the country for less than $5.00. It has a 10-inch nickel shell, wood lined. It has a well made imitation mahogany neck with fingerboard fitted with raised metallic frets. It has eleven brackets and is carefully and thoroughly made. Besides the usual outfit, we give with this banjo a complete course of instruction, consisting of ten weekly lessons, given by one of the best musical colleges in the country. Shipping weight, 12 lbs. Price. **$2.45**

OUR EDGEMERE BANJO. $3.80

No. 12E812 This banjo is sold throughout the country by dealers generally for from $5.00 to $7.00 It has an 11-inch head with nickel shell and strainer hoops, and seventeen nickel plated hexagon brackets. It has a wooden rim, imitation mahogany neck, ebony fingerboard with raised metallic frets and inlaid pearl position dots. It is a very satisfactory instrument in every respect; a great value at the price we ask. Besides the usual outfit, we give with this banjo a complete course of instruction. Shipping weight, 12 pounds. Price........ **$3.80**

$4.85 Our CONSERVATORY BANJO

No. 12E816 This Banjo is a splendid value at the price we ask. It has an 11-inch head, nickel shell and strainer hoop and maple rim. It has a well made, graceful neck and head veneered on front with rosewood. It has a rosewood fingerboard fitted with raised metallic frets and inlaid pearl position dots. It has 21 hexagon brackets and is a very handsome instrument in every respect. The frets are all accurately placed on the fingerboard, the nickel shell is highly polished and the entire instrument is well finished. Besides the usual outfit, we give with this banjo a complete course of musical instruction. Shipping weight, 12 pounds.

Price.. **$4.85**

Our NEW CENTURY BANJO. $6.85

No. 12E824 This is a regular $12.00 banjo and is sold at that price generally throughout the country. It has a nickel shell and strainer hoop, and is wood lined. It has an extension removable neck with metal truss and is tightened by two ebony keys. It has 25 hexagon brackets and genuine ebony fingerboard fitted with raised metallic frets and diamond and flower shaped position dots inlaid in mother-of-pearl. The front of the head is veneered with a heavy piece of ebony, as well as the heel, and fitted with ebony pegs We recommend this instrument as being something particularly good in a banjo at this price and we will be glad to send it to you for comparison and examination. Besides the usual outfit, we give with this banjo a complete course of instruction. See page 139 for full particulars. Shipping weight, about 12 lbs. Price. **$6.85**

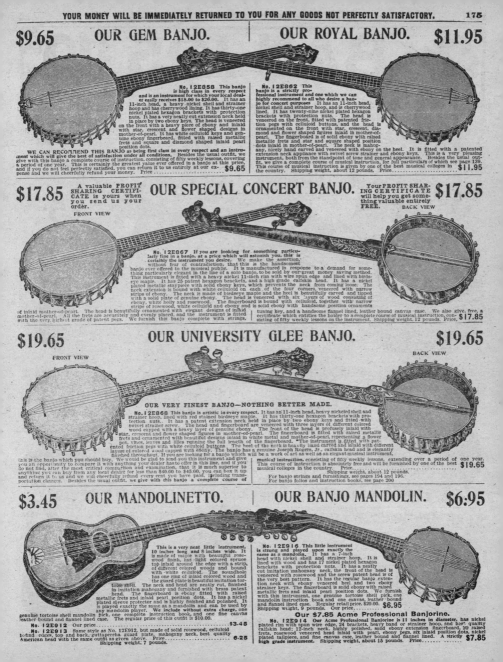

$9.65 OUR GEM BANJO.

No. 12E858 This banjo is high class in every respect and is an instrument for which your local dealer easily receives $18.00 to $20.00. It has an 11-inch head, a heavy nickel shell and strainer hoop and has cherrywood lining. It has thirty-one nickel plated hexagon brackets with protection nuts. It has a very neatly cut extension neck held in place by two ebony keys. The head is veneered on the front with a heavy piece of ebony and inlaid with star, crescent and flower shaped designs in mother-of-pearl. It has white celluloid keys and genuine ebony fingerboard, fitted with raised metallic frets and square and diamond shaped inlaid pearl position dots.

WE CAN RECOMMEND THIS BANJO as being first class in every respect and an instrument which will give the best of satisfaction under all conditions. Besides the usual outfit, we give with this banjo a complete course of instruction, consisting of fifty weekly lessons, covering a period of one year. This is certainly the greatest value ever offered in a banjo at this price, and if you do not feel perfectly satisfied, you can return it to us entirely at our expense and we will cheerfully refund your money. Price $9.65

OUR ROYAL BANJO. $11.95

No. 12E862 This banjo is a strictly professional instrument and one which we can highly recommend to all who desire a banjo for concert purposes. It has an 11-inch head, nickel shell and strainer hoop, and is cherrywood lined. It has twenty-nine nickel plated hexagon brackets with protection nuts. The head is veneered on the front, fitted with patented friction pegs with celluloid buttons, and the head is ornamented on the front with star, crescent, diamond and flower shaped figures inlaid in mother-of-pearl. The fingerboard is of solid ebony with raised metallic frets and star and square shaped position dots inlaid in mother-of-pearl. The neck is mahogany, nicely hand carved and veneered with ebony on the heel. It is fitted with a patented extension neck appliance with swivel screw strainer and ebony keys. This is a very pleasing instrument, both from the standpoint of tone and general appearance. Besides the usual outfit, we give a complete course of musical instruction, for full particulars of which see page 139. This course of musical instruction is given by one of the best musical colleges in the country. Shipping weight, about 12 pounds. Price.......................... $11.95

$17.85 OUR SPECIAL CONCERT BANJO. $17.85

A valuable PROFIT SHARING CERTIFICATE is yours when you send us your order.

Your PROFIT SHARING CERTIFICATE will help you get something valuable entirely FREE.

FRONT VIEW

BACK VIEW

No. 12E867 If you are looking for something particularly fine in a banjo, at a price which will astonish you, this is certainly the instrument you desire. We make the assertion, without fear of contradiction, that this is the handsomest banjo ever offered to the musical public. It is manufactured in response to a demand for something particularly elegant in the line of a solo banjo, to be sold by our great money saving method. This instrument is fitted with a heavy nickel 11-inch rim with wire spun edge and lined with birdseye maple. It has 25 patent hexagon brackets, and a high grade calfskin head. It has a nickel plated metallic staypiece with solid ebony keys, which prevents the neck from coming loose. The neck extension is bound with white celluloid on each of the four corners, veneered with narrow strips of ebony. The neck is made of birdseye maple and the heel is beautifully carved and tipped with a solid plate of genuine ebony. The head is veneered with six layers of wood consisting of ebony, white holly and rosewood. The fingerboard is bound with celluloid, together with narrow strips of rosewood, white celluloid and ebony and is solid ebony with handsome position ornaments of inlaid mother-of-pearl. The head is beautifully ornamented with elegant designs of inlaid mother-of-pearl. All the frets are accurately and evenly placed, and the instrument is fitted with the very highest grade of patent pegs. We furnish this banjo complete with strings, tuning key, and a handsome flannel lined, leather bound canvas case. We also give, free, a certificate which entitles the holder to a complete course of musical instruction, consisting of fifty weekly lessons on the instrument. Shipping weight, 12 pounds. Price, $17.85

$19.65 OUR UNIVERSITY GLEE BANJO. $19.65

FRONT VIEW

BACK VIEW

OUR VERY FINEST BANJO—NOTHING BETTER MADE.

No. 12E868 This banjo is artistic in every respect. It has an 11-inch head, heavy nickeled shell and strainer hoop, lined with red stained birdseye maple. It has thirty-one hexagon brackets with protection nuts. It has a patent extension neck held in place by two ebony keys and fitted with swivel strainer screw. The head and fingerboard are veneered with three layers of different colored wood capped with a heavy layer of genuine ebony. The front of the head is profusely inlaid with star, crescent and flower shaped figures in mother-of-pearl. The fingerboard is fitted with raised metallic frets and ornamented with beautiful designs inlaid in white metal and mother-of-pearl, representing a flower pot, vines, leaves and lilies running the full length of the fingerboard. The instrument is fitted with patented friction pegs with white celluloid buttons. The heel of the neck is heavily hand carved and inlaid with different layers of colored wood capped with ebony. The banjo has a genuine Joseph Rogers, Jr., calfskin head and is elegantly finished throughout. If you are looking for a banjo which will be a work of art as well as an elegant musical instrument, this is the banjo which you should buy. We would be glad to send you this instrument and give you an opportunity to compare it with anything your dealer has to offer in this line, and if you do not find, after the most critical comparison and examination, that it is much superior to anything you can buy from any local dealer for less than $40.00 to $45.00, you can box it up and return it to us and we will cheerfully refund every cent you have paid, including transportation charges. Besides the usual outfit, we give with this banjo a complete course of musical instruction, consisting of fifty weekly lessons, extending over a period of one year. This course of instruction is absolutely free and will be furnished by one of the best musical colleges in the country. Price.......................... $19.65

Shipping weight, about 12 pounds.

For banjo strings and furnishings, see pages 194 and 196.
For banjo folios and instruction books, see page 200

$3.45 OUR MANDOLINETTO.

OUR BANJO MANDOLIN. $6.95

This is a very neat little instrument, 10 inches long and 8 inches wide. It is made of maple with beautiful rosewood finish, has light colored spruce top inlaid around the edge with a strip of different colored woods and bound with white celluloid. The soundhole has one ring of inlaid colored wood and the guard plate is beautiful imitation tortoise shell. The neck and head are neatly cut, finished in imitation mahogany and furnished with brass patent head. The fingerboard is ebony fitted with raised metallic frets and inlaid pearl position dots. It has a nickel plated sleeve protector and is highly finished and polished. It is played exactly the same as a mandolin and can be used by any mandolin player. We include without extra charge, one genuine tortoise shell mandolin pick, one complete instruction book, and one fine canvas leather bound and flannel lined case. The regular price of this outfit is $10.00.

No. 12E912 Our price.......................... $3.45

No. 12E913 Same style as No. 12E912, but made of solid rosewood, celluloid bound edges, top and back, guttapercha guard plate, mahogany neck, best quality American head with the same outfit as given above. Price.......................... 6.25

Shipping weight, 7 pounds.

No. 12E916 This little instrument is strung and played upon exactly the same as a mandolin. It has a 7-inch head with nickel shell and strainer hoop. It is lined with wood and has 17 nickel plated hexagon brackets with protection nuts. It has a neatly cut imitation mahogany neck, the front of the head is veneered with rosewood and the screw patent head is of the very best pattern. It has the regular banjo extension neck with ebony veneered heel and two ebony strainer keys. The fingerboard is solid ebony with raised metallic frets and inlaid pearl position dots. We furnish with this instrument, one genuine tortoise shell pick, one mandolin instruction book and one canvas, leather bound and flannel lined case. Regular retail price, $20.00. Shipping weight, 9 pounds. Our price.......................... $6.95

Our $7.85 Acme Professional Banjorine.

No. 12E914 Our Acme Professional Banjorine is 11 inches in diameter, has nickel plated rim with spun wire edge, 24 brackets, heavy band or strainer hoop, and best quality calfskin head; 12-inch neck, highly polished, solid ebony extension fingerboard, 20 raised frets, rosewood veneered head inlaid with pearl, ebony pegs, six inlaid position dots, nickel plated tailpiece, and fine canvas case, leather bound and flannel lined. A strictly high grade instrument. Shipping weight, about 15 pounds. Price.......................... $7.85

THE AUTOHARP

has become one of the most popular of small musical instruments. Our trade in these instruments has become enormous, and is largely due to two points; our extremely low prices and the general excellence of the instruments we handle. These are favorite musical instruments, because it requires but little practice to play upon them, and the music is of the very highest order. Any-one who can read English and possesses ordinary intelligence can play upon an autoharp, because the music that we furnish is simply and plainly figured and the player will find no difficulty in following it. **With each autoharp we give a complete instruction book with many different selections of music.** Each one of these instruments is finished in the most beautiful manner, and carefully and durably constructed. If your time will not allow you to learn to play upon a violin, piano or other instrument of this class we would, by all means, advise you to purchase one of these instruments.

$1.75

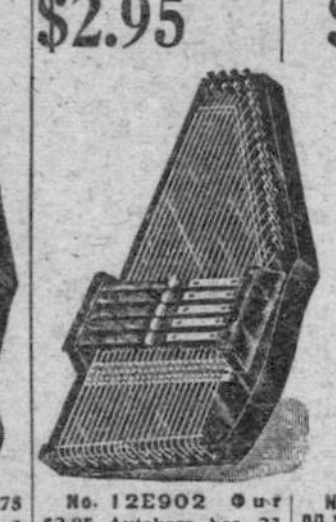

No. 12E900 Our $1.75 Autoharp has 20 strings, 3 bars and produces 3 chords. With this instrument the simpler airs and chords may be played. The best steel strings are furnished and the tone is remarkably sweet. Without a single exception, every purchaser has been delighted with this autoharp, and would not part with it at any price if another could not be secured. Weight, packed for shipment, 6 pounds.
Price..............$1.75

$2.95

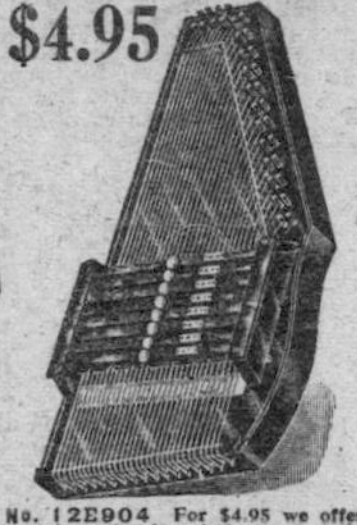

No. 12E902 Our $2.95 Autoharp has 23 strings, 5 bars and produces 5 chords. The possibilities of this beautiful instrument are unbounded, and while but little practice is needed for the beginner to play nicely, constant practice will enable the performer to produce very difficult music. Weight, packed for shipment, 7 pounds.
Price..........$2.95

$4.95

No. 12E904 For $4.95 we offer an autoharp that is entirely new, strictly first class in workmanship and susceptible of wonderful manipulation. This special autoharp is complete with 32 strings and is fitted with 8 bars, as it has 8 chords, as follows: C major, G seventh, F major, C seventh, Bb major, B minor, A seventh and G minor. The range of different music is very great and the possibilities of the instrument are beyond that of any other of similar construction and much higher price. You cannot purchase this autoharp from any other dealer for less than from $8.00 to $10.00. Weight, packed for shipment, 9 pounds. Price..............$4.95

$6.45

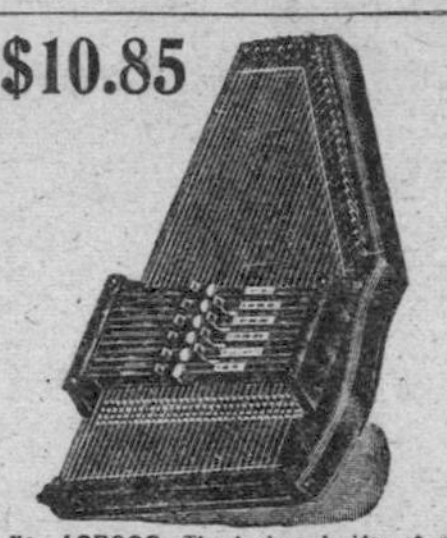

No. 12E906 This Autoharp is the very latest product of the manufacturers, and is destined to become the most popular style of their entire list. It has 37 strings and 12 chord bars; these bars are placed close together making the manipulation of them exceedingly easy. They produce 12 chords, as follows: G major, E seventh, C major, A minor, G seventh, E seventh, F major, D minor, C seventh, A seventh, Bb major and G minor. It is strung and tuned in a perfect chromatic scale. The finish is beautiful; highly polished ebony finish; altogether a handsome, useful musical instrument. Weight, packed for shipment, 10 pounds. Price........$6.45

$10.85

No. 12E908 The back and sides of this beautiful Autoharp are made of well seasoned hardwood and enameled in black. The top or sounding board is made of a carefully selected piece of beautifully close grain pine and finished in a light brown color. The edges are inlaid in white maple with a narrow strip of black between, giving the instrument a very elegant appearance. The bars and supporters are enameled in black and fitted with celluloid buttons for the fingers. It has six bars, by the use of which 16 chords are made possible. Weight, packed for shipment, 16 pounds.
Price..............$10.85

No. 12E909 Same as above, but packed in fine black wood autoharp case, flannel lined.
Price..............$11.85

GUITAR ZITHERS.

The Guitar Zither is an improved and simplified German zither, upon which may be rendered the most difficult music without the aid of a teacher. Our method of instruction is so easy that anyone can learn to play the instrument in a very short time. The bass notes are tuned in groups of chords. This is a very attractive feature because the various chords of the key are ready to be picked without effort. As an accompaniment of the voice these chords are invaluable. In connection with the violin, piano or other musical instrument, the guitar zither is especially delightful. It rewards individual skill more than any other harp in existence. These are musical instruments which charm alike the home circle and the concert audience. Every instruction book contains a list of music arranged for the instrument in figures easily comprehended. Our repertoire contains nearly everything published in the popular music of the day, besides all the standard music which has won the hearts of generation after generation.

$1.65

No. 12E921 The Guitar Zither, at $1.65, illustrated herewith, is made of maple, cherry stained and polished. It has a hand rest, 31 strings and 4 chords, namely, C, G, F major and G minor, complete with instruction book, key and ring. Lovers of music will find this a particularly fine instrument, as it is very easily learned and is delightfully entertaining. We will be glad to place this instrument in your hands for trial and examination, as we know you will find it to be an instrument which will meet your wants in every respect. Shipping weight, about 9 pounds.
Price..............$1.65

$1.98

No. 12E923 This is another splendid Guitar Zither, and is made of maple, ebonized and beautifully finished. It has hand rest, and is considerably larger in size than No. 12E921. It is inlaid around the soundhole with beautiful ornamentations, has 31 strings and 4 chords, namely, C, G, F major and G minor. Complete with instruction book, key and ring. This instrument will be found by players to be handsome in every respect, and possesses a deep tone which never fails to delight the listener. It is new in our line, and we highly recommend it for its many excellent qualities. Shipping weight, about 9 pounds. Price..............$1.98

$2.95

No. 12E925 This is another Guitar Zither, made of maple, ebonized and handsomely finished. It has hand rest, highly polished and is beautifully inlaid around the soundhole, has 41 strings and 5 chords, namely, C, G, F, D and A major. It is beautifully ornamented around the edge of the sounding board and is an instrument of which one may well be proud. We furnish a chart also with this instrument, which can be laid under the strings, giving the position of every note. It comes complete, with instruction book, key and ring. Shipping weight, about 9 pounds.
Price..............$2.95

$3.95

No. 12E927 This is a particularly fine instrument of great musical capacity. It is made of maple, ebonized, has hand rest, highly polished, and beautifully inlaid around the soundhole and the edge of the sounding board. Has nickel plated tuning pins, full chromatic scale with 51 strings and 6 chords, namely, C, G, F, D major and A minor. It has a deep, full, rich tone, and by the aid of the chart and instruction book which we send, it can be easily learned. We send it complete with chart, instruction book, key and ring, and the purchaser will find that it will prove a never ending source of entertainment and delight. Shipping weight, about 9 pounds.
Price..............$3.95

MANDOLIN-GUITAR-ZITHER.

$3.35

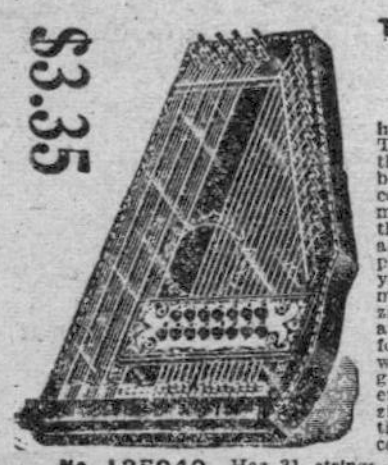

Three Instruments Combined at the Price of One.

The greatest musical instrument that has ever been placed before the public. The mandolin, guitar and zither, three of the sweetest toned instruments, are combined in this harp which is so simply constructed that anyone may become master of it in a very short time, without the aid of a teacher. No picks or rings are required to play the instrument, a patent keyboard being used instead. As you will see in the illustration, the instrument is made after the style of the guitar zither, having treble strings on which the air is played and accompaniment strings for the accompaniment. The keyboard, which is placed over the strings, is the greatest feature with which the mandolin effect is produced. These mandolin-guitar-zithers are made of selected material beautifully ebonized and decorated with decalcomania ornamentations around the edges.

$4.35

No. 12E940 Has 31 strings 4 chords G, C and F major and G dominant 7th. Price..............$3.35
Weight, packed for shipment, 9 pounds

No. 12E942 Has 41 strings 5 chords C, G, F, D and A major. Price..............4.35
Weight, packed for shipment, 12 pounds

Each packed in neat pasteboard box with instruction book and tuning key.

THE FAMOUS MARX PIANO HARP.

$2.65

No. 12E947 This is certainly the most wonderful instrument of its kind ever placed on the market. The mechanism of the instrument is so arranged that the performer gets a grand piano tone quality by the use of the hammers, as shown in the illustration. The instrument is picked with the right hand, same as an ordinary autoharp, while the hammers are manipulated with the left hand. These hammers are so arranged as to produce the chords of C major, G seventh, F major, C seventh, and their relative minors. The figured music which is used on this piano harp is the simplest ever offered in any instrument of this kind. By its use anyone, even though not familiar with music, can play any tune without any previous instruction. It has 23 strings and 7 hammers. It differs from the ordinary autoharp in the important particular that there are no dead strings over which the performer has to play. It is 11 inches long, and 20 inches wide, and weighs, boxed for shipment, 10 pounds. With this instrument we furnish one tuning key, one pick, one music holder and 30 pieces of figured music. Price..............$2.65

OUR GEM ROLLER ORGAN, $3.25.

OUR LEADER

THE GREATEST VALUE EVER OFFERED IN A MUSICAL INSTRUMENT. PRICE REDUCED FROM $4.20 TO $3.25. This reduction was made possible by our contracting for the entire output of the factory which makes this wonderful little instrument, AND NO DEALER IS ABLE TO FURNISH YOU A GEM ORGAN AT AS LOW A PRICE AS WE QUOTE IT.

THE CASE of the Gem Roller Organ is made of imitation dark walnut; is 16 inches long, 14 inches wide and 9 inches high.

THE GEM ORGAN is distinctly a musical instrument of excellent quality; substantially made by the best manufacturers of this class of goods in the United States. It is so simply constructed that a child can operate it. The music is obtained from a roller, which has teeth or pins like those of the cylinder of a regular Swiss music box. These pins operate on valve keys and the roller is turned by a gear which also works the bellows. The reeds used are the same as those used in regular cabinet parlor organs and the tone is therefore similar to that of a regular cabinet parlor organ.

WE CAN FURNISH any kind of music, including Sacred, Spanish, German, Norwegian, popular airs and all of the latest up to date selections. These rollers cost less than the ordinary sheet music and therefore afford you the pleasure of playing or hearing all of the most desirable compositions of the day with but little expense.

THE INSTRUMENT... is durable and you can secure as many rolls and as many different kinds of music as you desire. We list below some of the best known and most desirable selections taken from our entire collection, and the complete list is furnished with every organ.

Price for the **GEM ROLLER ORGAN** including THREE ROLLERS is

$3.25

When ordering be sure to order by number.

No. 12E985

Shipping weight, 12 pounds.

WE FURNISH THREE ROLLERS FREE WITH EACH GEM ROLLER ORGAN AT $3.25.

IN ORDERING ROLLERS ALWAYS BE SURE TO GIVE A SECOND CHOICE SO IF THE FIRST MENTIONED ARE OUT OF STOCK WE CAN SUBSTITUTE WITHOUT DELAY.

Complete List of the Best Rollers for Gem and Concert-Roller Organs.

Series No. 12E986 Order by Number.

PRICE, PER DOZEN, $2.16; EACH .... 18 Cents.

If by mail, postage extra, each, 6 cents.

SACRED MUSIC.

1 The Sweet Bye and Bye
2 Nearer, my God, to Thee
3 I Need Thee Every Hour
4 From Greenland's Icy Mountains
6 Onward, Christian Soldiers
12 Hold the Fort
13 Just as I Am
14 America
18 He Leadeth Me
19 I Love to Tell the Story
20 The Home Over There
21 Is My Name Written There
22 Almost Persuaded
23 Where Is My Boy Tonight
24 Bringing in the Sheaves
25 Let the Lower Lights be Burning
26 Only an Armor Bearer
27 I Will Sing of My Redeemer
29 Pull for the Shore
30 Precious Name
65 What a Friend We Have in Jesus
67 Rock of Ages
68 Sweet Hour of Prayer
72 Pass Me Not
73 Jesus, Lover of My Soul
78 Beulah Land
81 We Shall Meet Beyond the River
90 All the Way My Saviour Leads Me
91 Rescue the Perishing
603 Knocking, Knocking, Who is There
634 Shall We Gather at the River
721 Anywhere With Jesus
726 Glory to His Name
729 The Haven of Rest
730 Everlasting Arms
734 Lead, Kindly Light

POPULAR SONGS, DANCES.

101 Waltz—Les Roses
103 When the Swallows Homeward Fly
106 The Soldiers' Joy
107 When the Leaves Begin to Fade
108 Sweet Violets
109 Marching Through Georgia
111 Waltz, My Queen
112 Old Uncle Ned
115 Climbing Up the Golden Stairs
118 Meet Me in the Lovely Twilight
119 Vienna Polka
121 Old Folks at Home
122 Sailors' Hornpipe
123 Home, Sweet Home
124 The Marseillaise Hymn
127 Die Wacht am Rhine
132 The Dreamland Waltz
138 The Parade March
144 Nellie Gray
146 Annie Laurie
149 The Last Rose of Summer
150 Waltz—German Hearts
152 See-Saw Waltz
153 Polka—On the Wing
155 The Beautiful Blue Danube
156 Listen to the Mocking Bird
157 Then You'll Remember Me
161 The Blue Bells of Scotland
163 The Wearing of the Green
166 Little Old Log Cabin
183 The Flyaway Galop
190 Yankee Doodle
194 The Golden Slippers
195 The Quilting Party
196 Love Comes—Waltz
200 I } Gay Life Quadrilles
201 II } Gay Life Quadrilles
202 III } Gay Life Quadrilles
203 IV } Gay Life Quadrilles
204 V } Gay Life Quadrilles
205 Dixie
207 The Arkansas Traveler
209 The Kiss Waltz
212 When You and I Were Young
213 College Hornpipe
217 Medley Jig
226 Bring Back My Bonnie to Me
229 Tramp, Tramp
230 Don't Be Angry With Me, Darling
232 Johnny Get Your Hair Cut
233 Poor Old Dad
234 Waltz—Cricket on the Hearth
238 Put My Little Shoes Away
243 Money Musk
246 The Irish Washerwoman
247 The Devil's Dream
251 I'll Take You Home Again
254 Jennie, the Flower of Kildare
256 The Little Fishermaiden
262 Old Black Joe
266 Killarney
268 Comin' Thro' the Rye
270 Massa's in de Cold, Cold Ground
272 Grandfather's Clock
273 The Star Spangled Banner
275 Maryland, My Maryland
277 Hail Columbia
279 Red, White and Blue
280 Tenting on the Old Camp Ground
283 The Old Oaken Bucket
290 In Her Little Bed We Laid Her
293 You Never Miss the Water
295 The Way to be Happy—Waltz
297 St. Patrick's Day
298 Miss McLeod's Reel
301 The Girl I Left Behind Me
309 Down Went McGinty
335 Little Annie Rooney—Waltz
336 Sweetbrier Waltz
347 Good Luck Mazurka
349 Dairy Maid Waltz
351 Free as a Bird
363 Only a Dream of My Mother
368 Schottische—Little Beauty
374 Some Day I'll Wander Back Again
375 Take Me Back to Home & Mother
390 The Battle Cry of Freedom
392 Come Back to Erin
399 John Brown
406 Schottische—Always Smiling
407 Waltz—Loves' Dreamland
410 Why Did They Dig Ma's Grave so Deep
416 Captain Jinks
420 Schottische—Happy-go-Lucky
421 My Mother's Old Red Shawl
423 Peep-O-Day—Polka
443 Oh My Darling Clementine
444 Galop—Jolly Brothers
446 Manhattan Polka
450 Clayton's Grand March
452 Fresh Life, Waltz
453 Galop—Little Fairy
456 Racquet Waltz
457 Waltz—Estudiantina
476 Silver Threads Among the Gold
480 General Grant's Grand March
517 Mary and John
527 Farewell Till We Meet Again
577 The High School Cadets' March
578 The Skirt Dance
600 After the Ball
617 God Be With You
635 Happy Day
1003 Won't You Be My Sweetheart
1004 The Bowery
1006 Two Little Girls in Blue
1009 The Washington Post March
1016 The Miner's Dream of Home
1019 Molly and I and the Baby
1020 Little Alabama Coon
1030 In Love With the Man in the Moon
1036 Sweet Marie
1038 The Sidewalks of New York
1039 The Fatal Wedding
1050 I Don't Want to Play in Your Yard
1053 Ben Bolt
1054 The Honeymoon March
1058 Just Tell Them That You Saw Me
1059 Only One Girl in the World for Me
1061 The Sunshine of Paradise Alley
1069 My Old Kentucky Home
1070 The Darkies' Dream
1071 Sweet Rosie O'Grady
1083 Hot Time in the Old Town
1084 Bombasto March, Two Step
1086 There'll Come a Time
1087 All Coons Look Alike to Me
1090 On the Banks of the Wabash
1096 Stars and Stripes Forever, March
1100 Sunny Side Clog
1101 She was Bred in Old Kentucky
1102 Break the News to Mother
1107 Georgia Camp Meeting
1112 Hello, Ma Baby
1113 High Born Lady
1114 Smoky Mokes
1115 Eli Green's Cake Walk
1116 Whistling Rufus
1117 Just as the Sun Went Down
1118 Just One Girl
1119 Zenda Waltzes
1120 Home to Our Mountains
1121 Narcissus
1122 Intermezzo Rusticana
1123 The Moth and the Flame
1124 Sunny Tennessee
1125 El Capitaine—No. 1
1126 El Capitaine—No. 2
1127 Soldiers in the Park
1128 Holy City
1129 Mosquito Parade
1130 Good Bye, Dolly Grey
1131 Fishers' Hornpipe
1132 Creole Belle
1133 Tale of the Kangaroo
1134 Down Where the Cotton Blossoms Grow
1135 I Left Because I Love You
1136 In the Good Old Summer Time
1137 Mister Dooley
1138 Bill Bailey
1139 Hiawatha
1140 By the Sycamore Tree
1141 Laughing Water

OUR $7.60 CONCERT ROLLER ORGAN.

THIS ORGAN is of somewhat higher grade than the Gem roller organ, has greater musical capacity, is much better constructed and a finer instrument in every way. The cylinder and all of the mechanism are enclosed and covered with a glass door, which effectually excludes dust and dirt. It is operated in the same way as the Gem roller organ and uses the same cylinder, so that in ordering cylinders for this organ you can make your selections from the list on the preceding page.

THIS IS A VERY DESIRABLE INSTRUMENT, produces delightful music and, as the cylinders are removable, a great many different pieces can be played. The tone is similar to that of a parlor organ, as the tone is produced by reeds operated by a cylinder containing teeth, which open and close the valves. It is made of genuine black walnut, is 17 inches long, 14 inches wide and 13 inches high.

PART of our profit is given back to you under our **PROFIT SHARING SYSTEM** as explained on the last pages.

The Rollers Cost as Follows:

Series No. 12E986 Price, for extra rollers, each **$0.18**
Per dozen **2.16**
If by mail, postage extra, each, 6 cents.

Five Tunes Furnished Free With Each Concert Organ.

No. 12E988 Concert Roller Organ. Price $7.60
Weight, packed for shipment, 30 pounds.

No. 12E988

GRAND ROLLER ORGAN—A MUSICAL WONDER

No. 12E990

IN OFFERING the Grand Roller Organ we aim to furnish an instrument to fill the middle ground between the instruments of small cost and those ranging in price to several hundred dollars.

It has a compass of thirty-two notes, and thereby opens up a large field for the better class of music, such as overtures and classical selections, which could not very well be played on the small instruments. The tone is pure, sweet and full, having a volume sufficient for a large hall and yet pleasing in a small apartment. The mechanism is of the first order, nothing about the whole instrument being slighted or cheapened, and is as simple as can be devised to do the

...PROPER WORK...

NOTE—Rollers or cylinders to play any of the following pieces can be obtained by indicating the number of the piece desired.

No. 12E990

THE ROLLER used in the Grand Roller Organ is a marvel of mechanical skill, each roller having from 2,500 to 4,000 separate pins which must be absolutely perfect in position. The roller is 13 inches long, 2¼ inches in diameter and makes 8 full revolutions in completing a tune.

All wearing parts, such as keys, pins, etc., are made of steel, and all adjustments made to insure durability. The case is of oak finish, full nickel trimmed and is a handsome addition to any apartment. A complete list of music will be sent at any time upon application.

WE FURNISH FREE WITH EACH

GRAND ROLLER ORGAN

THREE ROLLS OF MUSIC.

No. 12E990 Price, complete. $14.95
Price for extra rollers, each.. .65
Price, per dozen.................. 7.80
If by mail, postage extra, single roller 25 cents.

Large quantities should be shipped by express or freight.

LIST OF BEST SELECTIONS:

Series No. 12E992 Order by Number.

POPULAR AIRS.

2001 Auf Wiedersehn Waltz
2002 Autograph Waltz
2003 The Thunderer March
2004 En Avant March
2008 Blooming Youth Waltz
2009 Four Little Curly Headed Coons
2010 The Nightingale's Song
2011 The Washington Post March
2015 Dramatic News Waltz
2018 After the Ball—Waltz Song
2019 Gracious Heavens—Martha
2020 The Oxford Minuet
2021 The Wedding of the Lily and the Rose
2022 The Gypsy Song—An Chorus
2023 The Bowery—Waltz
2024 Par Ci Par La—Polka
2025 The High School Cadets March
2026 Mosquito Skirt Dance
2027 "Wang" Waltzes
2030 The Virginia Skedaddle
2031 Push Dem Clouds Away
2033 I Wish I Was in Dixie Land
2040 Tannhauser March
2043 Home, Sweet Home
2044 "1492" Waltzes
2046 Gondolier Waltzes
2047 I and II } Mardi Gras Quadrilles
2048 IV and V }
2050 I and II } Palermo Quadrilles
2051 IV and V }
2054 Overture—Caliph of Bagdad
2055 Sweet Marie Waltz
2059 Wedding March
2060 Overture—Tancredi
2062 Overture—William Tell
2063 The Liberty Bell March
2064 Wedding March from Lohengrin
2065 I and II } Gondoliers Lanciers
2066 IV and V }
2067 The Belle of Chicago
2070 The Fatal Wedding
2071 America, Star Spangled Banner
2073 Because I Love Thee So
2074 Skirt Dance—Faust Up to Date
2075 Coronation March—The Prophet
2080 { I. Mrs. Flarity, What Did You Mean by That; II. Do, Do, My Huckleberry
2081 Rock-a-Bye, Baby
2086 { The Sidewalks of New York; I Long to See the Girl I Left Behind
2088 Overture—Poet and Peasant
2090 Yankee Doodle. My Old Kentucky Home
2091 { I Don't Want to Play in Your Yard; He Never Cares to Wander from His Fireside
2092 Military March
2097 Dream Waltz—Black Hussar
2099 Kerry Dance
2101 The Honeymoon March
2103 Old Hundred
2104 America
2107 Auld Lang Syne
2109 Beautiful Blue Danube Waltz
2112 Selection from Overture, Semiramis
2114 Sounds from the Vienna Woods
2116 Selections from Mignon
2119 Maggie Mooney. My Pearl is a Bowery Girl
2121 Slumber So Gently—Princess Bonnie
2122 Morning Leaves—Waltz
2123 Thousand and One Nights Waltz
2124 Crusaders' March—Il Talisman
2126 The Band Played On
2127 When the Swallows Homeward Fly
2129 Monastery Bells
2131 I'll Tell Papa on You. Oh, Uncle John
2132 Only One Girl in the World for Me
2134 { My Best Girl's a New Yorker; The Sunshine of Paradise Alley
2135 Yale March—Two Step
2137 { Just Tell Them That You Saw Me; I Love Only You
2138 Priest March—Opera Athalia
2139 Autophone, Melody
2140 { Battle Cry of Freedom. Tramp, Tramp. Red, White and Blue. Home, Sweet Home. Marching Through Georgia

SACRED MUSIC.

3001 O, Rest in the Lord. (Elijah)
3002 I Know that My Redeemer Liveth
3003 Come Unto Me
3004 Lead, Kindly Light
3005 Nearer, My God, to Thee
3006 Onward, Christian Soldiers
3007 Hold the Fort
3008 Jesus, Lover of My Soul
3009 Only an Armor Bearer
3010 Let the Lower Lights be Burning
3012 Sweet Hour of Prayer
3013 Beautiful Valley of Eden
3014 Sweet Bye and Bye
3015 From Greenland's Icy Mountain
3016 Portuguese Hymn
3017 Antioch

When ordering rollers always be sure to give a second choice so if the first mentioned are out of stock we can substitute without delay.

Our No. 12E1096 Concertina.

No. 12E1096 This concertina is not only a beautiful instrument in appearance, but possesses also an excellent quality of tone. It is made of solid mahogany fancy carved, bellows of eight folds, full leather bound. It has 20 bone keys and is finished splendidly throughout. The frame of the instrument is highly polished and the ornamentation throughout is in the very best taste. We unhesitatingly recommend it to all who desire a fine concertina at an extremely low price. This is a concertina for which your dealer asks you from $6.00 to $7.00, and you cannot buy it elsewhere for less than these prices. We buy these instruments under a special contract, and are thus able to procure the very best possible terms, and we sell you the instrument at exactly what it costs us, but with one small percentage of profit added. In this way you are able to purchase the instrument at an extremely low price. We guarantee it to be satisfactory and we assure our friends that it is a concertina of which anyone may well be proud. Remember, we do not ask you to keep it unless you find it satisfactory in every respect and equal, if not superior, to concertinas sold by dealers generally at twice the price. Weight, boxed, about 8 pounds.

Price **$3.45**

Our S., R. & Co.'s Special Anglo-German System Concertina No. 12E1098.

No. 12E1098 This is one of the most beautiful concertinas ever manufactured and the engraving falls far short of giving any idea of its handsome appearance and splendid finish. It is made of solid mahogany, highly polished and most exquisitely carved. It has leather covered bellows of six folds, has 21 bone keys and is fitted with extra fine quality reeds. It is put up in a leather covered case with lock and key. Why should you go to the retail music dealer and purchase a concertina in the usual way when you can purchase one from us of the very same grade for one-half what the dealer asks you. You cannot buy a concertina of this grade from any local dealer for less than $12.00 or $13.00, and we are willing to ship you this instrument with the understanding that if you do not find this to be the case, you can return it to us, we will cheerfully refund your money and pay transportation charges both ways. We guarantee this concertina to be satisfactory and we assure our customers that they take no risk whatever in ordering it, because we take all the chances and responsibilities of shipment. Under our plan of sale our customers are given an opportunity to try our instruments entirely at our expense. Weight, boxed, about 10 pounds. Price **$6.65**

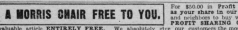

A MORRIS CHAIR FREE TO YOU.

For $50.00 in **Profit Sharing Certificates** we give a handsome, luxurious Morris Chair **FREE as your share in our profit.** Send us your orders for everything you need, get your friends and neighbors to buy with you, and you will be surprised how quickly you will accumulate $50.00 in **PROFIT SHARING CERTIFICATES** and can then get a beautiful Morris Chair or some other valuable article **ENTIRELY FREE.** We absolutely give our customers the most of our profit. We make our prices as low as possible, and send you a **PROFIT SHARING CERTIFICATE for every purchase, enabling you to participate in OUR GREAT PROFIT SHARING PLAN** as explained on last pages.

OUR BÖHM LINE OF SOVEREIGN ACCORDIONS.

A FINE LINE OF LOW PRICED ACCORDIONS. **We assure all admirers of the accordion that they will find in these instruments the greatest values ever offered in low priced accordions.** They are made especially for us by a maker who has an international reputation for manufacturing these instruments. They are all well and thoroughly made throughout, and we know that we can sell them to you at a price much lower than what other dealers will ask for the same grade of instruments. We ship them upon the same terms that we ship out other musical goods and allow full ten days' trial. They are all handsomely finished and ornamented and are instruments which we can conscientiously recommend to our customers. With each instrument we include a complete and comprehensive instruction book, by the aid of which anyone can learn to play on these instruments without the aid of a teacher. This is a line of old favorite accordions and we have been so successful in handling them that we have come to look upon them as a staple article in the accordion line. Our contract with the manufacturer of these accordions is such a favorable one that we are in a position to make prices which are lower than ever before As a proof of this we ask you to examine the accordions shown below and compare the prices which we quote with anything any other dealer has to offer If you are looking for an accordion of sterling merit, handsome in appearance, well made and beautifully toned at prices one-half lower than you can obtain elsewhere we will recommend any accordion in this line. Why should you go to the local dealer and purchase an accordion in the usual way, paying a price which is more than half made up of intermediate dealers' profits and selling expenses, when you can purchase just as good an accordion from us at about one-half the price?

WITH EACH ACCORDION WE GIVE A COMPLETE INSTRUCTION BOOK.

No. 12E994 This is a very fine accordion, is highly polished and finished with fancy fluted mouldings, and has double bellows with eight folds, with corner protectors and nickel clasps. It is very prettily ornamented with nickel strips on the inside of the panels and is fitted with ten keys and two sets of reeds and stops We can recommend this accordion very highly as being a durable and splendidly made instrument. It is well built and handsomely finished throughout, and has great volume and mellowness of tone. We sell all accordions under our offer to refund your money and pay the express charges both ways should you decide that you did not care to keep it after a thorough trial and examination. It is exactly such an accordion as those for which you would be compelled to pay your local dealer from $3.50 to $4.00. We are satisfied that you will gladly admit this, if you could see it and test it, which you can do under our liberal offer. Size, 6x7x10¼ inches. Weight, boxed about 8 pounds.
Price **$1.65**

No. 12E995 This is a very fine accordion with fluted, ebonized mouldings and dark red panels, triple bellows, nine folds, in three alternate colors, red, black and green. Highly ornamented corner protectors, ten nickel plated keys, two sets of reeds, two stops, fancy gold paper ornamentations around the frame. Nickel plated clasps and trimmings throughout. Fitted with strips of fancy webbing. A beautiful instrument at a medium price. Should you purchase an accordion of this same grade from your local dealer he will charge you from $4.00 to $4.50 for it. Give us an opportunity of placing this splendid instrument in your hands for examination, with the understanding that we will receive it back and refund your money if it does not prove satisfactory in every particular. We guarantee the instrument to be a high class accordion in every respect. We have sold a good many thousands of these instruments, and they have given universal satisfaction. Size, 5¼x7x10¼ inches. Weight, boxed, about 10 pounds.
Price **$1.95**

No. 12E996 Fancy fluted mouldings finished in imitation ebony. Keyboard also in imitation ebony; rich deep blue panels, with gold decorations. Triple bellows of nine folds with corner protectors, bellows and all leather work being in two colors, green and brown with rich Turkish red paper between the folds. Ten long nickel keys, clasps and trimmings, three sets of steel bronze reeds, three stops. A regular $5.00 instrument and sold for this price by dealers throughout the country. We will be glad to have you compare it with any accordion your local dealer has to offer in the same grade at double the price. We offer it to you and challenge competition of the all music dealers. We sell this accordion with the understanding that if you do not find when you receive it, that you have saved at least $3.00 on your purchase, that it is the greatest bargain you ever saw, you are to return it to us, and we will refund your money and pay the express charges. Size, 6x7¼x12¼ inches. Weight, boxed, about 12 pounds. Price **$2.65**

No. 12E997 This is undoubtedly the best double row accordion for the money yet placed on the market. It is finished with fancy fluted mouldings, highly polished ebonized keyboard, and is also furnished in imitation ebony, beautiful green panels ornamented with gold pencil design, double bellows of ten folds, and each fold is protected by metal protectors. The clasps are all nickeled, and it is trimmed in three colors, red, black and green. It contains four sets of reeds, nineteen keys, four stops and four basses. This accordion is sold under our guarantee for quality and is shipped out with the distinct understanding and agreement that if it is not all that you expect or if it is not entirely satisfactory after a thorough trial and examination, it is to be returned to us at our expense and all money paid by you is to be refunded in full. This is the offer we make on all our accordions. Size, 7¼x12 inches. Weight, boxed, about 14 pounds. Price **$4.25**

No. 12E998 The same accordion as described above except that it has twenty-one keys. Weight, boxed, about 14 pounds.
Price **$4.65**

OUR WEIDLICH ACCORDIONS.

A SPLENDID LINE OF ACCORDIONS AT AN EXTREMELY LOW PRICE.

This line of accordions is manufactured by one of the best known makers of accordions in Germany, and they are all furnished for us under special contract with the manufacturers. We guarantee each instrument to be satisfactory and the purchaser has the privilege of returning any instrument he may order from us should it fail to satisfy him in any particular. These accordions are all finely finished with the metallic parts beautifully nickel plated and the frames ebonized and stained in beautiful colors. There are many imitations of these accordions on the market, but for strictly guaranteed instruments of good grade and standard reputation, our prices are far below any competition. We include, free with each instrument, a complete, valuable instruction book, by the aid of which anyone can learn this instrument without a teacher. **Your Profit Sharing Certificate** will help you get some valuable article absolutely **FREE** of cost to you.

No. 12E1001 This is the greatest bargain in our line of accordions. It is 10¼ inches high by 6½ inches wide. The case is made of imitation mahogany, beautifully polished and finished. It has ten nickel keys, two stops and two sets of reeds, and double bellows with nickel corners and clasps. Our Empress Accordions have established themselves in public favor to a wonderful extent, and this popularity is due altogether to the fact that these instruments give perfect satisfaction to all purchasers. We recommend this entire line as being something particularly fine at the extremely low prices quoted. Weight, boxed for shipment, 7 pounds. Price **$1.85**

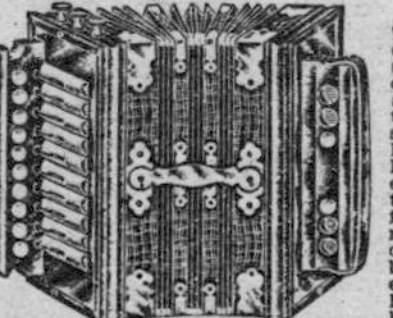

No 12E1007 We offer this accordion as something new and particularly desirable. It has three stops, controlling three sets of powerful steel bronze reeds. It has two basses and ten keys with highly nickeled valves. It has triple bellows of nine folds furnished with nickel corner protectors. The auxiliary bellows folds are covered with green and light brown pebbled leatherette, and protected with broad nickel corner protectors. The instrument is fitted with two nickel clasps to keep it closed when not in use, and the woodwork is finished in black enamel. It measures 5½ inches in depth, is 10 inches wide and 10 inches long. It is a very powerful, sweet toned instrument, and one which we are sure will be a welcome addition to this line. Weight, boxed for shipment, 10 pounds.
Price **$2.25**

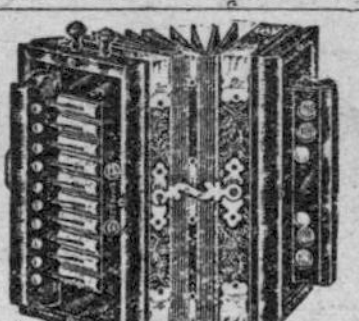

No. 12E1003 Genuine Celebrated Empress Accordion It is 9x10¼x5¾ inches in size. The frame is beautifully made, with highly polished ebonized mouldings with gilt lines; has nickel corners and clasps, ten nickel keys, leather straps, two ebonized stops, powerful double bellows with the center fold protected with nickel corners. The space will not allow us to dwell with any great length upon the merits of this instrument. It has two sets of extra broad reeds, giving it a specially strong and beautiful quality of tone. Weight, boxed for shipment, about 10 pounds.
Price **$2.35**

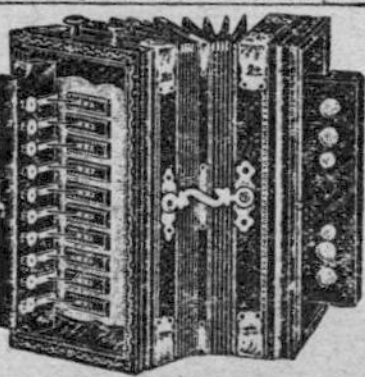

No. 12E1005 Empress Accordion. This is a handsome instrument with great musical capacity and powerful tone. It has a double bellows of eight folds bound with red cloth. It has a sunken keyboard enameled in silver and the entire instrument is finished in black and yellow enameled wood, red and green cloth ornamented with silver bronze and corners fitted with nickel protectors. It has two powerful basses, ten keys fitted with elegant mother-of-pearl buttons, two stops controlling two sets of richly toned reeds, making it suitable for all kinds of concert music. This is one of the neatest accordions in our Weidlich line and we recommend it to all who desire a handsome and durable instrument at a price which is within the reach of all. If you should buy this same accordion from the dealer you would find that he would be compelled to ask you a very much higher price than we do. This instrument is 11½ inches high, 10 inches wide and 5¾ inches deep. Weight boxed for shipment, about 10 pounds. Price **$2.75**

No 12E1004 We offer this accordion in competition with any instrument you can buy elsewhere at from $4.00 to $6.00. This accordion is 13 inches in height, 6¼ inches in width, has beautiful ebonized case; fancy cut corners, handsome gilt ornaments on corners and top. Beautiful gilt beading around same. Has two stops and two sets of reeds. Open action, nickel corners and clasps. Double bellows. This is an especially handsome instrument and we have sold thousands to professionals and amateurs alike, who desire an instrument which will meet all their demands. The workmanship and material throughout is the very best that possibly can be put into an accordion at this price, and we know that the instrument will surprise and delight you, because it is one of the very best low priced accordions on the market. In tone, quality and general appearance it is in every way equal to accordions sold throughout the country at double the price. Weight, boxed, about 12 pounds
Price. **$2.85**

No. 12E1022 The Empress Professional Instrument. This a large accordion, being 14½ inches high by 9 inches wide, with broad mahogany moulded frame, mahogany panels and keys, ornamented with handsome gilt and nickel ornaments. Clasps and corners are fully nickel plated, sunken open keyboard, double ribbed bellows, ten keys, eight stops, four sets of reeds, tuned in chords. Complete instruction book free. This is the best we offer, and is an instrument of great capacity and volume of tone. It is our very best Empress accordion, and is highly ornamented throughout. We will be glad to place this instrument in your hands and give you an opportunity to compare it with any accordion which your dealer has to offer at from $10.00 to $12.00. It is elegantly finished, and no accordion at this price on the market can in any way equal it in quality and volume of tone. Weight, boxed, about 15 pounds. Price **$6.40**

SEE OUR CUSTOMERS' PROFIT SHARING DEPARTMENT ON THE LAST PAGES OF THIS BOOK.

THE CELEBRATED PITZSCHLER ACCORDIONS.

Pitzschler is recognized as one of the best manufacturers of accordions in Germany, the home of this instrument. In presenting our line of Pitzschler Accordions we have selected five of the very large number of instruments made by this celebrated maker, and by special arrangement and by contracting for a large quantity, we are able to list them at prices representing the very greatest value ever quoted in instruments of this kind. Anyone desiring to purchase an accordion should see and try our Pitzschler's before deciding to purchase elsewhere. Most remarkably superior in richness and purity of tone, ease of action as well as details of construction.

THIS LINE OF ACCORDIONS IS SO WELL KNOWN that it is not necessary for us to say much in its favor. These instruments are in universal use not only in the United States, but throughout Europe as well. An accordion player who has one of these accordions can very well feel that he is prepared for any demand which may be made upon him. We ask you to examine the accordions kept in stock by your local dealer and we know that you will see at once that we are prepared to sell you a high class instrument for about one-half the price which he would charge you. **ALL OF THESE ACCORDIONS ARE FITTED WITH PEARL BUTTON KEYS. WITH EVERY ACCORDION WE GIVE A COMPLETE INSTRUCTION BOOK.**

No. 12E1080 **This accordion is 6½x7½x13 inches.** Is beautifully made and highly finished; has nine folds in the bellows with nickel corners; two stops and two sets of reeds, open action two basses. The keys are mounted in mother of pearl buttons, making them easily operated and especially adapted to the touch of the fingers. This instrument is beautifully decorated and a handsomer accordion cannot be found except at a much higher price than we ask. We include with each accordion a complete instruction book. This is the accordion which you will find in your local musical dealer's window priced at from $6.00 to $6.50. He cannot afford to sell such an instrument as this for any less than that amount, because he has not the same buying and selling advantage which we have. We sell so many thousands of these accordions that we can afford to be contented with a very small profit, and can sell them at the manufacturer's price with but our one small margin of profit added. Every instrument is carefully packed. Shipping weight, 10 pounds. Price..................**$3.85**

No. 12E1082 **This accordion measures 7x8½x13½ inches.** It is of ebony finish, the moulding highly polished; has ninefold triple bellows with metal corners; three sets of reeds and open keyboard; two basses. This is an exceptionally powerful accordion and a great bargain. If you will order one of these accordions, give it a thorough trial and examination and are not convinced that you could not buy it from your local dealer for less than $10.00, you can return it to us, and we will cheerfully refund the purchase price. We include with each accordion a complete instruction book. We feel justified in recommending this accordion to our customers, as it is one of the greatest triumphs for our method of sale and is certainly a magnificent bargain in every respect. Every instrument is carefully packed. Shipping weight, 10 pounds. Price..................**$4.90**

No. 12E1084 **This accordion is one of the latest designs; measures 7x9x13½ inches.** The mouldings are all finished in imitation ebony, highly polished and beautifully decorated. Has 10-fold extra broad single bellows. The end of the bellows are entirely covered with nickel and the corners are mounted with beautiful fancy brass caps, making this one of the handsomest accordions ever offered by any music dealer. This instrument has a sunken keyboard, with open action. The keys are all mounted with mother of pearl buttons. This accordion has three sets of reeds, three stops and two basses, and produces a beautiful and powerful tone. An examination of the illustration will give you some idea of the fine appearance of this accordion, but no illustration however good can give you any idea of its beautiful appearance and splendid tone. We include with each accordion a complete instruction book. Every instrument is carefully packed. Shipping weight, 11 pounds. Price.......**$5.80**

No. 12E1086 **This instrument is one of the best of the Pitzschler make.** It measures 7¾x7½x13¾ inches. The mouldings are all made in imitation ebony, highly polished and decorated. Has 10-fold, double, very powerful bellows protected with nickel corners; four stops, four sets of reeds and two basses. Sunken keyboard, open action. The keys are fitted with mother of pearl buttons, making the accordion easy to play. The tone of this instrument is especially powerful and of excellent quality. Accordions of this grade are sold generally throughout the country for about $12.00, and are considered to be great bargains at that price. Our money saving method of sale enables us to sell them to you at the wonderfully low price quoted. If you will compare this accordion with any instrument offered at the same price at the music stores you will find that everything that we have told you in regard to the great saving which we offer you is absolutely true in every respect. We recommend this instrument as the finest accordion that can be purchased anywhere in the country at this price. Shipping weight, about 20 pounds. Price.........**$6.40**

No. 12E1088 **This is the finest Pitzschler Accordion we handle.** It has fine fluted mouldings in imitation mahogany; panels genuine mahogany; all woodwork finely polished and finished; sunken open action keyboard; double row, nineteen nickel keys; heavy double bellows, with nickel protectors; nickel plated corners and clasps; four stops; four fine sets of reeds. Size, 14 inches by 8 inches. A complete instruction book free. Weight packed, about 20 pounds.
Price..................**$7.40**

No. 12E1090 **Genuine Pitzschler Accordion,** is just the same in every way as No. 12E1088, described above, but has twenty-one nickel plated keys, as shown in the illustration. The additional three keys on this instrument increase the volume of tone to a wonderful extent and give the instrument a much greater musical capacity. The slight addition in price is more than compensated for in the greater musical value which will be obtained. Weight packed, about 20 pounds.
Price..................**$7.80**

KALBE ACCORDIONS.

The name Imperial, together with the "double anchor" trade mark, on an accordion is a guarantee of its being of the very highest grade. While the price of these goods may be a trifle higher than others, the satisfaction derived from them, on account of the perfect workmanship and wearing qualities will amply repay for the difference in price, and they will be found much the cheapest in the end. We guarantee every one to arrive in perfect playing condition. You cannot make a mistake in buying a Kalbe Imperial for you get the very best article of the kind that is made. Attention is especially called to the patent simplex keys, which are made of heavy metal, in one piece, and are extremely durable. All of the styles of Imperial Accordions that we carry are supplied with patent metal bellows corners and patent folding clasps. Every part of these instruments is of the very best material and workmanship. The Kalbe Accordions are known throughout the world as standard instruments in every way, and we have sold an enormous number since we first begun to handle them. The name Kalbe on an accordion is an evidence of the finest grade, most thorough workmanship and most beautiful tone. **You will get a PROFIT SHARING CERTIFICATE with your purchase and can soon share in our profit, get some valuable article FREE, shown on the last pages, and in this way your Accordion will cost you even less money. At the same time our prices are as low as possible, guaranteed lower than you can get from any other dealer.**

Our Kalbe Accordion at $3.19.

No. 12E1100 **This is a splendid Kalbe instrument with an ebonized maple frame very handsomely finished.** It is very highly polished and is ornamented with fluted moulding. It has a powerful double bellows of eight folds, with nickel plated corner protectors. Highly polished nickel trimmings and clasps, two sets of reeds and two stops. This accordion is fitted with a tremolo or vox humana attachment, which gives the tone a wavy and undulating effect in imitation of the human voice. The tremolo can be thrown in and out of action at the will of the player by means of a lever, operated by the thumb of the right hand. The instrument is splendidly fitted throughout and will be sure to satisfy all players upon the accordion. Weight, boxed for shipment, about 10 pounds.
Price..................**$3.19**

Our Kalbe Accordion at $3.40.

No. 12E1104 **Kalbe's Imperial Miniature.** Beautifully polished ebonized frame, open action, patent simplex keys, which are very durable; double bellows, with hand painted artistic design on bellows frame, patent nickel plated corners on bellows, thus protecting the weakest part of the accordion. Ten keys, two stops, two sets of reeds and patent clasps. The size of this accordion is 10¼ inches high by 6¼ inches wide. This is a very ornamental instrument, very highly finished and attractive. It has a very beautiful tone and is accurately tuned. Its good quality has caused an immense sale as it is one of the favorites in the Kalbe line. If you desire a small accordion which will be satisfactory in every way, at a price which no dealer can approach, we take pleasure in recommending this instrument to your notice. Weight, boxed for shipment, about 10 pounds.
Price..................**$3.40**

No. 12E1112 **Kalbe Imperial Accordion.** This is an instrument of great sweetness and volume of tone, very rich in appearance with highly polished ebonized case. The corners are protected by fancy ornamental nickel bands and the corners of the bellows panels are protected in the same way. It is handsomely ornamented and decorated throughout, has triple bellows of eight folds. The bellows folds are ornamented in gold trimming and the entire instrument is one of the handsomest on the market. It has two sets of reeds and two stops and fitted on each side with patent clasps to keep the instrument closed when not in use. Size of instrument, 6¼ inches deep and 12½ inches wide. Weight, boxed for shipment about 10 pounds. Price..................**$4.40**

No. 12E1116 **Kalbe Imperial Accordion** Very fine ebonized case, highly polished, beautiful nickel plated strips all around the panels. Has double bellows of ten folds, giving great volume of tone to the instrument. Has broad nickel plated corner protectors and is a handsome instrument in every respect. Three sets of reeds and three stops. This is an instrument which the purchaser will be proud to own and pleased to show to his friends. It is 6½ inches deep and 11¾ inches wide. We believe that if you will examine some of the accordions offered by different dealers throughout the country you will find that none of them are offering accordions of this grade for less than from $10.00 to $12.00. We are prepared to ship you this instrument under our distinct promise to save you at least $5.00 on your purchase, and if you do not find when you receive it that we are doing so you can return it to us and we will cheerfully refund your money. Weight, boxed for shipment, about 12 pounds.
Price..................**$4.95**

No. 12E1120 **Kalbe Imperial Accordion.** This is a splendid instrument in every respect and has a very nicely finished ebonized case; has broad nickel plated corner protectors, and handsome clasps on each side to keep it closed when not in use. Has powerful double bellows of ten folds, four sets of reeds and four stops. Is very highly ornamented throughout and we guarantee it to give satisfaction. Size, 6½ inches deep by 11¾ inches wide. This is certainly one of the handsomest accordions on the market and is not only a beautiful musical instrument, but is a fine piece of workmanship as well. This accordion at $6.45 represents a wonderful saving in price to you. We could not afford to sell this magnificent instrument at this price if it were not for the fact that we buy them in such enormous quantities that we secure the lowest possible price, a price that represents the actual cost of making at the factory to which we add our one small margin of profit. Weight, boxed for shipment, about 12 pounds. Price..................**$6.45**

THE CELEBRATED HOHNER HARMONICAS.

In every trade, in every business, there can generally be found one firm that stands at the head of all the rest; and so in the small musical goods business, the firm of M. Hohner is known throughout the world as the largest manufacturers of these instruments. Not only do the Hohner goods enjoy a very large sale in the United States, but also in Europe and in all other foreign countries; and no business as extensive as the Hohner stands today, could possibly have been built up and held, had not the lines laid down at the very inception—of superior quality in material and superlative excellence of workmanship—been strictly adhered to during the intervening years. Through the efforts on the part of M. Hohner, Sr., founder of the business, whose adaptability to his chosen work, coupled with sterling qualities which always command success, has established a trade of which one has every reason to feel justly proud; the name Hohner, as applied to harmonicas, has become a household word in all parts of the globe. The factories of M. Hohner stand at the head of all others in this industry, and their products are unquestionably of the best materials, expert workmanship and excel in tone. The customer can, therefore, rest assured that any instrument bearing the name of M. Hohner carries with it the same good qualities that have specified the Hohner harmonicas during the past half century.

M. HOHNER

During the past fifty years the Hohner Harmonicas have been leading the market as the best mouth organs made, and have grown steadily in popularity and perfection on account of their admitted excellence. This success is not the result of chance but of superior skill and conscientious work along the line of harmonica betterment. The primary efforts of these years have been to perfect the tone. With the tone perfected, it was a comparatively easy matter to obtain the most modern machinery and to carry out all improvements and new ideas. To satisfy the constantly increasing demand for these harmonicas there are employed in the main factory and its fifteen branches over 1,500 men who turn out daily over 20,500 of these instruments. We are glad to be able to announce that we are prepared to sell these harmonicas by our great money saving method of giving our customers an opportunity to purchase them at prices away below what other dealers are prepared to make. Each one of these harmonicas is sold with our absolute guarantee of merit and we recommend them to all players who desire harmonicas of beautiful appearance and splendid tone at exceedingly low prices. The engravings shown below give but a very poor idea of the handsome appearance of these instruments, and no matter how fine the illustration may be it will always be necessary for the player to thoroughly test the tone, to prove the merits of the harmonica.

No. 12E1604 M. Hohner Marine Band Harmonica. This is a beautiful little instrument, is exactly suited to performers who desire an instrument of good compass and volume to carry in the pocket. It is handsomely and durably made and accurately tuned. It has ten single holes and twenty silver toned reeds set in brass plates. It is fitted with heavy convex brass covers with open back handsomely nickel plated. We send each one of these instruments complete with neat hinged pasteboard case. 4 inches long; furnished in A, B, C, D, E, F and G. When ordering, be sure and specify key desired.
Price.......(If by mail, postage extra 6 cents)........**19c**

No. 12E1608 Hohner's Marine Band. This is a beautiful little harmonica, 4¼ inches long, very neatly finished and durably made. It has ten double holes, twenty reeds, brass plates, nickel plated convex covers with flat sides. We send each one of these harmonicas out in a fine leatherette pouch, which closes with button clasp, the style of which has never before been used in the harmonica line. Not only is this pouch very handy and durable, but it also keeps the mouth organ in much better condition than the old style pasteboard box. Furnished in A, B, C, D, E, F and G. When ordering, be sure to state the key desired. Price........................**45c**
If by mail, postage extra, 6 cents.

No. 12E1612 Hohner's Autovalve Harp. This is absolutely a new idea in an harmonica and is fitted with a wind saving device, which is the greatest improvement that has been made in the harmonica line within the last 20 years. This improvement makes a concert harp as easy blowing as any single reed mouth organ. It has ten double holes, forty silver toned reeds, brass plates, nickel plated covers in new design, and is sent out complete in a handsome leatherette pouch shown in the engraving. 4½ inches long. Furnished in A, B, C, D, E, F and G. When ordering, be sure to state key desired.
Price....(If by mail, postage extra, 6 cents)........**70c**

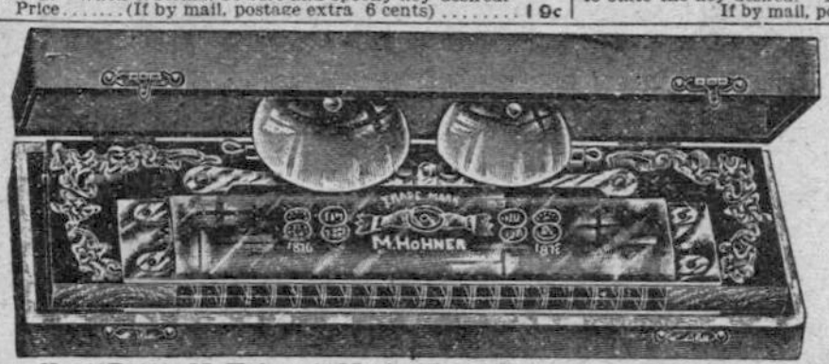

No. 12E1616 M. Hohner's Marine Band Tremolo Bell Harmonica. This is a splendid instrument with twenty double holes, forty reeds, brass plates, nickel covers, extension ends, fancy gilt stamp, tremolo with two extra clear toned bells. These bells are accurately tuned and a very beautiful effect can be obtained by using them in connection with music played on the reeds. This is one of Hohner's finest harmonicas, and it has rapidly increased in popularity with harmonica players since its appearance on the market. For performers who do considerable concert work on the stage, this instrument is invaluable and never fails to call forth admiration and applause. Each one of these harmonicas goes to the customer complete with a handsome hinged case with nickel clasps, and the instrument is very ornamental as well as of great musical value. 7½ inches long.
Price............(If by mail, postage extra, 8 cents)..................**85c**

MAKE YOUR ORDER $1.00 OR MORE, SO THAT YOU CAN GET A VALUABLE PROFIT SHARING CERTIFICATE, AND SHARE IN OUR PROFITS. SEE THE LAST PAGES.

No. 12E1620 The Hohnerphone is an harmonica with a brass horn which amplifies the tone and increases it in volume. By placing the right hand over the end of the bell the finest crescendo effect can be obtained, and much more conveniently than by using a glass tumbler for the same purpose. For concert work on the stage as well as for home playing this attachment is of great importance. The harmonica has ten double holes, forty reeds, brass plates and nickel covers. The length of the horn is 6½ inches. This is the first time that this fine instrument has been offered to the public at this wonderfully low price. Our contract with the manufacturer is such that we are able to sell this instrument by our direct from the factory to customer method and thus offer it to you for about one-half the price generally asked by dealers for the same instrument.
Price............(If by mail, postage extra, 10 cents)..............**75c**

No. 12E1628 Hohner Trumpet Call. This is one of the very latest designs in the Hohner line, and it is an instrument which will be welcomed with enthusiasm by harmonica players throughout the country. It has twenty-four double holes, forty-eight bell metal reeds, extra heavy brass reed plates and heavy nickel plated covers with flaring edges. By a special construction a beautiful tremolo effect is given to the music produced on this harmonica and we recommend this instrument for all kinds of concert work. We ship this instrument to the customer in a very fine leatherette case, and guarantee it to give satisfaction in every way. 7½ inches long. Furnished in A, B, C, D, E, F and G. In ordering, be sure to specify key wanted. Price....(If by mail, postage extra, 8 cents)...**58c**

No. 12E1624 Hohner's Triple Tremolo Harmonica. This instrument is offered in response to a demand for a harmonica which can be played in three different keys. The instrument is supplied with three sides, each tuned to a different key, and the changes from one key to another can be made instantly. The instrument is handsomely finished throughout and furnished with turning bars on each end for turning the instrument from one harmonica to the other. It has forty-eight double holes, ninety-six reeds, brass plates, nickel covers, three sides and three keys and is a wonderful instrument in many ways. The fact that this instrument is tuned in three different keys is of great importance when playing with other instruments or for accompaniments to songs. 6⅝ inches long. Price.... **$1.25**
If by mail, postage extra, 10 cents.

HOHNER'S MARINE BAND ECHO HARMONICA—ELEVEN AND ONE-HALF INCHES LONG.

No. 12E1632 This is a grand concert instrument in every respect, and is intended for those who desire an instrument of great capacity and volume of tone. It is tuned in different keys so that the performer can change instantly from one key to another. It is with a great deal of pleasure that we offer this instrument to the harmonica players of this country, and we know it will fill a long felt want and will be an instrument which will always be useful to the purchaser who requires an instrument that will meet all of the demands which may be made upon him. This instrument has sixty-four double holes, one hundred and twenty-eight reeds, brass plates, nickel plated convex covers and handsomely decorated extension ends. Each instrument comes in four keys. It goes to the customer complete with a fine case fitted with hinges and ornamented metallic clasps. We cannot recommend this instrument too highly, and desire to place it in the hands of every harmonica player who does concert playing. Like all other harmonicas which we handle, this instrument goes to the customer under our absolute guarantee of merit and with the distinct understanding that if the customer do not find, when he receives it, tha is getting an instrument of the grade as the one for which asks double the pr turned to us, and refund the money long.

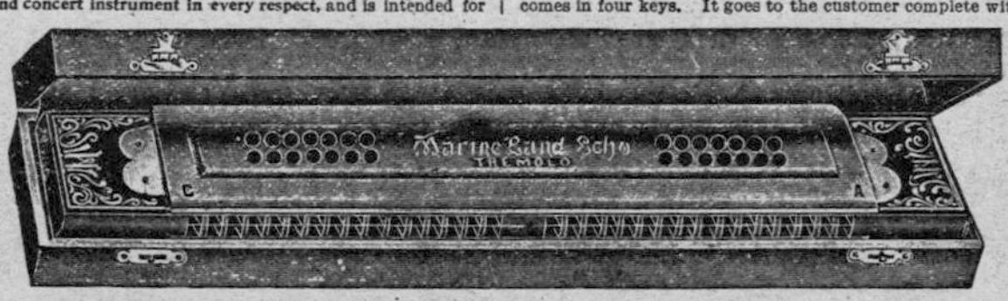

No. 12E163
If by mail, post

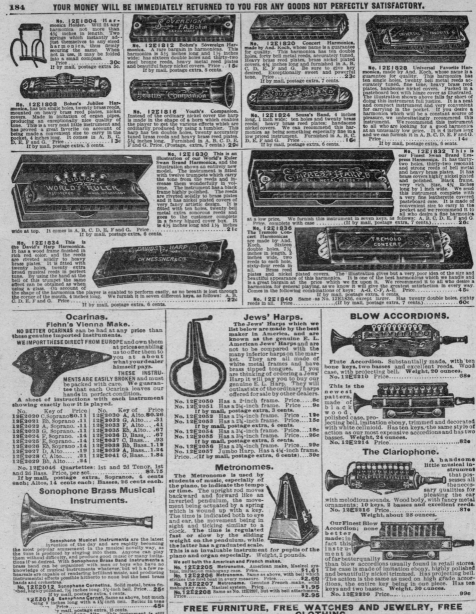

No. 12E1804 Harmonica Holder. Will fit any harmonica not more than 4¾ inches in length. Two springs which instantly adjust themselves to any sized harmonica, thus firmly securing the same. When not in use, it may be folded into a small compass. Price 30c
If by mail, postage extra 5c.

No. 12E1808 Bohm's Jubilee Harmonica, has ten single holes, twenty brass reeds, mounted on heavy brass reed plates, nickel covers. Made in imitation of organ pipes, producing an exceptionally nice quality of tone. This is a very neat little instrument and has proved a great favorite on account of being made a convenient size to carry in the pocket, 4 inches long. It comes in A, B, C, D, E, F and G. Price 13c
If by mail, postage extra, 5 cents.

No. 12E1812 Bohm's Sovereign Harmonica. A rare bargain in harmonicas. This harmonica is 5½ inches long and 1½ inches wide; has sixteen double holes and thirty-two steel bronze reeds, heavy metal reed plates and beautiful fancy nickel covers. Price .. 15c
If by mail, postage extra, 8 cents.

No. 12E1816 Youth's Companion. Instead of the ordinary nickel cover the harp is made in the shape of a horn which enables the player to get the various effects which are ordinarily produced by using a tumbler. This harp has ten double holes, twenty accurately tuned brass reeds and heavy brass reed plates. 5¾ inches long. Furnished in A, B, C, D, E, F and G. Price. (Postage, extra, 7 cents.) . 29c

No. 12E1820 Concert Harmonica, made by And. Koch, whose name is a guarantee for quality. This harmonica has ten double holes, forty bell metal reeds, accurately tuned. Heavy brass reed plates, brass nickel plated covers, 4¾ inches long and furnished in A, B, C, D, E, F and G. Be sure to give key desired. Exceptionally sweet and powerful tone. Price 23c
If by mail, postage extra, 7 cents.

No. 12E1824 Sousa's Band, 4 inches long, 1 inch wide; ten holes and twenty brass reeds; heavy brass reed plates; handsome nickel covers. We can recommend this harmonica as being something especially fine in a low priced instrument. Furnished in A, B, C, D, E, F and G. Price 16c
If by mail, postage extra, 6 cents.

No. 12E1828 Universal Favorite Harmonica, made by And. Koch, whose name is a guarantee for quality. This harmonica has ten single holes, twenty bell metal reeds accurately tuned, fine tone, heavy brass reed plates, handsome nickel covers. Packed in a pasteboard box with hinge cover as illustrated. The illustration shown above falls far short of doing this instrument full justice. It is a neat and compact instrument and very convenient for carrying in the pocket. If you desire a harmonica which will be a constant source of pleasure, we unhesitatingly recommend this instrument. We recommend this instrument to all who are looking for a good harmonica at an unusually low price. It is 4 inches long and we can furnish it in A, B, C, D, E, F and G. Price 14c
If by mail, postage extra, 6 cents.

No. 12E1830 This is an illustration of our World's Ruler Swan Brand Harmonica, and the illustration shows an entirely new model. The instrument is fitted with twelve trumpets which carry the tone from the reeds and increase them wonderfully in volume. The instrument has a black frame highly polished. The reeds are riveted solidly to brass plates and it has nickel plated covers of very fancy artistic design. It is fitted with ten holes, twenty bell metal extra sonorous reeds and goes to the customer complete in a fancy hinged cover box. It is 4½ inches long and 1½ inches wide at top. It comes in A, B, C, D, E, F and G. Price 21c
If by mail, postage extra, 6 cents.

No. 12E1834 This is the David's Harp Harmonica. It has a wood frame finished in rich red color, and the reeds are riveted solidly to heavy brass plates. It is fitted with twenty holes, twenty extra broad musical reeds in perfect tune. By using the hand at the bell of this trumpet the same effect can be obtained as when using a glass. On account of the shape of the harmonica the player is enabled to perform easily, as no breath is lost through the corner of the mouth, 4 inches long. We furnish it in seven different keys, as follows: A, B, C, D, E, F and G. Price 22c
If by mail, postage extra, 6 cents.

No. 12E1832 This is our Finest Swan Brand Empress Harmonica. It has thirty-two holes, thirty-two resonant and strong reeds of bell metal and heavy brass plates. It has brass covers highly nickel plated and polished. Black frame, very rich. Size, 4¾ inches long by 1 inch wide. We send this instrument complete with a very fine leatherette covered pasteboard case. It is made of convenient size to carry in the pocket and we recommend it to all who desire a fine harmonica at a low price. We furnish this instrument in seven keys, as follows: A, B, C, D, E, F and G. Price, complete with case .... (If by mail, postage extra, 7 cents.) 26c

No. 12E1836 The Tremolo Concert Harmonicas are made by And. Koch. Sixteen double holes, 7¼ inches in length, 2 inches wide, two reeds to each hole, sixty-four reeds in all. Brass reed plates and nickel plated covers. The illustration gives but a very poor idea of the size and beautiful appearance of this harmonica. It is one of the best harmonicas which we handle and is a great bargain at the price which we fix upon it. We recommend it to all who desire a harmonica for general playing, as we know it will give the greatest satisfaction in every way. Comes in the following combinations of keys: A-G, C-F, A-E. Price 45c
If by mail, postage extra, 6 cents.

No. 12E1840 Same as No. 12E1836, except larger. Has twenty double holes, eighty reeds in all. Price .... (If by mail, postage extra, 7 cents.) 60c

Ocarinas.

Fiehn's Vienna Make.

NO BETTER OCARINAS can be had at any price than these genuine imported instruments.

WE IMPORT THESE DIRECT FROM EUROPE and own them at prices enabling us to offer them to you at about what your dealer himself pays.

THESE INSTRUMENTS ARE EASILY BROKEN and must be packed with care. We guarantee that each Ocarina leaves our hands in perfect condition.

A sheet of instructions with each instrument showing exactly how it is played.

No.	Key of	Price	No.	Key of	Price
12E2020	C, Soprano	$0.11	12E2030	A, Alto	$0.26
12E2021	Bb, Soprano	.11	12E2032	G, Alto...	.31
12E2022	A, Soprano.	.11	12E2033	F, Alto...	.41
12E2023	G, Soprano.	.11	12E2035	Eb, Alto..	.67
12E2024	F, Soprano.	.14	12E2036	D, Bass...	.67
12E2025	E, Soprano..	.14	12E2037	C, Bass...	.93
12E2026	Eb, Soprano	.14	12E2038	Bb, Bass..	1.12
12E2027	D, Alto.....	.19	12E2039	A, Bass...	1.24
12E2028	C, Alto.....	.21	12E2041	G, Bass...	1.84
12E2029	Bb, Alto....	.24			

No. 12E2046 Quartettes: 1st and 2d Tenor, 1st and 2d Bass. Price, per set $2.75
If by mail, postage extra, Sopranos, 4 cents each; Altos, 14 cents each; Basses, 26 cents each.

Sonophone Brass Musical Instruments.

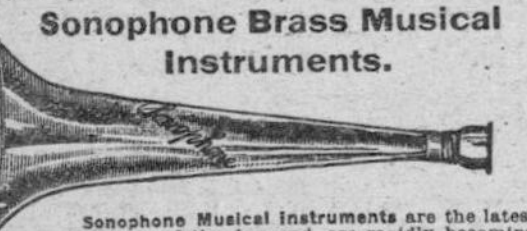

Sonophone Musical Instruments are the latest invention of the day and are rapidly becoming the most popular amusement in the musical novelty way, as the tune is produced by singing into them. Anyone can play them without difficulty, and produce good music or many imitations if so desired. With **Sonophone Brass Band Instruments** a brass band can be organized with men or boys who have no knowledge of musical instruments whatever, but with a few rehearsals are capable of rendering brilliant music, and producing instrumental effects possible hitherto to none but the best brass bands and orchestras.

No. 12E2012 Sonophone Cornetina. Solid metal, brass finished, highly polished, 7½ inches long; 3⅛-inch bell. Price... 25c
If by mail, postage extra, 4 cents.

[illegible]12E2014 **Sonophone Cornet.** Same as above, but much [illegible]being 9 inches long with a 4⅛-inch bell. Better in tone [illegible] Price 45c
[illegible]y mail, postage extra, 15 cents.

[illegible] **Sonophone Alto.** This instrument is still [illegible]E2014. Its tone is lower and deeper. Used to [illegible]to or second tenor in a quartette with great [illegible]es long, 6-inch bell. Price........ 60c
[illegible]nail, postage extra, 25 cents.

Jews' Harps.

The Jews' Harps which we list below are made by the best maker in America, and are known as the genuine E. L. American Jews' Harps and are not to be compared with the many inferior harps on the market. They are all made of white metal frames and have brass tipped tongues. If you are thinking of ordering a Jews' Harp it will pay you to buy our genuine E. L. Harp. They will outlast six of the ordinary harps offered for sale by other dealers.

No. 12E2050 Has a 2-inch frame. Price 8c
No. 12E2051 Has a 2¼-inch frame. Price 9c
If by mail, postage extra, 3 cents.
No. 12E2052 Has a 2½-inch frame. Price ... 12c
No. 12E2053 Has a 2¾-inch frame. Price.... 15c
If by mail, postage extra, 4 cents.
No. 12E2054 Has a 3¼-inch frame. Price.... 18c
No. 12E2055 Has a 3½-inch frame. Price.... 26c
If by mail, postage extra, 5 cents.
No. 12E2056 Has a 3¾-inch frame. Price.... 29c
No. 12E2057 Jumbo Harp. Has a 4¼-inch frame. Price... (If by mail, postage extra, 6 cents).... 39c

Metronomes.

The Metronome is used by students of music, especially of the piano, to indicate the tempo or time. The upright rod moves backward and forward like an inverted pendulum, the movement being actuated by a spring which is wound up with a key. The time is indicated both to eye and ear, the movement being in sight and ticking similar to a clock. **The time is regulated fast or slow by the sliding weight on the pendulum, while the latter has a graduated scale. This is an invaluable instrument for pupils of the piano and organ especially.** Weight, 2 pounds.

We sell both the American and French makes.

No. 12E2205 Metronome. American make, Maelzel system, imitation mahogany case. Price........ $1.61
No. 12E2206 Metronome. Same as above, with bell which strikes the first beat in every measure. Price........ $2.60
No. 12E2207 Metronome. Genuine French make, solid mahogany case. Maelzel system. Price........ $1.95
No. 12E2208 Same as No. 12E2207, but with bell attachment. Price........ $2.95

BLOW ACCORDIONS.

Flute Accordion. Substantially made, with ten bone keys, two basses and excellent reeds. Wood case, with projecting bell. **Weight, 20 ounces.**
No. 12E2210 Price........ 68c

This is the newest pattern, made of black wood, polished case, projecting bell, imitation ebony, trimmed and decorated with white celluloid. Has ten keys, the same style of action as our most expensive accordions and has two basses. **Weight, 24 ounces.**
No. 12E2214 Price........ 82c

The Clariophone.

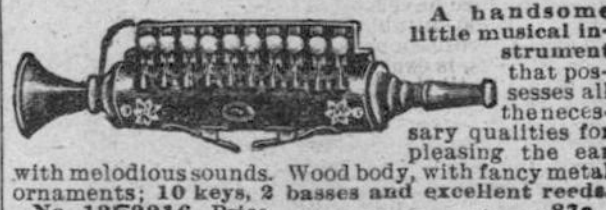

A handsome little musical instrument that possesses all the necessary qualities for pleasing the ear with melodious sounds. Wood body, with fancy metal ornaments; **10 keys, 2 basses and excellent reeds.**
No. 12E2216 Price........ 87c
Weight, about 28 ounces.

Our Finest Blow Accordion; none better made; in fact this instrument is of far better quality than blow accordions usually found in retail stores. The case is made of imitation ebony, highly polished and beautifully nickel trimmed. Has projecting bell. The action is the same as used on high grade accordions, the entire key being in one piece. Has ten keys and two basses. **Weight, 30 ounces.**
No. 12E2220 Price........ 99c

FREE FURNITURE, FREE WATCHES AND JEWELRY, FREE CLOTHING.

See the last pages for our WONDERFUL PROFIT SHARING OFFERS by which you get valuable goods ENTIRELY FREE OF CHARGE. At the same time we guarantee our prices below any kind of competition, and will refund your money immediately if you have not saved money on your purchase.

OUR BAND INSTRUMENT DEPARTMENT.

THREE SPLENDID LINES OF BRASS INSTRUMENTS FOR WHICH WE ARE SOLE AGENTS FOR THE UNITED STATES. SOLD BY OUR DIRECT FROM MANUFACTURER TO CUSTOMER PLAN, WHICH GUARANTEES AN IMMENSE SAVING TO THE PURCHASER.

EVERY INSTRUMENT WARRANTED AND SATISFACTION GUARANTEED.

EVERY INSTRUMENT FULLY WARRANTED.

YOUR MONEY RETURNED IN FULL IF OUR INSTRUMENTS DO NOT PROVE SATISFACTORY.

READ THIS LETTER.

Pittsburg, Penn. March 7th, 1905.
9 Gaskil St., Mt. Washington.

Messrs. Sears, Roebuck & Co.,
Chicago, Ill.

Gentlemen:-

Having recently organized a Concert Band in connection with the First Pentecostal Church of Pittsburg, and having, with two exceptions, purchased the entire set of instruments from you, I feel in duty bound to give this testimonial. The instruments sent on approval originally, were given a thorough test, and before placing the order, I secured the opinion of several impartial experts outside of the organization. The balance of the instruments have been carefully tested and compared with other high grade instruments and in no particular have we found them surpassed, the tone and valve action being all that could be desired. This set of instruments costs us $952.19 and we could not have purchased instruments of the same high grade from any other concern for less than $1600.00. I cannot speak too highly of your business methods and shall certainly look to you to supply future needs.

Very respectfully yours,
C. H. J. Osborne, Band Master.

THREE SPLENDID LINES OF BAND INSTRUMENTS SOLD AT PRICES NEVER BEFORE OFFERED.

EACH INSTRUMENT GUARANTEED SATISFACTORY.

WE DESIRE TO IMPRESS THE BANDMEN **of this country with the fact that we are in a position to sell them all classes of band instruments equal, and, in most cases, superior in grade to the instruments generally handled by dealers throughout the country.** Also that we are prepared to sell these instruments at an extremely small margin of profit, guaranteeing to the purchaser a saving of at least 30 per cent. There is no class of goods so susceptible of false valuation as musical instruments. The ordinary performer seldom possesses the technical knowledge necessary to discriminate between a good instrument and a poor one upon first trial, and the beginner is absolutely at the mercy of the dealer. Every one of our instruments is thoroughly examined by our buyer, who is an expert in this line, who fixes their true values before we purchase them. To this value we add our one small margin of profit, thus enabling the purchaser to buy the instruments at the manufacturers' prices with only our one small margin of profit added. Other large dealers and manufacturers find it necessary to fix very high prices upon their band instruments in order to take care of the large discounts which they make, to take old instruments in exchange, to sell upon the installment plan, and to protect their dealers in such prices as they may desire to make. We do not find it necessary to do this because we ship our goods directly to our customers, and are therefore enabled to sell these instruments at the same small profit which we make on our groceries, dry goods, etc.

UP TO WITHIN A RECENT PERIOD **the entire trade in band instruments and supplies has been in the hands of a few firms who have found it expedient to establish and maintain high prices on account of their expensive methods of handling the goods.** This method is to pass the goods from the manufacturer to the wholesaler, from the wholesaler to the retailer and finally from the retailer to the customer. Under this method it naturally follows that every dealer through whose hands the goods pass must make his profit and this profit must be included in the price which the purchaser eventually has to pay. The final result of this system is that the price paid by the customer is generally double the original cost of manufacturing. It is thus apparent at a glance that the cost of the goods to the purchaser does not depend upon the cost of making them, but depends almost entirely upon the expense incurred in getting them from the factory through the hands of the different dealers to the customer.

WE ARE OFFERING YOU **in the following pages three magnificent lines of brass instruments,** and in offering these lines we have a distinct object in view. We desire to furnish instruments which will be suitable for three classes of musicians, namely—beginners, amateurs and professionals. The first line that we illustrate, made by Marceau & Co., of Paris, is exactly suited for bands, who do not wish to invest a large sum of money until they are certain that they can learn to play acceptably. These instruments are extremely low in price and are of exceptionally good quality. A comparison of our instruments and prices through our entire line will prove that we can save bands a large amount of money if they will purchase their instruments from us.

OUR DUPONT PROFESSIONAL LINE **is considerably higher in grade and we offer them to advanced amateur and local concert bands.** We have handled this line with great success for some years and have sold a large number of sets in this country. They have never yet failed to give satisfaction, and we recommend them for the use of amateur bands who desire to do fine concert work.

WE OFFER THE PEERLESS LINE, TOURVILLE & CO. BAND INSTRUMENTS **made by Tourville & Company, of Paris, for professionals and the higher class of amateur concert bands.** We are willing to place this line in competition with any line of brass instruments on the market. In beauty of appearance and grandeur of tone they are unexcelled by any band instruments now being offered to the public. Bandmen all over the country are taking advantage of the extremely low prices which we make on these instruments and the enthusiastic praise which they have everywhere received proves to us that they are destined to become as famous in this country as they are in Europe. All of our brass instruments are fitted with French light action silver piston valves and are shipped to the customer complete with mouthpiece, music rack and instruction book. They are all short concert model and fully guaranteed by us.

OUR C. O. D. OFFER.

IN THE FIRST PLACE **we guarantee every instrument to be perfectly satisfactory, and in order that the customer may satisfy himself fully before investing his money, we send any instrument, where desired, by express C.O.D., subject to examination.** We always require a deposit of $1.00 in such cases as an evidence of good faith on the part of the purchaser. The instrument can be thoroughly tested at the express office, and if found satisfactory the customer can pay the balance of the price and take it to his home for further trial. Should the instrument not be found satisfactory at the express office, it can be returned to us, we will refund the $1.00 deposited and pay the express charges both ways.

OUR TEN DAYS TRIAL OFFER.

AFTER THE CUSTOMER HAS ACCEPTED **the instrument at the express office and taken it to his home, we allow him to try it for ten days,** and if at any time within that period it should prove unsatisfactory, it can be returned to us and we will refund the full price paid and pay express charges both ways. This fully protects the customer against any possible loss, and we make him the sole judge of the merits of the instruments. We ship all our band instruments and musical goods upon these terms, as we desire our customers to be perfectly satisfied before finally accepting their purchases.

WE PROTECT OUR CUSTOMERS AGAINST LOSS.

OUR CUSTOMERS **will see by the above terms that we are prepared to protect them in every way against all possible loss.** We desire an opportunity to demonstrate what we can do for them in the line of high grade band instruments, and we will be glad to correspond at any time with any band desiring to purchase a new set of instruments. You do not take any chances whatever in ordering from us, we take all of the risks of shipment and stand ready at all times to refund money for goods that do not prove satisfactory.

YOU WILL SHARE IN OUR PROFIT **if you send us an order from this department. We send you a profit sharing certificate showing the amount of your purchase for every order** and when these certificates amount to certain sums you can get various kinds of goods, entirely free of charge, as fully explained in the last pages of this book.

A COMPLETE COURSE IN MUSIC FREE. **With each cornet sold by us we give absolutely free to the purchaser a certificate which entitles him to a complete course, consisting of 50 weekly lessons, extending over a period of one year.** This course of lessons is so complete and thorough that the student will have no difficulty in understanding them. The lessons will be given by one of the best musical colleges in the country, the only expense to the student being the cost of the music and stationery, which we guarantee not to exceed 13 cents a week. You will find this course of lessons fully outlined and explained on page 139 of this catalogue, which we ask you to read carefully. The fact that we give this course of lessons absolutely free does not in any way affect the extremely low prices which we make on our instruments, and we shall continue to offer to our customers the very highest grade of instruments that can be secured at the very lowest possible prices.

OUR SPECIAL BAND CATALOGUE. **We especially recommend that you select your band instruments from this big catalogue rather than to cause a delay by first writing for our free Special Band Catalogue,** since we fully illustrate all of the principal instruments, and guarantee that any you may select from this catalogue will be in every way satisfactory. We also guarantee that you will find these instruments very much better than other instruments you can buy elsewhere at anything like the prices we offer, and that you will make a large saving in the cost to you. If you do not find this to be true, you are at liberty to return the instruments to us at any time within ten days, we will refund the price paid and pay the transportation charges both ways. If, however, you find yourself unable to make a selection from the illustrations and descriptions shown in this catalogue, and you feel that you would like to have a larger variety to select from with larger illustrations and more complete descriptions, then do not think of purchasing the instruments elsewhere until you first get our free Special Band Catalogue. This catalogue will be sent to you upon receipt of a postal card with request for it, and it will only be necessary for you to say, "Please send me your Band Catalogue."

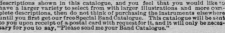

OUR CELEBRATED MARCEAU BAND INSTRUMENTS.

GREATEST BARGAINS IN BAND INSTRUMENTS EVER OFFERED TO THE BANDMEN OF AMERICA.

THIS IS ONE OF THE FINE LINES of band instruments which we have been handling for years and which have given such immense satisfaction.

MUSIC RACKS and INSTRUCTION BOOKS are sent with all of these instruments.

YOU GET A PROFIT SHARING CERTIFICATE WITH EVERY PURCHASE, AND CAN SOON GET SOMETHING VALUABLE FREE OF COST, AS EXPLAINED ON THE LAST PAGES.

WE GUARANTEE EVERY INSTRUMENT in this line and sell them on the same terms that we sell all of our other band instruments. Each horn is fitted with celebrated French piston light action valves and is splendid in model and finish. On page 185 of this catalogue you will find the terms upon which we sell these instruments fully given and also estimates of bands of different sizes, which may prove of interest to you.

Marceau E Flat Cornet.

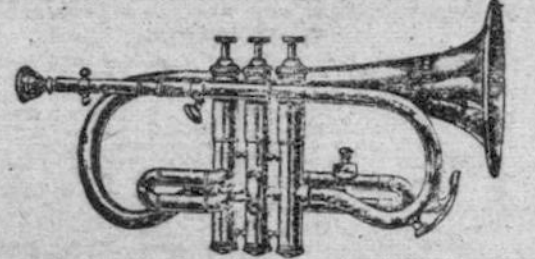

A clear toned splendid instrument for the use of leaders. Guaranteed in every way. Beautiful in model, perfect in tune and tone. The E flat cornet is never used except for playing in a band. If you wish a cornet for general playing, you should order a B flat cornet.

No. 12E7980 Brass, highly polished........$5.75
No. 12E7981 Nickel plated, highly polished 6.65

Marceau B Flat Cornet.

SINGLE WATER KEY.

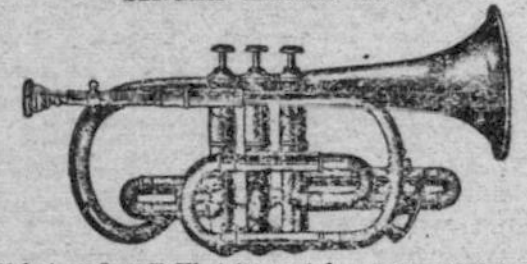

This is a fine B Flat Cornet in every way and is suitable for use in either band or orchestra. We send with it an A shank for use in orchestra, and it is a splendid instrument in every way.

No. 12E7984 Brass, highly polished $5.85
No. 12E7985 Nickel plated, highly polished 6.75

Marceau C Cornet.

We can also furnish this cornet in the key of C at the following prices:

No. 12E7988 Brass. Price....................$6.05
No. 12E7989 Nickel plated. Price............ 6.95

Artists' Model Marceau B Flat.

DOUBLE WATER KEY CORNET.

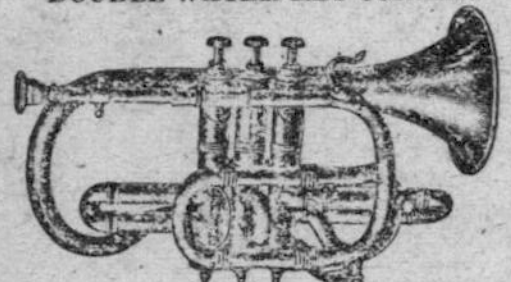

This Double Water Key Cornet has been a favorite with bandmen for a long time on account of its beautiful model and splendid tone.

No. 12E7996 Brass, polished.....................$ 9.95
No. 12E7997 Nickel plated, highly polished.. 11.05

Marceau Solo Altos.

These instruments are manufactured for solo alto purposes and have been great favorites ever since their appearance. They are easy blowing, have a splendid tone and a handsome appearance.

No. 12E8011 Brass, highly polished...........$ 9.25
No. 12E8012 Nickel plated, highly polished.... 10.75

Marceau E Flat Altos and B Flat Tenors.

These instruments are splendid for harmony work in a band, and we recommend them highly for those who desire fine altos and tenors at extremely low prices. They have a splendid tone, a beautiful model and a handsome appearance. They are perfect in tune and tone and so well constructed that they will last a lifetime. The action of the valves is extremely light and either one of these instruments can be used very nicely for solo purposes. We guarantee them to be satisfactory, and we believe that alto and tenor players will find in these instruments just what they desire at a very small cost. We desire to place them in the hands of all who are looking for something in this line at a moderate price, and we do not ask the customer to take any chances as we assume all the risk of shipping them.

No. 12E8013 Alto, brass, polished........$ 9.75
No. 12E8014 Alto, nickel, polished....... 11.25
No. 12E8015 Tenor, brass, polished...... 10.65
No. 12E8016 Tenor, nickel, polished...... 13.05

REMEMBER OUR WONDERFUL

PROFIT SHARING PLAN,

AS WELL AS THE ENORMOUS SAVING WHEN YOU BUY FROM US.

Marceau B Flat Baritone.

These instruments have been used with great success in all sorts of solo playing and general band work. A large number of bandmen have pronounced them the finest baritones on the market for less than double the price given below. Their tone is full and sonorous without being dull, and is light and clear without being too snappy. The model is handsome and the general workmanship on the instruments is all that can be desired. We recommend these baritones highly to baritone players throughout the country and we are always willing to have them compared with instruments offered by other dealers for twice the price.

No. 12E8017 Brass, highly polished.
Price.................................$12.15
No. 12E8018 Nickel plated, highly polished.
Price.................................$15.15

Marceau B Flat Bass.

These instruments can be used with excellent effect to fill in between the E Flat Bass and the B Flat Baritone. They are very effective when used in the bass solos which frequently occur in band selections, and they serve to balance up the instrumentation in excellent shape. Their tone is everything that could be asked for in an instrument of this nature and in model and finish they are splendid in every way.

No. 12E8019 Brass, highly polished..... $13.65
No. 12E8020 Nickel plated, highly polished.
Price.......................................$16.95

Marceau E Flat Bass.

We wish to call your attention particularly to this instrument and will say, without fear of contradiction, that it has never been equaled, price considered. It has a deep, rich tone and furnishes an excellent fundamental bass for any brass band. It has enough volume to answer for a large instrumentation and the tone is full and sweet enough for use, if desired, in orchestras. The model is fine and the tubing is so thoroughly braced and reinforced that it will not break down under severe use. The valves are all quick and responsive and we guarantee the instrument to be satisfactory in every particular.

No. 12E8021 Brass, highly polished $19.35
No. 12E8022 Nickel plated, highly polished.23.45

Marceau Circular Alto.

This style of alto horn has become very popular with all kinds of military and concert bands in the last few years on account of its beautiful mellow tone. It is used almost exclusively by all of the larger bands and we recommend its use to all bandmen. Its circular model makes it a very easy blowing and sensitive instrument and not only does it add to the appearance of the band but it gives the music a coloring which can be obtained in no other way. It is made by the same celebrated makers who manufacture the balance of this line, and is a valuable addition to the well known Marceau & Co. band instruments which we have handled so successfully for years. If your band does not possess altos of this model you should by all means procure them without delay, and you will find that the beautiful effect which you will obtain will much more than compensate for the small expense incurred.

No. 12E8033 Brass, highly polished.
Price.................................$17.95
No. 12E8034 Nickel plated. Price, 20.45

Marceau Valve Trombones.

These Trombones are all fine in every respect and have that deep, rich tone so peculiar to trombones. Each band should be fitted with at least two of these, as they give a coloring harmony, which could be obtained in no other way.

No. 12E8020 E Flat Alto Trombone, brass. Price... ....$ 9.75
No. 12E8024 E Flat Alto Trombone, nickel plated. Price........ 11.25

Special Hillyard Long Model Marceau Trombones.

No. 12E8029 B Flat Tenor Trombone, brass. Price..............$11.25
No. 12E8030 B Flat Tenor Trombone, nickel plated. Price...... 13.15

Marceau Slide Trombones.

We know that these instruments will appeal to all trombone players who desire good, serviceable trombones at an extremely low price. For band and orchestra use they will be found equal to all requirements. For solo playing they have given general satisfaction. The slide works with ease and rapidity and the tone is mellow and powerful.

No. 12E8031 Brass, highly polished..$6.65
No. 12E8032 Nickel plated, highly polished 8.55

$38.75 FOR OUR NEW 1906 BIKE GEAR RUNABOUT

YOUR $38.75 PROFIT SHARING CERTIFICATE will almost pay for another big valuable article. SEE LAST PAGES.

No. 11E2400

GREATLY IMPROVED FOR 1906. Combines every up to date feature of every other high grade, new, 1906 style bike runabout on the market, all our own features, all new improvements. HANDSOMER, STRONGER, EASIER RIDING, LIGHTER DRAFT, more stylish, more lasting, in every way a better runabout rig than you could buy elsewhere at $15.00 to $25.00 more money. OUR $38.75 price barely covers the cost of material and labor in our own factory with but our one small profit added. WE CAN MAKE IMMEDIATE SHIPMENT, for we carry a large number.

WE HAVE THESE RIGS IN STOCK at our factory in Evansville, Indiana, ready for immediate shipment, so if you send us your order it will take only a few days for your order to reach us and the runabout to reach you. You will find that the freight will amount to next to nothing compared to what you will save in price.

OUR OFFER.

Send us your order for one of these new 1906 style runabouts at $38.75, enclose our price; we will send the rig to you with the understanding and agreement that you can give it ten days' trial, during which time you can put it to every test, and if you do not find it perfectly satisfactory, one of the neatest, most stylish, best finished, strongest built, highest grade runabouts on the market, if you are not convinced you have gotten a better rig from us than you could have gotten elsewhere, you can return the rig to us at our expense, and we will immediately return your money, together with any freight charges paid by you.

Understand, the rig goes to you complete, every piece and part, all covered by our binding guarantee. We guarantee it to reach you promptly and in perfect order and agree to return your money if you are not satisfied in every way.

We could build a much cheaper bike runabout, but under our policy we use only the highest grades of materials throughout, extra high grade wheels, such bike axles, gear, gear irons, spokes and hangers, such body construction bracing, bolting, staying, etc., such painting, trimming and finish as goes out of no other factory, and you will find this bike wagon that you will buy from us for $38.75 will be in better condition after five years' wear than the ordinary factory grade work after one year's wear.

Below we give a detailed description of this rig, but want of space prevents our telling you all the wonderful advantages in this rig over the common bike wagons. You must see, examine and compare this bike runabout with bike wagons of other makes to appreciate how much better we make our work than is made in factories generally.

BODY. Piano box style, 23 inches wide by 54 inches long, thoroughly well made, with a hardwood body frame; corner posts and seat frame; convex panels thoroughly glued, clamped, screwed and plugged. The edges of the panels are fitted with oval edge irons at the top and at the corners; hardwood step strips are gained into sills. The seat risers are concave, in fact, the body throughout is thoroughly well made, strong and durable.

GEAR. This gear is of our own design and manufacture, we make it right in our blacksmith shop, we do not use any wood axle bed or axle caps, but use the high arch naked steel axles, made of the best steel, 15-16-inch spindles. The axles have a 3½-inch arch; they are swedged, top and bottom; spindles are the celebrated dust and mudproof, self oiling, long distance spindles, fitted with the bell collars. The fifth wheel is riveted and brazed to the front axle; the rear reach circle is connected to the center of the rear axle; the braces, running from the reaches to the point of the axle, are bolted to the reaches, and riveted and brazed to the axle, making a very strong connection. The reaches are selected second growth hickory, ironed full length, with a 3-16-inch reach plate. We use 36-inch oil tempered, easy riding, open head, full bright springs, clipped to our own pattern of Bailey body loops, the neatest designed body loops on the market. We use a heavy wrought iron fifth wheel.

WHEELS. Wheels on this job are made of selected second growth hickory, fully warranted, they are the Sarven's patent style; 36 inches front and 38 inches rear. We use wheels slightly lower than the regular wheel used on a top buggy, on account of the high arch axle. This makes the body about the regulation height from the ground. The wheels are thoroughly made throughout, the spokes are selected second growth hickory; the rims are ⅞ inch, with a screw on each side of the spoke, they are fitted with oval edge steel tires regular, the tires are full bolted between each spoke. We sell a large portion of these runabouts however, with the rubber tires, ⅞ inch, as quoted opposite.

PAINTING. We paint this runabout in the best possible manner, the body being painted a plain black with a mirror finish. We use more coats of paint and rub and polish this body more than any other runabout we build, except our No. 11E400, which gets the same treatment. We finish this job as good as any runabout sold, no matter what price you may pay. The gear is finished in the best possible manner, regularly a rich carmine, neatly striped with black. We sometimes have call for the gear to be furnished New York red, Brewster green or canary yellow, and we are always pleased to furnish this way if specified in the order.

TRIMMINGS. We upholster this job in the best possible manner, using regularly a heavy light colored Bedford cord, which is heavier than a whipcord. The seat and back are both upholstered in this material. We put springs in the cushion and use a polished 10-inch bent panel back; there is a double bent stick seat, full length velvet carpet, Stanhope seat fenders, 13-inch padded patent leather dash, good storm apron wrench, and a fine pair of shafts trimmed with leather 36 inches back from the points, round shaft straps and Bradley shaft couplings.

TRACK—4 feet 6 inches only, not built in the wide track.

No. 11E2400 Price, complete, with double braced shafts and steel tires . . $38.75
Price, fitted with ¾-inch Kelly Springfield guaranteed rubber tires 51.85
Price, fitted with ⅞-inch Kelly Springfield guaranteed rubber tires 53.40
Price, fitted with 1⅛-inch cushion rubber tires 56.85
For cheaper rubber tires, see page 201.

EXTRAS.

Pole in place of shafts, Bradley couplings $1.90
Both pole and shafts, Bradley couplings 4.25
Genuine leather upholstering 1.75
Weight, crated under 30 inches, 400 pounds. Shipped from factory.

NEW 1906 PRIZE WINNER RUNABOUT $39.95

FOR $39.95 we offer this handsome Prize Winner Boulevard Runabout with all the new 1906 improvements, with its handsome combination panel and stick seat, Stanhope seat fenders, beautiful panel back, with our new special gear construction, our new system of bracing, bolting and staying, a rig that will ride easier, run lighter and wear longer than any runabout rig you could buy elsewhere at $20.00 more money, a runabout made in our own factory and put out under our binding guarantee as the highest grade work on the market. More than a hundred little special features in the manufacture go to make a smoother, handsomer, more stylish, more lasting and better runabout in this, our Prize Winner at $39.95, than any runabout you could buy at $50.00 to $60.00.

No. 11E402

No illustration will do this rig justice. You must see it to appreciate it, and if you will send us your order for this rig at $39.95 we will send it to you with the understanding and agreement that you can give it ten days' thorough trial, and if it does not prove perfectly satisfactory, the most wonderful runabout value you ever saw or heard of, you can return it to us at our expense and we will immediately return your money.

IF YOU COULD BE IN OUR FACTORY

and see what we do in wheel construction, gear making, body making, trimming, painting, finishing, etc., to make our buggies wear longer, look new longer and give better satisfaction than any work you could buy elsewhere, you would not think of buying a runabout from your dealer at home or sending to any other house. We have these rigs on hand and can make immediate shipment. It will take but a few days for your order to reach us and the rig to reach you. The freight will amount to next to nothing compared to what you will save in price. Don't think of comparing this runabout with any of the cheap factory grade rigs on the market. Let us send it to you to examine, test and compare. If it doesn't please you and save you money, send it back at our expense and get your money back.

No. 11E400

BODY. Body is 23 inches wide by 55 inches long, it is built in the best possible manner, with a hardwood frame; corner posts and seat frame. The panels are thoroughly glued, clamped, screwed and plugged to this hardwood frame. The panels are thoroughly air seasoned bone dry stock, convex with concave seat risers; the step strips are made of hardwood, gained into the sills of the hardwood frame, body is thoroughly well made throughout.

GEAR. 15-16-inch arched axles, of the long distance pattern, with dust and mudproof bell collars, the axles are fitted with a selected hickory wood axle cap, which are cemented and clamped to the axle, then sanded down so as to make a perfect joint; has a large wrought iron fifth wheel, with selected hickory reaches, ironed full length, with a 3-16-inch reach plate; the stays and braces are of wrought iron, thoroughly bolted and clipped to the axles and reaches. A strong gear, one that has just the right proportions to give it style. We use 36-inch open head, oil tempered, easy riding springs, to which are clipped our new style body loops, the best on the market, the gear throughout could not be made better.

WHEELS On this job we use 42-inch front wheels and 46-inch rear wheels, although if desired, and it is so specified, we will furnish 40-inch front and 44-inch rear wheels. The wheels are made throughout of carefully selected second growth hickory, they are Sarven's patent style, with the rims screwed on either side of the spokes; the rims are ⅞ inch wide, fitted when furnished with steel tires, with a regular oval edge steel tire, which is bolted between each spoke to the rim, the majority of these runabouts, however, we furnish with rubber tires.

PAINTING. The way this job is painted and finished makes it one of the most attractive runabouts on the market today, we spare no pains to make this the best finished runabout that goes out from any factory. We furnish the body plain black with a mirror finish, the panel or solid part of seat is finished in a handsome dark maroon, the gear is painted a rich carmine, striped with black. The combination of painting makes it one of the most attractive and stylish runabouts on the market today, it has just enough color to make it attractive, at the same time it is not in any sense of the word flashy. We can furnish, when so ordered, the gear painted New York red, with black striping.

TRIMMINGS. This job we upholster regularly with a heavy light colored Bedford cord, which is a heavy whipcord. We furnish springs in the cushion, and upholster it in the best possible manner, and, as shown in the illustration, we upholster in a very fine pattern, with a 10-inch bent panel back. The job comes complete with a full length velvet carpet, padded patent leather dash, good storm apron, Stanhope seat fenders, Bradley shaft couplers, and a nice pair of shafts trimmed with leather 36 inches back from the points, and round shaft straps.

TRACK—4 feet 8 inches narrow or 5 feet 2 inches wide.

No. 11E400 Price, complete, with double braced shafts and steel tires $39.95
Price, fitted with ¾-inch Kelly Springfield guaranteed rubber tires 53.05
Price, fitted with ⅞-inch Kelly Springfield guaranteed rubber tires 54.60
Price, fitted with 1⅛-inch cushion rubber tires 60.60
For cheaper rubber tires, see page 201.

No. 11E402 This job is the same as No. 11E400, except it has solid panel seat, as shown in small illustration. Price 38.95

EXTRAS.

Pole in place of shafts, Bradley couplings $1.90
Both pole and shafts, Bradley couplings 4.25
Genuine leather upholstering in place of Bedford cord 1.75
Weight, crated under 30 inches, 400 pounds. Shipped from factory.

SOLID COMFORT CONCORD RUNABOUT.

DONT FAIL TO STATE WIDTH OF TRACK

$37.85

No. 11E225

BODY—27 inches wide by 56 inches long, making it very roomy. Body is extra well made of selected material, with hardwood sills, beams and seat frames, ironed and braced; seat is extra wide and deep, with a high, solid panel spring back. Seat measures 32¼ inches across top of cushion.

GEAR—Full Concord gear, with three reaches made of carefully selected second growth hickory, ironed and braced; 1-inch long distance axles, fitted with dust and mudproof bell collars. The axle caps are selected hickory, cemented and clipped to the axles; extra long Concord side, 1⅜-inch four-plate springs, hung on equalizers, both front and rear; an extra strong gear throughout.

WHEELS—Sarven's patent, second growth hickory spokes, ⅝-inch screwed rims, fitted with oval edge steel tires, 38 inches front and 42 inches rear. If ordered, we can furnish compressed band wood hubs, also 40-inch front and 44-inch rear wheels.

PAINTING—Body and seat panels, black, nicely striped, shutter work on the seat risers being painted carmine to harmonize with the gear. Gear, blood carmine, neatly striped. Can furnish Brewster green gear if ordered, with shutter work on the seat risers to correspond.

TRIMMINGS—Seat cushion and back upholstered in genuine leather over solid panel spring back and box spring cushion, nicely tufted. Can furnish whipcord upholstering if ordered. Velvet carpet, handsome patent leather dash, quick shifting shaft couplers, double braced shafts, leather trimmed.

TRACK—4 feet 8 inches or 5 feet 2 inches.

No. 11E225 Price, complete, with shafts and steel tires........ **$37.85**
Price, fitted with ⅝-inch Kelly Springfield guaranteed rubber tires. **52.50**
Price, fitted with 1-inch Kelly Springfield guaranteed rubber tires. **55.70**

EXTRAS.

Pole in place of shafts.. **$ 1.60**
Both pole and shafts.. **3.75**
Can furnish with a three-bow leather quarter top for................ **11.25**
Weight, crated under 30 inches, 400 pounds. Shipped from factory.

OUR MODEL TOP BUGGY.

$28.90

No. 11E02

While this is the best buggy that was ever turned out of any vehicle factory for the money, you can secure far greater value for every dollar invested, by spending a few more dollars and buying our American Beauty Top Buggy at $38.50, shown in large illustration on page 206, or still better, one of our higher grades.

BODY—Piano body, 23x55 inches; convex side panels; hardwood frame, with step strips gained into sills; seasoned poplar panels, screwed, glued and plugged.

GEAR—Axles, 15/16 inch, double collar, fantailed; hickory wood parts, with axle beds cemented and clipped to axles; three and four-plate oil tempered elliptic springs.

WHEELS—Sarven's patent, ⅝-inch rims, fitted with ¾-inch oval edge steel tires, bolted between each spoke; 38 inches front and 42 inches rear. Can furnish 40 inches front and 44 inches rear if ordered.

TOP—Three-bow, rubber drill roof and quarters, with black enameled back stays, lined; dark green wool faced head lining; roll up back curtain, unlined side curtains. Can furnish four-bow top if ordered.

PAINTING—Body black, nicely striped and decorated, as shown in illustration; gear painted dark Brewster gear green, with neat striping to match body.

TRIMMINGS—Latest pattern cushion and back of Union body cloth, over solid panel back, with springs in both cushion and back; seat ends padded and lined; drill boot, carpet, storm apron, wrench, anti-rattlers and drill dash.

TRACK—4 feet 8 inches or 5 feet 2 inches.

No. 11E02 Price, complete, with double braced shafts and steel tires, **$28.90**

EXTRAS.

Pole in place of shafts.. **$1.60**
Both pole and shafts.. **3.75**
Genuine leather cushion and back.. **1.25**
Weight, crated under 30 inches, 400 pounds. Shipped from factory.

OUR $26.95 TOP BUGGY.

DONT FAIL TO STATE WIDTH OF TRACK

$26.95

No. 11E01

While this top buggy is covered by our binding guarantee and is a better buggy than you could buy elsewhere at $10.00 to $15.00 more money, to get the greatest value possible for your money, we advise you by all means, to add a few dollars and order our American Beauty at $38.50, as shown in the full page illustration, or one of our still higher grades.

BODY—23x55 inches, piano style, convex side panels, frame of hardwood, step strips gained into sills, panels of well seasoned poplar, glued, screwed and plugged.

GEAR—Axles, 15/16 inch, double collar, fantailed; hickory axle caps, reaches and spring bars; three and four-plate elliptic springs.

WHEELS—Selected hickory, Sarven's patent, ⅝-inch rims, fitted with ¾-inch oval edge steel tires, bolted between each spoke; 38 inches front and 42 inches rear.

TOP—Three-bow, enameled bow sockets, drill quarters, stays and roof. Dark green head lining and lined back stays; roll up back curtain with black knob fasteners; drill side curtains.

PAINTING—Body, plain black; gear, dark Brewster gear green, with two-line stripe on wheels.

TRIMMINGS—Imitation leather cushion and back, nicely upholstered on solid panel spring back and spring cushion, padded and lined seat ends; storm apron, drill boot, black enameled duck dash, wrench, anti-rattlers and carpet.

TRACK—4 feet 8 inches or 5 feet 2 inches.

No. 11E01 Price, complete, with double braced shafts and steel tires, **$26.95**

EXTRAS.

Pole in place of shafts.. **$1.60**
Both pole and shafts.. **3.75**
Weight, crated under 30 inches, 400 pounds. Shipped from factory.

OUR RIVAL LEATHER QUARTER TOP BUGGY.

$29.95

No. 11E05

This top buggy is covered by our binding guarantee, is the best leather quarter top buggy that was ever produced for the money, is better than you could buy for $10.00 or $15.00 more elsewhere, but we advise you by all means to spend a few dollars more and order our American Beauty Top Buggy, shown in large full page illustration on page 206, or still better, one of the higher grade rigs.

BODY—23x55 inches, piano body; hardwood frame, with step strips gained into sills; seasoned poplar panels, glued, screwed and plugged. Can furnish Corning body if ordered.

GEAR—15/16-inch double collar steel axles, fantailed; hickory reaches, ironed full length; axle beds cemented, sanded and clipped to axles; elliptic oil tempered springs, three-plate front, four-plate rear, clipped to Bailey body loops.

WHEELS—38 inches front and 42 inches rear; ⅝-inch rims, fitted with oval edge steel tires, full bolted, Sarven's patent hub. Can furnish 40-inch front and 44-inch rear wheels if ordered.

TOP—Three-bow, leather quarter top, with leather back stays; drill roof and back curtain; all wool faced head lining; roll up back curtain; drill side curtains. Can furnish four-bow top if ordered.

PAINTING—Body black, with fancy stripe and design on seat risers. Gear, dark Brewster green, striped to match. Will furnish carmine or New York red gear if ordered.

TRIMMINGS—Seat and back upholstered with good heavy cloth, over solid panel spring back, with springs in cushion. Seat ends padded and lined; boot, patent leather dash and lined panels, wrench, storm apron, etc.

TRACK—4 feet 8 inches or 5 feet 2 inches.

No. 11E05 Complete, with double braced shafts and steel tires.... **$29.95**

EXTRAS—SAME AS No. 11E02.

OUR AMERICAN BELLE.

$35.70

Four-Bow Top same price.

No. 11E104

BODY—Piano body, 23x55 inches, side panels 8 inches deep; hardwood frame with step strips mortised into sills; corners screwed, glued and plugged; concave risers, oval edge iron on top of panels, floor rabbetted into sills. Round seat corners.

GEAR—Axles, 1⅛ inch, fantailed, dust and mud proof long distance spindles; axle beds cemented and clipped to axles; double reach, ironed full length; full bearing fifth wheel; three and four plate 36-inch oil tempered elliptic springs; Bailey body loops.

WHEELS—Sarven's patent wheels, ⅞-inch screwed rims, fitted with ¼-inch oval edge steel tires, bolted between each spoke; 38 inches front and 42 inches rear. Boxes set true by hydraulic pressure in white lead. Perfect dish guaranteed. Can furnish wheels 40 inches front and 44 inches rear if ordered.

TOP—Three-bow, leather quarters and back stays; quarters cut deep and back stays lined and padded, with fancy needle work on lining; roof and back curtain heavy rubber; nickel curtain fasteners; wool head lining and lined back curtain. Comes complete with good side curtains. Can furnish four-bow top when ordered.

PAINTING—Body, black with neat decoration and striping. Gear, Brewster gear green, neatly striped. Will furnish blood carmine or New York red gear if ordered.

TRIMMINGS—Seat cushion and back upholstered with heavy dark green body cloth over coil spring cushion and solid panel spring seat. Seat ends padded and lined. Leather if specified, see extras. Storm apron, boot, quick shifting shaft couplers, carpet, lined panels, wrench, leather dash and leather trimmed shafts.

TRACK—4 feet 8 inches or 5 feet 2 inches. Net weight, about 290 pounds.

No. 11E104 Price, with double braced shafts and steel tires..... $35.70
Price, with ¾-inch Kelly Springfield guaranteed rubber tires....... 48.80
Price, with ⅞-inch Kelly Springfield guaranteed rubber tires....... 50.35
Price, with 1-inch Kelly Springfield guaranteed rubber tires...... 53.55
For cheaper rubber tires, see page 202.
EXTRAS SAME AS No. 11E124.
Weight, crated under 30 inches, about 450 pounds. Shipped from factory.

OUR SOLID COMFORT BEAUTY.

$38.70

No. 11E124

Three-Bow Top same price.

Roomy Phaeton Seat.

BODY—Piano body, 25x55 inches, side panels 8 inches deep. Hardwood frame with step strips mortised into sills. Corners screwed, glued and plugged. Concave risers, oval edge iron on top of panels, floor rabbetted into sills; round seat corners; large, roomy seat. Extra wide seat, 32¼ inches across top of cushion.

GEAR—Axles, 1⅛ inch, dust and mud proof long distance spindles; axle beds cemented and clipped to axles; double reach, ironed full length. Full bearing fifth wheel, three and four-plate oil tempered elliptic springs, 36-inch sweep. Bailey body loops.

WHEELS—Sarven's patent wheels, 1-inch screwed rims fitted with ¼-inch oval edge steel tires, bolted between each spoke; 40 inches front and 44 inches rear. Made of second growth hickory; fully warranted. 38 inches front and 42 inches rear if ordered.

TOP—Four-bow, leather quarters and back stays; quarters cut deep and back stays lined and padded, with fancy needle work on lining; roof and back curtain heavy rubber. Nickel curtain fasteners. All wool head lining and lined back curtain. Comes complete with good side curtains.

PAINTING—Body, black, with neat decoration and striping; gear, Brewster gear green, neatly striped. Will furnish blood carmine gear.

TRIMMINGS—Upholstered with heavy dark green body cloth over coil spring cushion and solid panel spring back. Storm apron, boot, quick shifting shaft couplers, carpet, lined panels, wrench, 15-inch leather dash and shafts leather trimmed.

TRACK—4 feet 8 inches or 5 feet 2 inches. Net weight, about 315 pounds.

No. 11E124 Price, with double braced shafts........................$38.70
Price, with ⅞-inch Kelly Springfield guaranteed rubber tires.... 53.35
Price, with 1-inch Kelly Springfield guaranteed rubber tires.... 56.55
For cheaper rubber tires, see page 202.

EXTRAS.

Pole in place of shafts.......$1.60 | Both pole and shafts..........$3.75
Genuine leather upholstering.. 1.65
Weight, crated under 30 inches, about 400 pounds. Shipped from factory.

OUR EASY RIDING SOUTHERN BUGGY.

THE MOST POPULAR BUGGY IN THE SOUTH.

BIGGEST SELLER IN SOUTHERN STATES.

$36.65

Three-Bow Top same price.

No. 11E119

BODY—Piano box body, 19x55 inches, hardwood frame, with step strips gained into sills; seasoned poplar panels, glued, screwed and plugged; convex seat panels and concave seat risers. Can furnish 23-inch body if ordered.

GEAR—Axles, 1⅛ inch, long distance with dust and mud proof bell collar; axle caps cemented, sanded and clipped to axles; long, easy riding side springs running from front to rear axle; no reaches.

WHEELS—Sarven's patent, ¾-inch screwed rims, fitted with oval edge steel tires; 38 inches front and 42 inches rear. Can furnish 36 and 40 inches if ordered. Can furnish ⅞-inch rims if ordered.

TOP—Two and one-half bow, leather quarters and back stays; heavy rubber roof and back curtain; padded and lined back stays; fancy stitched; back curtain lined; good heavy side curtains, all wool head lining; nickel curtain fasteners. Can furnish three-bow if ordered.

PAINTING—Body, plain black; gear, Brewster gear green, neatly striped. Can furnish New York red or blood carmine gear. Will stripe body if wanted.

TRIMMINGS—Seat and back upholstered with heavy, dark green keratol leather over Georgia drop back and spring cushion. Leather if specified, see extras. Padded and lined seat ends; double bar nickel arm rails; carpet and lined panels; patent leather dash, boot, storm apron, quick shifting shaft couplers, shafts leather trimmed, wrench, etc.

TRACK—4 feet 8 inches or 5 feet 2 inches.

No. 11E119 Price, with double braced shafts and steel tires...... $36.65
Price, fitted with ¾-inch Kelly Springfield guaranteed rubber tires. 49.75
Price, fitted with ⅞-inch Kelly Springfield guaranteed rubber tires, 51.30
Price, fitted with 1-inch Kelly Springfield guaranteed rubber tires, 54.50
For cheaper rubber tires, see page 202.
EXTRAS—SAME AS No. 11E124.
Weight, crated under 30 inches, 400 pounds. Shipped from factory.

OUR BREWSTER SIDE BAR BUGGY.

$36.45

Three or Four-Bow Top same price.

No. 11E160

BODY—Piano box style, 19 inches wide by 55 inches long. Hardwood frame; seasoned poplar panels, screwed, glued and plugged. Steps are of hardwood, gained into sills. Can furnish 17 or 23-inch body if ordered.

GEAR—1⅛-inch steel axles, fantailed; fitted with celebrated dust and mud proof bell collar long distance spindles; axle beds cemented and clipped to axles; single reach, ironed and braced; full bearing fifth wheel; combination King coil and Brewster side bar springs.

WHEELS—Sarven's patent, 38 inches front and 42 inches rear; ¾-inch screwed rims fitted with oval edge steel tires, full bolted between each spoke. Can furnish wheels 40 inches front and 44 inches rear, or 36 inches front and 40 inches rear if ordered. Can also furnish ⅞-inch rim wheels.

TOP—Two and one-half bow, leather quarters and back stays. Quarters cut deep and back stays lined and padded. Roof and back curtain, heavy rubber. All wool head lining. Comes complete with side curtains. Can furnish three or four-bow if ordered.

PAINTING—Body, black, neatly striped and decorated, as shown in illustration. Gear, blood carmine, neatly striped. Can furnish Brewster gear green if ordered.

TRIMMINGS—Seat and back upholstered with keratol leather. Lined seat ends. Georgia drop back and box spring cushion; carpet, panels lined, full leather dash, boot, storm apron, seat handles, quick shifting shaft couplers, nickel top prop nuts, double bar rope arm rail and seat rail, wrench, and shafts leather trimmed.

TRACK—4 feet 8 inches or 5 feet 2 inches. Net weight about 290 pounds.

No. 11E160 Price, complete, with double braced shafts..........$36.45
Price, with ¾-inch Kelly Springfield guaranteed rubber tires.... 49.55
Price, with ⅞-inch Kelly Springfield guaranteed rubber tires.... 51.10

EXTRAS.

Pole in place of shafts......$1.60 | Both pole and shafts.........$3.75
Weight, crated under 30 inches, about 400 pounds. Shipped from factory.

$38.50 AMERICAN BEAUTY

DON'T BUY A CHEAPER BUGGY, for while our lower priced top buggies are covered by our binding guarantee, and are MUCH BETTER IN QUALITY AND MUCH LOWER IN PRICE than you can buy elsewhere, and will give satisfaction in every case, **You Get More For Your Money When You Order Our AMERICAN BEAUTY at $38.50.**

WHILE WE SELL A GOOD TOP BUGGY, our own make, under our binding guarantee at $26.95, a better top buggy than you can buy in Chicago or elsewhere at $35.00; the difference in price between our cheapest top buggy of our own make, $26.95, and the price we ask for the American Beauty, $38.50, a difference of $11.55, permits of our adding so very much to the quality of the rig. This difference of $11.55 goes so far in improving every part, the wheels, the ironing, the gear throughout, the body, the painting, finishing, upholstering, gives us such an opportunity to add to the durability, the wearing qualities, the appearance, the very life of the buggy, that we know positively if you could be at our factory and see this, our new 1906 Model American Beauty Top Buggy, placed side by side with any buggy we can possibly build and sell at a lower price, you would gladly pay the difference. You wouldn't think of selecting the cheaper grade. Place this American Beauty, if you please, alongside of our cheapest top buggy, the $26.95 rig. While our cheapest $26.95 top buggy will look better, be better and wear better than any top buggy you can buy elsewhere at $35.00, yet you will see where in actual wearing qualities, in appearance, finish and all, there is to the man who buys the rig for his own use, more than double the difference we ask, more than twice the $11.55 difference. This difference of $11.55, the exact difference between our price on the new 1906 Model American Beauty and the cheapest top buggy we build, represents only the actual difference in cost to manufacture, the difference in the cost of the raw material, the fine workmanship and beautiful finish. Therefore, fully in the interest of the buyer, to anyone selecting a top buggy for their own use, we advise you to act as we know you would act could you be in our factory and examine the finished work, the different materials used, the workmanship and finish that goes onto the finished rigs, then we know you would select one of our higher grade buggies, either this, our $38.50 American Beauty, or one of the still higher grades.

ON OUR AMERICAN BEAUTY, a fine rig, the difference of $11.55 in manufacturing cost between the American Beauty and our cheapest top buggy, enables us to make this investment where it will do the most good and in offering you the American Beauty Top Buggy we have gone so far in this direction that we have decided to show this buggy in a large illustration with as complete a description as the page space will permit, in the hope that our customers, in selecting a buggy for their own use, rather than decide to select a top buggy at from $26.95 to $32.00, will pay just a few dollars difference, $38.50, and let us send them our really high grade new 1906 Model American Beauty for only $38.50.

IF YOU HAVE BEEN THINKING OF BUYING A TOP BUGGY at say from $27.00 to $35.00, and you will spend a few dollars more and select the American Beauty at $38.50, we know you will always be much better pleased with your selection. We know you will appreciate that the $2.00 extra you will put in the top, the trimmings, the wheels, gear and body, have been carefully, judiciously and honestly expended, placed only where they will add to the wearing qualities, beauty, comfort, style and lasting satisfaction the buggy will give.

OUR AMERICAN BEAUTY OFFER. If you have been thinking of buying a top buggy for less than $38.50, and are just a little bit undecided, as an inducement for you to get this beautiful rig in preference to any buggy we could possibly build for you at a lower price, as a guarantee that you will, after you have seen and used the American Beauty, feel confident that you have gotten at least two dollars of real intrinsic value for every dollar the American Beauty has cost you more than a lower priced buggy, we make you this special American Beauty buggy offer:

SEND US YOUR ORDER for an American Beauty top buggy, exactly as illustrated and described, enclose our price $38.50, and we will send you the buggy immediately, carefully crated; we will guarantee the buggy to reach you promptly and in perfect condition. If it should by chance be damaged in any way by the railroad company, we will agree to immediately take it back and return your money, although, the way we paper, crate and pack our buggies, they rarely ever reach their destination with even the slightest scratch or mar. After you have received the American Beauty buggy, which will be but a very few days, for our sales on this buggy are so large we always keep a stock on hand ready for immediate shipment, you then pay the railroad agent the freight charges which, by the way, amount to next to nothing compared with what you save in price; for example, the freight charges to points one hundred to five hundred miles from our factory at Evansville, Indiana, on a top buggy will be from one dollar to four dollars greater or lesser distances in proportion. You take the buggy home, give it ten days' trial, compare it with buggies made or sold by others at $20.00 to $30.00 more money, compare it, if you can, with any buggy you can buy anywhere at the same or a lower price, and if you are not perfectly satisfied if you do not find the American Beauty buggy equal or better than any buggy you could buy elsewhere at a much higher price if you are not convinced as between selecting the American Beauty at $38.50 and any top buggy at a lower price that you have made a wise selection, that for the slight difference in cost you have gotten really many times the difference in real intrinsic value, return the buggy to us at our expense of freight charges, and we will immediately return your money together with any freight charges paid by you; and remember, the American Beauty is covered by our written, binding one-year guarantee, as explained in this catalogue, and it is made of such material and built in such a way that with care it will really last a natural lifetime.

No. 11E105

THE ABOVE ILLUSTRATION, engraved by our artist from a photograph, will give you some idea of the appearance of this buggy; although pictures differ but little, while the different grades of work set side by side differ greatly. Space will not permit us to describe this buggy in detail, therefore we urge you to let us send you a buggy to try and examine, especially this, our American Beauty at $38.50, or one of our higher grades. If you want a top buggy please don't order a cheaper grade. In your own interest take this one or a better one. REMEMBER you get a PROFIT SHARING CERTIFICATE good for valuable articles FREE to you.

BODY. Body is 23 inches wide, 55 inches long, piano box, hardwood solid construction frame, hardwood corner post seat frame and cross pieces. There are more than twenty points in the construction of this body that takes it entirely out of the class of buggies made by others or any buggy we could sell you at a lower price; in short, it combines every up to date high grade feature.

GEAR. This gear is made better and is better than any gear you could buy elsewhere in a buggy at anything like the price, superior in many details to any gear we could furnish you in a top buggy at a lower price. It is hung on 15-16-inch steel axles, long distance, dust and mudproof Bell collar pattern, fitted with micrometer gauge for exact pitch and shape. The system of fitting the hickory axle caps, truing the gear to perfect track and gauge, our special high grade fifth wheel, specially finished elliptic end springs, full 36 inches; special iron body loops, double hickory reach, ironed full length; in short, the almost innumerable features go in the building up of this high grade gear puts it in a class by itself and prompts us to urge that you do not select lower priced work. Either order this buggy or one of our still higher grade rigs.

WHEELS. Sarven's patent second growth hickory wheels, carefully selected ⅞-inch rim, screwed on each side of spokes throughout, ¼-inch thick oval edge steel tire, set by our own special process, front wheels are 38 inches high, rear wheels 42 inches, or if desired, front wheels 40 inches high, rear wheels 44 inches. In the making of our wheels for this and the higher grade buggies we go farther than any other factory and make them perfect and make them well, but space prevents our giving but very little detail.

TOP. This top is longer, deeper and more graceful than you will find on any other work; has extra deep genuine leather quarters, genuine leather back stays, heavy rubber roof and back curtain, back stays are padded and lined, fancy stitched and scalloped, lined with wool head lining, lined back curtain. We use four roll-up straps to hold up the rear curtain. Good heavy side curtains. It is trimmed with nickel curtain fasteners, comes in three bows or we will furnish with four bows if desired. On this higher grade work we use such tops as you will find on no ordinary top buggy.

PAINTING. Body is painted black, neatly striped and decorated; fancy seat risers: gear we furnish regularly painted blood carmine, handsomely striped with black. When desired we can furnish the gear painted Brewster gear green or New York red. If you could follow this or any of our higher grade buggies through our painting department you would understand why our customers tell us that our buggies look better after three years' wear than the ordinary buggy will look after six months' wear.

TRIMMINGS. This is one of the most stylishly trimmed buggies in our entire line. You will note that it is trimmed in fancy colored keratol leather with a deep roll around the back, center is made up of small biscuits, neatly tufted The sides are plain, the whole effect is pleasing, back fitted with plenty of springs. It is easy riding and very attractive. Seat cushion is furnished in nicely tufted biscuit pattern, fitted with plenty of springs so as to make it easy riding. Seat ends are padded and lined. Back is of a solid panel pattern, handsomely finished, and when desired we upholster this buggy in fancy colored cloth in place of keratol leather, without any extra charge. This buggy is trimmed throughout in the best possible manner, nickel dash rail and top prop nuts, quick shifting shaft couplers, velvet carpet, inside body panels are lined with carpet, storm apron, boot, wrench, antirattlers and leather trimmed shafts.

TRACK. 4 feet 8 inches or 5 feet 2 inches. Net weight, about 280 to 290 pounds. If you have been in the habit of paying $35.00 or less for a top buggy, then this is by all means the top buggy we want you to order. It is so much better in every way than any buggy we could sell you at $35.00 or less, and so entirely different from any buggy you could buy from any other house even at $45.00 to $50.00. It differs in that it is large and roomy, nothing skimped to save cost, wide and roomy seats, liberally large body, dash, top, etc., a wonderfully substantial gear and wheels, especially good trimming and upholstering, a beautiful job of painting, accurately gauged, light draught, exceedingly comfortable, easy riding, positively the lowest price we have ever been able to name on such high grade work, and we furnish this wonderful value in our American Beauty at $38.50 and upward, according to the specifications as listed above.

EXTRAS.

Pole, in place of shafts	$1.60
Both pole and shafts	3.75
Genuine leather cushion and back in place of keratol	1.50
Full leather top with rubber side curtains in place of leather quarter top	3.15

No. 11E105 Price, complete, with double braced shafts and steel tires	$38.50
Price, complete, fitted with ¾-inch Kelly Springfield guaranteed rubber tires	51.60
Price, complete, fitted with ⅞-inch Kelly Springfield guaranteed rubber tires	53.15
Price, complete, fitted with 1-inch Kelly Springfield guaranteed rubber tires	56.35

For cheaper rubber tires, see page 201.

Shipping weight, crated under 30 inches, about 450 pounds. Shipped from factory.

Our Long Tug Spring Wagon Harness, $26.00 and $27.60

Bridles, ⅝ inch, box loop checks, square patent leather blinds, round winker braces, round side reins, with face piece or overcheck bridle, if wanted, and tie strap; **lines**, 1 inch wide by 20 feet long, with snaps; **hames**, low wood hames, iron bound, Hayden's holdback rigs, hame straps and spread straps; hame tug, 1¼ inches long, box loop, scalloped point, champion trace buckle; **traces**, 1¼ inches wide by 6 feet long, raised center, round edge finish, cockeyes sewed in; **breeching**, single strap hip breeching to snap under the horse in the martingale ring and buckle round crupper fork. Folded bellybands, 1½-inch martingales, with collar strap, 1¼-inch breast straps, with snaps and slides and buckle, adjustable; **pads**, racket coach pad, harness leather bottom, patent leather housings, iron tree, double and stitched skirts to buckle in the trace buckle, ⅞-inch turnback, scalloped, with crupper to buckle on, ⅞-inch heavy hip straps with patent leather drop; **trimmings**, brass and japan only. Weight of harness, packed for shipment, about 80 lbs.

No. 10E916 Price, without collars, japan trimmings **$26.00**

No. 10E917 Price, without collars, brass trimmings **27.60**

Extra for roller snaps on breast straps **$0.20**

Extra for 1½-inch traces **1.00**

Deduct from price of harness for breeching, if not wanted, $2.00.

Our New York Double Truck Harness, $35.00.

Bridle, ¾ inch, short, double and stitched check, with Concord flat reins, harness leather blinds, fancy spotted face piece, round winker stays, short flat reins, to check up over the hames, brass fronts and rosettes; **lines**, 1-inch wide, 15 feet long, heavy select line leather; **hames**, Scotch brass ball top, clip and staple; **traces**, 1¾ inches, double and stitched with three rows of stitching, 5 feet 8 inches long with a 30-inch heel chain; **breeching**, heavy folded harness leather body, 1½-inch heavy layer double and stitched, 1¼-inch back straps, single strap on the hames, 1-inch double hip straps, 1½-inch double and stitched side backers, snapping in the breeching and running to the neckyoke; **trimmings**, japan or brass. Weight of harness, boxed for shipment, about 95 to 100 pounds.

No. 10E919 Price, without collars, japan trimmings **$35.00**

No. 10E920 Price, without collars, brass trimmings **$36.40**

Extra for 2-inch traces **1.00**

Our Buffalo Heavy Concord Truck Harness, $28.25 and $33.16.

Bridles, ¾-inch, long check, spotted face piece, Concord blinds, round winker brace, **flat rein**; **lines**, fine selected Dundee oak leather, 1 inch wide and 18 feet long, with snaps; **hames**, red Concord bolt hames with brass balls; **traces**, 6 feet long, 12-inch chain, heavy selected stock, double and stitched, 1⅜-inch, with heel chains, 1⅜-inch bellyband billet and heavy folded bellyband, traces made as shown in illustration; **breeching**, heavy folded body, with 1½-inch layer; 1-inch side strap running to hame, 1-inch double hip strap, 1-inch side strap to snap in pole strap ring under horse; **breast straps**, 1½-inch, with roller snaps; **pole straps**, made Chicago style. This harness is full size for 1000 to 1250-pound horse. Shipping weight, boxed, about 88 pounds.

No. 10E940 Price, per set, without collars **$28.25**

Add extra for 1¾-inch traces on No. 10E940 .... **1.50**

No. 10E942 **Extra Heavy Concord Harness**, same style as No. 10E940 only made with 2-inch traces, 6 feet long, with 12-inch chains; extra heavy breeching, 1¼-inch side straps; 1¼-inch back straps; 1¼-inch double hip straps; 1¾-inch breast straps and martingale roller snaps; 1¼-inch by 20-foot lines; ¾-inch bridle, Dandy hame brass balls, balance of harness japanned trimmed. Price, without collars **$33.16**

Add for extras to price of harness. If wanted with 1¾-inch traces, deduct **1.50**

Add extra for harness large enough for 1400 to 1600-pound horse **3.00**

For No. 10E3480 curled hair face collars, each add **3.10**

For price on collars, see collar page.

Montana Concord Harness, $30.65.

This harness is largely used in Montana, Oregon, Idaho, Utah and, in fact, all the western states.

How this harness is made: This harness is made with great care, with extra heavy fine Concord pad stuffed bottom; brass loop on pad with buckle and billet end to buckle into trace buckle. **Made to be used on bolt hames. Quality of leather:** Leather used in this harness is our fine **Delhi oak tanned leather. Stock is well selected, carefully cut and blacked, and we think it is equaled by none and superior to all other grades of harness leather for this particular style and grade of harness.**

Bridles, ⅞-inch, box loop, Concord blinds, spotted face piece, heavy front, round winker brace, ⅞-inch flat rein to throw over hame; **hames**, No. 6 oiled Concord bolt hame, lace box loop hame tug, Champion trace buckle, 1¼-inch bellyband billet, heavy folded bellyband; **pads**, fine Concord pad, stuffed bottom, **brass** loop on top of pad; **traces**, 6 feet long, fine selected Dundee oak leather, 1½-inch double and stitched point, 2⅛-inch single strap body with cockeye sewed on; **breeching**, heavy folded body, with wide layer, 1⅛-inch back strap to run through loop on pad to hame, ⅞-inch double hip strap, ⅞-inch side strap to snap under horse in pole strap ring; **lines**, selected line leather, well made, 1-inch by 18 feet, with snap; **breast straps**, 1¼ inches, with roller snap, pole strap 1½ inches, with collar strap, spread strap and ring, tie strap. This harness is full size for 1000 to 1250-pound horses. Extra large harness for 1400 to 1600-pound horses will cost you $3.00 extra. Weight, about 85 pounds, boxed for shipment.

No. 10E950 Price, per set, without collars **$30.65**

Add extra for brass ball hames, brass trimmed bridles, brass buckle shields, balance of harness full japanned trimmed **$3.50**

Add for 1⅜ inches by 2⅛ inches single strap body traces **$1.50**

Add for 2 inches by 2¼ inches single strap body traces **$2.25**

Add for toggle on traces in place of cockeye .... **.50**

For No. 10E3480 collar, each, add **3.10**

For price on collars, see collar page.

Our Great Western Corcord Harness, $32.85.

Bridles, ⅞-inch box loop cheeks, heavy crown piece, fancy spotted face piece, heavy round fronts, large harness leather Concord blinds, round winker stays, flat side reins to check over the hames; **lines**, 1 inch wide, extra heavy, 18 foot long, buckles and billets, with snaps; **hames**, oil Concord bolt hames, 1¾-inch hame tugs, extra heavy, box loop, Champion trace buckle, and heavy billet, heavy folded bellyband; **traces**, 1¾ inches, Concord style, double and stitched point, 2½-inch extra heavy single strap body with toggles; **pads**, Concord style, stuffed bottom with double round leather loop for back strap, buckles into the trace buckle; **breeching**, extra heavy harness leather, folded body with heavy layer, double and stitched, 1⅛-inch double back strap, running to the hames, 1-inch double hip straps, 1⅛-inch double side straps to snap in the martingales, breast straps, 1½ inches, 5 feet long with snaps and slides, (roller snaps 22 cents extra), 1½-inch martingales, with leather safe at the ring, with heavy collar straps; **trimmings**, full japan trimmed. Weight of harness, boxed for shipment, about 85 pounds.

No. 10E955 Price, without collars **$32.85**

Extra for lines 1⅛ inches wide by 20 feet long .... **.65**

Extra for heavy 2-inch traces, double and stitched point, 2¾-inch single strap body **2.75**

Extra for roller snaps on breast straps .... **.22**

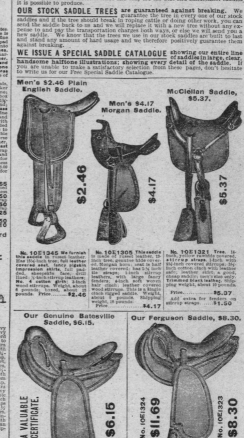

DEPARTMENT OF SADDLES.

WE GUARANTEE to furnish you a better saddle for less money than you can possibly get elsewhere. Our saddles are strictly high class, thoroughly well made, guaranteed in every way and our prices are lower than the wholesaler's or jobber's, very much lower than the retail dealer's prices. Our line of stock saddles is especially adapted for western and southwestern trade and they are the best and handsomest saddles it is possible to produce.

OUR STOCK SADDLE TREES are guaranteed against breaking. We guarantee the tree in every one of our stock saddles and if the tree should break in roping cattle or doing other work, you can send the saddle back to us and we will replace it with a new tree without any expense to and pay the transportation charges both ways, or else we will send you a new saddle. We know that the trees we use in our stock saddles are built to last and stand any amount of hard usage and we therefore positively guarantee them against breaking.

WE ISSUE A SPECIAL SADDLE CATALOGUE showing our entire line of saddles in large, clear, handsome halftone illustrations; showing every detail of the saddle. If you are unable to make a satisfactory selection from these pages, don't hesitate to write us for our Free Special Saddle Catalogue.

Men's $2.46 Plain English Saddle.

$2.46

No. 10E1345 We furnish this saddle in russet leather. Has 15½-inch tree; full leather covered seat, fancy pigskin impression skirts, full padded, sheepskin face, drill lined; ⅞-inch stirrup leathers; No. 4 cotton girth; 3-inch wood stirrups. Weight, about 6 pounds; boxed, about 12 pounds. Price **$2.46**

Men's $4.17 Morgan Saddle.

$4.17

No. 10E1305 This saddle is made of russet leather, 13-inch tree, genuine hide covered. Morgan horn; seat is half leather covered; has 1-⅛ inch tie straps; 1-inch stirrup leathers, with large fancy fenders; 4-inch soft woven hair cinch; leather covered wood stirrups. This is a single cinch rigged saddle. Weight, about 9 pounds. Shipping weight, 18 pounds. Price **$4.17**

McClellan Saddle, $5.37.

$5.37

No. 10E1321 Tree, 14-inch, yellow rawhide covered, **stirrup straps**, 1-inch with 2½-inch covered stirrups; 3½-inch cotton cinch with leather safe; leather skirt; a good, cheap saddle; men's size only. **Trimmed black leather.** Shipping weight, about 10 pounds.

Price **$5.37**

Add extra for fenders on stirrup straps **$1.50**

Our Genuine Batesville Saddle, $6.15.

No. 10E1322 Full leather covered leather seat, heavy stirrup straps, large fenders and round skirt, round loop on the near side, leather covered stirrups. **Tree**, 13-inch Mulley Morgan; **seat**, full leather covered; **tie strap**, 1½ inches to tie; **cinch**, 4-inch gray soft hair; **stirrup straps**, 1½ inches to buckle with large fender attached; **stirrups**, 3-inch wood stirrup, leather hooded cover. Weight of saddle, about 10 pounds. Packed for shipment, about 20 pounds. Price **$6.15**

Our Ferguson Saddle, $8.30.

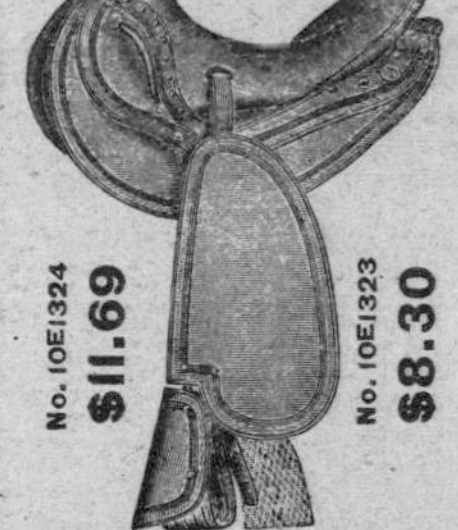

Made on a high grade Mosby tree, full leather covered, round leather skirt, round hand loop on the near side, heavy tie straps and large fender attached. This saddle is made in two sizes on a 14-inch tree and on a 17-inch tree. This is one of the very popular styles of single cinch saddles. **Tree**, 14-inch Mosby; **seat**, full leather covered; **tie straps**, 1¼ inches to tie; **cinch**, 4-inch white woven cotton; **stirrup straps**, 1¼ inches to buckle with large fender attached; **stirrups**, 3-inch wood covered stirrups. Weight of saddle, about 12 pounds. Packed for shipment, 20 pounds.

No. 10E1323 Price of saddle **$8.30**

No. 10E1324 Same style saddle as No. 10E1323, only extra large on a 17-inch Mosby tree, for men weighing from 180 to 225 pounds. Weight of saddle, about 19 pounds. Packed for shipment, about 27 pounds.

Price **$11.69**

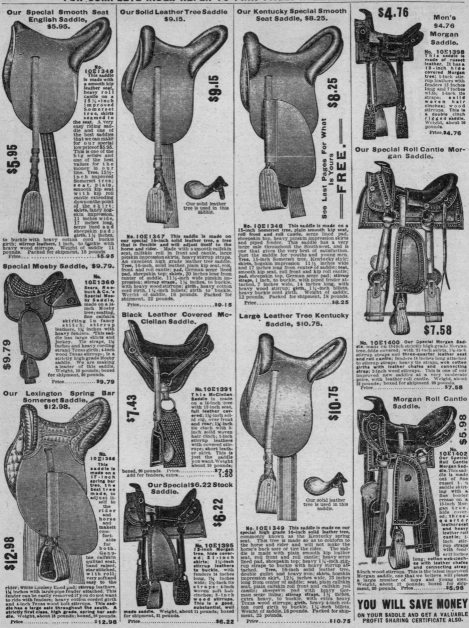

Our Special Smooth Seat English Saddle, $5.95.

No. 10E1346 This saddle is made with a smooth kip leather seat, heavy roll cantle on a 15½-inch improved Somerset tree, skirts seamed to the seat. A very easy riding saddle and one of the best saddles that we can make for our special low price of $5.95. This is one of the big sellers and one of the best values for the money in our line. Tree, 15½-inch improved Somerset tree; seat, plain, smooth kip seat with kip roll cantle extending down on the point of the skirt; skirts, fancy hogskin impression, 11 inches wide, 17 inches long, serge lined and sheepskin pad; girth, 1¼ inches, to buckle with heavy cotton cord buckle girth; stirrup leathers, 1 inch, to buckle with heavy wood stirrups. Weight of saddle 11 pounds. Packed for shipment, 18 pounds

Price........................$5.95

Special Mosby Saddle, $9.79.

No. 10E1360 Sears, Roebuck & Co.'s Special Mosby Saddle, made on a 14-inch Mosby tree; seating, fine calfskin skirting in fancy stitch; stirrup leathers, 1⅛ inches with heavy fenders. This saddle has large skirts and jockey. Tie straps, 1⅛ inches and heavy cording strand Texas girth; 4-inch wood Texas stirrups; is a strictly high grade Mosby saddle. We are making a leader of this saddle. Weight, 10 pounds; boxed for shipment, 20 pounds.

Price..............$9.79

Our Lexington Spring Bar Somerset Saddle, $12.98.

No. 10E1386 This saddle is made on a 17-inch spring bar tree, the best tree made, to adjust itself to the rider and horse and make it comfortable for both. Genuine calfskin quilted seat, hand raised, star stitched, with roll; very soft and easy to the rider; white Lindsey lined pad; stirrup leathers, 1⅛ inches with large pipe fender attached. This fender can be easily removed if you do not want to ride with fenders; heavy cotton corded girth and 4-inch Texas wood bolt stirrups. This saddle has a large sale throughout the south. A strictly first class, high grade, spring bar saddle. Weight, about 16 pounds; boxed, 26 pounds.

Price............ ....$12.98

Our Solid Leather Tree Saddle $9.15.

Our solid leather tree is used in this saddle.

No. 10E1347 This saddle is made on our special 16-inch solid leather tree, a tree that is flexible and will adjust itself to the horse and rider. Made with a smooth calfskin seat, calfskin roll in front and cantle, large pigskin impression skirts, heavy stirrup straps. An excellent high grade leather tree saddle. Tree, 16-inch, solid leather, plain kip seat, roll front and roll cantle; pad, German serge lined pad, sheepskin top; skirts, 20 inches long from center of saddle, 11½-inch wide pigskin impression; stirrup straps, 1⅛ inches, to buckle, with heavy wood stirrups; girth, heavy cotton cord girth, 1¼-inch billets; girth to buckle. Weight of saddle, 16 pounds. Packed for shipment, 22 pounds.

Price..............................$9.15

Black Leather Covered McClellan Saddle.

No. 10E1391 This McClellan Saddle is made on a 14-inch tree with 12-inch seat, full leather covered; 1⅛-inch solid rig, over front and rear; 1⅛-inch tie cinch with 5-inch solid woven hair cinch; 1-inch stirrup leathers with covered stirrups; short leather skirt. This is just the saddle you want. Weight about 10 pounds; boxed, 20 pounds. Price..................$7.43

Add for fenders, extra... .... 1.50

Our Special $6.22 Stock Saddle.

No. 10E1395 13-inch Morgan tree, hide covered; 21-inch skirts; 1⅛-inch stirrup leathers to buckle, with fenders 14 inches long, 7½ inches wide; 1⅛-inch tie straps; 4-inch woven soft hair cinches; 3-inch wood stirrups. This is a good, substantial, well made saddle. Weight, about 11 pounds; boxed for shipment, 21 pounds.

Price..................................$6.22

Our Kentucky Special Smooth Seat Saddle, $8.25.

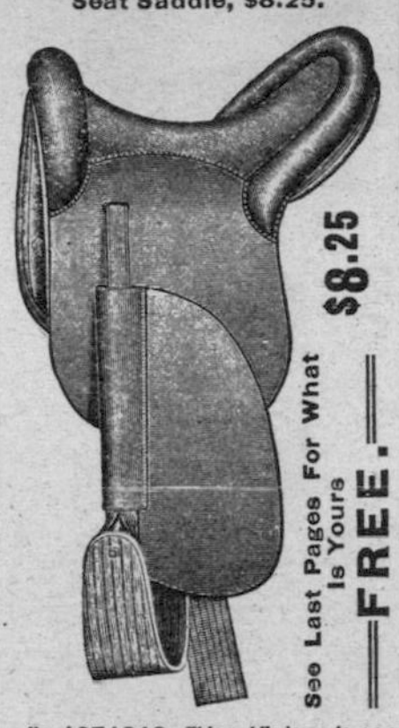

See Last Pages For What Is Yours FREE.

No. 10E1348 This saddle is made on a 15-inch Somerset tree, plain smooth kip seat, roll front and roll cantle, serge lined pad, sheepskin top, heavy pigskin impression skirts and piped fender. This saddle has a very large sale throughout the Southwest, and is one that gives the very best of satisfaction. Just the saddle for youths and young men. Tree, 15-inch Somerset tree, Kentucky style; skirts, hogskin impression 11½ inches wide and 17 inches long from center of saddle; seat, smooth kip seat, roll front and kip roll cantle; pad, sheepskin top, German serge pad; stirrup straps, 1 inch, to buckle, with piped fender attached, 7 inches wide, 14 inches long, with heavy wood stirrup; girth, 1¼-inch billets, heavy buckle cord girth. Weight of saddle, 12 pounds. Packed for shipment, 18 pounds.

Price..........................$8.25

Large Leather Tree Kentucky Saddle, $10.75.

Our solid leather tree is used in this saddle.

No. 10E1349 This saddle is made on our special high grade 16-inch solid leather tree, commonly known as the Kentucky spring seat. This tree is made so as to conform to the horse and rider and will not make the horse's back sore or tire the rider. The saddle is made with plain smooth kip leather seat, roll front and roll cantle; heavy serge lined pad, sheepskin top; heavy 1¼-inch stirrup straps to buckle with heavy stirrup attached. Tree, 16-inch solid leather tree, double gullet and heavy iron; skirts, hogskin impression skirt, 12½ inches wide, 23 inches long from center of saddle; seat, plain calfskin seat, plain calfskin roll front and calfskin roll cantle; sheepskin pad with heavy German serge lining; stirrup straps, 1¼ inches, extra heavy, to buckle, with extra heavy Texas wood stirrups; girth, heavy 4-inch cotton cord girth to buckle, 1¼-inch billets. Weight of saddle, 18 pounds. Packed for shipment, 25 pounds.

Price...............................$10.75

Men's $4.76 Morgan Saddle.

No. 10E1398 This saddle is made of russet leather. It has a 13-inch hide covered Morgan tree; 1-inch stirrup leathers with fenders 13 inches long and 7 inches wide; 1-inch tie straps; solid woven hair cinches; wood stirrups. This is a double cinch rigged saddle. Weight, about 10 pounds.

Price,$4.76

Our Special Roll Cantle Morgan Saddle.

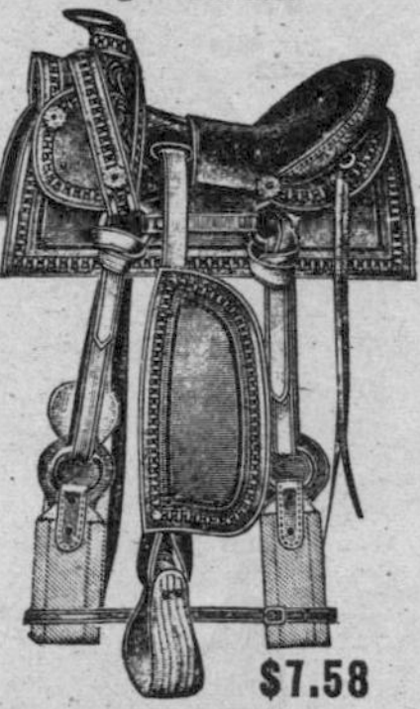

No. 10E1400 Our Special Morgan Saddle, made on 13-inch strictly high grade Morgan tree, hide covered; with 21-inch skirts, 1⅛-inch stirrup straps and three-quarter leather seat and roll cantle; fenders 14 inches long attached to stirrup straps; heavy tie straps, web cotton girths with leather chafes and connecting strap; 3-inch wood stirrups. This is one of our improved new saddles at a very moderate price, with leather roll cantle. Weight, about 12 pounds; boxed for shipment 20 pounds.

Price..................................$7.58

Morgan Roll Cantle Saddle.

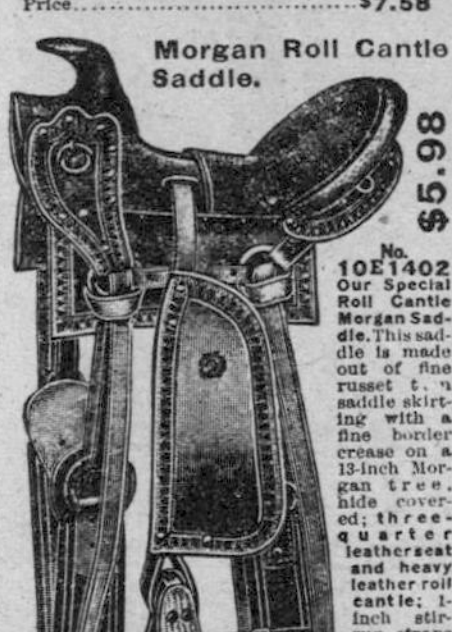

No. 10E1402 Our Special Roll Cantle Morgan Saddle. This saddle is made out of fine russet tan saddle skirting with a fine border crease on a 13-inch Morgan tree, hide covered; three-quarter leather seat and heavy leather roll cantle; 1-inch stirrup straps with fender 13 inches long; cotton web cinches with leather chafes and connecting strap; 3-inch wood stirrups. This is the latest improved Morgan saddle, one that we believe will please a large number of boys and young men. Weight, about 12 pounds; boxed for shipment, 20 pounds. Price................$5.98

YOU WILL SAVE MONEY

ON YOUR SADDLE AND GET A VALUABLE PROFIT SHARING CERTIFICATE ALSO.

Our Improved Morgan Full Leather Covered Seat Saddle, $5.97.

$5.97

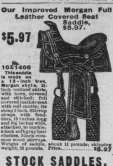

No. 10E1406 This saddle is made on a 13-inch tree, Morgan style, 21-inch unlined skirts, with horn, covered and stitched; full covered leather seat with roll cantle; tie strap 1 inch. Stirrup straps, with fenders, 15 inches long and 8½ inches wide, attached, to buckle; 4-inch soft gray hair cinches, 3-inch common wood stirrups. Weight of saddle, about 11 pounds; shipping weight, 22 pounds. Price................$5.97

STOCK SADDLES.

Our Missouri Saddle, $8.52.

No. 10E1415 Our Special Missouri Saddle, made on 14-inch steel fork, hide covered tree. Skirts 21 inches long, good, solid stock, unlined, with bars of tree lined with wool sheepskin. Stirrup leathers, 1½ inches, to buckle; fenders, 14 inches long and 8 inches wide; tie straps, 1 inch; 4-inch cotton cinches, 4-inch Texas wood stirrups. Weight, about 15 pounds; boxed for shipment, 30 pounds.

Price.....$8.52

Our Special Kansas Run-about Saddle, $9.36.

No. 10E1416 This saddle is made of selected skirting, seat and jockey in one piece, covered rings, solid, full length stirrup straps, steel horn and roll cantle, wool lined bars. Tree, 4-inch steel fork and hide covered; bar sheepskin covered; seat and jockey in one piece; full covered roll cantle, 21-inch skirts, 1½-inch stirrup straps, with fenders 14 inches long and 8 inches wide; 1½-inch tie straps; 4-inch soft gray cinches, and 4-inch plain Texas stirrups. Weight, about 18 pounds; shipping weight, 28 pounds. Price.............................$9.36

Our Popular $8.58 and $9.63 Saddle.

Our Gunnison Stock Saddle.

No. 10E1430 Our Gunnison Stock Saddle. We have lately improved this saddle by making it on a new steel fork Gunnison tree, hide covered, 14½-inch tree. The leather used in this saddle is a fine quality oil tanned skirting, well selected and well finished. The stirrup fenders and jockey are fancy stamped. The saddle is made with 22½-inch skirts and lined with an extra quality wool sheepskin, with steel strainer and roll cantle, raised and beaded gullet, 1¾-inch stirrup straps to buckle, with large fenders attached, size of fender, 14 inches long, 7 inches wide; 1¾-inch latigo straps, to tie, on a double cinch rig, genuine Mexican strong hair cinches and 3-inch California wood stirrups, leather bottom. This saddle is one of our leading sellers and, when compared with other saddles of like price, you will find it superior in quality of material and in workmanship. Weight, 20 pounds, net, and 45 pounds boxed for shipment. Price...................$10.62

Winfield Special Stock Saddle, $17.44

No. 10E1440 Made of selected all tan Oregon saddle skirting. All parts of saddle are given special attention where extra heavy strain is required. Made on a 15-inch Winfield steel fork tree, hide covered, with 24-inch sheepskin wool lined skirts. Full extended seat; seat and jockey in one piece. Steel strainer and bound cantle. Stirrup leathers, 2-inch to lace, with fenders, 15 inches long and 8 inches wide, attached. Tie straps, 1½-inch on near side, to tie, and 1¾-inch, to buckle, on the off side; 20-strand white Angora hair cinches; wool lined chafes and connecting straps; leather covered steel stirrups. We will make this saddle in roll cantle if wanted, but will always send bound cantle unless otherwise ordered. A strictly up to date good saddle, a saddle that would sell for $5.00 to $8.00 more than our special price. Weight, about 25 pounds; boxed, 35 pounds. Ea. $17.44

No. 10E1420 Our Popular Saddle is made on a thoroughly first class steel fork tree, with high horn. This tree is made for general purposes, for all kinds of ordinary use, and will stand a great deal of rough work. The leather used in the making of this saddle is a fine oil tanned skirting, well selected and nicely finished. The tree is 14½ inches (this is the only size we make this saddle), with 22½-inch unlined skirts. The seating is of solid leather, fancy stamped. The saddle is made with edged creasing throughout, with steel strainer and roll cantle, 1½-inch stirrup straps, with large fenders attached. Size, 15 inches long, 7 inches wide. It is double rig to tie with 1¾-inch tie straps, 4-inch woven cinches and 4-inch Texas wood stirrups. Weight of saddle, about 16 pounds; packed for shipment, about 30 pounds. We can highly recommend this saddle as being one of the best cheap stock saddles we handle, and is sure to give excellent service.

Price, with unlined skirts............$8.58

No. 10E1425 The same saddle made with sheepskin wool lined skirts.

Price..................................$9.63

Casper Big Heavy Stock Saddle, $29.99.

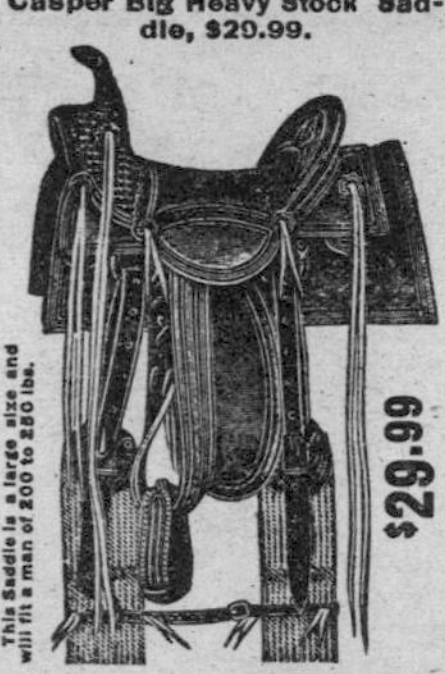

This Saddle is a large size and will fit a man of 200 to 250 lbs.

No. 10E1442 Made on a 17-inch Visalia tree, heavy steel fork, rawhide covered. We will also make this saddle on a 17-inch Nelson tree if wanted. Large, heavy 30-inch skirts; sheepskin wool lined. Extended full seat; bound cantle; seat and jockey in one piece. This is an extra large, roomy saddle, for a big, heavy, stout rider; 3-inch stirrup leathers, to lace, with extra heavy steel leather covered stirrups. Large, heavy fender, 18 inches long, 9½ inches wide, attached. Heavy, 20-strand, white hard hair cinches; wool lined chafes and connecting straps. 1¾-inch tie straps, 7 feet long on the near side, to buckle, and 2 inches wide on the off side, to buckle. We will make any changes in cinches wanted on this saddle; either all cotton or back band webbing cinches, but will send cinches listed regular with the saddle unless otherwise specified. We will also make this saddle in roll cantle if wanted. Remember, this saddle is made of an extra quality of fine Oregon heavy oil skirting, with full extended seat; seat and jockey in one piece. This saddle is made with lariat strap on the off side, and head string on the inner side. Weight of this saddle is about 38 pounds; shipping weight, 50 pounds. This saddle will sell in most places, from $45.00 to $65.00, and at our low price it is a special bargain.

Price...................................$29.99

Our Kit Carson Cowboy Saddle.

$20.76

No. 10E1445 This saddle is strictly new, made with full extended seat and jockey in one piece. Made on a 15-inch new San Juan tree, steel fork and hide covered. This is one of the new San Juan trees, 25-inch sheepskin lined skirts. Stirrup leathers, 2½ inches, to lace, with fenders, 16 inches long and 8½ inches wide, attached. Tie straps, 1½ inches wide on the near side and 1¾ inches, to buckle, on the off side. Cinches, California strand, white angora hair. XC iron stirrups, made in bound or roll cantle. Will always send bound cantle unless ordered roll cantle. Fine quality of saddle skirting. Every part of the saddle is well selected and well finished. Strictly high grade throughout. Weight, about 28 pounds; shipping weight, 40 pounds.

Price....................................$20.76

No. 10E1483 This saddle is made on a strictly high grade 15-inch Cherokee steel fork tree, hide covered; bastos 24 inches long and 11½ inches wide, wool lined; full seat and jockey in one piece; bound or roll cantle (will always send bound cantle unless ordered roll); full solid back rigged saddle; 2-inch stirrup leathers to lace with fenders 15x7 inches attached; 2½-inch Texas wood stirrups with leather bottom; 1¾-inch latigo on the near side and 1½-inch latigo on the off side. Covered rings and solid rigging in one piece. Cinches, California gray hair, with leather chafes and connecting strap. Weight of saddle, 20 pounds; boxed for shipment, 35 pounds.

Price....................................$16.69

Omaha Saddle, $15.38.

Improved La Platte Tree. New Omaha Style.

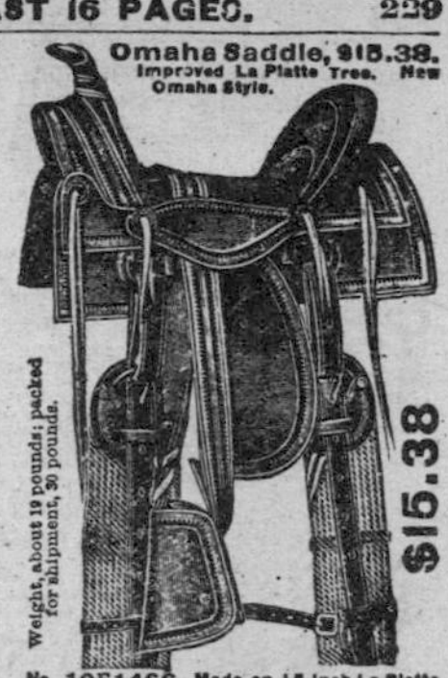

Weight, about 19 pounds; packed for shipment, 30 pounds.

No. 10E1466 Made on 15-inch La Platte steel fork tree, hide covered, solid leather seat, roll cantle, stitched jockey; 23½-inch wool lined skirts; tie strap to buckle, 1⅝ inches on near side, 1¾ inches on off side; double rig covered rings. Cinches; 20-strand, white angora hair, with chafes and tongue and connecting strap; stirrup straps, 2 inches to lace, with fender 14½ inches long attached; 4-inch wood Texas stirrups, leather covered. Price....$15.38

Our Special Kiowa Stock Saddle.

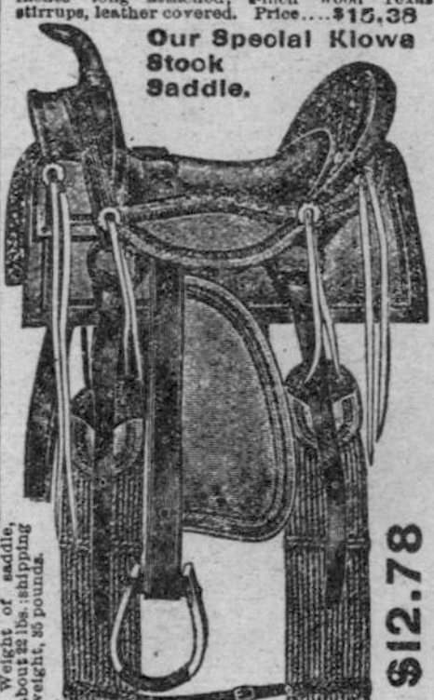

Weight of saddle, about 22 lbs.; shipping weight, 35 pounds.

No. 10E1454 This saddle is made on an Improved Kiowa tree, 14½ inches, steel fork and hide covered. Has the latest improved bars and is a very good easy riding saddle tree. The saddle is made of russet tanned oiled skirting. Roll cantle. The skirts, 22 inches long and 11½ inches wide, sheepskin wool lined. Stirrup leathers, 1¾ inches to buckle, with fender 8 inches wide and 14 inches long attached. Tie strap on the off side, 1½ inches to buckle, 1¾ inches on the near side to buckle; 15-strand soft hair cinches with leather chafes and tongues with connecting strap. Bent wood stirrups with leather bottom. This is one of the greatest bargains in our line. This saddle made in single cinch at same price. Price..........$12.78

Our Cherokee Stock Saddle.

$16.69

Our Special Montana Stock Saddle.

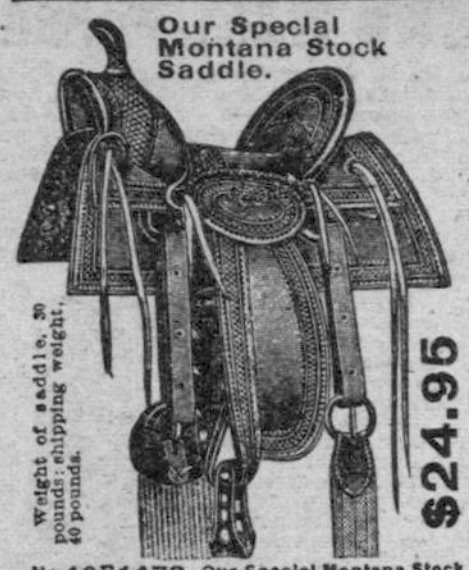

Weight of saddle, 30 pounds; shipping weight, 40 pounds.
$24.95

No. 10E1473 **Our Special Montana Stock Saddle made on a strictly new up to date Montana swell fork tree**; 15-inch full seat and jockey in one piece; rawhide trimmed, braided rawhide horn. This saddle is made in black skirting or russet skirting as desired, with white rawhide covered rings, rawhide covered bound cantle and gullet. This is a strictly new style of saddle; 27-inch wool lined skirts, 2¼-inch stirrup leathers with 9x16-inch fenders attached; iron stirrups; soft cotton front cinch, heavy belting web back cinch with connecting strap. We consider this saddle one of the greatest bargains in our line. Price..**$24.95**

Our California Stock Saddle.

Improved Western Tree.

Weight, about 34 pounds; boxed, 50 pounds.
$25.50

No. 10E1475 **This saddle is made on a 14½-inch steel fork, beef hide covered tree,** with 12-inch seat, high horn and cantle; full seat and jockey; in one piece; bound or roll cantle hand stitched 27-inch wool lined skirts; 1¾-inch tie strap on near side and 2-inch on off side to buckle; cinches, 44-strand extra hard laid fish cord with double connecting strap, wool lined chafes, 3-inch stirrup leathers with fenders 18 inches long; 7-inch wide steel leather covered stirrups. This is a very fine stock saddle, oiled skirting. Price..........................**$25.50**

Single cinch at same price.

Oklahoma Saddle, $15.87.

Improved El Reno Tree.

No. 10E1471 Tree, 15 inch El Reno, **steel fork, hide covered roll cantle, stitched jockey**; 24-inch wool lined skirts, double rig covered rings; tie strap to buckle, 1⅝ inches on near side, 1¾ inches on off side; 20-strand hair cinches with tongue and chafes, with connecting strap; stirrup leathers to lace, 2¼ inches wide, with fenders 15 inches long attached; stirrups, 3-inch wood, California style, leather bottom. Price..............................**$15.87**

Colorado Full Seat Stock Saddle.

No. 10E1482 **Improved and up to date Stock Saddle. Full seat and jockey tree;** 16-inch Nelson steel fork, hide covered shell seat, seat and jockey in one piece, hand stitched roll cantle; 30-inch wool lined skirts; tie strap, 1¾ inches to buckle on near side, 2 inches to buckle on off side; 20-strand gray California hard hair cinches with wool lined chafes and connecting strap, 3-inch stirrup straps with fenders 18 inches long and 9 inches wide; steel leather covered stirrups; ¾-inch rope strap on off side. Weight, about 35 pounds; boxed for shipment, 55 lbs.
Price..................................**$29.95**

Single cinch rig at same price.

Our $21.95 San Juan Saddle.

No. 10E1490 **This saddle is made on 16-inch improved San Juan steel fork tree;** 25-inch wool lined skirts, 2½-inch stirrup leathers to lace, with fenders 16 inches long and 8 inches wide; 1½-inch tie strap to buckle on near side, 1¾-inch on off side; Angora hair cinches with leather chafes and connecting strap with tongue; steel leather covered stirrups; roll or bound cantle. Will send bound cantle, unless order calls for roll. This is one of our big bargains in saddles. Weight, about 28 pounds; boxed, 40 pounds.
Price..................................**$21.95**

Our Idaho Stock Saddle, $31.95

No. 10E1498 **Big Horn Bucking Tree, Improved.** Our Big Horn bucking tree, 16-inch tree, steel fork, beef hide covered. This tree takes the place of bucking roll, full seat and jockey in one piece, bound or roll cantle, handstitched 30-inch wool lined skirts, 1¾-inch tie strap on near side, 2-inch on off side, to buckle; cinches, 20-strand white hard twisted cotton cord in front, 4-inch three-ply belting web in rear, double connecting strap, 3-inch stirrup leather with large fender attached, brass ox bow bound stirrups, leather bottom. Weight, about 38 pounds; boxed 50 pounds. Price...............**$31.95**

Our Sears' $24.95 Saddle.

No. 10E1511 **Sears' Special Stock Saddle. This is one of the latest improved saddles in our line.** Made on a 15-inch Spokane steel fork hide covered tree and we guarantee it to stand all kinds of heavy work. If the tree should break we will pay the transportation charges both ways on the saddle and put in a new tree free of charge. Made with a full seat and jockey in one piece. **The saddle seat** is built up solid with heavy leather and blocked to shape so as to be easy on the rider. Made in bound or roll cantle. (Will always send bound cantle unless ordered roll.) **Skirts**, 25½ inches long, 13 inches wide, full sheepskin lined. Stirrup leathers, 3 inches wide to lace with fenders 8 inches wide and 16 inches long attached, making a very heavy, strong and substantial stirrup strap. 2½-inch Moran pattern brass bound stirrups, full leather lined and leather capped; 1½-inch wide long latigo on the near side and 1¾-inch wide short latigo on the off side. Cinches, 20-strand Angora hair with leather chafes and connecting strap and buckle tongues. Heavy leather rigging back of cantle and over and around the horn with heavy leather covered rings. Lariat strap on the off side, long head string on the near side. **This is another of our great values in a moderate priced high grade stock saddle.** Remember, we guarantee the tree and will replace it if broken. Saddles not as good as this are sold at from $36.00 to $45.00. Weight of saddle, 30 pounds; packed for shipment, about 40 pounds.
Price...................................**$24.95**

Our Cowboys' Pride Saddle, $20.50.

No. 10E1513 This, our Special Cowboys' Pride Stock Saddle, is made on a high grade 15-inch Modock tree. It is a very easy riding saddle, well built up in the seat with the seat and jockey in one piece. Made in bound or rolled cantle. This saddle has the appearance of a much higher priced saddle. The stamping on this saddle is all done by hand, raised checkered stamping. It is a heavy double rigged saddle with leather covered rings, heavy stirrup straps and fenders, and strong cinches. This is a strictly new saddle and one we guarantee to give perfect satisfaction. **Tree,** 15-inch Modock, steel fork, hide covered; **seat,** full seat and jockey in one piece, bound or roll cantle (will always send bound cantle unless roll is ordered); **skirts,** 13 inches wide, 26½ inches long, sheepskin wool lined; **tie straps,** 1½-inch long tie strap to buckle on the near side, and 1¾-inch billets to buckle on the off side; **cinches,** 20-strand Angora front cinch and 3½-inch back band web rear cinch with leather chafes and connecting strap; **stirrup straps,** 2¼ inches wide to lace with large fender attached; **stirrups,** 3-inch wood, California pattern, leather bottom. Weight of saddle, about 25 pounds. Packed for shipment, about 35 pounds.
Price..................................**$20.50**

REMEMBER OUR PROFIT SHARING DEPARMENT AS SHOWN ON THE LAST PAGES.

Our Wild West Saddle, $35.75.

No. 10E1516 This is one of the highest grade saddles that we make. Made out of a very choice selection of Dundee oak saddle skirting. The leather is specially selected for all parts of this saddle. Made on a 16-inch Pocatella steel fork tree, beef hide covered, one of the best trees that can be made, has a wide pommel and low slanting cantle, a tree that is very easy on the horse and very easy on the rider. The stamping on this saddle is all done by hand. All figures and flowers are very handsome raised stamping. Nothing but the highest skilled mechanics can work on this saddle. Extra long sheepskin wool lined skirts, heavy 3-inch stirrup leathers with large fenders attached. Cotton cord girth and belting web back cinch; heavy double rigged with leather covered rings, full seat and jockey in one piece, bound or roll cantle (we will always send bound cantle unless roll cantle is ordered). If you want a strictly high grade up to date handsome hand raised stamped saddle this saddle will please you. **Tree,** 16-inch Pocatella steel fork tree, beef hide covered; **seat,** full leather seat and jockey in one piece, handsome raised stamped jockey and raised stamped seat, bound or roll cantle; **skirts,** 14 inches wide and 30 inches long, sheepskin, wool lined; **tie straps,** 1¾-inch long tie strap to buckle on the near side and 2-inch billets to buckle on the off side, **cinches,** 6-inch hard twisted cotton Mexican strong front cinch, 4-inch belting web rear cinch, with leather chafes and connecting straps; **stirrup straps,** 3-inch, to lace with large fender attached; **stirrups,** brass bound ox bow with leather bottom. Weight of saddle about 38 pounds. Packed for shipment, about 50 pounds. Price.......................**$35.75**

Our Big Horn Fancy Raised Stamped Saddle, $56.30.

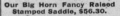

No. 10E1519 **This is the best high grade full raised stamped saddle that we make. It is equal to any saddle that is sold anywhere for $100.00 to $150.00.** We offer this saddle as the greatest bargain that was ever offered in a high grade full raised stamped saddle. It is made on an extra high grade quality steel fork Big Horn tree, beef hide covered; extra large skirts; extra large fenders; extra heavy stirrup straps double clear around, California style. The horn is rawhide braided. Only the highest skilled workmen are employed on this saddle. The stamping is all done by hand and the very choicest quality of Dundee saddle skirting is used on this saddle. **Tree,** 16-inch Big Horn steel fork, beef hide covered, rawhide braided horn; **seat,** full seat and jockey in one piece; seat and cantle in one piece; fancy raised stamped jockey and raised stamped seat; bound or roll cantle (will always send bound cantle unless roll is ordered); **skirts,** extra large, 16 inches wide, 30 inches long, sheepskin wool lined; **tie straps,** 1¾ inches extra long to buckle on the near side and 2 inches on the off side; **cinches,** 6-inch hard twisted cotton Mexican front cinch, 4-inch web back band cinch, chafes and connecting straps; **stirrup leathers,** 3-inch to lace, California style, double all around and laces to the fender. Extra large fender attached; **stirrups,** 1½-inch ox bow, brass bound, leather capped and leather lined; **horn,** rawhide, braided. Weight of saddle, about 45 pounds. Packed for shipment, about 60 pounds. Price...............**$56.30**

HOW TO MEASURE A ROOM AND HOW TO HANG YOUR OWN WALL PAPER.

RULES FOR MEASURING A ROOM. **Measure the length in feet of the four walls, add together, then** multiply by the height in feet, the result will give the total number of square feet of wall surface; now deduct for windows and doors. Multiply the height by the width of each door and window, add together the square feet of each and deduct from the amount; now you have the net total amount of wall surface to be papered, divide this total by 60, the result is the number of rolls required for the walls.

FOR SIDE WALL.

Example: Room 15 feet long, 12 feet wide, 9 feet high. One window, 6x4 feet; one door, 7x4 feet; one window, 3½x4 feet.

```
15          1 window, 6   x4=24 square feet.
15          1 door,   7   x4=28 square feet.
12          1 window, 3½x4=14 square feet.
12                        66 square feet.
---
54
 9  Multiply.
---
486
 66 Deduct.
60)420
   7 Rolls.
```

FOR CEILING.

The number of rolls required for ceiling is ascertained the same way, dividing the number of square feet by 60.
Example: Room 15 feet long, 12 feet wide.
15x12=180   60)180
Double rolls.... 3

FOR BORDER.

Measure the distance entirely around the room in feet, divide by 3, and you have the number of yards of border required.
Example: Room 15 feet long, 12 feet wide.
15+15+12+12=54   3)54
Yards of border needed....18

Wall paper weighs about 1½ pounds per double roll. We do not trim wall paper because the edges being exposed, if damaged in transit, would render perfect matching impossible.

INSTRUCTIONS HOW TO HANG YOUR OWN WALL PAPER.

No Experience Necessary. Our Illustrations Tell the Story.

Heretofore we have given our friends printed instructions only, which, while simple, did not convey the correct idea. We now show several illustrations which will assist our customers materially and anybody can do as good a job of paperhanging as any professional paperhanger.

Illustration No. 1.

PREPARATION. **Secure two boards about 8 feet long and 10 or 12 inches wide,** lay side by side, having the ends rest on a table or box at each end. The height should not exceed 3 feet. This will be your table. Now secure some plank for the platform on which to stand, which should be nearly as long as the width of the room you wish to paper. Make your platform sufficiently high so your head will be about 6 inches from the ceiling. This platform can be made by placing a board on two ordinary chairs or boxes. Secure the other necessary articles needed for your work. To apply the paste you will require a paste brush from 6 to 10 inches wide (a whitewash or calcimine brush will answer). A long pair of shears to secure a straight cut to trim the edges. **A smoothing brush** to smooth down the paper with after the same is hung and perfectly matched. If no smoothing brush is at hand, use a clothes brush or whisk broom. **A seam roller is required** to press down and smooth down the edges where each strip of paper laps over or is joined together. (You will note on the following pages that we offer all paper hangers' tools at actual cost). If you have no seam roller use a bed caster.

CAUTION—Do not use the seam roller until your paste on paper that is hung is partially dry—see further instructions. **Paper your ceiling first,** for in doing this work you are apt to touch the side walls with paper that has paste on, or with soiled hands, and your work will not look neat.

HOW TO TRIM WALL PAPER. **After you have ascertained the length of your room,** unroll the paper face up on your work table, then match and cut same. Be sure that you have at least 3 or 4 inches at each end to come down on side wall (see illustration No. 3). It is absolutely necessary to have your ceiling paper come down on the side wall a trifle so as to cover any space left blank after border is put on, caused by ceiling not always being perfectly level. The larger the design the more surplus is required for matching; this surplus will be covered by the border or side wall paper. Before starting to hang, cut sufficient lengths of paper to cover the entire ceiling. Turn all the paper face down and you are now ready to apply the paste on the first or top length.

Illustration No 2.

PASTING AND TRIMMING. **The bucket of paste should be placed on the right hand side of the operator.** Now apply the paste evenly on the top strip of paper, beginning on the left hand end of the table as you face same. After you have applied the paste on about one-half of the length, lay aside your brush and fold over the part of the paper that is pasted, using extra care that the sides are exactly even (see illustration No. 1). Now apply the paste to the other half and fold that over towards the center, same as first half. If the strip of paper is longer than your table, paste the left half; after folding allow the folded end to hang over the end of the table and rest on the floor while you are pasting and folding the other half. You now have an entire strip of paper before you, all pasted and folded, and the sides of the paper perfectly even and ready for trimming. Draw the strip of paper towards you about 3 inches from the edge of the table and proceed to trim, commencing at the right (see illustration No. 2). The great advantage in trimming paper after pasting is that the paste will then be more evenly distributed on the edges. It also takes less time, as you trim two thicknesses at once. **Always be sure to paper ceiling first.**

Illustration No. 3.

HOW TO HANG THE CEILING PAPER. **After the selvage is trimmed off, your paper will be 18 inches wide.** We have already explained when papering ceiling why the ends should come down a few inches on the side wall. For the same reason the first strip put up and also the last strip of ceiling should lap 2 inches on the side wall. As a guide for hanging the first length of ceiling paper properly, draw a line with chalk or charcoal 16 inches from the side wall. This is best done by driving a small nail in ceiling 16 inches from the side wall at each end of the room before starting to paper. Chalk a piece of cord, tie same to the nails, draw it tight, then take hold of the cord in the center, pull down and let go; the cord will strike the ceiling and leave a straight line. (We show this line in illustration No. 3.) Next you take the first piece of ceiling paper (which you have already pasted, folded and trimmed). Mount your raised platform, unfold the end to your right (as you start in the right hand corner of the room), let the other end, which is still folded, hang over a roll of paper which you hold in your left hand (see illustration No. 3). Commence in corner of ceiling, having the first strip come between the chalk line and the wall you face, allowing both the end and side of the paper to come down on the side wall 2 inches as explained. Now guide your paper with your right hand along the chalk line, at the same time pressing the paper to the ceiling with the flat of your hand as you move along and smoothing same with brush or whisk broom. When half of the first ceiling strip is put on, then unfold the other half and continue to the end of the first strip. When hanging the second length, you are guided by the edge of the first strip, and so on until the last strip of ceiling is put up. The edge of the last strip should also lap on the side wall. Care must be taken to have your patterns match.

Illustration No. 4.

HANGING SIDE WALL PAPER. **Always hang the side wall paper before hanging border.** Follow the same instructions for cutting paper for side wall as previously outlined for ceiling. Paper should be cut from 4 to 5 inches longer than the length required for the side wall that is to be papered. In cutting your side wall paper, you can allow for the space of wall that the border will cover. All borders are either 9 or 18 inches wide. Be sure to match the pattern (which is very simple) as you have allowed from 4 to 6 inches in cutting, you can raise or lower each strip or length of paper as the pattern may require. In matching your side wall paper on the work table you will find when a large pattern is selected that there will be at times a waste of 8 or 10 inches which will have to be cut off. The upper end of the side wall paper will be uneven but the border will cover same. The lower end which stops at the base board is either trimmed with a base trimmer (see wall paper tools) or a pair of shears. When using shears, paste your paper in place close down to the base board, use the back of the shears to mark with, running same over top of paper where top of base board and plaster meet, then lift your paper a little (the paste still being fresh will permit of this), then cut where you have marked with shears and smooth down with brush or whisk broom. To hang side wall paper, arrange your platform or step ladder so it is about 12 inches from the wall, commence at any door, this will be of great assistance to you in hanging the first piece of side wall paper straight, then continue around the room until finished. All short pieces can be used over doors and windows. Take your first length of paper that has been pasted, folded and trimmed, mount the platform or ladder, unfold both ends and the entire strip hangs perpendicular (see illustration No. 4), lean forward, looking down along the edge and when the pattern is properly matched, allow the paper to touch the wall and smooth down with a brush or whisk broom. **About ten minutes should elapse before using the seam roller** as the paste is still wet and will squeeze out at the edges. Occasionally it will happen that a strip is not properly matched after being hung, in such cases remove the strip at once and proceed over again.

Illustration No. 5.

HANGING THE BORDER. **The border should be hung last and can be cut in five or six pieces should it be easier to hang in that way.** Do not commence in the corner, but have the end lap over on the other wall about 4 inches. Cut the border through the center of the largest figure as a joint cannot be noticed after it is hung. Paste, fold and trim the border, same as you did in the side wall and ceiling. Take the folded strip of border, mount your platform or ladder, unfold the right end and proceed as shown in illustration No. 5. Should the ceiling be uneven it is best to draw a chalk line on the wall immediately under the ceiling. Make your chalk line in same manner as explained in our instructions for hanging first strip of ceiling (see line in illustration No. 5). This should be done on a line with the lowest part of the ceiling. This will leave the ceiling paper exposed above the border on the wall in some places. For this reason we recommend in our instructions on hanging ceiling paper to allow same to come down on side wall 2 inches. We trust the foregoing instructions are plain and that they will be of assistance to those who hang their own paper.

ABOUT ORDERING WALL PAPER. **After you have figured and ascertained the exact number of rolls required to paper your rooms, it is advisable to add an extra roll of each wall and ceiling and several yards of border. We do not want you to buy more paper than is actually needed, but we make above suggestion, having our customers' interest in mind. You may accidentally spoil a strip or when figuring you may overlook projections, such as chimneys, etc. Often an extra roll, worth a few cents, may avoid a great deal of inconvenience caused by waiting for additional paper to come on account of shortage.**

HOW TO MAKE PASTE. **Enough to paper a good sized room:** Take 3 pints of flour, rub smooth in 2 quarts of cold water, add 8 quarts of boiling water and let this boil slowly. Stir constantly for 10 minutes. When cold, stir in two tablespoonsful of powdered alum. Use about as thick as will run off the brush.

Starch Paste, which is considered very satisfactory, is made in the following manner: Dissolve 1 pound of best gloss starch in a quart of cold water. Use a large pail or dish pan. Boil a kettle of water and add same to starch gradually, stirring constantly until starch is cooked. When paste cools and is too thick, same can be reduced with cold water.

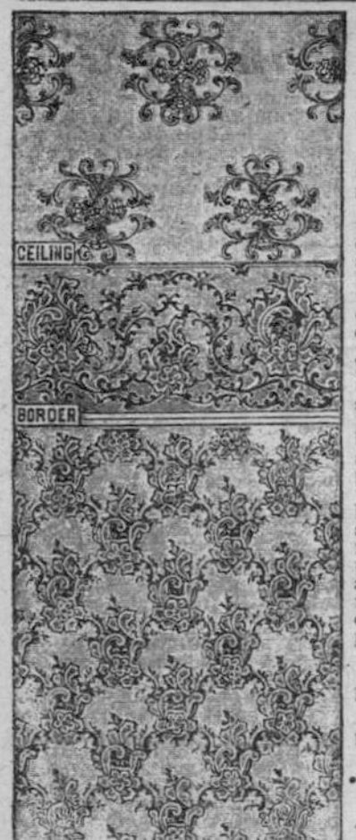

OUR PLAIN SET FIGURE PAPER WITHOUT BACKGROUND, 3c PER DOUBLE ROLL.

EXACTLY AS ADVERTISED, 1½c PER SINGLE ROLL, 3c PER DOUBLE ROLL.

This, our lowest priced paper, made in a neat set design, is finished without background, and while it will compare favorably with papers that sell generally at double the price, and is suitable for papering bedrooms, closets, kitchens, etc., but since it costs just as much to hang this paper as the richest, heavy background paper that will wear very much longer, be less susceptible to dust and dirt and look very much richer, we would especially recommend, that in selecting a paper, that you select one of our rich, heavy background papers at from 10 cents per roll upwards. For example, while 26 cents will supply enough of this paper to cover a room 11x11, 9 feet high, side wall, border and ceiling, less than $1.00 will supply the same amount of a rich, heavy background 10-cent paper, paper that will last twice as long, always look rich and beautiful; besides, the labor of hanging is exactly the same, so we always advise our customers, since the difference in the cost between this, our cheapest paper, and a rich, heavy background paper at 10 to 15 cents a roll, is only about $1.00 to a room, that in their own interest, as a matter of real economy, they select one of the richest patterns we have to offer.

No. 53E235 Wall. Price, per double roll, 3c
No. 53E1235 Border, 9 inches wide. Price, per yard, ⅛c; 8 yards for 1c
No. 53E236 Ceiling. Per double roll..... 3c

Cost of this paper for a room, size, 11x11 feet, height of ceiling 9 feet, will be as follows:
For side wall and border 20c
For ceiling 6c
Or total cost of wall, border and ceiling, 26c

On the price of 26 cents for the above sized room, we allow for four ordinary size openings, namely, two doors and two windows.

A VERY HANDSOME NEW DESIGN, 6c PER DOUBLE ROLL.

A neat set figure design in flat colors on a medium brown background. The lower part of the figure in light green, upper part in white, surrounded by a scroll in a darker shade of brown outlined in red. We can recommend this paper as one of the mose serviceable brown papers on the market, being a semi-dark paper it is especially recommended for rooms exposed to much dust, as this paper will not show the dust. We offer this heavy stock, pure color wall paper at only 6 cents per double roll, compare it with any paper sold at 12 cents per roll, and we are confident that our paper will be found superior in every way. Please bear in mind that every roll of wall paper sold by us is made in our own wall paper mill, this will explain why we are able to sell high grade paper for less money than others charge for a cheap grade. Made with a 9-inch border. The ceiling is decorated in similar colors on a light yellow background.

This beautiful new design of paper is shown by a sample in our Wall Paper Sample Book, sent to anyone on application. If you want to see it in its actual colors, write for the free Wall Paper Sample Book. While our price for this very pretty design is very low, only 6 cents per double roll, and while we always recommend the purchase of the higher qualities in all lines of merchandise, yet you will find this wall paper not only very beautiful, but very satisfactory, and representing wonderful value for the money.

No. 53E283 Wall. Price, per double roll. 6c
No. 53E1283 Border. 9 inches wide. Price, per yard .... ½c
No. 53E284 Ceiling. Price, per double roll 6c

SPECIAL NOTICE. We do not insist that our customers purchase complete combinations, we will gladly accept your order for all side wall, all border or all ceiling of any pattern. We manufacture every roll of wall paper we sell, consequently we can manufacture as many rolls of wall, border or ceiling as is found necessary.

OUR BEAUTIFUL STRIPE DESIGN, 11c PER DOUBLE ROLL.

We illustrate here a stripe effect which conveys a fair idea of the design but cannot show the beauty of this wall hanging. Stripes are always in demand, therefore we have endeavored to put on the market something very artistic and tasteful. The design shown here is made up in light colors, therefore a cheerful wall decoration for bedrooms, sewing rooms, small parlors, etc. The background consists of pure white and silver stripes over which are printed small roses in red and pink with sprays in green. The ceiling has similar flowers on a pure white ground. The border, 9 inches wide, is very pretty, consisting of festoons of small roses produced in colors to harmonize with ceiling and side wall.

This is one of our new 1906 patterns, and is equal to wall paper that retails at 16 to 20 cents per roll. You can send your order for this paper direct from this catalogue under our guarantee to please you, or if you would like to see the actual sample, do not fail to write for our free Wall Paper Sample Book.

No. 53E307 Wall. Price per double roll.. 11c
No. 53E1307 Border. 9 inches wide. Price, per yard 1c
No. 53E308 Ceiling. Price, per double roll.. 11c

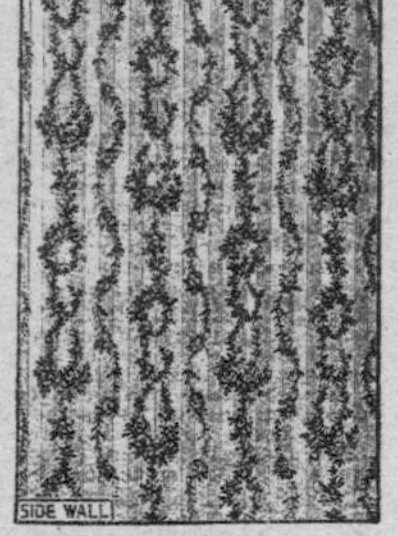

WE SHOW SAMPLES OF SIDE WALL, BORDER AND CEILING in our large 25-cent Wall Paper Sample Book. This book is made up especially for paperhangers and dealers from which they sell the paper again. If you must see a sample of the border and ceiling, it will pay you to send for this large sample book. The book will be sent to you by express, all charges paid, on receipt of 25 cents. The express charges alone will exceed 25 cents and the book costs us more than 25 cents to make. This book is larger, and contains better papers at lower prices, than any other sample book on the market.

RICH RED BACKGROUND PAPER, 10c PER DOUBLE ROLL.

We illustrate here our 10 cents per double roll pure red background gilt wall paper, a paper worth at least double the price we ask, red background papers have always sold at a high price, but owing to the enormous output of this department and the fact that we are the manufacturers of every roll of wall paper we sell, makes it possible for us to sell a high grade pure red background paper for 10 cents per double roll.

As the illustration clearly shows, the pattern is a pretty one and a paper which can be put in most any room in the house. The dark portion of the illustration is in pure red color, known as the background, the scroll or lighter portion is printed in two shades of pink, delicately blended, the scroll is also outlined in silver, which the illustration does not show; the leaves attached to the scrolls are printed in several shades of gold bronze giving the pattern somewhat of a Japanese atmosphere.

The border is 9 inches wide blending into a sage green ground ceiling with decorations to harmonize.

This is a very rich, warm effect paper, a decoration that will look good in almost any room, and with almost any combination of carpet and furniture. It is especially suitable for dining rooms, yet this style design is a great favorite for bedrooms also. While our sample book, sent free on request, shows a sample of this beautiful 10-cent pure red background paper, it must be seen on the wall in combination with the beautiful ceiling and border to really appreciate what we are offering. We know you could not duplicate this beautiful paper at retail for anything less than double the price we ask.

No. 53E237 Wall. Price, per double roll. 10c
No. 53E1237 Border. 9 inches wide. Price, per yard 1c
No. 53E238 Ceiling. Price, per double roll. 10c

SO THAT OUR READERS AND CUSTOMERS WILL UNDERSTAND THE DIFFERENT PHRASES OR THE LANGUAGE THAT IS USED BY WALL PAPER DEALERS, HANGERS AND AGENTS, WE WOULD LIKE TO OFFER THE FOLLOWING EXPLANATIONS.

A DADO PAPER is used from the baseboard to the chair rail, or where the back of a chair comes in contact with the wall. The part above that, which would naturally come between the chair rail and a plate rail or picture moulding, is called **the field.** If a large space of, say, 2 or 3 feet is left between the plate rail or moulding and the ceiling, this is called the **frieze.** If a narrow space of 9 or 18 inches is left in papering or putting up room moulding, it is generally called the **border space,** for all borders are made in 9 or 18-inch widths.

IN MANY INSTANCES, **a side wall and ceiling paper alone are used without any border whatever.** It is quite a fad in certain sections of the country to paper in this manner. When this is done, the ceiling paper is extended down the side wall as far down as the picture mouldings and you will have a very nice effect called the **drop ceiling.** In many instances moire or independent ceilings are used for this purpose.

YOU WILL ALSO PLEASE NOTE **that among our mouldings we offer a combination cove and picture moulding.** This is especially adapted for low ceilings and is placed on the side wall right up against the ceiling, which gives the room a much higher appearance. When this moulding is used you can hang your paper with or without a border, using side wall paper right up to the moulding, and use the ceiling paper on the ceiling only, the moulding will make a very nice frame in this manner for both side wall and ceiling. **We would call attention to our very fine line of mouldings which are made especially to match all of our papers that we offer this season.**

YOU WILL PLEASE NOTE **that we offer a very fine chair rail, our No. 53E72, of highly polished oak 2½ inches wide.** The same is recommended as a protection against marring the wall or injuring the paper or plaster where the backs of chairs would come in contact with same. Next above this, in a dining room, plate rails are recommended and are now used in all high class buildings throughout the country. **We show a very high grade line** in various widths and colors of these plate rails, which are quite an ornament to a dining room and are used for displaying odd pieces of crockery, china plates and bric-a-brac of all kinds. If our instructions are followed you will experience no difficulty in putting up these plate rails. We also show an end bracket for the plate rails, in order to give it a finished appearance. Above the plate rail, if desired, place any of the picture mouldings that we show in all colors to match the paper which you have selected for your dining room. In addition to the picture mouldings you will find cove mouldings. These are intended to be used where the ceiling and side wall meet. You will please note that they serve a double purpose, in the first place, giving a very handsome finish to the room; and secondly, a space is provided wherein to hang your picture hooks so that pictures can be suspended from same. When this moulding is used you will not require a picture moulding in the room. The cove mouldings we offer in a variety of colors and at very low prices. In addition to the above we offer mouldings and beadings to be used as dividers. For instance, you desire to use two different kinds of paper on your side wall and have no chair rail, plate rail nor picture moulding, on account of the room being too small or the moulding appearing too heavy, we would recommend our gilt beading, which is but one-half inch wide, in place of putting a plain ribbon of paper where the two different kinds of wall paper come together. This gilt beading will make a very handsome offset at a very small expense, and will add considerably to your room decorations. These beadings are also used in connection with the rosettes that we offer in our No. 53E17 for paneling purposes. The rosettes are hand carved and covered with gold leaf.

AMONG OUR MOULDINGS **we offer you plain oak, polished white enameled, burnished gilt, fancy colored, fancy figured mouldings, decorated mouldings, in imitation of bisque, mouldings stained and colored to harmonize with any wall paper that you may select.** The same are offered at prices exceedingly low and we guarantee all of our mouldings to be of the highest class manufactured. You will find them both ornamental and useful in decorating your home. The same are carefully packed and we guarantee safe delivery.

A NEAT, TASTEFUL PATTERN, VERY NEW, 8 CENTS PER DOUBLE ROLL.

A very neat design, suitable for any room in the house. The flowers in pink and white blended, with small sprays in white and green on a stone gray background. The design is a beautiful one and the colorings are such that any room in the house may be decorated with this paper.

This new heavy stock wall paper is offered at the unheard of low price, only 8 cents per double roll. We will leave it entirely to you to compare this paper with any 15-cent paper on the market, we are confident that our paper will be found better in quality and design.

Making this wall paper in our own mill, as explained in the introductory pages of this department, under the most economical conditions, we are able to undersell any manufacturer or dealer, to put into our paper a great deal more in quality, and yet sell at a much closer margin of profit than any other maker can. Our customers get the benefit of all this. Remember, you can order direct from this catalogue under our guarantee to please you or refund your money, but we will gladly send you our free Wall Paper Sample Book on request.

Made with a 9-inch border blending into a cream ground ceiling decorated with flowers to harmonize.

No. 53E249 Wall. Price, per double roll 8c
No. 53E1249 Border. 9 inches wide. Price, per yard .... ½c
No. 53E250 Ceiling. Price, per double roll 8c

OUR FREE SAMPLE BOOK

OF WALL PAPER CONTAINS ACTUAL SAMPLES OF OUR PAPER.

IT IS LARGER THAN ANY OTHER FREE SAMPLE BOOK ISSUED.

It contains more samples, better papers and lower prices than any other. If you do not care to order from these pages, by all means send for the free Sample Book of Wall Paper, it will be mailed to you promptly, postpaid.

CREAM TINT BACKGROUND, LARGE FLORAL PATTERN, 9c PER DOUBLE ROLL.

We illustrate here a 9-cent per double roll cream tint background paper with 18-inch border. Flowers in red and pink, with leaves in two shades of green, all in all, it is a pretty design and a paper that will give satisfaction in most any room in the house. There is no gilt nor silver, making it a modest yet cheerful wall paper.

We are able to offer this paper at only 9 cents per double roll because we own and operate one of the best equipped wall paper mills in the country, we have put in every improvement to lower the cost of manufacture and our customers are receiving the benefit of the reduced cost in being able to purchase new high grade heavy stock wall paper at less than one-half the price charged for similar paper.

This is one of our new and exclusive designs in low priced wall paper for 1906. It is a great advantage in buying from us, namely, that you will not find the same design offered by any other dealer. You are getting the benefit of exclusive patterns and this paper will have all the style, quality and effectiveness that you will find in paper offered by dealers and wall paperhangers at two or three times this price. If you would like to see a sample of this and our other new papers, just write and ask for our free Wall Paper Sample Book.

This design is made with an 18-inch border, blending into a white ground ceiling, decorated with similar flowers.

No. 53E255 Wall. Price, per double roll 9c
No. 53E1255 Border. 18 inches wide. Price, per yard 1c
No. 53E256 Ceiling. Price, per double roll 9c

WE HANDLE DOUBLE ROLLS ONLY

WE DO NOT HANDLE SINGLE ROLLS OF WALL PAPER.

All of our paper is put up in double rolls, therefore to avoid mistakes, please do not order single rolls. When wall paper is ordered in single rolls, a clerk may send the same number in double rolls. For instance, when a customer orders 12 single rolls, we fill the order by sending 6 double rolls, but a clerk may send 12 double rolls by mistake, not noticing that the order calls for single rolls, being accomstomed to handling double rolls only.

OUR NEW DAINTY BLUE PAPER. A REAL 25c QUALITY FOR 14c PER DOUBLE ROLL.

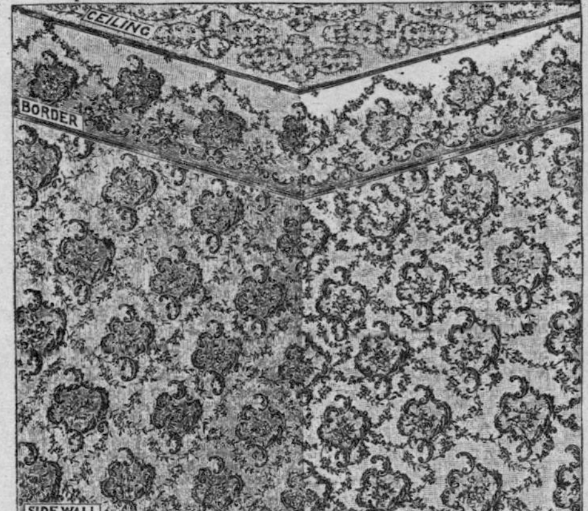

It is certainly unfortunate that we are unable to show the actual colors of the design illustrated herewith. We have here, without question, the best creation in blue ever shown, we will endeavor to describe this beautiful wall hanging. The background is a sky blue, the large figure shown in the illustration consists of a frame of scrolls in gold, in the center of which is a bouquet of pink and red flowers on a darker blue ground.

You can order this paper without seeing a sample with our guarantee that the paper will please, but if you prefer to see a sample first, write us at once for our free Sample Book of Wall Paper. This book will show a fair sized sample of the side wall and will give a correct idea of the design and colorings.

Please sit down and figure out what a little expense it will be to paper a room with this beautiful new blue wall paper. You cannot figure what an improvment it will be in the appearance of the room and how beautiful the effect will be, but you can figure out what a small cost to you it represents. $1.00 to $1.50 will buy enough of this wall paper, including border and ceiling, to paper an average size room. If you order this paper you will have something designed different from the paper sold in your own town, and such a handsome pattern as you would see in the finest stores from 25 to 30 cents per roll.

This number is made with an 18-inch border blending into a decorated ceiling with light cream ground.

No. 53E245 Wall. Price, per double roll 14c
No. 53E1245 Border. 18 inches wide. Price, per yard 2c
No. 53E246 Ceiling. Price, per double roll 14c

FLORAL EMBOSSED SILK STRIPE. A MAGNIFICENT WALL PAPER, 18c PER DOUBLE ROLL.

The illustration herewith represents our high grade floral embossed silk stripe with a 9-inch border. This is undoubtedly the prettiest silk wall hanging made, heavily embossed with rope embossing. The lighter stripe in the illustration is a pure white with a silver line running through center of same and gold dots on each side of the silver stripe; the dark narrow stripe is very much lighter than shown on the illustration, it is printed in gold and silver with a narrow green line on each side; the wide stripe is printed in a very light green with a spray in pure white running through the entire length, the stripe is broken at intervals of 8 inches by a twig of pink roses.

This paper positively cannot be purchased elsewhere for less than 35 cents per double roll, in fact, we do not believe that as pretty a paper can be had from any other manufacturer or dealer at any price.

The illustration will give you a good idea of the appearance of this handsome paper, and you can order it direct from this description with every assurance of being well pleased, but if you would like to see the exact colorings and quality, do not fail to write for our free Wall Paper Sample Book. This is another one of our prize designs and patterns that we are particularly proud of, and all who have seen it agree that it is one of the handsomest embossed silk striped wall papers ever produced. On the introductory pages of this department we give plain instructions how to order, and how to calculate the quanity of paper you need.

No. 53E291 Wall. Price, per double roll 18c
No. 53E1291 Border. 9 inches wide. Price, per yard 2c
No. 53E292 Ceiling. Price, per double roll 18c

WONDERFUL VALUE IN A NEW FLORAL AND SCROLL WALL PAPER AT 14 CENTS.

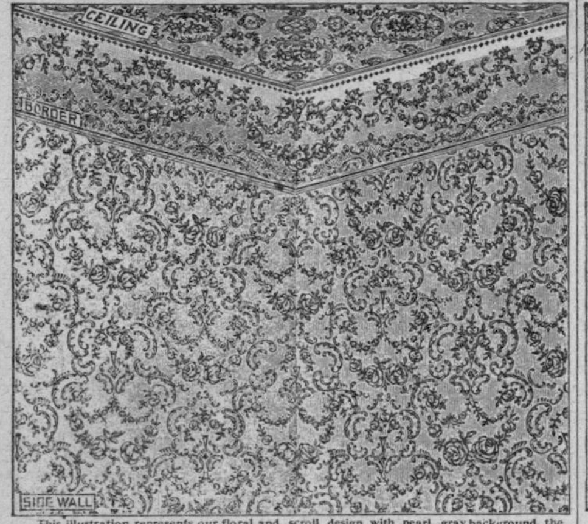

This illustration represents our floral and scroll design with pearl gray background, the scrolls in silver and gold with natural color red and pink roses and natural color green leaves. The background of this paper is a very popular color and a similar paper, listed last season, was one of our best sellers. While this paper is sold at the wonderful low price of 14 cents per double roll, we guarantee that a better paper cannot be had elsewhere at 30 cents per roll. If you desire a parlor, dining room, or large bedroom paper in cheerful colors, you can order this number with the assurance that you will be thoroughly pleased with the paper after received. Side wall and border are heavily embossed. The border is 18 inches wide and blends into a decorated ceiling with light gray ground.

In our Wall Paper Sample Book, sent free on request, we show a sample of this beautiful new pattern. Do not fail to write for the free Wall Paper Sample Book if you are unable to make a satisfactory selection direct from this book. We guarantee that this paper is one of the very highest quality. The color and pattern effect is beautiful, and we know that you will be more than pleased with it. This is a design suitable for almost any room in the house, and is sure to prove one of our most popular patterns.

No. 53E239	Wall.	Price, per double roll	14c
No. 53E1239	Border	18 inches wide. Price, per yard	2c
No. 53E240	Ceiling.	Price, per double roll	14c

NO HANDSOMER WALL PAPER WAS EVER OFFERED AT 25c. OUR PRICE 15c.

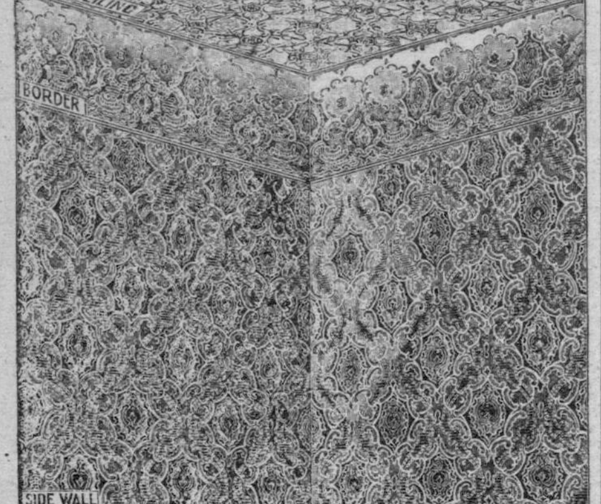

It would be impossible to correctly describe this beautiful wall hanging, the design is one of the best we have see and the coloring is certainly artistic and beautiful. The background is a medium dark green, the scrolls are in green bronze outlined in gilt. In the center of the figure are small scrolls in green bronze and gilt surrounded by small figures in black with a red choke, or to better describe it, the background of the figure is in red. It is a well covered paper and in a set figure design there is nothing more beautiful on the market.

We manufacture every roll of paper shipped by us, we own and operate one of the best equipped wall paper mills in the country, we can manufacture wall paper at a lower cost than any other mill because we do not have to employ a large number of clerks to look after other accounts, we save all this and give our customers the benefit in low prices.

If you think you would like this paper send us your order for as many rolls as you need. See the introductory pages of this department how to figure the quantity, and we will send the paper to you with the understanding and agreement that if you are not more than pleased with your purchase you can return it to us, and we will promptly return your money, and pay all transportation charges. Our free Wall Paper Sample Book shows a sample of this and all of our other papers. This paper is made with an 18-inch border blending into a yellow ground ceiling. Both border and ceiling carry similar decorations.

No 53E311	Wall.	Price, per double roll	15c
No. 53E1311	Border.	18 inches wide. Price, per yard	2c
No. 53E312	Ceiling	Price, per double roll	15c

INGRAIN WALL PAPER AT PRICES NEVER BEFORE HEARD OF.

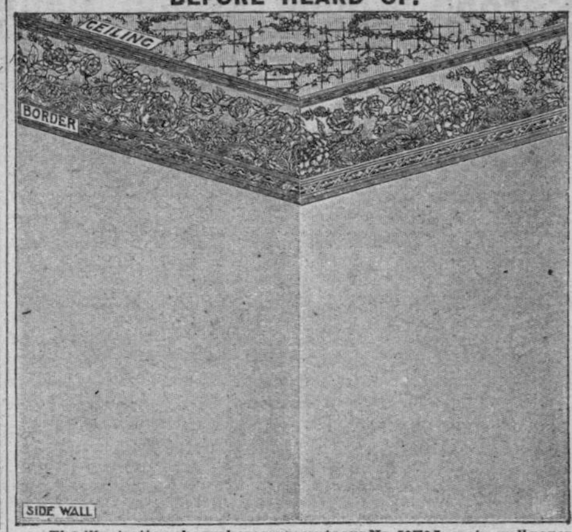

The illustration shown here represents our No. 53E9 Ingrain wall paper with a floral border and ceiling. The term Ingrain, as applied to wall decoration, means a plain paper without figure decoration of any kind. Ingrain side wall papers are plain, made in various colors on heavy stock. The borders and ceilings are decorated with flowers or figures in colors to harmonize with the side wall.

Ingrains are used in parlors, dining rooms, stores, art galleries, drawing rooms, etc. Where pictures are to be hung, ingrains are generally preferred because there is no figure or decoration to detract from the picture itself.

Ingrain side wall papers are usually put up in rolls 30 inches wide, which makes it very difficult to hang, therefore, for the convenience of our customers, we have reduced the width to 19½ inches, the same as ordinary wall paper and in figuring you will measure the same as for ordinary wall paper.

All of the borders are 18 inches wide. We cannot furnish 9-inch borders with Ingrain papers.

No. 53E1	Wall.	**Vermont Stone.** Price, per double roll	15c
No. 53E15101	Border.	Price, per yard	2c
No. 53E5101	Ceiling.	Price, per double roll	15c
No. 53E3	Wall.	**Light Green.** Price, per double roll	16c
No. 53E15103	Border.	Price, per yard	2c
No. 53E5103	Ceiling.	Price, per double roll	16c
No. 53E4	Wall.	**Light Blue.** Price, per double roll	16c
No. 53E15104	Border.	Price, per yard	2c
No. 53E5104	Ceiling.	Price, per double roll	16c
No. 53E5	Wall.	**Terra Cotta.** Price, per double roll	15c
No. 53E15105	Border.	Price, per yard	2c
No. 53E5105	Ceiling.	Price, per double roll	15c
No. 53E6	Wall.	**Yellow.** Price, per double roll	15c
No. 53E15106	Border.	Price, per yard	2c
No. 53E5106	Ceiling.	Price, per double roll	15c
No. 53E9	Wall.	**Dark Green.** Price, per double roll	17c
No. 53E19109	Border.	Floral design. Price, per yard	2c
No. 53E9109	Ceiling,	to match. Price, per double roll	17c
No. 53E1109	Border.	Set design. Price, per yard	2c
No. 53E109	Ceiling,	to match. Price, per double roll	17c
No. 53E10	Wall.	**Dark Red.** Price, per double roll	17c
No. 53E15110	Border.	Floral design. Price, per yard	2c
No. 53E5110	Ceiling,	to match. Price, per double roll	17c
No. 53E1110	Border.	Set design. Price, per yard	2c
No 53E110	Ceiling,	to match. Price, per double roll	17c
No. 53E12	Wall.	**Old Rose.** Price, per double roll	15c
No. 53E15112	Border.	Price, per yard	2c
No. 53E5112	Ceiling.	Price, per double roll	15c

INDEPENDENT OR MOIRE CEILING PAPER.

The following ceiling papers are especially made to be used with the Ingrain wall paper, they can also be used with nearly every pattern shown in this book. Preferred by many to the flowered or figured ceiling.

No. 53E14	**White Moire Ceiling.**	Price, per double roll	7c
No. 53E15	**Yellow Moire Ceiling.**	Price, per double roll	7c
No. 53E16	**Green Moire Ceiling.**	Price, per double roll	7c
No. 53E17	**Blue Moire Ceiling.**	Price, per double roll	7c
No. 53E18	**Pink Moire Ceiling.**	Price, per double roll	7c

VARNISHED TILE PAPER.

Varnished Tile Papers are principally used in bathrooms and kitchens. The paper has a varnished surface which can be washed when soiled. We do not manufacture varnished tile paper but if you are interested write us for samples, which will be mailed free. We have secured several fine patterns from a large eastern manufacturer and will furnish the paper at 30 cents per double roll for wall and ceiling and 2 cents per yard for 4-inch border, this is the regular width of varnished tile border.

COLORED BURLAP FOR DECORATING.

Our Burlap for Decorating Purposes is the Best Manufactured.

It is sized and ready to be put on the wall, a coat of special sizing being on the back of the burlap. **Burlap is now extensively used for high class decorating,** being principally used for dados or wainscoting. It is pasted on the wall, same as wall paper, with any good wall paper paste.

No. 53E25	**Dark Red.** Price, per yard	22c
No. 53E12	**Dark Green.** Price, per yard	22c
No. 53E42	**Yellow.** Price, per yard	22c
No. 53E32	**Dark Blue.** Price, per yard	22c
No. 53E47	**Brown.** Price, per yard	22c
No. 53E2	**Painted.** Price, per yard	20c

The burlap is 36 inches wide.

WE CANNOT SELL LESS THAN 6 YARDS OF A COLOR. SAMPLES MAILED ON APPLICATION.

Seroco Ready Mixed House Paint.

FOR A READY MIXED PAINT for houses, for interior or exterior work, or even for barns, fences, for wood or iron where an extra grade, an extra durable and handsome, easy working and fine finish paint is desired, the very best ready mixed paint made, we especially recommend this, our own Seroco Ready Mixed Paint.

REMEMBER, Seroco Ready Mixed Paint is made in our own factory, we guarantee every gallon to be full weight and full measure, to give perfect satisfaction or we will refund your money. At 85 cents to 98 cents per gallon, according to quantity ordered, we furnish this, our Seroco Ready Mixed Paint, made in our own paint factory, at prices that are based on the actual manufacturing cost, the cost of the raw material and labor, with but our one small percentage of profit added, and you can buy this, the highest grade ready mixed house paint from us at a lower price than dealers can buy their paint from other sources in any quantity.

YOU CAN ORDER DIRECT from this catalogue, selecting the color wanted from the colors listed below, with our guarantee that the color and quality will please you, or we will immediately return your money; but if you prefer to see the exact colors before ordering, write us and we will mail you our special Paint Color Sample Booklet free, with our compliments. This booklet shows samples of the actual colors of all the different paints we handle.

WE FURNISH our Seroco Ready Mixed House Paint, the highest grade house paint on the market, at prices ranging from 85 cents to 98 cents per gallon, according to package, as follows:

DIRECTIONS FOR SEROCO READY MIXED HOUSE PAINTS. For first coat, thin the paint with boiled linseed oil, in the proportion of one-half gallon oil to one gallon ready mixed paint. For second coat, use the paint as received, unless it should be very thick, when a little linseed oil may be added.

OUR GUARANTEE: We guarantee our Seroco Ready Mixed House Paint to wear for five years, if the directions are carefully followed. Seroco Ready Mixed House Paint will not peel, scale, blister or chalk, our guarantee covers this.

Our 98-Cent Seroco House Paint.

At 98 cents per gallon we furnish the Seroco Ready Mixed Paint put up in 1-gallon tin pails, exactly as illustrated. The difference in price between 85 and 98 cents per gallon only represents the difference in cost of the package to us. If you require five gallons or more it will pay you to order this paint in buckets or barrels. Understand, it is put out under our binding guarantee that if it does not please you, if you don't find it better than any ready mixed paint made, regardless of price, return it to us at our expense, and we will immediately refund your money.

AT 93 CENTS PER GALLON we furnish our Seroco, the highest grade ready mixed paint made, in 5-gallon buckets, exactly as illustrated.

In this package, in a 5-gallon wooden baled bucket, we can furnish our Seroco Paint at 93 cents per gallon. 93 cents barely covers the actual cost of material and labor; made, ground and put up in our own factory, with but our one small percentage of profit added. If you buy this paint from us you will get such value as you could not get from any other house.

88 Cents per Gallon for Seroco Mixed Paint, in 25-Gallon Half Barrels.

88 cents per gallon buys our highest grade Seroco Ready Mixed House Paint, put up in 25-gallon half barrels, exactly as illustrated.

This shows the style in which we put up Seroco paint in half-barrel lots and are able to offer it at 88 cents per gallon, just enough to cover cost of manufacture, with but our one small profit added.

85 Cents per Gallon for Seroco Paint in Full 50-Gallon Barrels.

At 85 cents per gallon, made in our own factory.

In 50-gallon barrels this excellent Seroco Ready Mixed Paint is offered at 85 cents per gallon. Remember, every gallon of Seroco Ready Mixed Paint is guaranteed to give satisfaction in wearing qualities and covering capacity. This means you are absolutely safe when purchasing a barrel of this paint. The money paid will be promptly refunded if for any reason you should think that the paint is not as represented.

Prices and List of Colors of Seroco Ready Mixed House Paint.

No. 30E100 Always order by color number as well as catalogue number.

201	French Gray	226	Willow Green
202	Lavender	227	Drab
203	Straw	229	Red
204	Pea Green	230	Brown
205	Light Drab	231	French Yellow
206	Canary	233	Slate
207	Lemont Stone	235	Light Stone
208	Pearl	237	Dark Gray
209	Beaver	239	Black
210	Pink	240	Yellow Stone
211	Milwaukee Brick	241	Green Tint
213	Nile Green	242	Light Slate
214	Olive Drab	243	Outside White
215	Cream	244	Sky Blue
216	Fawn	246	Colonial Yellow
217	Pure Blue	250	Azure Blue
218	Buff	251	Orange
219	Terra Cotta	252	Oakwood
220	Apple Green	254	Cream Tint
221	Leather Brown	255	Flesh Color
223	Light Blue	256	Tinted White
224	Maroon	IW	Inside White
225	Bronze Green		

Prices for above colors.	Each	Gallon
1-quart cans	28c	
2-quart cans	53c	
1-gallon cans	98c	
5-gallon buckets		93c
25-gallon half barrels		88c
50-gallon barrels		85c

Special Colors.

5-gallon kits,

No. 30E102	per gal.	1 gal.	2 qts.	1 qt.
232 Myrtle Green	$1.25	$1.30	70c	40c
234 Vermilion	1.75	1.80	95c	50c
236 Emerald Green	1.25	1.30	70c	40c
247 Carmine	1.75	1.80	95c	50c
253 Golden Green	1.25	1.30	70c	40c

Special to Dealers.

We will furnish the Seroco House Paints in lots of one dozen cans at the following prices. We cannot send assorted colors in this offer; we will allow two selections of colors, six cans of each shade.

Prices for all shades under catalogue No. 30E100.

Price, 1-quart cans, per dozen	$ 3.10
Price, ½-gallon cans, per dozen	6.10
Price, 1-gallon cans, per dozen	11.40

Prices for all shades under catalogue No. 30E102.

	1-gal. cans, per doz.	½-gal. cans, per doz.	1-qt. cans, per doz.
232 Myrtle Green	$15.00	$ 8.00	$4.40
234 Vermilion	21.00	11.00	5.50
236 Emerald Green	15.00	8.00	4.40
247 Carmine	21.00	11.00	5.50
253 Golden Green	15.00	8.00	4.40

Brushes to Use With Seroco Ready Mixed House Paint.

For inside wall painting, use a No. 30E551 or No. 30E552 wall brush, any size, 3½ or 4-inch recommended. For interior wood work use a round paint brush, No. 30E545 or No. 30E546, any size, 3-0 or 4-0 recommended. For windows use a sash tool, No. 30E543 or No. 30E544; sizes 4 to 8 are best adapted for this work.

For outside house painting the following brushes are required: Wall brush, round paint brush, two or three sash tools. No. 30E551 or No. 30E552 wall brush, sizes 3½, 4 or 4½ inches in width are recommended for the walls. No. 30E545 or No. 30E546 round paint brushes, sizes 3-0 to 5-0, for applying the trimming colors. No. 30E543 or No. 30E544 sash tools, one each, sizes 4 and 8, for general trimming and used where the round paint brush will be found too large.

Seroco Ready Mixed Floor Paints.

No. 30E104 Made from the very best pigments, by the latest and most improved machinery. Absolutely the best floor paint made; guaranteed to please or can be returned at our expense. Paint will dry in one night.

The best wearing paint for interior floors, outside porch floors, steps, etc. Has wonderful covering power and will wear longer than any other paint made.

510	Light Yellow
530	Drab
540	Lead
550	Maroon
560	Oxide Red
570	French Gray
580	Dark Yellow
590	Floor Green

Price, 1-quart cans	28c
Price, 2-quart cans	53c
Price, 1-gallon cans	98c
Price, 5-gallon kits, per gallon	93c

Use a No. 30E551 or No. 30E552 wall brush for applying above Seroco Floor Paint, 3, 3½ or 4 inches in width recommended.

SPECIAL PRICES IN LOTS OF ONE DOZEN CANS.

We cannot send assorted colors. We will allow two selections, six cans of each shade.

Seroco Ready Mixed Floor Paint, No. 30E104.

Price, 1-quart cans, per dozen	$ 3.10
Price, ½-gallon cans, per dozen	6.10
Price, 1-gallon cans, per dozen	11.40

Iron Paint Paddle.

No. 30E493 Many a poor job of painting can be traced direct to the paint pot, in that the paint was not properly stirred. This paint paddle will mix the paint thoroughly in less time than can be done with a wood paddle, furthermore, a wood paddle will float and be always in the way of the brush. Made of malleable iron, strong and durable.

Price, small size, for 1-gallon cans, each	$0.10
Per dozen	1.05
Price, large size, for 5-gallon kits, each	.12
Per dozen	1.30

Seroco Weatherproof Mineral Barn, Roof and Fence Paint.

Seroco Weatherproof Mineral Barn, Roof and Fence Paint, the most durable mineral paint, finely ground and thinned with linseed oil, the very best barn, roof and fence paint that we handle, is especially recommended for these purposes and for all purposes where the paint is especially exposed to the weather.

As a preservative this paint cannot be excelled, and we recommend it in every way for shingles, tin or iron roofs, structural iron work, barns, elevators and posts or timbers to be put under the ground. This mineral and weatherproof paint is acknowledged to be the best preserver of wood and the most durable. It is also water and rustproof, will stop leaks, prevent corrosion and is free from acids. One gallon covers about 300 square feet of surface two coats. We know that our Seroco Weatherproof Mineral Barn, Roof and Fence Paint will cover more surface, last longer, will give better satisfaction and is altogether the most desirable and durable paint for these purposes ever manufactured, and considering the covering surface and wearing qualities, it is worth double the price of any ordinary roof, fence or barn paint.

While our Free Color Sample Booklet shows the six different colors of this special weatherproof mineral barn, roof and fence paint and will be sent to any address on application, we would advise you to send your order direct from the catalogue, stating which of the six colors you desire; we will send the paint to you, guaranteeing the color to please you and the paint to prove satisfactory, or you can return it to us at our expense and we will immediately refund your money. Put up in 1-gallon cans, 5-gallon buckets, one-half barrels containing 25 gallons, and barrels containing 50 gallons. Made in six shades.

OUR GUARANTEE: We guarantee our Seroco Weatherproof Mineral Barn, Roof and Fence Paint to wear for five years if the directions are carefully followed. Our guarantee covers any and all defects due to the quality of the paint.

Prices and List of Colors of Seroco Weatherproof Mineral Barn, Roof and Fence Paint.

No. 30E108 Give catalogue number as well as name and number of color when ordering. Colors:

800	Oxide Red
810	Lead Color
820	Dark Gray
830	Yellow
850	Maroon
860	Natural Green

	Gallon
Price, 1-gal. can	65c
Price, 5-gal. bucket	60c
Price, 25-gal. barrel	55c
Price, 50-gal. barrel	50c

READ WHAT A FEW OF OUR CUSTOMERS SAY ABOUT SEROCO READY MIXED PAINT. THOUSANDS WRITE THE SAME WAY.

THIS EXPERT PAINTER SAYS THE SPREADING QUALITIES ARE EXCELLENT.

Sears, Roebuck & Co., Chicago, Ill. Evansville, Ind.

Gentlemen:—Being a practical painter and having used your Seroco Ready Mixed Paint can say that its equal would be impossible to find. Its spreading qualities are excellent, almost doubling those of other paints. It is easily worked and finishes handsomely with less than one-half the labor of the ordinary paints on the market. Ordinary mixed paints are much dearer than your Seroco Ready Mixed Paint would be at $1.75 per gallon.

Yours truly, E. F. ELBRECHT.

Experienced Painter's Verdict.

Carlton Center, Mich.

Sears, Roebuck & Co., Chicago, Ill.

Gentlemen:—I am very much pleased with your paint. The man that did my painting says it is the best ready mixed paint he ever used, and he is an experienced painter. It holds its color well and will not peel off as I have seen some other brands. I think I saved 30 per cent in buying my paint of you.

Yours truly, JOHN USBORNE, SR.

The Kind of Brushes to Use with Seroco Barn, Roof and Fence Paint.

For painting roofs and the walls of barns, sheds, etc., use a No. 30E551 or No. 30E552 wall brush, 4 or 4½ inches in width. For fences use the same brush but narrower, 3 or 3½ inches in width, or No. 30E545 or No. 30E546 round paint brush, size 3-0. For trimming use a round paint brush, No. 30E545 or No. 30E546, size 6-0.

Seroco Graphite-Creosote Paint.

No. 30E110 For barns, roofs, iron work, etc. Some prefer a graphite paint for painting barns, roofs, etc.; for this reason we have made a paint which consists of pure air-floated graphite, sufficient mineral to give it the proper color, creosote and linseed oil. While it makes an excellent barn paint, it is especially recommended for surfaces under water, such as posts and timbers to be put under ground.

360 Dark Red 361 Brown 363 Dark Lead 362 Willow Green 364 Black

Price, 1-gallon cans, per gallon........70c
5-gallon buckets, per gallon........65c
½-barrel, 30 gallons, per gallon........58c
1-barrel, 50 gallons, per gallon........53c

Seroco Graphite-Creosote Paint is applied with the same brushes recommended for our Seroco Weatherproof Mineral Barn, Roof and Fence Paint.

Pure Graphite Ready Mixed Paint.

No. 30E111 This paint is made of absolutely pure graphite and pure boiled linseed oil. It is the purest that can be made. Used extensively for painting smokestacks, tin and iron roofs, and structural iron and wood work.

Pure graphite paint is a dark slate color. The black listed below is the pure graphite paint, with the addition of lamp black. No. 1, graphite color; No. 2, black. Be sure and state kind wanted.

Price, 1-gallon cans, per gallon........$1.00
Price, 5-gallon kits, per gallon.........95
Price, 25-gallon ½ barrels, per gallon........90
Price, 50-gallon barrels, per gallon........87

Seroco Shingle Stain and Preservative.

No. 30E112 While our Mineral Paint is highly recommended for shingled roofs, still some prefer a shingle stain. These stains are the best manufactured, the shingles can be dipped in same or it may be applied with a brush. A shingled roof coated with these stains will last twice as long. When applied with a brush, one gallon will cover about 150 square feet of surface, one coat, or 100 square feet two coats. When dipped, 2½ to 3 gallons will cover 1,000 of the regulation 4x16 shingles. Two-thirds the length of the shingle only need be dipped. **Furnished in the following shades. Red, Moss Green, Dark Green, Brown, Light Slate, Dark Slate, and Black.**

Price, 1-gallon cans, per gallon........60c
Price, 5-gallon kits, per gallon........55c
Price, 25-gallon barrels, per gallon........50c
Price, 50-gallon barrels, per gallon........45c

Apply above Seroco Shingle Stain with a No. 30E551 or No. 30E552 wall brush, the largest size recommended.

Seroco Buggy Paints.

No. 30E115 Our buggy paints are ground in the best coach varnish. The colors are guaranteed not to fade. It is prepared especially for buggies and carriages but can be used on chairs, settees, benches, or any article exposed to the weather. One coat makes a beautiful and durable finish. Ready for use and no varnish required.

Do not fail to state color wanted.

Colors:

600 Yellow **640 Dark Green**
610 Vermilion **650 Blue**
620 Light Wine **660 Dark Wine**
630 Coach Green **670 Coach Black**

Price, ½-pint can........$0.20
Price, 1-pint can........30
Price, 1-quart can........50
Price, 1-gallon can........1.85

Apply Seroco Buggy Paint with a varnish brush, we recommend No. 30E516 or No. 30E520 for fine work. A 2-inch brush is the best size.

Wagon Paint.

No. 30E116 Wagon Paint, ground in pure linseed oil and the best coach varnish. It is the best wagon paint, extremely tough and will not crack. The colors are permanent and will not fade. One coat of Seroco wagon paint, at a small expense, will preserve your wagon or implement and make it look like new. Dries hard with a high gloss. Colors: red, green, blue, vermilion, yellow and black. Apply with a No. 30E516, 30E518 or 30E520 varnish brush, 1, 2 or 2½ inches in width.

Price, 1-quart can........$0.45
Price, ½-gallon can........80
Price, 1-gallon can........1.50

Liquid Weatherproof Canvas Coating.

No. 30E117 The greatest waterproof preparation for cotton duck. A coat of this material applied on cotton duck or canvas of the lightest weight will make it absolutely waterproof. The canvas can be folded without the danger of cracking, it acts like rubber. Especially adapted for **hay stack covers,** tents, wagon covers, tarpaulins, awnings; in fact, it can be applied to anything made of canvas or cotton duck and make it absolutely waterproof. Five gallons will cover an ordinary hay stack cover. In 1-gallon cans. Price, per gallon........60c
In 5-gallon cans. Price, per gallon........50c
In 10-gallon cans. Price, per gallon........48c

Radiator Enamel.

No. 30E118 This enamel is especially made for radiators, steam pipes and other steam heated surfaces. It is ready for use and dries with a fine glossy finish, very durable and tough. Apply with a No. 30E544 Sash Tool, size 6 or 8.

	Gallon	Quart	Pint
Maroon	$1.05	$0.30	18c
Pea Green	1.25	.35	20c
Terra Cotta	1.25	.35	20c
BronzeGreen	1.25	.35	20c
Aluminum	2.60	.70	42c

Gold Radiator Enamel.

No. 30E118 A satisfactory ready mixed gold radiator enamel cannot be made. We will send you the powder and liquid in separate packages and it must be mixed in equal proportions when ready to use. Do not mix more than required for immediate use. By following these directions this enamel will look better and wear longer than any other.

Liquid and powder to make one pint........$0.50
Liquid and powder to make one quart........95
Liquid and powder to make one gallon........3.50

Seroco Decorative Enamel.

No. 30E120 For all decorative work; is ready mixed, can be applied on anything and everything, any kind of furniture, iron beds, shelves, wicker work, baby carriages, clocks, etc. One half pint can is sufficient for an ordinary iron bed and will make it look like new. When ordering, be sure and mention color wanted: White, pink, light blue, light green, yellow, vermilion, red, brown, maroon, chrome green and black. Apply with a varnish brush, 1 or 1½ inches in width. No. 30E518 and No. 30E520 will do good work. For painting very small articles use a Sash Tool, No. 30E543 or 30E544, size 2 or 4.

Price, ½-pint can........20c
Price, 1-pint can........35c

Cannot be sent by mail.

Aluminum Enamel.

No. 30E122 Can be applied to anything, any kind of metal or wood, picture frames, furniture, shelves, clocks, stoves, mantels, etc.; it dries in a few hours with a silver finish and will not rub off. Water and heat will not affect it. Apply with a camel's hair brush, No. 30E507, size ⅛, ⅜ or ¾ recommended for small work. No. 30E508 or 30E509, size 1 or 1½ recommended for flat surfaces.

	Dozen	Each
Price, ⅛-pint can	$1.15	11c
Price, ¼-pint can	1.90	18c
Price, ½-pint can	2.90	28c
Price, 1-pint can	4.75	42c
Price, 1-quart can		70c

Cannot be sent by mail.

Seroco Gloss Enamel for Interior Use.

No. 30E125 This enamel produces a beautiful luster on walls, plastered or wood, and is a desirable article for kitchens, dining rooms, bed rooms and hospital wards, as it is easily cleaned. We furnish it in twelve shades, as follows: Pearl, light slate, cream, apple green, pea green, nile green, light blue, dark blue, lavender, pink, lilac, carmine, also white, ivory and black. Apply with a wall brush No. 30E551 or 30E552, size 3, 3½ or 4 inches.

1 Pint	1 Quart	½ Gallon	1 Gallon
24c	45c	78c	$1.48

Bath Tub Enamel.

No. 30E126 White Bath Tub Enamel, Liquid Porcelain. A common iron tub coated with this preparation will have a beautiful appearance. Apply with a good varnish brush. No. 30E520, 1½ inches in width is recommended.

Price, ½-pint can........25c
Price, 1-pint can........45c

Cannot be sent by mail.

Saved 52 Cents a Gallon.

Sears, Roebuck & Co., Chicago, Ill. Boydon, Iowa.
Gentlemen:—Seroco Ready Mixed is as good a paint as I ever used; was well pleased with it. The same paint I would have to pay $1.50 per gallon for here, I got of you for 98 cents; so you see I have saved 52 cents per gallon. Yours truly, ALBERT DEAN.

Wire Screen Enamel.

No. 30E128 Green or Black Wire Screen Enamel. Ready for use and easily applied; does not clog meshes of screens, and one coat gives to old, rusty screens a rich, brilliant and lasting finish. Apply with a varnish brush, 1 or 1½ in. wide.

Price, ½-pint can........15c
Price, 1-pint can........30c

State color wanted.

Cannot be sent by mail.

Black Iron and Roof Paint.

No. 30E130 Black Iron and Roof Paint cannot be excelled for general durability and preservative qualities. It is made especially for covering all kinds of metal work, dries rapidly with a hard, glossy black finish, and is absolutely water and acid proof. This is a paint universally used by railroads and steamboat companies for smoke stacks, bridges, etc., and should not be confounded with cheap mineral or black paints. **The best paint for iron work, all purposes.** In black only. Will cover from 600 to 800 square feet of smooth, metal surface per gallon, making it an economical paint to use. Apply with a wall brush, No. 30E551 or 30E552, the largest size recommended.

Price, 1-gallon can........85c
Price, 5-gallon jacket can, per gallon........75c
Price, 10-gallon jacket can, per gallon........70c
Price, 50-gallon barrel, per gallon........65c

Sapolin Stove Pipe Enamel.

No. 30E132 Sapolin Stove Pipe Enamel. Especially prepared for use on stove pipes, stoves, furnaces, grates, steam and water pipes, boilers, smoke stacks, garden tools, iron fences, brackets, etc. **One coat produces a brilliant black finish; very elastic.** Will not crack, chip, peel or burn off. Ready for instant use. Apply with a varnish brush. No. 30E517 or 30E518, size 1 or 1½ inches.

Price, ½-pint can. Weight, ⅝ pound........$0.15
Price, 1-pint can. Weight, 1⅛ pounds........26
Price, 1-gallon can........1.60

Cannot be sent by mail.

Egyptian Stove Pipe Enamel.

No. 30E133 The most satisfactory stove pipe and iron enamel ever put on the market. It is not so extensively advertised as some brands, but it will wear longer and produce a better finish than anything you can possibly obtain in stove pipe enamels. We furnish a brush free with each can.

Price, ½-pint can, including brush........$0.12
Price, 1-pint can, including brush........20
Price, ½-gallon can, including brush........70
Price, 1-gallon can, including brush........1.25

Cannot be sent by mail.

Pumice Stone Bricks.

No. 30E138 Pumice Stone Bricks are used by the painter and varnisher for rubbing down. These bricks are now used by the thousands for scouring stone window sills, steps and sidewalks. Price, each........$0.15
Weight, about 1¾ pounds.
Per dozen........1.70

Powdered Pumice Stone

No. 30E139 Finest Imported Powdered Pumice Stone. Price, per pound........5c
100-pound drums, per pound........4c

Plaster Paris.

No. 30E140 Price, per barrel of about 250 pounds........$2.00
Less quantity, per pound........02

Pure French Ochre in Oil.

No. 30E150 Pure French Ochre in oil, in 12½ and 25-pound cans. Price, per lb..4c

English Venetian Red in Oil.

No. 30E151 English Venetian Red, especially adapted for painting brick buildings. In 12½ and 25-pound cans.
Price, per pound........4c

White Ochre in Oil.

No. 30E152 White Ochre Ground in Oil. Ground in pure linseed oil and used as primer only. 12½ and 25-pound cans. Price, per pound........4c

Zinc in Oil.

No. 30E158 Pure Green Seal French Zinc, in oil, 12½ and 25-lb. cans. Price, per pound........12½
No. 30E159 Pure Green Seal French Zinc, in oil, 1 to 5-lb. cans. Price, per pound........15c
No. 30E160 Zinc in Oil, American Snow White, 12½ and 25-lb. pails. Price, per pound........7c

Putty.

No. 30E165 Putty in bladders, 10 to 25 pounds.
Price, per pound........2½c

Glaziers' Points.

No. 30E166 Zinc Glaziers' Points, for fastening glass in sash; put up in ¼-pound papers. Price, per paper........5c

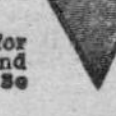

White Lead.

No. 30E171 Great Western White Lead in Oil; a special grade. Kegs of 12½, 25, 50 or 100 pounds.
Price, per pound........4c

Seroco Brand Painters' White Lead.

No. 30E172 A combination of absolutely pure white lead and zinc ground in pure linseed oil. A lead that will wear longer and work better than strictly pure white lead. We guarantee it. Kegs of 12½, 25, 50 and 100 pounds. Price, per pound....6c

National Lead Co.'s Brands White Lead.

No. 30E176 The following brands of white lead are manufactured by one concern, the National Lead Co., therefore we have no control over the price. The price quoted below was the lowest market price at the time this catalogue went to press. We reserve the right to advance the price should the market go higher but, on the other hand, if a decline, we will give you the benefit and refund the difference to you in cash. We handle the following brands: Red Seal, Shipman, Southern, Collier and Eckstein.

Be sure and mention the brand desired, if none is given we will ship Red Seal brand. Put up in 12½, 25, 50 and 100 pound kegs. Price, per pound........7c

The Seroco Colors in Oil.

For tinting paints. Ground in pure linseed oil, strong and permanent.

		1 and 5-lb. cans. Price, per lb.
No. 30E200	Blacks. Refined Lamp Black	15c
	Coach Black	13c
	Ivory Black	12c
	Drop Black	10c
No. 30E201	Blues. Prussian Blue	34c
	Ultramarine Blue	15c
	Cobalt Blue	25c
No. 30E202	Browns. Raw and Burnt Umber	12c
	Raw and Burnt Sienna	11c
	Vandyke Brown	12c
No. 30E203	Greens. Blind Green	16c
	Chrome Green	13c
No. 30E204	Reds. English Venetian	8c
	Indian Red	14c
	Tuscan Red	16c
	Unfading Red	28c
	English Rose Pink	17c
	English Rose Lake	26c
	Scarlet Vermilion	18c
No. 30E205	Yellows. Chrome, L. M. & O.	15c
	Yellow Ochre	8c
No. 30E206	Graining Colors. Light Oak, Dark Oak, Antique Oak, Walnut, Cherry, Mahogany	12c

All of the above colors furnished in 25-pound cans, at 2 cents per pound less.
Cannot be sent by mail.

Oil Stain.

No. 30E215 Perfect imitations of natural wood, cherry, rosewood, mahogany, walnut, light oak, dark oak, antique oak. For staining interior woodwork or any work not finished. This stain cannot be applied over varnished or painted surfaces. One or two coats of varnish applied over it will produce a fine finish. Nos. 30E300, 30E302 and 30E298 or 30E299 varnishes can be used in connection with these stains. Apply with a varnish brush. Price, ¼ pint can........$0.14
Price, 1-pint can........ .20
Price, 1-quart can........ .35
Price, ½-gallon can........ .67
Price, 1-gallon can........ 1.25
Cannot be sent by mail.

Varnish Stain.

No. 30E216 Stain and varnish used separately, on new work, produce a better finish than varnish stain, but for refinishing painted or varnished surfaces, such as old furniture or painted or varnished woodwork, this varnish stain is recommended. It stains and varnishes in one operation. Dries hard with a fine luster. Furnished in the following natural wood colors: cherry, rosewood, mahogany, walnut, light oak, dark oak, antique oak. Do not fail to mention color wanted. Apply with a varnish brush, 2-inch brush recommended.

In selecting a color it is necessary that the color selected is of a similar shade as the old finish; for instance, a piece of furniture finished in mahogany cannot be refinished in light oak by applying the light oak varnish stain. The varnish stain in this case will have to be of a dark color, either mahogany or walnut.
Price, ½-pint can........$0.15
Price, 1-pint can........ .21
Price, 1-quart can........ .38
Price, ½-gallon can........ .72
Price, 1-gallon can........ 1.30
Cannot be sent by mail.

Whiting.

No. 30E218 Extra Gilders' Whiting, fine quality, bolted. Barrels about 400 pounds, per pound........1c
Less quantity, per pound........2c

Dry Colors.

The following dry colors are used for tinting calcimines, making graining colors and other purposes. Some use these dry colors for painting purposes by mixing them with linseed oil. This we do not recommend unless the mixture is put through a paint mill, as you will have nothing but a coarse mixture which is not fit for anything. If a mineral paint is desired at a low price you will profit by purchasing the Seroco Weatherproof Mineral, Barn, Roof and Fence Paint, as then you will have a substantial paint, a paint that will wear three times as long, therefore cheapest in the end.

We handle only best qualities.	Bbl., per lb.	Per lb.
No. 30E220 Yellow Rochelle Ochre, 400 pounds in barrel	1c	2c
No. 30E221 Imported Marseilles Yellow Ochre, strong in color, 100-pound drums	3½c	4c
No. 30E222 Italian Buff (light), 500 pounds	1c	2c
No. 30E223 American Venetian Red, 350 pounds	¾c	1½c
No. 30E224 Imperial English Venetian Red, 336 pounds	1½c	2c
No. 30E225 Snow White Wood Filler, 400 pounds	1½c	2c
No. 30E226 Prince's Brown Mineral, 350 pounds	1c	2c
No. 30E227 White Ochre, 400 pounds	1½c	2c
No. 30E228 Lampblack, Germantown, 80 pounds	9c	10c
No. 30E229 Burnt Turkey Umber, 350 pounds	3½c	6c
No. 30E230 Raw Turkey Umber, 350 pounds	3½c	6c
No. 30E231 Burnt Italian Sienna, 350 pounds	4½c	7c
No. 30E232 Red Lead, 100 lbs.	6¾c	8c
No. 30E233 Raw Italian Sienna, 350 pounds	4½c	7c
No. 30E234 Chrome Green, best		8c
No. 30E235 Chrome Yellow Lemon		10c
No. 30E236 French Gray or Slate, 400 pounds in barrel	¾c	1½c
No. 30E237 Ultramarine Blue		7c
No. 30E238 Whitewash or Lime Blue		8c

Limeproof Colors for Tinting Calcimines and Whitewash.

A small quantity will tint a large bucket of calcimine or whitewash.
No. 30E240 Limeproof Green, per pound....12c
No. 30E241 Limeproof Blue, per pound....12c
No. 30E242 Limeproof Red, per pound....11c
No. 30E243 Limeproof Yellow, per pound....11c

Soluble Blue for Manufacturing Bluing.

This soluble blue is used by the large bluing manufacturers. Guaranteed the best on the market. If interested in manufacturing liquid bluing, we will be pleased to furnish the formula.
No. 30E244 Soluble Blue. Price, per lb....38c
25-pound drums, per pound........35c

Seroco Water Paint.

No. 30E250 Only requires mixing with water. Sanitary, fireproof. A dry powder. In white and various colors.

A water paint for the interior painting of residences, and on account of its sanitary nature and fireproof qualities, it is admirably adapted for the interior painting of factories, warehouses, docks, public buildings, breweries, stables, air shafts and court yards, and can be applied on sand finished walls, stone, brick or any solid surface. The average covering power of this paint is from 20 to 80 square feet to the pound, according to the surface to be painted. Full directions with each package.

Seroco Water Paint Price List.

		400-lb. bbls., per lb.	100-50-25 lb. kegs, per lb.	5-lb. package, per lb.
No. 10	White	5c	6c	7c
No. 20	Slate	7c	8c	9c
No. 30	Buff	7c	8c	9c
No. 40	Canary	7c	8c	9c
No. 50	Nile Green	7c	8c	9c
No. 60	Red	7c	8c	9c
No. 70	Dark Gray	7c	8c	9c
No. 80	Dark Blue	7c	8c	9c
No. 90	Light Blue	7c	8c	9c
No. 100	Pink	7c	8c	9c
No. 120	Blind Green	10c	11c	12c

Seroco Sanitary Calcimine.

Durable wall finish; absolutely healthful; mixed with water only; will not rub off; cannot fade. Made in 16 colors and white.

The Sanitary Wall Finish is ready for use when it is mixed with water and is unequaled for plain or high class decorative work on walls and ceilings. It covers well and one coat will generally be found sufficient. It can be recoated at any time when necessary, it forms a durable coating which will not decay, peel away or rub off if applied to a solid surface. One pound properly mixed and applied, covers from 60 to 100 square feet, according to the surface. To obtain good results, all surfaces that have been calcimined should be thoroughly cleaned, and all lime and whitewashed walls should be well scraped and sized before applying.

In ordering, be sure to give number and color.

Color No.		Color No.		Color No.	
11	Ivory	100	Medium Green	44	Light Green
55	Yellow				
99	Light Pink	33	Salmon Pink	66	Cream
133	Pea Green	88	Buff	122	Blue
22	Lavender	144	Slate	166	Drab
77	Olive Gray	111	Pink	155	Green

No. 30E254 White, per 5-pound package $0.24
Per case, containing 20 5-pound packages.. 4.20
Tints, per 5-pound package........ .26
Per case, containing 20 5-pound packages.. 4.80

Pure Graphite Paint Paste.

No. 30E262 To 12½ pounds (1 gallon) paste, add 3 gallons boiled oil, making 4 gallons of Pure Graphite Paint, ready for use. Will cover 500 square feet smooth metal per gallon. Will not crack, blister or peel off; is not affected by heat or cold, smoke, steam, moisture, acids, alkali or brine, or by climatic changes. For use on roofs, stacks, boilers, bridges, structural iron work of any kind. This paint is manufactured from pure graphite and absolutely pure linseed oil. Is a dark slate color.
Price, per 5 -pound can........$0.40
Price, per 12½-pound can........ .85
Price, per 25 -pound can........ 1.60

Seroco Floor Oil.

No. 30E275 Seroco Floor Oil. A special preparation for floors of residences and stores. A very small quantity applied with a cloth will bring out a rich color; also, it will do away with scrubbing, as floors oiled with Seroco Floor Oil are easily cleaned by simply washing them with soap and water.
Price, per pint can........$0.20
Price, per quart can........ .30
Price, per ½-gallon can........ .52
Price, per 1-gallon can........ .90
Price, per 5-gallon jacket can........ 4.00

Seroco Floor Wax.

No. 30E273 Seroco Floor Wax. A lasting brilliant polish can be obtained on floors when using our prepared floor wax. It is perfectly transparent and will not change the color of wood. Dirt and dust will not stick to floors waxed with the Seroco floor wax. One pound will cover about 300 square feet. Directions are simple and plainly printed on every can. Put up in 1-pound cans.
Price, per can........25c

Dancing Floor Wax.

No. 30E277 Dancing Floor Wax. (Powdered.) This is the best preparation for dancing floors, easily applied and can be used on new, old or canvas covered floors. Guaranteed not to soil the most delicate fabric. Sprinkle it on the floors and the dancers will do the rest. Put up in 1-pound cans. Price, per can 30c

Seroco Floor Color Varnish in Natural Wood Colors.

No. 30E278 Softwood floors can be made to look like hardwood by applying this wonderful Color Varnish. The most artistic finish can be put on any kind of floors with very little labor or expense. It can be applied over painted floors and hardwood imitated to perfection.

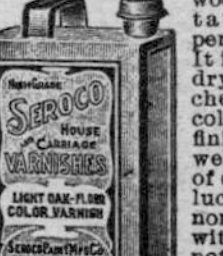

It is made from an elastic, hard drying varnish, combined with chemically pure, soluble oil colors. It cannot be surpassed for finishing floors of all kinds, as well as furniture and woodwork of every description. It is translucent, free from sediment and non-fading. Dries hard over night with a fine tone and luster and will not scratch or mar white. Made in five shades—dark oak, light oak, mahogany, cherry and walnut.

5 Gallons	1 Gallon	½ Gallon	Quart	Pint
$7.25	$1.55	88c	48c	26c

Seroco Filler.

No. 30E279 Seroco Filler for Cracks in Floors. A specially prepared, elastic, non-shrinkable compound for filling cracks of floors or furniture before applying paint or varnish; also adapted for smoothing rough surfaces.

Price, 1-pound can 13c
Price, 5-pound can 60c

Seroco Paste Wood Filler.

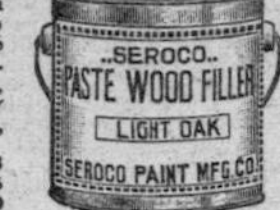

No. 30E285 All open grained hardwoods, such as oak, ash, etc., must be filled in order to produce a perfect varnish finish. This filler is the best made, easily applied and dries very hard. Made in two shades, light oak and dark oak.

Price, 1-pound can..$0.08
Price, 5-pound can.. .35
Price, 25-pound can.. 1.50

Seroco Liquid Wood Filler.

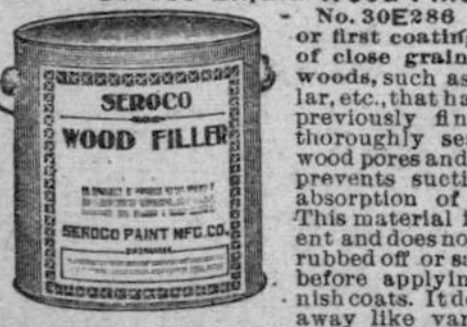

No. 30E286 For filling or first coating all kinds of close grained natural woods, such as pine, poplar, etc., that have not been previously finished. It thoroughly seals up the wood pores and effectually prevents suction or the absorption of moisture. This material is transparent and does not need to be rubbed off or sandpapered before applying the varnish coats. It does not sink away like varnish, but dries on the surface, thus equaling, for work of this nature, two coats of varnish. A coat or two of varnish applied over this material produces a really remarkable finish.

5 Gallons	1 Gallon	½ Gallon	Quart	Pint
$5.25	$1.15	65c	35c	20c

Steel Wool and Shavings.

No. 30E288 Steel Wool is a mass of fine fibres of steel resembling curled hair, which, while sharp, does not scratch but will cut as smoothly as the finest sandpaper, emery or pumice stone. For many purposes it is superior to sandpaper, etc. Used for rubbing down fillers and varnishes; in fact, it takes the place of sandpaper or pumice stone and will be found a much better article to use. Steel shavings is a coarse grade and is used for removing rust from iron preparatory to painting, also for cleaning floors or any surface of old varnish.

No. 0. Very fine. Price, per pound.......... 45c
No. 1. Fine. Price, per pound.......... 35c
No. 3. Fine. Price, per pound.......... 30c
Steel shavings, coarse. Price, per pound.......... 25c

VARNISH DEPARTMENT.

SEROCO HOUSE VARNISHES.

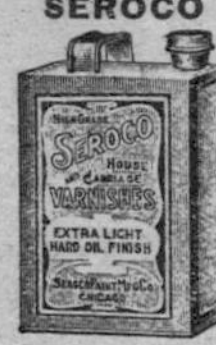

The following varnishes are made by one of the largest and best varnish manufacturers in the country. The very same varnishes are sold under the manufacturers' brands at from 50 cents to $1.50 per gallon higher than the prices we are quoting. We guarantee every ounce of our varnishes and no matter how costly the job, we guarantee satisfaction or money refunded. **Let us have a trial order, it will cost you nothing should it fail to give satisfaction.**

Seroco Extra Light Hard Oil Finish.

No. 30E298 Especially designed for finishing all kinds of natural wood surfaces where the grain and color are to be preserved. Works freely and dries in about 24 hours with an elegant gloss. This material may also be used with marked satisfaction on wainscoting, baseboards and inside doors.

5 Gallons	1 Gallon	½ Gallon	Quart	Pint
$6.00	$1.30	75c	42c	23c

Seroco No. 1 Hard Oil Finish.

No. 30E299 Splendidly adapted for general interior woodwork. Is pale, free flowing and durable and possesses a full and substantial body. Dries free from dust in 2 to 3 hours.

5 Gallons	1 Gallon	½ Gallon	Quart	Pint
$4.75	$1.05	63c	35c	20c

Seroco Furniture Varnish.

No. 30E300 This varnish may be used to brighten up worn and lusterless furniture of every description. It dries over night and imparts a fine gloss finish. For general repair work in the household on articles in daily use that must be finished hurriedly, this material is recommended.

5 Gallons	1 Gallon	½ Gallon	Quart	Pint
$3.75	85c	53c	28c	16c

Seroco Cabinet Finish.

No. 30E301 This varnish is designed for highest grade interior woodwork that is to be rubbed and polished; also gives a beautiful finish when left in the gloss. Is exceptionally rich and lustrous and on account of its elasticity, is extremely durable. Dries dust free in 3 to 4 hours and sufficiently hard for rubbing in 60 hours.

5 Gallons	1 Gallon	½ Gallon	Quart	Pint
$7.00	$1.50	85c	47c	25c

Seroco Interior Varnish.

No. 30E302 A high grade varnish, especially adapted for first class interior woodwork finishing and fine furniture. This varnish is of substantial body, light in color and works with great freedom. It gives a lasting and elegant finish and dries in from 10 to 12 hours.

5 Gallons	1 Gallon	½ Gallon	Quart	Pint
$5.00	$1.10	65c	37c	20c

Seroco Interior Spar Finish.

No. 30E303 For high class interior wood work. Exceedingly pale, free working and very durable. It dries free from dust in 4 to 5 hours. Can be safely rubbed in from 2 to 3 days and polished to a high and permanent luster in 4 days.

5 Gallons	1 Gallon	½ Gallon	Quart	Pint
$8.00	$1.70	95c	52c	28c

Seroco Durable Floor Varnish.

No. 30E304 Unequaled for finishing floors of all kinds, natural wood, painted or oil cloth. Will not turn white under repeated washing or foot friction, and dries to walk on over night. It is easily applied and gives an elegant and durable finish. This is undoubtedly the best floor varnish on the market.

5 Gallons	1 Gallon	½ Gallon	Quart	Pint
$8.25	$1.75	98c	53c	29c

Seroco Outside Spar Varnish.

No. 30E305 For finishing all kinds of exposed surfaces, such as outside doors, vestibules and store fronts. It is also especially recommended for finishing inside blinds and the woodwork in bath rooms and on sinks, where a very elastic and durable varnish should be employed.

5 Gallons	1 Gallon	½ Gallon	Quart	Pint
$10.75	$2.25	$1.25	65c	35c

Seroco White Damar Varnish.

No. 30E307 Made from imported Batavia gum. For finishing over any enameled surfaces, white or ivory, without producing discoloration. It may also be used with excellent satisfaction on fine wall paper hangings or on delicately tinted painted walls. Is of good body and dries well.

5 Gallons	1 Gallon	½ Gallon	Quart	Pint
$7.00	$1.50	85c	47c	25c

Seroco Black Asphaltum.

No. 30E309 For finishing all kinds of castings, smoke stacks, stove pipes, fenders, coal hods, iron work of agricultural implements, etc. It produces a jet black, brilliant finish and absolutely prevents rust or corrosion. It is heavy in body and quick drying.

5 Gallons	1 Gallon	½ Gallon	Quart	Pint
$2.50	60c	33c	22c	13c

Seroco Turpentine Japan Dryer.

No. 30E310 A first class house painters' japan, dependable in all kinds of weather. A good binder and a sure and quick dryer. It contains no acids and will not cause the paint with which it is mixed to burn, blister, crack, chalk or peel. It mixes readily with oil and does not detract from the elasticity of the paint.

5 Gallons	1 Gallon	½ Gallon	Quart	Pint
$3.50	80c	50c	30c	18c

Seroco Oil Shellac.

No. 30E312 This is a clear first coater or filler for new woods that have not been previously finished. It has a good body and produces a substantial and safe surface or base coat. It dries to sandpaper in 6 to 8 hours.

5 Gallons	1 Gallon	½ Gallon	Quart	Pint
$6.50	$1.40	80c	45c	25c

FINE CARRIAGE VARNISHES.

Seroco Wearing Body Varnish.

No. 30E313 A brilliant, durable and elastic varnish for finishing carriage and buggy bodies. It works and flows with surprising freedom and may be used on the largest surfaces, such as carriage bodies, with the greatest safety and satisfaction. It is very pale and will not darken or injure the lightest shades of body color. It dries free from dust in 12 to 16 hours and hardens properly in from 2 to 3 days.

1 Gallon	½ Gallon	Quart	Pint
$3.00	$1.60	85c	45c

Seroco Medium Drying Body.

No. 30E314 For finishing carriage bodies when time will not permit the use of our best Wearing Body Varnish. Varnish is pale, elastic and very durable. Works and flows with freedom and may be used with safety on larger panels. It dries hard in from 36 to 48 hours.

1 Gallon	½ Gallon	Quart	Pint
$2.75	$1.48	78c	42c

Seroco Elastic Gear.

No. 30E315 Used for finishing gear parts and wheels. Is free working, brilliant and durable. It sets in 6 to 8 hours and dries hard in 36 to 48 hours. This varnish may also be used for body finishing when drying despatch is an important consideration. This is a superior all around varnish for carriage finishing.

1 Gallon	½ Gallon	Quart	Pint
$2.85	$1.55	80c	43c

Seroco Quick Rubbing Varnish.

No. 30E316 This is an excellent material intended for undercoats of gears and bodies where time is a matter of consideration. Dries inside of 2 days to admit of being rubbed without sweating.

1 Gallon	½ Gallon	Quart	Pint
$2.40	$1.30	69c	36c

Seroco Hard Rubbing Body.

No. 30E317 For undercoats of gears or bodies. This is a magnificent material of light color and good body. It rubs without sweating in about 4 days and sets free from dust in from 8 to 12 hours.

1 Gallon	½ Gallon	Quart	Pint
$2.60	$1.40	75c	40c

Seroco Quick Black Rubbing.

No. 30E319 Made from our Medium Rubbing Varnish and the best Drop Black. Will rub without sweating in about 2 days.

1 Gallon	½ Gallon	Quart	Pint
$3.10	$1.65	87c	45c

Seroco One Coat Coach.

No. 30E320 A splendid varnish for general repair work. On carriages when work is simply dull or lusterless, otherwise in good condition, one coat of this varnish on the entire vehicle will produce a finish practically equal to a new job. It is light in color, elastic, brilliant and durable. Dries free from dust in about 12 hours and hardens to admit the use of the vehicle in about 3 days.

1 Gallon	½ Gallon	Quart	Pint
$2.70	$1.45	77c	40c

Seroco Wagon and Implement Varnish.

No. 30E321 For agricultural implements, wagons, etc. A good varnish for general outside work. Has a good body, a fine luster and is light in color and wears well. Dries in about 10 to 14 hours.

1 Gallon	½ Gallon	Quart	Pint
$1.65	93c	50c	27c

Seroco Gold Size.

No. 30E322 Especially adapted for use in binding colors and for rough stuff; it is also a reliable gold leaf sizing.

1 Gallon	½ Gallon	Quart	Pint
$2.25	$1.25	65c	35c

Seroco Coach Japan.

No. 30E323 A reliable japan for binding and drying colors and rough stuff.

1 Gallon	½ Gallon	Quart	Pint
$1.75	98c	53c	30c

Orange Shellac.

No. 30E326 Orange Shellac.

1 Gallon	½ Gallon	Quart	Pint
$2.25	$1.20	65c	35c

Seroco W. A. White Shellac.

No. 30E327 Seroco W. A. White Shellac.

1 Gallon	½ Gallon	Quart	Pint
$2.25	$1.20	65c	35c

Seroco Varnish and Paint Remover.

No. 30E328 Guaranteed to remove paints, varnish or oil from wood, iron or bath tubs without damage to the wood, veneer, glue or filler. Nor does it injure the hands of the operator in any way.

1 Gallon	Quart	Pint
$1.40	40c	23c

Seroco Furniture Polish.

No. 30E330 Adapted for use on old as well as new furniture. It has the advantage over other polishes of not gumming up in the corners, and therefore will not collect dust or dirt. It is perfectly harmless and will not affect the varnish in any way. It can be used as well on ordinary furniture as on the finest piano, organ and other highly finished work. This is without question the finest and safest polish on the market.

Price, per pint can.......... $0.25
Per quart can.......... .45
Per gallon can.......... 1.70

Seroco Paint and Varnish Reviver.

No. 30E332 This reviver combines the properties of a cleanser as well as a renewer for any painted or varnished surface. Where the paint or varnish is in good condition but very dirty or greasy, a small quantity of this Reviver with a little rubbing will produce a surface equal to new. Guaranteed not to injure the paint or varnish. Convince yourself of its value by giving it a trial.

Price, per pint can.......... $0.23
Per quart can.......... .42
Per gallon can.......... 1.50

Seroco Liquid Metal Polish.

No. 30E342 For polishing brass, zinc, tin, nickel, copper or silver. Can be used on anything made of metal, and is especially recommended for outdoor metal work, such as brass and zinc signs, show cases, railings, metal parts of harness, etc. Warranted not to injure the finest metals. No other polish will give the brilliant and lasting luster obtained when using Seroco Liquid Metal Polish.

Price, per ½-pint can.......... 10c
Price, per pint can.......... 18c

Flitters.

No. 55E02725 Bronze Flitters or Leaf Brocades, for sign work. Highest grade flitters made. Used everywhere by professional sign painters and decorators.

Color.	Price, per lb.	Price, per oz.
Pale gold and rich gold	$0.68	6c
Copper and crimson	.72	7c
Blue, orange, fire, green and lemon	.83	8c
Silver and aluminium	1.10	9c

One-half pound lots furnished at pound rates. Less than one-half pound lots at ounce rates only.

No. 55E02730 Best Gold Bronze Powder, for ornamental and decorative uses. Furnished in three shades, light or rich gold, medium or pale gold and deep gold.

Price, per pound, 72c; per ounce.......... 7c

No. 55E02735 Liquid for Mixing Bronze Powder.

Price, per 4-oz. bottle	Price, per 1-pint can	Price, per 1-quart can	Price, per 1-gallon can	Price, per 5-gallon can
8c	14c	25c	90c	$3.50

AUBREY ENGRAVED HAMMERLESS

OUR PATENT GLOBE SIGHT FREE WITH THIS GUN

$16.35

GENUINE DAMASCUS

CHOKE BORED

PAT. APPLIED FOR

OUR PATENT GLOBE SIGHT FREE WITH THIS GUN.

BORED FOR BLACK OR SMOKELESS POWDER.

THIS 12-GAUGE double barrel, full engraved, hammerless, quadruple lock action, breech loading shotgun is made by the Meriden Fire Arms Company of Meriden, Connecticut, a factory owned, controlled and operated by us, designed, modeled by and built under the direct personal supervision of Mr. A. J. Aubrey, vice-president and general manager of the Meriden Fire Arms Company, and maker of the highest grade double barrel breech loading shotguns made in America. Mr. A. J. Aubrey is recognized as authority in this country on high grade gun building, and he has been associated in the past years with a number of the largest American gun factories, where he has designed, modeled and brought out their very finest guns, guns made to retail as high as $500.00 each.

The A. J. AUBREY GUNS have a distinctiveness in design, mechanical construction, up to date features, shooting qualities,

IN FACT, in every essential point, an individuality found only in guns of the Aubrey make, and they are such guns as can be compared only with the highest grade guns made in this country and in Europe. They are from the lowest priced to the highest priced models, free from every earmark of cheapness common to American guns that sell at $30.00 and under.

THE AUBREY DOUBLE HAMMERLESS GUN, whether you buy our cheapest gun at $13.85, as shown on preceding page, or the finest Aubrey gun we build for stock, our $69.00 Aubrey, you will find in the gun every essential feature of the highest grade guns made in the world, an Aubrey individuality throughout, a mechanism that stands alone. You will have a gun there is practically no wear out to, a gun you cannot shoot loose, a gun with a locking or bolt mechanism unequaled by any other gun made, the mechanical construction throughout stands alone, shooting qualities unexcelled by any gun at any price, a gun that is evenly balanced, beautiful in outline and shape, an A. J. Aubrey contour, a gun that hangs beautifully, one that you can handle quickly for quick wing shooting, a gun possessing the good qualities of every other high grade double barrel breech loading hammerless gun made, with the defects of none.

WE HAVE BROUGHT OUT THE A. J. AUBREY double barrel hammerless breech loading shotgun in a variety of designs to suit all buyers, the armory steel barrel, plain hammerless gun with line engraving, at $13.85, as described on preceding page, gotten up in various grades of engraving, barrels, trimmings, etc., at prices ranging $16.35, $18.85, $29.75, $39.75, $49.75 and $69.00, as illustrated and described on this and the following pages; but whether you order the armory steel barrel at $13.85 or the very finest double Aubrey gun we build at $69.00, the mechanical construction, the working parts, the shooting qualities, the lasting qualities, the satisfaction the gun will give will be the same in every Aubrey gun, regardless of price.

Illustration shows our

No. 6E34

AT

$18.85

DETAILED DESCRIPTION

See preceding page for detailed description of the bolting mechanism. The bolting mechanism is exactly the same on all double barrel hammerless Aubrey guns. See preceding page for description of locks, break, safety barrel, extension rib, bolt construction, etc. In this regard all double barrel Aubrey guns are alike.

SIGHTS. This gun is furnished with front and rear sight, a very desirable feature and one which most shooters have affixed to their guns by a gunsmith at an extra expense of 75 cents to $2.00, while on this gun we furnish the front and rear sight free, the rear being 12 to 14 inches back of the front sight, a valuable assistance in "lining up" a gun for a good center shot. Without the rear sight the shooter is very liable to sight down one side of the rib and miss his bird.

THIS, OUR SPECIAL high grade Aubrey double barrel hammerless, which we furnish at $16.35 and $18.85, according to barrels, is elaborately engraved in fond creux leaf design. From the illustration, engraved by our artist from a photograph, you can form some little idea of the general appearance of the gun. With its beautiful engraved locks, frame, guard, etc., its specially selected walnut stock, with special fancy hand checkering on the full pistol grip and fore end, it makes a finished double barrel hammerless shotgun, the equal of which you could not buy elsewhere at less than $40.00. It's a gun you must see, examine and compare with guns that sell at $40.00 and upward to appreciate the value we are giving.

LET US SEND YOU THIS GUN TO EXAMINE.

Enclose our price; or, if you prefer, enclose $1.00, balance payable after received, state whether you wish this beautiful hand engraved gun with finest twist barrels, at $16.35, or with genuine two-blade Damascus steel barrels as illustrated, at $18.85, state whether you wish 30 or 32-inch barrels and the weight of gun wanted, and we will send the gun to you with the understanding and agreement that you can give the gun ten days' thorough trial, during which time you can put it to every test, test it for long range hard shooting, test it for penetration, for pattern, compare it with any hammerless double gun you can buy elsewhere at $40.00 to $50.00, compare the treble bolt extension rib and automatic locking device with any gun made, regardless of price, and if you are not perfectly satisfied with your purchase, if you are not convinced you have gotten such a double barrel hammerless breech loading shotgun as you could not have bought elsewhere at less than $40.00, if you do not feel you have saved from $15.00 to $25.00 by sending your order to us, you can return the gun to us at our expense and we will immediately return your money.

HOW WE MAKE THE PRICE SO LOW

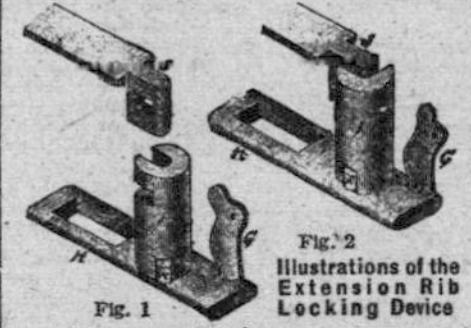

Fig. 1 Fig. 2 Illustrations of the Extension Rib Locking Device

Fig. 1 shows how the rib J enters into bolt I. Fig. 2 shows how rib J is locked by bolt I. H is the bolt which locks the lugs of barrels, and swivel G is the part which operates the bolts I and H all at the same time. All are operated by the top lever.

UNDERSTAND, the A. J. AUBREY guns are made in our own factory, made by the Meriden Fire Arms Company, at Meriden, Connecticut, a factory we own, control and operate. In this factory all our guns are made at a cost to us covering only the cost of material and labor, to this we add our one small percentage of profit, and as a result we can sell you one gun of the Aubrey make, a genuine Aubrey gun, a gun that can be compared only with the highest priced guns made in America; this gun we can sell you at less than dealers can buy guns that will in any way compare with the Aubrey, even in dozen or hundred lots.

NO ILLUSTRATION that we can engrave and print on paper, no description that we can give will give you any idea of how much more value for your money we can furnish you in the A. J. Aubrey guns than you can possibly get in any other gun you can possibly buy from your dealer at home or elsewhere. You must see, examine and compare these guns with guns sold by others to appreciate the value we are giving. We, therefore, especially urge that before you buy a gun elsewhere you, at least, let us send you one of these guns to examine.

WE FURNISH THIS GUN IN 12-GAUGE ONLY, in 30 or 32-inch barrels as desired, in the different weights as listed below, at the special prices named below, namely $16.35 and $18.85.

NOTICE OUR SPECIAL PRICES ON SMOKELESS POWDER SHELLS. We lead all sporting goods dealers and hardware merchants in ammunition. None can compete with us.

REMEMBER OUR PROFIT SHARING PLAN. You get a PROFIT SHARING CERTIFICATE for every purchase, and will soon be able to get some valuable article of furniture or other goods ABSOLUTELY FREE OF COST TO YOU, shown on the last pages of this catalogue.

Catalogue No.	Grade	Style of Barrels	Gauge	Length of Barrels Inches	Weight Lbs.	Finish	Price
6E30	A. L. E.	Genuine Laminated Steel	12	30 or 32	7½ to 8	Leaf Style	$16.35
6E34	A. D. E.	Genuine 2-Blade Damascus	12	30 or 32	7½ to 8	Engraving	18.85

Weight, packed for shipment about 14 pounds.

No. 6E34

ORDER BY NUMBER.

THE AUBREY ELABORATELY ENGRAVED $19.35

Made in our own factory, The Meriden Fire Arms Co., Meriden, Conn., under the personal supervision of Mr. A. J. Aubrey, one of the foremost gun makers in this country.

FOR $19.35 in the highest grade twist barrel or for $22.35 in the genuine two-blade Damascus barrel, with the elaborate fine line scroll and game hand engraving on the locks, frame, guard, etc., with special finish throughout, with specially selected and elaborately finished stock and fore end, with every new and up to date high grade feature, we furnish you this genuine A. J. Aubrey Hammerless Double Barrel Breech Loading Shotgun, exactly as shown in the illustration, under our guarantee that it is in every way the equal of any hammerless double barrel breech loading shotgun you can buy elsewhere for $50.00. We will gladly accept your order and, in fact, we especially urge that you let us send you this gun to examine. Either enclose our price, or, if you prefer, enclose $1.00, balance payable after received, and we will send the gun to you with the understanding and agreement that you can use it for ten days, during which time you can put it to every test, compare it with any gun made for long range shooting, penetration, target, for mechanical construction, and if you do not find it perfectly satisfactory, the equal of any double barrel hammerless gun you could buy elsewhere for $50.00, if you do not find the bolting mechanism, the locking device and all essential parts superior to any other hammerless gun on the market, regardless of name, make or price, if you do not feel you have saved from $20.00 to $30.00 dollars by sending your order to us, if you are not convinced you have gotten one of the highest grade double hammerless guns made, if you cannot see wherein this gun is worth double that of any of the cheaper grades of double hammerless guns on the market, you can return the gun to us at our expense and we will immediately return your money.

THIS GUN is made by the Meriden Fire Arms Company, of Meriden, Conn., under the personal direction of Mr. A. J. Aubrey, maker of the highest grade shotguns made in America. It combines every new, high grade, up to date feature of every other high grade double barrel hammerless shotgun made with the defects of none.

FOR FULL DESCRIPTION of bolting mechanism, of barrels, locks, frame and mechanical construction throughout, see preceding pages, or the description of the $13.85 gun. All Aubrey guns are in mechanical construction alike, and whether you buy the cheapest Aubrey double barrel gun at $13.85 or the one illustrated and described hereon at $19.35 or $22.35, or the highest grade Aubrey gun we make, the $69.00 gun, the mechanical construction, the shooting qualities, the durability are exactly the same. The difference in the price represents only the difference in the barrels, the difference in the elaborate engraving and finish, and in these more elaborately finished guns we actually furnish you from three to five times as much value for your money as you could possibly get elsewhere.

THIS SPECIAL, high grade, elaborately engraved A. J. Aubrey Hammerless Double Barrel Shotgun, which we furnish at $19.35 and $22.35, according to the barrels, has every late improvement, every up to date feature, is put out under our binding guarantee. We especially urge that you send us your order for this gun, either enclosing the full amount of cash, or if you prefer, enclose $1.00, balance payable after received, and if the gun isn't perfectly satisfactory you can return it to us at our expense and we will immediately return your money.

THIS GUN comes in 12-gauge only, in 30 or 32-inch barrels, the finest twist or laminated steel barrels or genuine two-blade Damascus barrels, as desired.

Cat. No.	Grade	Style Barrels	Gauge	Length of Barrels	Weight	Finish	Price
6E50	A. S. E.	Genuine Laminated Steel	12	30 or 32-in.	7½ to 8 lbs.	Fine Line Scroll and Game Engraving	$19.35
6E52	D. S. E.	Genuine two Blade Damascus	12	30 or 32-in.	7½ to 8 lbs.		22.35

Weight, packed for shipment, about 15 pounds.

NOTICE OUR PRICES ON AMMUNITION, especially Shotgun Shells. We beat all competitors, wholesale or retail; none can compete with us.

$29.75 WORTH $75.00

This genuine A. J. Aubrey Hammerless Double Barrel Breech Loading Shotgun, which we offer at $29.75, has a very elaborate fine line and game engraving, very rich finish; it has genuine four-blade Damascus steel barrels, carefully selected, beautifully finished and with rich hand engraving on lock, frame, guard, etc., with its English walnut stock, elaborately checkered grip and fore end, we guarantee it the equal of any hammerless double barrel breech loading shotgun you can buy elsewhere for $75.00; otherwise, it is exactly the same as the A. J. Aubrey Hammerless Guns described on preceding pages, 12-gauge only, 30 or 32-inch barrels, an especially high grade gun put out at $29.75, based on the actual cost of material and labor in our own factory, with but our one small percentage of profit added, guaranteed in every way the equal of any gun made, guaranteed in workmanship, style, finish, etc., the equal of any gun you can buy elsewhere for $75.00. **Order this gun, try it, compare it with guns you can buy elsewhere for $75.00, and if you do not find it in every way the equal, you can return the gun to us at our expense and we will immediately return your money.** If you want a very fine gun, four-blade Damascus steel barrels, bored for black or smokeless powder, extra fine finish, elaborately hand engraved, let us send you this gun to examine, enclose our price, or, if you prefer, enclose $1.00, balance payable after received, give the gun a thorough test, thorough trial, thorough examination and comparison, and then if you like you can return it to us at our expense and we will immediately return your money, together with any express charges paid by you.

No. 6E56 Our special price with very elaborate hand engraving, with very fine genuine four-blade Damascus steel barrels, elaborately finished throughout. 12-gauge, 30 or 32-inch barrels; weight, 7½ to 8 pounds........................ **$29.75**

Weight, packed for shipment, about 14 pounds.

$39.75 WORTH $100.00

$39.75 is our price for this genuine A. J. Aubrey Double Barrel, Hammerless, Breech Loading Shotgun, the very finest carefully selected, beautifully finished four-blade Damascus barrels, very elaborately hand engraved locks, frame, guard, plates, etc., selected English fine grain walnut beautifiluly finished stock and fore end, extra fine finish throughout. For detailed description of the mechanical construction, locking bolts, frame, action, etc., see the large illustrations of the Aubrey guns on preceding pages. This differs only from the Aubrey guns offered at lower prices in that it is more elaborately finished, richly hand engraved, has the finest four-blade Damascus steel barrels. This gun comes in 12-gauge only, 30 or 32-inch barrels. **Let us send you this gun to examine, enclose our price, or, if you prefer, enclose $1.00, balance payable after you receive it, examine it and give it a thorough trial, test it out in every way, and if you do not find it the equal of any double barrel hammerless shotgun you could buy anywhere for $100.00, you can return it to us at our expense and we will immediately return your money.**

No. 6E58 Our special price for this Genuine A. J. Aubrey Hammerless Double Barrel Breech Loading Shotgun, 12-gauge, 30 or 32-inch barrels, fancy four-blade Damascus barrels; weight, 7½ to 8 pounds.................................. **$39.75**

Weight, packed for shipment, about 14 pounds.

WE LET YOU SHARE IN THE PROFITS OF THIS BUSINESS, and you really cannot afford to buy elsewhere. Our prices are guaranteed lower than those asked by any other concern, our goods are guaranteed the highest quality, we guarantee to save you money on every purchase and you get a Profit Sharing Certificate good for something valuable shown on the last pages.

$49.75 WORTH $125.00

This is the Genuine A J. Aubrey Made to Order Hammerless Double Barrel Breech Loading Shotgun, made in our own factory, the Meriden Fire Arms Company, of Meriden, Conn., and offered to you at $49.75, under our guarantee that it is in every way the equal of any double barrel hammerless breech loading shotgun you can buy elsewhere at $125.00, and our $49.75 price barely covers the cost of material and labor, with but our one small percentage of profit added. This is the exact same style of gun, all working parts the very same as the lower priced hammerless A. J. Aubrey guns illustrated and described in detail on preceding pages. This gun differs in that it has the finest four-blade Damascus steel barrels, that it is very elaborately finished, that it is elaborately hand engraved on locks, frame, guard, barrels, trimmings, etc., it has a beautifully selected, imported English or Italian walnut stock, handsomely checkered, ornamented and finished, and is, in fact, in every way the equal of any hammerless gun you can buy elsewhere for $125.00.

MADE TO ORDER. **Our $49.75 and $69.00 guns are made to order. When a customer selects a gun at this price he usually has certain ideas how the gun should be built, so we show only the style of engraving.** The barrels will be best quality four-blade Damascus, the stock will be carefully selected and of a high order close grain and figured English or Italian walnut, and especial attention will follow these guns through the entire operations and only our most skilled workmen will be put on them under Mr Aubrey's supervision. Send us $49 75, send us the length, weight, drop of stock at butt and comb and the kind of choke wanted, allow us four to six weeks time and this gun will go to you exactly as you order it.

No. 6E60 The A. J. Aubrey Special Hand Engraved, Four-Blade Damascus Steel Barrel 12-Gauge Gun, 30 or 32-inch barrels; weight, 7½ to 8 pounds. Our special price...........(Weight, packed for shipment, about 14 pounds)........... **$49.75**

$69.00 WORTH $150.00

Our $69.00 Aubrey Hammerless Double Barrel Shotgun is made to order. When a customer orders a gun at this price he usually wants some special features, and these we are prepared to furnish. Send us your order, enclose our selling price of $69.00, send us the weight, length of barrels, length of stock, say which kind of choke you prefer, drop of stock at butt and comb, allow us six weeks to two months time and we will build this gun for you and it will be equal to any gun which you can get from any other house at $150.00, and will be just exactly as you order it. All our $49.75 and $69.00 guns will be built to order. We put our most skilled workmen on these guns. Select the finest material and steel, also the finest wood for the stocks, and all will go through under the personal supervision of Mr. Aubrey. This is the finest A. J. Aubrey made to order hammerless double barrel breech loading shotgun made, the most elaborately hand engraved, most beautifully finished, the highest grade American gun made, regardless of name, make or price; has the very finest four-blade Damascus steel barrels, finest imported English or Circassian finely figured, close grained walnut stock and fore end possible to produce, the hand engraving is the most elaborate shown on any gun made in this country or in Europe, elaborately hand engraved locks, frame, barrel, breech, guard, etc. In the mechanism the locks, locking bolts, mechanical construction are identically the same as the Aubrey gun shown in large illustrations on preceding page. It is positively the finest gun we make, the equal of any gun made, regardless of price.

No. 6E62 A. J. Aubrey Made to Order Finest Hand Engraved Four-Blade Damascus Steel Barrel Hammerless Double Barrel Shotgun, 12-gauge, 30 or 32-inch barrels; weight, 7½ to 8 pounds. Our special price.............................. **$69.00**

Weight, packed for shipment, about 14 pounds.

KNICKERBOCKER HAMMERLESS GUN, $15.50.

Made by the American Gun Co. of New York, factory in Connecticut.

12-Gauge Only.
Bored for Nitro or Black Powder.

Our Patent Globe Sight is FREE with this GUN.

ALIGNMENT. The Celebrated Knickerbocker Hammerless Double Barrel Shotgun, as turned out by the American Gun Co., possesses perfect alignment, in fact, the alignment is equal to that of any gun made, regardless of name, make or price.

Every minute feature has been studied with a view of producing a gun which "handles" nicely, which is a comfort to the shooter, a gun that makes a good pattern, has excellent shooting qualities and one which is bound to become a favorite with hunters or trap shooters.

The above illustration is engraved direct from a photograph of the gun itself, by our artist and will give you some idea of the appearance, but you should see the gun and examine it and compare it with high priced guns in order to get a proper idea of the gun. We recommend this gun very highly and know that you will be pleased with it.

THIS IS THE LATEST HAMMERLESS SHOTGUN ON THE MARKET. It is made from the best material that money can buy—made on fine lines, balances perfectly and is a neat, attractive and serviceable gun.

DESCRIPTION. **The Knickerbocker is fitted with top snap break**, laminated steel barrels, strong bar locks, beautifully matted L-shape Edwards' extension rib, double bolt locks, straight grained walnut stock and fore end handsomely checkered, Deeley & Edge patent fore end, full pistol grip capped with ornamental rosette, choke bored for close shooting; a good, sound, honest, hammerless gun. Weight, packed for shipment, about 14 pounds.

Catalogue Number	Grade	Style of Barrels	Gauge	Length of Barrels	Weight of Guns	Price
6E100	No. 7	Laminated Steel	12	30 or 32 in.	7½ to 8 lbs.	$15.50
6E102	No. 8	Genuine Damascus	12	30 or 32 in.	7½ to 8 lbs.	17.50

LOADED SHOTGUN SHELLS, $1.32 per 100. See page 300.

OUR HAND ENGRAVED CHICAGO LONG RANGE WONDER DOUBLE BARREL BREECH LOADING SHOTGUN,

$13.30 AND $16.30

Our Chicago Long Range Wonder Hand Engraved Double Barrel Hammerless Shotgun is almost identical with the gun described in the next column, except that the frame is handsomely engraved by hand, as illustrated above.

The barrel, machine work and other work is identical, except the hand engraved guns are fitted only with genuine laminated steel or twist barrels and genuine two-blade Damascus barrels. They are not fitted with armory steel barrels and we add only for the additional cost of the engraving to our plain finished guns, making the laminated or twist barrels cost $13.30 and the genuine two-blade Damascus cost $16.30. While these guns are $5.00 to $10.00 cheaper than you can buy similar guns from any other house and while they are good value to our customers and while they are good shooting guns, strong in penetration, still, if you wish a hand engraved gun of the very highest quality, one which compares with any gun made regardless of name, make or price, one which we send out under our strongest binding guarantee and liberal terms, by all means pay the additional price and order **an A. J. Aubrey hammerless double barrel shotgun, a** gun which we know will give you universal satisfaction and one which will make friends for the Aubrey gun. Our Chicago Long Range Wonder gun, as illustrated above, is fitted with top snap break, steel frame, Edwards' extension rib nicely tapered and matted, strong locking bolt in addition to the Edwards' extension rib, straight grained well seasoned walnut stock and fore end nicely checkered, stock fitted with ornamental rubber butt plate and the frame and top lever nicely engraved.

Catalogue Number	Grade	Style of Barrels	Gauge	Length of Barrels	Weight of Guns	Finish	Price
6E104	T. E.	Laminated Steel	12	30 or 32 in.	7¾ to 8 lbs.	En-	$13.30
6E106	D. E.	2-Blade Damascus	12	30 or 32 in.	7¾ to 8 lbs.	gr'd	16.30

Weight, packed for shipment, about 14 pounds.

OUR CHICAGO LONG RANGE WONDER HAMMERLESS DOUBLE BARREL BREECH LOADING SHOTGUNS.

$10.80 TO $14.80

OUR PATENT GLOBE SIGHT GOES FREE WITH THIS GUN.

FOR $10.80 we offer you our Chicago Long Range Wonder Double Barrel Hammerless Shotgun, fitted with genuine armory steel barrels; for $11.80 we offer you our Chicago Long Range Wonder Double Barrel Hammerless Shotgun, fitted with genuine laminated steel or twist barrels, and for $14.80 we offer you our Chicago Long Range Wonder Double Barrel Hammerless Shotgun, fitted with genuine two-blade Damascus barrels.

We offer these guns as the equal of any gun you can buy elsewhere at much higher prices, as guns which we put out in competition with other hammerless shotguns selling from $5.00 to $10.00 more.

Our Chicago Long Range Wonder guns are fitted with top snap break, steel frame, patent safety slide, Edwards' extension rib, nicely tapered and matted, strong locking bolt, straight grained well seasoned walnut stock and fore end, nicely checkered, fitted with ornamental butt plate, taper choke bored for close long range shooting, genuine armory steel barrels at $10.80; genuine laminated steel or twist barrels at $11.80, or genuine two-blade Damascus barrels at $14.80.

While the Chicago Long Range Wonder Double Barrel Hammerless Guns are equal to any guns on the market selling at $5.00 to $10.00 higher in price, still, if you wish a strictly high grade gun, a gun that is as well made as any gun on the market regardless of name, make or price, a gun that is calculated to give long and good service, by all means pay the additional price and buy an A. J. Aubrey hammerless double barrel shotgun, as illustrated and described on another page.

Catalogue Number	Grade	Style of Barrels	Gauge	Length of Barrels	Weight of Guns	Price
6E110½	S. P.	Armory Steel	12	30 or 32 in.	7¾ to 8 lbs.	$10.80
6E112½	T. P.	Laminated Steel	12	30 or 32 in.	7¾ to 8 lbs.	11.80
6E114½	D. P.	2-Blade Damascus	12	30 or 32 in.	7¾ to 8 lbs.	14.80

Weight, packed for shipment, 14 pounds.

THE NEW FOREHAND DOUBLE BARREL HAMMER GUN.

12-GAUGE ONLY **$12.45**

No. 6E117

For $12.45 we offer this season the celebrated Forehand Double Barrel Hammer Gun, fitted with fine twist barrels, low circular hammers, patent nitro cross bolt in the extension rib which locks the gun firmly when the barrel is closed. Straight grain walnut stock and fore end nicely checkered, rebounding hammers, patent top lever, fancy butt plate, elegantly case hardened frame and lock works, choke bored for close, hard shooting; a well made, good shooting, well balanced gun and one that is bound to give satisfaction. The factory price on this gun with twist barrels is $19.50, but owing to a large contract which we have made for them we are able to make you a reduced price of $12.45 this season and it is certainly a great bargain at this price.

No. 6E117 The New Forehand Double Barrel Hammer Gun, fitted with genuine twist barrels, 12-gauge, 30 or 32-inch barrels; weight, 7½ to 8 pounds. Factory price, $19.50, our price.......... **$12.45**

$1.32 PER 100 FOR HIGHEST GRADE LOADED SHELLS. SEE PAGE 300

OUR CELEBRATED BOX FRAME HAMMERLESS AUTOMATIC EJECTING DOUBLE BARREL SHOTGUN $18.75

FOR $18.75 we are now able to offer our customers a box frame hammerless double barrel breech loading shotgun, fitted with automatic shell ejector. This is the lowest price ever made by any house on a reliable double barrel shotgun, fitted with an automatic shell ejector, a gun of American manufacture, a gun which we can recommend for long range shooting qualities, penetration, durability and honest workmanship.

THIS GUN is manufactured by Messrs. Andrew Fyrberg & Sons of Hopkinton, Mass., which company has just been organized, installed a large line of new up to date automatic machinery suitable for manufacturing shotguns, and by placing a large contract, we have been able to figure the price so that we can offer our customers a double barrel automatic shell ejecting hammerless breech loading shotgun with genuine laminated steel barrels for only **$18.75.**

SIGHTS. This gun is furnished with front and rear sight, a very desirable feature and one which most shooters have added to their guns by a gunsmith at an extra expense of 75 cents to $2.00, while on this gun we furnish the front and rear sight FREE, the rear being 12 to 14 inches back of the front sight, a valuable assistance in "lining" up a gun for a good center shot. Without the rear sight the shooter is very liable to sight down one side of the rib and miss his bird.

ALIGNMENT of this double barrel hammerless automatic shell ejecting shotgun. This gun has been gotten out with a view of furnishing our customers a hammerless shotgun with the proper alignment such as is used on all high grade guns.

OUR PATENT GLOBE SIGHT GOES FREE WITH THIS GUN.

THE AUTOMATIC shell ejecting device is the most simple automatic shell ejecting device yet invented, a device which was invented by Mr. Fyrberg, where the entire operation for ejecting the shell is located on the cocking bolt and in the lug of the gun, and the cocking bolt is so constructed that it can be removed from the frame by taking out two screws from the frame under the barrel.

THE GUN can be put together and taken apart as easy as any hammer gun. The extractor is known as the split type extractor and will throw only the shell which has been fired, leaving the other one in the barrel and if you fire both shells, the automatic ejector will throw out the two shells upon opening the gun.

They handle and come up to the shoulder with the same ease and comfort of all high grade shotguns; a feature which commends itself to all shooters.

GENERAL DESCRIPTION. Our box frame hammerless automatic shell ejecting double barrel breech loading shotgun is fitted with a steel box frame, as shown in the illustration, top snap break, safety slide which keeps the hammer safe or ready to shoot at the option of the shooter, nitro cross-bite in the extension rib, strong locking bolt on the lug, handsomely matted extension rib, well seasoned straight grained walnut stock with pistol grip capped and handsomely checkered, fitted with ornamental butt plate, straight grained well seasoned walnut fore end nicely checkered, barrels flatted at breech, correct alignment, taper choke bored for black or smokeless powder the lock and working parts are made of best steel and the guns are fitted with genuine laminated steel barrels at **$18.75** or genuine two-blade Damascus barrels at **$21.75.**

Catalogue Number	Grade	Style of Barrels	Gauge	Length of Barrels	Weight	Price
6E120	G. L. S.	Laminated Steel	12	30 or 32 inches	7¼ to 8 lbs.	$18.75
6E122	T. B. D.	2-Blade Damascus	12	30 or 32 inches	7¼ to 8 lbs.	21.75

Weight, packed for shipment, about 14 pounds.

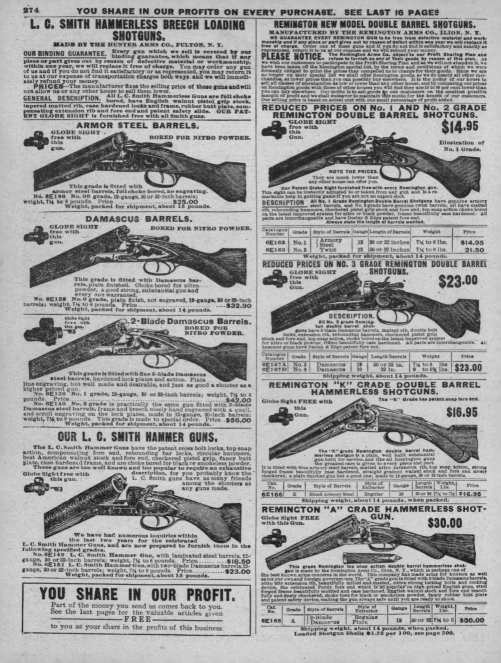

L. C. SMITH HAMMERLESS BREECH LOADING SHOTGUNS.

MADE BY THE HUNTER ARMS CO., FULTON, N. Y.

OUR BINDING GUARANTEE. Every gun which we sell is covered by our binding guarantee, which means that if any piece or part gives out by reason of defective material or workmanship, within one year, we will replace it free of charge. You may order any gun of us and if you do not find it satisfactory or as represented, you may return it to us at our expense of transportation charges both ways and we will immediately refund your money.

PRICES—The manufacturer fixes the selling price of these guns and will not allow us or any other house to sell them lower.

GENERAL DESCRIPTION. All L. C. Smith Hammerless Guns are full choke bored, have English walnut pistol grip stock, tapered matted rib, case hardened locks and frame, rubber butt plate, compensating extension rib and fore end and patent safety slide. OUR PATENT GLOBE SIGHT is furnished free with all Smith guns.

ARMOR STEEL BARRELS.

GLOBE SIGHT free with this gun.

BORED FOR NITRO POWDER.

This grade is fitted with armor steel barrels, full choke bored, no engraving.

No. 6E136 No. 00 grade, 12-gauge, 30 or 32-inch barrels; weight, 7¼ to 8 pounds. Price....................$25.00

Weight, packed for shipment, about 15 pounds.

DAMASCUS BARRELS.

GLOBE SIGHT free with this gun.

BORED FOR NITRO POWDER.

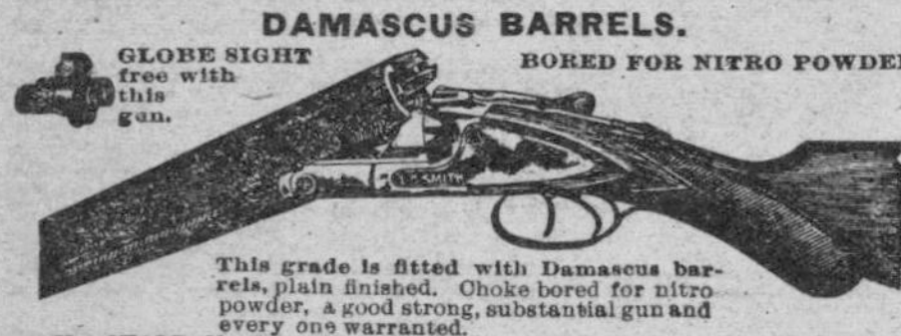

This grade is fitted with Damascus barrels, plain finished. Choke bored for nitro powder, a good strong, substantial gun and every one warranted.

No. 6E138 No. 0 grade, plain finish, not engraved, 12-gauge, 30 or 32-inch barrels; weight, 7¼ to 8 pounds. Price....................$32.90

Weight, packed for shipment, about 14 pounds.

2-Blade Damascus Barrels.

Globe Sight free with this gun.

BORED FOR NITRO POWDER.

This grade is fitted with fine 2-blade Damascus steel barrels, hardened lock plates and action. Plain line engraving, but well made and desirable, and just as good a shooter as a higher priced gun.

No. 6E136 No. 1 grade, 12-gauge, 30 or 32-inch barrels; weight, 7¼ to 8 pounds. Price....................$42.00

No. 6E140 No. 2 grade is practically the same gun fitted with 3-blade Damascus steel barrels, frame and breech nicely hand engraved with a quail, and scroll engraving on the lock plates, made in 12-gauge, 30-inch barrels; weight, 7¼ to 8 pounds. This grade is made to special order. Price..$56.00

Weight, packed for shipment, about 14 pounds.

OUR L. C. SMITH HAMMER GUNS.

The L. C. Smith Hammer Guns have the patent cross bolt locks, top snap action, compensating fore end, rebounding bar locks, circular hammers, best American walnut stock and fore end, checkered pistol grip, fancy butt plate, case hardened frame, and are choke bored for black or smokeless powder.

These guns are too well known and too popular to require an exhaustive description, for you probably know the L. C. Smith guns have as many friends among the shooters as any guns made.

Globe Sight free with this gun.

We have had numerous inquiries within the last two years for the celebrated L. C. Smith Hammer Guns, and are now prepared to furnish them in the following specified grades.

No. 6E149 L. C. Smith Hammer Gun, with laminated steel barrels, 12-gauge, 30 or 32-inch barrels; weight, 7¼ to 8 pounds. Price..........$18.50

No. 6E151 L. C. Smith Hammer Gun, with two-blade Damascus barrels, 12-gauge, 30 or 32-inch barrels; weight, 7¼ to 8 pounds. Price............$23.00

Weight, packed for shipment, about 15 pounds.

YOU SHARE IN OUR PROFIT.

Part of the money you send us comes back to you. See the last pages for the valuable articles given

—FREE—

to you as your share in the profits of this business

REMINGTON NEW MODEL DOUBLE BARREL SHOTGUNS.

MANUFACTURED BY THE REMINGTON ARMS CO., ILION, N. Y.

WE GUARANTEE EVERY REMINGTON GUN to be free from defective material and workmanship and if any piece or part gives out by reason of defect within one year we will replace it free of charge. Order one of these guns and if you do not find it satisfactory and exactly as represented, return it to us at our expense and we will refund your money.

PLEASE NOTICE. **The Remington Arms Co. object to our Profit Sharing Plan and refuse to furnish us any of their goods by reason of this plan.** As we wish our customers to participate in the Profit Sharing Plan and as we will not abandon it, we have been taken off the Remington special list, by the terms and conditions of which we were formerly obliged to print the prices they compelled us to charge for their goods. Since we are no longer on their special list we shall offer Remington goods, as we do nearly all other merchandise, at lower prices than you can possibly buy elsewhere. It is the policy of our house to sell all classes of merchandise as low or lower than any other house, and by comparing our prices on Remington goods with those of other houses you will find they are 10 to 30 per cent lower than you can buy elsewhere. Our motto is to sell goods to our customers on the smallest possible margin of profit and we shall endeavor to maintain this motto for the benefit of our customers. Our selling price is based on actual cost with one small percentage of profit added.

REDUCED PRICES ON No. 1 AND No. 2 GRADE REMINGTON DOUBLE BARREL SHOTGUNS.

GLOBE SIGHT free with this Gun.

$14.95

Illustration of No. 1 Grade.

NOTE THE PRICES. They are much lower than any other house can offer you.

Our Patent Globe Sight furnished free with every Remington gun. This sight can be instantly adjusted to or taken from any gun and is a remarkable help in getting game if you are not an expert shot.

DESCRIPTION All No. 1 Grade Remington Double Barrel Shotguns have genuine armory steel barrels, and No. 2 grade have genuine twist barrels; all have matted rib, rebounding hammers, checkered pistol grip stock and fore end, top snap action choke bored on the latest improved system for nitro or black powder, frame beautifully case hardened. All parts are interchangeable and have Deeley & Edge patent fore end.

Always state the length of barrels wanted.

Catalogue Number	Grade	Style of Barrels	Gauge	Length of Barrels	Weight	Price
6E163	No. 1	Armory Steel	12	30 or 32 inches	7¼ to 8 lbs.	$14.95
6E165	No. 2	Twist	12	30 or 32 inches	7¼ to 8 lbs.	21.50

Weight, packed for shipment, about 14 pounds.

REDUCED PRICES ON NO. 3 GRADE REMINGTON DOUBLE BARREL SHOTGUNS.

GLOBE SIGHT free with this Gun.

$23.00

DESCRIPTION. All No. 3 grade Remington double barrel shotguns have 2-blade Damascus barrels, matted rib, double bolt locks, extension rib, rebounding hammers, checkered pistol grip stock and fore end, top snap action, choke bored on the latest improved system for nitro or black powder, frame beautifully case hardened. All parts are interchangeable. All hammer guns have Deeley & Edge patent fore end.

Catalogue Number	Grade	Style of Barrels	Gauge	Length Barrels	Weight	Price
6E167A	No. 3	Damascus	12	30 or 32 in.	7¼ to 8 lbs	$23.00
6E167D	No. 3	Damascus	10	32 in.	9 to 9¾ lbs.	

Shipping weight, about 14 pounds.

REMINGTON "K" GRADE DOUBLE BARREL HAMMERLESS SHOTGUNS.

Globe Sight FREE with this Gun.

The "K" Grade has patent snap fore end.

$16.95

The "K" grade Remington double barrel hammerless shotgun is a plain, well built substantial gun built for service, and like all Remington guns the greatest care is given to every piece and part.

It is fitted with blue armory steel barrels, matted nitro extension rib, top snap action, strong forged frame beautifully case hardened, straight grained walnut stock and fore end nicely checkered; a plain finished gun but a good one; made in 12-gauge, 30 or 32-inch barrels.

Cat. No.	Grade	Style of Barrels	Style of Extractor	Gauge	Length Barrels	Weight, Lbs.	Price
6E166	K	Blued Armory Steel	Regular	12	30 or 32	7¼ to 7½	$16.95

Shipping weight, about 14 pounds, when packed.

REMINGTON "A" GRADE HAMMERLESS SHOTGUN.

Globe Sight FREE with this Gun.

$30.00

This grade Remington top snap action double barrel hammerless shotgun is made by the Remington Arms Co., Ilion, N. Y., which is perhaps one of the best known arms concerns in the world. This company has made arms for hunters as well as for our own and foreign governments. The "A" grade gun is fitted with 2-blade Damascus barrels, nitro bite extension rib, beautifully milled and matted, extra strong locking bolts and cocking device, the celebrated Purdy fore end which is so popular on high priced English guns, steel forged frame beautifully mottled and case hardened, English walnut stock and fore end beautifully and finely checkered, choke bore for black or smokeless powder, fancy rubber butt plate and patent safety device, making the gun always safe until you are ready to shoot.

Cat. No.	Grade	Style of Barrels	Style of Extractor	Gauge	Length Barrels	Weight, Lbs.	Price
6E168	A	2-Blade Damascus	Regular Plain	12	30 or 32	7¼ to 8	$30.00

Shipping weight, about 14 pounds, when packed.

Loaded Shotgun Shells $1.32 per 100, see page 300.

CELEBRATED THOMAS BARKER DOUBLE BARREL BREECH LOADING SHOTGUN, $9.80

Made in 16-gauge, 6½ to 7 pounds. 30-inch barrels.
20-gauge, 6¾ to 6¾ pounds. 30-inch barrels.

This illustration will give you some idea of the appearance of this gun. Over 50,000 now in use.

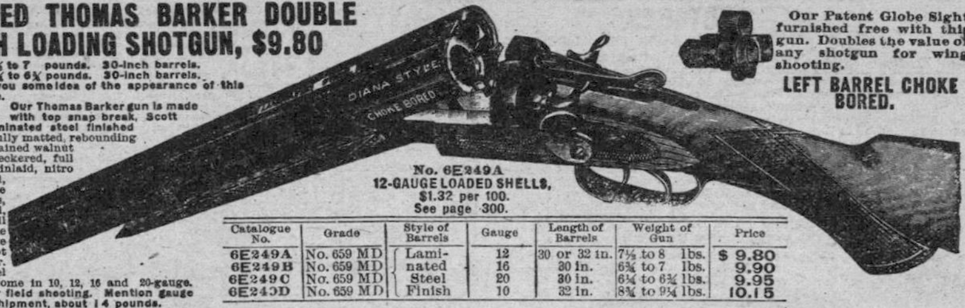

GENERAL DESCRIPTION. Our Thomas Barker gun is made with top snap break, Scott action, strong bar locks, laminated steel finished barrels, extension rib beautifully matted, rebounding circular hammers, straight grained walnut stock and fore end nicely checkered, full pistol grip stock with shield inlaid, nitro firing pins, patent snap fore end, chased engraving on locks, case hardened frame and lock plates, left barrel full choke bored, right barrel cylinder bored; all barrels bored smooth and true to gauge. A wonder for the money and a gun that will shoot black or smokeless powder. Always state length of barrel and gauge wanted. They come in 10, 12, 16 and 20-gauge. One of the best guns made for field shooting. Mention gauge wanted. Weight, packed for shipment, about 14 pounds.

Our Patent Globe Sight furnished free with this gun. Doubles the value of any shotgun for wing shooting.

LEFT BARREL CHOKE BORED.

No. 6E249A
12-GAUGE LOADED SHELLS,
$1.32 per 100.
See page 300.

Catalogue No.	Grade	Style of Barrels	Gauge	Length of Barrels	Weight of Gun	Price
6E249A	No. 659 MD	Lami-	12	30 or 32 in.	7½ to 8 lbs.	$ 9.80
6E249B	No. 659 MD	nated	16	30 in.	6¾ to 7 lbs.	9.90
6E249C	No. 659 MD	Steel	20	30 in.	6¼ to 6¾ lbs.	9.95
6E249D	No. 659 MD	Finish	10	32 in.	8¾ to 9¼ lbs.	10.15

OUR PATENT GLOBE SIGHT FURNISHED FREE WITH THIS GUN. Our sight adds many dollars' value to the shooting possibilities of a gun, but we furnish it FREE with this gun.

LOADED SHELLS $1.32 PER 100. SEE PAGE 300.

OUR $9.42 IMPORTED DOUBLE BARREL BREECH LOADER, WITH ENGRAVED LOCKS.

FOR $9.42 we offer you this genuine BAR LOCK DOUBLE BARREL BREECH LOADER

THIS IS A LOWER PRICE than most houses ask for a common plain back actionlock double barrel breech loader. All these guns have been put through the Belgian government rigid test, and for strength, durability and finish they are superior to any bar lock guns ever offered by any other house and present a handsome appearance.

No. 6E250

THIS GUN is made especially for us under season contract and will be found to give entire satisfaction for field shooting. THE BARRELS are made from celebrated RALEIGH STEEL and the frame from best forgings. The barrels are bored smooth and accurate and are chambered to gauge.

Catalogue No.	Grade	Style of Barrels	Gauge	Length of Barrels	Weight of Gun	Price
6E250	No. 639 ME	2-Blade Damascus Finish	12	30 or 32 in.	7¼ to 8 lbs.	$9.42

Weight, packed for shipment, about 14 pounds.

DETAILED DESCRIPTION. Our engraved lock gun is fitted with Scott action, top snap break, strong bar locks, two-blade Damascus finished barrels, rebounding circular hammers, straight grained well seasoned walnut stock and fore end nicely checkered, full pistol grip stock with inlaid shield, patent snap fore end, nitro firing pins, scroll engraving on the lock plates, case hardened frame and lock plates, bored smooth and true to gauge for black and smokeless powder, left barrel choke bored, right barrel cylinder bored, suitable for black or smokeless powder. Always mention length of barrel wanted.

OUR CARVED STOCK DOUBLE BARREL BREECH LOADING SHOTGUN. $10.98

Our Patent Globe Sight furnished free with this gun. Worth the price of the gun for wing shooting.

AT $10.98 we offer you this handsome double barrel genuine bar lock breech loading shotgun, fitted with our hexagon matted breech and two-blade Damascus finished barrels.

DESCRIPTION. Our Carved Stock Shotgun is fitted with Scott action top snap break, bar locks. Damascus finished barrels with matted hexagon breech beautifully matted as shown in the illustration. Extension rib, Edwards' patent, rebounding circular hammers, straight grained walnut stock and fore end beautifully carved in leaf design, pistol grip stock, nitro firing pins, patent snap fore end, case hardened frame and lock plates, left barrel choke bored, right barrel cylinder bored, bored true to gauge for black or smokeless powder. Always mention length of barrels wanted.

No. 6E257

Order by Number.

Send 10 cents for our Booklet of Useful Information to Shooters.

Catalogue No.	Grade	Style of Barrels	Gauge	Length of Barrels	Weight of Gun	Price
6E257	No. 669C	Damascus Finish	12	30 or 32 in.	7¼ to 7¾ lbs.	$10.98

Weight, packed for shipment, about 14 pounds.

OUR CELEBRATED EBONIZED DOUBLE BARREL BREECH LOADING SHOTGUN, $10.69

Our Globe Sight FREE with this gun.

MADE IN 12-GAUGE ONLY. LEFT BARREL CHOKE BORED.

AN IMPORTED GUN, MADE IN LIEGE, BELGIUM.

FOR $10.69 we furnish our celebrated ebonized black stock and black fore end double barrel hammer breech loading shotgun, one of the most attractive and well made shotguns ever offered by any house, a gun that must be seen to be appreciated, as it is so different from the regular walnut stock and fore end usually applied to shotguns.

WE ARE THE LARGEST IMPORTERS in the United States, selling goods from the manufacturers to the consumer. We import all our own foreign guns direct from Liege, Belgium, which is probably the largest gun making center in the world, and all our imported guns have the Belgium Government test, as explained on another page of this catalogue. When you buy a Belgium gun from us you do not pay a wholesaler's, jobber's, or retail dealer's profit, but you buy the gun at one small profit from the manufacturer to the consumer, thus making a great saving on your purchase.

OUR CELEBRATED EBONIZED STOCK and fore end double barrel breech loading shotgun is fitted with a forged breech, lock plates are nicely polished and handsomely nickeled, elegantly engraved in scroll design, as shown in the illustration. The barrel is finished in two-blade Damascus pattern with handsome matted rib, latest style Edwards' extension rib, bored smooth and true to gauge, the right barrel is cylinder bored and the left barrel is choke bored for field shooting.

THE LOCKS are of the bar lock type with rebounding hammers, which fly back to half cock after the gun is fired. The butt plate and top lever are nickel plated to conform with the frame and locks of the gun. The stock is beautifully finished in black ebonized color, checkered in diamond design with German silver pins in the diamonds; has scroll carving on the outer edge of the diamond field, as shown in the illustration. The general appearance of the ebonized stock, engraved nickel plated frame, locks and top lever, nickel plated butt plate and the two-blade Damascus finished barrels makes a combination of contrast pleasing to the eye.

Catalogue No.	Grade	Style of Barrels	Gauge	Length of Barrels	Weight of Gun	Price
6E258	No. 739	2-Blade Damascus Finish	12	30 or 32 in.	7½ to 8 lbs.	$10.69

Weight, packed for shipment, about 14 pounds.

HOW A SHOTGUN BARREL IS CHOKE BORED. For the benefit of our customers who are not familiar with choke boring, we give here illustration of how a shotgun barrel is choke bored. From the illustration you will imagine that a shotgun barrel has been cut in two the entire length, and you are looking at the inside of the barrel. You will notice that the chamber is large, the rest of the bore (cylinder bore) is smaller and of the same diameter until you come to about 1 inch from the muzzle, which is smaller than the cylinder bore from the chamber to the choke. This is known as taper choke; that is to say, the diameter is the same after it leaves the chamber until it meets the choke about 1 inch from the muzzle, when it tapers slightly, leaving the muzzle about one or two gauges smaller than the diameter of the cylinder bore from the chamber forward. It requires fine reamers and skill to taper choke a shotgun barrel. The difference between the cylinder and choke bore is hardly great enough to notice with the naked eye and the philosophy of choke bore is that the shot travels normally until it meets the choke when it becomes concentrated while leaving the barrel, and being concentrated puts a larger number of pellets in a 30-inch circle than if the shotgun was cylinder bored. Cylinder bored shotguns are similar, except that they are not smaller at the muzzle, the bore being the same from the chamber to the muzzle end of the barrel.

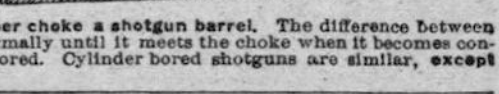

OUR COMBINATION SHOTGUN AND RIFLE, $14..6

Our Globe Sight FREE with this gun.

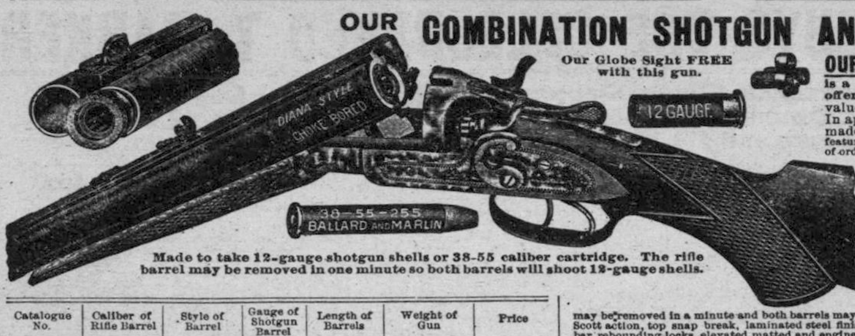

Made to take 12-gauge shotgun shells or 38-55 caliber cartridge. The rifle barrel may be removed in one minute so both barrels will shoot 12-gauge shells.

OUR $14.76 BELGIAN COMBINED RIFLE AND SHOTGUN is a gun equal to what retail gun stores offer at $25.00 to $30.00; it is such a gun value as has never before been offered. In appearance one of the handsomest guns made. Combines every strictly high grade feature, easily handled. A gun that cannot get out of order, a gun that will last a lifetime.

EVERY $14.76 GUN we put out will be a big advertisement for us. Everyone who sees the gun will admire it: every true sportsman will appreciate its splendid qualities, and every dealer in sporting goods will realize the wonderful value we are offering in this fieldpiece at only $14.76. On this basis we solicit your order, feeling confident we will give you such a gun at the price as cannot be duplicated elsewhere.

DETAILED DESCRIPTION. Our Combination Shotgun and Rifle is a new departure in this line, in that the rifle barrel is auxiliary and may be removed in a minute and both barrels may be used for shotgun shells. It is fitted with Scott action, top snap break, laminated steel finished barrels with Diana style breech. Strong bar rebounding locks, elevated matted and engine turned rib fitted with sporting rear and sporting front sight, Edwards' L-shape extension rib; rebounding circular hammers, straight grained walnut stock and fore end nicely checkered, full pistol grip with shield inlaid, patent snap fore end, nitro firing pins, left barrel choke bored, right barrel cylinder bored, case hardened forged frame and lock plates, suitable for birds and heavy game. The 38-55 cartridge is suitable for heavy game such as deer, moose, etc.

Catalogue No.	Caliber of Rifle Barrel	Style of Barrel	Gauge of Shotgun Barrel	Length of Barrels	Weight of Gun	Price
6E259	38-55 C. F. Takes cartridge 6E2342	Laminat'd Steel Finish	12	30 in.	9 to 9¼ lbs.	$14.76

Weight, packed for shipment, about 14 pounds.

OUR HIGHLY ENGRAVED DIANA STYLE BREECH, DOUBLE BARREL BREECH LOADER FOR ONLY $9.98

Our Patent Globe Sight furnished free with this gun. Doubles the value of any shotgun for wing shooting.

12-GAUGE LOADED SHELLS, $1.32 per 100. See page 300.

MADE IN 12-GAUGE ONLY.

This gun is made in Europe by one of the oldest and most reliable makers there, and we offer it for the first time at the remarkably low price of $9.98. Don't be deceived by anyone into buying any of the many cheap imitations. By reason of a large contract, which we have made for a quantity of these guns, we have gotten the manufacturer to figure the price down to the lowest point, and by paying cash for the goods we are able to obtain them based on the actual cost of labor and material, and by adding our one small percentage of profit, we are enabled to name you this heretofore unheard of price on the highly engraved Diana Style Breech, Double Barrel Breech Loading Shotgun.

No. 6E270
The above illustration, engraved from a photograph, will give you some idea of the appearance of this gun.

MINUTE DESCRIPTION. Our Diana Style Breech Gun is fitted with top snap break, laminated steel finished barrels, strong bar rebounding locks, L-shape Edwards' extension rib, rebounding circular hammers, imported walnut stock and fore end nicely checkered; full pistol grip with inlaid shield, patent snap fore end, nitro firing pins, flat matted rib, left barrel choke bored, right barrel cylinder bored; both barrels bored smooth and true to gauge for black and smokeless powder; case hardened forged frame and lock plates. A beautiful gun at a low price. Order by catalogue number and state length of barrels wanted.

Catalogue Number	Grade	Style of Barrels	Gauge	Length Barrels	Weight	Price
6E270	No. 839N	Damascus Finish	12	30 or 32 in.	7½ to 8 lbs.	$9.98

Weight, packed for shipment, about 14 pounds.

CELEBRATED GREENER ACTION BREECH LOADING SHOTGUN... $11.95

12-GAUGE ONLY

DESCRIPTION of our Greener Action Cross Bolt Shotgun. It is fitted with Scott action, top snap break, Damascus finished barrels, strongest bar action locks, with rebounding circular hammers, nicely matted extension rib with Greener action cross bolt in the extension; straight grained walnut stock and fore end nicely carved; pistol grip of inlaid design, giving the grip a handsome appearance; patent snap fore end, handsomely carved scroll engraving on the lock plates, left barrel choke bored, right barrel cylinder bored for field shooting; bored smooth and true to gauge for black and smokeless powder. Order by catalogue number and state length of barrels wanted.

You will get a PROFIT SHARING CERTIFICATE and will quickly get your share of our profit.

Notice our prices on J. C. Hand Traps

$11.95 BUYS A CROSS BOLT GUN With handsomely carved stock and fore end. The barrels of this gun are made of Wilson's best steel.

12-GAUGE LOADED SHELLS, $1.32 PER 100. SEE PAGE 300.

OUR PATENT GLOBE SIGHT furnished free with this gun. Worth the price of the gun for wing shooting.

Catalogue Number	Grade	Style of Barrels	Gauge	Length Barrels	Weight	Price
6E272	No. 365	Damascus Finish	12	30 or 32 in.	7½ to 8 lbs.	$11.95

Weight, packed for shipment, about 14 pounds.

OUR LADIES' LITTLE BREECH LOADING DOUBLE BARREL SHOTGUN.

$9.93

44-Caliber, or 40-85 Caliber Shotgun.

No. 6E276

We have had this little gun built for ladies or boys who like to hunt and for whom a 12-gauge gun kicks too hard. It is very effective for squirrels, birds or small game, and is made to take the 44 X. L. shot cartridge No. 6E2717. It can also be furnished to take the 40-85 primed shell which is about 3 inches long, and can be loaded heavier than the 44 X. L. shot cartridges are loaded. We cannot furnish the 40-85 shells loaded. The 40-85 shells are large enough to take about 40 grains of powder and ⅙-ounce of shot while the 44 X. L. will use only about one-half as much powder and shot. This little breech loader is fitted with 25-inch barrels and weighs about 4 pounds. Our patent Globe sight is not made small enough for this gun.

No. 6E276 Our 44-Caliber Double Barrel Breech Loading Shotgun, top snap, pistol grip stock, rebounding hammers, laminated steel finished barrels. Price....................$9.93

No. 6E2717 Shot Cartridges Caliber 44 X. L. Price, per box of 50....................75

No. 6E3232 Caliber 40-85 Primed Shells. (We cannot furnish these shells loaded). Price, per 100 shells....................$2.50

No. 6E277 Caliber 40-85 Loading Tools, consisting of recapper, cap extractor, wad cutter and charge cup. Price, per set....................55c

No. 57E4716 18-ounce Canvas Gun Cover with leather muzzle and lock protector for this gun. Price....................71c

This gun alone when packed for shipment, weighs about 8 pounds.

GIANT 8-GAUGE GOOSE GUN, 36-INCH BARRELS.

$21.10

Our 8-Gauge Double Barrel Goose Gun for Long Range Shooting. Strong French action. The illustration represents our new 8-gauge Lefeaucheaux Breech Loading Gun. This gun has bottom lever, genuine laminated steel barrels, best double key fore end, pistol grip stock, case hardened frame, fancy butt plate, rebounding locks, checkered grip; made for long range shooting. Our 8-gauge Goose Gun is made especially for us under contract, and nothing but the best material and the best barrels are used in the construction of this gun. We realize the importance of having guns intended for 8-gauge charges, strong at every point, and we have covered these points in the manufacture of these goose guns. Our Globe Sight can only be fitted to 10, 12 and 16-gauge guns.

No. 6E282 The Giant Goose Gun. Made 8-gauge, 36-inch barrels; weight, 12 to 14 pounds. Cylinder bored for buckshot. Price.................... $21.10

OUR AUXILIARY RIFLE BARREL, CALIBER 38-55, FOR 12-GAUGE SHOTGUNS, $4.95.

WITH THIS AUXILIARY RIFLE BARREL you can transform a double barrel shotgun into a combination rifle and shotgun by inserting the auxiliary barrel into the shotgun barrel and it will enable you to shoot a shot shell with the one barrel and a rifle cartridge with the other. It may also be used in a single barrel shotgun, but it is not intended to be used in magazine repeating shotguns.

UNDERSTAND, that for fine target shooting this barrel is impracticable, but for large game shooting a hunter can, with little practice, bring down large game at a distance of 50 to 100 yards by using the shotgun front sight and sighting over the rib of the gun instead of using a rear sight.

No. 6E284 Auxiliary Rifle Barrel, 38-55 caliber, to fit a 30 or 32-inch 12-gauge shotgun. State which length is wanted. Weight, 1¾ to 2 pounds. Price....................$4.95

If by registered mail, postage extra, 40 cents.

$11.22 BUYS THE CELEBRATED T. BARKER

Royal Damascus Finish, Elaborately Engraved, Silver Dog Inlaid, Bar Lock, Double Barrel Breech Loading Shotgun, in 10, 12 or 16-Gauge and $13.35 Buys a 36-inch Barrel 12-Gauge Gun.

Loaded Shells $1.32 per 100. See page 300.

Don't Order a Low Priced Double Barrel Shotgun.

WHILE WE SELL double barrel breech loading shotguns of the latest style as low as $6.35, and a number of others at prices lower than this, our celebrated T. Barker Royal Damascus finished gun, we especially urge that you order one of our higher grade guns, either this, our highest grade T. Barker Royal Damascus finish double barrel breech loader, or one of our American Gun Company's high grade, double barrel, breech loading shotguns. You will be much better satisfied by selecting this or a higher grade gun. You will find such a selection much cheaper in the end. In the shooting qualities, wearing qualities and general satisfaction, it pays to select one of our double barrel guns at from $11.22 and upward.

OUR OWN PATENT GLOBE SIGHT

FURNISHED FREE WITH THIS GUN.

This Globe Sight, which makes wing and fast shooting easy, a sight which can be quickly put on or taken off the gun, is furnished free with every T. Barker gun at $11.22. If you order this gun at $11.22 you will get with the gun, free of any cost, our own special patent Globe Sight as illustrated.

WHILE THE PROFIT IS THE SAME TO US, just our one small percentage of profit above the actual cost of material and labor, and the prices on all our guns are very much lower than you can buy from any other house, **wholly in the interest of our customers we urge you to select one of our higher grade guns, a double barrel breech loading shotgun at $11.22 and upward. You will get such gun value as was never before given, you will get such a gun as was never seen in your section at anything approaching the price,** and, remember, every gun is sent to you subject to your thorough test trial and approval, sent to you with the understanding that you can give it **TEN DAYS' TRIAL**, during which time you can put it to every test; you can compare it with guns made and sold by others, and if you are not convinced that we are giving you a better gun at a lower price than you can buy elsewhere, you can return the gun to us at our expense, and we will immediately

RETURN YOUR MONEY

together with any express charges you may have paid.

REMEMBER, with this and all our high grade guns

PART OF THE PROFIT IS YOURS.

We will send you a PROFIT SHARING CERTIFICATE and you can soon get a Fine Article entirely

FREE

AS EXPLAINED ON THE LAST PAGES.

THIS HANDSOME GUN is gotten out especially for us, following our own detailed specifications, with a view of giving our customers a higher grade, handsomer and better finished shotgun than can possibly be had elsewhere at anything approaching the price.

A NUMBER OF GUNS have been gotten out by various makers in imitation of this, our celebrated T. Barker gun, but you will find any gun offered by any other house bearing the appearance of this our T. Barker Special, will suffer by comparison; in other words, if you will order this gun from us and then order any of the imitations offered by others, and will compare them side by side, **you will find that they do not in any way compare with this.**

OUR SPECIAL T. BARKER GUN AT

$11.22

ILLUSTRATION SHOWING THE PATENT FORE END, FRAME AND INLAID FULL PISTOL GRIP.

FROM THE LARGE ILLUSTRATION, engraved by our artist from a photograph, we have endeavored to give you just a little idea of the beautiful finish, the elaborate appearance and the new up to date lines produced in this gun and OFFERED AT ONLY **$11.22**

THE ROYAL DAMASCUS FINISHED BARRELS

are thoroughly reliable as to quality and have all the handsome appearance of the most expensive barrels made, and each barrel is branded on the rib, Royal Damascus. These barrels are made and bored especially for field shooting, the right barrel being cylinder bored for an open target, and the left barrel choke bored for a close target. The locks and frame are elaborately engraved; **the gun is pistol grip, the grip and fore end neatly checkered.** It is finished with a handsome German silver shield or medallion in the full pistol grip. In short, **the gun has been gotten out according to our own specifications on lines more up to date, handsomer, more modern and in every way better than anything shown by any maker.**

AT ANY PRICE APPROACHING OUR $11.22 PRICE.

OUR FREE TRIAL GUARANTEE AND C. O. D. OFFER.

As a guarantee that this is in every way a better gun than any gun you can buy elsewhere at the price, we will accept your order and ship the gun to you with the understanding and agreement that you can give it ten days' trial, during which time you can put it to any test and if for any reason you become dissatisfied with your purchase, you can return it to us at our expense and we will return your money, together with any express charges paid by you.

DETAILED DESCRIPTION.

BARRELS—**The Royal Damascus finished barrels.** Each pair of barrels is branded on the rib "Royal Damascus." The right barrel is cylinder bored and the left barrel choke bored. The barrels have all the beautiful finish effect of the most expensive Damascus barrels made. They are finished with shell extractor, "L" shaped extension rib, making a strong locking device. They are fitted with heavy lugs, locking securely into the frame; they are nicely shaped and finished, have a neat, handsome matted rib and they are bored for either black, nitro or smokeless powder.

FRAME—The frame is solid steel, strong, beautifully finished, elaborately engraved, handsomely case hardened, made extra strong and of the latest model.

MOUNTINGS—The gun is mounted with neat low circular hammers, adjusted so that they are out of the line of sight; handsome top snap break; the locks are the latest type of bar lock, each lock branded "**T. Barker,**" and the left lock inlaid with a handsome solid silver hunting dog, which in connection with the hand engraving on the lock represents a strikingly beautiful appearance; has the latest style trigger guard, elaborately engraved; neatly shaped triggers; strong, heavy nitro firing pins; locks are rebounding and come back automatically to half cock on being fired.

STOCK—Stock is made from carefully selected and well seasoned black walnut, beautifully finished, made full pistol grip. The pistol grip is finished with a handsome German silver shield, grip is handsomely decorated as illustrated, fancy butt plate to stock; stock is beautifully shaped, giving the gun an even balance. Comes complete with handsome selected black walnut patent fore end, **which is handsomely checkered and beautifully finished.**

GAUGE—Our T. Barker gun is furnished in 10, 12 or 16-gauge as desired.

Our $11.22 price barely covers the cost of material and labor, with but our one small percentage of profit added. It is the greatest value ever shown in a gun at the price; **it is such a gun as can be had from no other house for only $11.22.**

FURTHER, IF YOU DO NOT WISH TO SEND THE FULL AMOUNT WITH YOUR ORDER, WE WILL ON RECEIPT OF $1.00 SEND THIS GUN TO ANY ADDRESS BY EXPRESS C. O. D.

You can examine it at your express office, and if found perfectly satisfactory and exactly as represented; if you are convinced you are getting in this our special **$11.22 T. Barker Gun,** a handsomer and better gun than you could get elsewhere at anything like the price, you can then pay the express agent the balance, $10.22, and express charges. Otherwise the agent will return the gun to us at our expense and we will immediately return to you the $1.00 sent to us.

FROM THE ILLUSTRATION engraved by our artist direct from a **photograph, you can get just a little idea of the appearance of the gun,** although you must see and examine this gun and compare it with guns sold by others at higher prices to appreciate the real value we are offering, yet the picture will give you just a little idea of the **HANDSOME EFFECT WORKED OUT IN THESE ROYAL DAMASCUS FINISHED BARRELS,** in the elaborate engraving of the frame and locks, of the solid silver dog inlaid in the lock, of the general handsome outlines of this

NEW, UP TO DATE, BEAUTIFULLY FINISHED SHOTGUN,

ALWAYS STATE LENGTH WANTED.

Catalogue No.	Grade	Style of Barrels	Gauge	Length of Barrels	Weight of Gun, pounds	Finish	Price
6E292A	No. 678	2 Blade Damascus Finish	12	30 or 32 in.	7½ to 8	Hand Eng'ved	$11.22
6E292B	No. 678		16	30 in.	6¾ to 7	Hand Eng'ved	11.45
6E292D	No. 678		10	32 in.	8¾ to 9¼	Hand Eng'ved	11.65
6E293E	No. 678		12	36 in.	8 to 8¼	Hand Eng'ved	13.35

Weight, packed for shipment, about 14 pounds.

OUR SPECIAL PRICE,

$11.22

for 30 or 32-inch barrels or

$13.35

for 12-gauge gun with 36-inch barrels.

LOADED SHELLS, $1.32 per 100. See page 300.

No. 6E292A ORDER BY NUMBER Price, $11.22.

OUR $10.48 DOUBLE BARREL AMERICAN BAR LOCK WONDER

Manufactured by the American Gun Co., New York, N. Y.
FACTORY AT NORWICH, CONN.

FOR $10.48 WE OFFER THIS STRICTLY HIGH GRADE, A1, AMERICAN MADE, EXTRA STRONG, FULL PISTOL GRIP, DOUBLE BARREL BREECH LOADING SHOTGUN, as the superior of any imported machine made gun sold generally at $20.00 to $30.00, and the first time a strictly high grade, bar lock, choke bored, genuine laminated steel, breech loading, genuine American gun WAS EVER OFFERED AT ANYTHING LIKE THE PRICE.

How the bird appears when using our Globe Sight.

OUR PATENT GLOBE SIGHT FURNISHED FREE WITH THIS GUN.

This sight can be instantly adjusted to, or taken off from any shotgun without in any way marring or scratching the gun barrel. When the gun is aimed at a bird on the wing, no matter how swiftly it flies or how inexperienced the marksman, it describes a large circle around the bird, and once the bird is within the circle and you fire you are sure of hitting the mark. It makes possible the most effective and accurate wing shooting, even in the hands of an inexperienced hunter. This sight really doubles the value of any shotgun for actual service. Once you have used our sight, you would not be without it even at the cost of the gun, and yet we furnish it free with this and all other shotguns. **Understand, we own and control the patent. The sight can only be had from us. It is free with this gun.**

GENUINE LAMINATED STEEL.

TAPER CHOKE BORED

WHERE THE GUN IS MADE.

THIS GUN is made for us under contract by a large manufacturer who has gained the reputation for the manufacture of strictly high grade breech loading shotguns, guns that are made and offered in competition with other American guns that sell at double the price. Only skilled mechanics are employed.

Every piece and part that enters into this gun is made true to gauge and is interchangeable. The locks are rebounding and all have double locking bolts.

$10.48

GENERAL DESCRIPTION.

BARRELS. The barrels are genuine laminated steel. They are made on the most approved process. Every barrel, before leaving the factory, is thoroughly tested with nitro (white and black) powder, tested to the greatest possible strain. These barrels are choke bored on the latest taper system, with a view to giving the most perfect target, the greatest possible penetration, to insure long range effect such as can be had only from the highest grade American guns made.

FINISH OF BARRELS. These barrels are given an extra fine finish and polish. The illustration will give you some idea of the effect worked out on the coloring process, the barrels being browned, colored and decorated by the latest barrel coloring process.

RIB. The rib to these barrels is handsomely finished, beautifully matted, perfectly leveled and comes with a heavy genuine Edwards' lock extension rib.

EXTRACTOR. These barrels are fitted with the very latest shell extractor, as illustrated; positive in its action.

EXTRA HEAVY BOLTS. These barrels are fitted with extra heavy double bolts, made very strong, thus insuring perfect lock and a strength from which the gun, even with the use of white or black powder, cannot give out or wear loose or shaky.

LENGTH OF BARREL. The American Wonder comes with either 30 or 32-inch barrels, as desired. In ordering, be sure to state whether you wish 30 or 32-inch barrels.

WEIGHT. The American Wonder is made to weigh from 7¾ to 8 pounds.

AMERICAN WONDER FRAME. This gun is made with one of the heaviest, strongest and most durable steel gun frames made. The frames are extra heavy, strong in every part, extra well finished, case hardened and handsomely colored. They have the latest nitro firing pins, handsomely shaped; perfect acting top snap break, neat circular rebounding hammers, very strong genuine bar lock, with steel hardened interchangeable parts, perfectly finished.

STOCK. The stock is made from carefully selected straight grained walnut, thoroughly seasoned. It is perfectly shaped. The maker of these guns employs only the most expert stock makers. The stock is fitted to the frame by an automatic stock fitting machine that insures a perfect fit and the frame and stock are so constructed at the point of construction as to insure the strongest kind of a stock where many guns are weakened. This stock is full pistol grip with a handsome fancy cap on grip. The grip is handsomely checkered, as illustrated. Stock comes with handsomely ornamented butt plate.

FORE END. Our $10.48 American Wonder is fitted with the Deeley & Edge automatic fore end, made of selected walnut, handsomely checkered as here illustrated, beautifully finished, self locking in its application.

GAUGE. These guns come in 12-gauge only, but in shooting qualities, penetration, pattern and for long range work they are the equal of any ordinary 10-gauge American gun. For all kinds of game for which a shotgun is used this American Wonder is perfectly suited.

SAFETY AND DURABILITY. First, in considering hard, long range shooting, extra penetration, extra target, the question of strength, durability and safety has not been overlooked, and while it is not safe to use white or nitro powder in any cheap foreign made guns or many of the cheap American guns manufactured, this gun is built for shooting any white powder of proper load that can be safely used in any of the highest priced American guns made. It has been built extra strong, of the best material, strongly locked, strongly reinforced, especially strong where many guns are weak, all with a view of giving you a gun that will be always safe, always reliable; a gun that will last for years and give the very best of satisfaction.

SHOOTING QUALITIES. Too much cannot be said for the shooting qualities of our $10.48 Wonder. Nothing has been spared to make this gun in shooting quality the equal of any gun made, regardless of price. The gun was in every part designed by one of the best and most practical gun makers in this country. It was designed after considering all the strong points for shooting work of all other American guns, and has been built with a view of embodying the strong features of other double barrel breech loading American guns with the defects of none. If a strong point, one that would add to the target or penetration, anything that would help for long range shooting, was found in another American gun, it has been applied in this, so that we feel perfectly safe in assuring the purchaser that he will find in this gun a gun that will equal if not outdo in strength and shooting qualities any other gun he has ever used.

SEE WHAT IS FREE TO YOU

Look on the last pages and see what you get FREE for your

PROFIT SHARING CERTIFICATES,

free to you as your share of our profit.

$10.48

12-GAUGE LOADED SHELLS, $1.32 PER 100. SEE PAGE 300.

HOW WE MAKE THE PRICE SO LOW.

While a thoroughly reliable genuine American Double Barrel Breech Loading gun has never been sold at anything beginning to approach our special $10.48 price, determined that we would get out a genuine American gun at as low or a lower price than the very inferior machine made foreign or Belgian gun could be sold, we took the matter of manufacturing this high grade gun up with a celebrated New England gun maker, figuring how, by running a certain branch of his factory at its utmost capacity, the price of a reliable gun might be greatly reduced. We found by employing the very highest type of automatic working machinery for making the different parts, by buying the raw material, including the drop forgings, steel, walnut, etc., in large quantities, and by running the factory to its utmost capacity, the actual factory cost, the cost of material and labor, could be reduced even below what we ourselves or the manufacturer had any idea of reaching, and to this net factory cost, the cost of material and labor, we add our one small percentage of profit and name you the heretofore unheard of price of $10.48.

THE BARRELS ON THESE GUNS are all genuine laminated steel, and not imitation laminated steel as sold by some houses. We guarantee them just as represented or money refunded.

NO OTHER HOUSE will give you such a guarantee on a gun at the price which we offer you this gun, and it is certainly the best gun value offered by any house in the United States.

No. 6E362 ORDER BY NUMBER.

No. 6E362 Our American Bar Lock Wonder, 12-gauge, 30 or 32-inch barrels; weight, 7¾ to 8 pounds. State length wanted. Price........ **$10.48**

WHEN ORDERING PARTS for guns, rifles or revolvers, always give catalogue number in full, also give the name, caliber, gauge of the gun, rifle or revolver. This will save us from writing you for this information.

NOTICE. The Canadian government charges 30 per cent duty on guns shipped into Canada from this country.

WHILE WE ESPECIALLY URGE THE PURCHASE OF A REVOLVER MADE IN OUR OWN FACTORY, as illustrated and described on the preceding pages, we show on this and the following pages A LINE OF THE WELL KNOWN DOUBLE ACTION MAKES, AND AT PRICES LOWER THAN YOU CAN BUY ELSEWHERE.

IN ORDERING A SINGLE REVOLVER we advise sending it by mail. This can be done by enclosing enough extra money to cover postage. The postage is 1 cent per ounce, or fraction thereof. If sent by insured mail, allow 5 cents extra for revolvers valued at $5.00 or less, and 10 cents extra for revolvers costing $10.00 or less; and 15 cents extra for revolvers costing $15.00 or less, and if lost in transit you will be entitled to a new revolver.

ON RECEIPT OF $1.00 we will send any revolver by express C. O. D., subject to examination, balance to be paid after the revolver is received and found perfectly satisfactory. We recommend, however, that you send cash in full with your order and save the small extra charge on a C. O. D. shipment. Nearly all our customers send cash in full with their orders. DON'T FAIL TO COMPARE OUR PRICES WITH OTHER HOUSES. WE CAN SAVE YOU MONEY.

HOW TO TEST A PISTOL OR REVOLVER.

PLEASE NOTE that expert pistol and revolver shooting can only be accomplished by experience and when once you become an expert shot, it is difficult for you to do poor shooting when you are in good form. **ALL REVOLVERS ARE TESTED** at 12 to 20 yards except the high power strong shooting arms, which are tested at 50 yards, and if you do not make a good target, it is not the fault of the revolver, but is usually the fault of the sighting; for instance, a revolver that is tested at a target at 12 yards, and you can do good shooting at this range, you will find if you shoot the same revolver at 50 yards the bullets will fall under the target, so in order to become an expert shot it is quite necessary for you to become acquainted with the revolver you intend to shoot, and in a short time you will know whether to hold above or below the bull's eye in order to hit it. **WHEN TESTING A REVOLVER** always take a muzzle rest, and shoot 5 or 6 consecutive shots at a bull's eye without stopping, then examine your target and see how the shots group and how near the group is to your bull's eye. This will give you an idea whether you should hold high, low, to the right or to the left of your mark. Always bear in mind that the wind has more or less effect on target shooting, and 5-inch barrel revolvers are better than 3-inch for target shooting. It requires long practice to become skilled with a 3-inch barrel.

DOUBLE ACTION REVOLVERS, $1.44 TO $1.65.

$1.44 TO $1.65

All are self cocking, full nickel plated with checkered rubber handle, round and octagon steel rifled barrel, forged parts, and made from the best material that money can buy.

Made in 22 and 32-caliber rim fire, 32-caliber center fire and 38-caliber central fire.

Catalogue Number	Caliber	Length of Barrel	Style of Barrel	No. of Sh'ts	Shoots Cartridge	Weight	Price
6E1180	22 r.f.	2⅝ in.	Round	7	6E2336	10 oz.	$1.44
6E1182	32 c.f.	2½ in.	Round	5	6E2377	12 oz.	1.45
6E1183	32 r.f.	2½ in.	Octagon	5	6E2352	10 oz.	1.64
6E1185	32 c.f.	2½ in.	Octagon	5	6E2377	12 oz.	1.65
6E1186	38 c.f.	2½ in.	Octagon	5	6E2388	16 oz.	1.65

Extra for pearl stock for any of the above revolvers. Price $1.00

If by mail, postage extra, 12 to 20 cents.

CARTRIDGES, 70 AND 91 CENTS PER 100. SEE PAGE 301.

DOUBLE ACTION { 4½-inch Barrel....... $1.89 / 6 -inch Barrel....... 2.14

$1.89

THESE REVOLVERS are strictly first class in every respect and made especially for us under season contract. The quality of material and workmanship are the best. All have octagon rifled barrels and are good shooters; 5 or 6-shot. These are not toys, but good guns. No one can meet our prices on these goods. They are self-cocking, all full nickel plated and checkered rubber stocks, and parts are interchangeable, and they weigh about 16 and 18 ounces.

Catalogue Number	Caliber	Length of Barrel	Finish	No. of Sh'ts	Shoots Cartridge	Weight	Price
6E1189	32 c.f.	4½ in.	Nickel Plated	6	6E2377	15 oz.	$1.89
6E1190	38 c.f.	4½ in.		5	6E2388	18 oz.	
6E1191	32 c.f.	6 in.		6	6E2377	16 oz.	2.14
6E1192	38 c.f.	6 in.		5	6E2388	18 oz.	

Extra for pearl stock $1.00

If by mail, postage extra, 20 to 27 cents.

CARTRIDGES, 70 AND 91 CENTS PER 100. SEE PAGE 301.

DOUBLE ACTION REVOLVERS, $1.63.

Manufactured by the Hopkins & Allen Manufacturing Co., who bought the Forehand & Wadsworth factory.

Forehand & Wadsworth New Double Action, Self Cocking Revolver, full nickel plated, rubber stock, octagon rifled barrel, safe and reliable, accurate, rebounding lock, parts are interchangeable.

Catalogue Number	Caliber	Length of Barrel	Finish	No. of Sh'ts	Shoots Cartridge	Weight	Price
6E1195	32 c.f.	2½ in.	Nickel Plated	6	6E2377	15 oz.	$1.63
6E1196	38 c.f.	2½ in.		5	6E2388	15 oz.	

If by mail, postage extra, 20 cents.

If you wish us to send a revolver by insured mail, see top of this page for rates of insurance.

CARTRIDGES 70 AND 91 CENTS PER 100. SEE PAGE 301.

SAFETY HAMMER DOUBLE ACTION REVOLVER, $1.64.

Forehand & Wadsworth Safety Hammer, Double Action Revolver is now made by the Hopkins & Allen Manufacturing Co., who have purchased the tools, machinery and patents of the Forehand Co. All are full nickel plated, rubber stock, octagon rifled barrel, rebounding lock, safe, reliable and accurate, and weigh about 15 ounces.

Catalogue Number	Caliber	Length of Barrel	Finish	No. of Sh'ts	Shoots Cartridge	Weight	Price
6E1197	32 c.f.	2½ in.	Nickel Plated	6	6E2377	15 oz.	$1.64
6E1198	38 c.f.	2½ in.		5	6E2388	15 oz.	

If by mail, postage extra, 20 cents.

These goods are genuine, and new from the factory. Beware of imitations and shop worn goods, which are sold for new goods by some firms. We handle nothing but first class goods.

70c PER 100 FOR 32-CALIBER CARTRIDGES. 91c PER 100 FOR 38-CALIBER CARTRIDGES. SEE PAGE 301.

OUR BABY HAMMERLESS.

Our Baby Hammerless Revolver is manufactured by Henry M. Kolb, Philadelphia, Pa., who guarantees the revolver against defective parts. It is made to carry in the vest pocket, length of revolver is 4 inches, all parts made interchangeable.

22-caliber $1.63

All have folding trigger, rifled steel barrel, fancy rubber stock, fluted cylinder, can be loaded from the side, rebounding hammer, full nickel plated; taking 22-caliber rim fire cartridge No. 6E2336.

Catalogue Number	Caliber	Length of Barrel	Finish	No. of Sh'ts	Shoots Cartridge	Handles	Price
6E1249	22 rim	1¼ in.	Nickel Plated	7	6E2336	Rubber	$1.63
6E1250	22 rim	1¼ in.		7	6E2336	Pearl	2.53

If by mail, postage extra, 8 cents.

22-CALIBER CARTRIDGES, 19c PER 100. SEE PAGE 301.

IVER JOHNSON AUTOMATIC,

32 and 38-Caliber. $3.24

70c and 91c per 100 for Cartridges. See page 301.

The Iver Johnson Automatic Shell Ejecting, Safety Hammer Revolver, double action, self cocking, 5-shot, weight, 13 and 18 ounces, 3-inch and 3¼-inch barrels, finely nickel plated, neatly finished. Every one warranted. All take center fire Smith & Wesson cartridges.

Catalogue Number	Caliber	Length of Barrel	Finish	No. of Sh'ts	Shoots Cartridge No.	Weight, Ounces	Price
6E1253	32 c.f.	3 in.	Nickel Plated	5	6E2377	13	$3.24
6E1254	38 c.f.	3¼ in.		5	6E2388	18	

Pearl handles on any of the above will cost extra..........$1.10

70 AND 91 CENTS PER 100 FOR CARTRIDGES. SEE PAGE 301

IVER JOHNSON HAMMERLESS,

32 and 38-Caliber. $3.74

The above illustrated revolver is the celebrated Iver Johnson automatic, hammerless, double action; high grade finish and fine adjustments. Its trigger locking device makes it one of the safest revolvers to carry in the pocket. Automatic self ejector, rebounding lock, safety trigger locking device, chambered cylinder, rifled barrel. The 32-caliber is small frame, 5-shot; weight, 13 ounces; length of barrel, 3 inches; a revolver that retails at from $5.00 to $7.00.

Catalogue Number	Caliber	Length of Barrel	Finish	No. of Sh'ts	Shoots Cartridge No.	Weight	Price
6E1321	32 c.f.	3 in.	Nickel Plated	5	6E2377	13 oz.	$3.74
6E1322	38 c.f.	3¼ in.		5	6E2388	18 oz.	

If fitted with pearl stocks, extra..........$1.00

If by mail, postage extra, 17 to 22 cents.

THE STEVENS' TIP UP PISTOL.

22-CALIBER CARTRIDGES, 19c PER 100. SEE PAGE 301.

22-caliber only. 3½-inch barrel.

Stevens' Single Shot Pistol. Tip up barrel, nickel plated finish, 3½-inch blued steel barrel, 22-caliber only, rim fire. No better material put in rifles. A fine target pistol. Rifled barrel and well made throughout.

22 SHORT

No. 6E1343 For 22-caliber short cartridges No. 6E2336. (Postage extra, 15c) Price $1.95

STEVENS' DIAMOND MODEL TARGET PISTOL.

22-CALIBER CARTRIDGES 19 CENTS PER 100. SEE PAGE 301

The Celebrated Stevens' Target Pistol, the best pistol made for fine, close shooting. It has fine blued barrel, nickel plated frame, rosewood stock, 6-inch tip up barrel; fitted with fine globe and peep target sights, 22-caliber, rim fire. Shoots either 22 long rifle or 22 short cartriges; good for 50 yards. 22-caliber, 6-inch barrel.

No. 6E1344 Diamond model, with globe and peep sights. Price..........$3.95

No. 6E1345 The same pistol, but with open sights. Price..........(Postage extra, 16c)..........$3.97

REMINGTON DERRINGERS.

This is the genuine Remington Double Derringer. Don't buy imitations. The Remington Double Derringer, 41-caliber short, rim fire, takes cartridge No. 6E2360; checkered rubber stock; length of barrels, 3 inches, entire length of pistol is 5 inches; nickel plated.

$4.25

No. 6E1347 Price, nickel plated........ $4.25

No. 6E1348 Same, blued. Price........

If fitted with pearl handles, extra........ 1.25

If by mail, postage extra, 24 cents.

HARRINGTON & RICHARDSON'S REVOLVERS.

YOUNG AMERICA, LADIES' REVOLVER.

Double Action, Reduced-Size 22-Caliber, Rim Fire and 32-Caliber Central Fire.

Young America. $1.65 TO $2.55

Full nickel plated, 22-caliber, 7-shot or 32-caliber 5 shot, with 2-inch rifled octagon barrel. The Young America can be carried in the vest pocket as conveniently as a watch, and is designed especially for ladies' use. The Young America is positively the best double action self cocking revolver made. It may be had with pearl handles or rubber handles as priced below.

No. 6E1354

Catalogue Number	Caliber	Length of Barrel	Weight	No. of Sh'ts	Shoots Cartridge	Handles	Price
6E1352	22 r.f.	2 in.	7 oz.	7	6E2336	Rubber	$1.65
6E1354	22 r.f.	2 in.	7 oz.	7	6E2336	Pearl	2.55
6E1355	32 c.f.	2 in.	9 oz.	5	6E2377	Rubber	1.65
6E1357	32 c.f.	2 in.	9 oz.	5	6E2377	Pearl	2.55

If by mail, postage extra, 13 to 15 cents.

YOUNG AMERICA, SAFETY HAMMER, SELF COCKER.

$1.64 and $2.54

70 CENTS PER 100 FOR CARTRIDGES. See page 301.

Is reduced size, full nickel plated, rubber stocks, 5-shot, rifled octagon barrel with safety hammer.

32-CALIBER ONLY

The safety hammer is very much desired by many of our customers as it leaves no horn on the hammer to catch in the pocket when pulling it out quickly. Like the regular hammer revolver this safety hammer is one of the very best double action revolvers made.

Catalogue Number	Caliber	Length of Barrel	No. of Sh'ts	Shoots Cartridge	Weight	Handle	Price
6E1359	32 c.f.	2 in.	5	6E2377	15 oz.	Rubber	$1.64
6E1361	32 c.f.	2 in.	5	6E2377	15 oz.	Pearl	2.54

If by mail, postage extra, 15 cents.

YOUNG AMERICA TARGET REVOLVER.

22-CALIBER CARTRIDGES, 19c PER 100. SEE PAGE 301

Double Action, Reduced Size, 22-Caliber, Rim Fire, with 6-inch Rifled Octagon Barrel.

$2.16 and $3.05

The Young America is full nickeled, rubber or pearl stocks, 7-shot, 6-inch rifled octagon barrel; takes cartridge No. 6E2336 and weighs 10 ounces.

22 SHORT

Catalogue Number	Caliber	Length of Barrel	Finish	No. of Sh'ts	Shoots Cartridge No.	Handles	Price
6E1368	22 r.f.	6 in.	Nickel Plated	7	6E2336	Rubber	$2.16
6E1369	22 r.f.	6 in.		7	6E2336	Pearl	3.05

This is the only 22-caliber, 7-shot, target pistol on the market and we were the first to offer it to our customers. If by mail, postage extra, 14 cents.

HARRINGTON & RICHARDSON'S REVOLVERS.

H. & R. NEW MODEL PREMIER, 22-CALIBER, 3-INCH BARREL.

22-CALIBER CARTRIDGES, 19c PER 100. SEE PAGE 301.

22 SHORT

ILLUSTRATION OF No. 6E1372

Harrington & Richardson's "Premier" is automatic shell ejecting, small frame, 7-shot and is adapted to 22-caliber short or long rim fire cartridges. The working parts are drop forged. This is a fine 22-caliber automatic revolver. The frame, cylinder and barrel are steel, hammer is hardened, has automatic shell ejector, rubber stocks. Full nickel plated or blued finish, rifled barrel. Weight, 13 ounces, a good pocket size revolver and takes cartridge No. 6E2336 or No. 6E2338.

Catalogue Number	Caliber	Length of Barrel	Finish	No. of Sh'ts	Shoots Cartridge No.	Handles	Price
6E1370	22 r.f.	3 in.	Nickeled	7	6E2336, or 6E2338	Rubber	$3.25
6E1371	22 r.f.	3 in.	Blued	7		Rubber	3.50
6E1372	22 r.f.	3 in.	Nickeled	7		Pearl	4.25
6E1373	22 r.f.	3 in.	Blued	7		Pearl	4.50

If by mail, postage extra, 20 cents.

H. & R. PREMIER, 22-CAL. 5-INCH BARREL.

22-CALIBER CARTRIDGES, 19c PER 100. SEE PAGE 301.

SHORT

$3.75 AND $4.00

Harrington & Richardson's Premier is automatic shell ejecting, small frame, 7-shot, and is adapted to 22-caliber short or long rim fire cartridges. The working parts are drop forged. This is a fine 22-caliber automatic revolver. The frame, cylinder and barrel are steel, hammer is hardened; has automatic shell ejector, rubber stocks, rifled barrel. Full nickel plated or blued finish. Weight, about 14 ozs. Shoots cartridge No. 6E2336 or No. 6E2338.

Catalogue Number	Caliber	Length of Barrel	Finish	No. of Sh'ts	Shoots Cartridge No.	Weight, Ounces	Price
6E1374	22 r.f.	5 in.	Nickeled	7	6E2336	14	$3.75
6E1375	22 r.f.	5 in.	Blued	7	6E2338	14	4.00

Extra for pearl handles on these revolvers............$1.00
If by mail, postage extra, 22 cents.

H. & R. AUTOMATIC REVOLVER.

70 AND 91 CENTS PER 100 FOR CARTRIDGES. SEE PAGE 301.

32 and 38-Caliber.

$3.24 TO $4.00

Over 3,500,000 Harrington & Richardson's Revolvers now in use.

OUR $3.24 H. & R. AUTOMATIC REVOLVER.

This revolver would retail in any first class gun store at from $5.00 to $6.00. The celebrated Harrington & Richardson's Improved Automatic, self extracting, double action, self cocking revolver, modeled on the Smith & Wesson pattern, beautifully nickel plated, rubber stock, as accurate and durable as any revolver on the market, and equal to the Smith & Wesson in shooting. The 32-caliber is 6-shot, and the 38-caliber is 5-shot.

Catalogue Number	Caliber	Length of Barrel	Finish	No. of Sh'ts	Shoots Cartridge	Weight Ounces	Price
6E1385	32 c.f.	3¼ in.	Nickel Plated	6	6E2377	18½	$3.24
6E1386	38 c.f.	3¼ in.		5	6E2388	18½	
6E1387	32 c.f.	3¼ in.	Blued Steel	6	6E2377	18½	3.50
6E1388	38 c.f.	3¼ in.		5	6E2388	18½	
6E1391	32 c.f.	5 in.	Nickel Plated	6	6E2377	21	3.75
6E1392	38 c.f.	5 in.		5	6E2388	21	
6E1393	32 c.f.	5 in.	Blued Steel	6	6E2377	21	4.00
6E1394	38 c.f.	5 in.		5	6E2388	21	

Pearl handles on above revolvers will cost extra......$1.10
If by mail, postage extra, 18 to 24 cents.

H. & R. HAMMERLESS REVOLVERS.

70 AND 91 CENTS PER 100 FOR CARTRIDGES. SEE PAGE 301
32 or 38-Caliber. Adapted to S. & W. Cartridges.

H. & R. 38 HAMMERLESS.

$3.76 AND 4.25

This is Harrington & Richardson's latest production. The revolvers have automatic shell ejectors, forged parts, steel barrels and rubber stocks. The 32-caliber has a small light frame, making them a good convenient pocket size. They are full nickel plated. The 32-caliber uses cartridge No. 6E2377; 38-caliber uses cartridge No. 6E2388

Catalogue Number	Caliber	Length of Barrel	Finish	No. of Sh'ts	Shoots Cartridge	Weight	Price
6E1411	32 c.f.	3 in.	Nickel Plated	5	6E2377	13 oz.	$3.76
6E1412	38 c.f.	3¼ in.		5	6E2388	18 oz.	
6E1415	38 c.f.	5 in.	Nickel Plated	5	6E2377	21 oz.	4.25
6E1416	38 c.f.	5 in.		5	6E2378	21 oz.	

Blued steel finish on above, extra..........................$0.25
Pearl handles on above revolvers, extra.............. 1.10
If by mail, postage extra, 18 to 24 cents.

OUR $3.62 FRONTIER REVOLVER

This Frontier Revolver is offered as the BEST strong shooting arm made at a medium low price. The best revolver for the money for frontier use. This large, strong shooting and well finished revolver retails everywhere at from $6.00 to $8.00.

Takes Cartridge 6D2409.

$3.62

It is a 5½-inch barrel 6 shooter, with fine engraved rubber stock, 44-caliber, center fire, full nickel plated or blued finish. This revolver is adapted to 44-caliber Winchester cartridges, so that a person having a rifle need not change ammunition, but can use the same cartridges in both. Weight, 35 ounces.

Catalogue Number	Caliber	No. of Shots	Finish	Length of Barrel	Price
6E1434	44-40	6	Nickeled	5½ in.	$3.62
6E1436	44-40	6	Blued	5½ in.	3.87

If by mail, postage extra, 40 cents.

OUR FOREHAND AUTOMATIC, $3.24

32 and 38-Caliber.

Hopkins & Allen's Celebrated Forehand Automatic Revolver for $3.24; a revolver that retails at from $5.00 to $6.00. The very latest improved model, automatic shell extractor, rebounding locks, double action, self cocking, simple and accurate, interchangeable parts made from drop steel forgings. The frame is cast steel, no malleable iron about it; nickel plated throughout; fancy rubber stock, every revolver is fully warranted; length of barrel, 3¼ inches; weight, 17 ounces; entire length, 7¾ inches. The fact that our sales are constantly increasing on these revolvers is evidence of the general satisfaction they give.

Catalogue Number	Caliber	Length of Barrel	Finish	No. of Sh'ts	Shoots Cartridge	Weight	Price
6E1460	32 c.f.	3¼ in.	Nickel	6	6E2377	17 oz.	$3.24
6E1461	38 c.f.	3¼ in.	Nickel	5	6E2388	17 oz.	

If by mail, postage extra, 24 cents.

OUR FOREHAND HAMMERLESS, $3.75

70c PER 100 FOR 32-CALIBER CARTRIDGES. 91c PER 100 FOR 38-CALIBER CARTRIDGES. SEE PAGE 301.
SMALL FRAME.

32 and 38-Caliber.

We offer you at $3.75 our Hopkins & Allen's Forehand hammerless revolver which has never been retailed at less than $5.00. No other house will meet our price. Make a comparison and decide for yourself. This is the celebrated Forehand new style hammerless revolver, made by the Hopkins & Allen Manufacturing Co., who have bought out the Forehand Arms Co. No better revolver made. Automatic shell extractor, double action, self cocking, rebounding lock, absolutely safe catch to lock hammer, made of best material, beautifully finished throughout, accurate and reliable. All center fire, and nicely nickel plated finish. Uses Smith & Wesson centerfire cartridges, 32-caliber and 38-caliber, 5-shot.

Catalogue Number	Caliber	Length of Barrel	Finish	No. of Sh'ts	Shoots Cartridge	Weight	Price
6E1470	32 c.f.	3 in.	Nickel	5	6E2377	14 oz.	$3.75
6E1471	38 c.f.	3¼ in.	Nickel	5	6E2388	16 oz.	

If by mail, postage extra, 19 to 24 cents.

OUR REVOLVER STOCK, 63c.

Our Revolver Stock is made to be attached to any revolver and is a great assistance to revolver shooters for getting steady aim. With this stock you practically make a rifle out of your revolver. To attach this stock, wrap a piece of cloth around the revolver handle to prevent it from becoming marred, and screw it fast with the thumb nut. This stock will not take the Colt's Automatic Pistol as it interferes with the magazine of same.

No. 6E1488 Our Revolver Stock. Price..............63c
If by mail, postage extra, 20 cents.

OUR NEW LIBERTY 22-CALIBER REVOLVER, $1.05.

Owing to the many calls which we have had for a cheap 22-caliber single action revolver, we have ordered a quantity of the Liberty revolvers with 2½-inch barrel, 7-shot, fancy rubber saw handle, full nickel plated throughout, taking the 22-caliber, rim fire, short cartridge. Weight, about 7 ounces. Full length, 5¾ inches. These revolvers are not quite as good as the Young America revolver, but are intended to take the place of a cheap single action revolver. They are as well made as any single action revolver yet produced.

Catalogue Number	Caliber	Length of Barrel	Finish	No. of Shots	Weight	Price
6E1489	22 rim.	2½ in.	Nickeled	7	7 ozs.	$1.05

If by mail, postage extra, 10 cents.

22-CALIBER CARTRIDGES FOR THIS REVOLVER 19 CENTS PER 100. SEE PAGE 301.

THE GENUINE COLT'S MAGAZINE REVOLVERS.

MADE BY THE COLT'S FIRE ARMS CO., HARTFORD, CONN.

NOTICE—The manufacturer fixes the prices at which we shall sell these revolvers and will not allow us or any house to sell them any cheaper. THESE PRICES ARE GUARANTEED to be as low as offered by any reliable dealer in the United States, and should you be offered these goods lower by any dealer you will confer a great favor by advising us, in order to give us an opportunity of investigating the matter.

COLT'S AUTOMATIC MAGAZINE PISTOL, 32-CALIBER, $15.00.

QUARTER SIZE

The opposite illustration engraved direct from a photograph will give you some idea of the Colt's Automatic Pistol made in caliber 32 to shoot smokeless cartridges for powerful long range shooting. This is the latest creation of the Colt's Patent Fire Arms Co., of Hartford, Conn. The Colt's Automatic Pistol is designed and proportioned for a pocket size automatic pistol. Specifications. The entire pistol is made from the very best grade of crucible steel which can be procured regardless of price, the mechanism is of the same high order which follows the Colt line throughout their entire output; the parts are simple and strong, not liable to get out of order, the barrel is finely rifled for long range shooting; all metal parts are handsomely blued, fancy rubber handles, latest improved safety on the grip which renders the pistol perfectly safe until the owner is ready to shoot, the entire length of the Colt's Automatic Pistol is 7 inches, the weight is 24 ounces, will hold 8 cartridges in the magazine and 1 in the barrel, making it a 9-shot pistol, is accurate up to 300 yards, and will penetrate four one-inch pine boards at a distance of 15 feet. To shoot the pistol, first cock the pistol, fill the magazine and put a cartridge in the chamber. Each shot throws out the shell and puts in a new cartridge. All you have to do is pull the trigger.

No. 6E1500 Colt's Automatic Pistol, 32-caliber, 4-inch barrel, weight, 24 ounces. Price..............................$15.00
If fitted with pearl handles, extra.............................. 1.75
Extra magazine for the above pistol. Price.............. .90
If by registered mail, postage extra, 36 cents.
No. 6E2560 32 caliber Automatic Smokeless Rimless Cartridges with metal patched bullet. Price, per box of 50, 72c
Cartridges cannot be sent by mail.

COLT'S AUTOMATIC MAGAZINE 38-CALIBER PISTOL ONLY $19.50.

QUARTER SIZE.

This is the latest creation of the Colt's Fire Arms Co., one of the strongest pistols ever produced, 8 shots may be fired in one second, has a range of 500 to 1,000 yards, shoots the latest 38-caliber Colt Automatic high pressure cartridge, and has a velocity of 1,300 feet per second, and will penetrate eight 1-inch pine boards. In placing this pistol on the market, we predict an innovation in pistols, for this pistol is made on entirely different principles from revolvers, the magazine is in the handle, and it has no cylinder, whereby it differs from revolvers. To operate this pistol, place seven cartridges in the magazine, and one in the chamber, raise the hammer, and all you have to do after that is to pull the trigger, for the pistol cocks itself after every shot is fired by its own recoil, ejects the cartridge which has been fired, places a new cartridge in the chamber, and is ready to shoot again as soon as you are ready to pull the trigger, in other words, the pistol shoots, raises the hammer, ejects the empty shell, replaces another cartridge in the chamber, as fast as you can pull the trigger; the entire eight loads may be fired in eight seconds.
The Colt's Automatic Pocket Pistol has 4½-inch barrel.

Catalogue Number	Caliber	Length of Barrel	Finish	No. of Sh'ts	Shoots Cartridge	Weight	Price
6E1503	38 aut.	4½ in.	Blued	8	6E2580	31 oz.	$19.50
6E1505	38 aut.	6 in.	Steel	8	6E2580	35 oz.	

Extra for pearl stocks, fitted to the above pistol......$2.00
Extra magazines for above pistol. Each................ 1.35
If by registered mail, postage extra, 48 cents.
No. 6E2580 38-caliber automatic smokeless cartridges with metal patched bullets. Price, per box of 50........$1.07

COLT'S NEW POLICE REVOLVER.

32 and 38-Caliber.

32 and 38-Caliber Colt's New Police Double Action Side Ejecting Revolver, jointless solid frame combined with simultaneous ejector, the 32 using the 32 short or 32 long Colt, the 38 using the 38-caliber S. & W. cartridges. The 38-caliber revolver has the new positive safety lock and the firing pin cannot strike the cartridge until you pull the trigger. This is the revolver adopted by the City Police Departments of New York and other cities.

Catalogue No.	Caliber	Lgth of Brrl	Finish	No. of Shots	Shoots Cart'ge	Weight	Price
6E1511	32 c. f.	4 in.	Blued	6-shot	6E2380, 6E2381	18 ozs.	$12.70
6E1513	38 c. f.	4 in.	Blued	6-shot	6E2388	20 ozs.	13.90

32 caliber if fitted with pearl handles, $2.00 extra.
38 caliber if fitted with pearl handles, $2.00 extra.
If by mail, postage extra, 26 to 28 cents.

OUR $2.72 AUTOMATIC AND $3.25 HAMMERLESS REVOLVERS

ARE GUARANTEED TO BE EQUAL TO ANY REVOLVER USUALLY SOLD AT DOUBLE THIS PRICE.
Send us your order, compare our revolver with any revolver costing more money, keep it ten days, at that time if you are in any way dissatisfied, return the revolver to us and we will refund your money and transportation charges paid by you.

COLT'S NEW NAVY REVOLVER.

Colt's New Navy side ejecting, double action revolver has been adopted by the U. S. navy, and every one must pass a rigid inspection and test. This Colt's New Navy double action, self cocking, side shell ejecting revolver is fitted with rubber stock, beautifully finished, and made of finest material, length about 12¼ inches; six shooter; weight, 2 lbs.; blued steel finish. The 38-caliber takes cartridges No. 6E2392, and the 41-caliber takes cartridges No. 6E2400 or No. 6E2401.

Illustration showing the revolver open. 38 and 41-caliber.

This revolver is very similar to the New Army, differing slightly in the handle.

Catalogue Number	Caliber	Length of Barrel	Finish	No. of Sh'ts	Shoots Cartridge No.	Weight Ounces	Price
6E1521	38 c.f.	4½in.	Blued	6	6E2392	32	$13.90
6E1523	38 c.f.	6 in.	Blued	6	6E2392	32	
6E1525	41 c.f.	4½in.	Blued	6	6E2400 or 6E2401	32	13.90
6E1527	41 c.f.	6 in.	Blued	6		32	

If fitted with pearl stocks, extra........................$2.75

If by mail, postage extra, 40 cents.

COLT'S DOUBLE ACTION REVOLVER.

38 and 41-Caliber.

Colt's Double Action, sliding side ejector. Every one warranted. 38 or 41-caliber. It is a 6-shooter using center fire cartridges, made of best revolver steel throughout, fitted with rubber handles, blued steel finish. This is the old reliable Colt double action which has been popular for many years. The 38-caliber takes cartridges No. 6E2392, and the 41-caliber takes No. 6E2400 or No. 6E2401.

Catalogue Number	Caliber	Length of Barrel	Finish	No. of Sh'ts	Shoots Cartridge No.	Weight Ounces	Price
6E1531	38 c.f.	4½in.	Blued	6	6E2392	26	$11.60
6E1533	38 c.f.	6 in.	Blued	6	6E2392	28	
6E1537	41 c.f.	6 in.	Blued	6	6E2400 or 6E2401	28	12.95

If fitted with pearl stocks, extra........................$2.75

If by mail, postage extra, each, 40 cents.

COLT'S NEW ARMY MODEL 1892.

38 and 41-Caliber.

Colt's New Army Model 1892. Double action, self cocking, side ejecting revolver. Weight, 2 pounds, 6-shooter, 38 or 41-caliber, length of barrel, 4½ or 6 inches. Blued steel finish, rubber handles. The 38-caliber takes cartridges No. 6E2392 and the 41-caliber takes No. 6E2400 or No. 6E2401. This revolver is very similar to the New Navy, differing slightly in the handle.

Catalogue Number	Caliber	Length of Barrel	Finish	No. of Sh'ts	Shoots Cartridge No.	Wgt. Oz.	Price
6E1541	38 c.f.	4½in.	Blued	6	6E2392	32	$13.90
6E1543	38 c.f.	6 in.	Blued	6	6E2392	32	
6E1545	41 c.f.	4½in.	Blued	6	6E2400 or 6E2401	32	13.90
6E1547	41 c.f.	6 in.	Blued	6		32	

If fitted with pearl stocks, extra........................$2.75

If by mail, postage extra, each, 40 cents.

WE RECOMMEND THE FOLLOWING CALIBERS OF COLT'S REVOLVERS:
For small game, 32 short, 32 long and 41 short.
For medium size game, 32-20, 38 short; 38 long and 41 long.
For deer, bear, etc., 44-40 and 45-caliber.
For quantity of powder and weight of bullet in each above caliber, see central fire cartridges, loaded with black powder, on another page.

COLT'S NEW SERVICE DOUBLE ACTION REVOLVER.

45-Caliber.

The New Service Double Action, side ejecting revolvers, have jointless solid frame, combined with simultaneous ejector, using 45-caliber Colt's double action cartridges; 7½-inch barrel, rubber handles, blued steel finish only. Weight, about 2 pounds. They are powerful shooters and take cartridges No. 6E2413.

Catalogue Number	Caliber	Length of Barrel	Finish	No. of Sh'ts	Shoots Cartridge N	Wgt. Oz.	Price
6E1563	45 c.f.	7½in.	Blued Steel	6	6E2413	36	$16.20

If fitted with pearl stocks, extra........................$5.50

If by mail, postage extra, 44 cents.

SEND 10 CENTS for our Booklet of Useful Information to Shooters. It tells how gun barrels burst and gives interesting data to shooters.

COLT'S SINGLE ACTION "COWBOY" FRONTIER ARMY.

32, 41, 44 and 45-Caliber.

This is the old reliable Cowboys' Gun, and our price is $13.90 for all calibers and length of barrels; furnished in blued steel finish only. Colt's single action army revolver is a 6-shooter, rubber stock, solid frame, the best quality of steel and finish; warranted perfect and accurate in every detail. Barrel 5½ or 7½ inches: entire length, 12½ inches; 32, 41, 44 or 45-caliber, as desired. We can furnish these in blued finish only.

Catalogue Number	Caliber C. F.	Length of Barrel	Finish	No. of Sh'ts	Shoots Cartridge No.	Wgt. Oz.	Price
6E1571	32-20	5½in.	Blued Steel	6	6E2384	40	$13.90
6E1573	32-20	7½in.		6	6E2384	40	
6E1575	41 c. f.	5½in.	Blued Steel	6	6E2401	40	13.90
6E1577	41 c. f.	7½in.		6	6E2401	40	
6E1579	44-40	5½in.	Blued Steel	6	6E2409	40	13.90
6E1581	44-40	7½in.		6	6E2409	40	
6E1583	45 c. f.	5½in.	Blued Steel	6	6E2413	40	13.90
6E1585	45 c. f.	7½in.		6	6E2413	40	

Pearl stocks on any of the above revolvers, extra......$4.00

If by mail, postage extra, 44 cents.

Nickel Plated Colt's Revolvers are not carried in stock, but we ship these from factory. Send cash in full with order, as we cannot send C. O. D.

COLT'S SPECIAL PEARL HANDLE REVOLVER.

SINGLE ACTION FRONTIER.

This is our special Cowboy's Six Shooter with pearl handles. The right handle has an Ox Head carved in raised design and makes a handsome revolver. This illustration is engraved from a photograph of the revolver and will give you some idea of its appearance. Made in blued steel finish only. We handle these regularly in 32-20 and 44-40-calibers but can furnish them on special order in calliber 41 c. f. or 45 Colt's c. f. with 5½ or 7½-inch barrel at $20.00 each. Weight 41 ounces. When ordering, say which length barrel you prefer.

Catalogue Number	Caliber C. F.	Length of Barrel	Finish	No. of Sh'ts	Shoots Cartridge No.	Wgt. Oz.	Price
6E1587	32-20	5½in.	Blued Steel	6	6E2384	41	$20.00
6E1589	32-20	7½in.		6	6E2384	41	
6E1591	44-40	5½in.	Blued Steel	6	6E2409	41	20.00
6E1593	44-40	7½in.		6	6E2409	41	

Above may be had in 41 and 45-calibers or in blued steel to special order, cash with order.

If by mail, postage extra, 46 cents.

COLT'S SINGLE ACTION BISLEY MODEL.

The Colt's Bisley Model Revolver is patterned after the Colt's Single Action Army Revolver, but has a longer handle, a different shape hammer, and the lock work is somewhat different, and it makes a good smooth working revolver. The frame is case hardened, and the barrel and cylinder are blued. This revolver embodies all the high grade workmanship of the famous Colt's revolvers. We carry this revolver regularly in 32-20 and 38-40 calibers, but can furnish it in 45 caliber to special order.

Catalogue Number	Caliber	Length of Barrel	Finish	No. of Sh'ts	Shoots Cartridge No.	Weight Ounces	Price
6E1610	32-20	5½in.	Blued Steel	6	6E2384	40	$13.90
6E1611	32-20	7½in.		6	6E2384	40	
6E1612	38-40	5½in.	Blued Steel	6	6E2396	40	$13.90
6E1613	38-40	7½in.		6	6E2396	40	

If by mail, postage extra, 45 cents.

GENUINE SMITH & WESSON REVOLVERS.

OUR 22-CALIBER SMITH & WESSON SIDE EJECTING REVOLVER, $10.00.

This revolver is double action, has fluted cylinder, rifled steel barrel, rebounding hammer, rubber stock, blued steel or nickel plated finish; made in 22-caliber, taking rim fire cartridges Nos. 6E2336 or 6E2338; weighs about 10 ounces and is 7-shot. This is the latest model Smith & Wesson Revolver, and the highest grade 22-caliber revolver made.

Catalogue Number	Caliber	Length of Barrel	Finish	No. of Sh'ts	Shoots Cartridge No.	Wgt. Oz.	Price
6E1700	22 Rim	3½ in.	Nickeled	7	6E2336	10	$10.00
6E1701		3½ in.	Blued	7	6E2338	10	

If fitted with pearl handles, extra..............................90c

If by mail, postage extra, 14 cents.

GENUINE SMITH & WESSON REVOLVERS.

S. & W. SIDE EJECTING 32 AND 38-CALIBER, $12.00 AND $14.00.

This is double action and center fire, 6-shot, with solid frame, swing-out cylinder and side ejecting mechanism; 32-caliber has 4½ and 6-inch barrel, the 38-caliber has 5 and 6½-inch barrel; blued steel or nickel plated finish; using 32 S. & W. long No. 6E2376 and 38-caliber long Colt DA cartridge No. 6E2392. This revolver is Smith & Wesson's latest creation and is a revolver that is built for business. It will withstand hard usage and the 38-caliber has a movable firing pin on the nose of the hammer, which absolutely closes the firing pin hole and prevents any possible gas from going back of the frame. They are highly recommended for target shooting, and made in blued steel or nickel plated finish, fitted with rubber handles.

Catalogue No.	Caliber	Length of Barrel	Finish	No. of Shots	Shoots Cart'ge	Weight	Price
6E1704	32 c f	4½ in.	Nickel	6-shot	6E2376	19 oz.	$12.00
6E1705	32 c f	4½ in.	Blued	6-shot		19 oz.	
6E1706	32 c f	6 in.	Nickel	6-shot	6E2376	20 oz.	12.00
6E1707	32 c f	6 in.	Blued	6-shot		20 oz.	
6E1714	38 c f	5 in.	Nickel	6-shot	6E2392	30 oz.	14.00
6E1715	38 c f	5 in.	Blued	6-shot		30 oz.	
6E1716	38 c f	6½ in.	Nickel	6-shot	6E2392	32 oz.	14.00
6E1717	38 c f	6½ in.	Blued	6-shot		32 oz.	

FIRST QUALITY PEARL STOCKS ON THE ABOVE, EXTRA. 32-caliber, $1.00; 38-caliber........................$2.00

If by mail, postage extra, 32-caliber, 25 cents; 38-caliber, 40c

We cannot furnish Smith & Wesson Revolvers for 38-40 cartridges.

S. & W. DOUBLE ACTION REVOLVERS.

These revolvers are warranted genuine Smith & Wesson. Manufactured by Smith & Wesson, Springfield, Mass. All are self cocking and double action, with automatic shell extractor, finely rifled steel barrel, fine rubber stocks, nickel plated or blued steel finish. Made of the finest material that money can buy and the workmanship is equal in finish to that of any ordinary watch. If you want the best work for your money buy a Smith & Wesson. The 32-caliber takes cartridge No. 6E2377 and the 38-caliber takes cartridge No. 6E2388.

Catalogue No.	Caliber	Length of Barrel	Finish	No. of Shots	Shoots Cart'ge	Weight	Price
6E1724	32 c f	3½ in.	Nickel	5-shot	6E2377	13 ozs.	$11.00
6E1725	32 c f	3½ in.	Blued	5-shot	6E2377	13 ozs.	
6E1726	32 c f	6 in.	Nickel	5-shot	6E2377	15 ozs.	11.00
6E1727	32 c f	6 in.	Blued	5-shot	6E2377	15 ozs.	
6E1730	38 c f	3¼ in.	Nickel	5-shot	6E2388	18 ozs.	12.00
6E1731	38 c f	3¼ in.	Blued	5-shot	6E2388	18 ozs.	
6E1732	38 c f	4 in.	Nickel	5-shot	6E2388	18 ozs.	12.00
6E1733	38 c f	4 in.	Blued	5-shot	6E2388	18 ozs.	
6E1734	38 c f	5 in.	Nickel	5-shot	6E2388	19 ozs.	12.00
6E1735	38 c f	5 in.	Blued	5-shot	6E2388	19 ozs.	
6E1736	38 c f	6 in.	Nickel	5-shot	6E2388	20 ozs.	12.00
6E1737	38 c f	6 in.	Blued	5-shot	6E2388	20 ozs.	

FIRST QUALITY PEARL STOCKS, EXTRA..........$1.00

If by mail or prepaid express, 32-caliber, 18 cents; 38-caliber, 24 cents.

SMITH & WESSON HAMMERLESS.

Made by Smith & Wesson, Springfield, Mass. Latest type new model hammerless, automatic shell ejector, patent safety catch, self locking rebounding locks, double action, blued steel or nickel plated finish, fitted with rubber handles. This is positively the best hammerless revolver made. "A thing of beauty is a joy forever." If you own one of these revolvers you are certain to own one of the best revolvers made and one which always has a market value. The 32-caliber takes cartridge No. 6E2377 and the 38-caliber takes cartridge No. 6E2388.

Catalogue No.	Caliber	Length of Barrel	Finish	No. of Shots	Shoots Cart'ge	Weight	Price
6E1756	32 c f	3½ in.	Nickel	5-shot	6E2377	15 oz.	$12.00
6E1757	32 c f	3½ in.	Blued	5-shot	6E2377	15 oz.	
6E1760	38 c f	3¼ in.	Nickel	5-shot	6E2388	17 oz.	13.00
6E1761	38 c f	3¼ in.	Blued	5-shot	6E2388	17 oz.	
6E1762	38 c f	4 in.	Nickel	5-shot	6E2388	18 oz.	13.00
6E1763	38 c f	4 in.	Blued	5-shot	6E2388	18 oz.	
6E1764	38 c f	5 in.	Nickel	5-shot	6E2388	19 oz.	13.00
6E1765	38 c f	5 in.	Blued	5-shot	6E2388	19 oz.	
6E1766	38 c f	6 in.	Nickel	5-shot	6E2388	19 oz.	13.00
6E1767	38 c f	6 in.	Blued	5-shot	6E2388	19 oz.	

FIRST QUALITY PEARL STOCKS, EXTRA..........$1.00

If by mail, postage extra 18 to 30 cents. ☞ See our prices on cartridges.

$4.35 AND $4.65 THE IMPORTED AUTOMATIC DOUBLE ACTION REVOLVER.

This illustration, engraved from a photograph by our artist, will give you some idea of the revolver. It is central fire and has 5½-inch barrel, finished in blued or nickel plated. Made in 44-40-caliber only. It is 6-shot, has rebounding hammer, rubber stock, weighs 35 ounces and is automatic shell ejecting. This revolver takes the same cartridge as the Winchester Rifle, 44-caliber (No. 6E2409), so that a man who has a 44-caliber rifle can use the same ammunition in both the rifle and this revolver. We have contracted for a large lot of these revolvers in order to get the price so we can sell them with our one small percentage of profit at these figures.

If by registered mail, 45c extra.

Takes No. 6E2409 Cartridges.

If by mail, postage extra, 45 cents.

Catalogue Number	Caliber C. F.	Length of Barrel	Finish	No. of Sh'ts	Shoots Cartridge No.	Weight, Ounces	Price
6E1780	44-40	5½in.	Nickeled	6	6E2409	35	$4.[illegible]
6E1781	44-40	5½in.	Blued	6	6E2409	35	4.[illegible]

POINTER SMOKELESS LOADED SHELLS

$1.49 PER 100 $7.25 PER CASE OF 500 39¢ PER BOX OF 25

GUARANTEED HIGHEST GRADE SMOKELESS POWDER LOADED SHOTGUN SHELLS MADE. WARRANTED TO OUTSHOOT ANY OTHER SMOKELESS POWDER SHOTGUN SHELL ON THE MARKET, REGARDLESS OF NAME, MAKE OR PRICE.

WHY THEY ARE THE BEST AND HOW WE MAKE THE PRICE SO LOW.

We are sole owners of the Meriden Fire Arms Co., Meriden, Conn. Every fire arm that goes out of this factory is made, controlled and sold by ourselves, the sole owners of the factory. So it is with Pointer Smokeless Shells. We absolutely control them. We use a higher grade smokeless powder than goes into any other shells made, heavier, truer and better brass, full finished and properly gauged heads, the best primers made, heavier, stronger and better firing anvils. We use the highest grade waterproof paper known in shell making. We use speciallyprepared wads.

OUR SHELL MAKING MACHINERY is the latest, most modern and, therefore the most perfect shell making machinery, on the market. The top brass head, the anvil, the paper are all perfectly shaped, perfectly fitted, producing a finished product not approached by any other shell maker.

OUR LOADING MACHINERY is of our own special designs and guarantees an accuracy of measure, pressure, crimp and smoothness not approached by any other shells on the market; in short, with our equipment we get a loading effect that cannot be approached even by the most carefully hand loaded shells. There is an accuracy that can only be effected by the most accurate automatic machinery, an accuracy that insures every shell in the box being exactly alike, one shooting the same as the other.

USE POINTER SMOKELESS SHELLS once and you will never use any other again. Every hunter knows the joy that the long so called chance shot brings to him when, on the duck pass or in the field, you have on rare occasions brought your bird down from what appeared to be almost the clouds, or you have dropped your bird when apparently far out of range. Hunter, this is not always a chance shot, but very often a chance shell, one shell that was just right, almost as good as a Pointer Smokeless, which are all, every one in the box, exactly alike. They are the shells that bring down the bird, the quail or goose, dove or turkey after the bird is out of the range of all other ammunition. Pointer shells, in the poor gun, will give better results in the field than other ammunition in the most expensive guns made, and as there is a difference in the shooting qualities of guns, so there is a vastly greater difference in the ammunition you use.

DON'T USE BLACK POWDER. Don't use black powder shells when Pointer Smokeless Shells cost so little more, and double the sport and comfort of shooting.

DON'T USE ANY OF THE COMMON GRADES OF SMOKELESS SHELLS until after you once try Pointer Smokeless Loaded Shells. Try them in the field. If your bird seems out of range, never mind, take aim and pull. Try the Pointer at long range. When others refuse to shoot, you shoot Pointer Shells, for Pointer Shells claim the game others cannot reach.

SAFETY. **The Pointer Shells are positively the safest loaded shotgun shells made.** The brass head construction, the heavy anvil, the waterproof grade of smokeless powder used, the system of loading, the uniformity throughout, the evenness with which the primers are fitted and the grade of primers we use, everything combines to make Pointer Smokeless Shells in every way the safest shotgun shells on the market.

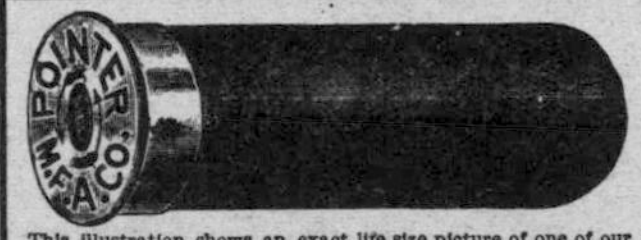

This illustration shows an exact life size picture of one of our 12-gauge Pointer Smokeless Loaded Shells.

SHOOTING QUALITIES.

WE GUARANTEE FOR OUR POINTER SMOKELESS POWDER SHELLS

GREATER PENETRATION, BETTER PATTERN, LESS RECOIL, BETTER COMBUSTION, BETTER EXECUTION IN EVERY RESPECT, THEREFORE, LONGER RANGE SHOOTING.

A BETTER BAG than can be accomplished with any other smokeless powder shells made, regardless of name, make or price, and we accept every order for Pointer Smokeless Powder Shells with the understanding and agreement that you can test the shells with any other make, and if you do not find that the Pointer Shells outshoot all others under all conditions, you can return them to us at our expense, and we will immediately return your money.

EVERY SHELL EXACTLY ALIKE. If you kill at 70 yards with the first shell, you can depend on it every shell in the box will produce the exact same results under the same conditions. Where is there another make that would do this?

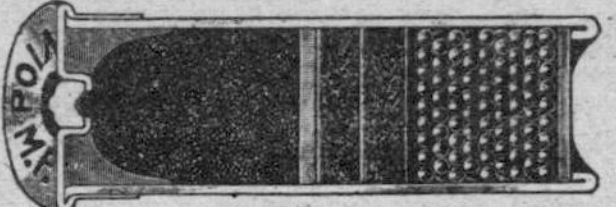

This illustration shows a shell split in half to show the loading, a finish, strength and evenness of load not approached in any other shell made.

HOW WE MAKE THE PRICE SO LOW.

OUR PRICE OF $1.49 PER HUNDRED AND UP, according to load, is so much lower than the prices you have been in the habit of paying for smokeless powder shells that you may wonder how we can possibly make such low prices. The lowest price at which loaded smokeless powder shells are sold by others is about $2.25 a hundred; others have asked from $2.25 upwards per hundred for smokeless powder shells that we guarantee will in no way compare with the smokeless powder shells we sell at $1.49 per hundred; in fact, our shells are put out under our guarantee with a thorough test and trial privilege, and if you do not find that the smokeless shells that you buy from us at $1.49 per hundred will outshoot any smokeless powder shells you can buy elsewhere at $2.25 per hundred, you can return them to us at our expense and we will immediatey return your money.

COMPARE OUR PRICES on the highest grade smokeless powder shells made with the prices others ask for the common black powder shells, and you will find that other houses ask from $1.60 per hundred upward for the most common grades of black powder loaded shotgun shells as against our price of $1.49 per hundred for the highest grade smokeless powder shotgun shells made.

OUR FACTORY AT MERIDEN, CONN., is run on the most economical lines. No high priced officers' salaries are paid; economy is studied in every way, every possible labor saving, automatic machine is employed, everything is done that can possibly be done to increase quality and lower cost, and you get the benefit of all this. Our price to you barely covers this cost of production, with but our one small percentage of profit added. No selling expense, no manufacturer's profit, no jobber's profit, no salesmen, no commissions, no losses, no expense allowance to pay for fancy trap shooters, no fancy publicity advertising expense, no losses, none of the multitude of expenses common to other manufacturers of loaded smokeless powder shells are figured into our cost. You pay for the material and labor only, with just our one small percentage of profit added. This is why we can furnish you the highest grade smokeless powder shells made in the world at less money than you can buy the most common black powder shells elsewhere, at a little more than one-half the price others charge for the common grades of smokeless powder shells, which we guarantee will, in shooting qualities, in no way compare with Pointer Smokeless Powder Shells.

Mr. Doolittle likes our Pointer Shells better than the Winchester Shells, because they are Longer Range.

Hunt, N. Y.

Sears, Roebuck & Co., Chicago, Ill.
Gentlemen:—I have been using Winchester Repeater Shells, but I like the Pointer Shells which you sent me much better, they shoot a greater distance than the Winchester repeaters.
Yours respectfully,
ALBERT DOOLITTLE.

39 CENTS PER BOX OF 25

This illustration shows a box of 25, the way in which our Pointer Shells are put up, 25 in a box, each box sealed with a handsome colored lithographed label. **Always look for the Pointer dog on the label to get the genuine.** The label is registered in Washington, D. C. Inside, outside, in appearance, finish, safety, regularity, comfort, shooting qualities—in every particular **Pointer Smokeless Shells stand ALONE**

ONE BOX FREE.

OUR TERMS, FREE TRIAL, COMPARATIVE TEST AND GUARANTEE OFFER ON ORDER FOR ONE CASE OF 500 OR MORE.

IF YOU DO NOT WISH TO SEND CASH IN FULL, although nearly all our customers send cash in full, you can send us $1.00, balance payable at your freight depot after shells are received; and in any case, whether you send $1.00 or cash in full, on all orders for 500 shells or more, we will send the shells to you with the understanding and agreement that you can shoot one box of 25 shells for careful test, and, if you do not find them by far the best shells you ever used, you can return the balance to us at our expense and we will immediately return your money, including any freight charges you paid, and **we will make no charge for the 25 shells** you used for test; these **25 shells will be FREE to you.**

Mr. Bell says Our Pointer Shells have greater Shooting Qualities than the High Priced Winchesters or Peters Shells.

Versailles, Ohio.

Sears, Roebuck & Co., Chicago, Ill.
Gentlemen:—I have tried your Pointer Smokeless Shotgun Shells. I find them to be up to the standard, they have greater shooting qualities than any of the high priced Winchesters or Peters. I am well satisfied with them.
Yours truly,
N. E. BELL.

POINTER SMOKELESS POWDER LOADED SHOTGUN SHELLS.

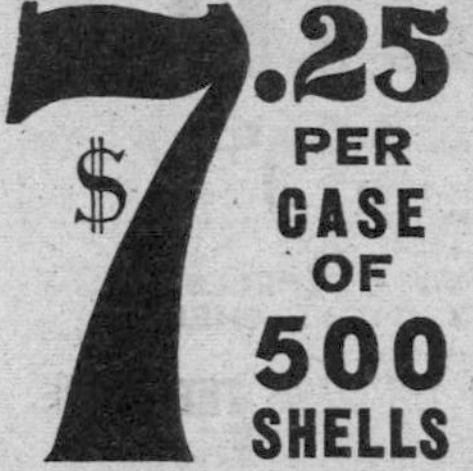

EXACTLY AS ILLUSTRATED

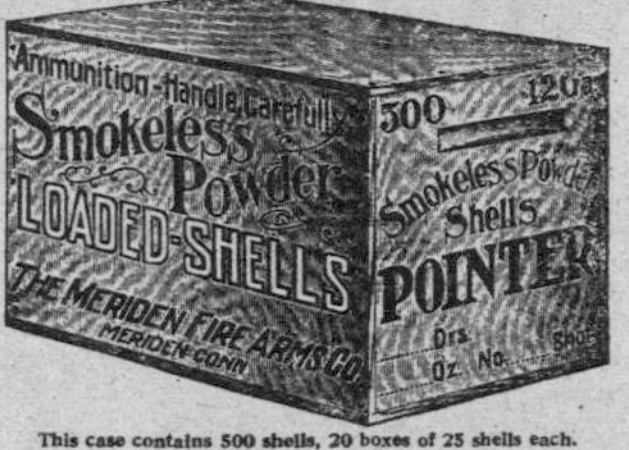

This case contains 500 shells, 20 boxes of 25 shells each.

$14.50 PER 1,000 TWO CASES SPECIAL TO

DEALERS, GUN CLUBS, MARKET HUNTERS, CLUB ORDERS,

OR ANY OTHER SPORTSMAN WHO WISHES TO TAKE ADVANTAGE OF OUR LOWEST QUANTITY OFFER.

AT $14.50 PER 1,000 OR $7.25 FOR CASE OF 500 for the lightest load, heavier loads in proportion, as shown in list, we furnish Pointer Smokeless Shells when ordered in one and two-case lots. Every shell, box and cover is branded **Pointer Smokeless Powder Shells, Meriden Fire Arms Co., Meriden, Conn.** Our name, S., R. & Co., does not appear anywhere, so any dealer, sporting goods house, gun store, hardware dealer, general store or other seller of shells can put Pointer shells in stock and add his profit, and no one will know where he bought them or what he paid for them. Sell **Pointer shells** once and your customers will never again have any other.

WE ADVISE EVERYONE to order 500 or 1,000 lots, by so doing you get our lowest quantity price, you get the **lowest possible freight rate,** you make the greatest possible saving.

NOTICE OUR PRICES ON CARTRIDGES, WE BEAT ALL COMPETITION

ORDER AT LEAST ONE CASE OF 500 SHELLS. Our shells will keep for years, but you will shoot 500 shells sooner than you realize, especially when you have Pointer shells. Order at least one case of 500, even if you have to get one or more neighbors to join with you in making up an order.

A full case of 500 shells for only **$7.25.** In quoting full case lots we furnish only one gauge and one size in a case, same as it comes to us from the factory.

WE CAN MAKE A PRICE OF $1.49 per hundred and upward for smokeless powder shells that will outshoot any other smokeless powder shells on the market for the following reasons:

AS MANUFACTURERS we reduce the cost of our shells to the actual cost of material and labor, the cost of brass, paper, powder, shot, wads, etc., as made in our factory, and the price we name to you on the highest grade smokeless powder shotgun shells made barely covers the cost of the different materials that enter into the construction, with but our one small percentage of profit added.

OUR GUARANTEE, SENT WITH EVERY CASE OF SHELLS, GUARANTEES EVERY SHELL MECHANICALLY PERFECT, HIGHEST GRADE MATERIALS AND THE STRONGEST, LONGEST RANGE SHOOTING SHELLS MADE IN THE WORLD.

Mr. Bremner says for penetration, good pattern and long range shooting, our Pointer Shells outdo the Winchester, Nitro Club or any other shells he ever used.

Kewanee, Ill.
Sears, Roebuck & Co.,
Chicago, Ill.
Gentlemen:
For the last two seasons I have used your Pointer Smokeless Powder Shotgun Shells. I formerly used Nitro Club and Winchester shells, but from experience and severe tests, I find that for a shell yielding the two essential qualities, a good pattern and penetration, that they outclass any shells I have ever used. For long range, and in fact any kind of shooting, they cannot be equaled.
Respectfully,
J. S. BREMNER.

Mr. Wilt says our Pointer Shells kill at longer range, and are the best shells on the market.

Portage, Penna.
Sears, Roebuck & Co.,
Chicago, Ill.
Gentlemen:
Your Smokeless Shells are number ONE. I shall use no other make as long as I can get the Pointer shell. Have tried all other makes and find the Pointer shell the best for long range and dead shot, have killed birds from 80 to 100 yards with No. 5 shot. Your shells make better pattern and greater execution. Will kill at longer range than any shell I have used before, they are the best shell on the market. Shall order more in next order.
Yours respectfully,
THOMAS WILT.

Mr. Dale likes our Pointer Shells better than the Winchester, Leader, U. M. C. or Arrow brands.

Twin Lakes, Minn.
Sears, Roebuck & Co.,
Chicago, Ill.
Gentlemen:
I bought from you some time ago the Pointer Smokeless Shotgun Shells. I must say that I was well pleased with what I received from you. I have used the highest priced shells made, the Winchester Leader, U. M. C., Arrow, etc., but cannot find a shell I like better than the Pointer made by the Meriden Fire Arms Company.
Yours, ever a customer,
H. G. DALE.

YOU GET BACK PART OF OUR PROFIT.

WHEN YOU SEND US AN ORDER for Pointer Shells, if your total order amounts to $1.00 or more, we send you a PROFIT SHARING CERTIFICATE, and these certificates entitle you to various valuable articles entirely free, as explained on the last pages. Do not forget this great feature—our Profit Sharing Department. Remember, also, that this profit sharing feature of our business does not add a fraction of a penny to our selling price, as it is a liberal free division of our profits with our customers, and we guarantee our prices always as low as possible, by far lower than the prices you can get from any other concern.

PRICES ON POINTER SMOKELESS SHELLS

Please notice we furnish only one size and one load in a case, just as they come to us from the factory at the case price.

SMOKELESS POWDER SHELLS, LOADED WITH DROP SHOT.

Catalogue No. 6E2322 — 12 Gauge — LOADED WITH SMOKELESS POWDER.

Load No.	Grains of Smokeless Powder Equal to	Wt. of shot	Size of Drop Shot	Price per box of 25 Shells	Price per 100 Shells	Price per Case of 500 Shells	Price per 1000 Shells
B6x 4 B6x 6 B6x 8 B6x10	3 Drams	1 Oz.	No. 4 No. 6 No. 8 No. 10	39c	$1.49	$7.25	14.50
B7x 2 B7x 4 B7x 5 B7x 6 B7x 7 B7x 8	3 Drams	$1\frac{1}{8}$ Oz.	No. 2 No. 4 No. 5 No. 6 No. 7 No. 8	43c	$1.65	$7.83	15.66

Catalogue No. 6E2320 — 10 Gauge — LOADED WITH SMOKELESS POWDER.

Load No.	Grains of Smokeless Powder Equal to	Wt. of shot	Size of Drop Shot	Price per box of 25 Shells	Price per 100 Shells	Price per case of 500 Shells	Price per 1000 Shells
A1 x 2 A1 x 4 A1 x 6 A1 x 7 A1 x 8	$3\frac{1}{4}$ Drams	$1\frac{1}{8}$ Oz.	No. 2 No. 4 No. 6 No. 7 No. 8	47c	$1.80	$8.56	17.12

Catalogue No. 6E2326 — 16 Gauge — LOADED WITH SMOKELESS POWDER.

Load No.	Grains of Smokeless Powder equal to	Oz. of shot	Size of Drop Shot	Price per box of 25 Shells	Price per 100 Shells	Price per box of 500 Shells	Price per 1000 Shells
C4 x 6 C4 x 8	$2\frac{1}{2}$ drams	1	6 8	40c	$1.53	$7.31	14.62

Catalogue No. 6E2328 — 8 Gauge — HAND LOADED WITH SMOKELESS POWDER.

Load No.	Grains of Smokeless Powder equal to	Oz. of shot	Size of Drop Shot	Price per box of 25 Shells	Price per 100 Shells	Price per case of 500 Shells	Price per 1000 Shells
8BB	$5\frac{1}{2}$ drams	$1\frac{1}{2}$	BB	$1.25	$5.00	$25.00	$50.00

SMOKELESS POWDER SHELLS, LOADED WITH CHILLED SHOT.

Shells loaded with smokeless powder and chilled shot give better penetration and more even patterns than drop shot. Loaded in 12-gauge only. The No. 7½ shot is our celebrated trap load. Order by catalogue number and load number.

Catalogue No. 6E2327 — 12 Gauge — LOADED WITH SMOKELESS POWDER.

Load No.	Grains of Smokeless Powder equal to	Ozs. of shot	Size of Chilled Shot	Price per box of 25 Shells	Price per 100 Shells	Price per case of 500 Shells	Price per 1000 Shells
B7Cx4 B7Cx6 B7Cx7½ B7Cx8	3 Drams	$1\frac{1}{8}$	No.4 No.6 No.7½ No.8	46c	$1.75	$8.35	16.70

Mr. Fisher says our Pointer Shells at 47 cents are far better than Peters' Shells sold at 60 cents per box.

Sunny Side, N. J.
Sears, Roebuck & Co.,
Chicago, Ill.
Gentlemen:
I received some of your special smokeless powder shotgun shells (the Pointer). I am greatly pleased with them for various reasons. First, they have a good penetration, second, they will kill at longer range, third, they have but little jar, fourth, they are quick and sure fire, fifth, they are much cheaper in price than any shells I have ever seen or bought. Your shells sell at 47 cents per box, while the Peters' Cartridge Company shells sell at 60 cents and are not so good a grade of goods. In fact, the Pointer Shells are a better shell in every respect than any other shells I have ever used.
Yours respectfully,
JAMES R. FISHER.

Mr. Tice gets better results from our Pointer Shells than any Shells he ever used.

Buford, N. D.
Sears, Roebuck & Co.,
Chicago, Ill.
Gentlemen:
I am well pleased with the Pointer Smokeless Shells I received from you. They will carry a great deal further and give much better penetration than any shell I have ever used. I have been using U. M. C., Nitro Club and Winchester Leader, and have no luck at all with them, as they would not carry far enough, so I gave your Pointer shells a trial, and have been more than pleased with the results I get. I remain,
Ever your customer,
WALTER TICE.

Mr. Gates likes our Pointer Shells better than the Winchester, U. M. C. or Peters.

Columbia Cross Roads, Pa.
Sears, Roebuck & Co.,
Chicago, Ill.
Gentlemen:
The Pointer Shells I got from you are the best shells I ever used. I have tried all kinds of shells, the Winchester, U. M. C., Peters' and several other makes, but I like Pointer shells the best for penetration and pattern, especially the three-dram and 1⅛-ounce shot load. Will order some more as soon as I need them.
Yours truly,
G. W. GATES.

Mr. Betz says our Pointer Shells are better for long range shooting than the Nitro Club, Winchester New Rival Shells.

Sears, Roebuck & Co., Ligonier, Penna.
Chicago, Ill.
Gentlemen:—I received your Pointer Shells, and found them just as they were recommended. They are better shells than any shell I have ever used before for long range and hard shooting. I was very well pleased with the shells, as they done fine work. I have used Nitro Club, New Rival, Winchester Repeater and other makes of shells, but found that they did not come up to your shells.
Yours truly, HARRY R. BETZ.

FLINT LOCK PISTOL, ONLY $2.75.

F is the flint.
C is cover of powder pan.

For $2.75 we offer you our special Flint Lock Pistol. Many people supposed that there were no more of these pistols to be had, but our European buyer succeeded in finding a small lot of them in Europe, and has sent them to us.

No. 6E1778 Flint Lock Pistol, 14-gauge, 9-inch barrel, weight about 2¾ pounds; a good relic. Price............$2.75

PARTS FOR GUNS, RIFLES OR REVOLVERS.

When ordering parts for guns, rifles or revolvers, always give the name, caliber, gauge of gun, rifle or revolver, or mail us the broken part. This will save us from writing you for this information.

HOW TO TAKE APART REVOLVERS.

The average revolver is usually taken apart by **First**—Removing the stocks. **Second**—Removing the main spring. **Third**—Removing the hammer. **Fourth**—Removing the pins which hold the guard. **Fifth**—Removing the pin which holds the trigger. The average revolver can be taken apart in this manner.

THE REMINGTON BULL DOG SINGLE SHOT PISTOL, $2.90.

For $2.90 we offer you this genuine Remington Single Shot Pistol, manufactured for the United States Government from the best material money can buy, all parts and pieces are made from the best steel procurable, made with a view of combining excellent workmanship and strength, made to shoot the old reliable Government 50-caliber pistol cartridge, and we give 20 cartridges free with each pistol, a pistol that was made to be used in the United States navy, and when they were used they were used with great effect.

DESCRIPTION.—Our Remington Single Shot Bull Dog Pistol is fitted with 8-inch accurately rifled steel barrel, handsomely blued, forged steel frame beautifully case hardened, straight grained walnut handle which is so constructed as to give a good grip, straight grained walnut fore end, the celebrated Remington safety breech block which cannot fly open when the hammer is down. The Remington breech block is a feature which made the Remington arms very popular in the past. In addition to shooting the 50-caliber Remington pistol cartridge, we have had these pistols chambered so they will take the 50-70-caliber primed shells, which can be loaded with about 40 grains of black powder, a cardboard wad and half an ounce of shot, which will make a good pistol for home defense, as well as a pistol for which you can load your own shells and use it to shoot small game, if you wish to do so.

No. 6E1790 Our Reliable Remington Single Shot Bull Dog Pistol, 50-caliber, 8-inch barrel. Weight, 36 ounces. Price, including 20 rounds of bullet cartridges............$2.90

No. 6E2415 Bullet Cartridges, .50-caliber, for the above pistol. Price, per hundred............$1.50

No. 6E3230 Primed Shells, 50-70-caliber Government, for the above pistol. Price, per hundred............$2.00

No. 6E277 Caliber 50-70 Reloading Tools, consisting of recapper, cap extractor, powder measure and wad cutter. Price, per set............56c
Weight, packed for shipment, about 5 pounds.

ATTENTION, BOYS!

Look at These Prices on AIR RIFLES.

THE NEW MODEL KING AIR RIFLE, SINGLE SHOT.

Our King Rifles we Guarantee the Highest Grade Made.

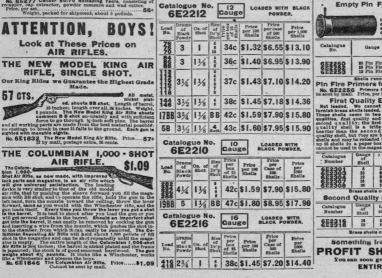

57 CTS. All metal, nickel plated, shoots BB shot. Length of barrel, 19 inches; length over all, 34 inches. Weight, 2 pounds. The New Model King Air Rifle shoots common B B shot accurately and with sufficient force to go through ¼-inch soft pine. The barrel and all working parts are made from the best material possible: no castings to break in case it falls to the ground. Each gun is sighted with movable sights.

No. 6E1832 The New Model King Air Rifle. Price....57c
If by mail, postage extra, 35 cents.

THE COLUMBIAN 1,000-SHOT AIR RIFLE. $1.09

The Columbian 1,000-Shot Air Rifle, as now made, with improved lock parts and magazine, is an air rifle which will give universal satisfaction. The loading device is very similar to that of the old model air rifle, that by pushing the sleeve forward you fill the magazine with BB shot, and to operate the rifle, hold the gun in the left hand, turn the muzzle toward the ceiling, throw the lever forward, same as you would with the Winchester rifle, and the gun loads itself. **Every time you throw the lever you put a shot in the barrel.** It is best to shoot after you load the gun or you will get several pellets in the barrel. **Should an imperfect shot get into the barrel,** it can easily be removed by cocking the gun and inserting a wire from the muzzle, which pushes the shot into the chamber, from which it can easily be removed. **The Columbian Repeating Air Rifle** will hold about 1,000 pellets of BB shot in the magazine and can be shot repeatedly until the magazine is empty. The entire length of the **Columbian 1,000-shot Air Rifle** is 34½ inches; the barrel is nickel plated and the frame is japanned; the stock is of good seasoned hardwood. **The gun weighs about 4¼ pounds.** It looks like a Winchester, works like a Winchester and pleases the boys.

No. 6E1846 The Columbian Air Rifle. Price......$1.09
Cannot be sent by mail.

OUR BLACK POWDER LOADED SHOTGUN SHELLS.

LOADED SHOTGUN SHELLS $1.32 PER HUNDRED AND UP for the highest grade loaded shotgun shells made, in both black and white powder, prices heretofore unknown. 12-gauge black powder shells ranging from $1.32 to $1.60 per hundred, and other sizes at proportionately low prices. We direct your attention to our illustrations, descriptions and incomparable low price quotations on the highest grade loaded shotgun shells made.

EVERY LOADED SHELL COVERED BY OUR BINDING GUARANTEE. We guarantee our loaded shells to be superior to any other loaded shotgun shell on the market, regardless of price.

WHILE OUR PRICES ARE VERY MUCH LOWER than you can buy elsewhere, we use a higher grade empty shell than other makers use, and if you wish to reload them, they will stand more reloading than any other paper shell made. No swelling, no sticking in the gun, the strongest, smoothest and best empty shell on the market.

QUALITY OF POWDER USED. We use a higher grade of black and smokeless powder than [illegible] in any other machine loaded shell on the market, and [illegible] our shells, loaded with the high grade powder we use, under our special system of loading and wadding, to give better penetration, better target, in short, to kill at longer range than any other machine loaded shell made, regardless of price

WE HAVE TESTED OUR LOADED SHELLS by the Chronograph Testing Machine with all other so called reliable makes of machinery shells, and have found, by the most accurate test, that the shot from our shells goes with greater rapidity, hence it shoots farther, gives more penetration, and more perfect target than any other machine loaded shell on the market. There is less recoil, no misfires; in short, there are no other machine loaded shells made that will in durability, safety and shooting qualities compare with ours.

ABOUT OUR LOW PRICES. The price we name barely covers the cost of material and labor, with but our one small percentage of profit added; hence, we can furnish loaded shotgun shells of a higher grade than you can buy elsewhere, and yet at a price very much lower than any other house can furnish you.

BUY EARLY. We aim to carry on hand at all times, one to three millions of loaded shells in the sizes which we advertise, but in the early spring and fall when hunting is at its height, it sometimes happens that we receive hundreds of orders in one day, from all parts of the United States, for the self same load, which temporarily exhausts our stock, and in these two seasons all loaded shell manufacturers are taxed to their utmost capacity, and even then are unable to supply the demand, so if you can give us a second choice of load number, when ordering, it will oftentimes assist us in filling your order promptly in case we are out of the particular load which you prefer. We advise buying shells early when you can do so.

THE VELOCITY OF OUR SHELLS. The velocity of our shells means that the shot travels a certain number of feet per second after leaving the shell. We have repeatedly tested our shells on the electrical chronograph, which is an electrical machine constructed to measure the number of feet that shot will travel per second, and our average velocity for black powder shells is 960 feet per second, and for smokeless powder shells is 1,050 feet per second; while other makes of shells which we have tested of the same size load as our own, do not in most cases come up to this average.

THE CHRONOGRAPH is a scientific electrical instrument made for testing velocity, and shells are tested with a chronograph as follows: One electric wire is attached from the chronograph to the trigger of the gun, and another electric wire is attached from the chronograph to a metallic target. As soon as the trigger is pulled the chronograph registers and when the shot strikes the target the chronograph ceases to register, which gives us the exact velocity of the shell

SEND GOODS BY FREIGHT. We advise sending goods by freight, as it is cheaper than by express. If you order a gun or a rifle, and you include enough needed goods from our big catalogue to make a shipment of 50 to 100 pounds, the entire shipment will be very near as cheap by freight as the gun alone would cost you by express When shipping 50 to 100 pounds or more by freight, it makes the freight cost practically next to nothing on each item.

NUMBER OF PELLETS TO ONE OUNCE OF SHOT.

We give below the number of pellets to one ounce of shot. The number is approximate. It may vary ten or more pellets.

Size of shot......	No. 10	No. 9	No. 8	No. 7½	No. 7	No. 6	No. 5	No. 4	No. 3	No. 2	No. 1	BB
Contains pellets.	850	570	390	335	290	220	170	130	105	85	70	60

OUR LINE OF BLACK POWDER LOADED SHELLS.

Why not get your friends to join with you and buy shells by the case or 1,000 and ship by freight! It will save you money in freight charges.

OUR CASE PRICE is for one size and one gauge in a case, just as it comes to us from the factory. We cannot sell less than a case at the case price, nor can we assort the case with different loads.

A case of 500 12-gauge shells weighs about 65 pounds.
A case of 500 10-gauge shells weighs about 75 pounds.
A case of 500 16-gauge shells weighs about 53 pounds.

Our terms on loaded shells are cash with order. We do not ship them C. O. D.

Order by catalogue number and load number.

Catalogue No. 6E2212 — 12 Gauge — LOADED WITH BLACK POWDER.

Load No.	Drams of Black Powdr	Oz. of Shot	Size of Dr'p Shot	Price per box of 25 Shells	Price per 100 Shells	Price per case of 500 Shells	Price per 1,000 Shells
76 78 70	3	1	6 8 10	34c	$1.32	$6.55	$13.10
84 86 88	3	1⅛	4 6 8	36c	$1.40	$6.95	$13.90
112 114 115 116 117 118	3¼	1⅛	2 4 5 6 7 8	37c	$1.43	$7.10	$14.20
144 146	3½	1⅛	4 6	38c	$1.45	$7.18	$14.36
17BB	3¾	1⅛	BB	42c	$1.59	$7.90	$15.80
5B	3½	1⅛	4 Buck	43c	$1.60	$7.95	$15.90

Catalogue No. 6E2210 — 10 Gauge — LOADED WITH BLACK POWDER.

Load No.	Drams of Black Powdr	Oz. of Shot	Size of Dr'p Shot	Price per box of 25 Shells	Price per 100 Shells	Price per Case of 500 Shells	Price per 1000 Shells
282 284 286 288	4¼	1⅛	2 4 6 8	42c	$1.59	$7.90	$15.80
19BB	5	1⅛	BB	47c	$1.80	$8.95	$17.90

Catalogue No. 6E2216 — 16 Gauge — LOADED WITH BLACK POWDER.

Load No.	Drams of Black Powdr	Oz. of Shot	Size of Dr'p Shot	Price per box of 25 Shells	Price per 100 Shells	Price per Case of 500 Shells	Price per 1000 Shells
416 418	2¾	1	6 8	38c	$1.45	$7.20	$14.40

Catalogue No. 6E2220 — 20 Gauge — LOADED WITH BLACK POWDER.

Load No.	Drams of Black Powdr	Oz. of Shot	Size of Dr'p Shot	Price per box of 25 Shells	Price per 100 Shells	Price per Case of 500 Shells	Price per 1,000 Shells
4206 4208	2½	⅞	6 8	39c	$1.48	$7.35	$14.70

We have taken great pains to select loads which are suitable for most purposes and these loads should meet all requirements. WE DO NOT SEND SHELLS C. O. D.

RUSTED AND DAMAGED GUNS.

Do not return to us a gun, revolver or rifle which is rusted, pitted or has the finish worn off, for we have no way of selling these guns. If you have a gun, revolver or rifle which needs repairing, first write us, fully describing the article and what is broken, and we may be able to send you the part necessary, thus saving the express charges on the gun both ways

Empty Pin Fire Paper Shells.

We cannot furnish these loaded. Order your ammunition and reloading tools from us and load your own shells to your own liking. These shells come 100 in a box and we cannot sell less than a box.

Catalogue No.	Gauge	Weight Per 100	Price Per 100
6E2250	20 Pin Fire	1½ pounds	53c
6E2252	16 Pin Fire	1¾ pounds	54c
6E2253	12 Pin Fire	2 pounds	62c

Shells cannot be sent by mail.

Pin Fire Primers for Above Paper Shells.

No. 6E2256 Primers for Pin Fire Paper Shells. Cannot be sent by mail. Price, per box of 100....................19c

First Quality Empty Brass Shells.

BEST QUALITY BRASS SHELL

Not loaded. We cannot furnish brass shells loaded. These shells come in two qualities, first quality and second quality; the first quality shell is a trifle heavier than the second quality shell, but they are both good, durable and serviceable shells and may be reloaded many times. These shells come put up 25 shells in a paper box and all use the No. 2 primer and cannot be used in the magazine of repeating shotguns.

Catalogue Number	Gauge of Shell	[illegible]gth [illegible]hell	Wt. Per Box of 25	Price Per Box of 25
6E2301	8	3 in.	2 lbs.	$2.00
6E2303	10	2⅞ in.	1¾ lbs.	1.15
6E2304	12	2⅝ in.	1¾ lbs.	1.10
6E2307	16	2½ in.	1½ lbs.	1.10
6E2308	20	2½ in.	1¼ lbs.	1.10

Brass shells cannot be sent by mail.

Second Quality Empty Brass Shells.

Catalogue Number	Gauge of Shell	Length of Shell	Wt. Per Box	Price Per Box of 25
6E2316	12	2⅝ in.	1½ lbs.	75c
6E2318	10	2⅞ in.	1½ lbs.	75c

Brass shells cannot be sent by mail.

Something free to you under our

PROFIT SHARING PLAN.

You can soon get Something Valuable ENTIRELY FREE.

SUPERIOR AMMUNITION

OUR HIGH GRADE LOADED PISTOL AND RIFLE CARTRIDGES AT LOWEST PRICES EVER KNOWN.

COMPARE OUR PRICES WITH OTHERS. NONE CAN COMPETE WITH US ON THESE GOODS.

WE GUARANTEE our Dominion rifle and pistol cartridges to be equal or superior to any cartridges made regardless of make, name or price. SEND US YOUR ORDER FOR CARTRIDGES, and if you find them otherwise, you may return them at our expense of transportation charges and we will return your money. COULD ANYTHING BE MORE FAIR?

LOADED METALLIC CARTRIDGES.

COMPARE OUR PRICES WITH OTHER HOUSES.

REMEMBER, our terms are cash with order on ammunition. These are the leading and popular selling cartridges. Cartridges can be shipped with other goods by express or freight, but cartridges cannot be sent by mail, because they are explosive. Prices subject to change without notice. Our ammunition is always fresh. We buy metallic and shotgun ammunition in carload lots. We sell large quantities, consequently have no old stock on hand. These illustrations are one-half size of the cartridges. In case you are in doubt about the correct caliber, send us a sample shell which has been shot, with your order, or send the cover of the box. Rim fire cartridges cannot be reloaded.

OUR HIGH GRADE RIM FIRE CARTRIDGES.

LOADED WITH BLACK POWDER.
Cannot be sent by mail.

No. 6E2331 No. 6E2332 No. 6E2336 No. 6E2338 No. 6E2340 No. 6E2342

No. 6E2344 No. 6E2346 No. 6E2348 No. 6E2352 No. 6E2353 No. 6E2356

No. 6E2357 No. 6E2360 No. 6E2363 No. 6E2366

No. 6E2367 No. 6E2368

Our ammunition is always fresh and loaded with first class powder. OUR TERMS ARE CASH WITH ORDER. WE CANNOT SEND C. O. D.

No.	CARTRIDGES Cannot be sent by mail. Caliber	Good for Yards	Grains of Powder	Grains of Lead	Weight per 100	Price for 50	Price for 100	Price for 1,000
6E2331	B. B. Caps (Round ball).....	15	....	21	7 oz.	......	$0.14	$1.35
6E2332	B. B. Caps (Conical ball) ...	20	....	24⅛	8 oz.	......	.17	1.60
6E2336	22 Short....................	35	3	30	9 oz.	10c	.19	1.90
6E2338	22 Long.....................	50	5	29	11 oz.	15c	.28	2.60
6E2340	22 Long Rifle...............	100	5	40	14 oz.	15c	.28	2.60
6E2342	22 Extra Long...............	125	6	30	15 oz.	......	.43	4.10
6E2344	22 Rim Special (Model 1890)..	125	7	45	18 oz.	22c	.43	4.10
6E2346	25 Stevens..................	150	11	65	29 oz.	35c	.70	6.65
6E2348	30 Short....................	75	6	55	20 oz.	22c	.44	4.30
6E2352	32 Short....................	100	9	82	27 oz.	24c	.48	4.56
6E2353	32 Long.....................	125	13	90	30 oz.	28c	.55	5.23
6E2356	38 Short....................	150	18	130	43 oz.	38c	.76	7.22
6E2357	38 Long.....................	200	21	148	48 oz.	43c	.86	8.17
6E2360	41 Short Rem. Derringer....	125	13	130	40 oz.	38c	.75	7.25
6E2363	44 Flat.....................	300	28	200	64 oz.	57c	1.14	10.83
6E2364	44 Long Ballard.............	300	28	220	4½ lbs.	60c	1.20	11.40
6E2366	56-50 Spencer	400	45	350	7 lbs.	99c	1.95	19.00
6E2367	56-52 Spencer	400	45	386	7 lbs.	99c	1.95	19.00
6E2368	56-56 Spencer	400	45	350	6¾ lbs.	99c	1.95	19.00

Cartridges cannot be sent by mail because they are explosive.

CENTRAL FIRE PISTOL AND RIFLE CARTRIDGES.

LOADED WITH BLACK POWDER. Explosives cannot be sent by mail. These illustrations are half the size of cartridges. If you are in doubt about the caliber, send a sample shell which has been shot, with your order, or send the cover of the box.

No. 6E2371 No. 6E2373 No. 6E2374 No. 6E2376 Hand Eject'r

No. 6E2377 No. 6E2380 No. 6E2381 No. 6E2384

No. 6E2388 No. 6E2392 No. 6E2396 No. 6E2401

No. 6E2405 No. 6E2406 No. 6E2409 No. 6E2413

CARTRIDGES CANNOT BE SENT C. O. D.

No.	CARTRIDGES Cannot be sent by mail. Caliber for following Rifles or Revolvers	Good for Yards	Grains of Powd'r	Grains of Lead	Weight per 100	Price for 50	Price for 100	Price for 1,000
6E2371	22 C. F. Single Shot Rifles	125	13	45	1½ lbs.	54c	$1.07	$10.17
6E2373	25-20 Single Shot Rifles..	200	19	86	2½ lbs.	68c	1.35	12.83
6E2374	25-20 Repeating Rifles....	200	17	86	2½ lbs.	57c	1.14	10.83
6E2376	32 Smith & Wesson Long.	125	13	98	2¼ lbs.	48c	.95	9.00
6E2377	32 Smith & Wesson	75	9	85	1½ lbs.	35c	.70	7.00
6E2380	32 Short Colt's Revolver.	75	9	82	1½ lbs.	39c	.78	7.41
6E2381	32 Long Colt's Revolver.	125	13	90	2 lbs.	46c	.91	8.08
6E2384	32-20 Repeating Rifles...	200	20	115	3 lbs.	57c	1.14	10.83
6E2388	38 Smith & Wesson.......	100	14	145	3¼ lbs.	46c	.91	9.10
6E2392	38 Long Colt's Revolver..	175	19	150	3¼ lbs.	52c	1.03	9.79
6E2396	38-40 Repeating Rifles....	300	40	180	4½ lbs.	68c	1.35	12.83
6E2401	41 Long Colt's Revolver.	175	21	200	4¼ lbs.	62c	1.24	11.78
6E2405	44 S. & W. American.....	200	25	205	4¼ lbs.	68c	1.35	12.83
6E2406	44 S. & W. Russian	175	23	255	5 lbs.	71c	1.42	13.49
6E2409	44-40 Repeating Rifles....	300	40	200	5 lbs.	68c	1.35	12:83
6E2413	45 Colt's Revolver.	300	40	250	5½ lbs.	79c	1.57	14.92
6E2415	50 Remington Pistol.	75	20	300	7 lbs.	75c	1.50	14.00

The above cartridges are reloadable and may be reloaded with Ideal or Bridgeport Gun Implement Co.'s loading tools.

DOMINION CENTER FIRE MILITARY AND SPORTING CARTRIDGES

LOADED WITH BLACK POWDER.

No. 6E2429 No. 6E2432

These illustrations are one-half size of cartridges. If you are in doubt about the correct caliber, send a sample shell, which has been shot, with your order, or send the cover of the box. Cartridges cannot be sent by mail.

No. 6E2434 No. 6E2439

No. 6E2438 No. 6E2440

No. 6E2474 No. 6E2490

CARTRIDGES CANNOT BE SENT C. O. D.

ALL THESE CARTRIDGES have lead bullets only, and are good for 200 to 500 yards. Explosives cannot be sent by mail. Cartridges cannot be sent C. O. D.

No.	Cartridges cannot be sent C. O. D. Caliber Kind	Grains of Powd'r	Grains of Lead	Weight per 100	Price for 20	Price for 100
6E2429	32-40 Ballard and Marlin	40	165	6 lbs	42c	$1.96
6E2432	38-55 Ballard and Marlin......	55	255	7 lbs	51c	2.40
6E2434	38-56 For Repeating Rifles.....	56	255	8 lbs	51c	2.40
6E2438	40-60 For Winchester Rifles....	62	210	7½ lbs	51c	2.32
6E2439	40-60 Marlin and Colt's Rifles.	60	260	8½ lbs	51c	2.40
6E2440	40-65 For Repeating Rifles.....	65	260	8 lbs	51c	2.40
6E2458	40-82 For Repeating Rifles....	82	260	9½ lbs	56c	2.63
6E2474	45-70-500 Government..........	70	500	12¼ lbs	58c	2.76
6E2490	50-70 Government.............	70	450	11½ lbs	57c	2.69

The above cartridges may be reloaded with Ideal tools, No. 6E4294.

SMOKELESS CARTRIDGES.

Metallic Cartridges, loaded with Smokeless Powder, are all the same shape and size as regular Black Powder Cartridges, but have less grains of Powder than Black Powder Cartridges.

30-30-160 Bullet. 30-30-160 Bullet.
Before Shooting. After Shooting.
These Cartridges are not loaded with Black Powder.

These two illustrations show a soft point bullet before and after shooting. The soft point bullets have a metal patch or jacket to the point, and when the bullet strikes it spreads at the point, as shown in illustration. **The full metal patched bullets** have a metal jacket covering the entire bullet and keep their shape after shooting. **We recommend soft point bullets for hunting purposes, but for powerful shooting, full metal patched are better;** for instance, a 30-caliber Army metal patched bullet will go through 58 pine boards, ⅞-inch thick, 15 feet from the muzzle of the rifle. A 30-30 caliber metal patched bullet will go through 35 boards, ⅞-inch thick, in the same distance, while a lead bullet would go through only about one-half as many boards.

RIM FIRE SMOKELESS. COME WITH LEAD BULLETS ONLY.

These illustrations are half size of cartridges. If you are in doubt about correct caliber, send us a sample shell, which has been shot, with your order, or send cover of box. No. 6E2535 No. 6E2539

No.	Rim Fire Smokeless Cartridges are not guaranteed for accuracy. Caliber	Grains of Powd'r	Grains of Lead	Weight per 100	Price for 50	Price for 100
6E2535	22 Short, Rim Fire..........	1¼	30	10 oz.	13c	26c
6E2539	22 Long, Rim Fire...........	2¼	35	12 oz.	18c	36c

CENTER FIRE SMOKELESS CARTRIDGES. RIFLE AND PISTOL SIZES.

CARTRIDGES CANNOT BE SENT BY MAIL NOR C. O. D.

All Smokeless Cartridges are the same style and size as Black Powder Cartridges, but they have less grains of powder than Black Powder Cartridges.

No. 6E2555 No. 6E2566 No. 6E2575 No. 6E2580

NOTICE: M. P. means Metal Patched Bullet. S. P. means Soft Point Bullet. Cartridges cannot be sent by mail.

The powder weight which we quote is Laflin & Rand's and it may vary in other brands.

No.	Cartridges cannot be sent C. O. D. Caliber Kind	Grains of Powd'r	Grains of Lead	Weig't per 100	Price for 50	Price for 100
6E2555	25-20 For Repeating Rifles......	3	86 Lead	2½ lbs.	$0.78	$1.56
6E2560	32 Colt's Automatic Pistol......	3¾	71 M.P.	2½ lbs.	.72	1.44
6E2566	32-20 For Repeating Rifles......	4	115 M.P.	3 lbs.	.83	1.65
6E2568	32-20 For Repeating Rifles......	4	115 S. P.	3 lbs.	.83	1.65
6E2573	38-40 For Repeating Rifles......	12	180 M.P.	4 lbs.	.99	1.98
6E2575	38-40 For Repeating Rifles......	12	180 S. P.	4 lbs.	.99	1.98
6E2580	38 Colt's Automatic Pistol......	8	105 M.P.	3 lbs.	1.07	2.14

REMEMBER you not only save money at our prices but you get your PROFIT SHARING CERTIFICATES and can soon get something valuable FREE—a wonderful plan for our customers to share in our profits.

OUR APOTHECARY SCALE With Weights.

FOR SMOKELESS POWDER.

Will weigh from 2 grains to 120 grains. The little weights made of sheet brass are the grain weights, weighing from 2 to 6 grains; the 10-grain weights are made of aluminum and stamped 10 grains. In addition to the above weights we also furnish the regular apothecary scruple and dram weights for druggists, 1 scruple being equal to 20 grains. These scales have 2-inch pans and come put up in a box 5½ inches long, 2½ inches wide and 1¼ inches deep.

No. 6E3451 Price.........35c
If by mail, postage extra, 6 cents.

DYNAMITE BLACK AND SMOKELESS POWDER.

In order to conform with the laws of the City of Chicago, and as a necessary economy in the way of getting a low rate of fire insurance, WE ARE UNABLE TO HANDLE, BUY OR SELL ANY KIND OF POWDER OR DYNAMITE.

Understand, this does not apply to loaded ammunition, such as shotgun shells and metallic cartridges. These we carry in immense stocks in a great variety of styles, which we sell in any quantity at much lower prices than you can buy elsewhere.

BULLETS FOR SMOKELESS CARTRIDGES.

S. P. means soft point. M. P. means full metal patched bullets. Order by catalogue number and style number.

Style No.	Catalogue No. 6E3460 and Caliber.	W'ght of Bullet. Grains	Wgt per 100. lbs.	Price per 100.
7A	25-35 Winchester, M. P.	117	1¾	$0.42
8A	25-35 Winchester, S. P.	117	1¾	.42
9A	25-36 Marlin, M. P.	117	1¾	.42
1B	25-36 Marlin, S. P.	117	1¾	.42
2B	30-30 Winchester, M. P.	160	2½	.50
3B	30-30 Winchester, S. P.	160	2½	.50
4B	30-40 U. S. Army, M. P.	220	3¼	1.30
5B	30-40 U. S. Army, S. P.	220	3¼	1.30
6B	32-40 Marlin, M. P.	165	2½	.70
7B	32-40 Marlin, S. P.	165	2½	.70
8B	38-55 Marlin, M. P.	255	3¾	.90
9B	38-55 Marlin, S. P.	255	3¾	.90
5C	303 Savage, M. P.	180	2¾	.90
6C	303 Savage, S. P.	180	2¾	.90

SHOT AND BAR LEAD.

Subject to market changes without notice.

Drop Shot.

1 2 3 4 5 6 7 8 9 10 11 12

Buckshot.

BB 4 5 6 7 8

Chilled and dropped shot in sacks of 5 pounds and 25 pounds at lowest market rates. We do not sell less than a sack. The price of shot fluctuates so much that we cannot quote permanent prices. Prices are subject to change without notice. Always mention size wanted. WE CANNOT SELL SHOT IN 5-POUND SACKS AT 25-POUND SACK RATE.

Catalogue Number	Kind of Shot	Size of Shot	Weight of Sack	Price, per Sack
6E3601	Drop	1 to 10	25 lbs.	$1.75
6E3603	Drop	1 to 12	5 lbs.	.42
6E3605	Chilled	1 to 10	25 lbs.	2.00
6E3607	Chilled	1 to 10	5 lbs.	.47
6E3609	Buck Drop	8 to 4	25 lbs.	2.00
6E3610	Buck Drop	8 to 4	5 lbs.	.47
6E3611	Buck Drop	BB	25 lbs.	2.00
6E3612	Buck Drop	BB	5 lbs.	.47

In case of fluctuation chilled shot is always 25 cents higher in 25-pound sacks and 5 cents higher in 5-pound sacks than drop shot. We will always bill shot at the lowest market rates.

No. 6E3613 Bar lead for running bullets at market price; average price about 7 cents per pound.

No. 6E3615 BB Shot in 1-pound packages for air rifles. Price, per pound.........10c

We always bill at lowest market prices.

We guarantee lowest market price on cartridges, shells, primers, wads, shot, etc. Prices are subject to change without notice.

B. G. I. LOADING TOOLS, 45c.

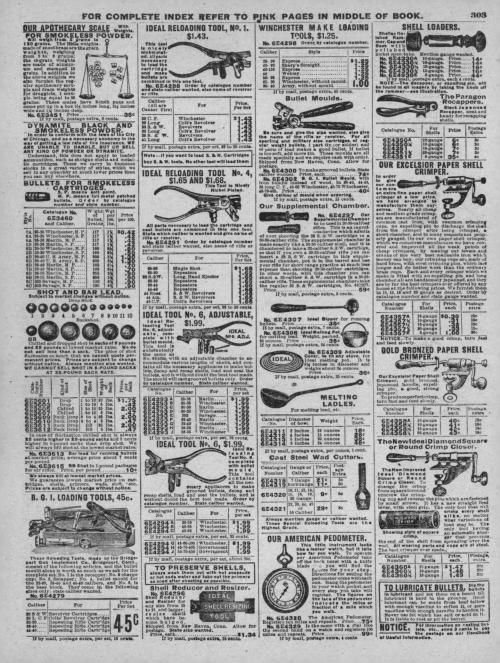

These Reloading Tools, made by the Bridgeport Gun Implement Co., Bridgeport, Conn., consist of the following articles, and the bullet mould alone is worth as much as we ask for the complete set. No. 1 is the recapper; No. 2 charge cup; No. 3, decapper; No. 4, bullet mould for the 32-20, 38-40 and 44-40 calibers, and No. 5, is the base block. They come in the following sizes only; state caliber wanted.

No. 6E4279

Caliber	For	Price Per Set
32 S & W	Revolver Cartridges	45c
38 L C F	Colts' Revolver Cartr'dgs	
32-20	Repeating Rifle Cartr'dgs	
38-40	Repeating Rifle Cartr'dgs	
44-40	Repeating Rifle Cartr'dgs	

If by mail, postage extra, per set, 18 cents.

IDEAL RELOADING TOOL, No. 1. $1.43.

This tool is nicely nickel plated. All parts necessary to load the cartridge and make bullets are combined in this one tool.

No. 6E4288 Order by catalogue number and state caliber wanted, also name of revolver or rifle.

Caliber (All are Center Fire)	For	Price, Per Set
32 C. F.	Winchester	$1.43
32 Long	Colt's Revolver	1.43
32 S. & W.	Revolvers	1.43
38 Long	Colt's Revolver	1.43
38 S. & W.	Revolvers	1.43
41 Long	Colt's Revolver	1.43

If by mail, postage extra, per set, 23 to 25 cents.

Note—If you want to load S. & W. Cartridges buy S. & W. tools. No other tool will load them

IDEAL RELOADING TOOL No. 4, $1.65 AND $1.68.

This Tool is Nicely Nickel Plated.

All parts necessary to load the cartridge and cast bullets are combined in this one tool. State which caliber is wanted and give name of rifle or revolver.

No. 6E4291 Order by catalogue number and state caliber wanted, also name of rifle or revolver.

Caliber	For	Price, Per Set
25-20	Single Shot	$1.68
25-20	Repeaters	1.68
32 S.&W.	Long, Hand Ejector	1.65
32-20	Repeaters	1.68
38-40	Repeaters	1.68
44-40	Repeaters	1.68
44 Russ.	S. & W. Revolvers	1.65
44 Am.	S. & W. Revolvers	1.65
45 C.F.	Colt's Revolvers	1.65

If by mail, postage extra, per set, 28 to 30 cents.

IDEAL TOOL No. 6, ADJUSTABLE, $1.99.

Ideal Reloading Tool No. 6, adjustable, complete with bullet mould. This tool is substantially the same as No. 6E4294, with an adjustable chamber to accommodate various lengths of shells, and contains all the necessary appliances to make bullets, decap and recap shells, load and seat the bullets, and is without doubt the best tool made. The mould will cast grooved bullets only. Order by catalogue number. State caliber wanted.

Catalogue No.	Caliber	For	Price, per set
6E4293 A	25-36	Marlin	$1.99
6E4293 B	25-35	Winchester	1.99
6E4293 C	30-30	Marlin	1.99
6E4293 D	30-30	Winchester	1.99
6E4293 E	303	Savage	1.99
6E4293 F	32-40	Marlin	1.99
6E4293 G	32-40	Winchester	1.99
6E4293 H	38-55	Marlin	1.99
6E4293 J	38-55	Winchester	1.99

If by mail, postage extra, per set, 32 cents.

IDEAL TOOL No. 6, $1.99.

Ideal Reloading Tool No. 6, complete with bullet mould. This tool contains all the necessary appliances to make grooved bullets, decap and recap shells, load and seat the bullets, and is without doubt the best tool made. Order by catalogue number. State caliber wanted.

Catalogue No.	Caliber	For	Price, per set
6E4294 A	38-56	Winchester	$1.99
6E4294 B	40-65	Winchester	1.99
6E4294 C	40-82	Winchester	1.99

If by mail, postage extra, per set, 32 cents.

Catalogue No.	Caliber	For	Price, per set
6E4294 G	45-60-300	Winchester	$1.99
6E4294 H	45-70-405	Government	1.99
6E4294 J	50-70-450	Government	1.99

If by mail, postage extra, per set, about 39c.

TO PRESERVE SHELLS,

always wash them out with hot soapsuds or hot soda water and take out the primers as soon after shooting as possible.

Shell Reducer and Resizer.

No. 6E4296 Shell Reducer and Resizer for any size from 25 to 25, and larger; resize shells which have become bulged. Shipped from New Haven, Conn. Allow for postage. State size wanted.

Price, each.........$1.34
If by mail, postage extra, 15 cents.

WINCHESTER MAKE LOADING TOOLS, $1.25.

No. 6E4298 Order by catalogue number.

Caliber	Style	Price
38-90	Express	$1.25
40-90	Sharp's Straight	1.25
40-110	Express	1.25
44	Webley	1.25
50-95	Express	1.25
25-35	Winchester, without mould	1.00
30-40	Army, without mould	1.00

If by mail, postage extra, 45 cents.

Bullet Moulds.

Be sure and give the size wanted, also give the name of the rifle or revolver. For all sporting and military size cartridges, of regular weight bullets, 1 part tin (or solder) and 40 parts of lead makes a good bullet. If bullet is too soft, add more tin. These moulds are all made specially and we require cash with order. Shipped from New Haven, Conn. Allow for postage.

No. 6E4300 To make grooved bullets. State caliber wanted. Price, each.........74c

No. 6E4302 B. G. I. Bullet Mould, with iron handle instead of wood, in 38-40, 44-40, 38 long C. F., 45-60 Winchester, 45-70 Winchester, 45-70-405. Price.........40c

Give caliber of mould when ordering.
If by mail, postage extra, 15 cents.

Our Supplemental Chamber.

No. 6E4297 Our Supplemental Chamber to be used in 30-30-caliber rifles. This is an ingenious device which admits of your shooting the 32 S. & W. cartridge in a 30-30-caliber rifle. The supplemental chamber is made exactly like a 30-30 caliber shell, and it is chambered to take a 32-caliber S. & W. cartridge, so that if you own a 30-30-caliber rifle you can insert a 32 S. & W. cartridge in this supplemental chamber, put it in the barrel and use your rifle for short range practice at much less expense than shooting 30-30-caliber cartridges. In other words, with this chamber you can shoot a 32-caliber S. & W. cartridge in a 30-30-caliber rifle. These supplemental chambers take the regular 32 S. & W. cartridges, No. 6E2377. Price.........59c

If by mail, postage extra, 2 cents.

No. 6E4307 Ideal Dipper for running bullets. Price.........35c
If by mail, postage extra, 7 cents.

No. 6E4308 Ideal Melting Pot for melting lead. Weight, packed, 25 ounces. Price.........35c
If by mail, postage extra, 26 cents.

No. 6E4309 Adjustable Cover, to fit any stove, for Ideal melting pot. It is 9¼ inches in diameter and weighs about 24 ounces. Price.........36c
If by mail, postage extra, 25 cents.

MELTING LADLES.

For melting lead, etc.

Catalogue No.	Diameter of bowl	Weight	Price, Each.
6E4311	3 inches	12 ounces	18c
6E4312	4 inches	15 ounces	28c
6E4313	5 inches	20 ounces	38c
6E4314	6 inches	24 ounces	48c

If by mail, postage extra, per ounce, 1 cent.

Cast Steel Wad Cutters.

Catalogue Number	Gauge or Caliber	Price, each	Postage Extra
6E4318	7 Gauge	21c	5c
6E4319	8 or 9 Gauge	11c	5c
6E4320	10, 11, 12, 14, 15, 16, 19, 20 Gauge	9c	5c
6E4321	32, 38, 44, 45 or 50 Caliber	29c	8c

Always mention gauge or caliber wanted. These Special Reloading Tools are the Highest Grade.

OUR AMERICAN PEDOMETER.

This little instrument looks like a ladies' watch, but it tells how far you walk. To operate our American Pedometer take off the back bezel with a knife blade ... you will find the figures for your step. Directions for setting the pedometer come with each one. Hang the pedometer in your watch pocket, and every step you take will register. The figures on the face of the pedometer indicate the miles or fraction of a mile which you walk.

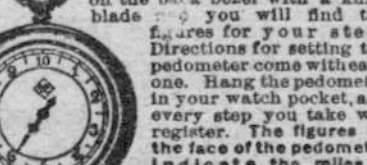

No. 6E4320 The American Pedometer. Registers ten miles and repeats. Price.........75c

No. 6E4329 Is the same with a dial like the second hand on a watch and registers 100 miles and repeats. Price.........99c

If by mail, postage extra, 4 cents.

SHELL LOADERS.

Shellac finished Rammer, Cap and Base with polished nickel spun tube. Mention gauge wanted.

No. 6E4330A 12-gauge. Price.....14c
No. 6E4330¼ 10-gauge. Price.....14c
No. 6E4330½ 16-gauge. Price.....16c
No. 6E4330¾ 12-gauge. Price.....16c
No. 6E4330E 8-gauge. Price.....44c

If by mail, postage extra, each 4 cents.

NOTE—The decapper, or expelling pin, will be found in all loaders by taking the knob off the rammer—see illustration.

The Paragon Recappers.

Black Japanned Recapper, neat and handy for recapping shells.

Catalogue No.	For Shells	Price	Postage Extra
6E4350A	12-gauge	6c	3c
6E4350¼	10-gauge	6c	3c
6E4351	16-gauge	7c	3c
6E4351½	20-gauge	7c	3c
6E4351E	8-gauge	35c	4c

OUR EXCELSIOR PAPER SHELL CRIMPER.

In order to give our customers an extra fine paper shell crimper at a low price, we have arranged to manufacture them ourselves. Nearly all cheap and medium grade crimpers are manufactured of common cast iron, with common crimping cups, no expelling pin to discharge the shell from the crimper after being crimped, a short chamber, and in many respects not properly gauged. On our own paper shell crimper, which we ourselves manufacture we have covered and improved all the weak points of cheap crimpers, by making our levers and cranks of the very best malleable iron which money can buy; our crimping cups are made of hard brass, with steel crimping pins, which last longer and do better work than the ordinary brass cups. Each and every crimper which we make is fitted with an expelling pin and long chamber, all are handsomely japanned, and they are by far the best crimpers ever offered by any house at the following prices. We furnish them in 10, 12, 16 and 20 gauge as desired. Order by catalogue number and state gauge wanted.

Catalogue Number	For Shells	Price, each	Postage extra
6E4357A	12-gauge	$0.30	18c
6E4357¼	10-gauge	.31	18c
6E4357½	16-gauge	.32	18c
6E4357¾	20-gauge	.33	18c
6E4357E	8-gauge	1.00	28c

NOTICE—To make a good crimp, turn fast and feed slowly.

GOLD BRONZED PAPER SHELL CRIMPER.

Our Excelsior Paper Shell Crimper, gold bronzed, japanned handle, expelling pin; a good, strong crimper.

To produce perfect crimp, turn fast and feed slowly.

Catalogue Number	For Shells	Price, each	Postage, extra
6E4358A	12-gauge	40c	18c
6E4358¼	10-gauge	41c	18c
6E4358½	16-gauge	42c	18c
6E4358¾	20-gauge	43c	18c

The New Ideal Diamond Square or Round Crimp Closer.

The New Improved Ideal Diamond Square or Round Crimp Closer. To change the crimp from square to round unscrew the crimping cup and reverse the pins which are fastened by small screws. It has a new straight feed lever, with steel grip. The only tool that will crimp every shell alike, no matter what variations of load may be. The only tool having an automatic plunger that prevents the end of the shell from spreading over the wad. All wearing parts and cups are of steel. The best crimper ever made.

Showing style of square crimp.

Catalogue Number	For Shells	Price, each	Postage, extra
6E4360A	12-gauge	$1.47	32c
6E4360¼	10-gauge	1.48	32c
6E4360½	16-gauge	1.49	32c

TO LUBRICATE BULLETS. Dip the bullets in lubricant and set them on a board till lubricant is hard in the grooves. Good lubricant can be made from beef tallow with enough vaseline to soften it, or pure vaseline with enough paraffin to harden it. Never use fat which has salt or acid in it. It is liable to rust or pit the barrel.

NOTICE. For information on casting bullets, etc., send 3 cents to pay the postage on our Handbook of Useful Information.

SHELL LOADING BLOCKS 85c.

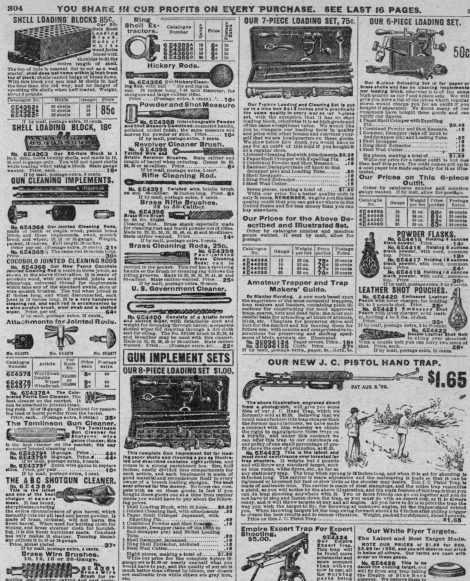

Our 50-Hole Shell Loading Block. Made of white wood, holes bored with shoulder to fit the entire length of shell. The top of hole is reamed out to act as a wad starter; **shell does not come within ⅛ inch from top of block**; shells cannot bulge or break down. With this block you can load 50 shells in half the time than the old way, and no danger of upsetting the shells when half loaded. Weight, about 3 pounds.

Catalogue No.	Holds	Gauge	Price
6E4362A	50 shells	12	85c
6E4362B	50 shells	10	
6E4362C	50 shells	16	

If by mail, postage extra, 53 cents.

SHELL LOADING BLOCK, 18c

No. 6E4363 Our 20-Hole Block is 1 inch deep, holds twenty shells, and made in 10, 12 and 16-gauge only. You will not upset shells while loading when using a block. State gauge wanted. Price, each.......................18c
If by mail, postage extra, 9 cents.

GUN CLEANING IMPLEMENTS.

No. 6E4364 Our Jointed Cleaning Rods, made of beech or maple wood; patent brass joints and three implements, swab, scratch brush and wiper; 10, 12 or 16-gauge. Weight, packed, 13 ounces. Full length 36 inches.
Price per set...(Postage extra, 10 cents)...21c
No. 6E4365½ The same rod 48 inches long. Price.......................30c

COCOBOLO JOINTED CLEANING RODS

No. 6E4366 Our New Fancy Cocobolo Jointed Cleaning Rod is made in three joints, as shown in the above illustration. It is made of cocobolo wood, with nickel plated joints and trimmings, universal thread for implements which take any of the standard swabs, slots or wire scratch brushes. The rod when joined is 37 inches long, and when disconnected, each joint is 13 inches long. **It is a very handsome cleaning rod, and is accompanied by a wire scratch brush, wool swab and a slotted wiper.** Price, per set.......................64c
If by mail, postage extra, 13 cents.

Attachments for Jointed Rods.

No. 6E4375 No. 6E4376 No. 6E4377

Catalogue Number	Article	For Rods No.	Price each	Postage extra
6E4375	Wool Swab	6E4365 or 6E4366	5c	4c
6E4376	Double Wiper		8c	4c
6E4377	Wire Brush		5c	4c

No. 6E4378A The Celebrated Ferris Gun Cleaner. The best cleaner on the market. It can be attached to jointed cleaning rods. 10 or 12-gauge. Excellent for removing lead or burnt powder from the barrel.
Price, each...(Postage extra, 5 cents.)..35c

The Tomlinson Gun Cleaner.

The Tomlinson Gun Cleaner for Shotguns; wire gauze cleaner; this is the best cleaner on the market; fits any standard jointed cleaning rod.
No. 6E4379A 12-gauge. Price.......44c
No. 6E4379B 10-gauge. Price.......44c
If by mail, postage extra, 5 cents.
No. 6E4379F Extra wire gauze to replace sides. Price, per pair.......................10c
If by mail, postage extra, 1 cent.

THE A B C SHOTGUN CLEANER.

No. 6E4380 This is the latest and one of the best shotgun cleaners made. It has broad, sharp blades covering the entire circumference of gun barrel, which instantly cuts out all lead and burnt powder. Is made of brass, nickeled, will not harm the finest barrel. When used for holding cloth for wiping, and brass strainer cloth for burnishing, it is the finest burnisher made. Constant use only makes it sharper. Turning thumb nut adjusts it to 10 or 12-gauge.
Price, nickel plated.......................37c
If by mail, postage extra, 4 cents.

Brass Wire Brushes.
10, 12, 16 or 20-Gauge.

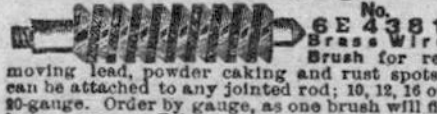

No. 6E4381 Brass Wire Brush for removing lead, powder caking and rust spots; can be attached to any jointed rod; 10, 12, 16 or 20-gauge. Order by gauge, as one brush will fit but one gauge. Price.......................37c
If by mail, postage extra, 2 cents.

McMillan's Shell Extractor.

No. 6E4383 The Universal Shell Extractor will extract any shell from 22-caliber to 8-gauge. Nickel plated. Price.......................8c
If by mail, postage extra, 1 cent.

Ring Shell Extractors.

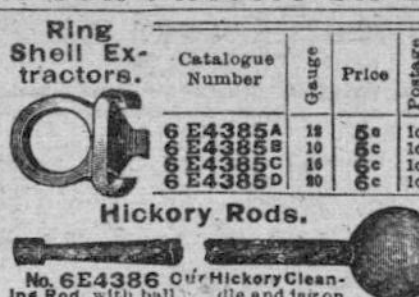

Catalogue Number	Gauge	Price	Postage Extra
6E4385A	12	5c	1c
6E4385B	10	5c	1c
6E4385C	16	6c	1c
6E4385D	20	6c	1c

Hickory Rods.

No. 6E4386 Our Hickory Cleaning Rod, with ball handle and jag on end. 38 inches long, 7-16 inch diameter; for shotguns and large caliber rifles.
Price......(Postage extra, 5 cents.).......10c

Powder and Shot Measure

No. 6E4388 Interchangeable Powder and Shot Measure Combined; enameled handle, polished nickel finish; the same measure will answer for powder or shot. Price........10c
If by mail, postage extra, 3 cents.

Revolver Cleaner Brush.

No. 6E4390 Twisted Wire and Bristle Revolver Brushes. State caliber and length of barrel when ordering. Comes in 22, 32, 38 or 44-caliber. Price.......................6c
If by mail, postage extra, 1 cent.

Rifle Cleaning Rod.

No. 6E4391 Twisted wire, bristle brush on end. 22-caliber. 24 inches long. Price...6c
If by mail, postage extra, 5 cents.

Brass Rifle Brushes.
22 to 50-Caliber.

No. 6E4396 Brass Wire Brush to fit No. 6E4398 Cleaning Rod. Brass shank especially made for cleaning rust and burnt powder out of rifles. Made in 22, 25, 30, 32, 38, 40, 44, 45 and 50-calibers. State caliber wanted. Price.......................14c
If by mail, postage extra, 2 cents.

Brass Cleaning Rods, 25c.

No. 6E4398 Four-jointed Brass Cleaning Rods; can be carried in the pocket. This rod has a revolving handle so the brush or cleaning rag follows the rifling grooves. Made in 22, 30, 32, 38, 44, 45 and 50-caliber. State caliber wanted. Price....25c
If by mail, postage extra, 10 cents.

U. S. Government Cleaner.

No. 6E4400 Consists of a bristle brush and slotted wiper, with detachable cord and weight for dropping through barrel; a separate slotted wiper for drawing through a dry cloth and for oiling. The No. 6E4396 brush in 32, 38, 44 and 50-caliber may be used with this cleaner. Made in 22, 32, 38, 45 or 50-caliber. State caliber wanted. Price......(Postage extra, 4c).....22c

GUN IMPLEMENT SETS

OUR 8-PIECE LOADING SET $1.00.

This complete Gun Implement Set for loading paper shells and cleaning a gun as illustrated and described contains eight articles, and comes in a strong pasteboard box. Size, 5x13 inches; neatly divided into compartments for each article, and each implement is made of good material and recommends itself to every owner of a breech loading shotgun. **The best ever offered for the money.** No house can compete with us on these goods; in fact if you bought these goods one at a time from regular stores you would have to pay about the following prices.

1 Shell Loading Block, with 20 holes......$0.25
1 Jointed Cleaning Rod, with attachments .35
1 Paper Shell Crimper Japanned, with Expelling Pin.......................45
1 Combined Powder and Shot Measure.......15
1 Rammer, Decapper (take off knob to find decapper pin) and Nickel Loading Tube.......................20
1 Shell Recapper, japanned.......................15
1 Ring Shell Extractor, nickeled.......................15
1 Steel Wad Cutter.......................15
Eight pieces, making a total of.........$1.85

While our price for the complete 8-piece 12-gauge set is $1.00 or nearly one-half what you would have to pay, and the quality of our set is much better than offered by others, our closers are malleable iron while others are gray iron, etc.

Our Prices for the Above 8-Piece Sets.

Order by catalogue number and state gauge wanted. If sent by mail, allow for postage.

Catalogue No.	Gauge	Weight of Set	Price, per Set	Postage extra
6E4401A	12	42 oz.	$1.00	45c
6E4401B	10	42 oz.	1.01	45c
6E4401C	16	37 oz.	1.02	40c
6E4401D	20	41 oz.	1.03	44c

OUR 7-PIECE LOADING SET, 75c.

Our 7-piece Loading and Cleaning Set is put up in a nice box 5x13 inches and is practically the same quality in every way as our 8-piece set, with the exception that it has no shell loading block, otherwise it is as high grade and of the same exceptional value. We would like you to compare our loading tools in quality and price with other houses and convince yourself that we are headquarters on these goods. We show below how much you would have to pay for an outfit of this kind if you bought it at a regular store.

1 Jointed Cleaning Rod with Attachments.$0.35
1 Paper Shell Crimper with Expelling Pin .45
1 Combined Powder and Shot Measure... .15
1 Rammer, Decapper (take off knob to find decapper pin) and Loading Tube........20
1 Shell Recapper.......................15
1 Ring Shell Extractor.......................15
1 Steel Wad Cutter.......................15
Seven pieces, making a total of........$1.60

While our price for a better quality outfit is only 75 cents. **REMEMBER**, we give you the best quality outfit that you can get anywhere in the United States and for less money than you can buy elsewhere.

Our Prices for the Above Described and Illustrated Set.

Order by catalogue number and mention gauge wanted. If sent by mail, allow for postage.

Catalogue No.	Gauge	Weight per Set	Price per Set	Postage Extra
6E4403A	12	33 oz.	75c	35 cents
6E4403B	10	33 oz.	76c	35 cents
6E4403C	16	33 oz.	77c	35 cents
6E4403D	20	33 oz.	78c	35 cents

Amateur Trapper and Trap Makers' Guide.

By Stanley Harding. A new work based upon the experience of the most successful trappers, trap makers and hunters, containing plain directions for constructing the most approved traps, snares, nets and dead falls; the most successful baits for attracting all kinds of animals, birds, etc. Chapters for preparing skins and furs for the market and for tanning them for future use; with concise and comprehensive instructions for preserving and stuffing specimens of birds, animals, etc. Illustrated.
No. 3E096124 Paper covers. Price..18c
No. 3E096125 Cloth. Price.......27c
If by mail, postage extra, paper, 3c., cloth, 5c.

OUR 6-PIECE LOADING SET.

50c

Our 6-piece Reloading Set is for paper or brass shells and has no cleaning implements nor loading block, otherwise it is of the same high quality as our 7 and 8-piece sets. We will give you here a list of the prices which regular stores would charge you for an outfit if you bought it separately. No doubt many of our customers have bought these goods and can verify our figures.

1 Paper Shell Crimper with Expelling Pin.......................$0.45
1 Combined Powder and Shot Measure. .15
1 Rammer, Decapper (take off knob to find decapper pin) and Loading Tube. .20
1 Shell Recapper.......................15
1 Ring Shell Extractor.......................15
1 Steel Wad Cutter.......................15
Six pieces, making a total of.........$1.25

While our price for a better outfit is but less than half this price. The outfit comes put up in a neat paper box made especially for it as illustrated.

Our Prices on This 6-piece Outfit.

Order by catalogue number and mention gauge wanted. If by mail, allow for postage.

Catalogue No.	Gauge	Weight per Set	Price per Set	Postage Extra
6E4406A	12	21 oz.	50c	22 cents
6E4406B	10	24 oz.	51c	26 cents
6E4406C	16	20 oz.	52c	23 cents
6E4406D	20	20 oz.	53c	22 cents

POWDER FLASKS.

No. 6E4415 Holding 4 ounces black powder. Price.......14c
No. 6E4416 Holding 8 ounces black powder, with cord, common top. Price.......................18c
No. 6E4417 Holding 12 ounces black powder, with cord, common top. Price.......................24c
No. 6E4418 Holding 16 ounces black powder, with cord, common top. Price.......................30c
If by mail, postage extra, 6 to 9 cents.

LEATHER SHOT POUCHES.

No. 6E4420 Embossed Leather Pouch with lever charger, for holding 2½ to 3 pounds shot. Price.....25c
No. 6E4421 Embossed Shot Pouch with lever charger, solid leather, holding 4 to 5 lbs. of shot. Price.......................35c
If by mail, postage extra, 8 to 10 cents.
No. 6E4422 Double Leather Shot Belt to sling over shoulder. With a double belt you can carry two sizes of shot. Price, each.......................28c
If by mail, postage extra, 11 cents.

OUR NEW J. C. PISTOL HAND TRAP.

$1.65

PAT. AUG. 5, '02.

The above illustration, engraved direct from a photograph, will give you some idea of our J. C. Hand Trap, which we formerly sold at $3.25. Believing that we could manufacture this trap cheaper than the former manufacturer, we have made a contract with him whereby we obtain the right to manufacture these traps on a royalty, and under this contract we can offer this trap to our customers on our policy of one small percentage of profit above the cost of production, at $1.65.

No. 6E4423 This is the latest and most novel contrivance ever invented for trap shooters. It weighs but 6 pounds and will throw any standard target, such as blue rocks, white flyers, etc., as far as any stationary trap. The trap when sprung is 39 inches long, and when it is set for shooting is 24 inches long. The carrier is made adjustable and the mainspring is made so that it can be tightened or loosened for fast or slow birds as the shooter may desire. This J. C. Pistol Trap is made of malleable iron. The carrier is made of steel stampings, and the entire trap resembles a pistol, as you will notice by the above illustration, and the main feature of this trap is that you can do trap shooting anywhere with it. Two or more friends can go out together and you do not have to stop and fasten down the trap, as you must do with an expert trap, as it is always ready, and it will throw targets at any and all angles. All you have to do is to point the trap the way you wish the target to fly; for throwing at unknown angles, let the trapper stand behind you. When throwing targets let the trap swing forward about 4 to 6 inches after pulling trigger to obtain the best results and to reduce vibration. Weight, packed for shipment, about 9 pounds.
Price on this J. C. Pistol Trap.......................$1.65

Empire Expert Trap For Expert Shooting, $5.00.

No. 6E4424 Our Empire Expert Trap. This trap will be found more substantial and more compact than others now in use; all the working parts being large, strong and bearings well fitted, assuring positive action in every detail. The Empire Expert Trap is constructed with a lever trigger pull, which allows the trap to be changed to any desired angle without interfering with the pulling device, and the ropes always have the same length and tension of the pull. These traps will throw any standard target, such as the blue rock, white flyer, black bird and others, at all angles. Weight, packed for shipment, 40 pounds. Price.............$5.00

Our White Flyer Targets.

The Latest and Best Target Made.

NOTE OUR PRICES of $1.99 for 500, $3.95 for 1000, and you will observe our price is below all others. Our terms are cash with order on these goods.

No. 6E4426 This is no doubt the coming target, and will fly from any trap taking the Empire or Blue Rock pigeons. We believe them to be superior in quality to all other targets, and have made arrangements with the manufacturer for an enormous quantity. They have a white rim, make a lighter colored target than the others, which will be a great advantage on gloomy days. **Try a barrel of White Flyers and you will surely want more.** Weight, per barrel (500 targets), 148 pounds.
Price, per barrel (500).......................$1.99
Price, per 1000.......................3.95

Our terms are cash with order on these goods.

Money Belts.

No. 57E4495 Money Belts, made of soft chamois skin; to be worn around the waist, under the clothing; the safest way to keep money. It is soft and comfortable, and made with three compartments. Price..........34c
If by mail, postage extra, 3 cents.

No. 57E4496 Money Belts. Made of soft tanned horsehide; same style as above. Strong and durable. Price..........54c
If by mail, postage extra, 3 cents.

No. 57E4498 Money and Gold Dust Belts. Four inches wide; made of the very finest oil tanned calfskin; very soft and pliable; will never get stiff and is just the thing to carry money or gold dust in; it is double stitched all around; made with three compartments; the center pocket is 8 inches long; the two end pockets are 5 inches long, each; the outside cover folds over very closely and is fastened by snap buttons. This is the finest belt on the market for the purpose. Price..........$1.05
If by mail, postage extra, 8 cents.

Rubber Cushion Leather Recoil Pads.

Give length of butt plate.

No. 57E4503 S. R. & Co.'s Rubber Cushion Recoil Pad. Solid leather, with lacing, will not become loose; has patent rubber cushion pad to rest against the butt plate to prevent recoil of gun from bruising the shoulder. Give length of butt plate when ordering. Price...42c
If by mail, postage extra, 10 cents.

No. 57E4505 The Acme Pure Red Rubber Recoil Pad. The best pad in the market. Lined with elastic cloth so it will not stick to the varnish on the gun stock. Give length of heel plate on gun for which you want the pad. They come in three sizes: No. 2 is 5 inches long; No. 3 is 5¼ inches long and No. 4 is 5½ inches long. Mention length of butt plate. Price..........59c
If by mail, postage extra, 7 cents.

Heike's Hand Protector.

No. 57E4510 Heike's Hand Protector, for shotgun barrels; a protection from cold barrels or hot barrels, made of spring steel, morocco leather covered. A necessity to trap shooters. It slips over the barrels and comes for 10, 12 or 16-gauge guns. State gauge wanted. Price..........60c
If by mail, postage extra, 3 cents.

Our Combined Leather Cheek and Recoil Pad.

Give length of butt plate.

No. 57E4512 The Combined Leather Cheek and Recoil Pad, made of soft russet leather oil tanned, will protect the stock and at the same time protect the cheek and shoulder of the shooter. It will fit any gun stock. This pad is fitted with a corrugated rubber cushion, the same as that used on the best recoil pads. The cheek pad on the comb of stock is left open at one end so that the shooter can remove or add padding as he desires. Price..........60c
If by mail, postage extra, 4 cents.

Our Arkansaw Bowie Knife.

No. 57E4515 Bowie Knife, buckhorn handle, 6-inch steel clip blade, leather sheath, with loop to attach to belt; entire length, 11 inches. Price..........65c

No. 57E4516 Bowie Knife, with 7-inch blade. Price, with leather sheath..........75c

No. 57E4517 Bowie Knife, with 8-inch blade. Price, with leather sheath..........85c
If by mail, postage extra, 10 cents.

Our Montana Hunting Knife.

No. 57E4518 Our Montana Hunting Knife, nicely checkered handle, 6-inch blade, leather sheath with loops to attach to a belt. The best hunting knife on the market for the money. Price..........47c
If by mail, postage extra, 9 cents.

Deer Foot Hunting Knives.

No. 57E4519 Hunting Knife, deer foot handle, 6-inch clip blade, leather sheath, nickel bolster and hilt. Price..........$1.00

No. 57E4520 Hunting Knife, deer foot handle, 7-inch clip blade, best steel, leather sheath, with loop to attach to belt, nickel bolster and hilt. Price..........$1.10
If by mail, postage extra, 12 cents.

Hunters' Pocket Knife.

No. 28E0920 T. T. C. Hunters' Pride Knife. It has stag handle, long, heavy German silver bolsters, cap and shield, brass lining, highly finished inside and out. The blades open and close freely without wearing. The knife blade is always true in the center, and it is these little points to which we pay so much attention, that cause our knives to give better satisfaction than those you can procure from any other dealer. Length of handle, 4½ inches; length with large blade open, 8 inches. Price..........60c
If by mail, postage extra, 6 cents.

For a full line of pocket cutlery, see our Cutlery Department.

Sportsmen's Folding Lock Blade Knife.

No. 57E4521 Sportsmen's Folding Lock Blade Knife, with 3¾-inch (scimiter) blade of finest steel and 4½-inch genuine deer foot handle, making the entire length, when open, 8¼ inches. It has dagger hilt, with German silver bolster, patent lock, which holds the blade either open or closed, and a corkscrew in the handle. Just the knife for camping. Price..........$1.40
If by mail, postage extra, 12 cents.

Pearl and Stag Handle Daggers.

No. 57E4523 Our Finest Quality Ladies' Dagger. This is a little beauty, with the very finest quality of steel in blade. Length of blade, 4 inches, both edges sharp, with beautiful pearl handle and dagger hilt, furnished with fancy leather sheath. This is the finest quality of a dirk knife, and the metal is warranted. Price. (Postage extra, 8c)..$1.05

No. 57E4524 Our Stag Handle Dagger, 4-inch blade of good quality steel, with leather sheath. Price......(Postage extra, 8c)......60c

Hunting Knife Sheath.

No. 57E4530 Leather Hunting Knife Sheaths.

For 6-inch Bowie..	20c	For 8-inch Bowie.	28c
For 7-inch Bowie..	24c	For 9-inch Bowie.	32c

If by mail, postage extra, 4 cents.

No. 57E4771 Leather Belts, for knife sheaths, 1¾ inches wide. Price..........18c
If by mail, postage extra, 8 cents.

Hunters' Axes.

No. 57E4533 Hunters' Axe, with handle, extra cast steel blade, weight, 1¾ pounds; with heavy russet leather sheath, as per illustration. A very convenient tool; makes a light axe or a heavy hatchet for putting up tents, etc., when camping. Weight, with sheath, 2 pounds. Price, with carrying sheath..........78c

Thomas' Nipper No. 4.

No. 57E4552 Thomas' Nipper, nicely finished and nickel plated. This nipper locks automatically when it is put on the prisoner's wrist. Price..........$1.70
If by mail, postage extra, 8 cents.

Detectives' Double Lock Handcuffs.

These handcuffs are adjustable to any size wrist and lock automatically, but cannot be unlocked without a key. They are made of forged steel, strong and durable.

No. 57E4553 Nicely polished and finished. Price, per pair..........$2.90

No. 57E4554 Nicely polished and nickel plated. Price, per pair..........$3.50
If by mail, postage extra, 20 cents.

Police Permanent Lock Handcuffs.

These handcuffs unlock with a key but lock automatically and are adjustable to any size wrist. They are made of good quality steel, are light, and used generally by detectives and other officers of the law.

No. 57E4555 Nicely polished and finished. Price, per pair..........$2.70

No. 57E4556 Nicely polished and nickel plated. Price, per pair..........$3.15
If by mail, postage extra, 16 cents.

DARK LANTERNS—See our Hardware Department.

Police Billies.

No. 57E4573 Plaited Billy, leather covered head. Weight, about 7 ounces, hand made. Price..........17c
If by mail, postage extra, 7 cents.

No. 57E4576 Leather Billy, sewed down the side, loaded with shot, made of the best material and cannot be equaled for the price. Length, 6 inches. Weight, about 9 ounces. Price...(If by mail, postage extra, 9c)....32c

No. 57E4577 Russet Leather Billy, 8½ inches long, with sliding leather handle, filled with shot, sewed down the side and well made. Weight, about 12 ounces. Price..........60c
If by mail, postage extra, 14 cents.

The most necessary part of a hunter's equipment is a good canteen. See No. 57E4796 for a description of the best canteen made, endorsed by the U. S. army officers.

Canvas Shell Bags for Carrying Loaded Shells.

No. 57E4665 10-oz. Brown Canvas Bags, leather bound, with pocket. To hold 50 shells. Price..........24c
To hold 75 shells. Price..........27c
To hold 100 shells. Price..........30c
If by mail, postage extra, 10 to 14 cents.

OUR GUN AND RIFLE COVERS.

We have selected the following line of gun and rifle covers and placed a large season contract for them, so as to enable us to give you the best possible value for the least amount of money in this line of goods. When you order a gun cover from us you are getting it at a price based on the actual cost of material and labor with only our one small percentage of profit added. You will assist us materially when ordering these goods if you will give us the name of your gun or rifle, also length of barrel, and advise us whether it is a single barrel, double barrel, repeating shotgun or rifle for which you want the cover; this will enable us to furnish you the exact cover you wish without any delay. For special lengths not mentioned in this catalogue allow us one week's time to make them.

8-oz. canvas means a yard weighs 8 oz.
NOTICE. 10-oz. canvas means a yard weighs 10 oz.
12-oz. canvas means a yard weighs 12 oz.

The more ounces to the yard, the heavier the canvas.

Mention length of barrel and name of gun or rifle when ordering a gun cover.

Our 39-Cent Leather Bound Cover.

No. 57E4695 Rifle and Gun Cover, best 8-ounce brown canvas, leather bound, leather sling, cotton flannel lined, best quality. For 24, 26, 28, 30 or 32-inch barrels. Mention length of barrel when ordering and say if you wish it for a rifle or shotgun. Price..........39c
If by mail, postage extra, 13 cents.

Special Value for 64 Cents.

No. 57E4698 Heavy Tan 18-ounce Duck Cover, for rifles and shotguns. Full leather bound, with heavy sole leather lock and muzzle protector, with handle and sling. For 24, 26, 28, 30 or 32-inch barrels. Price..........64c
If by mail, postage extra, 16 cents.

Our $1.40 Leather Rifle and Shotgun Cover.

No. 57E4701 Soft Leather Cover, made of heavy, soft russet bag leather, with combined sling and handle. Bright trimmings. For 24, 26, 28, 30 or 32-inch barrels; give length of barrel and name of gun or rifle when ordering. Absolutely waterproof. The finest gun cover made. Price..........$1.40
If by mail, postage extra, 25 cents.

Give name of rifle or shotgun and length of barrel when ordering.

Rifle and Carbine Sheath.

No. 57E4703 Rifle Sheath, made of best russet leather, for sporting rifles. These sheaths are not full length covers, but are intended for carrying rifle on saddle, leaving stock of exposed so it may be easily grasped when needed. Be sure to give name of rifle, model length of barrel when ordering, as different makes require different sheaths. We furnish th for 24, 26 and 28-inch barrel rifles only. Price..........$1.20
If by mail, postage extra, 30 cents.

No. 57E4704 The same identical sheath for carbines. State name of carbine and length of barrel when ordering. We furnish these for 20 and 22-in. barrel carbines only. Price.$1.15
If by mail, postage extra, 25 cents.

Give name of rifle or shotgun and length of barrel when ordering.

Our Victoria Gun Case 98c

No. 57E4707 Victoria Gun Case, heavy 18-ounce waterproof canvas, reinforced with leather lock and muzzle protector, with pocket cleaning rod; also shell bag to hold 50 shells. The most complete cover offered to sportsmen and trap shooters. For 28, 30 or 32-inch barrels. State length wanted. Price..........98c
If by mail, postage extra, 35 cents.

8-Ounce Duck Gun Case, 43c.

No. 57E4713 Tan Colored Duck Gun Case, for take down shotguns, with rod pocket, made of 8-ounce canvas. For 28, 30 or 32-inch barrels. Weight, 9 ounces. Give length of barrel. Price..........43c

Our 18-Ounce Canvas Victoria Rifle Case for Take Down Rifles, only 71 Cents.

No. 57E4716 Heavy 18-ounce tan duck, with lock and muzzle protector, rod pocket on the side, Victoria style, flannel lined, well made. This case is made for take down rifles only and the Ladies' Little Double Gun. When ordering state for which gun or rifle you wish it, and say if barrel is 24, 26 or 28 inches long. Give length of barrel and model and name of rifle when ordering. Weight, about 20 ounces. Price..........71c

> IF YOU OWN A FINE GUN it pays to have a sole leather cover, as it protects the gun from bruises, dents, etc., when carrying it in a wagon, etc. For special lengths, not mentioned in this catalogue, allow us a week's time to make.

Our Sole Leather Victoria Gun Case, $2.20.

No. 57E4726 Victoria Gun Case, made of heavy russet leather, embossed, strongly stitched, with rod pocket, making it very strong and durable. For 28, 30 and 32-inch barrels. State length wanted. Weight, about 45 ounces. Price..........$2.20

English Victoria Gun Case

$2.75

No. 57E4731 English Victoria Gun Case, leg of mutton shape, oak tanned sole leather, flannel lined, handle and sling, lock buckle, name plate. The best case on the market for the money. For 30 or 32-inch barrels. State length wanted. Weight, about 60 ounces. Price..........$2.75

French Style Gun Cases.

No. 57E4736 French Style Leather Gun Case. This is the latest style case and is the most compact, neatest sole leather case ever placed on the market. This case is made of oak tanned sole leather, fitted with lock buckle, heavy leather handle and sling, lined with Canton flannel, with partition for barrels, adapted for any take down gun whether single barrel, double barrel or repeater. This case at the large end is 6¼ inches high by 3½ inches wide. Made for 28, 30 or 32-inch barrels. State length wanted. Weight, about 50 ounces. Price..........$2.70

Our U. S. Leather Mail Bag $2.50.

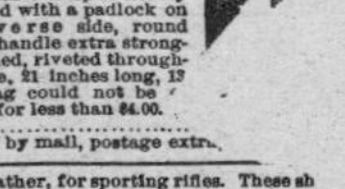

No. 57E4750 An ideal mail bag for rural mail carriers, hotels, merchants and manufacturers. This bag is made from regular mail bag leather, welted seams and sides and bottom, four loops with leather strap fastener, as shown in the illustration. The strap is made with a hasp so it may be locked with a padlock on the reverse side, round leather handle extra strongly stitched, riveted through-out. Size, 21 inches long, 13 same bag could not be dealers for less than $4.00. Price..........
If by mail, postage extra.

REVOLVER AND PISTOL HOLSTERS.

Our Line of Revolver Holsters.

By taking advantage of the leather market and laying in a supply of leather before the advance, we are enabled to make you the following prices. When you order holsters of us you are buying them on our system of one small percentage of profit from the maker to the consumer, and we are sure you will agree with us, that, quality considered, our prices are below any competition. When ordering holsters, always give the name of your revolver, length of barrel and caliber, to enable us to give you the exact size, for these holsters vary in size, according to caliber and length of barrel.

Our Acme Rubber Pocket Holsters.

Made of black rubber and lined with drilling, soft and pliable, with nickel plated clasp to hook to pocket, and made for pocket size revolvers only up to 4-inch barrel. Order by catalogue number in full.

Catalogue Number	Caliber of Revolver	Length of Barrel, Inches	Price, Each	Postage Extra
57E4755B	32	3 to 4	20c	5c
57E4755E	38	3½ to 4	22c	5c
57E4755G	44	4 to 5	25c	6c

Our Leather Flap and Open Top Holsters.

Made of best quality russet leather, nicely embossed, with loop for belt. When ordering, state make, caliber and length of barrel of your revolver. Order by catalogue number in full.

Flap Holster No. 57E4756 — Open Top Holster No. 57E4761

For Young America revolvers.

Caliber of Revolver	Length of Barrel, Inches	Catalogue No. 57E4756 Flap Holster Price, each	Catalogue No. 57E4761 Open Top Holster Price, each	Postage Extra
22	2	21c	16c	4c
22	6	22c	16c	4c

For Smith & Wesson, Harrington & Richardson, Hopkins & Allen, Forehand, Iver Johnson, Colt's New Pocket, Colt's Police and our own revolvers. Order by catalogue number in full.

[illegible]ber	[illegible]	Catalogue No. 57E4756 Flap Holster Price, each	Catalogue No. 57E4761 Open Top Holster Price, each	Postage Extra
	to 4	23c	17c	6c
	[illegible] to 5	24c	18c	6c
	5½ to 6	25c	19c	6c
	3½ to 4	26c	20c	6c
	4½ to 5	27c	21c	7c
[illegible]8	5½ to 6	28c	22c	7c

For Colt's New Navy, Colt's New Army, Colt's Double Action and Smith & Wesson Military revolvers. Order by catalogue number in full.

Caliber of Revolver	Length of Barrel, Inches	Catalogue No. 57E4756 Flap Holster Price, each	Catalogue No. 57E4761 Open Top Holster Price, each	Postage Extra
38 or 41	4½ to 5	33c	22c	8c
38 or 41	5½ to 6	[illegible]4c	23c	8c

For large frame revolvers, such as Colt's Frontier, Army, Single Action and Double Action, 32-20, 38-40, 44 and 45 caliber. Order by catalogue number in full.

Caliber of Revolver	Length of Barrel, Inches	Catalogue No. 57E4756 Flap Holster Price, each	Catalogue No. 57E4761 Open Top Holster Price, each	Postage Extra
[illegible]2-20 to 45	4½ to 5	35c	24c	10c
[illegible]-20 to 45	5½ to 6	36c	25c	10c
[illegible]20 to 45	7½	37c	26c	10c

Our Hand Carved Mexican Style Cowboy Holsters.

[illegible]de of heavy russet sad[illegible] to match our [illegible]oys' saddle. [illegible]rs are all hand [illegible] are not to be [illegible]ith the holsters [illegible]ouses sell as the [illegible]y holster, which [illegible]sed under a large [illegible]hese are the [illegible] and best [illegible]arket. [illegible] holsters [illegible] Smith [illegible]ton & [illegible]ins & [illegible]ver John[illegible] Pocket and New Police and our [illegible] revolvers in 38 caliber only. They [illegible]ot made for 32 caliber revolvers. When [illegible]ring, give the catalogue number in full.

Catalogue Number	Caliber of Revolver	Length of Barrel, Inches	Price, Each	Postage Extra
57E4767E	38	3½ to 4	$0.90	8c
57E4767F	38	4½ to 5	.95	8c
57E4767G	38	5½ to 6	1.00	8c

The following holsters are made to fit the Colt's Double Action, Colt's New Navy and New Army revolvers and Smith & Wesson Military and Police revolvers.

Catalogue Number	Caliber of Revolver	Length of Barrel, Inches	Price, Each	Postage Extra
57E4767H	38 or 41	4½ to 5	$1.10	10c
57E4767J	38 or 41	5½ to 6½	1.15	10c

The following holsters are made to fit the large Frontier and Army frame revolvers, 32-20, 38-40, 44-40 and 45 caliber.

Catalogue Number	Caliber of Revolver	Length of Barrel, Inches	Price, Each	Postage Extra
57E4767K	32-20 to 45	4½ to 5	$1.20	10c
57E4767L	32-20 to 45	5½ to 6	1.25	10c
57E4767M	32-20 to 45	7½	1.35	10c

Texas Shoulder Holster.

Keeps revolver always safe and ready. Made of fine soft russet leather, nicely embossed, with leather strap to pass around the chest to hold holster on shoulder, as shown in the illustration. When ordering, always give catalogue number in full and state the make and style of your revolver, give length of barrel, and we will fit your revolver.

No. 57E4768A For 22-Caliber Young America Revolvers. Mention length of barrel wanted. Price. . .(Postage extra, 5c.).....**40c**

For Smith & Wesson, Harrington & Richardson, Hopkins & Allen, Forehand, Iver Johnson, Colt's New Pocket and New Police and our own revolvers.

Catalogue Number	Caliber of Revolver	Length of Barrel, Inches	Price, Each	Postage Extra
57E4768B	32	3 to 4	45c	5c
57E4768C	32	4½ to 5	46c	5c
57E4768D	32	5½ to 6	47c	5c
57E4768E	38	3½ to 4	48c	5c
57E4768F	38	4½ to 5	48c	5c
57E4768G	38	5½ to 6	49c	5c

To fit Colt's Double Action New Navy and New Army, 38 and 41 caliber, and Smith & Wesson Military and Police revolvers.

Catalogue Number	Caliber of Revolver	Length of Barrel, Inches	Price, Each	Postage Extra
57E4768H	38 or 41	4½ to 5	50c	8c
57E4768J	38 or 41	5½ to 6½	51c	8c

To fit large frame 44 or 45 caliber revolvers.

Catalogue Number	Caliber of Revolver	Length of Barrel, Inches	Price, Each	Postage Extra
57E4768K	32-20 to 45	4½ to 5	52c	8c
57E4768L	32-20 to 45	5½ to 6	53c	8c
57E4768M	32-20 to 45	7½	54c	8c

OUR HOLSTER AND CARTRIDGE BELTS.

We would like you to compare our line of belts with any line offered by any other house, and, quality considered, we think you will find that our prices are equal to those paid by the largest dealers. Our leather goods are the best in the market. Always give waist measure and caliber when ordering.

Plain Leather Belts and Cartridge Belts.

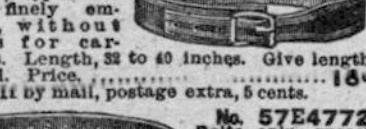

No. 57E4771 Belts only, russet leather, 1¾ inches wide, finely embossed, without loops for cartridges. Length, 32 to 40 inches. Give length wanted. Price.....**16c**

If by mail, postage extra, 5 cents.

No. 57E4772 Belts only, russet leather, nicely embossed edge, with loops for cartridges; 22, 32, 38, 41 or 44 caliber, 1¾ inches wide, plain roller buckle, 30 to 40 inches long. Give length and caliber wanted. Price.....**26c**

If by mail, postage extra, 5 cents.

Russet Leather Cartridge Belt.

No. 57E4773 Belt only, fine russet leather, nicely embossed edge, with loops for cartridges, 32, 38, 44 or 45 caliber; 2¼ inches wide, large nickel plated buckle, 32 to 40 inches long. Give length and caliber wanted. Price.....**44c**

If by mail, postage extra, 10 cents.

Combination Cartridge and Money Belts.

Mexican Combined Cartridge and Money Belt. Made of the very best soft russet leather; belt is 3 inches wide; soft and pliable and will not get hard and crack; neatly embossed. Mention caliber wanted.

No. 57E4774 32-caliber, give waist measure. Price.....**95c**

No. 57E4774½ 38-caliber, give waist measure. Price.....**95c**

No. 57E4774½ 44 or 45 caliber, give waist measure. Price.....**95c**

No. 57E4774¾ 50-caliber, give waist measure. Price.....**95c**

Don't forget to state caliber wanted, also waist measure.

If by mail, postage extra, 15 cents.

No. 57E4775 The Cowboy Combined Cartridge and Money Belt. Made of heavy russet tanned leather; strong and durable; nicely embossed; edges double stitched; designed to match our cowboy scabbard and holster; 32, 38, 44 or 45 caliber. Mention caliber wanted and give waist measure. Price.....**$1.15**

If by mail, postage extra, 18 cents.

Web Cartridge Belts.

No. 57E4776 Web Belts, for rifle and pistol cartridges; 32, 38, 44 or 45 caliber. Made of heavy web with loops for cartridges. A very strong and durable belt, not impaired by any kind of weather. Mention caliber and waist measure wanted when ordering. Price.....**35c**

If by mail, postage extra, 5 cents.

Shell Belts for Shotgun Shells.

Shell Belts with loops for carrying shotgun shells. Made of web and russet leather and with shoulder straps to go over the shoulder. Order by number and give waist measure.

No. 57E4786

Catalogue Number	Made of	Size Gauge	Price	Post'g extra
57E4786A	Web	12	30c	8c
57E4786B	Web	10	30c	8c
57E4786C	Web	16	30c	8c
57E4786D	Web	20	30c	8c
57E4787A	Rus. Leather	12	45c	10c
57E4787B	Rus. Leather	10	45c	10c
57E4787C	Rus. Leather	16	45c	10c
57E4787D	Rus. Leather	20	45c	10c
57E4787F	Rus. Leather	8	62c	16c

YOU GET A

Profit Sharing Certificate

with every order of $1.00 or more. You will be able to share in our profits, and **FREE** gets something valuable absolutely very quickly if you send us your orders. We guarantee our price to be lower than you can get elsewhere, the quality of goods the very highest, and under our **PROFIT SHARING PLAN** you are able to share with us in the profits of this business.

The New Anson Mills Woven Shell Belts.

No. 57E4791 In these Mills belts, the loops are woven into the belts, making them very strong and durable in all kinds of weather; 10 or 12-gauge, with shoulder strap and game hooks. Mention gauge wanted. Price**$1.16**

If by mail, postage extra, 22 cents.

No. 57E4794 Anson Mills Hunters Belt. The loops are woven, closed at the bottom, protecting the crimped end of the shell; no sewing whatever on the belt; 10, 12 or 16-gauge. Mention gauge wanted. Price...**79c**

If by mail, postage extra, 20 cents.

For Indian Snow Shoes

See Our Shoe Department.

The Lanz Canteen.

No. 57E4796 The only canteen which will keep water in palatable condition in any climate. With the Lanz Canteen a doctor can always have a cool drink of water in summer, or warm coffee or tea in winter, when making long rides through the country.

With it, the farmer and ranchman always have a cool drink at hand, when at work in the field, or upon the prairie.

Automobile tourists' or sportmen's tongues never parch when carrying a Lanz Canteen.

Where water in an ordinary canteen would freeze solid, under like conditions water in this canteen would not fall below a temperature of 60 degrees. The same theory applies to this canteen used in hot climates. Where water in an ordinary Government canteen would reach a temperature of 125 degrees, water in this canteen would not exceed a temperature of 82 degrees. Endorsed by doctors, explorers, soldiers and government officials. The canteen is made of heavy tin covered with a layer of felt, which in turn is covered with a removable canvas cover. Fitted with an adjustable web sling strap. The canteen is 9 inches in diameter, holds 45 fluid ounces, weighs about 1 pound. Price.....**$1.00**

If by mail, postage extra, 20 cents.

OUR HUNTING CLOTHING.

We are the largest handlers of hunting clothing selling direct to the consumer in the United States, and we know that we are offering greater value in this line of goods than it is possible for you to obtain elsewhere. Our hunting clothing is guaranteed to be made of the highest grade full weight canvas, full size, made with the same care and finish found in tailor made goods. **Quality, both in material and workmanship, considered, our prices cannot be equaled,** as they are based on our one small profit, manufacturer to consumer plan, and by reason of our enormous trade in this line, our cost of production is far smaller than that experienced by other manufacturers. In ordering, state number of inches around the chest under the arms, and state what size dress coat you wear. **Special sizes not mentioned in the following descriptions, will have to be made specially, and will cost 35 per cent more than the prices named below.**

NOTICE: DO NOT FAIL TO GIVE SIZE. Hunting clothing should be ordered one size larger than regular clothing to allow plenty of freedom.

Our Best 12-ounce Army Duck Coat, $3.80.

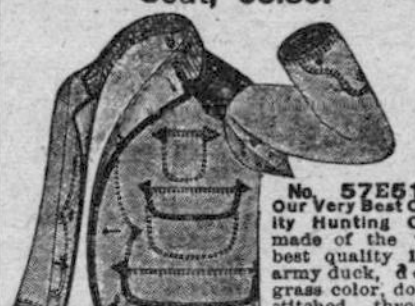

No. 57E5135 Our Very Best Quality Hunting Coat, made of the very best quality 12-oz. army duck, dead grass color, double stitched throughout, lined throughout the entire back with best quality 8-ounce army duck, sleeves lined with Walker's sateen, corduroy collar and adjustable cuffs lined with corduroy, **reinforced waterproof padded leather shoulder pieces,** leather bound throughout, including the pocket flaps; silk crow's foot stitching at the pockets and silk stitched buttonholes. **Note the gusset under the arms, as shown in the illustration. This enables you to freely raise your arms without feeling the weight of shells and game in the pockets.** The pockets are made on the cut in principle, with large flaps, which is very neat, and the game pockets are made so as to be accessible from the front and at the side seams, as shown in illustration. This is our best hunting coat, has six outside pockets and three spacious game pockets, with best quality of horn buttons, and no pains have been spared to make this hunting coat the best canvas hunting coat on the market, and is as nearly waterproof as a canvas coat can be. It comes in sizes of 36 to 46 inches. Give measure when ordering. Price.....**$3.80**

Cannot be sent by mail, as it weighs over 4 pounds. 12-ounce canvas weighs 12 ounces to the yard.

NOTICE — DO NOT FAIL TO GIVE SIZE. Hunting clothing should be ordered one size larger than regular clothing to allow plenty of freedom. . . .

Our 10-ounce Army Duck, Leather Bound Hunting Coat, $2.25.

No. 57E5137 Best quality 10-oz. army duck, dead grass color, lined with 8-oz. army duck, full pattern, reinforced shoulders, corduroy collar, corduroy lined adjustable cuffs, six outside pockets with flaps, three game pockets with entrance from front edge and side seam, double stitched throughout; leather bound all around. Sizes, chest measure, from 36 to 46 inches. Give chest measure when ordering. Price.....**$2.25**

If by mail, postage extra, 45 to 55 cents.

Our 10-ounce Canvas Special Value Coat for $1.82.

No. 57E5139 Hunting Coat, made of 10-oz. duck, dead grass color, three-quarter drill lined, corduroy collar and adjustable corduroy lined cuffs, shoulders reinforced, double stitched throughout, five outside shell pockets with flaps, reinforced, three game pockets with entrance from front edge and side seam, fancy stitching around entrance to game pockets. Sizes, chest measure, from 36 to 46 inches. Give chest measure when ordering. Price.....**$1.82**

If by mail, postage extra, 35 to 45 cents.

ORDER YOUR HUNTING COAT ONE SIZE LARGER THAN YOUR DRESS COAT, TO ALLOW PLENTY OF FREEDOM.

Our 10-ounce Sage Green Hunting Coat for $1.75.

No. 57E5140 This Hunting Coat is one of the most popular coats on the market; is made of 10-ounce sage green canvas, which is an excellent color for fall and late spring shooting; lined throughout with 8-ounce duck, has six flap pockets and large game pockets, entrance to game pockets either through front edge or through side seam. Corduroy collar and adjustable corduroy lined cuffs. **Note the gusset under the sleeves; this is a special feature and enables you to raise your arm without lifting the entire weight of shells and game in the pockets.** Sizes, chest measure, 36 to 46 inches. Give chest measure when ordering.
Price **$1.75**
If by mail, postage extra, 35 to 45 cents.

Our 8-ounce Canvas Hunting Coat, $1.32.

No. 57E5143 Hunters' Coat, made of 8-ounce duck (a yard of this canvas weighs 8 ounces), skirt drill lined, dead grass color, corduroy collar, adjustable corduroy lined cuffs, five outside pockets with flaps, three game pockets with entrance from front edge and side seams, shoulders reinforced, double stitched, three buttons. Sizes, chest measure, 36 to 46 inches. Give chest measurement when ordering. Price **$1.32**
If by mail, postage extra, 35 to 45 cents.

No. 57E5144 Exactly the same coat as No. 57E5143, but made from heavy, 10-ounce canvas instead of 8-ounce canvas. Sizes, chest measure, from 36 to 46 inches. Give chest measure when ordering. Price **$1.55**
If by mail, postage extra, 35 to 45 cents.

No. 57E5147 Made of heavy drill, dead grass color, five outside pockets, two inside skirt game pockets. A nice, light hunting and fishing coat for mild weather. This coat has no flaps over pockets and is not adjustable sleeve. Sizes, chest measure, 36 to 46 inches. Give chest measure when ordering. Price. **56c**
If by mail, postage extra, 20 to 35 cents.

Our Boys' Hunting Coat, $1.30.

No. 57E5150 We have had so many calls for Boys' Hunting Coats that we were persuaded to put in a line of these in 30, 32 and 34 inches chest measure. Made of 10-ounce canvas, has five outside pockets with flaps, two game pockets, corduroy collar, adjustable cuffs lined with corduroy, and made up in first class style, same as our regular men's coats. **Give chest measure when ordering.** Price **$1.30**
If by mail, postage extra, 28 to 34 cents.

Our $2.80 Corduroy Coat.

No. 57E5152 Is made of good quality corduroy, mouse color, well stitched, flaps over pockets, four outside pockets, two inside game pockets of large size, lined with drilling, reinforced shoulders. A dandy for the money, made in 36, 38, 40, 42 and 44 inches chest measure. Give chest measure when ordering.
Price..... **$2.80**
If by mail, postage extra, 35 to 42 cents.

Hunting Vests, 69c.

No. 57E5155 Hunting Vest, with loops for cartridges. Made of 8-ounce duck, unlined; holds about 36 shells, 10 or 12-gauge. Sizes, from 34 to 44 inches. **Give gauge and chest measure when ordering.** Price **69c**
If by mail, postage extra, 12 to 18 cents.

Duck Hunting Pants.

No. 57E5158 Hunting Pants. Made of 8-ounce duck; dead grass color, with four patch pockets. Sizes, from 28 to 40 inches waist measure. **Give waist measure and leg measure of inseam when ordering.** Price, per pair **72c**
If by mail, postage extra, 25 to 30 cents.

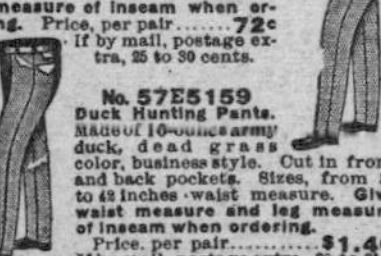

No. 57E5159 Duck Hunting Pants. Made of 10-ounce army duck, dead grass color, business style. Cut in front and back pockets. Sizes, from 30 to 42 inches waist measure. **Give waist measure and leg measure of inseam when ordering.**
Price, per pair **$1.40**
If by mail, postage extra, 30 to 35c.

Corduroy Hunting Suit.

No. 57E5172 Corduroy Coat, made of best imported drab mouse color corduroy, sateen lined, seven outside pockets, three game pockets, adjustable cuffs. This is positively as fine a corduroy coat as can be made and the equal of coats sold at $8.00 to $12.00 by other dealers. We furnish it in sizes 36 to 44 inches chest measure.
Price **$4.85**
Cannot be sent by mail.

No. 57E5174 Corduroy Vest. Business style, with pockets, to match above coat. Give chest measure when ordering. Price **$2.08**
If by mail, postage extra, 20 to 25 cents.

No. 57E5175 Corduroy Pants. Business style. To match above coat. Give waist measure and inseam of leg measure when ordering. Price, per pair **$3.15**
If by mail, postage extra, 30 to 38 cents.

HUNTING HATS AND CAPS.

Canvas Cape Cap, 37 Cents.

No. 57E5189 Canvas Cape Cap, made of 8-ounce duck, dead grass color, single stiff visor, full cape, flannel lined, an excellent rough or cold weather cap. State size wanted.
Price **37c**
If by mail, postage extra, 7 cents.

8-ounce Canvas Duck Hat for 33 Cents.

No. 57E5192 Made of 8-ounce duck, dead grass color, round top, taped seams, double stitched, stitched brim. State size wanted.
Price.......(Postage extra, 7 cents.)...... **33c**

Our Automobile Style Hunting Cap, 75 Cents.

No. 57E5196 Made of fine drab color corduroy, sateen lined, finely finished, with large earlaps which snap over top of cap when not needed.
Price **75c**
If by mail, postage extra, 8 cents.

Our Improved Klondike Cap.

No. 57E5197 The best winter cap made. Just the thing for farmers, teamsters, railroadmen, ice cutters, explorers and hunters. Made of heavy duck, lined with soft tanned sheepskin with the wool left on, with flap over face and two rows of patent snap glove fasteners, large visor, green lined, to protect the eyes, with nose protector which can be folded back out of the way without altering size of cap. The best cap on the market to protect you from extreme cold weather. State size wanted. Price **$1.32**
If by mail, postage extra, 20 cents.

DOG MUZZLES.

NOTICE—When ordering Dog Muzzles, please give measurement around the dog's neck and around snout, 1 inch from the tip of the nose, and the length from tip of the nose to the top of head where the strap goes around his neck, and you will assist us in fitting the muzzle, for muzzles vary considerably in size.

Leather Strap Dog Muzzle.

Leather Strap Dog Muzzle, to buckle around neck and buckles to take up length around head if too large. Give measure when ordering.

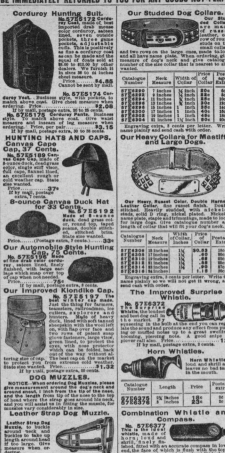

No. 57E5347 Small size. Price...... **20c**
No. 57E5348 Large size. Price...... **30c**
If by mail, postage extra, 4 cents.

OUR LINE OF DOG COLLARS.

Big Bargains.

We engrave names on collars for 3 cents per letter. Cash with order. If you wish a name engraved on the name plate, write the name PLAINLY, so we will not get it wrong.

NOTE—In taking measurements for dog collars the measures below are the length of collar from staple and middle hole, but for convenience of our customers we suggest that you give us the actual measurement around dog's neck by inches, specifying in the order actual measurement, and we will fit him every time. Prices on dog collars do not include padlocks.

Our Chain Dog Collars.

These collars have nickel plated flat links, as shown in illustration, lined with leather. When ordering, give catalogue number and length of collar that will fit your dog's neck.

Catalogue Number	Neck Measure	Width of Collar	Price of Collar	Postage Extra
57E6260	11 inches	½ inch	20c	5c
57E6262	13 inches	¾ inch	25c	7c
57E6264	15 inches	1 inch	30c	12c
57E6266	17 inches	1 inch	35c	16c

Engraving extra, 3 cents per letter. Write name plainly and send cash with order.

Our Studded Dog Collars.

Our Studded Collars are made of russet leather, one row of round studs on the small collars and two rows on the large ones, made to lock and all have name plate. When ordering, give measure of dog's neck and give catalogue number of the size collar that is nearest to size wanted.

Catalogue Number	Neck Measure	Width of Collar	Price of Collar	Postage Extra
57E6290	7 inches	½ inch	20c	6c
57E6292	9 inches	½ inch	22c	8c
57E6294	11 inches	⅝ inch	25c	10c
57E6296	13 inches	¾ inch	30c	12c
57E6298	15 inches	1 inch	35c	14c
57E6300	17 inches	1 inch	40c	16c
57E6302	19 inches	1 inch	45c	18c
57E6304	21 inches	1¼ inch	50c	20c

Engraving extra, 3 cents per letter. Write name plainly and send cash with order.

Our Heavy Collars for Mastiffs and Large Dogs.

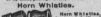

Our Heavy, Russet Color, Double Harness Leather Collar, fine russet finish. Double stitched. Heavily studded, with nickeled studs, solid D ring, nickel plated. Nickeled name plate, staple and trimmings, made to lock; for large dogs. Give catalogue number and length of collar that will fit your dog's neck.

Catalogue Number	Neck Measure	Width of Collar, Inches	Price of Collar	Postage Extra
57E6306	15 inches	1¼	$0.53	18c
57E6308	17 inches	1¼	.60	20c
57E6310	19 inches	1¼	.65	22c
57E6312	21 inches	1½	.85	25c
57E6314	23 inches	1½	.90	27c
57E6316	24 inches	2	1.15	30c

Engraving extra, 3 cents per letter. Write the name plainly so we will not get it wrong, and send cash with order.

The Improved Surprise Whistle.

No. 57E6372 The Surprise Whistle, the loudest and best dog call in the market. By squeezing in the bulb at the end you can regulate the sound and produce any effect from purling or muffled notes up to a great swelling, booming, piercing note. A good snipe or plover call also. Price **12c**
If by mail, postage extra, 2 cents.

Horn Whistles.

Horn Whistles, loud and shrill and leaves no bad taste in the mouth.

Catalogue Number	Length	Price	Postage extra
57E6375	2¾ inches	18c	2c
57E6376	3 inches	23c	2c

Combination Whistle and Compass.

No. 57E6377 This is the ideal whistle, made of horn; loud and shrill, finely finished, fitted with an accurate compass in lower end, the face of which is flush with the top of whistle. Length of whistle, about 2¼ inches. Price **35c**
If by mail, postage extra, 3 cents.

Drilled Key Dog Collar Locks.

No. 57E6400 Padlock, 1x¾ inch, all nickel plated, with key. Price **15c**

No. 57E6402 Our Little Secret Dog Collar Lock. A very neat and substantial lock; as strong as any lock and does not require a key. Keyhole has center post and is opened by pressing pin to the right. Price **10c**
If by mail, postage extra, 2 cents.

Kennel Chains.

Kennel Dog Chain, polished steel, round wire, new style safety links, three swivels, two snap hooks, so it will not kink; well made and durable; no dog can break it; comes in two lengths and two sizes.

Catalogue No.	Size Links	Length Chain	Price	Postage Extra
57E6420	Medium	4½ feet	22c	10c
57E6421	Medium	6 feet	27c	10c
57E6425	Heavy	6 feet	35c	16c

Spratt's Dog Cakes.

No. 57E6454 Spratt's Patent Fibrine Dog Cakes (with beetroot); these celebrated biscuit are supplied to all the leading kennels and are used at the principal dog shows in America and England, and have been before the public for more than a quarter of a century; 5-pound boxes. Per box.. **$0.39**
No. 57E6455 25-pound boxes.
Price, per box **1.58**
Each cake weighs 5 to 6 ounces. 2 to 4 cakes per day for pointers and setters, 3 to 5 cakes per day for mastiffs, is considered sufficient food.

LAWN TENNIS GOODS.

Our line of tennis rackets has been selected with great care and we know that we are offering better rackets for far less money than any other house. Even our cheapest racket is a hand polished racket. These rackets are made especially for us; we guarantee them to exceed any rackets on the market in finish, stringing and balance. We recommend our Seroco Racket, in 12-ounce weight, as being an excellent racket for ladies.

No. 57E6650 Our Junior Racket is made from second growth ash, walnut throat, cedar handle, well strung with American gut, well balanced; for boys and girls. Price.... **75c**

No. 57E6651 Our Oak Park Racket, full size head; made from second growth ash, with walnut throat, cedar handle; closely strung with best American gut, leather capped, well balanced. An excellent low priced racket for youths and misses. Price **$1.25**

No. 57E6652 Our Seroco Racket, full size head; made from selected second growth ash, with walnut throat, cedar handle; strung with good quality selected imported gut, leather capped. Designed for rapid, effective work, well strung and well balanced. Price. **$1.75**

No. 57E6653 Our Volley Racket, full size, highly polished head; is made from selected second growth ash, five-piece walnut and maple throat, polished and scored cedar handle, closely strung with a fine quality imported gut, leather capped and well balanced. A racket suitable for amateur or professional work.
Price **$2.45**

No. 57E6654 Our Champion Tennis Racket. This is a full sized racket, large popular shaped head and full 5-inch grip. Frame is made of second growth white ash, fitted with five-piece throat, scored cedar handle. Strung with the highest grade oriental gut, trimmed at throat and at top of racket. Guaranteed to be the equal in finish, service, balance and quality to any of the $5.00 or $6.00 rackets on the market.
Price **$3.00**

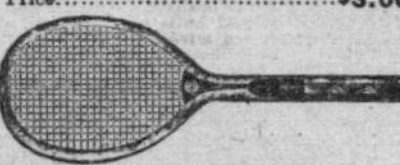

No. 57E6655 Our Expert Racket. This racket has proven to be the most popular high grade racket on the market. We have made a number improvements on same, which will make it even more popular and will cause it to excel any other racket on the market. The frame of this racket is made of selected white ash, fitted with five-piece walnut and maple throat, polished and scored extra large cedar handle 5¼ inches in circumference. This racket is strung with the very best clear white gut in the most improved manner. As shown in the illustration the racket is very closely strung through the center, giving it greater driving power and making it more effective for fast playing than any racket strung in the ordinary manner. Designed especially for professional work. Made as well as any racket on the market regardless of price and would ordinarily sell at from $6.00 to $8.00. Comes in 13, 13½, 14, 14½ ounce weights. Price **$3.75**
If by mail, postage extra, 14 to 16 cents.

RACKETS RESTRUNG WITH BEST CLEAR GUT, $1.50.

Racket Cover.

No. 57E6656 Mackintosh Cloth Waterproof Racket Cover. Keeps moisture from racket, saves racket and gut from injury. Price **80c**
No. 57E6657 Soft Felt Racket Cover.
Price **38c**
If by mail, postage extra, 6 cents.

Lawn Tennis Balls.

No. 57E6658 Regulation Felt Covered Tennis Balls. Price, each.. **$0.22**
Per dozen **2.58**
No. 57E6659 Goodrich Championship Tennis Balls. Positively the best ball made.
Price, each **$0.32**
Per dozen **3.60**
No. 57E6660 Wright & Ditson Championship Tennis Balls. Price, each **$0.35**
Per dozen **3.90**
If by mail, postage extra, 3 cents.

AWNINGS We manufacture Awnings of all sizes and descriptions. It is surprising what little money buys a good Awning. See page 324.

Lawn Tennis Nets.

Note our hand made double center net for $2.50.

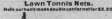

No. 57E6661 Tennis Nets, 27x3 feet, 12-thread. Weight, packed, 31 ozs. Price........**65c**

No. 57E6662 Tennis Nets, 36x3 feet, 15-thread. Weight, packed, 36 ozs. Price........**85c**

No. 57E6663 Tennis Nets, 42x3 feet, 15-thread. Weight, packed, 36 ozs. Price........**$1.08**

No. 57E6664 Tennis Nets, 42x3 feet, 15-thread, canvas bound. Weight, packed, 46 ounces. Price........**$1.52**

No. 57E6665½ Double Center Net, 42x3 ft., 21-thread, hand made, canvas bound. Weight, packed, 56 ounces. Price........**$2.50**

No. 57E6666 Back Stop Net to prevent balls from rolling out of grounds, 50x8 feet, 12-thread. Weight, packed, 68 ounces. Price........**$2.15**

Seroco Tennis Net Poles.

No. 57E6667 Solid (one piece) Tennis Poles, nicely finished, complete with guy ropes and pegs. Weight, 8½ lbs. Price, per pair, **85c**

Dry Tennis Court Marker.

No. 51E6668 Use a marble dust or air slaked lime, no mixing of material required. The wheel revolves on its axle. Comes fitted with handle. Price......**95c**

Tennis Double Court Marking Tapes.

No. 57E6669 Double Court Lawn Tennis Marking Tapes, complete with pins and staples. These tapes enable you to lay out your court in a few minutes' time and show the boundary lines very prominently on all kinds of grounds. Put up in paper box. Weight, about 10 pounds. Price, per set........**$2.90**

Our Seroco Croquet Sets.

No. 57E6678

No. 57E6670 Our Junior Four-ball Croquet Set, four striped mallets, four hardwood varnished and striped balls and striped and varnished stakes, ten wire arches; put up in neat, strong wood box with hinged cover. Weight, about 13 pounds. Price, per set....**54c**

No. 57E6672 Our Amateur Eight-ball Croquet Set, eight striped mallets, eight hardwood varnished and striped balls, two striped and varnished stakes, ten wire arches; put up in a strong wood box with hinged cover. Weight, about 22 pounds. Price, per set........**75c**

No. 57E6674 Our Favorite Eight-ball Croquet Set, consists of eight nicely painted and varnished mallets with five-inch heads, eight striped and varnished balls, two large fancy striped stakes, heavy wire arches; an excellent set at a low price; put up in a strong, durable wood box with hinged cover. Weight, about 24 pounds. Price, per set........**$1.25**

No. 57E6676 Our Champion Eight-ball Croquet Set, consisting of eight finely finished striped mallets, with eight-inch heads, eight hard maple striped and varnished balls, two striped fancy stakes, heavy pointed wire arches; well made and finished set in every respect; put up in strong wood box with hinged cover. Weight, about 27 pounds. Price, per set........**$1.45**

Our Professional Croquet Set.

No. 57E6678 Our Professional Eight-ball Croquet Set, consists of eight finely finished varnished and striped mallets, with eight-inch heads, eight finely finished striped hardwood balls, two handsome beaded striped stakes, heavy wire arches; an excellent set in every respect; put up in a strong wood box, hinged cover. Weight, about 31 pounds. Price, per set........**$2.20**

OUR BOXING GLOVE DEPARTMENT.

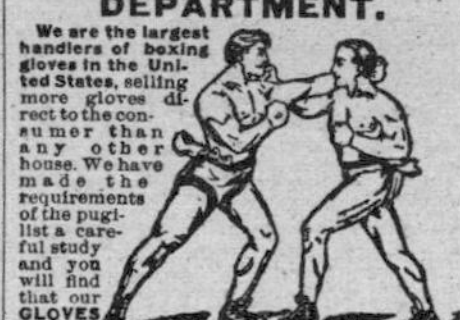

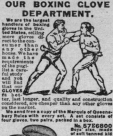

We are the largest handlers of boxing gloves in the United States, selling more gloves direct to the consumer than any other house. We have made the requirements of the pugilist a careful study and you will find that our **GLOVES** fit better, last longer, and quality and construction considered, are cheaper than any other gloves on the market.

We send free a copy of the Marquis of Queensbury Rules with every set. A set consists of four gloves, two pairs, packed in a box.

No. 57E6800 Boys' size, made of soft tanned kid leather, ecru color, stuffed with good quality short hair, ventilated palm, elastic wristband, good shape, a well made and durable glove. Weight, per set, boxed, about 28 ounces.
Price, per set of four gloves........**82c**
If by mail, postage extra, 31 cents.

No. 57E6801 Youths' size. Made of wine colored kid leather, soft and pliable, stuffed with good quality curled hair; stitched fingers, laced wristband, ventilated palm. Weight, per set, boxed, about 34 ounces.
Price, per set of four gloves........**$1.08**
If by mail, postage extra, 37 cents.

No. 57E6803 Our Frank Snyder Glove. Men's Standard Pattern, Improved. Made of claret colored California napa leather, with padded finger ends, ventilated palm, split and laced wrist, stuffed with good quality curled hair, drill lined. Weight, per set, boxed, about 46 ounces.
Price, per set of four gloves........**$1.25**
If by mail, postage extra, 49 cents.

No. 57E6804 Our Ben Hoerstal Corbett Pattern. Claret back, palm and wrist; ventilated palm, drill lined, laced wristband stuffed with good quality curled hair. Weight, per set, boxed, about 46 ounces.
Price, per set of four gloves........**$1.50**
If by mail, postage extra, 49 cents.

No. 57E6805 Our Original Corbett Pattern. Made of wine colored kid leather, serge lining, stitched fingers, ventilated palm, split wrist with laced wristband and padded cuffs; stuffed with best quality curled hair. Weight, per set, boxed, about 50 ounces.

Price, per set of four gloves........**$1.65**
If by mail, postage extra, 53 cents.

FLAGS.

See page 324 of this catalogue for lowest prices on Flags. We make our own flags, insuring you quality, size and value.

No. 57E6806 Trainer's Corbett Pattern. Made of selected green California napa leather, with stitched fingers, serge lining, laced wrist, ventilated palm, stuffed with best quality curled hair. Weight, per set, boxed, about 48 ounces.
Price, per set of four gloves........**$1.75**
If by mail, postage extra, 51 cents.

No. 57E6808 Instructor's Pattern. Made of selected especially tanned wine color kid, laced wrist, padded cuff, leather bound; best serge lining, ventilated palm, stuffed with extra quality curled hair, double silk stitched, with finger grip. Weight, per set, boxed, about 48 ounces.
Price, per set of four gloves........**$3.00**
If by mail, postage extra, 51 cents.

The Dudley Club Special, $3.75

No. 57E6811 The Dudley Club Special Boxing Glove. Corbett pattern, full heel pad below the lacing, center palm grip, full padded cuff, laced wristband, double stitched with silk, made from special selected, tan color, California tanned kid, stuffed with finest quality white curled hair, a new departure in boxing gloves, the latest on the market. Weight, per set, boxed, about 50 ounces.
Price, per set of four gloves........**$3.75**
If by mail, postage extra, 55 cents.

No. 57E6812 Barry Pattern. Made of selected, especially tanned French kid leather, green color with grip in center, thumb well padded on top, affording absolute protection, serge lined and leather binding, laced wrist with tape laces, wrist extra full padded, hand sewed; stuffed with extra quality curled hair, double stitched throughout with silk. Weight per set, boxed, about 48 ounces. Price, per set of four gloves..**$3.50**
If by mail, postage extra, 51 cents.

No. 57E6813 Approved Amateur Pattern Men's Size Gloves, made of best green color California kid leather, with finger grip and toe padded, ventilated palm, padded wrist, best serge lining, leather binding, laced wrist, stuffed with best quality curled hair, double stitched throughout. A good sparring glove.
Price, per set of four........**$2.15**
If by mail, postage extra, 48 cents.

Our Highest Grade Gloves at $3.10 per Set.

No. 57E6814 Special Fitzsimmons Pattern, with California thumb. Made of selected French kid leather, green color, with grip and side or heel pad, serge lined and leather binding, laced wrist with tape laces, wrist made with extra padded roll, hand sewed; stuffed with extra quality curled hair, double stitched throughout with silk. Weight, per set, boxed, about 52 ounces. Price, per set........**$3.10**
If by mail, postage extra, 53 cents.

Professional Fighting Gloves.

No. 57E6815 Our Official Professional Fighting Glove. Made of selected green California napa leather, with grip in center and toe pad, ventilated palm, lined throughout, laced and leather bound wrist; stuffed with very best quality curled hair, made extra strong for hard usage, double stitched with linen thread, padded cuff. Weight, per set, boxed, about 45 ounces.
Price, per set of four gloves........**$2.10**
If by mail, postage extra, 48 cents.

5-Ounce Fighting Gloves.

No. 57E6816 The Genuine Root Pattern Fighting Gloves, made of the very finest quality, selected tan color kid leather, and leather lined, made with padded wrist, finger grip, ventilated palm, deep laced wrist, double stitched with silk, stuffed with very best quality white curled hair. Each glove weighs 5 ounces. Regular price, $5.00; our price........**$3.90**
If by mail, postage extra, 35 cents.

STRIKING BAGS.

Bag punching is the most pleasant, least tiring and best of all exercises. Our line of striking bags is made especially for us in accordance with our specifications. Quality considered, they are superior to any bags on the market. They are all lined in the best manner and are guaranteed to hang absolutely true. Our bags have been used in many gymnasiums throughout the country for years and are highly endorsed by amateurs and professionals. **Price includes bag and bladder complete, with rope and screw eye.**

Single End Bags.

No. 57E6824 Made of good strong leather, drill lined, strong loop, all well made. This is a good practice bag for a very little money. Weight, about 10 ounces. Price, complete **90c**

No. 57E6825 Made of gold tan napa leather with strong loop. Drill lined, good, desirable and strong. 30 inches circumference when inflated. Weight, complete, about 10 ounces. Price, with bladder......**$1.12**

No. 57E6828 Made of olive tan leather, with strong loop and drill lined, very good strong bag, 32 inches circumference when inflated. Weight, complete, about 12 ounces. Price, with bladder........**$1.22**

No. 57E6829 Best quality, claret color, soft tanned leather, strong loop, drill lined, triple seams, making an extra strong bag, one of the best sellers, 32 inches circumference when inflated. Weight, complete, about 14 ounces. Price, with bladder........**$1.45**

No. 57E6830 Best quality California olive tan leather, strong loop, drill lined, welted seams, triple stitches, one-piece top, a fine bag and very fast. 32-inches circumference when inflated. Weight, complete, about 12 ounces.
Price, with bladder........**$1.70**

No. 57E6835 Soft tan satin calf, drill lined, triple seams, welted, strong loop, one-piece top. A good article, retails for $3.50. 32 inches circumference when inflated. Weight, complete, about 14 ounces. Price with bladder..**$2.18**

No. 57E6836 Expert Bag, made of special selected oil tan horsehide, very strong and tough. Drill lined, triple seams, welted, strong loop, one-piece top, made up first class in every respect; very fast and the finest bag made. 32 inches circumference when inflated. Weight, complete, about 14 ounces.
Price, with bladder........**$2.40**
If by mail, postage extra, 20 to 25 cents.

Our Pear Shape Bag.

This is the latest thing in punching bags. The pear shape bag is so made that the strain is on all sections of the bag instead of one place. The top and bottom are stitched by hand and the bag is built to withstand constant use—in fact, the bag is built for work.

No. 57E6838 Made of napa leather, plain seams, canvas lined, wine color, 30 inches circumference when inflated. Weight, complete, 11 ounces.
Price, with bladder........**$1.35**

No. 57E6839 Fine quality goatskin, olive green color, napa tanned, bound lips, eyeleted lace holes, welted triple seams, canvas lined, 32 inches circumference when inflated. Weight, complete, 11 ozs. Price, with bladder..**$1.80**

No. 57E6840 Fine quality selected horsehide, tan color, bound lips, eyeleted lace holes, welted seams, canvas lined, 32 inches in circumference when inflated, hand stitched top and bottom, with very best quality of rubber bladder that can be had; just the bag for professional bag punchers. Weight, complete, 11 ounces. Price, with bladder........**$2.45**
If by mail, postage extra, 22 to 25 cents.

Double End Bags.

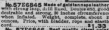

Here is a line of double end bags which are lively, good and can be put up anywhere where you can put in two screw eyes. Illustration shows a bag put up in a doorway. Bore a 1-inch hole in your door sill, turn a screw eye into it so it will be below the sill and out of the way; fasten a hook to the elastic cord and hook it to the screw eye, and you can take down the bag or put it up in a few seconds any time. These prices include the bag, bladder, a piece of rope, two screw eyes and a piece of elastic cord.

No. 57E6845 Made of gold tan napa leather, with strong loop, drill lined. Double end, good, desirable and strong, 30 inches circumference when inflated. Weight, complete, about 12 ounces. Price, with bladder, rope and elastic cord........**$1.33**

No. 57E6846 Best quality, claret color, soft tanned leather, drill lined, strong loop, triple seams, making an extra strong double end bag, and one of the best sellers; 32 inches circumference when inflated. Weight, complete, about 14 ounces. Price, with bladder, rope and elastic cord........**$1.71**

No. 57E6847 Soft tan satin calf, drill lined, triple seams, welted, the best double end bag on the market. A good article, retails for $4.00. 32 inches circumference when inflated. Weight, complete, about 15 ounces. Price, with bladder, rope and elastic cord........**$2.40**
If by mail, postage extra, 22 to 27 cents.

BOOMERANG.

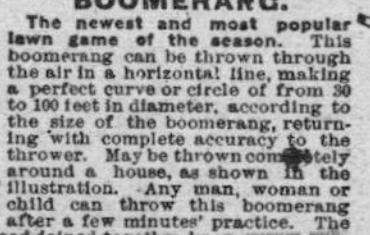

The newest and most popular lawn game of the season. This boomerang can be thrown through the air in a horizontal line, making a perfect curve or circle of from 30 to 100 feet in diameter, according to the size of the boomerang, returning with complete accuracy to the thrower. May be thrown completely around a house, as shown in the illustration. Any man, woman or child can throw this boomerang after a few minutes' practice. The boomerang is made of two blades of wood joined together by a screw running through the center, so shaped and curved to accomplish the results as above stated.

No. 57E6708 The Boomerang Game consists of six boomerangs, two rakahs, which are the nets used to catch the boomerang, and full instructions how to play the game as well as how to throw the boomerang. Each set put up in a nice strong paper box. Price, per set....**$2.00**

We will also sell the boomerangs separately at the following prices:

No. 57E6710 Boomerang. Blade, 7½ inches long; made of straight grained hard maple, nicely decorated, not weighted, cuts 45-foot circle. Price, each........**20c**

No. 57E6712 Boomerang. Blade, 7½ inches long; artistically decorated, blades weighted near ends, cuts 75-foot circle. Price, each........**30c**

No. 57E6714 Standard Boomerang with which all official games are played. 7½ inches long, made of the best clear grain maple wood, hand decorated, blades weighted near end, cuts 60-foot circle. Price, each........(If by mail, postage extra, 6 cents)........**40c**

Rakahs or Nets.

No. 57E6718 Daisy Rakah. Has straight grain white elm frame, natural wood finish hardwood handle, 24-thread cord net. Weight, 5½ ounces. Price, each........**40c**

Rugby Rubber Football Bladders.

Our bladders are all the best grade. We do not carry cheap composition bladders. They are worthless.

No. 57E6851 Pure Rubber for regulation Rugby foot balls. Price.......42c

No. 57E6851½ Rugby Bladders, for boys' footballs. Price.......35c

If by mail, postage extra, 5 cents.

Rubber Striking Bag and Football Bladders.

No. 57E6852 10-inch Bladders, made of pure Para rubber, for 30-inch striking bags and Association foot balls. Price.......42c

No. 57E6853 12-inch Bladders, made of finest quality pure rubber, for bags 33 inches in circumference. Price.......48c

If by mail, postage extra, 5 cents.

Striking Bag Swivel.

No. 57E6854 Striking Bag Swivel. Rope can be taken out without unscrewing from platform and permits bag to be punched in any direction without twisting rope. Price.......21c

If by mail, postage extra, 6 cents.

Striking Bag Knuckle Gloves.

No. 57E6855 The Celebrated Frazer Striking Bag Knuckle Glove, small, neat, made of the best oil tanned horsehide, heavily padded, thus making a complete protection for the knuckles. For ladies and men. Price, per pair..34c

If by mail, postage extra, 5 cents.

Striking Bag Mitts.

No. 57E6858 Striking Bag Mitts, made of kid, with grip in center, padded back, elastic wristband. This is the best mitt to use for bag punching.
Price, per pair.......60c

If by mail, postage extra, 10 cents.

Maple Indian Clubs and Dumb Bells.

No. 57E6856

No. 57E6857

Sold in pairs only, and made of the best first quality rock maple and finely polished. Weight given is the weight of each club or dumb bell. If you order one pair 1-pound clubs, you get two 1-pound clubs, etc. When ordering, state which weight you want.

Weight, of each Club or Bell	Indian Clubs No. 57E6856 Price, per pair	Dumb Bells No. 57E6857 Price, per pair	Weight, of each Club or Bell	Indian Clubs No. 57E6856 Price, per pair	Dumb Bells No. 57E6857 Price, per pair
½ lb.	14c	15c	2 lbs.	23c	24c
¾ lb.	16c	17c	3 lbs.	37c	38c
1 lb.	17c	18c	4 lbs.	44c	45c
1½ lb.	20c	Not Made.	5 lbs.	55c	Not Made.

Iron Dumb Bells.

No. 57E6859 Our Iron Dumb Bells are cast from pure gray iron. We make them in weights as follows: 1, 2, 3, 4, 5, 6, 8, 10, 12, 15, 20 and 25 pounds. These are the weights of each dumb bell. Sold by the pound. Mention weight you wish when ordering. Price, per pound.......4c

The Expert Striking Bag Swivel.

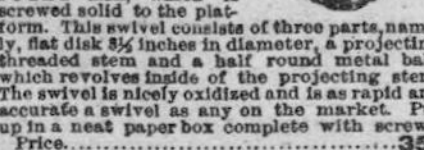

No. 57E6865 The Expert Striking Bag Swivel is undoubtedly the best swivel on the market. Bag can be instantly removed or a new rope inserted by unscrewing the projecting stem from the round disk, which is screwed solid to the platform. This swivel consists of three parts, namely, flat disk 3½ inches in diameter, a projecting threaded stem and a half round metal ball, which revolves inside of the projecting stem. The swivel is nicely oxidized and is as rapid and accurate a swivel as any on the market. Put up in a neat paper box complete with screws. Price.......35c

If by mail, postage extra, 8 cents.

Our Perfect Chicago Bag Platform, $3.25.

No. 57E6866 This platform is made of selected wood, 36 inches in diameter, well braced and is so constructed that the platform may be raised or lowered after it is fastened to the wall. The platform should be fastened so that the circle will be about 6½ feet from the floor. Price for the Chicago Punching Bag Platform (this price does not include the punching bag or swivel), only.......$3.25

Weight, crated for shipment, about 85 pounds.

Elastic Floor Attachments.

No. 57E6867 Elastic Floor Attachments for Double End Bags, made of elastic and covered with braided cotton and used for attaching the bottom of the bag to the floor. Price.......18c

If by mail, postage extra, 5 cents.

Exercising or Swinging Rings.

No. 57E6869 Wooden Rings, three pieces, made of walnut and maple, glued together, 6 in. in diameter. Per pair.......45c

If by mail, postage extra, 5 cents.

Horizontal Bars.

No. 57E6870 Made of the best quality of second growth, straight grain hickory, square ends.

4½ feet long. Price	$1.05
5 feet long. Price	1.25
5½ feet long. Price	1.50
6 feet long. Price	1.65

Weight, 4½ to 6 pounds.

Whiteley Chest Pull.

No. 57E6871 Just the thing to broaden your shoulders and to strengthen the muscles of your back and arms. More beneficial than the heavy chest weights, and far less expensive. Made of three strands of elastic cable, attached to two wood handles with nickel plated trimmings. Comes in three tensions.

A—Light tension, for ladies and children, 27 inches. Price.......45c

B—Medium tension, for youths, 30 inches. Price.......50c

C—Heavy tension, for men, 33 inches. Price.......55c

If by mail, postage extra, 12 cents.

Whiteley Exercisers.

No. 57E6873 Made of elastic cord with wood pulleys, plain handles and foot attachment. Price.....$1.50

If by mail, postage extra, 22 cents.

No. 57E6874 Made of elastic cord with metal pulleys running in brass bushings, enameled handles with foot attachment. Price.....$2.20

If by mail, postage extra, 30 cents.

No. 57E6875 Made of elastic cord, with fancy decorated pulleys, nickel plated trimmings, enameled handles with foot attachment. Price.......$2.85

If by mail, postage extra, 30 cents.

No. 57E6877 Whiteley Special Exerciser, for adults or children, full size, OO grade, made of elastic cable with plain wood pulleys and wood handles, nickel plated trimmings, complete with hinge attachments, screw eyes, also chart of exercising. Packed in neat paper box. Price.......95c

Massage Rollers.

The wood balls revolve on wire spindles, causing no friction or irritation of the skin, giving a better massage than that obtained at the hands of an expert. Very beneficial to sore or stiff muscles, also in such diseases as rheumatism, neuralgia, insomnia, etc.

No. 57E6876 Massage Roller, 18 balls with non-elastic sides, complete with instructions. Price.......45c

No. 57E6879 Massage Roller, 22 balls elastic sides, making a combination exerciser and roller, complete with instructions. Price.......80c

If by mail, postage extra, 23 cents.

BASEBALL GOODS FOR AMERICA'S NATIONAL GAME

BASEBALLS.

The National League Ball.

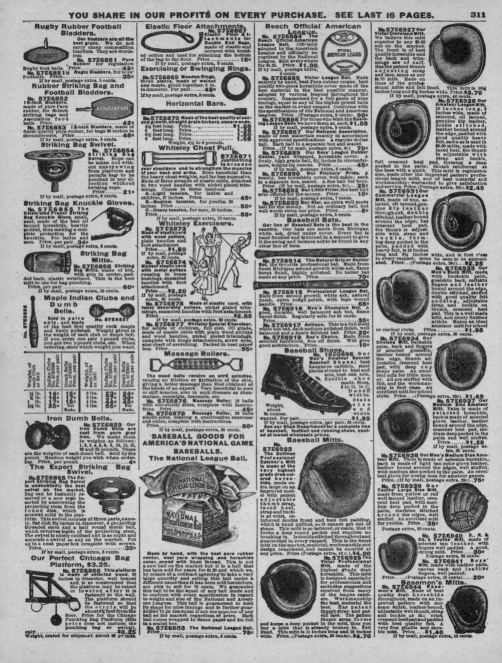

Made by hand, with the best pure rubber center, wool yarn wrapping and horsehide cover, sewed with linen thread. This is not a new ball on the market but it is a ball that has been sold for years for $1.25 and which we, by reason of a contract agreeing to take a very large quantity and selling this ball under a different name than it has been sold heretofore, are able to sell for 75 cents. We guarantee this ball to be the equal of any ball made and to conform with every specification in regard to weight and size of the National and American Leagues. This ball is guaranteed to hold its shape for nine innings and is further guaranteed to be the equal if not the superior of any ball on the market regardless of price. Each ball comes wrapped in tissue paper and tin foil in a sealed box.

No. 57E6883 The National League Ball. Price.......75c

If by mail, postage extra, 9 cents.

Reach Official American League.

No. 57E6884 The Reach Official American League Ball. Officially adopted by the American League and officially recognized by the National League. Sold everywhere for $1.25. Price..$1.00

If by mail, postage extra, 9 cents.

No. 57E6885 Victor League Ball. Made entirely by hand, best Para rubber center, best quality two-piece horsehide cover made of the best material in the best possible manner, adopted by various leagues throughout the country. Guaranteed for a full game of nine innings, equal to any of the higher priced balls on the market in every respect. Conforms with the specifications of the National and American leagues. Price..(Postage extra, 9 cents)..90c

No. 57E6886 For those who wish the Spalding League Balls we have them at, each, $1.05

If by mail, postage extra, 9 cents.

No. 57E6887 Our National Association, made of best materials exactly in accordance with approved specifications. A regular dollar ball. Each ball in a separate box and sealed. Price...(If by mail, postage extra, 8c) 70c

No. 57E6889 Our Boys' League Rubber Center, yarn wrapped, horsehide cover. A lively, high grade ball, 8½ inches in circumference, weighs 4¼ ounces. Price.......45c

If by mail, postage extra, 8 cents.

No. 57E6890 Our Pitchers' Pride. A beauty, has horsehide cover, well made; each in a separate box, sealed. A fine ball for boys. Price..(If by mail, postage extra, 8c).....25c

No. 57E6892 Our Little Victor, the best ball ever offered for the money. Price.......10c

If by mail, postage extra, 7 cents.

No. 57E6893 Our Star, an extra well made ball for the money. Not an ordinary ball, but well worth twice our price. Price.......5c

If by mail, postage extra, 5 cents.

Baseball Bats.

Our line of Baseball Bats is the best in the country. Our bats are made from Michigan white ash, dried under cover. Every bat is hand finished and is turned in a manner to give it the swing and balance not to be found in any other line of bats.

No. 57E6914 The Natural Grip or Bunter Bat, the favorite professional bat. Made from finest Michigan second growth white ash, flame burnt finish, highly polished. No better bat made at any price. Price.......70c

No. 57E6915 Professional League Bat. Made from second growth white ash, natural finish, extra rough polish, with tape wound handle. Price.......65c

No. 57E6916 Men's Champion Bat. A good, durable, well balanced ash bat, flame burnt finish. Regularly sells for 50 cents. Price.......35c

No. 57E6917 Antique. This is a full sized white ash bat, dark antique polished finish, well balanced and a finely finished bat. Price..20c

No. 57E6919 Boy's Choice. Made from selected hardwood, fine oil finish. Will give good satisfaction. Price.......10c

Baseball Shoes.

No. 15E0696 Our Men's Amateur Special Baseball Shoes; best kangaroo calfskin, steel plates riveted to heel and sole, best oak sole, flexible shoe made. Sizes, 6 to 11, in C, D and E widths. State size and width wanted. Weight, about 24 ounces. Per pair.......$1.85

If by mail, postage extra, per pair, 36 cents.

See our Shoe Department for a complete line of baseball, football and running shoes, quoted at lowest wholesale prices.

Baseball Mitts.

No. 57E6923 The Sullivan Professional Catcher's Mitt is made of the very highest grade drab colored horsehide, made extra large on an improved model with patent adjustable thumb strap, laced heel, strap and buckle at wrist, reinforced double front and best felt padding, which is hand quilted, so it cannot get out of shape. This mitt is so tailored, or made, that it forms a deep round pocket and requires no breaking in. Is double stitched throughout and guaranteed in every respect. This is the finest mitt on the market, material, workmanship and design considered, and cannot be excelled at any price. Price (Postage extra, 40 c.), $4.00

No. 57E6925 The Victor Professional Mitt, made of the highest grade drab horsehide. This mitt is designed especially for professionals and embodies suggestions received from many of the league catchers. Workmanship the best, material the best. Has patent thumb strap and patent lace. The patent thumb strap forms and keeps a deep pocket in the mitt, thus you buy a mitt that is already broken in. Felt lined. This mitt is 11 inches long and 10 inches wide. Price..(Postage extra, 38 cents)..$4.70

No. 57E6927 Our Victor Cleveland Mitt. We believe this mitt superior to any $5.00 mit on the market. The front is of best quality horsehide and the back and trimmings are of calf. Has the patent thumb adjusting strap and lace, same as our $4.70 mitt. Made on lines of the professional mitts and felt lined. This mitt is 10½ inches long and 9½ inches wide. Price.$3.70

If by mail, postage extra, 40 cents.

No. 57E6928 Our Amateur League Mitt, 10 inches long, 9 inches wide, made of selected, oil tanned, genuine kip leather, double stitched, leather bound around the edge, padded with good quality heavy felt, same as is used in $5.00 mitts, made with laced heel, the thumb is adjustable with strap and buckle, full crescent heel pad, forming a deep pocket in the palm; thumb reinforced at the base with a quirk. This mitt is regulation size, made after the improved pattern professional league mitt, and of best material and workmanship; warranted to give satisfaction and service. Price.(Postage extra, 33c).$2.45

No. 57E6931 Our Commercial League Mitt, made of fine, selected, oil tanned, genuine kip leather throughout, double stitched, leather bound around the edge; has crescent heel pad, the thumb is adjustable with strap and buckle, forming deep pocket in the palm, padded with heavy felt, is 10 inches long and 9½ inches wide, and is first class in every respect; must be seen to be appreciated. Price...(Postage extra, 35c).$2.25

No. 57E6933 Our Men's Buck Mitt, made with buckskin palm, goatskin back, calfskin fingers and leather bound around the edge, double stitched, stuffed with good quality felt padding, adjustable strap and buckle on thumb, crescent heel pad. This is a well made mitt, and nicely finished article. Makes an ideal amateur mitt for school or clerical clubs. Price.......$1.85

If by mail, postage extra, 30 cents.

No. 57E6934 Our Chelsea Mitt, buckskin palm, back and fingers of selected goatskin, leather bound around the edge, thumb adjustable, crescent heel pad, with deep cup shape palm. An excellent mitt for little money. All are stuffed with felt, and the workmanship is first class. An excellent mitt for school clubs. Price...(Postage extra, 30c)..$1.65

No. 57E6937 Our Medium Size Amateur Mitt. Palm is made of selected horsehide, back is made of selected glove leather, leather bound around the edge, crescent heel pad, medium deep pocket in the palm and well stuffed. Price.......$1.25

If by mail, postage extra, 28 cents.

No. 57E6938 Our Men's Medium Size Amateur Mitt. Palm is made of asbestos buckskin, back is made of light tan color glove leather, leather bound around the edges, well stuffed, with medium size pocket in the palm. An excellent glove for young men for amateur games. Price..(If by mail, postage extra, 28c)..75c

No. 57E6939 Our Youths' Large Size Mitt, made from yellow or red well tanned leather, crescent heel pad, with medium deep pocket in the palm, machine stitched around the edges, well stuffed. An excellent mitt for youths. Price.......38c

Postage extra, 20 cents.

No. 57E6940 S., R. & Co.'s Youths' Mitt, made of selected tan leather, with fingers well padded. A good, strong mitt. Price.......30c

Postage extra, 20 cents.

No. 57E6941 Boys' Mitt, made with leather palm, canvas back and leather fingers, well padded. Price.....(Postage extra, 18 cents).......20c

Basemen's Mitts.

No. 57E6944 Basemen's Mitt. Made of best quality drab horsehide throughout, made on an improved pattern with outseam finish, leather bound, adjustable web thumb, strap and buckle at the wrist, crescent heel pad and padded with best quality felt. A very fine pliable and durable mitt. Price.......$1.40

If by mail, postage extra, 12 cents.

Basemen's Mitts.

No. 57E6946 Basemen's or Outfielder's Mitt. Made with horsehide front, fine glove leather back with fingers like a catcher's mitt, padded with good grade of felt, crescent heel pad, web thumb, strap and buckle at the wrist. This is a mitt that will give excellent service at a medium price. Price..**82c**
If by mail, postage extra, 10c.

Fielder's Gloves.

No. 57E6950 League Fielder's Glove. Made of very finest high grade light drab color buck, on the latest improved model, extra large size pattern with large little finger, heavily padded on the heel, forming large, deep pocket in the palm, leather lined, leather bound, welted seams, strap and buckle at the wrist, web between thumb and first finger. This glove contains all of the best features of the most popular gloves on the market and the quality of the stock and workmanship are the best obtainable.
Price..**$2.50**
If by mail, postage extra, 14 cents.

No. 57E6952 The Professional Style Fielder's Glove of latest improved Pattern, is made of the very best, fine selected oil tanned leather, very soft and pliable, made on very large pattern with large little finger and correctly padded. Has heavy padding at the heel forming a large deep natural pocket in the palm. Leather lined, leather bound, strap and buckle wrist and welted seams. The glove is so constructed that it does not require "breaking in," and is guaranteed to be equal and to wear as long as any $3.50 glove on the market. No better to be had at any price, and it must be seen to be appreciated. Price.......................**$2.15**
If by mail, postage extra, 14 cents.

No. 57E6954 The Victor Professional Fielders' Glove. Made of horsehide, correctly padded, crescent pad extending in a semicircle around palm, with adjustable web between the thumb and first finger, as shown in the illustration, making a deep pocket, correctly padded.
Price.....**$1.95**
If by mail, postage extra, 11 cents.

No. 57E6956 Basemen's and Infielders' Glove, made of good quality buckskin, crescent heel pad, palm and fingers heavily padded, lined with good quality felt, web between thumb and first finger, a medium priced professional glove and a good one. Price.......................**$1.25**
If by mail, postage extra, 14 cents.

No. 57E6958 Our Chicago Glove, men's size, made of napa tanned horsehide, well padded, with finger tips; crescent padded palm, full men's size, first class workmanship. A glove that will give you satisfaction. Leather finger tips will be popular this season.
Price.........**$1.00**
If by mail, postage extra, 13 cents.

No. 57E6959 Made in men's large size, of buckskin leather, felt lined, crescent heel pad, heavily padded palm, web thumb and first finger, leather bound edges, button wrist. A first class semiprofessional glove.
Price...................**75c**
If by mail, postage extra, 13c.

No. 57E6961 Made of Napa tanned glove leather; felt padded palm and fingers, leather bound edges, button wristband. Price.........**40c**
If by mail, postage extra, 8c.

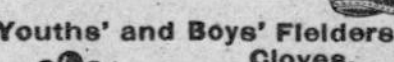

Youths' and Boys' Fielders' Gloves.

No. 57E6964 Our Youths' Infielders' Glove, made of finest oil tanned leather, heavily padded crescent heel pad, leather bound all around, button fastener. A regular boys' professional glove.
Price...................**35c**
If by mail, postage extra, 3c.

Our 18c Boys' Glove.

No. 57E6966 Our Boys' Infielders' Glove, made of fine, colored sheepskin, palm is felt lined and padded, well stitched seams, elastic fastener. Price.....**18c**
If by mail, postage extra, 3 cents.

Baseball Catchers' Masks.

This illustration shows the patent pneumatic cushion or pad we are placing on our Nos. 57E6972 and 57E6973 baseball masks. Unquestionably these pneumatic pads represent the best invention within the past five years in baseball goods. The old style leather pads were hard and rigid, they would never conform to the face of the wearer and were never comfortable. These pneumatic pads of ours are made of rubber, covered with perspiration proof brown khaki cloth, extend around the face and across the chin, conform to the contour of the face and are at all times comfortable, making our masks the most perfect fitting and most comfortable masks on the market. These pads are inflated or deflated by means of the nozzle shown in the illustration. One operation inflates the entire pad.

No 57E6972 Our patent neck protecting pneumatic pad mask. The best mask on the market, fitted with our pneumatic pads as above described, made of the best annealed steel wire of extra heavy gauge, covered with black enamel to prevent the reflection of light. Fitted with an extension at the bottom of mask to give protection to the neck, which extension does not in any way interfere with the free movement of the head. Endorsed by professional and amateur players throughout the country.
Price.......................................**$2.10**
If by mail, postage extra, 30 cents.

No. 57E6973 Men's Professional League Mask, fitted with our pneumatic pads, as above illustrated and described. This mask is full size, made of black enamel wire, 5-32 and 6-32 inch in diameter. The pneumatic pad extends around the face and across the chin, making this mask more comfortable and better fitting than any other mask. This mask is 10½ inches long, 7½ inches wide and weighs about 24 ounces. Price.......................................**$1.85**
If by mail, postage extra, 29 cents.

No. 57E6977 Men's Professional League Mask. Black enameled wire of 5-32 and 6-32 inch diameter, which prevents the reflection of the light; temple and cheek pads, with head and chin pieces; weight, 22 ounces; an A1 quality mask; 10½ inches long, 7½ inches wide. A strong mask. Price..**$1.25**
If by mail, postage extra, 27 cents.

No. 57E6978 Men's Professional Mask. Black enameled wire, 5-32 inch in diameter, temple and cheek pads, head and chin pieces; well made; weight, 18 ounces; 10 inches long, 7 inches wide.
Price...................**90c**
If by mail, postage extra, 18 cents.

No. 57E6980 Men's Amateur Mask. Bright wire, 4-32 inch in diameter; temple and cheek pads; nicely finished; weight, 11 ounces; 10 inches long, 7 inches wide.
Price...................**50c**
If by mail, postage extra, 16 cents.

No. 57E6983 Youths' Mask. Bright wire, 3-32 inch in diameter; temple and cheek pads; nicely finished; weight, 6 ounces; frame, 10 inches long, 6 inches wide. Price...................**35c**
If by mail, postage extra, 9 cents.

No. 57E6984 Boys' Mask. Bright wire, 3-32 inch in diameter; temple and cheek pads; nicely finished; weight, 4 ounces; frame, 9 inches long, 5 inches wide. Price..........**18c**
If by mail, postage extra, 6 cents.

Baseball Catchers' Body Protectors.

No. 57E6990 Our Special Professional League Body Protector, made of the very best rubber, inflated with air; light, pliable, and does not interfere with movements of the wearer. When not in use air may be let out and the protector rolled into a small package.
Price...................**$3.50**
Postage extra, 40 cents.

No. 57E6991 Our Special Amateur Body Protector, inflated with air, similar to our league, but has fewer air compartments. It is made with the same care as our professional and all are warranted perfect when they leave our store. Price...................**$2.50**
If by mail, postage extra, 40 cents.

No. 57E6992 Our Boys' Body Protector, made of canvas, well stuffed and quilted, same shape as our league but smaller, for boys. Price...................**60c**
If by mail, postage extra, 20 cents.

No. 57E6993 Our Men's Body Protector, made of canvas, with soft leather front, stuffed and quilted. Price...................**$1.00**
If by mail, postage extra, 30 cents.

Baseball Shoe Plates.

Our professional league shoe plates are made of finest tempered razor steel, guaranteed the best shoe plates on the market. Come put up in an envelope complete with screws.

No. 57E6996 Professional League Razor Steel Toe Plates. Price, per pair...................**30c**

No. 57E6997 Professional League Razor Steel Heel Plates. Price, per pair...........**31c**
If by mail, postage extra, 4 cents.

Amateur Shoe Plates.

No. 57E7001 Amateur Toe Plates, complete with screws. Price, per pair...........**9c**

No. 57E7002 Amateur Heel Plates. Price, per pair...................**8c**
If by mail, postage extra, 3 cents.

No. 57E7003 Pitchers' Brass Toe Plate. For either left or right foot. State which is wanted when ordering.
Price, each...................**18c**
If by mail, postage extra, 3 cents.

Athletic Guides.

No. 57E7028 Annual Baseball Guide, giving official rules of this game. Not issued before April 1st of each year. Price...................**10c**

No. 57E7029 Annual Tennis Guide, giving rules and instructions.
Price...................**10c**

No. 57E7039 Annual Basketball Guide. Price...................**10c**

No. 57E7040 Annual Football Guide. **10c**
If by mail, postage extra, 7 cents.

BASEBALL UNIFORMS.

WRITE FOR OUR FREE SAMPLE BOOK SHOWING SAMPLES OF THE DIFFERENT MATERIALS WE USE FOR BASEBALL UNIFORMS WITH FULL INFORMATION REGARDING THE PRICES AND STYLES.

We make to special order, out of the best grades of athletic flannel, complete baseball uniforms at $2.75, $3.50, $4.50, $6.00 and $7.00 and we also make and sell the separate shirts and pants. We letter the shirts as desired. **For samples of the material we use, instructions how to measure and how to order, write and ask for our free sample book of baseball suits.** We do not describe and price our baseball uniforms in this catalogue for the reason that it is more satisfactory if you have the sample of the material to select from. Don't fail to send for our sample book showing the flannels used in our uniforms, also detailed description how to order, etc., before you place your order with anyone.

Our business in baseball uniforms exceeds that of any other house. This is due entirely to the fact that we have won the confidence of the baseball player by giving him the very best suits for the smallest amount of money. We have made the requirements of the baseball player a careful study and we have made our uniforms in accordance with these requirements. You will find our uniforms look better, feel better, last longer, and, quality considered, are cheaper than any other uniforms on the market. We make each and every uniform especially to order in accordance with specifications furnished by the customer. If you are interested in baseball uniforms, we especially urge that you send for our sample book and measurement blank which show the quality of the flannel used in our uniforms and give full description at lowest prices. Send a postal card for our sample book of baseball uniforms and we will be pleased to send same at once.

Baseball and Football Belts.

No. 57E7079 Our Leather Belt, with one large leather covered buckle. Strong serviceable belt. Price.........(If by mail, postage extra, 3 cents)...................**45c**

No. 57E7080 Cotton Web Belt, single buckle, leather billet. Price...................**20c**
If by mail, postage extra, 3 cents.

Baseball and Football Stockings.

No. 57E7081 Heavy Weight Ribbed Cotton Stockings, black only, excellent serviceable stockings. Price, per pair.........(If by mail, postage extra, per pair, 8 cents)...........**25c**

No. 57E7082 Medium Weight Wool Stockings, ribbed, black, navy or maroon color. Give size when ordering. Price, per pair.........(If by mail, postage extra, per pair, 8 cents)...**60c**

No. 57E7083 Our Heavy Weight Ribbed Worsted Stockings, black, navy blue or maroon. Price, per pair.........(If by mail, postage extra, per pair, 8 cents)...........**90c**

Grain Leather Association Round Footballs.

No. 57E7085 The High School Association Football. Made of the best American tanned grain leather, hand sewed, canvas lined, rawhide lace, regulation size. Price, with bladder.....**$2.10**
If by mail, postage extra, 15 cents.

No. 57E7086 Association Football, made of good quality pebbled cowhide, canvas lined, raw hide lace and bladder. A very strong, well made ball, that retails at $2.00. Our price....(Postage extra, 15c.)......**$1.35**
For Football Bladders, see No. 57E6852.

The Victor Rugby Football, Oval Pattern.

No. 57E7087 The Victor Intercollegiate Official Rugby Football. Made of best imported grain leather, with all possible stretch removed, stitched with wax thread and has patent double laced opening. The highest grade football on the market, guaranteed; has lacing needle and pump. Price, with bladder...**$3.20**
If by mail, postage extra, 12 cents.

No. 57E7088 Rugby Football, made of the best quality selected American grain pebbled leather, lined with canvas, stitched on lock stitch machine, with waxed thread, furnished with rawhide lace, lacing needle and pure rubber bladder. An extra strong regulation size ball. Price.....(Postage extra, 18c.)....**$1.50**

No. 57E7089 Rugby Football, made of good quality pebbled cowhide, canvas lined, full size and well made. Rawhide lace and bladder. A very good strong ball for a little money, that looks like a $2.50 ball. Price...........**$1.15**
If by mail, postage extra, 12 cents.

No. 57E7090 Our Leader Rugby Football, made of good quality pebbled leather, well lined and well made, a genuine bargain for the boys. Will give them satisfaction.
Price, with bladder...................**75c**
If by mail, postage extra, 12 cents.
For Rugby Football Bladders, see No. 57E6851½.

Black Rubber Footballs.

American Round Rubber Footballs. These footballs are inflated through the key. When inflated turn key to right to close the valve.

No. 57E7092 Order by catalogue number and size number.

Size	Diameter	Weight	Price
No. 1	6-inch	6 ounces	32c
No. 2	7-inch	8 ounces	42c
No. 3	8-inch	10 ounces	47c
No. 4	9-inch	13 ounces	54c
No. 5	10-inch	15 ounces	64c
No. 6	11-inch	16 ounces	66c

If by mail, allow 1 cent per ounce.

No. 57E7093 Extra keys for football..**5c**
If by mail, postage extra, 1 cent.

Football and Striking Bag Inflaters.

No. 57E7094 Pocket Football and Striking Bag Inflaters, nickeled tubes, for pumping up bladders.
Price.......(Postage extra, 4 cents).....**15c**

Basket Balls.

No. 57E7095 Amateur Basket Ball, made of high grade pebbled leather, canvas lined and well made, cheapest basket ball on the market. Will give good service and worth much more than we ask for it.
Price, with bladder..**$1.45**
If by mail, postage extra, 20 cents.

No. 57E7096 Our Regulation Basket Ball, made of best quality American grain pebbled leather, best lining and stitched with waxed linen thread, furnished with rawhide laces and pure rubber bladder. A ball that will stand lots of hard service. Price...................**$2.70**
If by mail, postage extra, 28 cents.

No. 57E7097 Pure rubber bladders for basket balls. Price...................**50c**
If by mail, postage extra, 5 cents.

Basket Ball Goals.

No. 57E7098 Basket Ball Goals, regulation style, made of iron frame with cotton netting, Per pair...................**$2.75**

BASEBALL AND FOOTBALL JERSEYS.

No. 57E7099 Our All Wool Jersey, made of fine quality hard twisted worsted yarn, closely knitted, made to stand wear on the football field as well as for other athletic work; a perfect jersey with roll collar, made in three solid colors only, navy blue white or maroon. Give chest measure when ordering.
Price...................**$1.80**
If by mail, postage extra, 15c.
We can furnish these in stripes when ordered in lots of 9 or more, made to special order and shipped from our factory in the east at $1.00 each.

No. 57E7099½ Our Full Weight Cotton Jersey, same style as above, navy blue or maroon. Sizes, 32 to 40. Price...........**80c**
If by mail, postage extra, 14 cents.

FOOTBALL GOODS.

Football Jackets, Full Sleeves.

These jackets are made to order. Send cash with the order.

No. 57E7100 Made of white twilled drilling, laced front, well sewed, a good, strong jacket; give chest measure under arms. Price...**50c**
If by mail, postage extra, 12 cents.

No. 57E7102 Made of tan colored army khaki cloth, which is growing in favor as football material, because it is light and strong, made in laced front, reinforced with double seams; give chest measure under the arms. Price...........**73c**
If by mail, postage extra, 22 cents.
Send for free sample card of football suits.

Sleeveless Football Jackets.

No. 57E7107 Made of white twilled drilling, laced front, well sewed; a good strong jacket; give chest measurement under the arms. Price.....37c
If by mail, postage extra, 11 cents.

No. 57E7110 Made of tan colored army khaki cloth, which is the coming material for football clothing, made with laced front, double seam reinforced, well made and well finished; give chest measure under the arms. Price.........58c
If by mail, postage extra, 16 cents.

Superior Football Pants.

The knees and hips of all our pants are heavily padded and all have elastic bottoms.

No. 57E7116 Made of white twilled drilling, laced front, quilted, give waits measure.
Price, per pair.......58c

No. 57E7118 Made of sage green 8-ounce duck, laced front, cane reeds at thighs, large loose pads at hips and knees, well made; give waist measure.
Price, per pair $1.00

No. 57E7119 Made of tan colored army khaki cloth, made laced front, full padded and quilted at hips and knees, cane reeds at thighs, the latest thing in football pants; well made and well finished; give waist measure. Price, per pair.............$1.20
If by mail, postage extra, 28 to 36 cents.
Send for a sample card of football material.
For a complete line of football shoes, see our Shoe Department.

FOOTBALL SUNDRIES.

Rubber Nose Mask.

No. 57E7122 Made of finest rubber with detachable mouthpiece. Fastens around the head. Gives absolute protection to nose and teeth, and hangs by neck band when not in use.
Price.....75c
Extra mouthpiece. Each.....10c
If by mail, postage extra, 10 cents.

Head Helmet.

No. 57E7123 Our Regular Head Harness, specially intended to protect the head and ears; made of oil tanned horsehide, padding for ears of soft material and open in center, allowing same to entirely surround ear and rest on head without pressing ear or obstructing hearing.
Price.....$1.10
If by mail, postage extra, 10c.

Shin Guards.

Shin Guards. Made of lightweight canvas, padded and stiffened with rattan, very substantial, double stitched all around and quilted.
No. 57E7124 9 inches long, for boys. Price, per pair.....35c
No. 57E7125 12 inches long, for men. Price, per pair.....58c
If by mail, postage extra, 7 cents.

Indoor Baseball.

No. 57E7148 The Victor Official Indoor Baseball. 14 inches in circumference; weight, 11 ounces; best quality horsehide cover. The official ball. Price, 75c
If by mail, postage extra, 12 cents.
No. 57E7149 Regulation Indoor Baseball Bat, made from second growth hickory, with tape wound handle. Weight, about 25 ounces.
Price.....35c

ATHLETIC ELASTIC BANDAGES.

See our Drug Department.

Morton's Supporters.

No. 57E7139 Improved Morton Supporter. Made of canton flannel, lace-front. Give waist measure when ordering.
Price.....18c

Our Elastic Combination Jockey Strap Suspensory.

No. 57E7142 This Suspensory is made entirely of elastic, except the front piece, which is made of fine balbriggan. It is self adjusting and conforms to the body in any position, is never too loose or too tight. This is the most practical and by far the most comfortable supporter made. Can be washed in lukewarm water. When ordering, give waist measurement. Price.....45c
If by mail, postage extra, 6 cents.

Leather Wrist Supporter.

No. 57E7146 A perfect support and protection to the wrist. Invaluable to baseball, tennis and cricket players or in any game where the strain is on the wrist. In domestic grain leather, tan or black. Price, each.....16c
If by mail, postage extra, 2 cents.

The Hackey Ankle Supporter.

No. 57E7150 Hackey Supporter relieves pain immediately, cures a sprain in a short time and prevents turning of the ankle. Made of fine, soft calfskin and is worn over stocking, lacing very tight in center, loose at top and bottom. The shoe usually worn can be used. These supporters are not made in children's sizes. Mention size shoe you wear when ordering.
Price, per pair....65c
If by mail, postage extra, 3 cents.

FENCING FOILS.

Weight, 13 to 16 ounces each.

No. 57E7175 No. 1 Fencing Foils, with steel blades, iron mounted figure 8 guard, corded handle. Price, each.....58c
No. 57E7176 No. 2 Fencing Foils, with Solingen steel blades, iron mounted figure 8 guard, leather handles. Price, each.....86c
No. 57E7177 No. 3 Fencing Foils, best Solingen steel blades, 4-inch bell guard or hilt, leather wound handles. Price, each $1.40
If by mail, postage extra, 16 cents.

Fencing Mask.

No. 57E7178 Our Fencing Mask, Face and Ear Guards, made of finest quality wire, extra small mesh, the best mask made.
Price, each.....$1.05
If by mail, postage extra, 40 cents.

Fencing Glove.

No. 57E7179 Our Gauntlet Fencing Glove, made of fine quality buckskin, with red gauntlet, lined, made for either right or left hand. Unless otherwise specified, glove for right hand will be sent. Price, each.....75c
If by mail, postage extra, 5 cents.

Y. M. C. A. Trousers.

No. 57E7180 Our Regulation Y. M. C. A. Gymnasium Trousers are made of good quality gray color athletic flannel, with belt loops and elastic foot straps. The material and style of these pants is the same as is used in nearly all gymnasiums. Give measure of waist and inseam when ordering. Price, per pair...$1.20
If by mail, postage extra, 20 cents.

ATHLETIC AND THEATRICAL SUITS.

Full Sleeve Shirts.

No. 57E7190 Full Sleeve Fine Cotton Shirt, black or flesh color. Give chest measure.
Price.....50c
If by mail, postage extra, 10c.

Quarter Sleeve Shirts.

No. 57E7196 Quarter Sleeve Shirt. Medium quality worsted, solid colors, seamless, made in black or navy blue. Give chest measure when ordering.
Price.....$1.35
If by mail, postage extra, 12 cents.
No. 57E7197 Cotton Shirt, quarter sleeve, good quality. Made in solid colors of black or navy blue. Give chest measure when ordering. Price.....35c
If by mail, postage extra, 10 cents.

Full Length Theatrical Tights.

No. 57E7200 Full Length Tights, made of medium grade worsted, in solid colors of black or navy blue. Give waist and inseam measure when ordering.
Price, per pair.....$1.95
If by mail, postage extra, 10 cents.
No. 57E7201 Full Length Cotton Tights, in solid colors of black, navy or flesh color. Give waist and inseam measure when ordering. Price, per pair....80c
If by mail, postage extra, 8 cents.

Athletic Knee Tights.

No. 57E7203 Made of medium grade worsted in solid colors of black or navy blue. Give waist measure.
Price, per pair.....$1.25
No. 57E7204 Cotton Tights. Good quality cotton tights, made in solid colors of black or navy blue. Give waist measure. Price, per pair...30c
If by mail, postage extra, 6 to 10c.

Velvet Puff Theatrical Trunks.

No. 57E7206 Beautiful Velvet Puff Trunks, made of the finest velvet, full puff, either black, turquoise blue, navy blue, emerald green or maroon color, for theatrical or athletic exhibitions.
Price, per pair.....78c
If by mail, postage extra, per pair, 7 cents.

BATHING SUITS.

Our One-Piece Best Cotton Bathing Suit is made like a union suit (buttons over shoulder). Made in solid colors and fancy stripes, and ranging in size from 32 to 44 inches chest measure. When ordering give chest measure.

No. 57E7208 Cotton One-piece Suit, in solid color, black or navy blue; give chest measure.
Price.....65c
No. 57E7210 Cotton One-piece Suit, in fancy stripes, assorted patterns; give chest measure. Sizes, 34 to 46. Price....75c
If by mail, postage extra, 12 cents.

Two-Piece Bathing Suits.

GIVE CHEST AND WAIST MEASURE.

No. 57E7216 Two-Piece Cotton Bathing Suit, consisting of quarter sleeve shirt and knee pants, made in black or navy blue colors.
Price, per suit.....55c
No. 57E7217 Same in fancy stripes.
Price, per suit.....70c
No. 57E7218½ High grade worsted two-piece Bathing Suit, consisting of sleeveless shirt and trunks. Navy blue or black with fancy stripes around the bottom of the garments. Most up to date and best bargain on the market. If you wear a worsted suit, you will not experience that chill so disagreeable to bathers.
Price, per suit.....$2.25
If by mail, postage extra, 15 cents.

Our Swimming Trunks.

Our Cotton Swimming Trunks, made up in assorted designs of stripes, with draw string; assorted sizes for men or boys. When ordering, give waist measure.

No. 57E7219 Men's and Boys' Swimming Trunks. Give waist measure.
Price, per pair.....20c
If by mail, postage extra, 5 cents.

Capoc Swimming Jacket.

This jacket, as shown in the illustration is made in two parts, front and back. It is 9½ inches wide, length of each half about 25 inches. Weight about 2 pounds. It is hung over the shoulders with tapes, fastened round the body in such a manner as not to interfere with the free movement of the limbs. Can be instantly removed. Capoc is a vegetable wool and is very buoyant. These jackets are guaranteed to support any average person. Comes in two styles, for men, ladies and children.

No. 57E7225 For ladies and children. Price.....80c
No. 57E7226 For men. Price.....85c
If by mail, postage extra, 37 cents.

OUR LINE OF HAMMOCKS.

The strongest and handsomest hammocks made. Notice our spring pillow styles No. 57E7243, No. 57E7244 and No. 57E7245.

Our Hand Knitted Seine Twine Hammock, 95c.

This hammock is knitted by hand, of double seine twine, forming a 2-inch square mesh, and each hammock is made in white and one other neat attractive color. The edge on each side is chain braided, and interwoven into the meshes, making a strong, substantial and durable hammock, and with ordinary care will last a number of years. The entire hammock is about 13 feet long and the bed is about 7 feet long, and we furnish it without spreaders.

No. 57E7230 Our hand made double seine twine hammock. Price.....95c
If by mail, postage extra, 32 cents.

Our Hann's Patent Canvas Hammock.

The Hann Patented Hammock is the latest and most comfortable hammock yet produced. It is so constructed that by simply moving the arm rest from one place to another along the ropes, the hammock may be changed from one position to another instantly. By removing the arm rests the hammock may be used as a regular hammock, and by inserting the arm rests, as shown in the above illustration, the hammock has the effect of a reclining chair, and is an excellent thing for invalids as well as being one of the most comfortable hammocks on the market. All are made of striped canvas. Bed is 30 inches wide and 78 inches long, and weighs about 7½ pounds.

No. 57E7234 Made of striped canvas with spreader, pillow and valance. Price...$1.35
When hanging a hammock always hang it so that head will be higher than the foot.

Open Weave Cotton Hammock, 55 Cents.

No. 57E7235 Open Weave Cotton Hammock. Fine cotton weave, quarter color, with fancy colored stripes. Size of bed, 6 feet long, 3 feet wide. Strong and durable; fitted with good wood spreader; without pillow. A good hammock for children. Weight, 2 pounds.
Price.....55c

Cotton Weave Hammock with Pillow and Spreader, 85 Cents.

No. 57E7237 Cotton Hammock, with close woven body, of the best cotton weave, full fancy colors, with spreader and pillow. Size of bed, 6½ feet long, 3 feet wide. A hammock that sells regularly at $1.25 to $1.50. Weight, 3½ pounds.
Price, with fancy pillow and spreader. 85c

Canvas Weave Hammock with Pillow and Spreader, $1.00.

No. 57E7239 Hammock made of closest fancy canvas weave, in full fancy bright colors. Made with three-ply warps, with fancy colored pillow and spreader. A very strong hammock. Retail from $1.75 to $2.00. Size of bed, 6½ feet long, 3 feet wide. Wt., 3½ lbs. Price...$1.00

Special Value with Fringe Valance for $1.25.

No. 57E7241 Cotton Hammock, close excelsior weave, with short fancy fringe valance, full fancy bright colors, with pillow and spreader. Size of bed, 6½ feet long, 3 feet wide. A first class hammock in every respect. Sells regularly at $1.50 to $1.75. Weight, 4 pounds.
Price.....$1.25

Our Leader, $2.25 Value for $1.50.

No. 57E7242 Fine Canvas Weave Hammock, has deep woven valance with fringe, full fancy bright colors, with one spreader and one pillow. Size of bed, 6½ feet long, 3 feet wide. A beauty for the money. Weight, about 5 pounds. Price.....$1.50

This illustration shows the Torsion Braided Wire Pillow used on the following three styles of hammocks, No. 57E7243, No. 57E7244 and No. 57E7245. This pillow is undoubtedly the greatest improvement on hammocks within the past five years. It is entirely free from the heat and stuffiness of the ordinary pillow, self-ventilating, very soft and comfortable and accommodates itself to every movement of the head. It will always retain its shape and elasticity and will not rust. Other manufacturers charge from 50 cents to $1.00 more for a pillow of this kind. We are furnishing the following three numbers of hammocks fitted with our spring pillow for less money than other dealers charge for the same quality of hammock with the ordinary stuffed pillow.

Our Damask Weave Spring Pillow Hammock $1.90.

No. 57E7243 Our Big Leader Hammock, made in figured fancy weave, damask pattern, full fancy fluted valance, with fringe and scroll pattern. One strong spreader at head, with fancy patent spring pillow, also one short wood spreader at the foot. Size of bed, 40x80 inches. One of the most beautiful hammocks ever placed on the market. Strong and durable, and one which generally sells at retail for $3.00. Weight, 6½ pounds. Price...$1.90

Our Old Gold Pattern Spring Pillow Hammock $2.45.

No. 57E7244 Our Large Size, Torsion Spring Pillow Hammock. This hammock is made in full fancy colors, strong spreader and full size spring pillow at one end with extra wood bar at the foot. Full deep valance at the sides. Size of bed, 40x80 inches. Made of heavy three-ply warp, color of old gold effect, and we consider this one of the best bargains which we offer in hammocks. Weight, 10 lbs.
Price, for this full size hammock....$2.45

Our Highest Quality Spring Pillow Hammock, $2.75.

No. 57E7245 Hammock, extra heavy fancy close canvas weave, fine fancy bright colors, in contrasting designs, extra deep fluted valance with fancy extra large patent spring pillow, heavy strong spreader. One short wood bar at the foot. Size of bed, 46x88 inches. This is a large size hammock, strong, durable and very showy. Weight, 9 pounds. Price $2.75

Hammock Hooks.

No. 57E7266 Screw Hammock Hooks, tinned, 7-16 inch diameter, screw in. Price, each ......5c Postage extra, 3c.

No. 57E7267 Plate Hammock Hooks, tinned, 7-16 inch in diameter to fasten with screws. Price, each 6c

No. 57E7266

No. 57E7267 If by mail, postage extra, 3 cents.

Lawn Swings, $3.25 and $4.00.

For Children and Adults.

This is the best Lawn Swing on the market. It is made of hard pine and gum wood, with connections well bolted and well braced, painted in red color, and after they are started the swinging is continued by pressing the feet on the footboard. It is great fun for the children, and adults will find them very comfortable. These swings are shipped from factory in Illinois and cannot be sent with other goods. Not sent C. O. D.

No. 57E7271 Adults' size, about 8½ feet high. The seat is 20 inches wide, which is wider than the ordinary chair, and will hold two grown persons or four children. Weight, about 100 pounds. Shipped from our factory and cannot be sent with other goods. Price.....$3.25

No. 57E7272 Large size, 8½ feet high, seat 33 inches wide, large enough to seat four adults or six children. Weight, about 140 pounds. Shipped from our factory and cannot be sent with other goods. Price $4.00

Our Acme Folding Lawn or Porch Settee, 83 Cents.

No. 57E7274 For 83 cents we offer you our Acme Lawn Settee, made of selected wood, painted in a bright attractive color, the seat is in natural wood finish. Unlike other settees, the slats are not nailed but are screwed to the frame. This lawn settee is made so it may be folded up and set away during the winter or it may be left on a porch, as desired. The Acme lawn settee is a very useful and desirable article and will recommend itself to our customers; in fact, it requires no care or attention and saves many times its value in the wear and tear of regular household furniture. Our Acme lawn settee, 3½ feet long, painted. Weight, 20 pounds. Price 83c

The Chicago Folding Porch Chair, 80 Cents.

No. 57E7278 The Chicago Folding Porch Chair. Made of wood frame with denim body. All joints riveted and may be folded when not in use. Weighs about 10½ pounds and the back may be adjusted to various angles for comfort. All have arm rests and high back, are easily carried about and save the household furniture. Price 80c

Hammock Ropes.

No. 57E7282 Hammock Ropes, 6½ feet long, adjustable anchor fastening that remains where you place it; no knots to tie after attached to hammock, no slipping in hammock. Hammock can be raised and lowered in an instant. Price, per pair, 15c; each..........8c If by mail, postage extra, each, 8 cents.

Metal Telescope Collapsing Cup.

Our Fine Metal Collapsing Cup. It can be folded into a very small space and carried in vest pocket. Neat and substantial, nicely nickel plated and the body fits into the cover. Large size about size of an ordinary tumbler.

No. 57E7286 Medium size. Price. 17c

No. 57E7287 Large size, aluminum; satin finish. Price..........25c

If by mail, postage extra, 3 to 5 cents.

Rubber Drinking Cups.

No. 57E7290 Soft, White Rubber Drinking Cup, tumbler shape, will hold about as much as a common table tumbler. Flexible, and can be folded and put in a vest pocket. Price..........13c

If by mail, postage extra, 8 cents.

FISHING TACKLE DEPARTMENT.

By referring to the following pages you will find a most complete line of highest quality fishing tackle of great variety. We have been very careful to uphold the standard of quality in this line and our rods, lines, baits, etc., quality considered, are the best values ever offered. Our lancewood and bamboo rods are not imitations, but are genuine. They are not wrapped with cotton, but are wrapped with silk. Our reels, lines and baits are made of the best material and finished in the most high grade manner. We call attention to the exceedingly low prices we are making on steel fish rods.

JAPANESE RODS.

We are offering our customers this season a line of Japanese jointed rods which we believe are better value than you can get from any other house in the United States, quality considered. We have endeavored to get most of this line of Japanese rods all fitted with solid reel seat and zylonite butt, which makes a very attractive and expensive looking rod, and by placing a large contract for these goods, we were able to get the cost of manufacture down to the lowest point, and by adding our one small percentage of profit we are able to give you such value as we believe you cannot get anywhere else in the United States.

Japanese Two-Piece Rod, 7½ to 8½ Feet, 12 Cents.

No. 57E8597 Japanese Two-Piece Bamboo Rod. Natural color, double telescope ferrules, ringed guides for line. Length, about 7½ to 8½ feet. Price.... (Postage extra 8 cents).....12c

Japanese Two-Piece Rod with Zylonite Butt, 7 to 8 Feet, 45c.

No. 57E8600 Japanese Two-Piece Rod, about 7½ feet long. Made of genuine Japanese cane fitted with nickel telescope ferrules, solid reel seat above the grip, black zylonite butt, line guides for line. The best rod on the market for the money. Weight, about 12 ounces. Price .... (If by mail, postage extra, 14 cents)..........45c

Japanese Three-Piece Rod with Zylonite Butt, 8½ to 9 Ft., 58c.

No. 57E8602 Japanese Three-Piece Rod, about 8½ to 9 feet long, made of genuine Japanese cane, nickel plated telescope ferrules, solid reel seat above the grip, black zylonite butt, line guides for the line. The best 3-piece rod on the market for the money. Weight, about 13 ounces. Price .... (If by mail, postage extra, 15 cents)..........58c

Japanese Four-Piece Rod, with Zylonite Butt, about 14 Ft. 85c.

No. 57E8603 Japanese Four-Piece Rod, about 14 feet long, made of genuine Japanese cane, fitted with nickel plated telescope ferrules, solid reel seat above the grip, black zylonite butt, line guides for line. The best long rod on the market for the money. Weight, about 24 ounces. A good rod to fish from the shore. Price .... (If by mail, postage extra, 26 cents)..........85c

Japanese Mottled Three-Piece Casting Rod.

No. 57E8605 Our Japanese Three-Piece Bamboo Casting Rod is a handsome mottled rod, fitted with large Kalamazoo ring guides, full nickel mounted throughout, with solid nickel plated reel seat and finger hook and cord wound grip. This rod is silk wrapped between the guides, which greatly strengthens the rod and adds to its appearance. Three joints, each 24 inches long, total length, 6 feet. Put up in neat partitioned cloth bag. Weight, about 10 ounces. Price, each..........95c

Calcutta Four-Piece Trunk Rod, About 8 Feet, 75 Cents.

No. 57E8606 Calcutta Four-Piece Trunk Rod. 7½ to 8 feet long. Made of genuine mottled Calcutta cane, nickel plated telescope ferrules, strong line guides for line, solid reel seat above the grip, zylonite butt, nickel plated trimmings. Each piece is 24 inches long, so it may be carried in a trunk or grip. Weight, 8 ounces. Price....(Postage extra, 12 cents)....75c

Calcutta Four-Piece Splashing Rod, 12 to 16 Feet, 85 Cents.

No. 57E8607 Calcutta Four-Piece Bamboo Rod, double telescope ferrules, ringed for line, with butt cap and reel bands. An excellent rod for splashing or spatting or trolling among the weeds and lily pads. Length, 12 to 16 feet. Weight, about 3 pounds. Price..........85c

LANCEWOOD RODS.

There are about thirty to fifty styles of Lancewood rods manufactured by the various makers, and each style necessitates a change in equipment, machinery, etc., and by reducing the number of styles of our lancewood rods, we are able to save the expense of these changes, which expense is necessarily added to the rods when so many styles are handled by one house. We have decided to reduce the number of styles of lancewood rods in order to handle a few.

St. Croix River Lancewood Fly Rod, 10 to 10½ Feet, 82 Cents.

No. 57E8616 Our St. Croix River Lancewood Fly Rod, made in three pieces, with an extra tip, genuine lancewood throughout, nickeled mountings and raised telescope ferrules. Silk wound tie guides and silk whippings at each mounting. Solid reel seat below hand. Zylonite corrugated grip. Length, about 10 to 10½ feet. Put up in neat partitioned cloth bag. Weight, about 9 ounces. A fine looking rod. Price..........82c If by mail, postage extra, 12 cents.

GENUINE LANCEWOOD BAIT CASTING ROD FOR 75 CENTS.

No. 57E8621 Owing to a contract we placed early in the season we are able to furnish a genuine lancewood Bait Casting Rod, 8 to 9 feet in length, for 75 cents. This rod is made of genuine lancewood, 3 joints, with extra tip, has double shouldered nickel plated telescope ferrules, select silk wound round wire tie guides, which are guaranteed not to cut the lines, is nicely wrapped with silk, solid nickel plated reel seat above handsome corrugated zylonite grip. Weight, about 9 ounces. This rod is put up in a neat, partitioned cloth bag, is a fine looking rod, very strong and pliable, a regular $1.50 to $2.00 rod. Our price..........(If by mail, postage extra, 18 cents)..........75c

Agate Tip fitted to this rod, 65 cents extra; Agate Guide fitted to this rod, 65 cents extra; Agate Tip and Guide, $1.20 extra over the stated price of the rod.

Eight in One Combination Lancewood Rod, $2.85.

No. 57E8623 The best combination rod on the market. You can make eight different rods of this rod, can place the reel seat above or below the handle, and with the aid of the shortener carried in the butt of rod make a short, medium or long bait casting rod or a fly rod, as desired. The rod can be shortened when in use without taking the line from the entire rod by drawing the line to the side of the guides, which are open for that purpose. Made of the best grade lancewood, solid nickel reel seat, nickel mounted throughout, fitted with frictionless guides, beautifully wrapped at close intersections with silk. Comes put up four joints and extra fly tip making five joints in all, with detachable cord wound grip, in a neat partitioned cloth bag. Price..........$2.85 If by mail, postage extra, 19 cents.

OUR SPLIT BAMBOO RODS.

This illustration will give you as near as it is possible an idea of how a split bamboo rod is made. At first the bamboo cane is split in a sort of triangle shape, as shown in illustration, and glued together, forming a hexagonal shape. This is where the rod derives its name—Split Bamboo—(the bamboo is split and glued together).

Our Western Expert Split Bamboo Bass Rod 5½ Feet $2.00.

No. 57E8629 This rod was designed by us to meet the large demand for a high grade short length bait casting rod, and is one that is generally sold for from $4.00 to $5.00. This rod is original with us. It was made in exact accordance with the specifications furnished by us, made by a manufacturer who has been in business for years and whose rods ordinarily sell for very fancy prices. This rod is made of special selected clear straight grain, hand split bamboo, the joints are beautifully tapered and balanced, giving this rod just the right amount of life and elasticity which has always been so hard to obtain in a cheap rod. It is handsomely and closely wrapped with alternate wrappings of black and red silk, is fitted with German silver anti-friction trumpet guides, double hole funnel tip, handsome solid nickel plated reel seat with nickel plated finger hook, corrugated black and white celluloid grip, nickel plated butt cap, heavy welded shouldered ferrules, shouldered dowels, put up three joints and an extra tip on a flannel covered wood form, incased in a flannel bag; a rod that will please the expert at a price fully $2.00 less than it could possibly be duplicated for elsewhere. Weight, 5½ ounces. Length, 5½ feet. Price..........$2.00 If by mail, postage extra, 20 cents.

Agate tip fitted to this rod, 65 cents extra; agate guide fitted to this rod, 65 cents extra; agate guide and tip fitted to this rod, $1.20 extra over stated price of the rod.

Our Climax Split Bamboo Bass Rod, 8 to 9 Feet, 75 Cents.

No. 57E8630 Solid reel seat above the hand. This rod is one that we are making a run on at an exceedingly low price and are positive the rod cannot be duplicated for twice the amount anywhere in the country. Split and glued bamboo bass rods, nickel plated telescope ferrules, silk wound line guides, with alternate wrappings, nickeled mountings, three pieces, with an extra tip. Put up on a wooden form in a cloth bag. About 8 to 9 feet long. Weight, about 11 ounces. Price..........(If by mail, postage extra, 20 cents)..........75c

Agate tip; fitted to this rod, 65 cents extra; agate guide fitted to this rod, 65 cents extra; agate tip and guide fitted to this rod, $1.20 extra over the stated price of the rod.

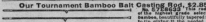

Our Tournament Bamboo Bait Casting Rod, $2.85.

No. 57E8633 This rod is made of the highest grade selected split bamboo, beautifully tapered from grip to tip, giving it the needed elasticity for accurate and distance bait casting. It is beautifully wrapped with two colors of silk, the wrappings are very closely clustered, presenting a most handsome appearance. The rod is full nickel mounted, shouldered welded ferrules, reel seat is fitted with a finger pull. Rod is fitted with a double mottled cord wound grip, large two-ring Kalamazoo guides. Comes three joints and extra tip. 5 feet long. Weighs 6 ounces. Put up in partitioned flannel bag. This same rod sells for $5.00 or $6.00 all over the country, and at our price of $2.85 is the best value ever offered in a split bamboo bait casting rod. Price $2.85
If by mail, postage extra, 16 cents.

Our Acme Split Bamboo Fly Rod, 9½ to 10 Feet, 82 Cents.

No. 57E8634 Solid reel seat below the hand. This rod is the same quality as our Climax, except that the reel seat is below the hand for trout and light fishing. Has silk wound ring guides, with wrappings of fine silk every few inches; solid reel seat and nickel plated telescope ferrules and mountings. Length, about 9½ to 10 feet. Weight, about 11 ounces. **Worth $1.75 anywhere. Comes in three pieces with an extra tip on a wood form and in a cloth bag.** Price....................................82c
If by mail, postage extra, 19 cents.

Our Special Wilowemock Split Bamboo Fly Rod, 9½ to 10 Feet, $1.50.

No. 57E8641 Solid reel seat below the hand. This rod is made of special selected bamboo, hexagonal in shape, with close wrappings of colored silk, full nickel plated telescope ferrules and mountings, cork grasp. Put up in three pieces with an extra tip on a fine covered wood form and in a neat bag. Length, about 9½ to 10 feet. A rod that retails at $3.00 in stores. Weight, 6 ounces. Price.................(If by mail, postage extra, 18 cents.)..........$1.50

Sunday Pocket Fly Rod, $2.85.

No. 57E8645 This is an ideal rod for the man that wants a rod he can carry in his pocket or in a small grip. The joints of this rod are but 13 inches long, made of select split bamboo, closely wound with two colors of silk, fitted with improved snake guides, welded ferrules, nickel plated reel seat, below the cork grip. With the heavy tip you can make a short six-piece rod, 6 feet long, by placing the heavy tip in the fifth joint. By using the light tip you can make a seven-piece rod, 7 feet long. This is a high grade rod in every respect, and while the joints are short they do not in any way injure the life and spring of the rod. The rod has as much life as any rod with joints twice as long. Put up in neat partitioned cloth bag. Price....................................$2.85
If by mail, postage extra, 10 cents.

Our High Grade Split Bamboo Fly Rod, 9 to 10 Feet Long, $3.15.

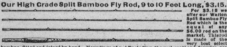

For $3.15 we offer our Walton Split Bamboo Fly Rod which is the equal of any $6.00 rod on the market. This rod is made of the very best select bamboo, fitted and joined by hand. Mountings of rod, including the reel seat and ferrules, are **solid German silver.** To add strength and beauty to the rod it is fitted with an extra inlaying of cedar at the butt; wrappings are of silk and are beautifully clustered at close intervals. Fitted with improved snake guides and cork grip. Put up three joints and an extra tip on a handsome covered wood form in a flannel bag. Each joint is about 36 inches long and rod weighs about 7 ounces. This is the liveliest, handsomest and strongest fly rod ever offered at anything like the price.
No. 57E8668 Our Walton Split Bamboo Fly Rod. Price....................................$3.15
If by mail, postage extra, 17 cents.

STEEL FISHING RODS.

Manufactured by the Horton Manufacturing Co., of Bristol, Conn.

Note the exceptionally low prices we are making on our line of steel rods. These are excellent rods in every respect and we guarantee each and every one to give satisfaction. **We guarantee them for one year against breakage caused by defective material or workmanship.** This guarantee, however, does not apply when the rods are broken through careless handling. If the joints go together rather tightly, do not file the ferrule but put a drop of oil, a bit of graphite or soap on the ferrule and the joints will go together very easily.

Our High Grade 10-Foot Jointed Steel Fly Rod, $2.35.

No. 57E8675 Steel Fly Rod, 10 feet long, full nickel mounted, with solid reel seat below the hand. This rod is jointed and fitted with two-ring German silver tie guide and one-ring German silver fly tip. Is made with three pieces and handle; each joint being 38 inches long. **Does not telescope.** Weight, 9½ ounces. With cork grip. Price....................................$2.35
If by mail, postage extra, 13 cents.

Genuine Henshall 8½-Foot Steel Bass Rod, $2.25.

No. 57E8677 Full nickel mounted with solid reel seat above the hand. This rod is jointed and fitted with two-ring German silver tie guides and German silver three-ring tip. Is made with three pieces and handle: each joint being 32 inches long. **Does not telescope. This rod is the best bass or pickerel rod made.** Weight, 10 ounces. With cork handle. Price....................................$2.25
If by mail, postage extra, 15 cents.

The Expert 6½-Foot Steel Bass Rod, $2.32.

No. 57E8681 The Expert Steel Bait Casting Rod, 6½ feet long, full nickel mounted, with solid reel seat above the hand. This rod is jointed and fitted with two-ring German silver tie guides and German silver three-ring tip. It is made with three pieces and handle; the joints are 24 inches long. This is a fine rod for long casts and for heavy work. **Does not telescope, but is jointed.** Weight, 8¾ ounces. With cork grip. Price....................................$2.32
If by mail, postage extra, 13 cents.

The Kalamazoo Steel Bait Casting Rod $2.95.

No. 57E8686 This rod has a short cork grip, large polished German silver two-ring guides, and solid agate double hole tip. The reel seat is so arranged that the reel is brought close to the grip, which enables the fisherman to thumb the reel without tiring his hand. The free running qualities of the large guides and tip are such that a novice can cast from 75 to 100 feet after a few trials. Length, 5 feet. Weight, 8¾ ounces. Price....................................$2.95

No. 57E8689 The Champion Steel Bait Casting Rod, 5½ feet long with agate tip and one agate guide, which saves the wear on the line, the other guides are German silver, trumpet style. This rod is intended for those who prefer a short rod, which is rapidly becoming more and more popular, being more readily handled and not so severe on the wrist. This rod does not telescope, but is jointed and fitted with cork handle. Weight, 8¾ ounces. Price....................................$3.65
If by mail, postage extra, 13 cents.

Emergency Tip.

No. 57E8690 Emergency Tip, to be used with Bristol steel fishing rods only. In case of accident to the regular tip joint or in place of the tip joint, to make a very stiff trolling rod. Can be carried in the vest pocket. About 2½ inches long. Every owner of a Bristol rod should have one. Price....................................18c
If by mail, postage extra, 2 cents.

Steel Rod Shortener.

No. 57E8695 Our Steel Rod Shortener. This shortener fits in the grip of jointed steel rods and in doing so takes only the two smallest joints, leaving out the joint which fits in the grip. With this shortener you can make an 8½-foot rod 6 feet long. Price..........(If by mail, postage extra, 2 cents)..........24c

Our Apollo Steel Boats.

The best boats made for shooting, fishing or pleasure. These boats are made of steel; wooden boats are obsolete. All modern battleships and steamers, even sail boats are made with steel hulls. One of our steel boats will outlast six ordinary wood boats. With heavy loads in collision with stumps and rocks, these boats will hardly show a scratch where wooden boats would be stove in. Furthermore our boats are **non-sinkable.** They **do not leak, do not expand or contract and are non-rustable,** being made of galvanized steel painted with silver pegamoid, a preparation with which our steel navy is painted. **Our steel boat being properly constructed will slide through the water with ⅛ less friction than a wood boat of the same dimensions,** has 50 per cent more buoyancy and will last forever. These boats have light draft, are suitable for shallow water, are not as easily capsized as wooden boats and **if capsized the air chambers will enable it to float all passengers even though the boat is filled with water.** We have three styles of this boat, one Clinker style, which is built with a keel, one flat bottom boat and a duck boat. **Not sent C. O. D.**

No. 57E8700 Our Apollo Clinker Boat is the most graceful boat on the market. It is especially designed to meet the requirements of either high class livery or family use where a strong, reliable boat of great carrying capacity and small dimensions is required. Length, 14 feet; width amidship, 45½ inches; depth amidship, 14 inches; height of bow, 22 inches; height of stern, 24 inches; distance between ribs, 4 inches. Has air chambers at each end which cause great buoyancy and assure absolute safety. Weight, 150 pounds. Crated about 175 pounds. Price of boat in natural wood finish, including one pair of ash oars and oar locks....................................$26.00

No. 57E8702 Our Flat Bottom Apollo Steel Boat is an ideal boat for hunting or fishing, has an extra heavy steel bottom, with three oak strips running full length, one in center, one on each side to protect boat from rocks and rough usage. Length, 12 feet, width amidship, 41½ inches; depth amidship, 12 inches; height of bow, 15 inches; height of stern, 15 inches. Fitted with three seats; distance between ribs, 5 inches. Weight, about 100 pounds; crated, about 135 pounds. Price of boat in natural wood finish, including one pair of 6½-foot ash oars fitted with oar locks....................................$21.00

Our Winner Duck Boat.

No. 57E8705 Our Winner Duck Boat is without question the best duck boat on the market. It is superior in strength, speed, construction, material and buoyancy to any duck boat made, regardless of price. This boat is 12 feet long, 44 inches wide amidship; cockpit is 5½ feet long, 28 inches wide and 12 inches deep. The hull of this boat is made of steel, same as the boats above described. The deck is made of thin spruce, covered with heavy weight waterproof canvas. **Boat has air chambers at each end,** and has a lighter draft than any duck boat on the market, barring none. This boat weighs but 100 pounds, so that a man can easily pick it up and carry it. Weighs, crated, about 175 pounds. Comes complete with copper tipped paddle and push pole. This boat is not fitted with oars and oarlocks, as it has been found that a boat of this kind can be handled far more advantageously with a paddle. Price, including copper tipped paddle....................................$24.00
These boats are shipped from the factory at Detroit, Mich., and take four times first class rate.

The Comfort Boat Seat Back Rest.

This back rest was invented by a fisherman who experienced the uncomfortable sensation of sitting in a boat for several hours without any support to his back. Adjustable to any boat seat, instantly attached without any tools, nails or screws, and as quickly detached. This back rest is made of canvas attached to two wood posts ⅞ inch in diameter, which are set in malleable iron sockets to which two steel hooks are hinged, by means of which hooks the rest is attached to the boat seat. When in position this back rest is 17 inches high and 13 inches wide. Folds up in a small space, 18 inches long and 7 inches in circumference. Weight, 2 pounds. Not only good for fishermen, but women and children find it very comfortable. When folded can be packed in most any grip or suit case.

Folded.

No. 57E8709 Price, each..........(If by mail, postage extra, 33 cents)..........60c

WHITE ASH OARS.

One pair or 6½-foot oars weigh about 6 pounds and one pair of 8½-foot oars weigh about 13 pounds. **All our oars are first quality.**

Plain Ash Oars.

No. 57E8710 Length given is length of each oar.

Length...	6 ft.	6½ ft.	7 ft.	7½ ft.	8 ft.	8½ ft.
Price, pr.	88c	93c	$1.00	$1.08	$1.17	$1.24

Copper Tipped Ash Oars.

No. 57E8711 Length given is length of each oar.

Length	6 ft.	6½ ft.	7 ft.	7½ ft.	8 ft.	8½ ft.
Pair...	97c	$1.04	$1.10	$1.20	$1.25	$1.34

Spruce Paddles.

No. 57E8712 Single, straight grained, first quality Spruce Paddle. None better made. Price, each....................................$1.30

Copper Tipped Spruce Oars.

No. 57E8713 Genuine Adirondack Spruce Oars. Lighter than ash oars and strong, copper tipped.

Length	6-foot	7-foot
Price, per pair	$1.05	$1.25

Oar Locks.

No. 57E8714 North River Oar Lock, galvanized, malleable iron, 3 inches between horns. Weight, per pair, about 2 pounds. Price, per pair....................................20c

No. 57E8715 Socket Oar Locks, malleable iron. Weight, per pair, 2 pounds. Width, 2 inches between horns. Price, per pair....................................18c

No. 57E8717 Safety Side Plate Oar Locks. Impossible to pull horn out of socket accidentally. Made of malleable iron. Weight, per pair, 2½ pounds. Price, per pair...35c

Universal Bow Facing Oar Locks.

No. 57E8718 Do not row backwards because your grandfather did. Buy a pair of Universal Oar Locks and face the way you are rowing. This oar lock is very simple, made of malleable iron, contains but few parts and can be easily attached to a boat by most anyone. Weight, per pair, 8 pounds. Price, per pair....................................$2.00

Life Preservers.

No. 57E8719 Never Sink Solid Cork Jackets. Adopted as standard and the government inspector's stamp on each one; easily put on, durable and has great buoyancy. Weight, 8 lbs. Price....$1.40

No. 57E8720 Life Belts, made of square blocks of cork around the body. One of the best in the market; safe and durable. Weight, 8 lbs. Price....$1.15

Notice—We do not use granulated cork in our life preservers—we use solid block cork only.

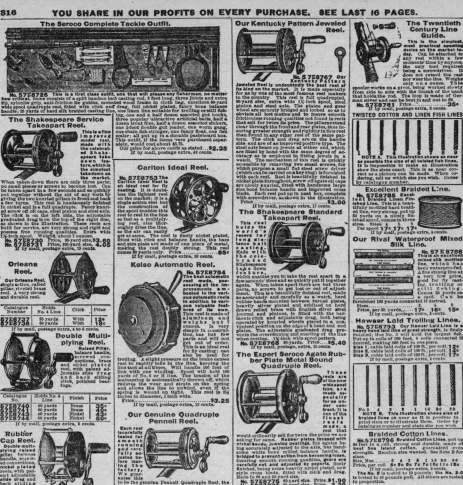

The Seroco Complete Tackle Outfit.

No. 57E8726 This is a first class outfit, one that will please any fisherman, no matter how critical. Same consists of a split bamboo bait casting rod, 8 feet long, three joints and extra tip, zylonite grip, anti-friction tie guides, mounted wood frame in cloth bag, excellent 60-yard wide spool quadruple reel, fitted with click and drag, full nickel plated, fancy bone balance handle; 25 yards of hard silk braided casting line, one linen line suitable for trolling or still fishing, one and a half dozen assorted gut hooks, three popular attractive artificial baits, half a dozen trout flies, half a dozen assorted sinkers, one 3-foot double gut leader, one worm gang, one chain fish stringer, one fancy float, one fish scaler; all put up in a durable pasteboard box. This outfit, if the items were purchased separately, would cost about $3.75.

Our price for above outfit as stated... **$2.35**
If by mail, postage extra, 42 cents.

The Shakespeare Service Takeapart Reel.

This is a fine improved model reel, made with the celebrated Shakespeare take down feature, which is the simplest takedown on the market. When taken down there are only three parts; no small pieces or screws to become lost. Can be taken apart in a few seconds and as quickly put together without the aid of any tools by giving the two knurled pillars in front and back a few turns. This reel is handsomely finished in nickel and is a full quadruple. Fancy knurled screw off oil caps, steel pinion and steel axle. The click is on the left side, the adjustable graduated drag is on the top of the right disc, as shown in the illustration. These reels are built for service, are very strong and rigid and possess free running qualities. Extra wide 1⅛-inch spool. Weight, about 7 ounces.

No. 57E8730 Price, 80-yard size, **$3.60**
No. 57E8731 Price, 100-yard size, **4.05**
If by mail, postage extra, 15 cents.

Orleans Reel.

Our Orleans Reel, single action, raised pillar, riveted brass reel. A very strong and durable reel.

Catalogue Number	Holds No. 4 Line	Click	Price
57E8737	25 yards	With	12c
57E8738	60 yards	With	18c

If by mail, postage extra, 4 to 6 cents.

Double Multiplying Reel.

Raised Pillar, balance handle, screwed connections, brass and nickel plated reel, with patent adjustable slide drag and back sliding click, polished bearings.

Catalogue No.	Holds No. 4 Line	Finish	Price
57E8740	40 yards	Brass	35c
57E8741	60 yards	Brass	40c
57E8743	40 yards	Nickel	43c
57E8744	60 yards	Nickel	50c

If by mail, postage extra, 9 cents.

Rubber Cap Reel.

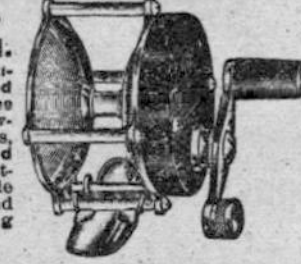

Double multiplying raised pillar, balance handle, screwed connections, **nickel plated** reels, with patent adjustable **slide drag and back sliding click.**

Catalogue No.	Holds No. 4 Line	Price
57E8746	40 yards	55c
57E8747	60 yards	60c
57E8748	80 yards	70c

If by mail, postage extra, 9 cents.

Our Ideal Quadruple Reel.

The best low price Quadruple Reel on the market, has round disc, wide spool, balance handle, screw off oil cap, the oil cap, disc, handle and post are milled, giving it a handsome appearance; is fitted with steel axle and steel pinion, also fitted with click and drag, making it a very durable, handsome reel; each reel is carefully examined, guaranteed to run absolutely true.

Catalogue No.	Holds No. 4 Line	Price
57E8750	40 yards	$0.95
57E8751	60 yards	1.10
57E8752	80 yards	1.20

If by mail, postage extra, 14 cents.

Carlton Ideal Reel.

No. 57E8753 The Carlton Ideal Reel is an ideal reel for fly casting. It is doubtless the lightest reel on the market; it is a single action reel but the construction of the spool enables this reel to reel in the line as fast as a multiplying reel, also thoroughly dries the line, as the air can easily get at same. The reel is finely nickel plated, fitted with click and balance handle, the base and side plate are made of one piece of metal, making the reel doubly strong. This reel comes 80 yards only. Price... **85c**
If by mail, postage extra, 10 cents.

Kelso Automatic Reel.

No. 57E8754 The best automatic reel made, possessing all the improvements embodied in the various automatic reels in addition to various valuable features of its own. This reel is made of aluminum and weighs but 7 ounces. Is very simple in construction, has but few parts and will not get out of order. This is an ideal reel for fly casting; can also be used for trolling. A slight pressure on the brake causes reel to rapidly take in the line, keeping the line taut at all times. Will handle 100 feet of line with one winding. Spool will hold 100 yards of No. 6 or H line. The tension of the mainspring is automatically thrown off, which relieves the wear and strain on the spring and allows the line to unwind, even if the spring is wound up tight. This reel is 3½ inches in diameter, 1 inch wide.
Price... **$3.25**
If by mail, postage extra, 12 cents.

Our Genuine Quadruple Pennell Reel.

Each reel is carefully tested for smooth running and carefully adjusted before leaving the factory. We guarantee this to be the genuine Pennell Quadruple Reel, the best reel for bass fishing or trolling. **Our Quadruple Pennell Round Disc Reel** is fitted with adjustable sliding click and drag, steel pivots, bridge over gear made of the best material possible, handsomely nickeled, fancy bone balance handle.

Catalogue No.	Holds No. 4 Line	Price
57E8755	40 yards	$1.65
57E8756	60 yards	1.90
57E8757	80 yards	2.00

If by mail, postage extra, 15 cents.

Shakespeare Universal Quadruple Reel.

A low priced reel made in a high grade manner. This reel is full quadruple, is of the wide spool pattern, full nickel plated, fitted with strong click, steel pivot, bridge over cogs, fitted with fancy bone balance handle, every reel stamped with the maker's name.

No. 57E8764 40 yards. Price... **$0.75**
No. 57E8765 60 yards. Price... **.90**
No. 57E8766 80 yards. Price... **1.00**
If by mail, postage extra, 12 cents.

Our Kentucky Pattern Jeweled Reel.

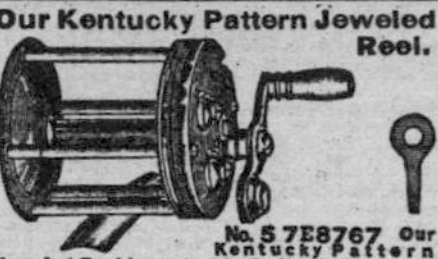

No. 57E8767 Our Kentucky Pattern Jeweled Reel is undoubtedly the best reel of its kind on the market. It is made especially for us by one of the most famous reel makers in the country. This reel is full quadrupled, 80-yard size, extra wide 1⅛-inch spool, steel pinion and steel axle. The pinion and gear wheel are securely bridged and locked so as to obviate all lost motion and to insure smooth frictionless running qualities not found in reels that sell for twice its price. The pillars extend clear through the front and rear plates, thus insuring greater strength and rigidity in this reel than found in any other reel of the same pattern. The click and drag are on the handle side and are of an improved positive type. The steel axle bears on jewels at either end, which are fitted by hand with the same degree of accuracy as is employed in fitting jewels in a watch. The mechanism of this reel is quickly accessible by removing two small screws, for which purpose a small flat steel screw driver (which can be carried on a key ring) is furnished with each reel. Reel is beautifully finished in nickel plate throughout, screw off agate oil caps are nicely knurled, fitted with handsome large size bone balance handle and improved cross blade. Each reel put up in neat box, complete with screwdriver, as shown in the illustration.
Price... **$3.00**
If by mail, postage extra, 17 cents.

The Shakespeare Standard Takeapart Reel.

This reel holds the world's record for long distance bait casting. Made with the celebrated Shakespeare take down feature, which enables you to take the reel apart in a few seconds' time and as quickly put it together again. When taken apart there are but three parts, no screws to get lost or out of adjustment. This is a beautifully finished reel, made as accurately and carefully as a watch, hard rubber heads mounted between turned plates, heavily silver plated and oxidized on hard drawn rolled brass with English silver steel journal and pinions, is fitted with the harmonic click and adjustable drag, both being operated by knurled wheels placed in a convenient position on the edge of a head and end plates. The adjustable graduated drag prevents the overrunning and snarling of the line when casting. 1⅛-inch wide spool pattern.
No. 57E8768 80-yards. Price... **$5.40**
If by mail, postage, extra, 15 cents.

The Expert Seroco Agate Rubber Plate Metal Bound Quadruple Reel.

These reels are of the new wide spool type, are made especially for us under contract. It is one of the finest reels made, a reel that would ordinarily sell for twice the price we are asking for same. **Rubber plates incased with nickel bands, jeweled bearings**, the agates being accurately adjusted to the axle, has handsome white bone milled balance handle, **is bridged to prevent action from becoming loose**, insuring smooth running qualities, **gears are carefully cut and adjusted by experts**, finely finished, being extra heavily nickel plated, new style cross blade, fitted with click and drag. Made in 60 and 80-yard size.
No. 57E8775 60-yard size. Price. **$1.90**
No. 57E8776 80-yard size. Price. **2.20**
If by mail, postage extra, 15 cents.

Perfection Pennell Takeapart Reel.

No tools required. This reel may be taken apart in a moment's time by unscrewing the ring at either end. This reel is made by the most skilled mechanics, built on entirely different principles than other reels, and is the strongest, simplest, swiftest reel on the market. **Has a scientific friction device by which any degree of friction can be instantly secured on the spool.** The pinion gear of quadruple style is cut upon a solid steel shaft running through and securely fastened into the non-corrosive German silver spool. The pivots are turned upon this hardened steel shaft and have cone end bearings. The large gear is perfectly cut in bronze, and is securely bridged on the cap of the reel. **The fancy bone handle** is screwed upon the solid post of this gear **and can be placed in four different positions.** This reel is of the wide spool pattern, is the best bait casting reel of its kind ever placed upon the market. Absolutely true and accurate.

No. 57E8777 60 yards. Price... **$2.60**
No. 57E8778 100 yards. Price... **2.75**
No. 57E8779 This reel is the same as that above described except the frame instead of having riveted pillars and cross blade is made of one solid piece, making a very strong, substantial reel and guarding against loose joints, otherwise same as No. 57E8777. Comes 80 yard size only, wide spool pattern. (If by mail, postage extra, 14 cents) Price... **$4.00**

The Twentieth Century Line Guide.

This is the simplest, most practical spooling device on the market today. Can be attached to any reel within a few moments' time by anyone, the only tool required being a screwdriver. It does not retard the cast nor wear the line. Weighs only one ounce. This spooler works on a pivot, being worked slowly from side to side with the thumb of the hand that holds the rod. The loop is made of German silver and can be bent in and out to fit.
No. 57E8781 Price... **35c**
If by mail, postage extra, 2 cents.

TWISTED COTTON AND LINEN FISH LINES

1 2 3 4 5 6 7 8 9

NOTE A. This illustration shows as near as possible the size of all twisted fish lines. It is impossible to make an illustration show the sizes exact. This is as near correct as a picture can be made. When ordering, tell us which size you wish. Order by catalogue number.

Excellent Braided Line.

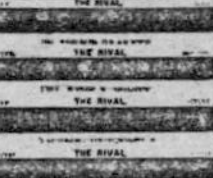

No. 57E8785 Excellent Braided Linen Finished Line. This is a beautifully mottled hard braided line, very strong, put up 50 yards on a nicely finished spool, comes in three sizes. Sizes 4 5 6
Per spool **17c 17c 17c**
If by mail, postage extra, 4 cents.

Our Rival Waterproof Mixed Silk Line.

No. 57E8788 This is an excellent mixed silk mottled line, which has been waterproofed. A fine strong line at a very low price, good for fly casting, trolling or still fishing. Comes 25 yards on a card. Can be furnished 100 yards connected if desired.
Sizes... 3 4 5
Price, per 25 yards... **17c 16c 15c**
If by mail, postage extra, 3 cents.

Hawser Laid Trolling Lines.

No. 57E8793 Our Hawser Laid Line is a heavy hand laid line of great strength. is finely finished; line No. 3 will hold the largest fish. Put up in coils of 100 feet, 6 coils connected if desired, making 600 feet in one piece.
Size 1, cable laid coils of 100 ft., per coil, **12c**
Size 2, cable laid coils of 100 ft., per coil, **14c**
Size 3, cable laid coils of 100 ft., per coil, **17c**
If by mail, postage extra, 4 cents.

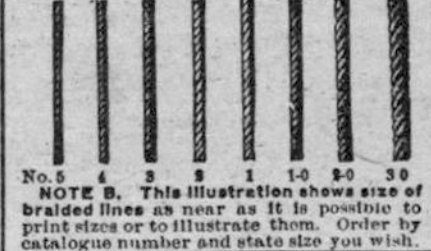

NOTE B. This illustration shows size of braided lines as near as it is possible to print sizes or to illustrate them. Order by catalogue number and state size you wish.

Braided Cotton Lines.

No. 57E8796 Braided Cotton Lines, put up 84 feet in a coil, strong and durable, made of best Sea Island cotton, guaranteed even strength. Mention size wanted. See Note B for sizes.
Size, Nos... 5 4 3 2 1 1-0 2-0 3-0
Price, per coil.. **5c 5c 6c 7c 7c 10c 11c 12c**
If by mail, postage extra, 3 cents.
The No. 5 is tested to 10 pounds; **the No. 3-0** is tested to 40 pounds pull. All others are tested in proportion.

Hard Braided Linen Lines.

No. 57E8798 Hard Braided Linen Lines, put up 25 yards in a coil and may be had four coils connected, making 100 yards. Much stronger than twisted or laid lines. The best bass and trolling line in the market. Made from best Scotch linen fibre, evenly braided and well finished. The No. 5 is tested to 25 pounds; the No. 2-0 to 50 pounds, and all the other sizes are tested in proportion. See illustration Note B for sizes. State size wanted. Order by catalogue number and size number.
Size, Nos. 5 4 3 2 1 1-0 2-0
Per coil.. **13c 13c 13c 15c 15c 16c 18c**
If by mail, postage extra, 3 to 10 cents.

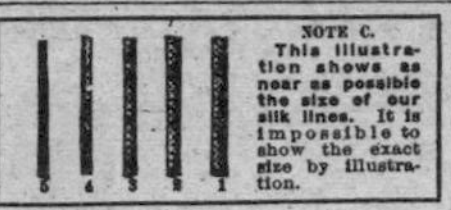

NOTE C. This illustration shows as near as possible the size of our silk lines. It is impossible to show the exact size by illustration.

Our Famous Braided Oil Silk Lines in Coils.

No. 57E8810 Fine Quality Braided Oil Silk Lines, put up 25 yards in a coil and may be had four coils connected, making 100 yards. This is a very strong line, closely braided, of the finest silk, oiled, making it a waterproof line; soft and pliable. A good line for trolling and fly casting. For sizes, see illustration Note C. State size wanted. Order by catalogue number and size number.

Size, Nos.	5	4	3	2
Price, per 25 yds.	25c	34c	39c	44c

If by mail, postage extra, 4 cents.

Our Kingfisher Special Silk Bass Lines.

This line is the highest quality dressed silk casting line made. It is specially braided to our order under contract that it will stand the test we print. This line has been tested by experts and pronounced perfect for bass and game fish. It runs freely on the reel and does not kink. Put up 50 yards on a spool and may be had two spools connected, making 100 yards, if wanted. This is the genuine Kingfisher line.

Catalogue Number	Size	For Fish Weighing	Price, per Spool
57E8811	No. 5	1 to 3 lbs.	50c
57E8811¼	No. 4	3 to 4 lbs.	60c
57E8811½	No. 3	4 to 10 lbs.	70c

If by mail, postage extra, 7 cents.

Martin's Special Enameled Silk Trout Lines.

No. 57E8814 Our Extra Quality Kingfisher, Enameled Oil Silk Trout Lines are giving excellent satisfaction and the demand for these lines is becoming greater each season, they being of small diameter and possessing great strength. This result is obtained not only by using the highest grade of silk, but by braiding more strands into each line and plaiting very close. Try one of these lines and you will want more. 25 yards on neat card.

Price, per card.....(Postage extra, 3c).....32c

Kingfisher Special Enameled Finish Potomac Bass Lines.

No. 57E8815 Our Special Potomac Bass Line Comes 25 yards in a coil and may be had two or four coils connected, or 50 yards, if so wanted.

Price, per coil of 25 yards.....44c

If by mail, postage extra, 2c

Our Italian Enameled Silk Fly Casting Line.

No. 57E8816 Our Italian Enameled Silk Waterproof Flexible Fly Casting Line, made from the best Italian silk, braided over a silk core. It is undoubtedly the best fly casting line on the market. The enamel is guaranteed not to crack or become sticky as is the case with many enameled silk lines. Put up 25 yards in a coil. May be had four coils connected if desired.

Sizes	6	5	4	3
Price, per 25 yards	45c	52c	58c	65c

If by mail, postage extra, 2 cents.

Genuine Italian Braided Silk Bass and Trout Lines.

Our Genuine Italian Braided Silk Line is intended for expert fishermen, for the man who wants the best line that money can buy. This line is made from selected stock, perfectly braided over a silk core, is a hard line free from any imperfections. This same line is sold by dealers under various names at $1.50 a spool. It comes put up 50 yards, on a spool, two spools connected.

Catalogue Number	For	Yards on Spool	Price, per Spool
57E8818B	Bass	50 Yards	85c
57E8818T	Trout	50 Yards	70c

If by mail, postage extra, 2 cents.

Cuttyhunk Linen Lines.

The Strongest Reel Line Made.

No. 9, No. 12, No. 15, No. 18, No. 21

No. 57E8820 Cuttyhunk Linen Reel Line, the old reliable; the strongest line made for its size. Made of the finest quality of Scotch linen, always runs smooth and even and never kinks. The best linen reel line on the market. Put up 150 feet on a spool, or may be had two spools connected, making 300 feet of line. This line is twisted, and when used with swivel on end will not untwist. Can be used same as a braided line. See illustration for sizes. State size wanted. Order by catalogue number and size number.

Size, Nos.	9	12	15	18	21
Price, per 150 ft.	22c	24c	29c	34c	37c
Price, per 300 ft.	43c	47c	57c	67c	72c

If by mail, postage extra, 4 to 9 cents.

Furnished Lines.

Furnished Lines, rigged complete. Line with hook, float and sinker, all ready to drop in the water. Put up one on a winder, convenient to carry.

No. 57E8826 Medium Laid Cotton Line, rigged complete, with fancy adjustable float for still fishing. Price....(Postage extra, 2 cents)...5c

No. 57E8832 Finest Quality Silk Line, rigged complete, with gut hook, fancy float and sinker, for still fishing. Price..............13c

If by mail, postage extra, 3 cents.

Fish Hooks, Double Refined and Tempered Steel.

Order by Number.

This illustration shows the exact size of the ringed hooks, such as Limerick, Kirby, Carlisle and all other kinds of hooks, as nearly as possible, measuring from the point of the hook to the shank.

The other difference in the various hooks is in the length of the shank and the style of bend.

We cannot sell less than 100 hooks of a size.

On above sizes, No. 2-0 is the smallest and No. 10-0 is the largest size. The sizes grow larger gradually from No. 2-0 up, as shown in above illustration.

1 2 3 4 5 6 7 8 9 10 11 12

This illustration shows the Kirby style hooks, about two-thirds the actual size. Order by size number and catalogue number. Postage on ringed hooks, sizes 1 to 8, 1 and 2 cents; sizes 1-0 to 10-0, 3 to 23 cents.

Ringed Fish Hooks.

Kirby, Limerick and Carlisle, made of superfine steel, ringed. Put up in a box of 100 each. We cannot sell less than 100 of a size, but our price is the same whether you buy 100 or 1,000. We give the lowest price always. See illustration of sizes on this page and state size wanted. Order by catalogue number and size number. **Our Carlisle Hooks are the celebrated Milward English "Iron Arm" brand.** No better hooks made.

KIRBY — LIMERICK — CARLISLE

Milward's "Iron Arm" Brand.

Size No.	KIRBY Catalogue Number 57E8848 Price for Box of 100	LIMERICK Catalogue Number 57E8850 Price for Box of 100	CARLISLE Catalogue Number 57E8853 Price for Box of 100
1	5c	6c	8c
2	5c	6c	8c
3	5c	6c	8c
4	5c	6c	8c
5	5c	6c	8c
6	5c	6c	8c
7	4c	5c	8c
8	4c	5c	8c
10	4c	5c	....
11	4c	5c	....
12	4c	5c	....
1-0	7c	8c	9c
2-0	8c	9c	11c
3-0	10c	10c	13c
4-0	11c	11c	16c
5-0	13c	......	19c
6-0	14c	13c	24c
8-0	20c	19c	30c
10-0	35c	......	......

POSTAGE ON HOOKS.

Sizes	Per box	Sizes	Per box
1 to 12	2c	8-0	10c
1-0 to 4-0	3c	9-0	13c
5-0 and 6-0	5c	10-0	18c
7-0	7c		

NOTICE—The above prices are not the prices of hooks but are the postage necessary to send hooks by mail.

The Smith Weedless Hook.

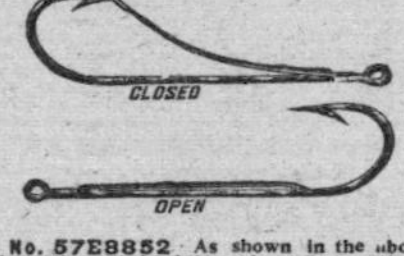

No. 57E8852 As shown in the above illustration this hook is made on an entirely different principle than other weedless hooks. The spring on this hook holds it open instead of closed. When spring is set against point of hook it is absolutely weedless, spring being instantly released the moment the fish strikes, fitting snug against the shank of the hook, leaving nothing to prevent the hook from catching in the mouth of the fish. One size only, 6-0. Best quality Carlisle hook.

Price each, weighted.....................13c
Price, without weight.....................10c

If by mail, postage extra, 2 cents.

The Maloney Weedless Bass Hook.

No. 57E8855 This is the latest and most practical weedless hook on the market. It is so made and weighted that when casting for bass, the frog is always right side up. They are made in sizes 2-0, 3-0, 4-0 and 5-0. See illustration of ringed hooks for sizes and state size wanted. Price, each.....................8c

If by mail, postage extra, 1 cent.

Greer's New Lever Hooks.

Illustration shows the hook when set and sprung.

Greer's Patent Lever Fish Hooks. No more fish lost and baits to reset, no coming home without your largest fish; a dead sure thing on getting your fish if it bites. It is easily adjusted to all kinds of fishing, by sliding the little clamp on the rod. Made of 1-0 and 3-0 Carlisle hooks.

GREER NEW LEVER SLOT HOOK — SET — SPRUNG

No. 57E8857 Size, 1-0. Price, each..8c
No. 57E8857½ Size, 3-0. Price, each..9c

If by mail, postage extra, 2 cents.

Spring Fish Hooks.

No. 57E8858 The Snap and Catch 'Em Spring Fish Hook. The hook's spring points outward, and it is easily set. Fish cannot get away when he is once hooked. No. 20, for small fish; No. 19, for medium size fish; No. 18, for large fish. Say which you want. Price, each.....................8c

If by mail, postage extra, 2 cents.

Kelso Worm Gang.

No. 57E8858¼ This is just the thing for still fishing and will catch the nibbler every time. As shown in the illustration, this bait consists of three No. 8 hooks tied to a piece of gut same as an ordinary snell hook, except you have three hooks around which you twine your angle worm. You will not have your bait nibbled off if you use the Kelso Worm Gang when you go still fishing. Price, each............6c

If by mail, postage extra, 1 cent.

The Payson Automatic Weedless Hook.

No. 57E8859 This is the best weedless hook on the market. It lands the frog or minnow belly down and has sufficient weight to aid in bait casting. The nickel plated weed guard hangs down, leaving the hook well exposed. When in contact with weed or snag, the guard closes over the point of the hook. The hooks are removable. You can change the hook according to the size fish you are after. Two hooks accompany each guard. Sizes 4-0 and 7-0. State size wanted when ordering.

Price, each.....................25c

If by mail, postage extra, 4 cents.

AN OUTFIT FOR BASS, PICKEREL, ETC.

Consists of 1 Bait Casting Rod, 5 to 6½ feet, 1 Quadruple Reel, 1 Silk Line, 3 or 4 spoons No. 4 to 4½, a few sinkers, a few pieces of pork rind, 3 inches long, ¼ inch wide, cut to look like a fish and fastened to one of the treble hooks on the spoon. With this outfit you are ready for business.

If you go on a long trip take an extra cheap rod and a few extra articles in case you break a rod or lose some tackle in the lake.

SNELLED HOOKS.

Our snelled hooks are put up one-half dozen of a size in a package, and we cannot sell less than one-half dozen of a size. All our snelled hooks are specially hand tied and no house can compete with us in quality and prices. All our gut hooks are tied with silk. **Our Carlisle and Cincinnati Bass Hooks** are put **in a patent folding metal holder which is indestructible.** Will keep your hooks together without tieing or fastening same.

Limerick Spear Point Snelled Hooks.

Tied to best quality single and double gut, full length. We cannot sell less than one-half dozen of a size.

No. 57E8860 Limerick Single Gut.

Size No.	8	7	6	5	4	3
Price, per doz.	10c	10c	10c	10c	10c	10c
Size No.		2	1	1-0	2-0	3-0
Price, per doz.		10c	10c	12c	13c	14c

If by mail, postage extra, per dozen, 2 to 4 cents.

No. 57E8862 Limerick Double Gut.

Size No.		4	3	2	1	
Price, per doz.		12c	12c	12c	12c	
Size No.	1-0	2-0	3-0	4-0	5-0	6-0
Price, per doz.	14c	15c	16c	21c	26c	32c

If by mail, postage extra, per dozen, 2 to 4 cents.

This illustration shows the patent metal wrapper we furnish with every half dozen of our Carlisle and Cincinnati bass hooks.

Carlisle Snelled Hooks.

Carlisle Spring Steel Hooks, special quality, silk tied to full length single or double gut. Put up one-half dozen in a **patent metal holder.** We cannot sell less than one-half dozen of a size.

No. 57E8867 Carlisle Single Gut.

Size No.	8	7	6	5	4	3
Price, per doz.	15c	15c	15c	15c	15c	15c
Size No.		2	1	1-0	2-0	3-0
Price, per doz.		15c	15c	19c	21c	24c

No. 57E8869 Carlisle Double Gut.

Size No.	4	3	2	1	1-0
Price, per doz.	18c	18c	18c	18c	21c
Size No.	2-0	3-0	4-0	5-0	6-0
Price, per doz.	23c	26c	30c	34c	40c

If by mail, postage extra, per dozen, 2 to 4 cents.

Cincinnati Bass Hooks, Snelled.

No. 57E8875 Cincinnati Bass Hooks. Double Gut, silk tied to best quality double gut, full length, and warranted the best hooks in the market for the money. Put up one-half dozen of a size in a **patent metal holder.** We cannot sell less than half dozen of a size.

Size No. 24 equal to No. 3, per dozen..18c
Size No. 23 equal to No. 2, per dozen..18c
Size No. 22 equal to No. 1, per dozen..18c
Size No. 21 equal to No. 1-0, per dozen..20c
Size No. 20 equal to No. 2-0, per dozen..22c
Size No. 19 equal to No. 3-0, per dozen..24c
Size No. 18 equal to No. 4-0, per dozen..28c
Size No. 17 equal to No. 5-0, per dozen..30c
Size No. 16 equal to No. 6-0, per dozen..32c

If by mail, postage extra, per dozen, 2 to 5 cents.

Plain Treble Hooks.

Don't throw away your spoon bait if you have lost the hook, but buy a hook for it.

No. 57E8884 Plain Treble Hooks; ringed, made of best quality spring steel and well finished. Sizes compare with regular fish hooks.

Size No.	4	3	2	1			
Price, each	2c	2c	2c	2c			
Size No.	1-0	2-0	3-0	4-0	5-0	6-0	7-0
Price, each	3c	3c	3c	4c	4c	4c	5c

If by mail, postage extra, 1 to 3 cents.

Our Phantom Minnow.

No. 57E9008 One of the most successful baits made. The body is made of silk, waterproofed, nicely mounted, assorted in blue, silver and brown colors. We claim our Phantom Minnow equal to any upon the market, regardless of price. Order by catalogue number and mention length of minnow wanted when ordering.

Sizes....	1	2	3	4	5	6	8
Length, inches,	2	2¼	2¾	3	3½	4	4½
Price, each....	22c	23c	24c	26c	27c	30c	32c

If by mail, postage extra, 3 to 7 cents.

RUBBER BAITS.

Excellent Substitutes where the Natural Bait Cannot Readily Be Found.

Shrimp Bait.

No. 57E9012 Shrimps, about 3 inches long. Price....20c
If by mail, postage extra, 3 cents.

Helgamites.

No. 57E9014 Helgamite, or Dobson, soft rubber, with swivel. Price....16c
Postage extra, 3 cents.

Our Special Fly Minnow.

No. 57E9015 Fly Minnow, 1½ inches long, a good imitation of a minnow, for still fishing. Price...(If by mail, postage extra, 2c.)...13c

The Kalamazoo Swimming Frog.

No. 57E9018 This is a new departure in artificial baits. This frog is made of soft rubber with hollow body. The natural position of the legs of this frog are at right angles to the body. In pulling the frog through the water the legs kick backwards with identically the same motion used by a live frog when swimming. The hooks being protected by the feet of the frog are practically weedless. Finished in exact imitation of a live frog. Very durable; will catch fish wherever they are to be found. Price ... 68c
If by mail, postage extra, 4 cents.

Grasshopper Bait.

No. 57E9019 Grasshopper, soft rubber, 1½ inches long, quite natural. Price..........12c
If by mail, postage extra, 1 cent.

Rubber Frogs.

No. 57E9020 Genuine Soft Rubber Frogs, colored as natural as life. An excellent bait for "splashing" or casting. Tied with strong gut loop to treble hook. Colored green and brown. About 1¾ inches long. Price...............20c
If by mail, postage extra, 3 cents.

Floating Meadow Frog.

No. 57E9021 Made of satin cork, very artistically painted, has a lifelike appearance. The treble hook is secured to the belly of the frog on a spiral eye, enabling fishermen to change hooks when desired. This treble hook insures hooking your fish when he strikes. Entire length, 3 inches. Price...(If by mail, postage extra, 4c)....23c

Soft Rubber Angle Worms.

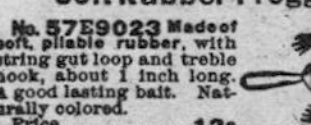

No. 57E9022 Angle Worms; a perfect imitation of red, live worms; about 3 inches long. Price....15c
If by mail, postage extra, 2 cents.

Soft Rubber Froggies.

No. 57E9023 Made of soft, pliable rubber, with string gut loop and treble hook, about 1 inch long. A good lasting bait. Naturally colored. Price..................13c
If by mail, postage extra, 2 cents.

Shakespeare Revolution Bait.

No. 57E9032 This is one of the most popular baits on the market. It is made entirely of aluminum, with two paddles and three treble hooks. The body, head and paddles revolve rapidly when the bait is drawn through the water, resembling a fish, making a very attractive lure. This bait has been on the market but a short time, but its killing qualities has made it one of the most popular baits now on the market. Price..................40c
If by mail, postage extra, 2 cents.

Genuine Dowagiac Wood Minnows.

These minnows are guaranteed to hold their color and not to chip or crack. They are beautifully finished with mottled green back and white belly. The patent socket device prevents the hooks from interlocking. Spinners at either end revolve freely. This minnow always comes in right side up and is guaranteed to retain its finish and color.

No. 57E9025 Dowagiac Minnow, 2¾ inches long, fancy back and fitted with three treble hooks and two spinners. Suitable for bass, pike and pickerel. Price....................50c

No. 57E9026 Dowagiac Minnow, large size, 3½ inches long, fancy mottled back fitted with five treble hooks and two spinners, suitable for large fish, including muskallonge. Price....................65c
If by mail, postage extra, 4 cents.

Our Sure Catch Minnow Trap.

No. 57E9033 Our Sure Catch Minnow Trap is made of galvanized sheet steel and wire screening with cone shaped ends, and so constructed that it may be separated in the center and one end can be telescoped into the other. When baited with stale bread, meat or other bait, the bait is exposed to view through the wire screen and when the minnows, crawfish or other small fish once get into this trap it is difficult for them to find their way out. The Sure Catch Minnow Trap is 18 inches long, 10 inches in diameter and weighs about 3½ pounds. Price 70c

Keystone Fish Stringers.

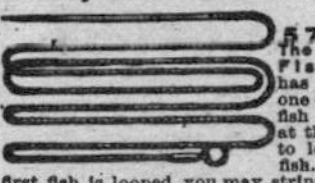

No. 57E9036 The Keystone Fish Stringer has a needle at one end to string fish and a ring at the other end to loop the first fish. After the first fish is looped, you may string as many as the string will hold. The Keystone is 6 feet long. Price..........................12c
If by mail, postage extra, 2 cents.

Chain Fish Stringers.

No. 57E9038 Chain Fish Stringers, brass links, heavy nickel plated, strong and durable; will hold 100 pounds of fish and not break. Price, 13c
If by mail, postage extra, 3 cents.

Fish Spears.

No. 57E9048 Has four tines, 2½ inches long, with socket for pole. Price..................15c
If by mail, postage extra, 6 cents.

No. 57E9049 Has five prongs, 5 inches long, with socket for pole. Price.......42c
If by mail, postage extra, 18 cents.

Our Special Hand Forged Spear.

The best spear on the market.

No. 57E9050 Hand Made Fish Spear, all best steel except socket and wedge; beards of each tine made on solid shank, screws into socket and makes its own thread in wood (of handle); the outside tines can be removed if smaller spear is wanted at any time by putting in larger wedge. Width, about 4½ to 4¾ inches; entire length of tines, about 6½ inches; entire length, 22 inches. Weight, about 1¾ pounds. None better. Price.........................$1.38
If by mail, postage extra, 26 cents.

No. 57E9052 Is same as No. 57E9050 but lighter weight, weighing 8 ounces. Total length, 14½ inches; length of tines, 4½ inches; width across tines, 4 inches. A good hand made spear with threaded shank to screw into the handle and nickeled ferrule. Price..........65c
If by mail, postage extra, 22 cents.

The Lion Gaff.

The Strongest, Best Automatic Gaff Hook made. Illustration shows the gaff hook open, ready for action. Owing to the trigger arrangement you can catch a fish lying close to the bottom of the lake as well as up near the surface. To set gaff hook pull jaws apart until they lock. For convenience in transportation and packing we furnish our gaffs without handle, as any broom handle can be fitted to the socket.

No. 57E9055 No. 1 Gaff, blued finish, measuring 3½ inches between the points of jaws when open. Price.........................90c

No. 57E9056 No. 2 Gaff, blued finish, measuring 5½ inches between the points of jaws when open. Price.........................70c
If by mail, postage extra, 12 to 20 cents.

Tackle Boxes.

No. 57E9060 An Excellent Tackle Box, 10½ inches long, 4 inches high and 5½ inches wide. Hinged cover with improved latch. This box is finished on the outside with two coats of high grade rich green enamel, gold stripes; inside the box is black; has one compartment suitable for snelled hooks, floats, spoons, etc.; one compartment large enough to hold one 100-yard reel; one compartment suitable for lines, leaders, etc.; one tray divided into five spaces. Price....50c
If by mail, postage extra, 38 cents.

No. 57E9061 This box was designed for a fisherman desiring a flat box that can be packed in a suit case or large grip. This box is 9½ inches long, 3½ inches high, 7 inches wide, with handle on the side, the same as a suit case, finish same as No. 57E9060; has one compartment large enough for a 100-yard reel or two smaller reels; one compartment the full length of the box for snelled hooks and flies; three smaller compartments for spoon baits, wood minnows, etc., and one tray divided into four compartments. A strong, well made, finely finished box. Price......64c
If by mail, postage extra, 45 cents.

No. 57E9062 Our Large Tackle Box, 12½ inches long, 5½ inches wide, 6½ inches high. This is an extra strong box, with hinged cover, with strong hasp, with handle on top of box. Finished on the outside with two coats of rich green enamel, gold striped, and finished inside in jet black. Has one compartment large enough for two or three reels; one compartment suitable for leader box, fly book, lines, etc.; one tray divided into three compartments suitable for snelled hooks, spoon baits, floats, etc.; one small tray, as shown in the illustration, divided into six compartments suitable for swivels, sinkers, etc. This is the best box for fishermen desiring a large, roomy box. Price.........................70c
If by mail, postage extra, 55 cents.

Seroco Tackle Books.

No. 57E9071 Seroco Tackle Book. Made to hold snelled hooks or flies. This book has durable pebbled leather cover, made with pocketbook fastening. Size, 6x3½ inches. Has four sheets of yellow parchment with bar and center clips to hold four dozen flies, with two flannel leaves for drying, has also deep pocket suitable for gut leaders. This is a neat, durable book, just the right size for the pocket. Price...40c
If by mail, postage extra, 6 cents.

Our Bray Style Tackle Book.

No. 57E9072 The cover of this book is heavy calf leather, lined with soft glove leather, has two leather pockets, also two celluloid envelopes. This book has celluloid leaves, Bray style spring in center, holds four dozen flies. In addition it has two flannel leaves for drying flies or keeping leaders moist. Size, 3¾x7 inches, has single strap fastening, all leaves are celluloid, is undoubtedly the best tackle book on the market. Price.......$1.20
If by mail, postage extra, 8 cents.

Bait Boxes.

All our Bait Boxes are of tin, neatly painted and finished.

No. 57E9079 The Padlock Bait Box, 3½ inches wide, 3 inches deep, shaped very much like a fish basket, with a top cover and a safety pin on the back so it can be pinned to the coat—no losing of bait or upsetting of bait box. Price.........................10c
Postage extra, 5 cents.

S., R. & Co.'s Celebrated Minnow Buckets.

No. 57E9085 Handiest, lightest, most noiseless and most complete minnow bucket ever put on the market. Free circulation of air and water, attracts the fish to it, thereby making good fishing around the bucket. If desired to keep the minnows fresh while in transit put a little ice in the bottom of your bucket. When you arrive at the lake drop the inside bucket into the water, where it can be kept on the surface by a string tied to the boat. The inside bucket is made of wire screening and so open that it affords full flow of fresh water all the time, bringing to your minnows the insect food upon which they exist, as well as attracting other fish to it. Weight, 3 and 3½ pounds.

Buckets for holding........	8 quarts	10 quarts
Price.....................	63c	82c

Midget Minnow and Frog Bucket.

No. 57E9086 Our Two-Quart Minnow and Frog Bucket is an ideal bucket for the lone fisherman. Same is nicely lacquered in deep blue, has perforated hinged cover, self locking, bail handle. This bucket is 6 inches in diameter, 4½ inches high, weighs 9 ounces. Tie a string to the handle and drop bucket overboard and your bait will remain fresh. Small, strong, neat, efficient. Price.........................18c
If by mail, postage extra, 12 cents.

Our Universal Live Nets, to Keep Fish Fresh When Caught.

No. 57E9088 These nets are made with wire hoops and tan colored netting, are collapsible and take up very little room. An excellent thing to keep fish alive and fresh when caught.

Price, 10 inches diameter...26c
Price, 12 inches diameter...31c
Price, 14 inches diameter...36c
If by mail, postage extra, 18 cents.

Minnow Dip Nets.

No. 57E9089 Minnow Dip Nets made of No. 20 6-ply Sea Island cotton, superior in strength and durability to linen nets and far less expensive. Prices are for nets only; do not include frames.

Price, 16 inches deep..................16c
Price, 18 inches deep..................20c
Price, 20 inches deep..................25c
Price, 24 inches deep..................30c
Price, 30 inches deep..................40c
Price, 36 inches deep..................48c
If by mail, postage extra, 5 cents.

Linen Landing Nets.

No. 57E9090 Price is for netting only, and does not include frame. For landing large fish.

Price, 20 inches deep..................15c
Price, 24 inches deep..................20c
Price, 30 inches deep..................30c
If by mail, postage extra, 5 cents.

Our Chicago Landing Net, 75 Cents.

No. 57E9091 Our Complete Landing Net, with solid round ring, fitted with 18-inch net, ¾-inch mesh and 4-foot jointed bamboo handle, finely finished. Price, complete.........................75c
If by mail, postage extra, 27 cents.

Bucket and Aquarium Net.

No. 57E9093 Our Minnow Net is designed to take minnows out of a bucket, which is more convenient than taking them out by hand; this net is made with a round frame, short handle, and can easily be carried in the coat pocket. Price.........14c
If by mail, postage extra, 4 cents.

The Superior Folding Net Ring, Complete with Net.

Complete with net and handle. This is undoubtedly the best folding net on the market. Can be taken apart in a moment's time, is very light and strong, being made of the best tempered steel. No parts to get lost ring can be folded without moving the net. Put up in neat partitioned cloth bag.

No. 57E9095 No. 1 Ring, 14x15 inches, mounted with a square bottom linen waterproof net, fitted with 4-foot jointed, nicely finished handle. Price.........................$1.35
If by mail, postage extra, 20 cents.

Fishing Hats.

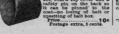

No. 57E9098 No. 57E9099

No. 57E9098 Collapsible Brown Muslin, green lined, rolls up and may be carried flat in the pocket. On a windy day pin it fast to coat collar. The finest thing out, cool and light. Price.........................20c

No. 57E9099 Same as the above, with a mosquito shield, a mosquito proof hat. Price..(If by mail, postage extra, 4c.)..40c

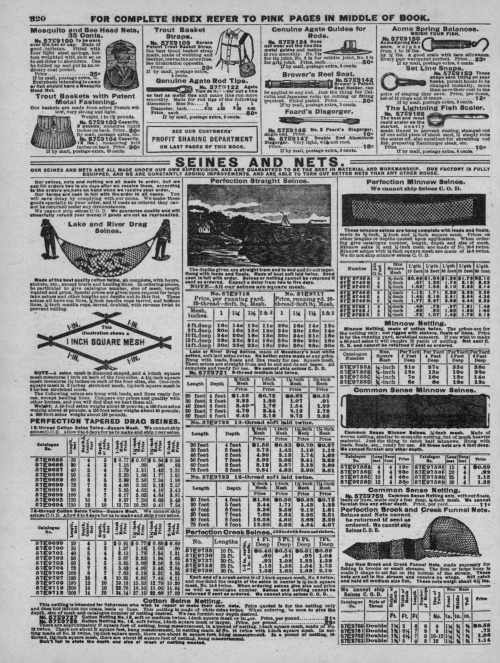

Mosquito and Bee Head Nets, 35 Cents.

No. 57E9100 To be worn over the hat or cap. Made of good tarletan. Fitted with four light steel springs, bottom weighted with shot so as to set close to shoulders. Can be folded up and put in an ordinary coat pocket.
Price 35c
If by mail, postage extra, 7c.
Everybody intending to camp or fish should have a Mosquito Head Net.

Trout Baskets with Patent Metal Fastening.

Our baskets are made from select French willow, very strong and light.

Weight, 1 to 1¼ pounds.
No. 57E9103 Capacity, 9 pounds; measures 7½x12 inches on back. Price..80c
By mail, postage extra, 15c.
No. 57E9104 Capacity, 12 lbs.; measuring 9x13 inches on back. Price..90c
If by mail, postage extra, 20 cents.

Trout Basket Straps.

No. 57E9109 Seroco Patent Trout Basket Strap, the best trout basket strap made, made of webbing and leather, leaves the arms free. See illustration opposite.
Price 20c
If by mail, postage extra, 4 cents.

Genuine Agate Rod Tips.

No. 57E9122 Agate Tips do not wear out a line as fast as metal tips and make line run more smoothly. Made for rod tips of the following diameters: Size No..... 4/0, 3/0, 1/0, 1
Diameter, inch........3-32, 4-32, 5-32, 6-32
Price, each 50c
If by mail, postage extra, 2 cents.

SEE OUR CUSTOMERS'
PROFIT SHARING DEPARTMENT
ON LAST PAGES OF THIS BOOK.

Genuine Agate Guides for Rods.

No. 57E9124 Does not wear out the line like metal guides and makes it run smoothly. No. 7 is for tip joint, No. 6 is for middle joint, No. 5 is for grip joint. Price, each....................50c
If by mail, postage extra, 2 cents.

Brower's Reel Seat.

No. 57E9142 Brower's Patent Reel Holder, can be applied to any rod. Just the thing for Calcutta and Japanese rods; no cutting or fitting required. Nickel plated. Price............20c
If by mail, postage extra, 3 cents.

Foard's Disgorger.

No. 57E9146 No. 2 Foard's Disgorger, single end. Price....................10c
No. 57E9147 Double End Aluminum Disgorger. Very light, will not rust.
Price....................18c
If by mail, postage extra, 3 cents.

Acme Spring Balances.

WEIGH YOUR FISH.

No. 57E9150 AcmeSpring Balance, weighs from 1 to 10 lbs. by ¼ lbs. A good scale with tare allowance. Every pair warranted perfect. Price....23c
If by mail, postage extra, 5 cents.

Set Line Snaps.

No. 57E9153 These snaps save tieing on your hooks, permit hooks to be changed instantly, more than save their cost in the price of staging they save. Price, per dozen, set of 12 rings and 12 snaps....................12c
If by mail, postage extra, 2 cents.

The Lightning Fish Scaler.

No. 57E9166 The best and most rapid scaler on the market, neatly made, tinned to prevent rusting, stamped out of one solid piece of sheet steel, it simply rubs the scales off, also excellent for shredding cod fish, preparing Hamburger steak, etc.
Price 10c
If by mail, postage extra, 6 cents.

SEINES AND NETS.

OUR SEINES AND NETS ARE ALL MADE UNDER OUR OWN SUPERVISION, AND ARE GUARANTEED TO BE THE BEST IN MATERIAL AND WORKMANSHIP. OUR FACTORY IS FULLY EQUIPPED, AND WE ARE CONSTANTLY ADDING IMPROVEMENTS, AND ARE ABLE TO TURN OUT BETTER NETS THAN ANY OTHER HOUSE.

Our seines, nets and netting are all made to order, but we can fill orders two to six days after we receive them, according to the orders we have on hand when we receive your order.

Our terms are cash in full with the order in all cases. You will save delay by complying with our terms. We make these goods specially to your order, and if made as ordered they cannot be returned under any circumstances.

We cannot ship seines C. O. D. **We guarantee quality and will cheerfully refund your money if goods are not as represented.**

Lake and River Drag Seines.

Made of the best quality cotton twine, all complete, with buoys, sinkers, etc., except brails and hauling lines. In ordering seines, be particular to give catalogue number, size of mesh, length wanted and price. Special prices are given upon request for large lake seines and other lengths and depths not in this list. These seines all have top lines, ⅜-inch manila rope tarred, and bottom lines, ⅜-inch manila rope, tarred, doubled, with reverse twist to prevent rolling.

NOTE—A seine mesh is diamond shaped, and a 1-inch square mesh measures 1 inch on each of the four sides. A 1½-inch square mesh measures 1½ inches on each of the four sides, etc. One-inch square mesh is 2 inches stretched mesh; 1½-inch square mesh is 3 inches stretched mesh.

The following seines are hung with leads, and lines ready for use, except hauling lines. Compare our prices and quality with other houses, and you will find that we beat them all.

Weight: A 50-foot seine weighs about 20 pounds; a 100-foot seine weighs about 40 pounds; a 150-foot seine weighs about 80 pounds; a 300-foot seine weighs about 180 pounds.

PERFECTION TAPERED DRAG SEINES.

12-thread Cotton Seine Twine—Square Mesh. We cannot ship seines C.O.D. Allow 2 to 6 days for us to make and ship your seine.

Catalogue No.	Length, feet	Depth, Center, feet	Depth, at ends, feet	1-inch Mesh, Price	1¼-inch Mesh, Price	1½-inch Mesh, Price	2-inch Mesh, Price
57E9685	20	4	3	$0.77	$0.67	$0.64	$0.56
57E9686	30	4	3	1.16	.99	.96	.83
57E9687	40	5	4	1.79	1.51	1.42	1.21
57E9688	50	5	4	2.23	1.88	1.77	1.51
57E9689	60	6	5	2.99	2.50	2.34	1.96
57E9690	72	7	6	4.06	3.33	3.12	2.57
57E9691	90	8	7	5.55	4.52	4.18	3.43
57E9692	100	8	7	6.17	5.02	4.64	3.81
57E9693	120	10	8	8.87	7.20	6.68	5.45
57E9694	150	12	10	12.73	10.20	9.41	7.54

16-thread Cotton Seine Twine—Square Mesh. We cannot ship seines C.O.D. Allow 2 to 6 days for us to make and ship your seine.

Catalogue No.	Length, feet	Depth, Center, feet	Depth, at ends, feet	1-inch Mesh, Price	1¼-inch Mesh, Price	1½-inch Mesh, Price	2-inch Mesh, Price
57E9699	20	4	3	$0.91	$0.77	$0.68	$0.60
57E9700	30	4	3	1.37	1.16	1.03	.90
57E9701	40	5	4	2.13	1.79	1.54	1.31
57E9702	50	5	4	2.67	2.23	1.94	1.65
57E9703	60	6	5	3.65	3.02	2.58	2.15
57E9704	72	7	6	5.03	4.09	3.46	2.84
57E9706	100	8	7	7.63	6.19	5.21	4.25
57E9707	120	10	8	10.95	8.89	7.48	6.11
57E9709	180	12	10	19.16	15.33	12.79	10.20
57E9710	200	14	10	23.76	18.10	15.06	11.94
57E9712	300	14	10	34.14	27.15	22.60	17.92

Perfection Straight Seines.

The depths given are straight from end to end and do not taper. **Hung with leads and floats. Made of best soft laid twine. Send cash in full with order. Seines or netting cannot be returned if sent as ordered. Expect a delay from two to five days.**

NOTE.—All our seines are square mesh.

Mesh, inches.	No. 57E9716 Price, per running yard. 12-thread—Soft. Sq. Mesh. 1	1¼	1½	2 & 3	No. 57E9717 Price, running yd. 16-thread-Soft Sq. Mesh. 1	1¼	1½	2 & 3
6 ft. deep	16c	14c	12c	11c	20c	16c	14c	12c
8 ft. deep	20c	16c	15c	12c	24c	20c	16c	14c
10 ft. deep	24c	20c	18c	15c	30c	24c	21c	16c
12 ft. deep	28c	22c	21c	16c	35c	28c	23c	18c
14 ft. deep	30c	25c	22c	18c	39c	30c	26c	20c

Lake or River Drag Seines, made of **Woodbury's best white cotton,** soft laid seine twine. **No better seine made at any price.** Hung with leads, floats and line ready for use. Square mesh. These seines are straight from end to end and do not taper. All complete and ready for use. **We cannot ship seines C. O. D.**

No. 57E9721 9-thread medium laid twine.

Length	Depth	¾-inch Mesh Price	1-inch Mesh Price	1¼-inch Mesh Price	1½-inch Mesh Price
20 feet	4 feet	$1.28	$0.72	$0.62	$0.53
30 feet	5 feet	2.23	1.20	1.07	.91
40 feet	6 feet	3.40	1.76	1.54	1.29
50 feet	7 feet	4.76	2.44	2.13	1.76
60 feet	8 feet	6.40	3.18	2.75	2.26

No. 57E9722 12-thread soft laid twine.

Length	Depth	¾-inch Mesh Price	1-inch Mesh Price	1¼-inch Mesh Price	1½-inch Mesh Price
20 feet	4 feet	$1.56	$0.83	$0.70	$0.67
30 feet	5 feet	2.72	1.42	1.19	1.12
40 feet	6 feet	4.20	2.12	1.74	1.62
50 feet	7 feet	5.92	2.95	2.41	2.23
60 feet	8 feet	8.12	3.87	3.13	2.89
75 feet	8 feet	9.84	4.83	3.90	3.61

No. 57E9723 16-thread soft laid twine.

Length	Depth	¾-inch Mesh Price	1-inch Mesh Price	1¼-inch Mesh Price	1½-inch Mesh Price
20 feet	4 feet	$1.88	$0.98	$0.83	$0.73
30 feet	5 feet	3.44	1.71	1.43	1.23
40 feet	6 feet	5.36	2.58	2.12	1.81
50 feet	7 feet	7.60	3.64	2.95	2.51
60 feet	8 feet	10.28	4.80	3.88	3.26
75 feet	8 feet	12.80	5.98	4.84	4.07

Perfection Creek Seines. All fitted with floats and sinkers.

No.	Lengths		4 Ft. Deep	5 Ft. Deep	6 Ft. Deep	7 Ft. Deep
57E9735	10 ft.	1-2 in. center, 1 in. at ends.	$0.46	$0.54	$0.61	$0.69
57E9736	15 ft.		.69	.81	.92	1.04
57E9737	20 ft.		.93	1.08	1.23	1.38
57E9738	25 ft.		1.15	1.35	1.54	1.73
57E9739	30 ft.		1.38	1.65	1.88	2.10

Each end of a creek seine is of 1-inch square mesh, No. 9 twine; and one-third the length of the seine in center is ½-inch square mesh, No. 14-6 twine. When ordering seines give size and price as well as catalogue number. Seines and netting cannot be returned if sent as ordered. We cannot ship seines C. O. D.

Cotton Seine Netting.

This netting is intended for fishermen who wish to repair or make their own nets. Price quoted is for the netting only and does not include the floats, leads or lines. This netting is made of white seine twine. When ordering, be sure to give the depth, size of mesh and catalogue number of netting desired. We can furnish any depth desired.

No. 57E9727 Cotton Netting No. 12, soft or medium twine, 1-inch square mesh or larger. Price, per pound............31c
No. 57E9728 Cotton Netting No. 16, soft twine, 1-inch square mesh or larger. Price, per pound....................29c

There are approximately 37 square feet of netting, hung measurement, in a pound of netting, 1-inch square mesh, made of No. 12 twine. There are about 31 square feet, hung measurement, in netting made of No. 16 twine with 1-inch square mesh. In netting made of No. 12 twine, 1½-inch square mesh, there are about 64 square feet, hung measurement. In a pound of netting, 16-thread, 1½-inch square mesh, there are about 50 square feet of netting, hung measurement.

Don't fail to state the depth and size of mesh of netting wanted.

Perfection Minnow Seines.

We cannot ship Seines C. O. D.

These minnow seines are hung complete with leads and floats, made in ⅜-inch, ¼-inch and ½-inch square mesh. Prices on other lengths or depths quoted upon application. When ordering give catalogue number, length, depth and size of mesh. Minnow seine ⅜ and ¼-inch mesh are made of No. 20-6 twine. Minnow seines with ½-inch square mesh are made of 14-6 twine. We do not ship minnow seines C. O. D.

Number	Depth Feet	Size Square Mesh	L'gth 10 feet	L'gth 15 feet	L'gth 20 feet	L'gth 25 feet	L'gth 30 feet
57E9740A	3	⅜-inch	$0.69	$1.04	$1.38	$1.73	$2.10
57E9740B	4	⅜-inch	.87	1.30	1.74	2.18	2.63
57E9740C	5	⅜-inch	1.05	1.58	2.10	2.63	3.14
57E9746D	3	¼-inch	1.13	1.71	2.26	2.83	3.38
57E9746E	4	¼-inch	1.45	2.19	2.91	3.64	4.36
57E9746H	5	¼-inch	1.77	2.67	3.56	4.44	5.33
57E9752I	3	½-inch	.49	.73	.97	1.21	1.46
57E9752J	4	½-inch	.60	.90	1.20	1.50	1.80
57E9752K	5	½-inch	.72	1.07	1.43	1.79	2.13

Minnow Netting.

Minnow Netting, made of cotton twine. The prices are for the netting only; **not rigged with sinkers, floats or lines.** Price is by the running yard, stretched measure. If you wish to make a 50-yard seine it will require 75 yards of netting. **Not sent C. O. D. and cannot be returned if sent as ordered.**

Catalogue Number	Size, Square Mesh	Per Yard 3 Feet Deep	Per Yard 4 Feet Deep	Per Yard 5 Feet Deep	Per Yard 6 Feet Deep
57E9755A	⅛-inch	21c	27c	33c	38c
57E9755B	⅜-inch	12c	15c	19c	22c
57E9755C	½-inch	7c	10c	12c	14c
57E9755D	¾-inch	6c	8c	10c	12c

Common Sense Minnow Seines.

Common Sense Minnow Seines, ⅛-inch mesh. Made of woven netting, similar to mosquito netting, but of much heavier material. Just the thing to catch bait minnows. Hung with leads, floats, etc., ready for use. **All these nets are 4 feet deep. We cannot furnish any other depth.**

Catalogue No.	Long feet	Deep feet	Price	Catalogue No.	Long feet	Deep feet	Price
57E9758A	4	4	19c	57E9758E	15	4	$0.69
57E9758B	6	4	28c	57E9758F	20	4	.92
57E9758C	10	4	46c	57E9758G	25	4	1.15
57E9758D	12	4	56c	57E9758H	30	4	1.38

Common Sense Netting.

No. 57E9759 Common Sense Netting only, without floats, leads or lines, made only 4 feet deep, ⅛-inch mesh. **We cannot furnish this any other depth.** Price, per yard....................11c

Perfection Brook and Creek Funnel Nets.

Seines and Nets cannot be returned if sent as ordered. We cannot ship Seines C. O. D.

Our New Brook and Creek Funnel Nets, made expressly for fishing in brooks or small streams. The first or large hoop is made D shape to set flat on the bottom of the stream. **These nets are set in the stream and require no wings. Will catch and hold all medium size fish. These nets weigh about 4½ lbs.**

Catalogue No. (We cannot ship Seines C. O. D.)	Style of Throat	Height of Mouth, Ft.	Width of Mouth, Ft.	Length, Ft.	Number of Hoops	Size of Twine, No.	Size Mesh Front, In.	Size Mesh Middle, In.	Size Mesh Tail, In.	Price
57E9760	Double	1¼	3	6	8	9	1¼	¾	⅝	$0.58
57E9761	Double	1¾	3½	7	9	9	1¼	¾	⅝	.73
57E9762	Double	1¾	4¼	7	9	16-12	1¼	¾	⅝	1.08
57E9763	Double	1⅝	5	8	9	16	1½	¾	⅝	1.14

The Perfection Peerless Fyke or Hoop Net.

Send cash with order. We cannot ship Nets C. O. D.

Lengths which we give on wings are for each wing. **Hoops are on outside of netting, thus greatly saving the same. Made of best quality cotton twine.** Hung ready for use. Netting can be furnished without hoops to your order if desired. **Expect a delay of from two to five days. Cannot be returned if made as ordered.**

Wts. 2 ft. 10 lbs.
Wts. 2½ ft. 12 lbs.
Wts. 3 ft. 20 lbs.
Wts. 4 ft. 25 lbs.
Wts. 5 ft. 35 lbs.
Wts. 6 ft. 46 lbs.

No.	Style Throat.	Height, Mouth	Length of Net	Number of Hoops	L'gth Right Wing	Length Left Wing	Size of Twine	Size of Mesh, Inches Square: Front	Middle	Tail	White Twine Price
		ft	ft		ft	ft	No				
57E9765	Single...	2	6	4	6	6	9	¾	¾	¾	$1.27
57E9766	Single...	3	10	6	9	9	24	1¼	1¼	1¼	2.02
57E9768	Double..	2½	8	6	6	6	16	1	1	1	1.87
57E9769	Double..	3	10	6	9	9	24	1¼	1¼	1¼	2.10
57E9770	Double..	4	16	7	12	12	24	2	1¾	1½	2.91
57E9771	Double..	4½	18	8	15	15	24	2½	2	1½	3.81
57E9772	Double..	5	18	8	15	15	28	2½	2	1½	3.89
57E9773	Double..	6	18	8	20	20	28	2½	2	1½	5.59

For Fyke Nets made of tarred twine, add ten per cent to the above prices. When hoops are not wanted, deduct one-fifth from above prices.

NOTE. We make all kinds of fish nets to order. If you will fully describe what you want and send diagram of shape, we will quote prices on the style and mesh you wish. They cannot be returned when made as ordered.

PERFECTION FUNNEL NETS, WITHOUT WINGS.

Same style as above, but have no wings. With hoops complete. Made of the best quality cotton twine. When ordering nets give size, price and catalogue number, to avoid error. Expect a delay of from two to five days.

Cannot be returned if sent as ordered and we cannot ship C. O. D.

Description: No.	Style Throat	Weight, lbs.	Height Mouth	Length of Net	Number Hoops	Size of Twine	Size of Mesh, Inches Square: Front	Middle	Tail	Price
			ft.	ft		No	in.	in.	in.	
57E9780	Single.	7	2	6	4	9	¾	¾	¾	$0.77
57E9781	Single.	10		10	6	24	1¼	1¼	1¼	1.46
57E9783	Double	9	2½	8	6	16	1	1	1	1.43
57E9784	Double	15	3	10	6	24	1¼	1¼	1¼	1.54
57E9785	Double	20	4	16	7	24	2	1¾	1½	2.22
57E9786	Double	25	4½	18	8	24	2½	2	1½	2.84
57E9787	Double	30	5	18	8	28	2½	2	1½	2.92
57E9788	Double	35	6	18	8	28	2½	2	1½	4.07

PERFECTION LINEN GILL NETTING.

The best linen netting for all gill nets or for inside of trammel nets, made of best silver gray, 3-cord linen twine. Any depth required. Mention depth when ordering. This netting is for gill or set nets, and not for drag seines, the twine being too small for such use. **Cannot be returned when made to order**

No. 57E9810 Size of Twine	1-inch square mesh, per lb.	1¼-inch square mesh, per lb.	1½-inch square mesh, per lb.	1¾-inch square mesh, per lb.	2-inch square mesh, per lb.
18x3 cord.........	$1.52	$1.44	$1.38	$1.34	$1.29
20x3 cord.........	1.61	1.53	1.48	1.43	1.38
25x3 cord.........	1.75	1.67	1.61	1.57	1.52
30x3 cord.........	1.89	1.81	1.75	1.71	1.66
35x3 cord.........	2.19	2.11	2.05	2.00	1.96
40x3 cord.........	2.42	2.34	2.28	2.23	2.19

Size 25x3-cord, 1-inch mesh, contains about 180 square feet to the pound. **Size 40x3-cord, 1-inch mesh, contains about 380 square** feet to the pound. Larger mesh contains more square feet to the pound in proportion.

See No. 57E9915 for sizes. **We do not send this C. O. D.**

No. 57E9811 Cotton Netting. No. 16 soft twine, intended for outside of trammel nets. Size, 6 to 8-inch square mesh. Price, per pound.......... **29c**

PERFECTION SQUARE COTTON DIP NETS.

No. 57E9850 Made of cotton seine twine. Roped all around edges, with loops at corners. All are made 1-inch square mesh of No. 12 soft twine. Price is for netting only. No frame comes with these nets. **Cannot be returned if sent as ordered.**

	Price	Postage extra
4x4 feet, square shape.........	$0.23	10c
5x5 feet, square shape.........	.36	12c
6x6 feet, square shape.........	.46	15c
8x 8 feet, square shape.........	.79	23c
10x10 feet, square shape.........	1.19	38c
12x12 feet, square shape.........	1.66	40c

BEST QUALITY TRAMMEL NETS.

Our Prices are below any Competition, Quality Considered.

We handle only the Perfection Nets and Seines, recognized the world over as THE BEST. We could furnish poorer goods at less money, but the Perfection Seines are so far superior to all others, and our prices to you being but our small percentage above actual cost to make, are **so very low**, that we feel sure you will want the best. **Do not buy a cheap net or seine.** You will find it dear at any price. Perfection goods will always satisfy you.

The Perfection Trammel Net has three nets hung upon a single top and a single bottom line. Of the three nets the two outside have large meshes of cotton seine twine. The inside net is made of best linen gilling twine, which is hung slack, forming a bag in which fish coming from either side are caught and unable to escape. **These nets are not "drag seines," but are to be "set" stationary in the water, the same as a gill net. We do not ship C. O. D.**

Price is per running yard in length, hung measure, for the net complete. The mesh sizes are square mesh. **Weight, per yard about ½ pound. Nets cannot be returned when made as ordered.**

No.	Depth	Outside Mesh	Inside Mesh	Inside Linen Twine	Outside Cotton Twine	Price per Yard
	Feet	Inches	Inches	No.	No.	
57E9820	3½	6	¾	25	All No. 16-Thread Soft Laid Twine.	16c
57E9821	3½	6	1	25		14c
57E9822	3½	6	1¼	25		13c
57E9823	4	6	1	25		16c
57E9824	4	6	1¼	25		13c
57E9826	4½	7	1¼	25		14c
57E9827	4½	7	1½	18		13c
57E9829	4½	7	2	18		11c
57E9830	5	8	1	25		19c
57E9831	5	8	1½	18		14c
57E9832	5	8	2½	18		11c
57E9833	5	8	3	18		11c
57E9834	6	8	1	25		22c
57E9835	6	8	1½	18		18c
57E9836	6	8	2	18		14c
57E9837	6	8	2½	18		13c
57E9838½	6	8	3	18		13c
57E9838	7	8	1¼	25		20c
57E9839	7	8	1½	18		19c
57E9840½	7	8	2	18		16c
57E9842	8	8	1¼	25		22c
57E9843	8	8	1½	18		21c
57E9844	8	8	1¾	18		19c
57E9845	8	8	2	18		18c
57E9846	8	8	2½	18		16c
57E9847	8	8	3	18		15c

Other styles made to order. Meshes as given above are diamond square. Hung complete for use except hauling lines. **When ordering nets give size, price and catalogue number. Allow us two to five days to make.**

NOTE—Trammel Nets are made to order only, and if order is filled correctly we cannot take the goods back, as we seldom have any two orders just alike in every particular. Consequently if the net were returned it would be a dead loss to us.

NOTICE—If you intend to use your net in water where there is a very swift current, same must be rigged accordingly. We can rig nets extra heavy with leads and floats at an additional expense of 10 per cent over catalogue prices.

LINEN GILL OR SET NETS.

A gill net is a single net, hung with floats and leads complete, without hauling lines. Made of best imported linen twine. **These nets cannot be used for drag seines,** the twine being too fine. They are set in the water and allowed to remain from 5 to 24 hours.

The fish are caught by the gills, hence the name gill or set nets.

Rigged complete ready for use. Made of linen twine. Price per running yard in length; hung measure. **Weight, per yard, about ¼ pound.**

Nets cannot be returned if sent as ordered. Allow us two to five days to make.

No.	Depth feet	Size Linen Twine	Sq. Mesh, 1 inch Price, pr. yd.	Sq. Mesh, 1¼ in. Price, pr. yd.	Sq. Mesh, 1½ in. Price, pr. yd.	Sq. Mesh, 2 in. Price, pr. yd.	Sq. Mesh, 2¼ in. Price pr. yd.
57E9860	3½	All 40-3 Cord	......	......	......	6c	......
57E9861	4		12c	11c	8c	7c	......
57E9866	5		13c	12c	10c	7c	7c
57E9873	6		15c	13c	11c	8c	8c
57E9880	7		......	......	12c	10c	......
57E9883	8		......	......	13c	11c	......

Other styles made to order. Our gill nets are made of Knox best Scotch linen twine.

PERFECTION COTTON GILL NETS.

We furnish these nets in the following sizes only, made in 1¼, 1½, and 2-inch square mesh of No. 28 4-ply Sea Island cotton gill netting. **Cannot be returned if sent as ordered. Be sure to specify size of mesh wanted, also depth and number of yards. Following prices are per running yard, hung measure, rigged complete with leads and floats.**

No.	Depth	1¼-inch Mesh, Price, per yard	1½-inch Mesh, Price, per yard	2-inch Mesh, Price, per yard
57E9890A............	4 feet	7c	6c	6c
57E9890B............	5 feet	8c	7c	6c
57E9890C............	6 feet	10c	8c	6c
57E9890D............	7 feet	10c	8c	7c
57E9890E............	8 feet	11c	10c	7c

PERFECTION COTTON TROT LINES.

Cotton Trot Lines, to use as set lines and top and bottom lines on small nets; in 50-foot coils, six rolls connected or 300 feet. Best quality. Sold in any quantity at dozen rates.

No. 57E9900 No.	Weight, per doz.	Price, per doz. coils or 600 ft.
1..........	15 oz.........	$0.17
2..........	16 oz.........	.23
3..........	19 oz.........	.28
4..........	20 oz.........	.37
5..........	23 oz.........	.43
6..........	24 oz.........	.57
7..........	32 oz.........	.66
8..........	36 oz.........	.79
9..........	44 oz.........	.93
10..........	52 oz.........	1.08
11..........	56 oz.........	1.20
No. 12 is $\frac{5}{16}$-inch diameter......	96 oz.........	1.50

PERFECTION COTTON GILL NETTING.

This Gill Netting is made from No. 28x4-ply Sea Island Cotton Twine, in any depth, and is made to special order, according to your specifications, and cannot be returned if sent as ordered; when ordering, mention depth desired, **also mention size mesh** wanted. Understand, this is not a rigged net; it is the netting only and does not have the floats, leads and lines. This cotton netting is very fine and strong, and runs just twice as much to the pound as the heavier, coarser netting, hence the difference in price. **Allow us two to five days to make.**

No. 57E9853 Cotton Gill Netting, 1-inch square mesh, mention depth wanted. Price, per pound.............. **$1.61**

No. 57E9854 Cotton Gill Netting, 1¼, 1½, 1¾ or 2-inch square mesh, mention depth and mesh wanted. Per lb. **$1.38**

PERFECTION LINEN GILLING TWINE.

THE BEST QUALITY IMPORTED.

OUR GILL TWINE is made of the **highest grade linen, and** quality considered, is offered for less money than it has ever been sold before. **Gilling Twine is a small, all** linen twine used for gill or set nets, and cannot be used to make drag, lake or river nets. **For Gill Netting see No. 57E9810.**

PRICES OF LINEN GILLING TWINE.

Catalogue Number	Size of Twine	No. of yds. per pound.	Comes in balls of	Price, per pound
57E9915 A...	12x3 cord	1,200	½-lb. each	$0.81
57E9915 B...	16x3 cord	1,600	½-lb. each	.89
57E9915 C...	18x3 cord	1,800	½-lb. each	.92
57E9915 D...	20x3 cord	2,000	½-lb. each	.98
57E9915 E...	25x3 cord	2,500	½-lb. each	1.08
57E9915 F...	30x3 cord	3,000	½-lb. each	1.26
57E9915 G...	35x3 cord	3,500	½-lb. each	1.48
57E9915 H...	40x3 cord	4,000	½-lb. each	1.71

PERFECTION WHITE SEINE TWINE.

Comes in skeins or hanks, and we cannot sell less than 2 pounds of one size. State size wanted.

Catalogue Number	Style of laid	No. 6, per pound	No. 9, per pound	No. 12, per pound	No. 16 and larger, per pound
57E9925	Soft	28c	25c	24c	23c
57E9926	Medium	28c	25c	24c	23c
57E9927	Hard	37c	26c	26c	25c

No. 9 Twine will average 600 yards per pound.
No. 12 Twine will average 425 yards per pound.
No. 16 Twine will average 325 yards per pound.

Showing sizes of Seine Twine as near as possible. These illustrations appear larger than the twine.

Our Seine Twine is the best in the market, laid smooth and even and uniform in size. We do not handle the loosely laid, bunchy, cheap goods.

RIGGING MATERIAL.

OUR RIGGING MATERIAL is the best on the market.

No. 57E9950 Cedar Trammel Net Floats.	Size, 1¼ x 5,			per 100, 31c	
No. 57E9951 Cedar Gill Net Floats.	Size, 1¾ x 5,			per 100, 61c	
No. 57E9952 Cedar Seine Floats.	Size, 2 x 3, per 100, 35c	Size, 2½ x 3, per 100, 49c	Size, 2¼ x 4, per 100, 57c	Size, 3 x 4, per 100, 77c	Size, 3 x 5, per 100, 92c

No. 57E9960 Lead Sinkers for trammel nets or seines. 16 to the pound. Price, per pound........ 8c
10 to the pound. Price, per pound................ 8c
4 to the pound. Price, per pound................ 7c

No. 57E9965 Hoops for Fyke and Funnel Nets.
5 in. to 2 ft. in diameter, ½ in. timber. Price...... 12c
2¼, 2½, 2¾ and 3 feet in diameter, ⅜x1 in. timber... 13c
3¼, 3½, 3¾ and 4 feet in diameter, ⅜x1 in. timber .. 18c
4½, 4¾ and 5 feet in diameter, ⅜x1 in. timber...... 21c
5½ and 6 feet in diameter, ⅜x1 in. timber. Price..., 52c

SEINE NEEDLES.

No. 57E9935 Seine Knitting Needles, made of prepared maple wood, finely finished; very tough and strong.

Width, inches.....	½	¾	1	1¼	1½
Price, each........	6c	7c	7c	7c	8c

If by mail, postage extra, 1 cent.

THE OTTER FOLDING CATCH-ALL MINNOW NET.

No. 57E9970 This Net supplies a long felt want. A minnow net that can be folded into a small space and when spread out is large enough to be practically used as a minnow dip net. This net has a steel frame, 3½ feet square. This frame can be folded in a moment's time; when folded occupies a space 2 inches square, 2½ feet long. The net itself is heavy common sense netting ⅛ inch mesh, reinforced at corners, fitted with a brass ring in each corner to attach to frame. This net is not fitted with handle, frame has a large ring to which a handle or rope can be attached.

Price, complete with bag................................$1.15
If by mail, postage extra, 25 cents.

Our Patent Tent Slide.

This illustration shows our patent tent slide used on all our tents. This slide is far superior to the wood slide universally used by all other manufacturers. It is made of coppered wire, it positively will not slip, it is instantly adjusted, cannot break, will not rust, cannot be lost from the guy rope. These patent slides greatly increase the actual value of the tent and are furnished on all of our tents without any extra charge whatsoever.

OUR TENT AND COVER DEPARTMENT.

WHY WE MANUFACTURE OUR OWN TENTS AND COVERS. We manufacture our own tents and covers in order to insure our customers receiving exactly what they order and exactly what they pay for. We know of no business where so much fraud and deception are practiced as in the tent business, and to guard our customers against this and to insure them getting tents that are full weight and full size at the lowest possible prices, we installed our own tent and cover factory.

WHY A COMPARISON OF PRICES does not indicate which tents or covers are the cheapest. After going into the tent manufacturing business thoroughly and after years' of experience in selling tents, we have found that the selling price of tents differs from the selling price of other merchandise in the fact that in nearly all other classes of merchandise, the selling price is based on the cost, and that in the tent business the cost is based on the selling price. In other words, in order to meet competition, dealers will skimp the tent and reduce the cost of manufacturing. It is not alone a question of price in the tent business. A dealer who handles any quantity of tents will get five or six prices on supposedly the same size and weight of tent. We know from our own experience instances where we have been quoted prices 20 per cent lower than our cost of making an honest tent, and our cost of production is less than that of any factory in the country.

HOW A TENT IS ROBBED IN ORDER TO BE SOLD AT OR BELOW OUR PRICE. From time to time we get samples of tents offered by dealers throughout the country and we find there are about a dozen different ways in which the quality of a tent is reduced in order to offer the tent at competitive figures. In nearly all instances the center height of the tent is from 4 to 6 inches short. **We have frequently found in examining tents offered as being the same size and weight as ours, that the 8-ounce tent was made of 7-ounce duck and that the 10-ounce tent was made of 9-ounce duck.** A difference of one ounce in the weight of duck means a difference in cost of from fifty cents, in small sized tents, to several dollars in the larger tents. Another plan of deception is to make the door of the tent of lighter canvas than the rest of the tent, also to make the door but 4 to 6 inches wide, whereas, our way of making a tent, is to make the door of tents up to and including 12x14 feet, one-half width of canvas, over 12x14, 15 inches, and to make all 16x18-foot tents with a full width door. Another manner in which the selling price of tents is reduced to meet our price, is to use jute rope. Anyone familiar with ropes knows that jute rope, after it once becomes wet, is absolutely worthless. It becomes hard and rots very quickly. We do not use jute rope; in the small sized wall tents we use the best pure sisal rope. In wall tents larger than 12x18 feet, and on all refreshment and photographers' tents we use the best pure manila rope. We have enumerated a few of the methods dealers use throughout the country to meet our prices on tents. We know that the average man knows little or nothing about tents, that in placing an order he will naturally make a comparison of prices, and we know that a comparison of prices will not place him in a position to order intelligently and to his best interest, unless a comparison of quality is also made.

QUALITY AND PRICE GUARANTEE. We guarantee every tent in this catalogue to be lower in price than the same quality of goods can be bought elsewhere. If any house ever meets or cuts our price on any article, they do it at the expense of quality. If you do not find this so by comparing the goods, or if you ever buy anything from us that is not lower in price than the same high quality of goods can be bought from any other house, you are especially requested to return our goods at our expense and get your money back at once. We guarantee our tents and covers to be exactly as described in our catalogue. We guarantee them to be full weight 29-inch canvas, and to be full size. We guarantee the door of the tent to be of the same weight canvas as the rest of the tent. If you purchase a tent of us and do not find it exactly as we represent it, you have the privilege of returning it to us at our expense and your money and transportation charges to be refunded to you. Weigh one of our tents or covers and one of our competitors' make and note which weighs the most.

DELIVERIES. We make all our tents and covers to order and therefore ask our customers to anticipate a delay of from two to six days when ordering.

HOW TO PITCH A TENT. Having unrolled the tent in the exact position you want it to be when up, place the ridge pole, round side up, inside the tent, and on a line with the large eyelet holes, which are in the center of the roof; then insert the uprights in the holes bored in the ridge pole, and let the spikes in the upright pole come through the top of the tent. If a fly is used, let the spikes also go through that in precisely the same way as the tent, then take hold of the uprights and raise tent and fly together, secure the corner guys first and then the others between them. **Do not drive the pegs straight,** but slanting; they hold very much better in this way. The tent being now up and guys all adjusted so that they bear equal strain, then proceed to dig a V-shaped trench all around the tent, about three inches deep; **this will insure you a dry floor at all times. Do not take the tent down when wet or even damp.** Heat and dampness are the cause of mildew, which destroys more tents than all other causes combined.

WALL TENTS.

Why the sizes of our tents differ from those quoted by other houses. After going into the tent manufacturing business thoroughly, we found that the sizes, which have been quoted for years, in a good many instances were wrong. We found that in some cases the tents could not be made economically in the sizes that they were quoted, in other words, the size quoted would not permit the canvas for the tent to be cut to good advantage, there would be too much waste and that therefore the tents were misrepresented, the tents were not as quoted. In such instances we reduced the size of the tent to a size that would cut to good advantage and would enable us to give our customer full value for his money. We also found that some tents, if properly made, would be larger than the sizes previously quoted, for example we found that a tent formerly quoted as being 9 feet long and 9 feet wide, if properly made, would measure 9½ feet long by 9½ feet wide. We accordingly changed the sizes of our tents to conform with actual measurements as made by us. **Tents cannot be returned,** as they have to be made to order. We warrant them to be exactly as represented. **In ordering, give catalogue number, length, breadth and price. Allow three to five days' time for making tents, and in June and July allow ten to fifteen days, according to the number of orders we have on hand at the time we receive your order. Send for samples of canvas which goes into our tents.**

No. 57E10350 Wall Tent.

We give weight of tents with poles below on 8-ounce ten[t] 10-ounce will weigh about ¼ more and 12-ounce about ½ m[ore] than 8-ounce. The weights may vary slightly, as poles do [not] always run alike. Allow three to five days' time to make te[nts] and in June and July allow ten to fifteen days. A 9½x12 f[t.] tent makes a good out house or summer kitchen.

Warning—We do not use jute rope in our tents, we use the best pure sisal rope up to and including the 12x18-foot tent, larger than 12x18, we use the best pure manila rope. On all wall tents size 12x12 and larger, we furnish top guy ropes at each end.

Order by catalogue number and style number.

No. 57E10350 **We do not ship tents C. O. D.**

Style No.	Length and Breadth	Height Wall	Height Pole	Weight, 8-ounce	Our Prices include Pole Pegs, Guys, Guy Ropes etc., Complete, ready to set up.		
	Feet	Ft.	Ft.	Lbs	8-oz. Duck	10-oz. Duck	12-oz. Duck
A	7 x 7	3	7	30	$4.48	$ 5.24	$5.85
B	7 x 9 ½	3	7	35	5.32	5.92	6.06
C	9 ½ x 9 ½	3	7½	40	6.13	7.17	8.12
D	9 ½ x 12	3	7½	45	7.21	8.43	9.52
E	9 ½ x 14½	3	7½	50	8.20	9.58	10.79
F	12 x 12	3½	8	55	8.57	10.05	11.38
G	12 x 14½	3½	8	60	9.69	11.31	12.82
H	12 x 16	3½	8	70	10.75	12.57	14.20
J	12 x 18	3½	8	70	11.12	13.96	15.76
K	14½ x 14½	4	9	70	11.54	13.52	15.31
L	14½ x 16	4	9	80	12.71	14.12	16.96
M	14½ x 18	4	9	85	14.20	16.66	18.75
N	14½ x 20½	4	9	100	15.79	18.34	20.50
P	14½ x 24	4	9	120	17.81	20.66	23.24
Q	16 x 16	5	11	90	15.79	18.59	20.92
R	16 x 18	5	11	110	17.33	20.38	22.97
S	16 x 20½	5	11	120	19.10	21.98	24.94
T	16 x 24	5	11	145	21.76	25.31	28.44
U	16 x 30	5	11	170	26.32	30.66	34.53
W	18 x 20½	5	11	175	21.84	25.41	28.70
X	18 x 24	5	11	180	24.42	28.48	32.00
Y	18 x 30	5	11	240	29.26	34.10	36.62
Z	18 x 35	5	11	290	32.56	37.97	42.70

"A" or Wedge Tents.

We do not ship Tents C. O. D.

The weight which we give includes center poles. 10-ounce will weigh one-fourth more, and 12-ounce will weigh one-half more. When poles are not wanted with tents deduct 5 per cent from these prices.

No. 57E10340 The following prices include poles:

Style No.	Length and Breadth	W'ght, 8-oz.	Height	Price, 8-oz. Duck	Price, 10-oz. Duck	Price, 12-oz. Duck
A	7 x 7 ft.	25 lbs.	7 ft.	$3.46	$4.15	$ 4.80
B	7 x 9½ ft.	27 lbs.	7 ft.	4.23	4.95	5.24
C	9½ x 9½ ft.	32 lbs.	7 ft.	4.65	5.51	6.44
D	9½ x 12 ft.	38 lbs.	7½ ft.	5.76	6.77	7.89

Miners' Tents.

For Miners, Prospectors, or may be used as play tents for children. The weight which we give includes poles. 10-ounce weighs one-fourth more than 8-ounce and 12-ounce one-half more than 8-ounce. Tents cannot be returned if sent as ordered. Send for samples of canvas which goes into our tents.

Without pole, deduct 15 cents from price quoted.

Tents are not shipped C.O.D.

Style No.	No. 57E10342 We do not ship Tents C. O. D. Size of Base	Weight, 8-ounce	Price, Complete with Pole Ht.	8-oz. Duck.	10-oz. Duck	12-oz. Duck
A	7 x 7 feet	15 lbs.	7 ft.	$2.40	$2.80	$3.37
C	9½ x 9½ feet	22 "	8 ft.	3.69	4.25	5.04
F	12 x 12 feet	30 "	9 ft.	5.60	6.45	7.90

REFRESHMENT TENTS.

Oblong or Refreshment Tent, made of plain white duck, as shown in illustration. Price includes poles, pins, guy ropes, etc., **complete, ready to set up.** We furnish all refreshment tents **with double corner guy ropes** made of best manila and fitted with **our patent non-breakable, non-slip metal slides.** This illustration shows front open and folded at the sides; the front may be closed or stretched out in front for an awning or taken off altogether, as it is put on with hooks for these changes. **Tents are made to order and cannot be returned if made as ordered.**

NOTICE—Our 12-ounce refreshment tents are made of 12-ounce double filled duck throughout. Some manufacturers make the side walls of lighter duck; we make side walls and top of 12-ounce double filled duck.

No. 57E10344 Cannot be shipped C. O. D.

Size	Weight, 8-oz.	Hgt., Wall	Height, Center	8-oz. White Duck	10-oz. White Duck	12-oz. D. F. White Duck
9x14	50 lbs	6 ft.	10 ft.	$12.55	$14.25	$17.85
9x19	80 lbs.	6 ft.	10 ft.	15.60	17.75	21.75
12x19	100 lbs.	6 ft.	11 ft.	17.14	19.60	24.30
14x21½	125 lbs.	6 ft.	11 ft.	21.10	24.10	30.15
14x23½	130 lbs.	6 ft.	11 ft.	26.00	29.75	36.50

Tent Without Poles. 5 per cent Less Than Above Prices.

EXTRAS AND DEDUCTIONS.

Where higher wall is wanted, add 5 per cent of the cost of the tent for each 6 inches extra height of wall.

Poles and pins are included in above prices.

A tent fly makes an extra movable or double roof to a tent, and affords a greater protection from sun and rain, and can be made to serve as an awning, either in front or rear of tent. They **are not really necessary, and are not included in prices of tents,** but we can furnish them, if ordered, at one-half the price of tents of corresponding size and quality, for instance, a fly for a **$10.00 tent will cost $5.00.**

When tent poles are not wanted with tents, deduct 5 per cent from above prices of tents.

Tents cannot be returned if sent as ordered.

THE SEROCO VIEW CAMERA.

5 x 7 Outfit....	$23.00
6½x8½ Outfit...	28.95
8 x 10 Outfit....	32.25

MADE IN OUR FACTORY AT ROCHESTER.

Our special prices are actual factory cost, with only our one small profit added, less than corresponding trust cameras cost the largest dealers.

SPECIFICATIONS: SOLID MAHOGANY, PIANO FINISH; NICKEL PLATED METAL WORK; KERATOL BELLOWS; REVERSIBLE BACK; RACK AND PINION SLIDING FRONT, RACK AND PINION FOCUS MOVEMENT; RACK AND PINION DOUBLE SWING, CENTRALLY PIVOTED; BOTH FRONT AND BACK FOCUS; EXTRA LONG DRAW; THREE SECTION, DOUBLE GROOVED BED.

THE FOCAL CAPACITY of the Seroco View Camera constitutes a most important feature, the 5x7 size having a bellows length of 24 inches, the 6½x8½ size, 27 inches and the 8x10 size, 30½ inches.

The Seroco View Camera and Combination Tripod.

THE SEROCO VIEW CAMERA is the highest grade view camera made, combining convenience, strength, rigidity, compactness and adaptability for the widest possible range of work to a degree never before attained. We honestly believe the Seroco View Camera to be the best view camera made, regardless of price.

THE SEROCO VIEW CAMERA meets all requirements for the very best amateur or professional work. It is a camera that is elegant in appearance, a camera that will give you perfect results and a camera that you will enjoy using.

THE WOODWORK of the Seroco View Camera is solid mahogany throughout, thoroughly seasoned and highly polished.

THE METAL PARTS are all of nickel plated brass, highly finished, carefully and accurately adjusted.

FOCUSING may be accomplished by moving either the front or the back, both being operated by fine rack and pinion adjustment.

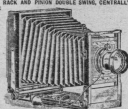

The Seroco View Camera with rear section of bed detached.

THE BACK is reversible and may be instantly changed to either upright or horizontal work.

The Seroco View Camera Folded.

THE DOUBLE SWING, which is pivoted at the center, is easily and quickly adjusted to any desired angle, both vertical and side swings being operated by fine rack and pinion movement

THE FRONT is adjustable, permitting a wide range of movement either above or below the center, operated by rack and pinion, and is securely clamped at any height by simply tightening a milled head screw.

THE BELLOWS is made from the best grade of keratol, lined with a special light proof gossamer cloth; elegant in appearance, absolutely light tight; strong and durable; the best bellows possible to make.

FOR WIDE ANGLE WORK the back may be racked close up to the front, thus permitting the use of the shortest focus lenses made, leaving no part of the bed in range of the lens.

THE BED is made in three sections, the front section hinged and arranged to fold back against the camera. The rear section is detachable, being necessary only when the extreme length of draw is used.

STRONG, RIGID, SUBSTANTIAL AND AT THE SAME TIME LIGHT AND COMPACT.

THE TRIPOD. We furnish with the Seroco View Camera a high grade Combination Tripod, a combined sliding and folding tripod with detachable head, made from selected ash, strong, substantial, absolutely rigid, the best tripod that can be made. This tripod is easily and quickly set up, readily adjusted to any desired height, and folds up so compactly that it can be put into the carrying case with the camera.

THE LENS AND SHUTTER. We equip the Seroco View Camera with either our Seroco Rapid Rectilinear Lens and Unicum Shutter (for prices see No. 20E2208 below), or with our Seroco Extra Rapid Symmetrical Lens and Automatic Shutter (for prices see No. 20E2209 below.) For illustrations and complete descriptions of these lenses and shutters we refer you to page 333.

THE CARRYING CASE. We put the Seroco View Camera in a fine carrying case, with compartments for containing the camera, the tripod, the lens and shutter and six extra plate holders. Compare the convenience of this outfit in which everything is contained in one easily carried case, with other outfits in which the case contains only the camera and about two holders, making it necessary to carry the lens and shutter, the tripod and the extra plate holders in separate packages.

The Carrying Case, with compartments for Camera, Lens and Shutter, Tripod and six Double Plate Holders.

FOR PRICES On these Cameras with ANASTIGMAT LENSES See Page 334.

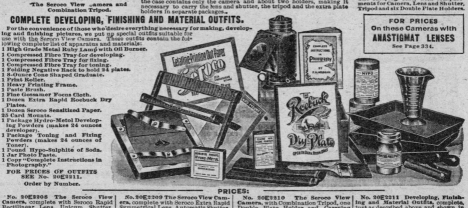

COMPLETE DEVELOPING, FINISHING AND MATERIAL OUTFITS.

For the convenience of those who desire everything necessary for making, developing and finishing pictures, we put up special outfits suitable for use with the Seroco View Camera. These outfits contain the following complete list of apparatus and materials:

- 1 High Grade Metal Ruby Lamp with Oil Burner.
- 1 Compressed Fibre Tray for developing.
- 1 Compressed Fibre Tray for fixing.
- 1 Compressed Fibre Tray for toning.
- 1 Folding Negative Rack to hold 24 plates.
- 1 8-Ounce Cone Shaped Graduate.
- 1 Print Roller.
- 1 Heavy Printing Frame.
- 1 Paste Brush.
- 1 Fine Gossamer Focus Cloth.
- 1 Dozen Extra Rapid Roebuck Dry Plates.
- 1 Dozen Seroco Sensitized Paper.
- 25 Card Mounts.
- 1 Package Hydro-Metol Developing Powders (makes 24 ounces developer).
- 1 Package Toning and Fixing Powders (makes 24 ounces of Toner).
- 1 Pound Hypo-Sulphite of Soda.
- 1 Jar Photo Paste.
- 1 Copy "Complete Instructions in Photography."

FOR PRICES OF OUTFITS SEE No. 20E2211.

Order by Number.

PRICES:

No. 20E2208 The Seroco View Camera, complete with Seroco Rapid Rectilinear Lens, Unicum Shutter, Combination Tripod, one Double Plate Holder and Carrying Case.

Size	Price
Size, 5 x 7.	$23.00
Size, 6¼ x 8½.	28.95
Size, 8 x 10.	32.25

No. 20E2209 The Seroco View Camera, complete with Seroco Extra Rapid Symmetrical Lens, Automatic Shutter, Combination Tripod, one Double Plate Holder and Carrying Case.

Size	Price
Size, 5 x 7.	$38.25
Size, 6¼ x 8½.	43.80
Size, 8 x 10.	52.10

No. 20E2210 The Seroco View Camera, with Combination Tripod, one Double Plate Holder and Carrying Case, but **without Lens or Shutter.**

Size	Price
Size, 5 x 7.	$13.50
Size, 6¼ x 8½.	14.20
Size, 8 x 10.	15.50

No. 20E2211 Developing, Finishing and Material Outfits, complete, just as described above and shown in the illustration on this page.

Outfit for 5 x 7 Camera....	$3.24
Outfit for 6¼ x 8½ Camera....	3.86
Outfit for 8 x 10 Camera....	4.92

Extra Holders, 5x7, 60c each; 6¼x8½, 79c each; 8x10, $1.10 each. See No. 20E2510

FILM CAMERAS.

No. 2 Buster Brown Film Camera, $1.65.

FOR PICTURES, 2¼x3¼.

No. 20E2236 THE No. 2 BUSTER BROWN CAMERA is a thoroughly reliable and practicable camera, although sold almost at the price of a toy. **This camera takes pictures 2¼ inches wide by 3¼ inches long,** and is suitable for making pictures of buildings, residences, street scenes, landscapes, pictures of animals, groups, portraits, interior views, etc. In fact it can be used for general all around work, just the same as higher priced cameras.

THE LENS is a first quality single achromatic, guaranteed to make good sharp pictures The shutter is of very simple construction, not liable to get out of order, and arranged for both time and instantaneous exposures.

THE No. 2 BUSTER BROWN CAMERA is made from thoroughly kiln-dried wood, covered with imitation leather, carefully and accurately constructed, all metal parts nickel plated and finely finished.

THIS CAMERA USES FILM ONLY and the film comes in rolls of six exposures each.

Price...... **$1.65**

If by mail, postage extra, 25 cents.

See No. 20E2970 for prices on films for Buster Brown cameras.

"COMPLETE INSTRUCTIONS IN PHOTOGRAPHY" FREE with the Buster Brown cameras. See page 325.

No. 20E2237 THE No. 1 BUSTER BROWN CAMERA, same style as the No. 2 described above, but smaller size. Takes pictures 2¼x2¼ inches

Price...... **85c**

If by mail, postage extra, 20 cents.

No. 1 Ansco Film Camera, $4.10.

FOR PICTURES 3½x3½.

No. 20E2240 No. 1 ANSCO FILM CAMERA. This is a small, compact camera, thoroughly well made throughout, guaranteed to make perfect pictures and exceedingly simple of operation. It is covered with the best grade of seal grain morocco leather, fitted with first quality single achromatic lens of universal focus, with three diaphragms and automatic shutter, arranged for three speeds of instantaneous exposures or time exposures of any length.

THE CAMERA IS COMPLETE in itself, there are no loose parts to become broken or lost. Fitted with one brilliant finder and tripod socket, all metal parts nickel plated and polished. Price...... **$4.10**

No. 20E2242 No. 2 ANSCO FILM CAMERA. Same style of construction as the No. 1, but of larger size, making **pictures 3¼x4¼ inches,** and fitted with two view finders and two tripod sockets, adapting the camera to either horizontal or vertical pictures. Weight of camera, 25 ounces. Size, 6⅞x4⅞x4⅜ inches. Price, complete...... **$4.95**

No. 20E2243 No. 3 ANSCO FILM CAMERA. Same as No. 2 described above, but larger size, making **pictures 4x5 inches.** Price...... **$5.85**

"COMPLETE INSTRUCTIONS IN PHOTOGRAPHY" FREE with the Ansco cameras. See page 325.

Nos. 6 and 7 Folding Pocket Ansco Film Cameras.

DAYLIGHT LOADING.

3¼ x 4¼, $13.25 **4 x 5, $16.25**

Nos. 6 AND 7 FOLDING POCKET ANSCO FILM CAMERAS. Perfect and complete film cameras in every respect, fitted with all the latest adjustments, highest grade workmanship throughout. These cameras are fitted with high grade double rapid rectilinear lenses, carefully selected and tested, and equipped with the new improved Wollensak automatic shutters with Iris diaphragms, making instantaneous exposures of various speeds, bulb exposures and time exposures.

THE Nos. 6 AND 7 FOLDING POCKET ANSCO FILM CAMERAS are made throughout from the finest selected mahogany; all metal parts, except the shutter, are nickel plated and highly polished, and the covering is the best grade of black seal grain morocco leather, genuine leather double extension bellows, fine rack and pinion focus movement, brilliant reversible finder, two tripod sockets, in short, all the latest improvements.

No. 20E2280 No. 6 Folding Pocket Ansco Film Camera, for 3¼x4¼ pictures. Price...... **$13.25**

No. 20E2284 No. 7 Folding Pocket Ansco Film Camera, for 4x5 pictures. Price...... **$16.25**

"COMPLETE INSTRUCTIONS IN PHOTOGRAPHY" FREE WITH THESE ANSCO CAMERAS. SEE PAGE 325.

THE REFLEX CAMERA.

LATEST 1906 MODEL.

WITH FOCAL PLANE SHUTTER FOR HIGH SPEED INSTANTANEOUS WORK.

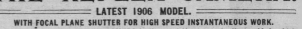

THE REFLEX CAMERA is the greatest camera in the world for high speed instantaneous work. It is made especially for

Photographing Race Horses at Full Speed, Athletic Work, Yacht Races, Birds and Animals, Football and Baseball Games, Street Scenes, Newspaper Work, etc.

THE REFLEX CAMERA IS USED BY NEWSPAPER MEN in getting **pictures for their papers, because it is the only camera that fully meets the exacting requirements in this line of work.** Newspaper men must make pictures when and where they are wanted, irrespective of light and weather conditions, irrespective of the time of day or night, and without regard to rapid movement on the part of the subject. **They must be able to make pictures under the most difficult conditions,** with poor light, with rapidly moving and changing scenes, hampered by the presence of big crowds, etc., and **the Reflex Camera is the only camera that fulfills all the conditions for this difficult class of work.**

THE REFLEX CAMERA is not only adapted to the difficult lines of work mentioned above, but at the same time is suitable for the every day needs of the amateur photographer, being capable of doing not only all work any ordinary camera does, but in addition it does the high speed, exacting work referred to above.

IN APPEARANCE the Reflex Camera is not unlike the ordinary box camera, and it is made throughout from the finest carefully selected kiln dried mahogany, covered with the very best grade of heavy morocco leather, and all metal work is finished in dead black, with nickel plated trimmings.

REFLEX CAMERA OPEN FOR USE.

PRINCIPLE OF CONSTRUCTION. The great difference between the Reflex Camera and cameras of the ordinary style lies in the fact that a very fine optically perfect mirror is placed between the lens and the plate at such an angle that the image is reflected to **the ground glass which is located in the top of the camera. THIS ARRANGEMENT PERMITS THE OPERATOR TO SEE THE IMAGE ON THE GROUND GLASS RIGHT SIDE UP UNTIL THE VERY INSTANT OF EXPOSURE.** Focusing is accomplished by a milled screw conveniently located on the left hand side of the camera, **and the picture can be focused right up to the very instant of exposure.**

THE ADVANTAGES of being able to focus and of seeing the image on the ground glass, right side up, until the very instant of exposure, will be readily appreciated by anyone who has ever tried to photograph rapidly moving objects. Remember, that the slide can be drawn from the plate holder before the camera is focused; you can insert the plate holder in the back of the camera, draw the slide, and then, **while actually looking at the picture on the ground glass,** you can move around with the camera, follow your moving object, watch it closely all the time on the ground glass, **changing the focus** as the distance between the camera and the subject is changed, until, when everything is just exactly right, the subject in just exactly the position you wish it, and the picture focused perfectly sharp, the button is pressed and **the picture is made just exactly as you saw it on the ground glass right up to the instant of exposure.**

REFLEX CAMERA CLOSED.

THE SHUTTER with which the Reflex Camera is equipped is an extra high grade focal plane shutter, that is, a curtain shutter working at the back of the camera, directly across the face of the plate. This shutter makes instantaneous exposures of any desired length from $\frac{1}{8}$ of a second up to the $\frac{1}{1500}$ part of a second. **The speed** of this shutter is varied by changing the width of the slit in the curtain, and by changing the tension of the spring, both of which adjustments are made without opening the camera. **The shutter is set** from the outside by means of a large milled head screw, and the width of the slit in the shutter curtain is also adjusted by means of this same screw. The speed of the shutter is adjusted by means of a small lever, also located on the outside of the camera. **The focal plane shutter,** with which the Reflex Camera is equipped, is, without any exception, the simplest focal plane shutter made, the least liable to get out of order and the easiest to operate.

THE BACK OF THE REFLEX CAMERA is reversible and instantly detachable, making the camera available for either upright or horizontal pictures, and the plate holder can be inserted from either the right or left hand side of the camera, as desired

WE FURNISH THIS CAMERA WITHOUT LENS, or with any of our regular styles of lenses, as described in this catalogue. We recommend, however, that, in order to take full advantage of the special features of this camera, a lens of large aperture; that is, a very rapid working lens, be selected. We particularly recommend for use with this camera our Series II Busch Anastigmat Lens, which works at a speed of F 5.5, which will be found in practice amply sufficient for high speed work. Under favorable conditions as to light, for example, on a sunny day in the summer, exposures of $\frac{1}{1500}$ part of a second, made with the Reflex Camera and the Series II Busch Anastigmat Lens, will give fully timed negatives. For athletic events, running races, pole vaulting, football games, etc., exposures varying from $\frac{1}{300}$ to $\frac{1}{500}$ of a second are usually found sufficiently short to produce a sharp picture.

REMEMBER that the Reflex Camera is always ready for instant action. With the ordinary camera it is necessary first to focus, then to set the shutter, insert the plate holder and draw the slide, and during the time elapsing while all this is being done the picture may change entirely, but with the Reflex Camera the plate holder is in place, the slide is drawn, the shutter is set, and **the operator sees the image on the ground glass and can focus right up to the very instant of pressing the button** to make the exposure. No time whatever elapses between the moment when the picture is seen on the ground glass and the exposure itself.

NO FOCUS CLOTH IS NECESSARY, as the ground glass is located in the top of the camera and entirely protected by a fine leather focusing hood. This hood is collapsible and folds compactly into the camera when not in use.

WHEN YOU ARE TAKING PICTURES with the Reflex Camera "there is nothing to watch but the ground glass."

REMEMBER that the prices we quote on the Reflex Camera are for the latest 1906 style, embodying all of the improvements which several years of practical experience have brought to the makers of this wonderful camera, making this camera not only the simplest but at the same time the most effective camera in the world.

YOU SHARE IN OUR PROFITS, as explained on the last pages.

PRICES ON THE 1906 MODEL REFLEX CAMERA.

No. 20E2225

EQUIPMENT	Size, 4x5	Size, 5x7	Size, 6½x8½
Camera with Focal Plane Shutter, but without Lens	$52.00	$60.00	$72.00
Camera complete, with Focal Plane Shutter and Seroco Rapid Rectilinear Lens, F 8.	57.60	66.65	81.75
Camera complete, with Focal Plane Shutter and Seroco Extra Rapid Symmetrical Lens, F 6	66.90	79.10	95.85
Camera complete, with Focal Plane Shutter and Busch Series II Anastigmat Lens, F 5.5	73.20	86.45	114.00
Camera complete, with Focal Plane Shutter and Busch Series III Anastigmat Lens, F 7.7	66.00	75.75	103.50
Camera complete, with Focal Plane Shutter and Seroco-Goerz Series II Anastigmat Lens, F 6.8	60.65	88.00	106.90

All above prices include one Double Plate Holder.

"COMPLETE INSTRUCTIONS IN PHOTOGRAPHY" FREE with the Reflex Camera. See page 325.

No. 20E2226 Extra Plate Holders for Reflex Camera. Price, each, 4x5, **75c**; 5x7, **94c**; 6½x8½, **$1.20**

Our Special Portrait Outfit.

No. 20E2300 THIS OUTFIT CONSISTS OF AN 8x10 CAMERA, Camera Stand and Reversible Cabinet attachment.

CAMERA IS MADE FROM BEST HARDWOOD, finely finished. All adjustments are automatic and self locking. Has 30-inch bed, best India rubber bellows.

STAND IS THE WIZARD No. 7, fitted with automatic balancing device, raises and lowers with the lightest touch, can be locked in any position by lever at side. Firm and rigid, made of hardwood, finely finished. Top measures 17x32½ inches.

THE NELSON AUTOMATIC HOLDER is included, the best studio plate holder made. Plates are put in or removed without turning a button, the back does not require to be opened, no spring to press on back of plate. Takes any size of plate from 8x10 to 2x2.

THE REVERSIBLE CABINET ATTACHMENT has spring actuated ground glass, and uses modern double plate holders.

THE FOLDING RACK is made of hardwood, holds twelve double plate holders, and is attached to side of stand.

KITS FOR 6½x8½, 4¼x6½ and 3¼x4¼ plates are furnished so that the outfit is complete for any size work from 8x10 down.

Price, complete..**$34.75**

No lens or shutter is included. Make selection from this and next page to suit your requirements.

Our Best Penny Picture Camera.

No. 20E2320 THIS CAMERA IS MADE FROM CAREFULLY SELECTED HARDWOOD and handsomely finished. It can be used for any regular portrait work in the studio, up to and including 5x7; also for copying. As a multiplying or penny picture camera, it makes 1, 4, 9, 12, 16, 20, 30 or 42 pictures on one 5x7 plate. **Only one lens required.** The mechanism is exceedingly simple, very easy to operate. Made with rising front and self locking focus lever. This camera has a 30-inch bed, rubber bellows and uses double plate holders of modern style.

Price, with one double plate holder........................**$16.90**

Extra plate holders, each..**.65**

We especially recommend our Portrait Lens No. 20E2432 for use with this camera.

The Expo Watch Camera.

No. 20E2230 A True Vest Pocket Detective Camera. The Expo camera is the smallest practical camera ever made, and, although it is so small that it can readily be carried in the vest pocket, it is at the same time a strictly high class practical instrument in every way. The Expo camera is a daylight loading camera using film, and can be loaded for twenty-five exposures at a time. This camera looks exactly like a fair sized watch and pictures can be taken with it anywhere without any one suspecting that a camera is being used. The pictures taken with the Expo camera are ⅞ of an inch long by ⅝ of an inch wide, the exact size shown in our illustration. This camera can be used for either time or instantaneous exposures and is suitable for landscapes, street scenes, groups, portraits, etc., in fact, just exactly the same kind of work which is accomplished by larger and more expensive cameras. The Expo camera is carefully constructed from metal throughout, nickel plated, fitted with a fine achromatic lens and is guaranteed in every respect. So perfect are the negatives made with this little vest pocket camera that the pictures can be enlarged without sacrificing the detail or other good qualities.

Expo Picture, Exact Size.

No. 20E2230 The Expo Watch Camera.
Price, complete, without film........................**$2.25**
If by mail, postage extra, 10 cents.

No. 20E2231 Daylight Loading Film for Expo Camera, twenty-five exposures to the roll.
Price, per roll..**18c**
If by mail, postage extra, 1 cent

The Expo Enlarging Camera.

No. 20E2235 The Expo Enlarging Camera. This is a special enlarging camera for enlarging pictures made with the Expo vest pocket watch camera, as described above. In appearance it resembles the ordinary box camera, being constructed from wood, covered with imitation leather, and so arranged that the little Expo-negative can be inserted in one end, and a piece of sensitized developing paper in the other end. The lens is located back of the negative in such a manner that the picture is projected onto the developing paper, producing, in a very few moments, an enlargement from the little negative measuring 2 by 2¾ inches. Any kind of developing paper, such as the various styles of Darko, or any brand of Bromide paper may be used for making the enlargements. Price, complete........................**$1.30**
If by mail, postage extra, 16 cents

PHOTOGRAPHIC LENSES.

The Monarch Wide Angle Lens.

No. 20E2415 The Monarch Wide Angle Lens embraces an angle of 90 degrees, making it especially adapted to photographing the interiors of buildings, out of door views in confined situations; in fact, any work where it is difficult or impossible to get far enough away from the subject in order to get it all on the plate with an ordinary lens. **Our Monarch Wide Angle Lenses** are handsomely mounted in lacquered brass with fine Iris diaphragm. Made expressly for us by the Bausch & Lomb Optical Company, and represents the latest advances in the making of lenses of this type. **The speed of this lens is F 16.**

Size of View, inches	Equivalent Focus, inches	Diameter Across Hood, inches	Price, with Iris Diaphr agm
4 x 5	3⅛	1 9/32	$5.70
5 x 7	5¼	1 9/32	6.80
5 x 8	5⅛	1 9/32	7.10
6½ x 8½	6½	1 9/32	9.90
8 x 10	8	1 9/32	12.80

Seroco Rapid Rectilinear Lens.

No. 20E2421 The Seroco Rapid Rectilinear Lens, a double lens of the rapid rectilinear type, very handsomely mounted in lacquered brass with Waterhouse diaphragms. **This lens is perfectly rectilinear,** rendering the straight lines of buildings, or other subjects, absolutely without distortion, possesses a remarkable depth of focus and flatness of field, giving the most brilliant definition and detail. **This lens is unsurpassed for landscape work,** views of buildings, and other architectural subjects, flash lights, groups and instantaneous work. **Represents better value than any other lens on the market, and is superior in every respect to many lenses** sold at double the prices. In sizes 4x5 to 8x10 inches, inclusive, we furnish the Seroco Rapid Rectilinear Lens either with or without the Unicum Shutter. **The speed of this lens is F 8.**

The Unicum Shutter gives automatic exposures of 1 second, ½ second, ¼ second, 1/25 second or 1/100 second, with one pressure of the bulb. With indicator set to "B" a pressure of the bulb opens the shutter, which remains open until the pressure is released. With indicator set to "T" the first pressure of the bulb opens the shutter, which remains open until the bulb is again pressed. Back of the shutter blades is a perfect **Iris Diaphragm,** the opening being instantly adjustable to any desired size by the index lever at lower margin of shutter. **Accuracy and entire freedom from jarring are secured by a pneumatic retarding device,** and the actuating mechanism of the shutter is fully protected from injury or dust. Made from bronze metal, with nickel plated trimmings, very handsomely finished throughout.

The Seroco Rapid Rectilinear Lens with Unicum Shutter.

Size of View, inches	Equivalent Focus, inches	Diameter Image Circle, inches	Diameter Across Hood, inches	Price of Lens Complete With Unicum Shutter
4 x 5	6¾	9	1⅛	$ 8.50
5 x 7	8¾	10⅛	2 1/16	9.50
5 x 8	9¼	11	2 1/16	11.25
6½ x 8¼	12	13¼	2 11/32	14.75
8 x 10	14¾	16	3	16.75

A COMBINATION PORTRAIT AND VIEWING LENS.

SPEED F 6. THE QUICKEST RECTILINEAR LENS MADE.

No. 20E2430 The Seroco Extra Rapid Symmetrical Lens is particularly well suited to most rapid instantaneous work and for use on dark, cloudy or misty days, where an ordinary lens would utterly fail. **Requires only one-half the exposure** that must be given with the ordinary rectilinear lens. **For all around work, including landscapes, general viewing, high speed instantaneous work, etc., the Seroco Rapid Symmetrical Lens offers advantages over any other existing type of lens on the market today.** This lens is perfectly rectilinear, rendering the straight lines of buildings or other subjects absolutely without distortion, possesses **great depth of focus,** flatness of field and **brilliant definition. The great speed of this lens,** almost equal to that of an ordinary portrait lens, makes it particularly desirable for **portrait work,** and for those who do not care to invest in both a rectilinear lens and a portrait lens, we can especially recommend the Seroco Extra Rapid Symmetrical Lens, **which will answer both requirements.**

Size of View, inches	Equivalent Focus, inches	Diameter Image Circle, inches	Diameter Across Hood, inches	Price of Lens Complete with Automatic Shutter
4 x 5	6⅜	8¾	1 9/16	$20.55
5 x 7	8	10¾	1 23/32	24.75
6½ x 8½	9 7/16	12¾	1 31/32	29.62
8 x 10	11¼	15⅛	2 11/32	36.60

THE SEROCO PORTRAIT LENS.

SERIES I. SPEED F 6.

No. 20E2432 This lens possesses those peculiar optical qualities necessary in portrait work, working very rapidly and yielding soft, brilliant negatives. **The ¼ size is particularly suitable for penny picture work and for small portraits.** Many photographers purchase ordinary rectilinear lenses for penny picture work on account of the comparatively low price of such lenses as compared with regular portrait lenses, but in this lens we offer you an opportunity to equip your outfit with a lens designed and made expressly for portrait work, a true portrait lens, at a price even lower than the cost of a rectilinear lens. **The ½ size and 4-4 size are both designed for regular cabinet work** and of the two the 4-4 size is the most popular, as it can also be used for small groups and full figures.

Size	Plate covered, inches	Diameter lenses, inchbs	Back Focus, inches	Price, with Iris Diaphr'gm
¼	3¼x4¼	1⅝	4⅛	$ 7.50
½	4¼x6½	2⅝	7	13.35
4-4	6½x8½	3¼	11	26.70

The Seroco Rapid Portrait Lens.

SERIES II. SPEED F 5.

No. 20E2436 The Seroco Rapid Portrait Lens, Series II, is a true portrait lens of the most approved type of portrait lens construction. These lenses are ground from the best imported optical glass, composed of two systems of two glasses each, the front system cemented and the rear system made with an air space between the two glasses. The special formula by which these lenses are ground, combined with their large diameter, gives them a high working speed, producing brilliant negatives with plenty of detail with the shortest possible exposures.

We recommend the Series II Seroco Rapid Portrait Lens as the very best moderate priced portrait lens ever placed on the market, and for general all around work in the studio these lenses can not be surpassed. These lenses are beautifully finished in lacquered brass with black trimmings, and fitted with a very fine Iris diaphragm.

Size of Plate Covered, Inches	Diameter of Lens, Inches	Equivalent focus, Inches	Distance for Stand'g Cabinet, Feet	Price with Iris Diaphragm
4 x 5	1⅞	7	8	$11.65
5 x 7	2¼	10	10½	13.50
6½ x 8½	2½	12.	13	18.75
8 x 10	3	14	15	30.00

The Seroco Extra Rapid Portrait Lens, Series IV.

SPEED F 4. THE QUICKEST LENS MADE.

No. 20E2441 At $58.00 we offer the 6½x8½ **Seroco Extra Rapid Portrait Lens as the equal in every way of portrait lenses heretofore sold at several times our price.** In quality of glass, perfection of finish, careful adjustment and fine workmanship; in softness, delicacy and depth of focus; in speed, flatness of field and brilliancy of illumination; **the Seroco Extra Rapid Portrait Lens** is not equaled by any other portrait lens on the market, regardless of price or maker. **The Seroco Extra Rapid Portrait Lens** represents the very latest advances in scientific lens grinding, possessing all those peculiar optical qualities and special brilliancy of definition so necessary in high grade portrait work. **The Seroco Extra Rapid Portrait Lens** preserves that softness and roundness so essential in portrait making, even when stopped down, a quality possessed by no other portrait lens made, as all other lenses become distinctly wiry when a small diaphragm is employed. **We particularly invite comparison of the Seroco Extra Rapid Portrait Lens with any other portrait lens on the market, regardless of price or maker,** as we know that in all these special points, whereby a portrait lens is judged, the **Seroco Extra Rapid Portrait Lens** is the best that money can buy. **Made by the Bausch & Lomb Optical Co. and sold everywhere at double our price.**

Number	Size of Plate Covered, inches	Diameter of Lenses, inches	Back Focus, inches	Diameter Across Hood, inches	Price, with Iris Diaphr'gm
1	5 x 8	3 5/16	8½	4 9/16	$44.00
2	6½x 8½	4 1/16	11½	5 9/16	58.00
3	8 x10	4¼	13½	5 9/16	89.00

Quarter Size Gem Lenses, $7.95 per Set.

No. 20E2445 First Quality Quarter Size Gem Lenses in sets of four, mounted on a brass plate, for ferrotype work. Price, for the set complete........................**$7.95**

Series II Busch Anastigmat Lens.

SPEED F 5.5.

No. 20E2447 The Series II Busch Anastigmat Lens works at an aperture of F 5.5, which is about double the speed of the ordinary anastigmat lens.

Absolute flatness of field and complete absence of astigmatism are obtained over the entire angle of 75 degrees, and equal definition is secured over the entire surface of the plate when the lens is used at full aperture. The use of smaller diaphragms greatly increases the covering power and renders the lens very valuable as a wide angle lens, when used on a plate larger than the size for which it is listed.

Both the front and rear combinations are perfectly corrected for spherical and chromatic aberration and astigmatism, and the back lens can be used alone (with small diaphragm) for landscape and portrait work, having a focal length one and three-fourth times that of the complete lens.

REMEMBER, that a lens having a large aperture will do any work that a lens of smaller aperture will do, and in addition will do very many things that cannot be done with a lens of smaller aperture. For instantaneous exposures on dark or cloudy days this lens is indispensable. **For portrait work** the length of exposure is greatly shortened, an advantage which will be readily appreciated. **For high speed, instantaneous work this lens is undoubtedly the very best lens on the market today.**

We furnish the Series II Busch Anastigmat Lens in Wollensak Optical Co.'s Automatic Shutter, or in the celebrated Bausch & Lomb Optical Co.'s Volute Shutter.

The Volute Shutter is the highest type of Iris diaphragm shutter, extra rapid, very compact, dust proof and durable. It is beautifully finished throughout; made like a watch in point of accuracy and fine workmanship. Recognized everywhere, by experts as the finest shutter made.

This is a large lens and can be fitted only to cameras having large lens boards and plenty of room in front. Send us your front board when you order, and we will mount the lens without charge.

The prices are for the lens complete with automatic shutter, bulb and tube.

ze of plate overed at ll aperture	Size of plate covered at F 11	Equivalent Focus, inches	Price, with Automatic Shutter	Price, with Volute Shutter
4x5	5x7	6	$25.00	$34.40
5x7	6½x8½	7½	31.00	40.00
6½x8½	8x10	10	48.00	57.65
8x10	11x14	13	Not furnished.	75.00

eries III Busch Anastigmat Lens.

SPEED F 7.7.

No. 20E2448 This lens is constructed upon xactly the same principle as the Series II Busch Anastigmat Lens described above, and in optical ualities is exactly the same in every respect, but is a much smaller lens, being of lesser diameter, permitting its use in smaller and more compact cameras.

The speed of the Series III Busch Anastigmat Lens is F 7.7, very much faster than the ordinary rectilinear lenses with which most cameras are equipped.

This is an ideal lens for any style of folding camera, and its small size and compact style of construction make it available for use with any kind of a camera. We particularly recommend this lens to those who desire to equip their cameras with a genuine anastigmat lens at the very lowest possible cost, as we are selling these lenses at lower prices than have ever been made for genuine anastigmat lenses.

Remember, this Series III lens is in every respect equal to the Series II described above, possessing the same high degree of correction, the same freedom from astigmatism, the same flatness of field, the same brilliant definition over the entire plate, the only difference being the working speed, which in this series is F 7.7.

Furnished either in the Wollensak Automatic Shutter or the Bausch & Lomb Volute Shutter.

The following prices include the lens complete with shutter, bulb and tube:

Size of plate covered at full aperture	Size of plate covered at F 45	Equivalent focus, inches	Price, with Automatic Shutter	Price, with Volute Shutter
4x5	5x8	6	$17.50	$24.50
5x7	7x9	7½	19.75	26.75
6½x8½	9x12	10	37.00	43.50
8x10	12x16	13	46.00	52.00

The Wollensak Skyshade Shutter.

No. 20E2450 The Wollensak Skyshade Shutter is an auxiliary shutter, which enables the operator to give correct exposure to both sky and foreground at the same time, which is impossible with any other style of shutter. It is a well known fact that if a sufficiently short exposure be made to give the correct exposure to the sky, the foreground will be under timed, and, on the other hand, if the exposure is timed correctly for the foreground, as is usually the case, the sky is very much over-exposed. If any clouds are present they are entirely lost in the resulting negative, because of the over-exposure of the sky.

The Skyshade Shutter is so arranged that it opens slowly from the bottom in such a manner that the foreground is given several times as much exposure as the sky, resulting in a negative that is correctly timed all over. For example, set for 1 second the shutter blade rises slowly until the top is reached, then instantly descends so that the foreground receives 1 full second of exposure, while the sky receives only about ⅛ of a second, the same ratio existing with the shutter set for other speeds.

As there are two regulating levers, each with its own mechanism, it is possible to give an infinite variety of exposures, and the operater can handle the lighting of a picture almost as an artist would his paint brush in painting.

The Skyshade Shutter can be attached to any lens. It requires no fitting whatever and can be attached to the front of your lens right over your regular shutter. The pressure of two small levers opens the flange at the back so that it can be slipped over the front of the lens, and releasing the pressure on the two levers allows the flange to grip the lens, holding it firmly in place without any further adjustment or manipulation of any kind. The shutter is thus instantly and easily attached to any lens, and just as easily detached.

This shutter is also excellently adapted to studio use, as it is almost noiseless.

Number	Light opening, inches	For Lens with free diameter of, inches	Will fit lens mounts with outside diameter of, inches	Price
1	1 5/16	1 or smaller	1¼ to 1 9/16	$ 6.95
2	1 9/16	1½ to 1⅜	1⅝ to 2 1/16	9.50
3	2 1/16	1½ to 1⅞	2⅛ to 2¾	11.50
4	2¾	2 to 2⅝	2 13/16 to 3⅞	15.00

Some lenses are made with a hood (like our No. 20E2421) and when using Skyshade Shutter this hood is removed. If your lens has a hood, take measurement for "outside diameter" with hood removed.

Seroco Cameras With Anastigmat Lenses.

ANTI-TRUST CAMERAS, WITH ANTI-TRUST LENSES, AT ANTI-TRUST PRICES.

Catalogue Number	Camera		Price, with Series II Busch Anastigmat Lens	Price, with Series II Seroco-Goerz Anastigmat Lens	Price, with Series III Busch Anastigmat Lens
20E2451	4 x5	Long Focus	$32.00	$25.80	$24.50
20E2452	5 x7	Long Focus	40.35	33.85	29.10
20E2453	6½x8½	Long Focus	59.60	49.85	48.60
20E2454	8 x10	Long Focus	*89.50	62.80	60.50
20E2455	4 x5	Dbl. Exten.	36.50	30.30	29.00
20E2456	5 x7	Dbl. Exten.	44.80	38.30	33.50
20E2457	6½x8½	Dbl. Exten.	64.00	54.30	53.00
20E2459	5 x7	View	44.50	38.00	33.25
20E2460	6½x8½	View	62.20	52.40	51.20
20E2461	8 x10	View	*90.50	63.80	61.50

The above prices all include Automatic Shutters, except those marked (*) which include Volute Shutters.

IF VOLUTE SHUTTER is wanted, with styles not marked (*) **add to above price** the difference between price of lens with Automatic Shutter and price with Volute Shutter as quoted under Nos. 20E2447, 20E2448 and 20E2449.

With the **Long Focus and Double Extension** cameras at above prices, we include sole leather carrying case and one plate holder.

With the **View** cameras, at above prices, we include canvas carrying case, one plate holder and combination tripod as shown on page 338.

Ray Filters.

No. 20E2470 A Ray Filter is a small device to be slipped over the hood of the lens during exposure. It absorbs the violet and ultra-violet rays of light and produces a picture in which the color values are correct, that is it enables us to produce, in monochrome, photographs with true color values. **Certain colors** or combinations of colors, such as white clouds and blue sky, or reds and yellows, show little or no contrast when photographed without a ray filter. **Clouds in a photograph** improve the artistic value of the picture wonderfully, and except under very unusual conditions they cannot be obtained at al without using a ray filter. **Landscapes** photographed with the ray filter possess a brilliancy and contrast which it is impossible to obtain otherwise and in the photographing of flowers, paintings or any brightly colored subjects, the ray filter is practically indispensable.

No. 1 for lenses 1 5/16 inches in diameter...... $0.60
No. 2 for fixed focus or box cameras........ .60
No. 3 for lenses 1 7/16 inches in diameter...... .60
No. 4 for lenses 1⅝ inches in diameter...... .75
No. 5 for lenses 1¾ inches in diameter...... .90
No. 6 for lenses 2 inches in diameter...... .90
No. 7 for lenses 2¼ inches in diameter...... 1.05
No. 8 for lenses 2½ inches in diameter...... 1.20
No. 9 for lenses 2¾ inches in diameter...... 1.35
No. 10 for lenses 3 inches in diameter...... 1.50
No. 11 for lenses 3¼ inches in diameter...... 1.80
No. 12 for lenses 3½ inches in diameter...... 2.10
No. 13 for lenses 4 inches in diameter...... 2.50
No. 14 for lenses 4½ inches in diameter...... 3.00

If by mail, postage extra, on Nos. 1 to 6, 3 **cents;** Nos. 7 to 10, **5 cents;** on Nos. 11 to 14, **8 cents.**

Any of the above sizes are suitable for lenses ¼ inch less in diameter than size mentioned.

State exact diameter of lens when ordering.

AUXILIARY ENLARGING AND COPYING LENSES

No. 20E2475 These lenses are used in connection with the regular lens of any folding camera, greatly increasing its power. By the use of these lenses, copying and enlarging may be done with any folding camera, enabling one to copy other pictures or photograph small articles to their full size or even larger. **A 4x5 photograph copied with an ordinary camera will make a picture about the size of a postage stamp, but when copied with the aid of this lens can be made full size or larger. Many uses for this valuable discovery will readily suggest themselves to the user.**

No. 1 for 4x5 camera with lens 1 5/16 in. in diam $0.90
No. 2 for 5x7 camera with lens 1 5/16 in. in diam. .90
No. 3 for fixed focus or box cameras............ .90
No. 4 for 4x5 camera with lens 1 7/16 in. in diam. .90
No. 5 for 5x7 camera with lens 1 7/16 in. in diam. .90
No. 6 for 4x5 camera with lens 1½ in. in diam. 1.20
No. 7 for 5x7 camera with lens 1½ in. in diam. 1.20
No. 8 any size camera with lens 1¾ in. in diam. 1.35
No. 9 any size camera with lens 2 in. in diam. 1.50
No. 10 any size camera with lens 2¼ in. in diam. 1.65
No. 11 any size camera with lens 2½ in. in diam. 1.80
No. 12 any size camera with lens 2¾ in. in diam. 1.95
No. 13 any size camera with lens 3 in. in diam. 2.10

If by mail, postage extra, on Nos. 1 to 7, **3 cents;** Nos. 8 to 10, **4 cents;** Nos. 11 to 13, **5 cents.**

In measuring your lens, take the outside diameter, remembering that the enlarging lens slips over your regular lens same as a cap.

Any of the above sizes are suitable for lenses ¼ inch less in diameter than size mentioned.

Auxiliary Portrait Lenses.

No. 20E2478 In making portraits with the ordinary folding hand camera the great difficulty heretofore has been the small size of the faces. **This** portrait lens, however, entirely overcomes this difficulty and enables anyone with any kind of a folding camera to make portraits in which the faces are large and distinct. Constructed in the same style and used in same manner as the enlarging lens No. 20E2475.

No. 1 for 4x5 camera with lens 1 5/16 in. in diam. $0.90
No. 2 for 5x7 camera with lens 1 5/16 in. in diam. .90
No. 3 for fixed focus or box cameras........... .90
No. 4 for 4x5 camera with lens 1⅜ in. in diam. .90
No. 5 for 5x7 camera with lens 1⅜ in. in diam. .90
No. 6 for 4x5 camera with lens 1½ in. in diam. 1.20
No. 7 for 5x7 camera with lens 1½ in. in diam. 1.20
No. 8 any size camera with lens 1¾ in. in diam. 1.35
No. 9 any size camera with lens 2 in. in diam. 1.50
No. 10 any size camera with lens 2¼ in. in diam. 1.65
No. 11 any size camera with lens 2½ in. in diam. 1.80
No. 12 any size camera with lens 2¾ in. in diam 1.95
No. 13 any size camera with lens 3 in. in diam. 2.10

If by mail, postage extra, on Nos. 1 to 7, **3 cents;** Nos. 8 to 10, **4 cents;** Nos. 11 to 13, **5 cents.**

In measuring your lens, take the outside diameter, remembering that the portrait lens slips over your regular lens same as a cap.

Any of the above sizes may be used on lenses ¼ inch less in diameter than size given.

The Seroco-Goerz Series II F6.8 Anastigmat Lens.

No. 20E2449 This high class anastigmat lens is made expressly for us by C. P. Goerz, of Berlin and New York, the most celebrated lens maker in the world. The name **"C. P. Goerz,"** which is engraved on everyone of these lenses, is in itself an absolute guarantee of quality.

The Seroco-Goerz Series II Anastigmat Lens is corrected to the fullest extent for spherical, chromatic and astigmatic aberration. Will cover the plate sharp at full opening F 6.8 over an angle of 64 degrees and with a small diaphragm over an angle of 70 degrees.

The single combinations, when used with medium or small diaphrams, make very valuable landscape lenses of about double the focal length of the complete objective.

We particularly recommend these lenses to owners of hand cameras, who desire to improve their pictures by discarding the ordinary lenses with which such cameras are equipped and replacing them with one of these high class, genuine Goerz objectives. We furnish these Seroco-Goerz anastigmat lenses equipped with either **the Wollensak Automatic Shutter** or **the Bausch & Lomb Volute Shutter.** In our illustration we show the lens equipped with the volute shutter.

This lens can be fitted to any folding camera.

Size of plate covered at full aperture	Equivalent Focus, inches	Price, with Automatic Shutter	Price, with Volute Shutter
4 x5	6	$18.76	$25.76
5 x7	7	24.50	29.50
6½x8½	9½	38.22	44.22
8 x10	10	48.30	54.30

Scenery or Shooting Spectacles.

Nos. 55E230 to 55E234

While these spectacles are commonly known as shooting spectacles, they are largely used by tourists in looking at scenery, especially where the light is bright and dazzling or when the ground is covered with snow, which reflects the light and tires the eyes. **The peculiar amber tint of the lenses, not only improves the view but enables one to see more plainly at a distance,** and is very pleasant and soothing to the eye. **The lenses are known as diaphragm lenses,** being sanded or ground in such a manner as to exclude the view except through the clear circle in the center of each lens.

No. 55E230 Shooting Spectacles, steel frames, straight temples, good quality, nickel plated, amber tinted diaphragm lenses. Price........16c

No. 55E231 Shooting Spectacles, steel frames, straight temples, best quality, finely tempered with bronze finish. Best amber tinted diaphragm lenses. Price........36c

No. 55E232 Shooting Spectacles, steel frames, same as illustration, but with riding bow temples, fine quality, extra finish with amber tinted diaphragm lenses. Price........28c

No. 55E234 Shooting Spectacles, steel frames, straight temples, best quality, finely tempered and extra finish, with best grade smoke tinted diaphragm lenses. Price........42c

If by mail, postage extra, each, 5 cents.

Goggles.

The use of Goggles as a protection to the eyes from light, dust, etc., is so common and well known that no comment upon them is necessary.

Nos. 55E240 and 55E241

No. 55E240 Goggles, ordinary quality, wire gauze with common smoke, blue, green or clear glasses. Price........7c

No. 55E241 Goggles, good quality, wire gauze, velvet bound edges, with smoke, blue or clear glasses. Each pair in cloth bound box. Price........20c

No. 55E243 Goggles, steel frame, velvet bound, finely finished, with stiff nose piece and tempered riding bow temples. Extra fine wire gauze and highest grade light smoke lenses. Each pair in fine case. Price........95c

If by mail, postage extra, each, 5 cents.

Eye Protectors.

These eye protectors, being extremely light and also well ventilated, are very comfortable, and as a protection against excessive light, blinding storms of sleet, snow or rain, floating cinders, mud, dust, flying sparks, are unexcelled. They are used by wheelmen, streetcarmen, railroadmen, stonecutters, firemen, millers, harvesters, in fact, by all who are in any way exposed to the danger of injuring the eyes.

No. 55E248 Celluloid Eye Protector, well made from the best transparent celluloid, felt bound, in clear, blue or green. Price, including case.....**(If by mail, postage extra, 2 cents)**.....16c

No. 55E249 Mica Eye Protector. Made of selected mica, substantially constructed and bound with corrugated felt. This Eye Protector is hinged at the center, thus folding into small space, and is made with either smoke, blue or clear mica. Price, with morocco case....30c

If by mail, postage extra, 2 cents.

Boracine Eye Remedy.

The purest and best remedy for curing all sore and inflamed eyes and for keeping them well and strong. Modern hygienic rules as laid down by the up to date physician and specialist include the occasional cleansing of the eyes the same as the use of the bath and the daily washing of the body. In using Boracine, the purest and best remedy, a few drops at a time will remove inflammation, heal any irritation or swelling, act as a tonic to the mucous membrane of the eye and restore tired eyes immediately to their natural condition and brilliancy.

Boracine is an eye remedy, not an eye water. Is absolutely harmless and highly beneficial, when used as an eye cleanser and eye protector. It will cure all forms of sore eyes, red, inflamed or scaly, itching or granulated eyelids. Complete directions will be furnished with each bottle.

No. 55E254 1-ounce size. Price, each.....$0.22
Per dozen bottles........2.10

12 cents extra for mailing tube and postage.

Eyeglass Chains and Hooks.

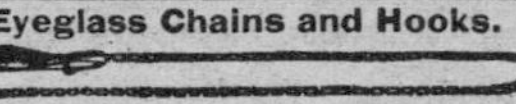

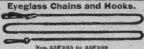

Nos. 55E265 to 55E269

No. 55E265 Eyeglass Chain, gold filled. Price, with snap and hook, 35c; with snap and hairpin, 32c; with snap and earloop........30c

No. 55E267 Eyeglass Chain, extra quality, gold filled, fully guaranteed. Price, with snap and hook, 58c; with snap and hairpin, 55c; with snap and earloop........52c

No. 55E269 Eyeglass Chain, best quality, solid 10k gold. Price, with snap and hook, $1.20; with snap and hairpin, $1.15; with snap and earloop........$1.10

Postage extra, on any style chain, 4 cents.

No. 55E275 Eyeglass Hook, fine quality gold filled. Price........15c

No. 55E277 Eyeglass Hook, solid gold, extra quality. Price........62c

Nos. 55E275 and 55E277

If by mail, postage extra, 2 cents.

Eye Shades.

No. 55E281 Eye Shade, best grade transparent green celluloid, very light and comfortable. Held in place by light elastic cord, self adjusting. Price.....7c

Postage extra, 4 cents.

READING GLASSES

are very desirable for reading fine print, and as they are strong magnifiers and give a large range of vision they are very restful to the eyes and especially desirable for old people. **They are also used for looking at photographs and other pictures, as they bring out the detail and add greatly to** the beauty of the picture, the principle being the same as the graphoscope.

Powerful Burning Glasses.

Any of these reading glasses are powerful sun or burning glasses, readily setting fire to light materials such as paper, shavings, dry leaves, etc. The larger the glass the greater is its burning power.

German Reading Glasses.

These glasses, Nos. 55E335 to 55E339 are fitted with first quality lenses, nickel plated frames and black enameled handles.

No. 55E335 German Reading Glass, 2¼ inches in diameter. Price........21c

If by mail, postage extra, 12 cents.

Nos. 55E335 to 55E339

No. 55E336 German Reading Glass, 2¾ inches in diameter. Price........37c

If by mail, postage extra, 14 cents.

No. 55E337 German Reading Glass, 3¼ inches in diameter. Price. **(If by mail, postage extra, 18c)** 53c

No. 55E338 German Reading Glass, 4 inches in diameter. Price........64c

If by mail, postage extra, 20 cents.

No. 55E339 German Reading Glass, 5 inches in diameter. Price...**(Postage extra, 25 cents)**..$1.22

Best Grade Reading Glasses.

Nos. 55E345 to 55E349

These glasses, Nos. 55E345 to 55E349, are the highest grade manufactured, with strongly made nickel plated frames, and wood handles, finished in black enamel, high magnifying power. Better or more powerful glasses than these are not manufactured.

No. 55E345 Reading Glass, 2 inches in diameter. Price........36c

If by mail, postage extra, 12c.

No. 55E346 Reading Glass, 2½ inches in diameter. Price....46c

If by mail, postage extra, 14c.

No. 55E347 Reading Glass, 3 inches in diameter. Price....62c

If by mail, postage extra, 17c.

No. 55E348 Reading Glass, 4 inches in diameter. Price....96c

If by mail, postage extra, 20c.

No. 55E349 Reading Glass, 5 inches in diameter. Price..$1.68

If by mail, postage extra, 25 cents.

Pearl Handle Reading Glass.

No. 55E350 The handle of this beautiful **Reading Glass** is made of brilliant iridescent oriental pearl, the rim is finely gold plated and the lens is best grade manufactured. Diameter, 3¼ inches. The handsome appearance and fine quality make it **especially suitable for a birthday or Christmas gift.** Price....**(If by mail, postage extra, 20c)**....$2.58

Our 69-Cent Dust Protector.

No. 55E400 Against dust it is the greatest protector ever made. For thrashers, grain men, millers, farmers and everyone whose duties call him into dusty places. **It is worth a thousand times its cost** as a protection to the lungs, to the general health and comfort. **Thousands of men are saved from consumption by the use of this protector. It protects the nose and mouth** from the intrusion of dust which is so injurious to the head and lungs. **No miller, grain buyer, thrasher or farmer is safe** without one. They afford perfect protection with perfect ventilation. **Made of fine metal,** handsomely nickel plated, bound with chamois skin, adjustable to anyone by strong elastic band, absolutely indestructible and worth a thousand **times the trifling cost** as a safeguard to health. Each protector comes packed in a neat box with full instructions for use. Price........69c

If by mail, postage extra, 5 cents.

Conversation Tubes.

Conversation Tubes are undoubtedly the best device ever made for the relief of deafness, and these are the very highest grade of conversation tubes made; finely constructed throughout, with a peculiar metallic spiral lining, which gives the tube great flexibility and at the same time keeps it fully distended in any position.

No. 55E411 Mohair Conversation Tube, medium size, tapered, covered with flexible mohair, hard rubber ear piece and bell. Price........$1.00

No. 55E412 Mohair Conversation Tube, same as No. 55E411, but larger size, 3 feet in length. Ea. $1.10

No. 55E413 Silk Conversation Tube, very highest grade manufactured, covered with finest quality black silk, tapered tube, medium size. Price. $1.05

No. 55E414 Silk Conversation Tube, same style and quality as No. 55E413, but larger size, 3 feet in length. Price........$1.15

Hearing Horns.

These horns are exactly the same as those advertised by many dealers at prices ranging from $8.00 to $15.00 each. These London Hearing Horns are constructed of light metal upon an entirely new principle. They may be carried in the pocket and when in use are easily concealed in the hand. **They are designed for the use of those who are** only moderately deaf and enable one to hear not only an ordinary conversation but sounds at a distance as well, making them suitable for use anywhere—at home, in church, or public entertainments.

Made in Two Sizes, with Black Oxidized Finish.

No. 55E420 London Hearing Horn, medium size. 2¼ inches in length. Price........$1.00

If by mail, postage extra, 5 cents.

No. 55E421 London Hearing Horn, large size, 4 inches in length. Price........$1.10

If by mail, postage extra, 8 cents.

Your money will be promptly refunded if the horn does not give entire satisfaction.

Miss Greene Hearing Horn.

No. 55E425 This is a new device, being an improvement in shape over all other Tin Trumpets, and is more easily carried. The sound receiving end is flat oval shape, 5¼ inches in diameter by 1¾ inches in depth. Its peculiar formation is especially adapted to gather in sounds and convey them audibly and distinctly to the ear; is one of the best arrangements for conversation or public speaking; can be held to the ear without raising the hand; made of metal, in two pieces, japanned black. Price........90c

Our $1.70 Opera Glass

No. 55E450 This is a good practical glass, made with a good quality achromatic lenses, 1⅛ inches in diameter; covered with black morocco leather; draw tubes and trimmings are black. It is an excellent instrument for so little money.

Price $1.70

By mail, postage extra, 16 cents.

Genuine Colmont Opera Glass, $6.85.

No. 55E460 This opera glass is beautifully finished in pearl and gold, and is strictly high grade throughout. Finest achromatic lenses, 15 lignes (1¼ inches) in diameter; oriental pearl body, pearl tops and pearl focusing screw. Draw tubes, cross bars and trimmings heavily gold plated. Price... $6.85

If by mail, postage extra, 18c.

Our $4.29 Pearl Opera Glass.

No. 55E465 We offer this gold and pearl opera glass as the best instrument of the kind ever sold for so low a price. All metal parts are gold plated. Warranted not to tarnish, fine pearl body, good achromatic lenses, 1⅛ inches in diameter. Price............ $4.29

If by mail, postage extra, 18c.

Only $12.95 for Our Highest Grade Genuine Jena Special Field Glass.

No. 55E560 This large illustration, engraved by our artist direct from a photograph, will give you an idea of the appearance of our JENA SPECIAL FIELD GLASS. The lenses of this field glass are ground from the famous Jena special optical glass, made in the Jena glass factory in Germany.

It is from this special new glass, this latest result of the experiments and investigations of the most skilled and scientific glass makers of Europe, that the lenses for our Jena Special Field Glasses are ground. They are ground by the most skilled lens grinders, they are fitted with the utmost care, and they are accurately adjusted. These lenses combine, to a degree never before attained, the highest power with the most marvelous definition and clearness.

We offer the Jena Special Field Glass not merely as the equal of glasses sold by other dealers at several times our price, but we offer it as absolutely the best field glass that can be obtained at any price. We sell this glass under a positive guarantee, and if you do not find it superior to any field glass to which you may compare it, you may return it at our expense and we will refund your money.

Bear in mind that our special $12.95 price is for the large size Jena Special Field Glass with lenses 26 lignes in diameter. This field glass measures 6 inches high when closed and 7⅝ inches when extended, weighs 33 ounces, and the magnifying power is seven times. The draw tubes, cross bars, tops and trimmings are all finished in fine black enamel and the covering is the best grade of morocco leather.

Price, complete with fine case and strap.. $12.95

No. 55E561 OUR JENA SPECIAL ALUMINUM FIELD GLASS. Exactly the same as our No. 55E560, except that all metal parts are made of aluminum, thus reducing the weight and adding to its handsome appearance. The highly polished draw tubes are finished in the natural silvery color of aluminum, all trimmings are finished in black and the covering is morocco leather. Weight, only 18 ounces.

Price, complete with fine case and strap.. $15.60

Maxim Binocular Telescope for $17.60.

An exceedingly small and compact instrument of high magnifying power.

This is a genuine Maxim Double Telescope, made by Maxim, the celebrated Paris telescope maker, and is the handiest and most efficient instrument of this kind ever devised. It is an ideal glass for tourists, farmers, hunters, ranchmen, stockmen or anyone requiring a powerful instrument which at the same time is small in size, light and compact. Our special Binocular Telescope weighs only 9 ounces and is so compact that it may be carried in the coat pocket as easily as a pocketbook, yet has a magnifying power of nine times or one-half again as high a power as the best field glasses. Our illustration shows the glass in the fine silk lined morocco leather pocket case, which is included without extra charge. When closed our Special Binocular Telescope measures only 4¾ inches high, the distance from side to side is only 3½ inches and the barrels are only ¾ of an inch in diameter. The length when extended for use is 6¾ inches. The lenses with which our Special Binocular Telescope is fitted are the best quality achromatic, accurately fitted and adjusted. The magnifying power is nine times and the definition is exceptionally fine.

No. 55E565 Maxim Double Telescope.

Price complete with morocco pocket case, as shown in illustration $17.60

If by mail, postage extra, 20 cents.

FIELD GLASSES.

We contract every season with the best known and most famous makers of field glasses in Paris and Germany to furnish us with the largest quantity of high grade field glasses ever purchased by any one house. In this way we induce the manufacturers to figure the cost to us on a basis of the actual cost of material and labor. To this price, figured on actual shop cost, we add simply our one small percentage of profit, and as a result we offer in our cheapest field glass at $3.55, an instrument for which you would pay the ordinary optician from $8.00 to $10.00.

REMEMBER You get a valuable PROFIT SHARING CERTIFICATE, enabling you to share in our profit, and get fine goods entirely FREE of cost, as explained on the last pages.

Our $3.55 Delmar Field Glass.

No. 55E500 For $3.55 we furnish this Delmar Field Glass fitted with genuine achromatic lenses, bars, draw tubes and trimmings finished in black and body covered in black morocco leather. We offer this Delmar Field Glass as the equal of field glasses sold by retail dealers at prices ranging from $8.00 to $10.00. The Delmar Field Glass measures 6 inches high when closed and 7¼ inches when extended. The object glasses are 24 lignes in diameter and the weight is 17 ounces. Magnifying power four times.

Price, complete with leather case and strap. $3.55

If by mail, postage extra, 40 cents.

Tourists' Field Glass for $6.60.

No. 55E525 This is an exceptionally fine field glass, designed especially for tourists or those who expect to carry a field glass to a considerable extent, its small size and light weight making it very desirable. Our high grade tourists' field glass is fitted with the best achromatic lenses, very carefully ground, accurately fitted and adjusted. The finish throughout is extra fine, the trimmings, cross bars and draw tubes are the best quality black enamel, the covering is the best grade of fine morocco leather, and the workmanship throughout is the best. The extra high grade lenses of our Tourist Field Glass are noted for their definition and clearness; the magnifying power is four times. Our Tourist Field Glass measures only 4 inches high when closed and 5¾ inches when extended, the draw tubes being extra long in proportion to the size of the instrument. The weight is 16 ounces, and the object glasses are 19 lignes in diameter. Price, complete with case and strap... $6.60

If by mail, postage extra, 30 cents.

$6.95 Buys a $15.00 Field Glass.

No. 55E510 This Field Glass is provided with first quality achromatic lenses, carefully fitted, the draw tubes are finished in dead black and the trimmings are in bright black enamel and nickel plate. This glass possesses higher magnifying power than the Delmar Field Glass, and the lenses are of better quality, thus giving finer definition and greater clearness. Workmanship and materials throughout are first class. Our $6.95 Field Glass measures 5¾ inches high when closed, 7¾ inches when extended. The diameter of the object glasses is 24 lignes, the magnifying power is five times and the weight is 22 ounces.

Price, complete with leather case and strap.. $6.95

If by mail, postage, extra, 42 cents.

Turner-Reich Prism Binoculars.

The bodies of the Turner-Reich Binoculars are made of aluminum and the working parts are of brass. The bodies are covered with the finest quality pebbled morocco leather and all exposed metal parts are finished in lusterless black. One of the eye piece cells is so made that it may be adjusted to accommodate observers' eyes that are not of the same power, a much commoner defect than is generally supposed and frequently only noticeable when using a high power glass. Focusing is accomplished very easily by the large mill head in the hinge, which actuates a precision screw. The Turner-Reich Instruments are adjustable for pupillary distance and provide for any separation of the eyes. An adjustable click may be set at the desired pupilary distance so that the images of both barrels of the instrument may be made coincident by simply turning the barrels until the click springs into position.

No. 55E570 6-power Turner-Reich Prism Binocular. Linear magnifying power, 6 diameters. (Superficial power 36 times.) Real field of view 6 degrees. Diameter field of view at 1000 yards, 315 feet.

Price, with solid sole leather case and shoulder strap.............. $23.00

If by mail, postage extra, 42 cents.

No. 55E571 8-Power Turner-Reich Prism Binocular. Linear magnifying power, 8 diameters. (Superficial power 64 times.) Real field of view, 1¾ degrees. Diameter field of view at 1000 yards, 246 feet.

Price, with solid sole leather case and shoulder strap........................ $28.00

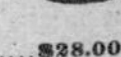

If by mail, postage extra, 42 cents.

No. 55E572 10-Power Turner-Reich Prism Binocular. Magnifying power, 10 diameters. (Superficial power, 100 times.) Real field of view, 3¾ degrees. Diameter field of view at 1000 yards, 204 feet.

Price, with solid sole leather case and shoulder strap $34.50

If by mail, postage extra, 42 cents.

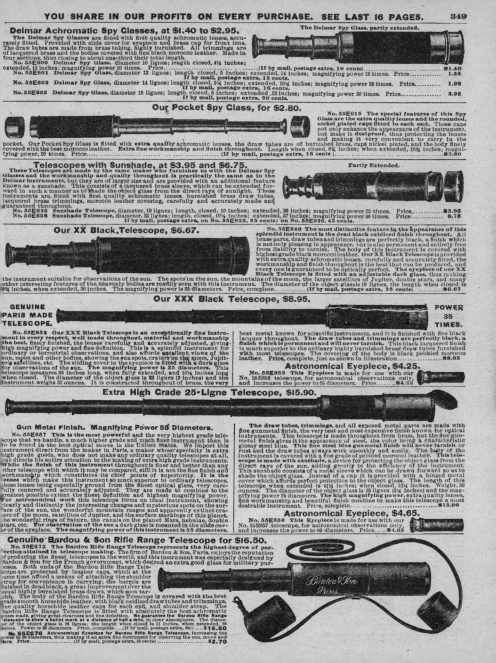

Delmar Achromatic Spy Glasses, at $1.40 to $2.95.

The Delmar Spy Glass, partly extended.

The Delmar Spy Glasses are fitted with first quality achromatic lenses, accurately fitted. Provided with slide cover for eyepiece and brass cap for front lens. The draw tubes are made from brass tubing, highly burnished. All trimmings are of lacquered brass and the bodies covered with fine black morocco leather. Made in four sections, thus closing to about one-third their total length.

No. 55E600 Delmar Spy Glass, diameter 10 lignes; length closed, 4¼ inches; extended, 13 inches; magnifying power 10 times. Price......(If by mail, postage extra, 10 cents)......$1.40

No. 55E601 Delmar Spy Glass, diameter 12 lignes; length closed, 5 inches; extended, 14 inches; magnifying power 12 times. Price...... 1.55
If by mail, postage extra, 12 cents.

No. 55E602 Delmar Spy Glass, diameter 14 lignes; length closed, 6¼ inches; extended, 16¼ inches; magnifying power 16 times. Price...... 1.98
If by mail, postage extra, 16 cents.

No. 55E603 Delmar Spy Glass, diameter 16 lignes; length closed, 8 inches; extended, 22 inches; magnifying power 20 times. Price...... 2.95
If by mail, postage extra, 20 cents.

Our Pocket Spy Glass, for $2.80.

No. 55E615 The special features of this Spy Glass are the extra quality lenses and the rounded, nickel plated caps fitted to each end. These caps not only enhance the appearance of the instrument, but make it **dustproof**, thus protecting the lenses and making it very convenient to carry in the pocket. Our Pocket Spy Glass is fitted with **extra quality** achromatic lenses, the draw tubes are of burnished brass, caps nickel plated, and the body finely covered with the best morocco leather. **Extra fine workmanship and finish throughout.** Length when closed, 6¾ inches; when extended, 16¾ inches; magnifying power, 20 times. Price......(If by mail, postage extra, 16 cents)......$2.80

Telescopes with Sunshade, at $3.95 and $6.75.

Partly Extended.

These Telescopes are made by the same maker who furnishes us with the Delmar Spy Glasses and the workmanship and quality throughout is practically the same as in the Delmar instruments, but they are of larger size and are provided with an additional feature known as a sunshade. This consists of a lacquered brass sleeve, which can be extended forward in such a manner as to shade the object glass from the direct rays of sunlight. These instruments are fitted with first quality achromatic lenses, burnished brass draw tubes, lacquered brass trimmings, morocco leather covering, carefully and accurately made and guaranteed throughout.

No. 55E625 Sunshade Telescope, diameter, 19 lignes; length, closed, 10 inches; extended, 30 inches; magnifying power 25 times. Price......$3.95
No. 55E626 Sunshade Telescope, diameter, 22 lignes; length, closed, 10½ inches; extended, 37 inches; magnifying power 30 times. Price...... 6.75
If by mail, postage extra, on No. 55E625, 25 cents; on No. 55E626, 45 cents.

Our XX Black Telescope, $6.67.

No. 55E640 The most distinctive feature in the appearance of this splendid instrument is the dead black oxidized finish throughout. All brass parts, draw tubes and trimmings are perfectly black, a finish which is not only pleasing in appearance, but is also permanent and entirely free from liability to tarnish. The body of this instrument is covered with highest grade black morocco leather. **Our XX Black Telescope** is provided with extra quality achromatic lenses, carefully and accurately fitted, the workmanship and finish throughout is the best that can be produced, and every one is guaranteed to be optically perfect. **The eyepiece of our XX Black Telescope is fitted with an adjustable dark glass**, thus making the instrument suitable for observations of the sun. The spots on the sun, the mountains of the moon, the larger satellites of Jupiter, double stars, and many other interesting features of the heavenly bodies are readily seen with this instrument. The diameter of the object glass is 19 lignes, the length when closed is 9¾ inches, when extended, 30 inches. The magnifying power is 25 diameters. Price, complete......(If by mail, postage extra, 25 cents)......$6.67

Our XXX Black Telescope, $8.95.

GENUINE PARIS MADE TELESCOPE. POWER 35 TIMES.

No. 55E652 Our XXX Black Telescope is an exceptionally fine instrument in every respect, well made throughout, material and workmanship the best, finely finished, the lenses carefully and accurately adjusted, giving high magnifying power and fine definition. This is a splendid instrument for ordinary or terrestrial observations, and also affords excellent views of the sun, moon and other bodies, showing the sun spots, craters on the moon, Jupiter's satellites, etc. The sliding cover in the eyepiece is fitted with a dark glass for observations of the sun. **The magnifying power is 35 diameters.** This telescope measures 36 inches long, when fully extended, and 10¼ inches long when closed. The diameter of the object glass is 22 lignes (2 inches) and the instrument weighs 32 ounces. It is constructed throughout of brass, the very best metal known for scientific instruments, and it is finished with fine black lacquer throughout. **The draw tubes and trimmings are perfectly black, a finish which is permanent and will never tarnish.** This black lacquered finish is much superior to the ordinary highly burnished brass draw tubes furnished with most telescopes. The covering of the body is black pebbled morocco leather. Price, complete, just as shown in illustration......$8.95

Astronomical Eyepiece, $4.25.

No. 55E653 This Eyepiece is made for use with our No. 55E652 telescope, for astronomical observations only, and increases the power to 55 diameters. Price......$4.25

Extra High Grade 25-Ligne Telescope, $15.90.

Gun Metal Finish. Magnifying Power 55 Diameters.

No. 55E657 This is the most powerful and the very highest grade telescope that we handle, a much higher grade and much finer instrument than is to be found in the best optical stores in the United States. We import this instrument direct from the maker in Paris, a maker whose specialty is extra high grade goods, who does not make any ordinary quality telescopes at all, but directs his entire attention to the making of extra high grade instruments. **While the finish of this instrument** throughout is finer and better than any other telescope with which it may be compared, still it is not the fine finish and workmanship which constitutes its chief points of superiority. **It is the lenses** which make this instrument so much superior to ordinary telescopes, these lenses being especially ground from the finest optical glass, very carefully centered and accurately adjusted. They are made to combine to the greatest possible extent the finest definition and highest magnifying power. **For astronomical work** this telescope forms an ideal instrument, showing clearly and distinctly the interesting changes and mysterious spots on the surface of the sun, the wonderful mountain ranges and apparently extinct craters of the moon, satellites of Jupiter, and the surface markings of this planet, the wonderful rings of Saturn, the canals on the planet Mars, nebulae, double stars, etc. **For observation of the sun** a dark glass is mounted in the slide cover of the eyepiece. **The magnifying power of this instrument is 55 diameters.** **The draw tubes, trimmings, and all exposed metal parts are made with** fine gunmetal finish, the very best and most expensive finish known for optical instruments. This telescope is made throughout from brass, but the fine gunmetal finish gives it the appearance of steel, the color being a characteristic glossy steel blue. **This fine steel blue gunmetal finish will never tarnish** or rust and the draw tubes always work smoothly and easily. The body of the instrument is covered with a fine grade of pebbled morocco leather. **This telescope is made with sunshade**, a device for protecting the object glass from the direct rays of the sun, adding greatly to the efficiency of the instrument. This sunshade consists of a metal sleeve which can be drawn forward so as to shade the object glass. Instead of a cap it is provided with a hinged metal cover which affords perfect protection to the object glass. The length of this telescope when extended is 41½ inches; when closed, 12¼ inches. Weight, 50 ounces. The diameter of the object glass is 25 lignes (2¼ inches) and the magnifying power 55 diameters. **The high magnifying power**, extra quality lenses, fine workmanship and beautiful finish combine to make this telescope a most desirable instrument. Price, complete......$15.90

Astronomical Eyepiece, $4.65.

No. 55E658 This Eyepiece is made for use with our No. 55E657 telescope, for astronomical observations only, and increases the power to 80 diameters. Price......$4.65

Genuine Bardou & Son Rifle Range Telescope for $16.50.

No. 55E675 The Bardou Rifle Range Telescope represents the highest degree of perfection attained in telescope making. The firm of Bardou & Son, Paris, enjoys the reputation of producing the finest telescopes in the world, and this instrument was especially designed by Bardou & Son for the French government, which desired an extra good glass for military purposes. Both ends of the Bardou Rifle Range Telescope are protected by leather caps, which at the same time afford a means of attaching the shoulder strap for convenience in carrying; the barrels are finished in dead black, a great improvement over the usual highly burnished brass draws, which soon tarnish. The body of the Bardou Rifle Range Telescope is covered with the best grade smooth horsehide leather, with black oxidized draw tubes and trimmings, fine quality horsehide leather caps for each end, and shoulder strap. The Bardou Rifle Range Telescope is fitted with absolutely the best achromatic lenses made, giving great clearness and fine definition. **We guarantee the Bardou Rifle Range Telescope to show a bullet mark at a distance of half a mile**, in clear atmosphere. The diameter of the object glass is 22 lignes; the length when closed is 11 inches, when extended, 36 inches. Power is 33 diameters. Price, complete....(If by mail, postage extra, 60c)....$16.50

No. 55E676 Astronomical Eyepiece for Bardou Rifle Range Telescope, increasing the power to 50 diameters, thus making it an extra fine instrument for observing the sun, moon and stars. Price......(If by mail, postage extra, 10 cents)......$2.70

MAGNIFIERS.

Tripod Microscope.

No. 55E710 Tripod Microscope, adapted to a variety of uses where a short focus and high magnifying power is desirable. Adjustable focus, extra high grade lens, strong, heavy brass mountings, with fine lacquered finish. The best tripod microscope made. Price....................30c
If by mail, postage extra, 6 cents.

Combination Microscope.

No. 55E719 Combination Microscope with lacquered brass case, 2 inches in length, has two lenses, one of very high power, the other of medium power; is especially adapted for the pocket. Price, including one insect holder..(Postage extra, 5 cents)....18c

Prospectors' Magnifying Glass.

No. 55E725 Prospectors' Magnifying Glass, heavy, well finished hard rubber case, two lenses, 1 inch and 1¼ inches in diameter, of high magnifying power. Strong and durable. **Especially adapted to the use of mineral prospectors,** being designed by a mining expert of long experience and made expressly for us by one of the best optical manufacturers in the world. Price, $1.95
If by mail, postage extra, 5 cents.

Triple Lens Magnifiers.

These are the most powerful instruments made in this style of construction, having three extra fine quality magnifying glasses, which can be used separately or all together, as desired, thus giving a range of power. The three lenses used together form an extra powerful magnifier. Mounted in finely finished rubber cases.

No. 55E746 Diameter of lenses, ½, ⅝ and ¾ inch. Price..**43c**
By mail, postage extra, 2 cents.

No. 55E747 Diameter of lenses, ⅝, ¾ and ⅞ inch. Price...(Postage extra, 2 cents)...**57c**

No. 55E748 Diameter of lenses, ¾, ⅞ and 1 inch. Price..........(If by mail, postage extra, 4 cents)..........**72c**

FOLDING CODDINGTONS.

These Coddington Magnifiers are made with folding metal cases, nickel plated, making them very convenient for carrying in the pocket. They are fitted with very fine double achromatic lenses of high power.

No. 55E781 Diameter, ¾ inch. Price..............**$0.75**
If by mail, postage extra, 3 cents.

No. 55E782 Diameter, 1 inch. Price..............**1.00**
If by mail, postage extra, 5 cents.

No. 55E783 Diameter, 1⅛ inches. Price..............**1.25**
If by mail, postage extra, 5 cents.

No. 55E784 Diameter, 1⅜ inches. Price..............**1.40**
If by mail, postage extra, 8 cents.

Gem Microscope, $1.75.

No. 55E805 This little instrument is designed especially for beginners in this fascinating study, and its simplicity, compact form and low price make it a very popular style. It is substantially made of brass throughout, stands 6 inches high, has one eyepiece and one objective giving magnifying power of 20 diameters. Beneath the stage a mirror is provided for illumination of transparent objects. The Gem Microscope has sufficient power to render the minute objects in mineral, animal and vegetable life distinctly visible and will prove a source of enjoyment and profitable instruction. Price, complete in polished wood case..............**$1.75**
If by mail, postage extra, 14 cents.

THERMOMETERS.

Distance Reading Thermometers.

In the Distance Reading Thermometers the scale and figures are large and very distinct, the tube magnifies the column of red spirit, and the temperature is therefore easily read at a distance of from 15 to 25 feet. They are very convenient and present a handsome appearance.

No. 55E914 Distance Reading Thermometer, enameled metal case, large black figures, red spirit tube, 7¾ inches long. Price..............**12c**
If by mail, postage extra, 6 cents.

No. 55E915 Distance Reading Thermometer, same style as No. 55E914, but 2¾ inches wide by 9¼ long, with extra large and plain figures, easily read at a distance of 25 feet. Price..............**15c**
If by mail, postage extra, 11 cents.

Tin Case Outdoor Thermometers.

No. 55E905 Japanned Tin Case Thermometer, ordinary grade, black figures on light metal scale; mercury tube. Length, 8 inches. Price..............**10c**
If by mail, postage extra 7 cents.

No. 55E908 Japanned Tin Case Thermometer, good quality, heavier, better made and more accurate than the preceding style; seasoned tubes of standard size, mercury only; good reliable thermometer for ordinary use. Length, 8 inches. Price..............**19c**
If by mail, postage extra, 8 cents.

No. 55E911 Japanned Tin Case Thermometer, best grade made, white figures and graduations upon black oxidized scale, thoroughly seasoned tubes of large size, good material and workmanship throughout, and guaranteed absolutely accurate; mercury only. Length, 8 inches. Retails everywhere at $1.00. Price..............**58c**
If by mail, postage extra, 10 cents.

No. 55E913 Japanned Tin Case Thermometer, with red spirit tubes, graduated to 50 or 60 degrees below zero. Carefully tested for accuracy and is perfectly reliable. Length, 12 inches. Price..............**39c**
If by mail, postage extra, 13 cents.

No. 55E911

Storm Glass Thermometers.

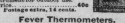

No. 55E930 The Old Original Poole's Barometer, a combined storm glass and thermometer, mounted upon varnished wood case, 3 inches wide by 9 inches long. This storm glass foretells the weather with a fair degree of accuracy for 24 hours in advance, and the thermometer shows correct temperature. Price..............**16c**
If by mail, postage extra, 12 cents.

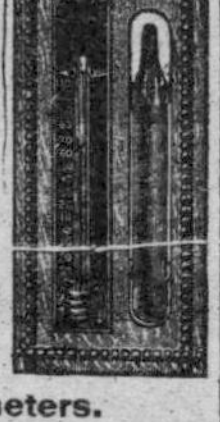

No. 55E932 Antique Oak Storm Glass and Thermometer combined, mounted upon carved oak back with fancy beaded edge, black oxidized metal scale to thermometer with brass mountings, extra large storm glass with etched lettering. A reliable and handsome instrument. Price..............**58c**
If by mail, postage extra, 17c.

No. 55E934 Copper Case Storm Glass and Thermometer, case made of polished copper, silvered metal scale, high grade thermometer with standard size tube, mercury. A very serviceable instrument for outdoor use. Price..............**40c**
Postage extra, 14 cents.

Fever Thermometers.

Clinical or fever thermometers are used, as the name implies, for taking the temperature in cases of sickness. **No family should be without a good fever thermometer, and we handle only the highest grade, as a cheap or inaccurate instrument is worse than useless.**

No. 55E940 Fever Thermometer, 4 inches long, magnifying tube, self registering, in hard rubber case, very accurate and guaranteed. A certificate of accuracy given with each one. Price..............**78c**
If by mail, postage extra, 3 cents.

No. 55E942 Fever Thermometer, 4 inches long, self registering, in hard rubber case, magnifying tube, very carefully tested and guaranteed, **registers in one minute.** Each thermometer accompanied by certificate of accuracy. Price..............**98c**
If by mail, postage extra, 3 cents.

No. 55E944 Fever Thermometer, 4 inches long, self registering; in black enameled case with gold trimmings, chain and clasp; cannot be lost out of pocket; magnifying tube; very carefully tested and certificate of accuracy with each one. Price.....**89c**
If by mail, postage extra, 3 cents.

Dairy Thermometers.

No. 55E950 Churn Thermometer, with flange scale, tested at 62 degrees, for churning. Price..............**8c**
If by mail, postage extra, 4 cents.

No. 55E957 All Glass Dairy Thermometer. New easy reading style, made with extra large plain figures, special red lettering at scalding, cheese, churning and freezing points. Red spirit column, easy to see. **Bulb weighted with shot, stands upright in cream. Very accurate.** Price..............**13c**
If by mail, postage extra, 5 cents.

No. 55E960 Dairy Thermometer, all glass. **This thermometer floats in the cream in upright position with entire scale exposed to view. Scale is hand graduated and very accurate. Red spirit,** magnifying tube, making it very easy to read.
Price..(If by mail, postage extra, 11 cents) **39c**

Incubator Thermometers.

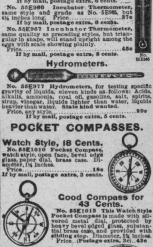

No. 55E965 Incubator Thermometer, extra large bulb and tube, very sensitive, white graduations on black oxidized metal plate. Absolutely accurate; 6 inches long. Price..............**42c**
If by mail, postage extra, 6 cents.

No. 55E966 Incubator Thermometer, same style and grade as No. 55E965, but 4½ inches long. Price..............**37c**
If by mail, postage extra, 6 cents.

No. 55E967 Incubator Thermometer, same quality as preceding styles, but triangular in shape, will stand upright among the eggs with scale showing plainly. Price..............**45c**
If by mail, postage extra, 8 cents.

No. 55E965

Hydrometers.

No. 55E977 Hydrometers, for testing specific gravity of liquids, eleven kinds as follows: Acids, alkalis, ammonia, coal oil, gasoline, salt, spirits, sirup, vinegar, liquids lighter than water, liquids heavier than water. **State kind wanted.**
Price, any style..............**29c**
If by mail, postage extra, 5 cents.

POCKET COMPASSES.

Watch Style, 18 Cents.

No. 55E1010 Pocket Compass, watch style, open face, bevel edge glass, paper dial, brass case. Diameter, 1¼ inches. Price..............**18c**
If by mail, postage extra, 3 cents.

Good Compass for 43 Cents.

No. 55E1015 This Watch Style Pocket Compass is made with silvered metal dial, protected by heavy bevel edged glass, substantial brass case, and provided with **sliding stop.** Diameter, 1¾ inches.
Price..(Postage extra, 3c)..**43c**

Jeweled Compass, 72 Cents.

No. 55E1020 This fine Pocket Compass has strong brass case with cap cover, heavy bevel edged glass, silvered metal dial, with full circle divisions, sliding stop and **jeweled cap to needle.** Diameter, 1¾ inches. An extra good compass at a very low price. Price..............**72c**
If by mail, postage extra, 4 cents.

Jeweled Compass, 95 Cents.

No. 55E1030 Our Watch Style Jeweled Pocket Compass is made with finely finished strong brass case with hinged cover, heavy beveled edge glass, silvered metal dial with full circle divisions and sliding stop. The needle is very sensitive and mounted with jeweled cap. Diameter, 2 inches. A compass that will last a lifetime and give perfect satisfaction under any conditions. Price..............**95c**
If by mail, postage extra, 5 cents.

Fine Jeweled Compass, $1.78.

No. 55E1033 An extra high grade pocket compass, made throughout in the most careful and accurate way. Strongly made lacquered brass case, 2⅝ inches in diameter, with cap cover, extra heavy beveled glass, automatic stop and best **grade jewel mounted English bar needle.** Bottom of compass is oxidized in black, with white lettering, and **the full circle divisions are engraved on a silvered metal dial raised to level of needle.** Price..............**$1.78**
If by mail, postage extra, 10 cents.

High Grade Compass, $1.90.

No. 55E1050 This is a very fine, compact compass, very convenient for carrying in pocket, made like a watch with **nickel plated dustproof case,** spring hinged cover, opened by pressing on stem, best jewel mounted English bar needle, automatic stop and heavy beveled glass. The full circle divisions are engraved on a silvered metal dial raised to level of needle. Diameter, 2 inches.
Price..............**$1.90**
If by mail, postage extra, 5 cents.

GRAPHOPHONES THAT USE STANDARD SIZE WAX CYLINDER RECORDS.

$7.50 COLUMBIA Type Q GRAPHOPHONE

No. 21E110 This is the genuine Type Q Graphophone, made by the Columbia Phonograph Company, one of the most perfectly constructed talking machines ever placed on the market at so low a price. This machine runs the regular standard size wax cylinder records just as perfectly as the higher priced machines, and is especially well suited for home entertainment purposes.

THE STRONGLY MADE SPRING MOTOR which operates the Q Graphophone, is enclosed in a dustproof barrel. Is made with a high grade governor, latest style speed regulator and is guaranteed to work perfectly. The reproducer is the latest style D, large sized aluminum reproducer, made with mica diaphragm and Brazilian pebble reproducing point.

THIS MACHINE REPRODUCES the standard size wax cylinder records just as perfectly as any talking machines costing three or four times as much.

Uses our 16-cent records, also the regular 25-cent Columbia XP records or any other make of standard size wax cylinder records.

No. 21E110 Price complete, with 10-inch japanned horn, and style D mica diaphragm aluminum reproducer. Shipping weight, 10 pounds.............. **$7.50**

COLUMBIA Type Q Special GRAPHOPHONE.

No. 21E116 Columbia Q Special Graphophone. This beautifully finished and thoroughly practical home entertainment graphophone is the regular genuine Columbia Phonograph Company's Type Q Special, made with large, heavy, substantial nickel plated and highly ornamental metal base, which not only adds to the attractive appearance of the machine, but gives it greater weight and stability, contributing to steadiness and thereby increasing the efficiency of the machine.

A fine aluminum horn 14 inches in length, with 7-inch bell, increases the volume of sound and very greatly improves the tone.

$8.40

LATEST STYLE D ALUMINUM REPRODUCER, made extra large, fitted with indestructible mica diaphragm and Brazilian pebble reproducing point, exactly the same as furnished with wax cylinder machines costing two or three times the price we ask for this outfit, enables this machine to reproduce all styles of wax cylinder records just as well as the higher priced machines.

No. 21E116 Our special price for the Type Q Special Graphophone complete, with nickel plated ornamental base, 14-inch aluminum horn and style D aluminum reproducer, just as shown in the illustration. Shipping weight, 16 pounds. Price.. **$8.40**

COLUMBIA Type AT GRAPHOPHONE,

$20.00

Runs our 16-cent Records, also the Columbia XP 25-cent Records, or any other style or make of standard size wax cylinder records.

This high grade Columbia Graphophone is an ideal machine for home entertainment, a genuine Columbia machine, made by the Columbia Phonograph Company, made with all the latest improvements, constructed with a view to strength and durability and at the same time with a view to beauty and elegance of design, making it an ornament to any parlor.

THE REPRODUCER furnished with the A T graphophone is the latest extra large style D aluminum reproducer, with indestructible built up mica diaphragm and genuine sapphire reproducing point.

An extra powerful triple spring motor is furnished with the A T machine, made with the most perfect governor and the latest speed regulator device, insuring perfect and natural reproduction, and this extra powerful motor enables the machine to run five records with one winding.

The cabinet is constructed from quarter sawed oak of elegant design, just as shown in our illustration, beautifully finished, first class workmanship throughout.

YOU CAN MAKE YOUR OWN RECORDS with this machine, as each machine comes complete with the latest improved recorder, and half the pleasure in owning a graphophone is derived from record making.

No. 21E120 Columbia A T Graphophone, complete with style D reproducer, 14-inch aluminum horn, handsome bent oak top (not shown in illustration) and latest style recorder. Shipping weight, 45 pounds. Price.................. **$20.00**

REMEMBER THAT ANY OF THESE MACHINES WILL USE OUR **16c RECORDS**

See pages 369 and 370 for particulars regarding Our Great Record Sale.

COLUMBIA Type AZ GRAPHOPHONE.

$25.00

This new type of genuine Columbia Graphophone is similar to the type AT previously described, made with solid quarter sawed oak cabinet, with special hard oil rubbed finish, a most handsome and ornamental machine in every respect, furnished with fine solid oak bent top (not illustrated), completely protecting the machine from dust, dirt or injury of any kind; made with extra powerful double spring motor, running eight records with one winding. Workmanship and finish throughout the very best.

Runs our 16-cent Records, also the Columbia XP 25-cent Records, or any other style of standard size wax cylinder records.

THE NEW LYRE SHAPED REPRODUCER is the special feature which distinguishes this machine from all other wax cylinder talking machines on the market. This new lyre shaped reproducer is the latest product of the Columbia Phonograph Company, a reproducer that is simply marvelous from a mechanical point of view and which reproduces any kind of standard size wax cylinder records without the slightest scratching or harsh metallic sound. This reproducer represents the acme of perfection in sound reproducing devices, works as smooth as velvet, producing a sweet, resonant and delightful tone.

REMEMBER, this machine, so far as the cabinet, the motor, the workmanship and general construction is concerned, is in quality exactly the same as the A T machine previously described, and its superiority over the A T machine lies simply in the new lyre shaped reproducer.

No. 21E125 Columbia Type A Z Graphophone, complete with lyre shaped reproducer, 14-inch aluminum horn, fine oak top (not shown in illustration). Price... **$25.00**

NOTE—No recorder is included with this machine. Shipping weight, 50 lbs.

COLUMBIA Type BE GRAPHOPHONE

$30.00

This is the very latest and most improved style of genuine Columbia wax cylinder talking machine, embodying all the very latest improvements, including the

NEW STYLE FLOATING WEIGHT REPRODUCER.

This is the best reproducer ever made, being so constructed that the lever raises only the reproducer point from the record instead of the entire reproducer, thus making it impossible to harm the record in any way. This new style floating weight reproducer is extra loud, reproducing the record with greater volume of sound and greater clearness than any other reproducer made. The triple spring motor, extra powerful, runs eight records with one winding, and is made with the latest style of speed regulating device and governor. Made with extra long winding crank, special machine cut gears, in short, everything that will contribute to uniformity of speed, smoothness in operation, and freedom from liability to get out of order. Oil cups are located in the rear of the machine, through which every gear and bearing in the machine can be oiled without trouble.

Runs our 16-cent Records, also the Columbia XP 25-cent Records, or any other style or make of standard size wax cylinder records.

THE CABINET is extra large and ornamental, of very handsome design, made from solid quarter sawed oak, beautifully finished, exactly as shown in our illustration, and in addition it is provided with a fine quarter sawed oak top or cover (not shown in the illustration.)

No. 21E131 COLUMBIA TYPE B E GRAPHOPHONE, complete with new floating weight reproducer, highest grade recorder, 14-inch brass horn, and ornamental quarter sawed oak cover (not shown in illustration, but is very handsome.) Shipping weight, 40 pounds. Price.................. **$30.00**

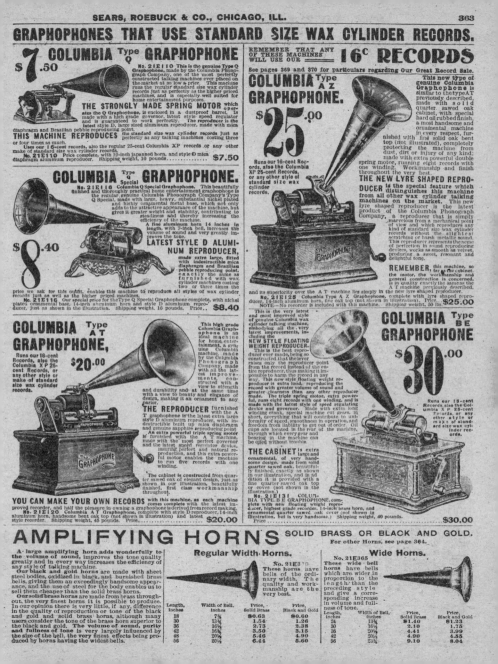

AMPLIFYING HORNS SOLID BRASS OR BLACK AND GOLD.

For other Horns, see page 364.

A large amplifying horn adds wonderfully to the volume of sound, improves the tone quality greatly and in every way increases the efficiency of any style of talking machine.

Our black and gold horns are made with sheet steel bodies, oxidized in black, and burnished brass bells, giving them an exceedingly handsome appearance, and the use of steel for the body enables us to sell them cheaper than the solid brass horns.

Our solid brass horns are made from brass throughout, the very finest horns it is possible to produce. In our opinion there is very little, if any, difference in the quality of reproduction or tone of the black and gold and solid brass horns, although many users consider the tone of the brass horn superior to the black and gold. **The volume of sound, purity and fullness of tone** is very largely influenced by the size of the bell, the very finest effects being produced by horns having the widest bells.

Regular Width Horns.

No. 21E3[illegible] These horns have bells of the ordinary width. The quality and workmanship are the very best.

Length, inches	Width of Bell, inches	Price, Solid Brass	Price, Black and Gold
18	7⅜	$0.63	$0.60
30	13¾	1.54	1.26
36	16⅛	2.73	2.38
42	16¾	3.50	3.15
48	20⅛	5.46	4.90
56	20½	6.44	5.60

Wide Horns.

No. 21E365 These wide bell horns have bells which are wider in proportion to the length than the preceding style and give a corresponding increase in volume and fullness of tone.

Length, inches	Width of Bell, inches	Price, Solid Brass	Price, Black and Gold
24	13¾	$1.40	$1.23
30	16½	2.10	1.75
36	20⅛	4.41	3.99
42	20½	4.90	4.55
56	23¾	9.10	8.04

$8.75 BUYS THE No. 1 HARVARD DISC TALKING MACHINE.

THIS TALKING MACHINE uses the wonderful disc records, the most marvelously realistic reproductions of sound ever made. This machine is strictly high grade in every respect, made from the very best materials, constructed in the most careful, accurate and substantial manner, exactly the same machine that is being sold today by other dealers for $15.00, and never before sold for less than $15.00. THIS DISC TALKING MACHINE is made with extra powerful clockwork spring motor, made with machine cut bevels and gears, and an improved form of governor, insuring an absolutely uniform rate of speed. THE MECHANISM is entirely enclosed within the case in such a way that it is perfectly protected from dust or injury and will require practically no attention whatever. THE CABINET is strongly and substantially constructed from solid oak, made in a very handsome design and finely finished.

THE SOUND BOX, also known as the reproducer, is of an improved type, made with the latest mica diaphragm, producing a volume of sound combined with a fullness and roundness of tone which is a revelation to those accustomed to the ordinary wax cylinder talking machines. This talking machine uses THE NEW PROCESS DISC RECORDS, THE GREATEST IMPROVEMENT IN RECORD MAKING SINCE THE INVENTION OF TALKING MACHINES.

THE DISC RECORDS ARE LOUDER AND CLEARER, and the reproduction is more perfect and more absolutely true to the original sound than has ever before been produced by any process. Those who have been accustomed to hearing the ordinary talking machine and the ordinary wax cylinder records will be astounded when listening for the first time to the latest new process disc records as used by this and our other disc machines.

FOR PUBLIC EXHIBITION WORK the disc machine is the only machine that should ever be used, as it is the only talking machine which reproduces the human voice, bands, orchestras and other instrumental music with sufficient volume, musical quality and absolutely perfect fidelity. THIS TALKING MACHINE WITH THE NEW PROCESS HARVARD OR COLUMBIA DISC RECORDS MUST BE HEARD TO BE APPRECIATED. It is impossible for anyone not having heard these wonderful machines to appreciate in any way the marvelous results which they give.

No. 21E207 No. 1 Harvard Disc Talking Machine, complete, as shown in illustration, with 16-inch japanned horn, improved sound box and 100 needles. Shipping weight, 28 pounds. Price **$8.75**

THE HARVARD TALKING MACHINE USES THE 7-INCH OR 10-INCH HARVARD RECORDS, 7-INCH OR 10-INCH COLUMBIA RECORDS, OR ANY OTHER MAKE OF 7-INCH OR 10-INCH DISC RECORDS.

THIS $12.00 HARVARD TALKING MACHINE, $8.40.

THIS IS A REGULAR HIGH GRADE $12.00 HARVARD TALKING MACHINE, USING CYLINDER RECORDS, NEVER BEFORE SOLD BY ANY DEALER IN THE WORLD FOR LESS THAN $12.00. OUR PRICE, $8.40.

$8 40

THIS IS THE EXACT SAME Talking Machine furnished by the makers and by all dealers in talking machines at $12.00, except that instead of the little 10-inch horn which all other dealers furnish with this machine at $12.00, we furnish a LARGE CONCERT SIZE, 26-inch Japanned Amplifying Horn with 12-inch bell and folding japanned horn stand, this horn and stand alone being sold by other dealers at from $1.00 to $2.00. THIS TALKING MACHINE is an exceedingly handsome machine, thoroughly well made in every respect and perfectly finished. The operating power is furnished by a powerful spring motor guaranteed not to get out of order. THE GEARS AND PINIONS are all machine cut, thus insuring perfect accuracy of action. THE GOVERNOR AND TENSION SCREW effectively maintain the speed at an absolutely uniform rate. LARGE SIZE REPRODUCER, extra loud, made from aluminum, with sapphire reproducing point and latest improved mica diaphragm.

THIS TALKING MACHINE is substantially mounted on a handsome oak base with highly finished bent oak cover with handle, thus forming in itself a convenient and effective carrying case for the machine.

NO BETTER, HANDSOMER OR MORE DURABLE talking machine was ever before offered by any dealer for less than $12.00, and our special price of $8.40 represents th~ very lowest price at which a strictly high grade first quality reliable talking m~ ~hine has ever been sold.

No. 21E216 Harvard Wax Cylinder Talking Machine, complete with aluminum reproducer, mammoth 26-inch amplifying horn and folding horn stand. Shipping weight, 25 pounds. Price **$8.40**

THIS HARVARD TALKING MACHINE AND 48 RECORDS $14.95

YOUR OWN SELECTION OF SUBJECTS FROM PAGES 369 AND 370.

No. 21E218 COMPLETE HARVARD TALKING MACHINE OUTFIT, consisting of Harvard Cylinder Record Talking Machine with 26-inch Amplifying Horn, japanned stand, large aluminum reproducer, just as shown in illustration and 48 genuine Columbia standard size wax cylinder P records, your own selection, as illustrated and described on pages 369 and 370. Shipping weight, 48 pounds.
Price for the entire outfit, all complete........................ **$14.95**

Extra Wide Flaring Horns.

No. 21E380 These extra wid~ flaring horns are the largest and finest horns made, regardless of price. In volume of sound and fullness of tone they are not equaled by any other horns made.

Length inches	Width of Bell inches	Price, Solid Brass	Price, Black and Gold
30	20¼	$ 4.20	$ 3.85
42	23¼	8.54	7.35
56	28	13.30	12.25

FOR OTHER HORNS, SEE PAGE 363

Flower Horns.

These new floral design or flower horns are the handsomest and most ornamental horns made for talking machines. In shape and design they are like an immense morning glory, and they are beautifully finished with a special enamel, either in black or in colors, with gold stripes or fancy decorations inside. This finish is baked on and is absolutely permanent and durable. These horns are made by a new process in such a way that all strain comes on the ribs, which are made of four thicknesses of metal, giving them great strength. The acoustic properties are unexcelled, giving full, rich, soft tones of great volume and clearness.

One size only, 31 inches long, with 22½-inch bell.

No. 21E390 Flower Horn, black, with gold stripes. Price.................. $1.20
No. 21E391 Flower Horn, maroon, with gold stripes. Price.................. 1.30
No. 21E392 Flower Horn, blue, with gold stripes. Price.................. 1.30
No. 21E393 Flower Horn, black, decorated inside. Price.................. 1.50
No. 21E394 Flower Horn, maroon, decorated inside. Price.................. 1.60
No. 21E395 Flower Horn, blue, decorated inside. Price.................. 1.60

Folding Horn Stands.

No. 21E540 Horn Stand, black japanned, folds into small space, suitable for 30-inch and smaller horns. Price........................ 35c

No. 21E542 Imperial Horn Stand, a handsome and efficient folding stand, finely made throughout and nickel plated; adapted to any size horn up to 42-inch. Price........................ 82c

No. 21E544 No. 1 Horn Stand, our best stand, extra strong and heavy; adapted to any size horn, including the largest 48-inch and 56-inch; nickel plated; folds very compactly. Price........................ $1.40

COLUMBIA TYPE A K DISC GRAPHOPHONE, $15.00

THIS MACHINE is one of the Columbia Phonograph Co.'s VERY LATEST PRODUCTIONS, embodying all of the features of the highest grade talking machines and yet sold at a moderate price. It is made with powerful clockwork spring motor and contained in a fine oak cabinet of handsome design. The sound box or reproducer is the latest type concert style with improved knife edge bearings, heavy mica diaphragm, the highest grade sound box furnished with any talking machine, regardless of price. The ornamental horn supporting arms, which are detachable, are of very handsome design and made of aluminum, this metal being most perfectly adapted for this purpose.

THE BLACK AND GOLD HORN is the highest grade horn made for Disc Talking Machines, the body of this horn being made from fine sheet steel with black oxidized finish and the bell of polished brass, giving it a very ornamental appearance.

Uses any kind of disc records, of any size or make.

No. 21E230 Columbia Type A K Disc Graphophone, complete with 16-inch black and gold horn and 100 needles. Price, **$15.00**

Shipping weight, 28 pounds.

COLUMBIA TYPE A J DISC GRAPHOPHONE, $22.50

THE TYPE A J DISC GRAPHOPHONE is made with hinged cabinet top, thus giving easy access to the motor for the purpose of oiling or cleaning. The clockwork spring motor is extra powerful, made with the latest improved governor and most perfect speed regulator. It runs two 10-inch or three 7-inch records with one winding. We particularly recommend this A J disc machine either for home entertainment or for public exhibition work, as it has proven the most popular talking machine we have ever handled. This disc graphophone, similar to the type A K described opposite, is a somewhat larger machine with a larger, heavier and more handsomely designed cabinet made from solid quarter sawed oak.

THE SOUND BOX OR REPRODUCER is the latest knife edge style, extra large size, made with mica diaphragm, and is the very highest grade sound box furnished with any talking machine, regardless of price.

Uses any kind of disc records, of any size or make.

No. 21E241 Columbia Type A J Disc Graphophone, complete with 16-inch horn and 100 needles. Price **$22.50**

Shipping weight, 30 pounds.

COLUMBIA TYPE A H DISC GRAPHOPHONE, $30.00

THE TYPE A H DISC GRAPHOPHONE is one of the highest grade automatic talking machines made by the Columbia Phonograph Co., and represents a very high degree of perfection in the making of talking machines. The cabinet is extra large and heavy of a very handsome and ornamental design, made from solid quarter sawed oak, and very finely finished throughout.

THE SOUND BOX is the very latest improved knife edge pattern, extra large, with heavy mica diaphragm, the most perfect reproducer yet constructed.

THE POWERFUL DOUBLE SPRING MOTOR with special governor and improved speed regulator is easily accessible for cleaning and oiling, and runs three 10-inch records, or five 7-inch records with one winding.

THE MOTOR IS ABSOLUTELY NOISELESS. THE ONLY DISC MACHINE MOTOR MADE WHIC OPERATES ENTIRELY WITHOUT SOUND.

Read about our **WONDERFUL PROFIT SHARING PLAN** on the last pages of this book. We guarantee to save you money on every purchase, to furnish better goods for less money than you can get elsewhere, and at the same time we allow our customers to share in the profits of this business. Don't forget that you will get a **Profit Sharing Certificate** for every purchase.

REMEMBER, that this graphophone, and all the other graphophones described on this page, use our **FAMOUS 28-CENT HARVARD DISC RECORDS.**

For list of selections, see page 367.

DON'T MISS THIS OPPORTUNITY to put in a good supply of high class, absolutely guaranteed disc records at only 28 cents each, or $3.25 per dozen.

THIS GRAPHOPHONE RUNS EITHER THE **7 OR 10-INCH COLUMBIA RECORDS, OR THE HARVARD DISC RECORDS,** A complete list of which you will find on pages 367, 368, 372 and 373.

IF YOU WANT A TALKING MACHINE which will create a sensation in your locality, a machine which people will come miles to hear, order this **A H MACHINE** and a selection of 10-inch records.

THE FINE BLACK AND GOLD HORN is of extra large size, being 22 inches long, with 11½-inch bell, the body of this horn being constructed from the finest quality sheet steel, oxidized in black, and the bell is made of extra heavy polished brass. This type of horn greatly improves the quality and sweetness of tone.

No. 21E250 Columbia Type A H Graphophone, complete with 22-inch black and gold horn and 100 needles. Price.. **$30.00**

Shipping weight, 65 pounds.

NEW COLUMBIA ALUMINUM TONE ARM GRAPHOPHONES CHAMPION, $30.00. STERLING, 45.00.

COLUMBIA CHAMPION DISC GRAPHOPHONE. $30.00

THE NEW ALUMINUM TONE ARM GRAPHOPHONES represent the latest and highest development in disc talking machines. In these machines the sound is transmitted directly from the reproducer, through the hollow aluminum tone arm, to the horn, securing in this way the **greatest possible volume of sound, the greatest beauty and naturalness of tone, and preventing, to a very large extent, the scratching sound** sometimes noticed with machines of other styles of construction.

THE MOTOR is noiseless in operation, made with the most perfect speed regulator and governor, fine machine cut gears, made to run noiselessly, uniformly, and so simple in construction that repairs of any kind are very seldom necessary, and **can be wound while playing.**

THE CABINET is made from solid quarter sawed oak, with dark finish, highly polished, handsome and ornamental design. It is fitted with a 10-inch turntable, making the machine suitable for disc records of any size.

THE REPRODUCER is the latest Columbia, knife edge, sound analyzing style, made with automatic needle clamp, by means of which the needle is inserted or removed simply by pressing a lever.

THE BEAUTIFUL FLORAL HORN adds greatly to the beauty of this instrument. This horn is made of steel, with black enamel satin finish, and gold bands, and is 17¾ inches long with 19-inch bell.

No. 21E261 Columbia Champion Type B H Graphophone, complete with aluminum tone arm, sound analyzing reproducer and black satin finish floral horn, just as described above and shown in our illustration. Price, complete........... **$30.00**

Shipping weight, 30 pounds.

COLUMBIA STERLING TALKING MACHINE. $45.00

THE COLUMBIA STERLING GRAPHOPHONE is a still larger, finer and more complete talking machine of the new aluminum tone arm construction, made with **extra powerful double spring motor, with worm gear, insuring the most perfect operation, absolute noiselessness, every part fitted with the same care that is used in making a watch.**

THE CABINET is very substantially made of **solid quarter sawed oak,** of very handsome and ornamental design, with piano finish.

THE SOUND ANALYZING REPRODUCER with automatic needle clamp, doing away entirely with the old style thumb screw, the most perfect reproducer made, is included with the Sterling graphophone.

THE HORN IS OF A BEAUTIFUL FLORAL DESIGN, resembling in shape a great morning glory, nickel plated and highly polished throughout, 17½ inches long, with 21¼-inch bell, contributing greatly to the perfection of sound reproduction, and adding greatly to the ornamental appearance of the machine.

THE NEW ALUMINUM TONE ARM constitutes the greatest improvement made in talking machines for many years. This type of construction gives the greatest possible volume of sound, the clearest and most natural reproduction, the finest and most perfect musical quality, and does away with the disagreeable scratching sound heretofore noticed in machines of the ordinary style of construction.

No. 21E263 Columbia Sterling Type B I Graphophone, complete with aluminum tone arm, sound analyzing reproducer, and nickel plated floral horn, just as described above and shown in our illustration. Price, complete.............. **$45.00**

Shipping weight, 45 pounds.

LATEST 1906 MODEL No. 3A HARVARD TALKING MACHINE.

No. 3A HARVARD DISC TALKING MACHINE, $14.90

Don't Miss Our Big Sale of

Genuine Harvard 7-inch and 10-inch Disc Records at 28c and 52c each.

For complete list of selections see pages 367 and 368. This Harvard Graphophone uses the Harvard Records, the Columbia Records, either 7-inch or 10-inch, or any other style of flat disc records.

THE No. 3A HARVARD DISC TALKING MACHINE is similar in principle to our No 1 Harvard, but is a larger and finer machine, made with a larger horn, a larger, more substantial and more ornamental cabinet and a larger and more powerful clockwork spring motor. We have designed this machine especially to meet the ideas of those who desire a somewhat better, larger and handsomer machine than the No. 1 Harvard Machine, and we have been able, in spite of the increased cost and the improvements made in this machine, to keep the price down to a figure within the reach of almost anyone.

THE POWERFUL SPRING MOTOR with which we equip the No. 3A Harvard Machine is the highest grade spring motor made for talking machines. It is made with machine cut gears, the latest type of governor and the most approved style of speed regulating device. It is a motor that we can absolutely guarantee to give satisfaction under any conditions.

THE SOUND BOX OR REPRODUCER is of the very latest type, designed expressly for the Harvard Talking Machines, made with extra heavy mica diaphragm, a sound box that is equal in volume, sweetness and perfect reproduction to any sound box with which it may be compared. This reproducer is made with the **latest automatic needle clamp,** by which needles are inserted or removed simply by pressing a little lever, doing away entirely with the annoyance of the old style thumb screw arrangement.

THE CABINET with which we equip the No. 3A Harvard Disc Talking Machine is made from solid quarter sawed oak, hard oil hand rubbed finish throughout, workmanship and material guaranteed in every way. In design this cabinet is very handsome, making the machine an ornamental addition to any parlor.

THE BLACK AND GOLD HORN is the same high grade horn that we use on all of the Harvard Machines, made of the best sheet steel, with solid brass bell, finished in black and gold, of large size, 21 inches long.

No. 21E282 No. 3A Harvard Disc Talking Machine, all complete, with 21-inch black and gold horn, improved sound box and 100 needles. Price.................... **$14.90**
Shipping weight, 40 pounds.

LATEST 1906 MODEL No. 4 HARVARD DISC TALKING MACHINE, $17.40

THIS IS THE HIGHEST GRADE HARVARD DISC TALKING MACHINE that we make, a machine that is equal in every way to disc talking machines sold by other dealers at from $30.00 to $40.00.

THE CABINET OF THE No. 4 HARVARD DISC TALKING MACHINE is in every way a beautiful piece of work, made from solid quarter sawed oak, especially selected, thoroughly kiln dried and put together by high class experienced workmen. It is made with a five-ply, built up top, hand turned decorations and lock cornered mitred moulding. The finish is the highest grade dead oil, hand rubbed finish, a finish that is not only pleasing in appearance, but at the same time durable.

THE MOTOR is an extra powerful tandem spring clockwork of the very latest type, made with machine cut gears, latest improved governor and patented speed regulating device.

THE SOUND BOX is our highest grade mica diaphragm Harvard reproducer, unsurpassed by any reproducer or sound box on the market in volume, naturalness of tone and freedom from scratch. This reproducer is made with the **latest automatic needle clamp,** by which needles are inserted or removed simply by pressing a little lever, doing away entirely with the annoyance of the old style thumb screw arrangement.

THE HORN is the same high grade black and gold horn with which we equip all of the Harvard Machines and is the largest size which we use on this line of machines, measuring 30 inches in length with bell 12 inches in diameter. This horn is made with solid sheet steel body, oxidized in black, with solid brass bell highly burnished.

REMEMBER,

This No. 4 Harvard Machine,

uses our famous **28-cent Harvard Records.** For complete list of selections, see page 367.

This machine runs five 7-inch records or three 10-inch records with one winding.

Besides the Harvard Records, this machine, and all other Harvard machines described on this page, use any style, any size or any make of flat disc records.

CONSIDER OUR PROFIT SHARING PLAN.

Your PROFIT SHARING CERTIFICATE will go a long way toward getting you something handsome and valuable, shown on the last pages of this catalogue.

IN APPEARANCE, SIZE, BEAUTY OF DESIGN, elegance of finish, and in all those points which mean quality and satisfaction in a talking machine, the No. 4 Harvard Machine is in every way equal and in most respects superior to disc talking machines sold by other dealers at more than double our price.

No. 21E284 No. 4 Harvard Disc Talking Machine, all complete, with solid oak highly ornamental cabinet, extra large 30-inch black and gold horn, improved Harvard sound box and 100 needles. Shipping weight, 60 pounds. Price.................... **$17.40**

Miscellaneous.

No. 21E585 Recorder, for Q, QC, QQ, or our special Home Graphophone. Price.................. **$2.50**

No. 21E590 Recorder, for BX, AT, AO, or Gem Graphophone.................................. **$5.00**

No. 21E595 Reproducer, for Q, QC, QQ, or our special Home Graphophone. Price............ **$2.50**

No. 21E599 Reproducer, Style D, for any wax cylinder graphophone **except** Q, QC, QQ and our special Home, Latest improved style, extra large, with built up mica diaphragm. Price.................. **$5.00**

SPECIAL OFFER: Send us your old reproducer and $3.00 in cash and we will send you this latest model improved "D" Reproducer.

No. 21E625 Diaphragm Glasses, best French glass. Price, per dozen, 30c; each.............................. **4c**

No. 21E628 Mica Diaphragms, for "D" reproducers only, best quality, built up. Price, each .. **19c**

No. 21E632 Mica Diaphragms, for sound boxes of any style Disc Graphophone. Price, each **10c**

No. 21E640 Rubber Gaskets, for reproducers or recorders. Price, per set of three, ordinary size... **5c**
Per set of two, for large "D" reproducer......... **4c**

No. 21E650 Reproducer Ball, made of Brazilian pebble, but sold by many dealers as sapphire.
Price, each.................................. **20c**

No. 21E651 Reproducer Ball, made of genuine sapphire, highest grade. Price, each.............. **75c**

No. 21E653 Governor Springs, for types Q, QC, QQ, BX, AB and our Special Home Graphophones. Price.. **10c**

No. 21E654 Governor Springs, for types AT, AO, AZ, AK, AJ, AH, AR and our $8.75 Disc Graphophones. Price.. **15c**

No. 21E660 Recorder Points, made of Brazilian pebble, but often sold as sapphire.
Price, each, in setting, flat edge.................. **52c**
Price, each, in setting, cupped edge. **60c**

No. 21E661 Recorder Points, genuine sapphire, highest grade made.
Price, each, in setting, flat edge................ **$1.10**
Price, each, in setting, cupped edge........... **1.80**

No. 21E670 Main Spring, single, for Q, QC, QQ, BX, AB and our special Home Graphophones.
Price, each.................................. **18c**

State kind of Graphophone for which spring is wanted.

No. 21E672 Main Spring, single, for AT, AK, AJ, AH and our $8.75 Disc Graphophones.
Price, each.................................. **45c**

No. 21E800 Speaking Tube, for use in record making, mohair covered, with spiral spring, lining and hard rubber mouthpiece; 22 inches long. Price **75c**

No. 21E830 Camel's Hair Brushes, 1½ inches wide, for dusting records. Price, each........... **15c**

No. 21E850 Needle Box, two parts, for used and unused needles. Price, each....................... **15c**

No. 21E875 Blank Cylinders, for record making. Standard size, same as P or XP records.
Price, each.................................. **15c**

Needles at 4 Cents per 100.

No. 21E900 These Needles, for disc talking machines of any make, are made from cold drawn, oil tempered steel wire, and guaranteed to be the finest needles manufactured. Put up in envelopes of 100 each. Price, per 100............ **4c**
If by mail, postage extra, 2 cents.
Put up in boxes. Price, per 1,000,................ **35c**
If by mail, postage extra, 8 cents.

No. 21E920 Rubber Hose, large size, for connecting large horns to any style talking machine.
Price, per foot.................................. **16c**

These remedies are neither patented nor secret preparations. We publish the ingredients so you may know what they contain. We positively guarantee that they contain the ingredients named and nothing else. They represent the best standard formulas in prepared form for the treatment of the conditions for which they are intended.

DR. WILDEN'S QUICK CURE FOR INDIGESTION AND DYSPEPSIA

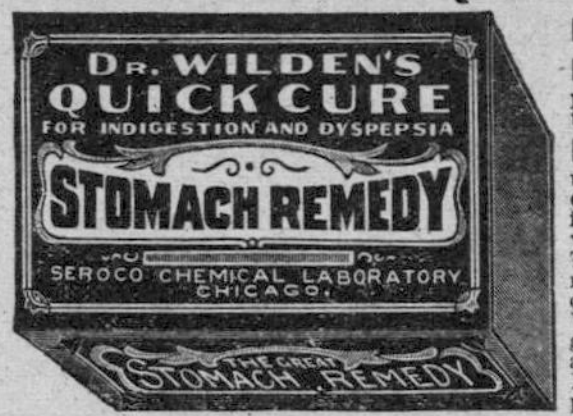

DO YOU SUFFER FROM INDIGESTION? Do you have dyspepsia? Does your food distress you?

DO YOU SUFFER from a stuffed up, choking feeling and difficulty in breathing, pain in the chest, as if a lump were there, after your meals? These are some of the easily recognized and sure symptoms of indigestion. Send for Dr. Wilden's Quick Cure for Indigestion and Dyspepsia, a stomach remedy of recognized merit. Each tablet contains in correct proportion

- Sodium Bicarbonate
- Powdered Rhubarb
- Powdered Gentian
- Powdered Capsicum
- Powdered Ipecac
- Powdered Pancreatin
- Powdered Willow Charcoal

THIS VALUABLE PRESCRIPTION is furnished by us, designated as Dr. Wilden's Quick Cure for Indigestion and Dyspepsia; is put in the form of chocolate coated, easily taken tablets and highly recommended for the treatment and cure of indigestion and dyspepsia. If you suffer from only an occasional attack of indigestion, even though your stomach is out of order but seldom, keep Dr. Wilden's Quick Cure for Indigestion and Dyspepsia on hand, take a tablet after your meals as a protection against the trouble. You can then enjoy your meals without suffering from a distressed condition of your stomach. In fact, you won't know you have such an organ as a stomach, as far as any pain is concerned.

Price only 35 cents per box, containing fifty doses, enough for fifty treatments.

FOR 35 CENTS we furnish a box of Dr. Wilden's Quick Cure for Indigestion and Dyspepsia, containing almost double the number of tablets or treatments found in boxes of other so called dyspepsia tablets that retail at 50 cents everywhere.

FOR 54 CENTS we furnish a large box containing as much as three small ones and more tablets than are contained in any other dyspepsia remedy that retails at $1.00.

DO NOT WAIT until your digestion or occasional stomach trouble has become chronic. Do not think that because you suffer from distress after meals only once in a while you should overlook it. With Dr. Wilden's tablets at hand for convenient use, you can check the trouble and at the slightest intimation of indigestion, the least fullness or uncomfortable feeling after eating, take a tablet (they dissolve easily) and in a short time you will be relieved. At the same time the stomach is toned and strengthened, better able to perform its natural functions and you are protecting yourself against after complications.

ONE TABLET OF DR. WILDEN'S QUICK CURE FOR INDIGESTION AND DYSPEPSIA helps the stomach to digest food. There is a recognized stimulating power to aid digestion in a single tablet of this stomach remedy and yet this splendid preparation does not contain one single particle of opium, calomel or any other harmful ingredient, but it nevertheless assists the stomach and strengthens the digestive organs.

YOU MAY PREFER TO HAVE YOUR PHYSICIAN take charge of your case and prescribe for you. You may wish to get information as to the merit of Dr. Wilden's Quick Cure for Indigestion and Dyspepsia, and he can judge by the printed formula and you will find that he will tell you in all fairness that this prescription is one of the best for the treatment and cure of indigestion and dyspepsia. We do not believe there is a preparation on the market that possesses more valuable properties to stimulate digestion as are found in Dr. Wilden's Quick Cure for Indigestion and Dyspepsia.

DR. WILDEN'S QUICK CURE FOR INDIGESTION AND DYSPEPSIA is the best remedy of its kind. It is, however, of importance to you to know whether it will reach your case or whether it will benefit your condition. We are therefore willing that you should send for a box of Dr. Wilden's Quick Cure for Indigestion and Dyspepsia, with the understanding that you can give it a trial, and if it does not benefit you, you simply tell us that you received no benefit from it and that it is the first package that you have tried, and we will immediately return your money. We have great confidence in this remedy and we do not want any of our customers to suffer, if we are able to offer them the means of relief and cure. We have supplied this preparation for many years, and from reports received from our customers, we feel justified in recommending Dr. Wilden's Quick Cure for Indigestion and Dyspepsia to those that need a remedy of this kind, believing that it will do for them what it has accomplished for thousands of others who have given it a fair trial and found it satisfactory in every respect.

No. 8E1 Price, per dozen regular size boxes, **$3.50**; per box **35c**
No. 8E2 Price, per dozen large boxes, **$5.60**; per box **54c**
If by mail, postage extra, small box, 2 cents; large box, 8 cents.

BROWN'S VEGETABLE CURE FOR FEMALE WEAKNESS.

One 20-ounce bottle, retail price $1.00
Our price, per bottle **$0.52**
Per dozen bottles **5.00**

BROWN'S VEGETABLE CURE FOR FEMALE WEAKNESS contains the following ingredients in correct proportion:

- Partridge Berry
- Helonias Root
- Blue Cohosh
- Black Haw
- Golden Seal
- Podophyllum
- Hydro-Alcoholic Menstruum
- Sugar q. s.

THIS REMEDY IS MOST HIGHLY RECOMMENDED for female disorders. If you have any of the following symptoms, give this preparation a test, it may afford you prompt relief and an easy cure.

NAUSEA AND BAD TASTE IN THE MOUTH, sore feeling in lower part of bowels, an unusual discharge, impaired general health, feeling of languor, sharp pains in region of the kidneys, backache, dull pain in small of back, bearing down feeling, a dragging sensation in the groin, courses irregular, timid, nervous and restless feeling, a dread of some impending evil, temper irritable, a feeling of fullness, pain in the womb, swelling in front, hysterics, sleep short and disturbed, headache, dizziness, morbid feeling and the blues, nerves weak and sensitive, appetite poor, spirits depressed, a heavy feeling and pain in the back upon exertion, fainting spells, etc.

IF YOU HAVE ANY OF THESE SYMPTOMS, try a bottle of Brown's Vegetable Cure and give this preparation a trial. It will be sufficient to show you whether Brown's Vegetable Cure is just the remedy you need, a remedy that will not only bring relief, but a cure, so far as a cure is possible, as it has in thousands of cases of suffering women, who have given this medicine a fair test. Invalids have found health from it. One bottle will be sufficient to convince you.

UNDER THE GENERAL HEADING OF FEMALE WEAKNESS are included a vast **array of systemic troubles,** including most derangements of the female organism and other difficulties. The term "female weakness" itself has no specific meaning and covers a multitude of ailments, in fact, given six different women with six different ailments peculiar to their sex, each one of them would be sure to characterize her trouble as female weakness. **Brown's Vegetable Cure** is a remedy that can be used with benefit in the treatment of diseases peculiar to women.

BROWN'S VEGETABLE CURE FOR FEMALE WEAKNESS is a prescription **that has proven highly efficient in a very large number of cases.** It is one of our household remedies, guaranteed to contain nothing harmful but made up of the ingredients named above, which are known to have the best effect in cases where the symptoms of female weakness are present. We offer it with every confidence and, if you are suffering, you can give this remedy a trial. If it affords you no relief it will not harm you and we will return you your money, if you have not used this remedy before.

No. 8E4 Price, per dozen bottles, **$5.00**; per bottle **52c**
Cannot be mailed on account of weight.

DR. ECHOLS' HEART CURE.

39 Cents and 69 Cents per Box, According to Size.

THIS REMEDY, which we supply under the name of Dr. Echols' Heart Cure, contains the following ingredients in correct proportions:

- Cactus Grandiflorus
- Digitalis
- Iron Pyrophosphate
- Caffeine

THESE INGREDIENTS comprise some of the best known remedies for the treatment of weak heart **and are considered the most valuable heart stimulants.**

THE HEALTH OF THE HEART IS MOST IMPORTANT. The heart is the great **human pump that sends the life giving blood to every part of the body.** The amount of labor it performs day and night, working incessantly year after year, is almost beyond belief. All this vast amount of work must be done and done each day. If not, your health will surely suffer in consequence of the least failure of the heart to properly perform its duties.

SYMPTOMS OF HEART TROUBLE. In order that one may determine **whether the heart is affected,** we call your attention to the following list of symptoms which denote heart disease. Fluttering of the pulse, palpitation of the heart, shortness of breath, tenderness and sudden sharp pains in the left side, dreaming of falling from a height, inability to sleep upon the left side, fainting or smothering spells, unconscious spells, dropsy, sudden starting in the sleep and noises in the ears. In describing these symptoms we have included the facts whereby heart trouble is recognized.

IT IS NOT CLAIMED that organic diseases of the heart can be cured. Such cases should be under the physician's care and attention, who, even if he cannot cure, can more accurately help to afford the patient at least temporary relief. There are, however, thousands of cases where the heart trouble is attributable to a reflex action upon that organ by other bodily ailments, and in such cases Dr. Echols' Heart Cure acts as a tonic stimulant, thereby affording the relief sought for by the sufferer.

IF YOU HAVE THE SLIGHTEST SUSPICION OF HEART TROUBLE, give this remedy a test. Dr. Echols' Heart Cure is a safe, scientific and carefully prepared remedy. It is based upon a prescription that has relieved hundreds of cases. It may fit your case exactly and it will afford you benefit and satisfactory results. If you are suffering from heart trouble, do not fail to take advantage of the opportunity of getting relief at a small expense and we are willing that you make a trial of Dr. Echols' Heart Cure. If you find that you have not received any benefit, simply write us to that effect and tell us that this is the first package of this remedy that you have tried and we will cheerfully refund your money. We do not want to sell our customers anything, whether it is an article of merchandise or a medical preparation, unless we know that they get value received for their money. The price of this remedy is very small indeed. If you know that you are a sufferer from heart weakness or other heart complications, we recommend to you giving a trial to Dr. Echols' Heart Cure. It has offered many a sufferer a means of relief and it may accomplish the same for you. Under our liberal terms you can ascertain whether Dr. Echols' Heart Cure is suitable for the treatment of your case without the slightest risk on your part. We are giving a list of ingredients that it contains and you will know that it cannot harm you and if it does not help you, you need only to notify us that the first box you have used of this remedy has not benefited your condition and we will return to you every cent you have paid for same.

DR. ECHOLS' HEART CURE is prepared in the form of a tablet and the remedy can be carried in the pocket without inconvenience. We furnish you a box containing forty doses for 39 cents, larger boxes containing one hundred doses for 69 cents.

THE PRICE OF THE REMEDY IS SMALL compared to its value and, if you have any heart complications, you should not be without a box of this valuable prescription.

No. 8E6 Price, per box, containing forty doses **$0.39**
Per dozen boxes **3.75**
No. 8E7 Price, per box, containing one hundred doses .... **.69**
Per dozen boxes **6.40**
If by mail, postage extra, per small box, 3 cents; large box, 6 cents.

CELERY MALT COMPOUND.

A HIGH CLASS PREPARATION. LARGE 20-OUNCE CAPACITY $1.00 BOTTLES.

OUR PRICE, ONLY 52c

• A NERVE BUILDER, BRAIN TONIC AND STIMULANT

CELERY MALT COMPOUND contains the following ingredients:

Celery Seed
Liquid Extract of Malt
Coca Leaves
Cinchona
Senna
Couch Grass
Rochelle Salts
Iron Phosphate
Hydro-Alcoholic Menstruum
Sugar q. s.

CELERY COMPOUND has for years been recognized as one of the best tonics. Our celery compound is improved by the addition of malt, making it superior to other similar remedies. We guarantee our Celery Malt Compound to be absolutely pure and unadulterated. It is regarded of superior merit as compared with any other Celery Compound on the market, regardless of name or price.

IT IS A TRUE NERVE TONIC, a genuine appetizer, a stimulant for both the young and old. We do not claim that Celery Malt Compound is an absolute specific for any chronic disease but it has a much wider range of usefulness, as it is just the preparation required in hundreds of cases and where no chronic disease has taken hold, it is very beneficial in hundreds of the ills that require a reconstructive tonic. It is a preparation of such usefulness that in many homes it is regarded as standard and is always kept on hand for immediate use.

CELERY MALT COMPOUND IS A RECOGNIZED NERVE AND BRAIN MEDICINE. It combines the tonic and quieting effects of celery and other standard tonics with the nutritive and digestive elements of malt and thereby gives an opportunity to secure relief in nearly every form of nerve trouble. This preparation contains in concentrated form the active medicinal properties of celery seed, well known to physicians as one of the best and most-controlling agencies for the nerves, also the phosphates, as required for a strong, healthy, vigorous body, and other medicinal properties in correct proportion, the value of which have been thoroughly demonstrated in all brain and nervous affections and in emaciated conditions. In addition it contains a large percentage of malt, which creates a tendency for building up strength. All this makes it an ideal combination, and it is not only a useful tonic and stimulant but an extremely pleasant tasting preparation as well. As a brain and nerve tonic, appetizer and stimulant it has few equals in the realm of medicine. For insomnia, nervousness or mental exhaustion, loss of appetite, impoverished blood and for that tired feeling that comes from close confinement or sedentary habits, it is very effective and infinitely better than all stimulants of an alcoholic nature.

IF YOU ARE NERVOUS, EXHAUSTED, CANNOT SLEEP, DIGESTION IMPERFECT, or if you are out of sorts generally and in a low physical condition, we recommend a trial of Celery Malt Compound. As a rule it will give new life and vigor and build up the entire system.

IF YOU ARE SUFFERING you can make a trial of this preparation, under our liberal offer, order one bottle, use it and if it does not benefit you, if you do not find that it is the remedy that suits your condition and will help you, all you have to do is to notify us that you have never used the remedy before and we will refund to you, upon request, the full amount that you paid us for the first bottle of this preparation. You assume not the slightest risk in making the test. The remedy can do you no harm and you can ascertain whether the Celery Malt Compound is the proper remedy indicated for the treatment of your condition. Large size (twenty-ounce bottle) covering about one month's treatment, 52 cents.

No. 8E8 Price, per dozen large bottles, **$5.00**; each **52c**

Cannot be mailed on account of weight.

YOU GET A

PROFIT SHARING CERTIFICATE

FOR EVERY ORDER OF $1.00 OR MORE.

You will be able to share in our profit and get something valuable absolutely free, very quickly, if you send us your orders. We guarantee our prices to be lower than you can get elsewhere, the quality of the goods the very highest, and now under our **PROFIT SHARING PLAN** you are able to share with us in the profits of this business.

Look at the last pages in this catalogue. See the beautiful articles you can get free, as your share of the profit in this business. Send us your orders for everything you need. You save money every time you buy from us. Get your friends and neighbors to order with you, thus get your **CERTIFICATES** for a larger amount and get a larger share of our profit.

WINE OF LIFE—"VIN VITAE"—WINE OF LIFE.

A TONIC STIMULANT FOR THE TIRED, WEAK AND SICK OF ALL CLASSES A RENEWER OF ENERGY; A STIMULANT FOR THE FATIGUED.

A STRENGTHENER FOR THE WEAK, AN EFFECTIVE AND AGREEABLE FOOD FOR THE BLOOD, BRAIN AND NERVES.

Retail price, per bottle..............................**$1.25**
Our price..............................**64c**

A popular medicine because it is delightful to the taste and to the stomach. Not merely a stimulant, but a genuine toner and strengthener.

A TONIC WHICH YOU WILL FIND TO REACH YOUR CASE.

WHAT IS VIN VITAE? Vin Vitae (Wine of Life) is a preparation combining the curative, healing and strengthening powers of ingredients named below with the invigorating tonic effects of the purest and finest wines of sunny California. The herbs supply the needed food and strength for the blood and nerves, the wine element counteracts the disagreeable, nauseous properties of the herbs and gives just the right fire and life to the preparation. It is a combination producing a pleasing and effective medicinal tonic.

VIN VITAE is an ideal tonic and strengthener for all, combining all the best elements of similar medicines with distinctive and peculiar advantages of its own that make it enjoyed and appreciated by all who try it. It produces a result and leaves no ill effects. A pleasant medical tonic to strengthen and tone up the nerves, purify and enrich the blood, invigorate brain, body and muscles, regulate the system.

VIN VITAE is an excellent tonic. It is in a class by itself. Are you easily tired? do you sleep badly? are you nervous? do you feel exhausted? have you lost your appetite? is your stomach weak? are you thin? is your circulation poor? are you weak, either constitutionally or from recent sickness? **You should take Vin Vitae,** because it may be just the very tonic you need.

TAKE VIN VITAE and the good effects will be apparent. You will get stronger, you will feel brighter, more fresh and active; you will feel your health and strength and energy improving. If you are easily tuckered out, if some especially hard task has exhausted your vitality, or if you have undergone any kind of a strain, mental or bodily, **Vin Vitae will act quickly** and remove fatigue and a feeling of dullness within a very short time.

VIN VITAE is agreeable to the taste and acceptable to the most delicate stomach. For tired nerves in men and women, exhaustion, overwork, weakness, weak stomach, loss of sleep, nervous trouble of any kind, for those recovering from a period of sickness, for all who feel tired, weak, wornout, **Vin Vitae,** taken according to directions, acts with quick and satisfactory results.

VIN VITAE MAKES WOMEN STRONG. Weak women, easily tired, worn out by ordinary household duties, should take Vin Vitae, the Wine of Life, as a tonic. Women sufferers from the diseases and troubles peculiar to their sex will realize benefit from the strengthening and tonic effects of Vin Vitae. It is a tonic for ailing and suffering women. Vin Vitae is giving thousands of women new health.

64 CENTS BUYS A LARGE BOTTLE OF VIN VITAE. Each bottle contains a commercial pint, a quantity sufficient for the initial treatment of ordinary cases. Vin Vitae is handsomely put up in keeping with the splendid preparation that it is.

VIN VITAE is compounded in our own laboratory, under the direction of our own skilled chemists, after a formula comprising the following ingredients:

Coca Leaves
Iron Pyrophos
Gentian
Corn Silk
Senna
Port Wine, q. s.

EVERY OUNCE IS CAREFULLY TESTED for strength and purity, so that we can offer it to our customers with our highest recommendation, for Vin Vitae has been known for years as the finest tonic wine stimulant, the most pleasant and powerful strengthener and rejuvenator. It can be taken with perfect safety. It is recommended by those who have tested it, and will be found to contain only the best ingredients and pure products that are noted for their stimulating, nourishing and strengthening properties, combined in such a way as to form a most agreeable tasting and effective preparation.

FOR LACK OF APPETITE, general lassitude, worn out nerves, Vin Vitae is recommended. It improves the appetite, assists digestion, purifies and enriches the blood, carries strength to every part of the body and induces a vigor and tone not usually obtained by the use of ordinary medicine. If you are not enjoying your usual good health, if you feel the need of a powerful tonic, you need not hesitate giving Vin Vitae a fair trial.

ORDER ONE BOTTLE as a test of this splendid preparation. We offer it on its merits, offer it to our customers as an excellent preparation. Every one who is in need of a tonic should try Vin Vitae. We offer it feeling confident that if you try it you will be pleased with its agreeable and strengthening effects, and that you will not fail to recommend Vin Vitae to your friends and neighbors.

IN FAIRNESS AND AS A PROTECTION to you, you are permitted under the terms governing the sale of our household remedies, to order a bottle of Vin Vitae, take it according to directions, and if you do not feel a decided improvement within a few days, if you do not feel that it renews your energy, soothes the nerves, improves digestion, induces restful sleep, brings back former strength, in fact, if you do not find that it does you more good than any medicinal tonic you have taken before, notify us, and we will not hesitate to refund to you on the first bottle that we ever supplied to you the full amount that you have paid for it.

No. 8E12 Price for Vin Vitae, the Wine of Life, per bottle..............**$0.64**
Per dozen bottles..............................**6.30**

Unmailable on account of weight.

SEROCO SPECIFIC FOR THE TOBACCO HABIT.

No matter in what form you are using tobacco, if you want to stop the habit, Seroco Tobacco Specific is the preparation you should try.

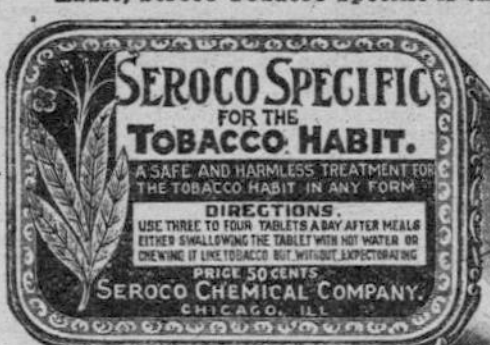

THIS SPECIFIC FOR THE TOBACCO HABIT is a preparation that is a result of long experience in the treatment of the tobacco habit. It has proven very successful to help men break this disagreeable habit. It acts without upsetting the nerves, without taking away your capacity for work and without disarranging your physical system. It is a preparation, that taken as directed, in many cases almost immediately helps to overcome the craving for tobacco and at the same time it has a beneficial effect upon the stomach and nervous system. It is therefore a tobacco specific which also has tonic effects. We do not hesitate to offer it to our customers under the liberal terms governing the sale of our household remedies. We believe many of our customers could get relief by giving this preparation a trial and, while we do not pretend to guarantee relief for every case, we offer the remedy for exactly what it is and nothing else. So much benefit has been derived from its use that we give every one the opportunity of making a trial and test for himself, and if no benefit is received, and it is the first package you have tried, we will gladly refund to you your money upon receipt of your report to that effect.

THE SEROCO TOBACCO SPECIFIC can do you no harm but only benefit when used in accordance with directions furnished. The most important ingredients which it contains are:

Powdered Chamomile, Roman
Powdered Golden Seal
Powdered Natrium Muriate
Powdered Ext. Glycyrrhiza
Powdered Cypripedium
Powdered Nux Vomica
Powdered Prunus Virginiana
Powdered Ginger
Powdered Bitterwort
Sugar of Milk q. s.

A COMBINATION which, from many experiments made, has been demonstrated as a specific for the treatment of men addicted to the tobacco habit.

Complete information and instructions how to get the best results from the use of Seroco Tobacco Specific are furnished with each package.

No. 8E16 Price, regular size box, per dozen, $3.60; each 39c

No. 8E17 Price, large box, per dozen, $6.30; each 67c

If by mail, postage extra, per box, 3 cents; large box, 4 cents.

DR. HAMMOND'S NERVE AND BRAIN TABLETS.

A GREAT REMEDY FOR WEAK MEN.

A special prescription in a prepared form for the treatment and cure of men's special diseases and all disturbances of the nervous system. Our price, per box, only 55 cents; six boxes for $2.80.

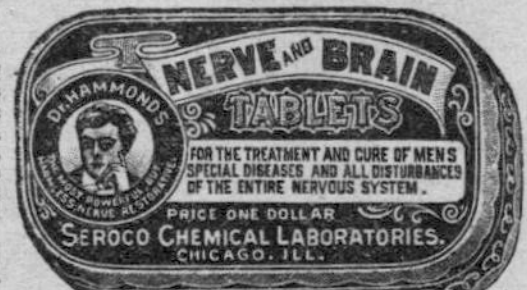

DR. HAMMOND'S NERVE AND BRAIN TABLETS are designated for the use of weak men and will not disappoint those who will use this treatment systematically and for a reasonable length of time, and a test of one single box of these tablets will be entirely sufficient to show the actual merit which they possess.

THOUSANDS OF MEN IN ILL HEALTH, or only slightly sick from other causes, yes, thousands of men who otherwise are strong and well, are suffering from a weakness which they are desirous and anxious to overcome. In some cases, owing to the peculiar cause of the weakness, it may require the personal supervision and treatment by a reliable physician. In such cases we warn you to be careful and under no circumstances place yourself in the hands of a so called advertising physician. Be sure that you personally know the physician as a man of standing, skill and reliability. To such a man explain your case freely and without reserve, without false pride and he will either do for you what medical science can do in such cases or else frankly give you the very best advice.

IN MANY CASES OF MEN'S WEAKNESS it requires, however, only a safe, yet powerful stimulant; a remedy that will reach the nervous system and build up the former strength and endurance without having a disturbing effect upon the digestive organs. There is one prescription that has been tested for many years that will do this; but one remedy that will meet, in the majority of cases, the expectations of those who require a medical treatment of this kind; a prescription which we have sold for many years—**Dr. Hammond's Nerve and Brain Tablets.** These tablets comprise the following ingredients, in correct proportion:

Dried Sulphate Iron
Potassium Carbonate
Asafetida
Ext. Damiana
Aloin
Zinc Phosphide
Ext. Nux Vomica

THE MERIT OF DR HAMMOND'S NERVE AND BRAIN TABLETS is perhaps best illustrated by the fact that their sale has steadily increased from year to year. Millions of these tablets are used today by men who have convinced themselves by actual test that these tablets are the best medicine for the treatment of that condition for which they are intended.

IF YOU HAVE USED THIS MEDICINE BEFORE, you will, of course, reorder it whenever you need the stimulating benefit they afford. If you have never tried **Dr. Hammond's Nerve and Brain Tablets,** you have the privilege of sending for one regular size box, containing about three or four weeks' treatment, use them as directed and if you are not entirely satisfied with the results, write us and we will refund to you at once the price of 55 cents which you have paid for them.

DR. HAMMOND'S NERVE AND BRAIN TABLETS is a very carefully compounded remedy; a preparation that took years of study and experimenting to perfect, in order to combine the elements that would restore vital force and revitalize the weakened sexual organism, and at the same time strengthen the heart action and tone up the stomach, liver and kidneys.

No. 8E22 Dr. Hammond's Nerve and Brain Tablets, per box $0.55

Per six boxes, $2.80 per dozen boxes 5.40

If by mail, postage extra, per box, 3 cents.

HAVE YOU CATARRH?

CATARRH OF THE THROAT? NASAL CATARRH OR CATARRH AFFECTIONS?

Do you suffer from catarrh of any kind, in any of its stages or from any of its effects? If so, try Dr. Hammond's Internal Catarrh Remedy.

Retail price $1.00
Our price, per bottle 51
Our price, per dozen bottles 5.00

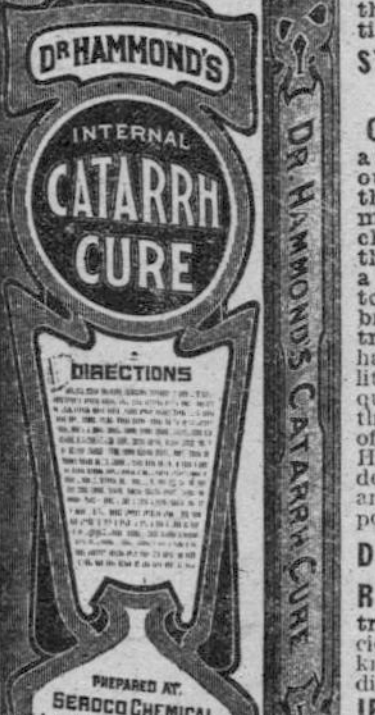

OUR CATARRH REMEDY, designated as Dr. Hammond's Internal Catarrh Remedy, contains the following ingredients in correct proportion:

Potassium Iodide
Burdock Root
Poke Root
Couch Grass
Golden Seal
Marigold
Rochelle Salts
Hydro-Alcoholic Menstruum

SYMPTOMS OF CATARRH are numerous. Among them are mucous discharge from the nostrils, a coated tongue, foul breath, slight deafness, watery eyes, throat troubles, indigestion, and in fact, catarrh has been mistaken in throat troubles for tonsilitis and other complications. Its effects are quite similar in these instances and often deceive those so afflicted. If you have any one or more of these symptoms, you are invited to give Dr. Hammond's Internal Catarrh Remedy a trial. It is designed to go straight to the root of the malady and enables the tissues affected to throw off poisons and perform their functions perfectly.

DR. HAMMOND'S INTERNAL CATARRH REMEDY is a preparation which has met with decided success in the treatment of this disease. It is a highly efficient preparation and composed of ingredients known for their beneficial action upon catarrhal diseases.

IF YOU KNOW THAT YOU ARE A SUFFERER FROM CATARRH, send for a bottle of Dr. Hammond's Internal Catarrh Remedy and give it a thorough trial, according to directions. Your experience, no doubt, will be the same as that of thousands of other customers who have received benefit by the use of this remedy right from the start and obtained final relief and cure by continuing the treatment a reasonable length of time.

DR. HAMMOND'S CATARRH REMEDY is designated as internal catarrh treatment because it reaches all kinds of catarrh, whether in the head or elsewhere, for it acts through the blood, enables it to throw off diseases and to fortify the entire system against catarrhal trouble of every description.

WE HAVE SUPPLIED DR. HAMMOND'S CATARRH REMEDY for many years to thousands of customers located in every state in the Union and particularly to those residing in the localities where catarrhal diseases are most prevalent and, judging from the reports received from those who have learned of the merit of Dr. Hammond's Internal Catarrh Remedy by its use and the benefit derived from it, we feel justified in saying to you: "If you need a remedy of this kind, send for a bottle, use it in the proper manner, and if not found suitable for your particular case, if the first bottle does not benefit you to a noticeable extent, do not proceed with the treatment, but notify us and we will pay you back every cent that you paid for this remedy." We believe, however, you will, as have thousands of others, decide to proceed with the treatment of Dr. Hammond's Internal Catarrh Remedy, so that by following up this treatment you can bring the beneficial change in your condition produced by the first bottle of this medicine, if possible, to an established cure.

PLEASE UNDERSTAND, however, that we want you to be the judge. We want you to know beyond a reasonable doubt that this remedy is really benefiting you before you are expected to proceed with the treatment.

No. 8E20 Price, per dozen bottles, $5.00; per bottle 51c

Unmailable on account of weight.

We Are Willing For You To Make a Trial

OF ANY OF OUR HOUSEHOLD REMEDIES

UNDER THESE CONDITIONS:

Send for a bottle or package, as the case may be, give the remedy a fair trial according to the directions and if you do not receive any benefit we will refund your money.

All you need to do is to write us and state that you have received no benefit and that this is the first bottle or package that you have tried.

We do not want to take anyone's money for the preparation, unless you get value received and unless you receive benefit from its use.

DR. ROSE'S ARSENOUS COMPLEXION TABULES, FOR PRODUCING A PERFECT COMPLEXION.

Per box of fifty treatments, 36 cents; per box of one hundred treatments, 62 cents. Perfectly harmless.

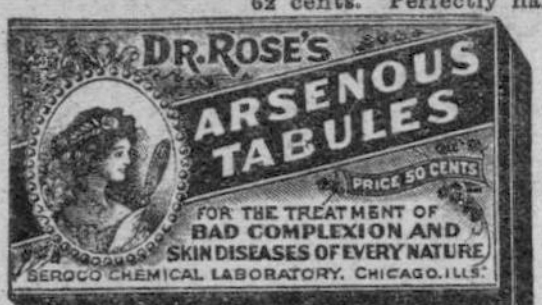

IN THIS REMEDY, designated as Dr. Rose's Arsenous Tabules, the value of the treatment depends upon the arsenous ingredients, selected with great care and the very best of materials used. By taking them according to directions, a clear, dainty, transparent and altogether beautiful complexion is possible. It is hard to realize what the active properties of these little tabules will accomplish until you have used them. Their effect upon the complexion practically starts from the very first day of their use and proceeds with the treatment, which may be discontinued when you have occasion to decide that the transformation is pleasing and satisfactory to you.

DR. ROSE'S SPLENDID TABULES produce a transparent and pellucid complexion. The effect of these arsenous tabules upon the skin and the muscular tissues of the body is to drive out impurities, banish unnatural oiliness and give a transparent texture and beauty. Many ladies object to the use of cosmetics, no matter how superior they may be, because many of them conceal rather than relieve skin imperfections. It is for this very large class that these exceedingly effective tabules are intended. This remedy clears and beautifies the skin by its action through the blood. There is nothing to apply externally, no sign that the most practiced eye can detect to tell that the complexion has been improved, the work of nature stimulated by the use of these arsenous tabules.

IF YOU WANT TO IMPROVE YOUR COMPLEXION, send for a box of Dr. Rose's Arsenous Complexion Tabules and observe their action. Follow directions carefully to obtain the best results. The expense is little, the improvement in your personal appearance, your attractiveness will be extremely gratifying to you and worth many times the small cost of the preparation. **Valuable hints on the care of the complexion and skin sent with every box.**

WE SEND FREE OF CHARGE with every box of Dr. Rose's Arsenous Complexion Tabules a book containing plain directions for their use, also directions how to care for the skin and complexion. A very valuable booklet written by an expert and authority on this subject. You can improve your complexion by using Dr. Rose's Arsenous Complexion Tabules, and nothing adds so much to one's attractive appearance as a clear skin.

LADIES WILL UNDERSTAND that they have the privilege of ordering one box of Dr. Rose's Arsenous Complexion Tabules, and if you have never tried them before, and if you find that they do not benefit your case, all that will be necessary is to report that fact to us and we will return to you every cent that you paid for them. One or two boxes will be sufficient to show you what this preparation will do for you and you will then know whether it is suitable for the treatment of your case and by following up the treatment in a systematic manner and for a reasonable length of time, final good results can be then obtained.

No. 8E25 Price, per dozen boxes, **$3.50;** per box of fifty treatments....**36c**
No. 8E26 Price, per dozen boxes, **$5.80;** per box of one hundred treatments....**62c**

If by mail, postage extra, per box, small, 2 cents; large, 3 cents.

DR. WORDEN'S FEMALE PILLS.

Female Diseases and Troubles, Peculiar to the Sex and Woman's Delicate System, Regulated by the Use of Dr. Worden's Female Pills.
PRICE, ONLY 33 CENTS PER BOX.

THIS REMEDY, designated as Dr. Worden's Female Pills, is a combination of ingredients well known for their value and effectiveness. These pills contain in correct proportion:

Extract Squaw Vine
Dried Ferrous Sulphate
Potassium Carbonate
Ext. Sumbul
Ext. Helonias
Po. Asafetida
Ext. Gentian
Ext. Viburnum

THOUSANDS OF WOMEN suffering from ailments peculiar to their sex have learned to regard this remedy as a valuable treatment and peculiarly adapted to overcome the ailments from which they are suffering.

FEMALE TROUBLE, as a rule, is indicated by headache, nausea, weakness, sickness, depression, etc., the direct result of a derangement of the delicate female organism and nature's regular functions. Nearly every woman understands the suffering her sex must undergo by what is known as female trouble, suffering which is usually borne in silence, because of the disinclination to place the case before a physician. With all due respect to your modesty, we believe, if your case is very serious and complicated, that you should not hesitate to place yourself under the treatment of a capable and responsible physician. In a number of cases a systematic treatment with Dr. Worden's Female Pills will bring the help that can be offered.

DR. WORDEN'S FEMALE PILLS are for the cure of female troubles. They contain nothing that will injure the most delicate woman. They are not cure-alls. They are intended to relieve only the troubles peculiar to women. They can be employed in cases where leucorrhea, irregular, suppressed or painful periods, thin blood, nervousness, sleeplessness (insomnia), sick headache, weakness, anemia, chlorosis or green sickness are present.

DR. WORDEN'S FEMALE PILLS ARE SAFE. Unlike drug compounds which depend upon violent minerals to force action, they relieve and act by their splendid tonic effect. These little pills have a good effect upon weak and run down systems. No harmful element is contained in them and they embody only ingredients named, which make for the upbuilding of the general system, the purifying of the blood and towards curing of so called female complaints. It has been demonstrated that no other prepared remedy offered to the ailing women has given better satisfaction than this remedy has in every form of female trouble.

DR. WORDEN'S FEMALE PILLS embody the very best prescription intended for the treatment of these symptoms. If you have used this remedy before, you will have had occasion to learn of its value and what it will accomplish in the treatment of ailments for which it is intended. If you have not used this remedy before, you can send for one box, give it a thorough trial and if you do not receive benefit and relief you need only to send us a report to that effect and we will refund to you the full amount you have paid for same, nor do we expect that you should continue with the treatment, unless you have by the use of the first box, convinced yourself that it is just the remedy for you, that it reaches your case effectively and you have become convinced that final good results can be secured by continuing for a further reasonable length of time.

No. 8E29 Price, per dozen boxes, **$3.10;** per box........................**33c**

If by mail, postage extra, per box, 2 cents.

DR. McBAIN'S BLOOD PILLS.

A Very Successful Blood Remedy in Pill Form. 27 Cents per Box, $2.30 per Dozen Boxes.

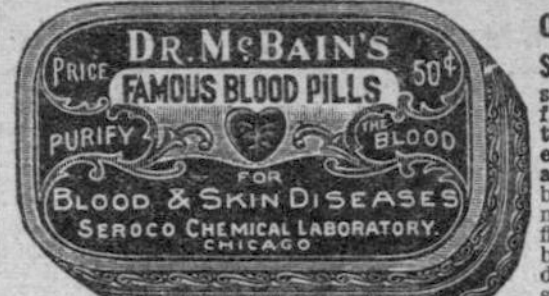

ONE-HALF OF ALL THE SICKNESS is due to impure blood. The results of impure blood are far reaching, as the blood is the medium through which every tissue of the body is fed and renewed. Therefore, impure blood, thin blood, poor blood, means lack of nourishment of the flesh, the nerves, the brain, the bones of the body and a general disorganization of the entire physical system.

GENERAL DEBILITY, GENERAL WEAKNESS, sallow or pale complexion, loss of appetite, pain in the back, nervous headache, etc., are all troubles and diseases usually arising from humors or impurities in the blood and the impurities become worse from day to day and aggravate the troubles until the blood and entire system becomes involved.

DR. McBAIN'S BLOOD PILLS are intended as a blood cleanser and purifier. The effect of these little blood pills is very beneficial. These pills are not of the cathartic nature; they do not upset the system by violent purging, but they act upon the blood, the seat of the trouble, vitalize it, renew the red corpuscles by feeding the proper nourishment to them, thus permitting the blood to purify itself. The elements of which these pills are compounded enrich the blood and also assist digestion, regulate the bowels and act upon the liver and kidneys. Dr. McBain's Pills are invaluable to men and women alike.

This remedy, designated as Dr. McBain's Blood Pills, contains in correct proportion:

Extract Iris
Extract Queen's Root
Extract Burr Seed
Extract Gentian
Extract Red Weed
Extract Couch Grass
Extract Leptandra

THESE BLOOD PILLS are offered by us to our customers for a fair trial and no one should overlook the opportunity we offer where so much benefit can be derived. If you are not benefited, it will not cost you one cent. If you have any trouble arising from impure blood, give this preparation a fair trial and convince yourself of the good it will do in your case.

DR. McBAIN'S FAMOUS BLOOD PILLS can be taken according to directions without any danger to either sex, and if carefully followed, will give splendid results. Weakness, poor, thin blood, sallow or pale complexion, loss of appetite, chlorosis or green sickness, pain in the back, nervous headache, and diseases resulting from humors in the blood, which cause erysipelas, sores, swellings, are benefited by this remedy.

ONLY 27 CENTS A BOX, $2.30 FOR A DOZEN BOXES is our price for this special remedy. It usually sells at from 50 cents to $1.00 per box. Sold by us with the privilege offered by no other firm. You can send for the first box, use it and if you do not find the benefit or relief expected, notify us and we will unhesitatingly refund the amount that you have paid for same.

THE PRICE OF THIS REMEDY IS EXTREMELY LOW. Don't think that this affects the value of the remedy, for Dr. McBain's Blood Pills represent a high class blood remedy. With every box of these pills you are furnished a booklet, "How to Have Pure Blood," which is a short treatise on the blood and its diseases, with a safe, sure and convenient method of treatment for men, women and children.

No. 8E31 Price, per dozen boxes, **$2.30;** each........................**27c**

If by mail, postage extra, per box, 3 cents.

DR. BARKER'S BLOOD BUILDER.

This remedy, designated as Dr. Barker's Blood Builder, contains in correct proportion:

Stillingia
Burdock
Blue Flag
Elder Flowers
Pipsissewa
Aromatics q. s.
Gran. Sugar q. s.
Hydro Alcoholic Menstruum

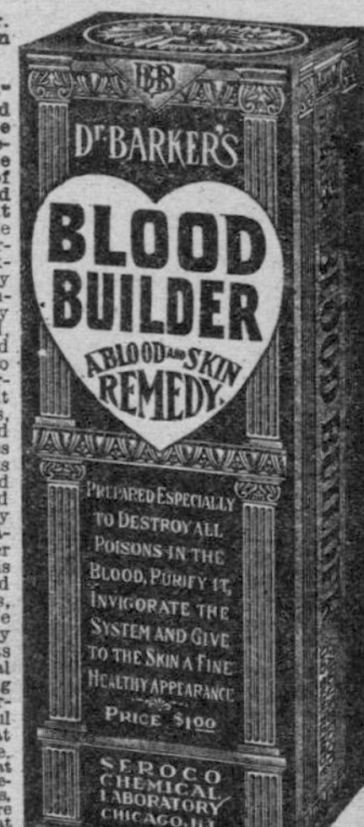

IF YOU ARE FEELING POORLY, and are not quite able to define what the trouble is, try a bottle of Dr. Barker's Blood Builder and give it a test. It is possible your blood needs nourishment and Dr. Barker's Blood Builder may prove exactly the remedy for you. It is certainly a remedy worthy of a test, for purifying the blood, building up the system and toning and strengthening every organ. It helps to eradicate and even prevent these disorders becoming chronic, when the patient is suffering from scrofula, cancer, pimples, chronic ulcers, boils and other painful and disfiguring maladies, which show themselves on the surface of the body or create serious disorders within. It purges the blood and is a remedy of merit for all forms of blood disorders, has been put to the test and many cases have yielded to its beneficial and curative influence. Dr. Barker's Blood Builder is of great value in eradicating all eruptions of the skin and face by improving the blood and by its effect on skin imperfections, helps to attain a perfect complexion. We offer you the opportunity to give this remedy a fair trial. The combination of ingredients includes some of the best known remedial agents for purifying the blood and building it up to a healthy condition and we guarantee its purity. There is nothing harmful in this preparation and it is very likely that you will receive great benefit from its use. Order a bottle under our liberal proposition that enables our customers to receive the greatest benefit from our splendid line of household remedies, namely, with the understanding that if results are not entirely satisfactory, you can write us to that effect and if this is the first bottle you have tried, we will gladly refund your money. We have received many reports of the benefits derived by those who have suffered owing to the poor condition of their blood, and who have used Dr. Barker's Blood Builder with very gratifying results.

WITH EVERY BOTTLE of Dr. Barker's Blood Builder we send free the booklet "How to Have Pure Blood," which explains in detail the action of this remedy and also gives important hints on the care and upbuilding of the system.

No. 8E34 Price, per dozen bottles, **$5.50;** per bottle, large size, each..**54c**

Unmailable on account of weight.

OUR WHITE LILY FACE WASH

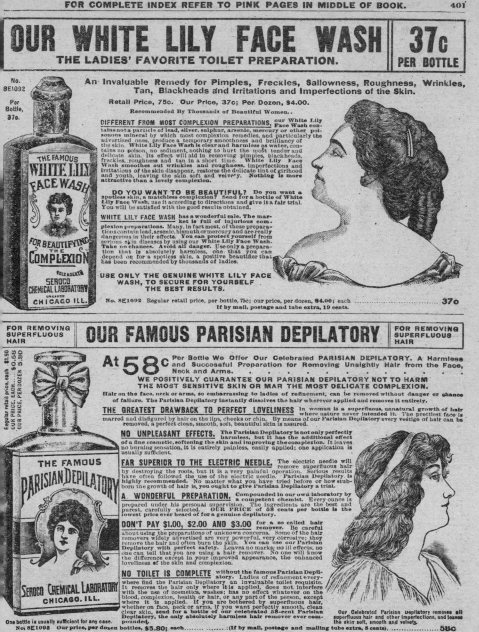

THE LADIES' FAVORITE TOILET PREPARATION.

37c PER BOTTLE

No. 8E1092

Per Bottle, 37c.

An Invaluable Remedy for Pimples, Freckles, Sallowness, Roughness, Wrinkles, Tan, Blackheads and Irritations and Imperfections of the Skin.

Retail Price, 75c. Our Price, 37c; Per Dozen, $4.00.

Recommended By Thousands of Beautiful Women.

DIFFERENT FROM MOST COMPLEXION PREPARATIONS, our White Lily Face Wash contains not a particle of lead, silver, sulphur, arsenic, mercury or other poisonous mineral by which most complexion remedies, and particularly the advertised ones, produce a temporary smoothness and brilliancy of the skin. White Lily Face Wash is clear and harmless as water, contains no poison, no sediment, nothing to hurt the most tender and delicate skin. Its effect will aid in removing pimples, blackheads, freckles, roughness and tan in a short time. White Lily Face Wash smoothes out wrinkles and roughness, imperfections and irritations of the skin disappear, restores the delicate tint of girlhood and youth, leaving the skin soft and velvety. Nothing is more attractive than a lovely complexion.

DO YOU WANT TO BE BEAUTIFUL? Do you want a spotless skin, a matchless complexion? Send for a bottle of White Lily Face Wash, use it according to directions and give it a fair trial. You will be satisfied with the good results obtained.

WHITE LILY FACE WASH has a wonderful sale. The market is full of injurious complexion preparations. Many, in fact most, of these preparations contain lead, arsenic, bismuth or mercury and are really dangerous in their effects. You can protect yourself from serious skin diseases by using our White Lily Face Wash. Take no chances. Avoid all danger. Use only a preparation that is absolutely harmless, one that you can depend on for a spotless skin, a positive beautifier that has been recommended by thousands of ladies.

USE ONLY THE GENUINE WHITE LILY FACE WASH, TO SECURE FOR YOURSELF THE BEST RESULTS.

No. 8E1092 Regular retail price, per bottle, 75c; our price, per dozen, $4.00; each 37c
If by mail, postage and tube extra, 19 cents.

FOR REMOVING SUPERFLUOUS HAIR

OUR FAMOUS PARISIAN DEPILATORY

FOR REMOVING SUPERFLUOUS HAIR

Regular retail price, each $1.50
OUR PRICE, EACH.... $0.58
OUR PRICE, PER DOZEN 5.80

At 58c Per Bottle We Offer Our Celebrated PARISIAN DEPILATORY. A Harmless and Successful Preparation for Removing Unsightly Hair from the Face, Neck and Arms.

WE POSITIVELY GUARANTEE OUR PARISIAN DEPILATORY NOT TO HARM THE MOST SENSITIVE SKIN OR MAR THE MOST DELICATE COMPLEXION.

Hair on the face, neck or arms, so embarrassing to ladies of refinement, can be removed without danger or chance of failure. The Parisian Depilatory instantly dissolves the hair wherever applied and removes it entirely.

THE GREATEST DRAWBACK TO PERFECT LOVELINESS in woman is a superfluous, unnatural growth of hair where nature never intended it. The prettiest face is marred and disfigured by hair on the lips, cheeks or chin. By means of our Parisian Depilatory every vestige of hair can be removed, a perfect clean, smooth, soft, beautiful skin is assured.

NO UNPLEASANT EFFECTS. The Parisian Depilatory is not only perfectly harmless, but it has the additional effect of a fine cosmetic, softening the skin and improving the complexion. It leaves no burning sensation, it is entirely painless, easily applied; one application is usually sufficient.

FAR SUPERIOR TO THE ELECTRIC NEEDLE. The electric needle will remove superfluous hair by destroying the roots, but it is a very painful operation. Serious results have often followed the use of the electric needle. Parisian Depilatory is highly recommended. No matter what you have tried before or how stubborn the growth of hair is, you ought to give Parisian Depilatory a trial.

A WONDERFUL PREPARATION. Compounded in our own laboratory by a competent chemist. Every ounce is prepared under his personal supervision. The ingredients are the best and purest, carefully selected. OUR PRICE of 58 cents per bottle is the lowest price ever heard of for a genuine depilatory.

DON'T PAY $1.00, $2.00 AND $3.00 for a so called hair remover. Be careful about using the preparations of unknown concerns. Some of the hair removers widely advertised are very powerful, very corrosive; they remove the hair and often burn the skin. You can use our Parisian Depilatory with perfect safety. Leaves no marks; no ill effects, no one can tell that you are using a hair remover. No one will know the difference except in your improved appearance, the enhanced loveliness of the skin and complexion.

NO TOILET IS COMPLETE without the famous Parisian Depilatory. Ladies of refinement everywhere find the Parisian Depilatory an invaluable toilet requisite. It removes the hair only where it is applied, does not interfere with the use of cosmetics, washes; has no effect whatever on the blood, complexion, health or hair, or any part of the person, except where it is applied. If you are bothered by superfluous hair, whether on face, neck or arms, if you want perfectly smooth, clean clear skin, send for a bottle of our celebrated 58-cent Parisian Depilatory, the only absolutely harmless hair remover ever compounded.

Our Celebrated Parisian Depilatory removes all superfluous hair and other imperfections, and leaves the skin soft, smooth and velvety.

One bottle is usually sufficient for any case.

No. 8E1095 Our price, per dozen bottles, $5.80; each........ ....(If by mail, postage and mailing tube extra, 8 cents). 58c

This is a life size illustration of the jar.

HOW TO BE BEAUTIFUL

FLORAL MASSAGE CREAM, THE GREAT AID TO BEAUTY.

A WONDERFUL TOILET PREPARATION.

A NEW PURIFYING, ANTISEPTIC, CLEANSING AND BEAUTIFYING MASSAGE CREAM, A MOST EXCELLENT PREPARATION. MAKES THE OLD YOUNG, THE PLAIN BEAUTIFUL AND REMOVES THE TELLTALE MARKS OF TIME.

REGULAR 50-CENT SIZE JARS 32c

Extra large size jar, one-half pound, enough for 60 treatments, regular retail price $1.00. Only.......... ....55c

THIS BOOKLET, A COMPLETE COURSE OF INSTRUCTIONS FOR FACIAL MASSAGE, SENT FREE WITH EACH JAR.

This booklet free with every jar.

COMPLETE DIRECTIONS for taking a complete course of massage treatment sent with each jar, a booklet written by a specialist, illustrated throughout with pictures and diagrams showing the same course of treatment society ladies receive in the fashionable city massage parlors at $1.00 per treatment. This booklet shows by pictures the exact way to massage the face, the various movements, the position of the hands, all explained by illustrations, so that anyone by following the plain and simple instructions, and the methods as shown by the pictures can get the same delightful, wonderful and improving effect from facial massage that makes this treatment so much appreciated by ladies of refinement and fashion everywhere.

WITH FLORAL MASSAGE CREAM and with the complete illustrated booklet of instructions you can do all this yourself at a mere fraction of the cost and get all the benefit and all the results that you would get if you went regularly to any of the fashionable massage parlors in large cities.

FLORAL MASSAGE CREAM is our latest and most improved toilet preparation, a standard, high grade and perfectly satisfactory facial massage cream, guaranteed by us as the very finest preparation of its kind on the market, very much superior in quality and effectiveness to the many creams and ointments on the market, many of which are widely advertised and sell through retail stores at two to three times the price that we ask for our matchless preparation.

FLORAL MASSAGE CREAM is a luxury which no woman, young, middleaged or old should deny herself. It is composed of the purest ingredients, perfectly harmless to the most delicate skin. Our Floral Massage Cream contains no grease of any kind, its emollient effects are greater, its cleansing and beautifying results more marked than can be obtained from any other combination prepared for massage purposes.

OUR FLORAL MASSAGE CREAM is based on a combination used so successfully by the leading professional masseurs in the massage parlors of the large cities, and is supplied by us exclusively to our customers for home massage. We have taken this basis of combination and by careful experiment we have refined and improved the preparation until it is now without question the most attractive and delightful toilet preparation ever offered, one that will appeal to ladies of refinement everywhere, who would not use any of the usual so called toilet preparations, cosmetics or skin preparations. Floral Massage Cream is a pure preparation, contains nothing to harm the most delicate skin, is not to be classed with cosmetics or other skin preparations. It is a preparation that no one can feel the slightest embarrassment in using. Our Floral Massage Cream is just as necessary an adjunct to the dressing table as a bottle of fine perfume; just as important to the toilet as a tooth brush.

FLORAL MASSAGE CREAM removes the horizontal lines from the brow, takes out the laughing wrinkles and crows' feet, removes the wrinkles under the eyes, makes the cheeks plump and round, cleanses the skin absolutely of all dirt, soot and impurities of all kinds, makes your complexion just what you want it to be, healthy, clear and rosy. For removing wrinkles, filling out the cheeks, clarifying the skin and bringing out that rosy color, Floral Massage Cream does indeed work wonders. It brings fresh bloom to faded faces, it smoothes away age lines and care marks. Underneath wrinkles and hollows and unbecoming flabbiness it builds firm sound healthy tissues; it is a food to the starved skin system and is absorbed with a grateful sense of delight.

THE BOOKLET, a complete course of instruction for facial massage, which we sen free with each jar is alone worth more than we ask for the enti preparation. Among the illustrations and directions in this booklet will be found instructio for removing horizontal wrinkles from the forehead, another picture illustrating removing laughing wrinkles and crows' feet, another illustration for hollow or drooping eyelids, anoth illustration for removing the wrinkles under the eyes, another illustration to make the chee plump and rounded, another illustration massaging the neck, etc., all with full instructio under each picture, showing how to get the best results with our toilet preparation Flor Massage Cream.

THE LARGE ILLUSTRATION will give you an idea of the appearance of th jar of Floral Massage Cream; the small illustra tion shows a complete package. Each jar is hermetically sealed, is tied with ribbon, bears a attractive label, is wrapped in tissue paper, and put up in a handsome lithographed paste board carton, as shown by the small illustration.

LET US SEND YOU a jar of Floral Massage Cream with your next order. Use just once, and if you do not admit that it is the most benef cial and the most delightful toilet preparation you ever used we won't expect your furth orders. In fact, we have so much confidence in this preparation that we will make you th free offer below.

FLORAL MASSAGE CREAM heals the skin. Removes from the pores the impu ities that make the skin rough and unwholesom Its use renders the skin soft, white and beautiful. It is antiseptic and eradicates the germs disease, yet it is perfectly harmless to the most delicate skin. Floral Massage Cream is no irritating, purifies and invigorates the pores of the skin, giving, at the same time, activity to th glands, which is always very desirable

IT IS GOOD FOR YOUNG AND OLD. Men appreciate a good facial massa as well as women; it is far superior the massage creams that barbers use, and we make this same free offer to the gentlemen well as to the ladies. If your barber has ever massaged your face you know the benefit fro this treatment. Then send us your order for a jar of Floral Massage Cream, get our bookl of instructions, give yourself the same massage treatment with a much better cream and in the comfort of your own room, and all at one-twentieth the expense.

HAVE YOU EVER TRIED FACE MASSAGE?

OUR FREE OFFER.

Send us an order for a jar of our Floral Massage Cream, use it according to directions, and if you are not more than pleased with the result, if you find any massage cream or other toilet preparation that will compare with ours, if you do not find it strictly a high class preparation intended for people of refinement, then simply write us to this effect, tell us you are not satisfied and if it is the first jar you have ever ordered we will, without further question, refund your money. Anyone who has ever tried Floral Massage Cream will never be without it. The cost is so little, the benefit so great, one extra large size jar, which we sell at only 55 cents, lasts so long and it is, therefore, so inexpensive that anyone who has ever used it and given it a fair trial will never be without it.

HAVE YOU EVER EXPERIENCED the peculiarly delightful, stimulating and exhilarating effects upon the facial nerves and muscles produced by a scientifically prepared and properly applied massage cream? Do you know that massaging the face is now considered a function which no progressive lady omits in order to produce and preserve that healthy glow, that pink complexion which makes beautiful features more beautiful, and adds to irregular ones attractions, the effect of which is really remarkable. We all know that exercise means increased circulation of the blood, but generally exercise is not entirely sufficient to produce the right results in the fullest measure for the facial perfection. Local exercise, in other words massage of the face, becomes necessary to induce increased circulation through the facial blood vessels, but even this is incomplete unless you use in connection with it the famous Floral Massage Cream which cleanses and clears the skin, arouses to activity every facial nerve and muscle, stimulates and feeds them, removes wrinkles under the eyes, on the brow, fills out the cheeks, making them plump and round, and insures a beautiful complexion in all cases. It is not surprising that the foremost professional masseurs will use nothing else in their work but Floral Massage Cream, which can be found in every fashionable massage parlor, where it is used almost exclusively.

IT IS NOT GREASY, it does not contain any animal fats, and therefore is not subject to decomposition. It is absolutely pure, therefore harmless and cleanly. It is prepared in the most scientific manner, therefore reliable and certain in results. It is, however, not necessary that you should employ the services of a professional masseur, for with our Floral Massage Cream you can massage your face in the privacy of your own home, and at an expense of only a cent or two. We supply the regular large $1.00 size of the genuine Floral Cream to our customers for 55 cents, sufficient for many months of facial massage treatment. Complete instructions are sent with each jar.

FLORAL MASSAGE CREAM is a delightful preparation and speedily renders facial muscles firm and healthy, clarifying the complexion quickly and permanently. Soothes and rests the nerves of the face, and produces a healthy glow and a sensation of ease and comfort.

No. 8E1099 Floral Massage Cream. Regular 50-cent jars. Price.......... **$0.32**
Per dozen jars **3.90**

If by mail, postage extra, each, 14 cents.

No. 8E1100 Large size (holding three times the quantity of 50-cent jars). Price **$0.55**
Per dozen jars **6.00**

Not mailable.

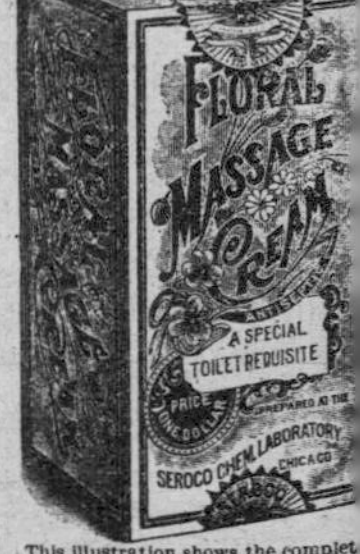

This illustration shows the complete package.

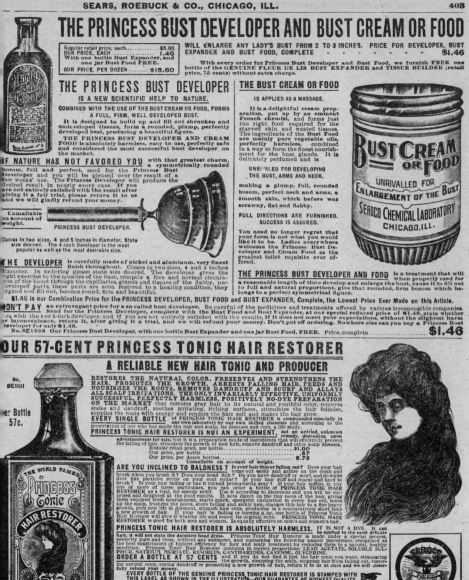

THE PRINCESS BUST DEVELOPER AND BUST CREAM OR FOOD

Regular retail price, each	$5.00
OUR PRICE, EACH	1.46
With one bottle Bust Expander, and one jar Bust Food FREE.	
OUR PRICE, PER DOZEN	$15.60

WILL ENLARGE ANY LADY'S BUST FROM 2 TO 3 INCHES. PRICE FOR DEVELOPER, BUST EXPANDER AND BUST FOOD, COMPLETE $1.46

With every order for Princess Bust Developer and Bust Food, we furnish FREE one bottle of the GENUINE FLEUR DE LIS BUST EXPANDER and TISSUE BUILDER (retail price, 75 cents) without extra charge.

THE PRINCESS BUST DEVELOPER

IS A NEW SCIENTIFIC HELP TO NATURE.

COMBINED WITH THE USE OF THE BUST CREAM OR FOOD, FORMS A FULL, FIRM, WELL DEVELOPED BUST.

It is designed to build up and fill out shrunken and undeveloped tissues, form a rounded, plump, perfectly developed bust, producing a beautiful figure.

THE PRINCESS BUST DEVELOPER AND CREAM FOOD is absolutely harmless, easy to use, perfectly safe and considered the most successful bust developer on the market.

IF NATURE HAS NOT FAVORED YOU with that greatest charm, a symmetrically rounded bosom, full and perfect, send for the Princess Bust Developer and you will be pleased over the result of a few weeks' use. The Princess Developer will produce the desired result in nearly every case. If you are not entirely satisfied with the result after giving it a fair trial, please return it to us and we will gladly refund your money.

Unmailable on account of weight.

PRINCESS BUST DEVELOPER.

Comes in two sizes, 4 and 5 inches in diameter. State size desired. The 4-inch Developer is the most popular as well as the most desirable size.

THE DEVELOPER is carefully made of nickel and aluminum, very finest finish throughout. Comes in two sizes, 4 and 5 inches diameter. In ordering please state size desired. The developer gives the right exercise to the muscles of the bust, compels a free and normal circulation of the blood through the capillaries, glands and tissues of the flabby, undeveloped parts, these parts are soon restored to a healthy condition, they expand and fill out, become round, firm and beautiful.

THE BUST CREAM OR FOOD

IS APPLIED AS A MASSAGE.

It is a delightful cream preparation, put up by an eminent French chemist, and forms just the right food required for the starved skin and wasted tissues. The ingredients of the Bust Food are mainly pure vegetable oils, perfectly harmless, combined in a way to form the finest nourishment for the bust glands. It is delicately perfumed and is

UNRIVALED FOR DEVELOPING THE BUST, ARMS AND NECK,

making a plump, full, rounded bosom, perfect neck and arms, a smooth skin, which before was scrawny, flat and flabby.

FULL DIRECTIONS ARE FURNISHED. SUCCESS IS ASSURED.

You need no longer regret that your form is not what you would like it to be. Ladies everywhere welcome the Princess Bust Developer and Cream Food as the greatest toilet requisite ever offered.

THE PRINCESS BUST DEVELOPER AND FOOD is a treatment that will when properly used for a reasonable length of time develop and enlarge the bust, cause it to fill out to full and natural proportions, give that rounded, firm bosom which belongs to a perfect symmetrical figure.

$1.46 is our Combination Price for the PRINCESS DEVELOPER, BUST FOOD and BUST EXPANDER, Complete, the Lowest Price Ever Made on this Article.

DON'T PAY an extravagant price for a so called bust developer. Be careful of the medicines and treatments offered by various irresponsible companies. Send for the Princess Developer, complete with the Bust Food and Bust Expander, at our special reduced price of $1.46, state whether you wish the 4 or 5-inch developer, and if you are not entirely satisfied with the results, if it does not meet your expectations, without the slightest harm or inconvenience, return it, after giving it a trial, and we will refund your money. Don't put off ordering. Nowhere else can you buy a Princess Bust Developer for only $1.46.

No. 8E1098 Our Princess Bust Developer, with one bottle Bust Expander and one jar Bust Food, FREE. Price, complete........................ **$1.46**

OUR 57-CENT PRINCESS TONIC HAIR RESTORER

A RELIABLE NEW HAIR TONIC AND PRODUCER

No. 8E1101

Per Bottle 57c.

RESTORES THE NATURAL COLOR, PRESERVES AND STRENGTHENS THE HAIR, PROMOTES THE GROWTH, ARRESTS FALLING HAIR, FEEDS AND NOURISHES THE ROOTS, REMOVES DANDRUFF AND SCURF AND ALLAYS ALL SCALP IRRITATIONS. THE ONLY INVARIABLY EFFECTIVE, UNIFORMLY SUCCESSFUL, PERFECTLY HARMLESS, POSITIVELY NO-DYE PREPARATION ON THE MARKET that restores gray hair to its natural and youthful color, removes scales and dandruff, soothes irritating, itching surfaces, stimulates the hair follicles, supplies the roots with energy and renders the hair soft and makes the hair grow.

EVERY SINGLE BOTTLE of PRINCESS TONIC HAIR RESTORER is compounded especially in our own laboratory by our own skilled chemists and according to the prescription of one who has made the hair and scalp, its diseases and cure, a life study.

PRINCESS TONIC HAIR RESTORER IS NOT AN EXPERIMENT, not an untried, unknown remedy, depending upon advertisements for sale, but it is a preparation made of ingredients that will effectively prevent the falling of hair, stimulate the growth of new hair, remove dandruff and other scalp diseases.

Regular retail price, per bottle	$1.00
Our price, per bottle	.57
Our price, per dozen bottles	5.75

Unmailable on account of weight.

ARE YOU INCLINED TO BALDNESS? Is your hair thin or falling out? Does your hair come out easily and gather on the comb and brush when you brush it? Does your head itch? Do you have dandruff or scurf, and do white dust like particles settle on your coat collar? Is your hair stiff and coarse and hard to brush? Is your hair fading or has it turned prematurely gray? If your hair suffers in any one or more of these particulars, you can order a bottle of PRINCESS TONIC HAIR RESTORER as a trial, for speedy relief. Use it according to directions and you will be surprised and delighted at the good results. It acts direct on the tiny roots of the hair, giving them required fresh nourishment, starts quick, energetic circulation in every hair cell, tones up the scalp, freshens the pores, stops falling and sickly hair, changes thin hair to a fine heavy growth, puts new life in dormant, sluggish hair cells, producing in a comparatively short time a new growth of hair. If your hair is fading or turning gray, one bottle of Princess Tonic Hair Restorer will give it healthy life and renew its original color. PRINCESS TONIC HAIR RESTORER is good for both men and women. Is equally effective on men's and women's hair.

PRINCESS TONIC HAIR RESTORER IS ABSOLUTELY HARMLESS. IT IS NOT A DYE. It can be applied to the most delicate hair, it will not stain the daintiest head dress. Princess Tonic Hair Restorer is made under a special process, perfectly pure and clear, without any sediment, and containing the following named ingredients, recognized as the best constituents of highest efficiency for hair and scalp treatment for restoring them to a natural, healthy condition. Princess Tonic Hair Restorer contains in correct proportions: LEAD ACETATE, SOLUBLE SULPHUR, NATRIUM MURIATE, RESORCIN, CANTHARIDES, CAYENNE, GLYCERINE.

ORDER A BOTTLE AT 57 CENTS and if you do not find it just the hair tonic you want, stimulating the growth, cleansing the scalp, stopping hair from falling out, restoring natural color, curing dandruff or promoting a new growth of hair, return it to us at once and we will cheerfully refund your money.

EVERY BOTTLE OF THE GENUINE PRINCESS TONIC HAIR RESTORER IS STAMPED WITH THIS LABEL AS SHOWN IN THE ILLUSTRATION—OUR GUARANTEE OF HIGHEST QUALITY.

This Label is your Protection. It shows that only the purest and finest ingredients are used.

YOU WILL FIND VARIOUS SO CALLED HAIR TONICS and hair restorers widely advertised in the newspapers and magazines. Some of them possess merit and others do not. Those that possess merit are sold for two and three times the price we ask for genuine Princess Tonic Hair Restorer, and are not equal to the preparation that we put out under our binding guarantee for quality. If you have any doubt as to the merit of the Princess Tonic Hair Restorer as against the preparations advertised and offered by others, we would be willing for you to order our preparation, and then send for any other preparation on the market, give both preparations a fair and honest trial, and if you do not find the Princess Tonic Hair Restorer better by far than any other hair tonic, you need only write us to this effect and we will return your money. By using the remedy properly it will overcome almost any hair trouble, and a single month's treatment is often sufficient to accomplish result, sometimes a few weeks will do the work, it depending somewhat on the length of time the trouble has existed.

No. 8E1101 Price, per dozen bottles, $5.75; per bottle........................ 57c

English Lavender Smelling Salts.

REFRESHING AND INVIGORATING.

For faintness, headache, etc. In pretty, glass stoppered bottles, a useful and handsome ornament for the dressing table.

No. 8E1104 Price, per bottle, **18c**

If by mail, postage and tube extra, 10 cents.

Malaga Almond Meal.

This is the genuine Oriental meal; much more emollient than the meal usually sold in this country. We import it direct in original bags and put it up in nice packages. It is splendid for the skin and can be used in place of soap. **Malaga Almond Meal is highly recommended to ladies who have a very sensitive skin;** one that is easily affected even by the slightest presence of acid in a toilet preparation.

No. 8E1107 ¼-lb. size. Price..**15c**
½-lb. size. Price..**25c**

If by mail, postage extra, small size, 8 cents; large size, 12 cents.

Milk of Roses for the Complexion.

A great beautifier used by the most fashionable ladies in Europe, and prepared from fresh white and pale colored roses by a simple process, which, however, secures and obtains by a superior extraction, the finest odor and other portions which always have a pleasant and softening effect on the skin when used for the treatment of same, especially when the skin is not entirely free from blemishes. The process for preparing this toilet article has been secured from the French manufacturer and chemist for our exclusive control in the United States.

No. 8E1110 Price.... **32c**

Unmailable on account of weight.

Genuine Juice of Lily Bulbs.

After many futile efforts we finally succeeded in obtaining the genuine and pure juice of the fresh bulbs of pond lilies, so that our customers are in a position to obtain from us the real, genuine article of this toilet preparation, recognized as one of the best in the world. When used for a limited time only this preparation always assures a clear complexion, soft and transparent, giving at the same time an extremely healthy color.

No. 8E1113 Price.............. **36c**

Unmailable on account of weight.

Creme de Marshmallow.

A very fine, fragrant, dainty toilet lotion, bland and soothing, for preserving the complexion. Especially recommended for an inflamed and irritated condition of the skin. Ladies doing domestic work will find it a perfect lotion for the skin. May be applied at any time. Quickly absorbed by the skin. **Unmailable.**

No. 8E1116 Price.................. **26c**

Milk of Cucumber.

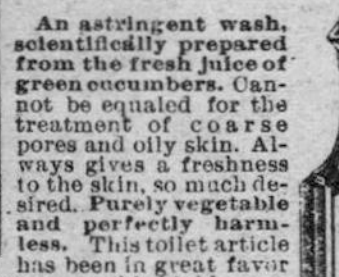

An astringent wash, scientifically prepared from the fresh juice of green cucumbers. Cannot be equaled for the treatment of coarse pores and oily skin. Always gives a freshness to the skin, so much desired. **Purely vegetable and perfectly harmless.** This toilet article has been in great favor the past few years, and is highly recommended by ladies having used the wash constantly, and always with the very best results. **Unmailable.**

No. 8E1119 Price.............. **18c**

Orange Flower Skin Food.

QUI VIVE.

This celebrated preparation has quickly grown into popular favor, and is today, by ladies of fashion, considered an indispensable toilet article. It acts as a skin nourisher and wrinkle remover, smooths roughness and fills out hollow cheeks, giving the natural healthy glow and beauty to the skin. Orange Flower Skin Food is today often preferred and used instead of preparations that would cost three and four times the price at which we can furnish same to our lady customers.

No. 8E1122 Regular sized jar. Price........ **20c**
4-ounce jars. Price .....(Not mailable)....... **33c**

If by mail, postage extra, regular size, 15 cents.

Creme Marquise.

QUI VIVE.

This cream is equally as popular as the Orange Flower Skin Food, and while it can be used successfully alone, most society ladies employ it together with the Orange Flower Skin Food. **It is especially effective for whitening, softening and preserving the skin.** When Orange Flower Skin Food and Creme Marquise are used together, they should be alternated by changing every other night.

No. 8E1125 Regular sized jar. Price......... **19c**
4-ounce jars. Price.......(Not mailable)....... **32c**

If by mail, postage extra, regular size, 15 cents.

Mme. Qui Vive Complexion Powder.

This is an equally well known toilet article, prepared from the famous Qui Vive formulas, is non-irritating, contains no mineral poisons and may be applied without danger to the most delicate skin. Three shades, flesh, brunette and white.

No. 8E1129 Price, per box................. **18c**

If by mail, postage extra, per box, 3 cents.

Always state which color is wanted.

Floral Complexion Powder.

Floral Complexion Powder is one of the very best powders the market affords, is delicately perfumed, fragrant with natural flower odors, and is composed of carefully selected ingredients of the purest kind, and cannot under any conditions whatever cause inflammation or the slightest irritation of the skin as many other complexion powders often do.

No. 8E1131 Price, per box...................... **25c**

If by mail, postage extra, per box, 7 cents.

La Dore's Powder de Riz.

Made from fine rice flour and exquisitely perfumed. This powder is very popular and preferred by many to any other complexion powder used for the purpose for which it is intended. Furnished in three shades, white, cream and flesh.

No. 8E1134
Price, per box...... **15c**

If by mail, postage extra, per box, 3 cents.

Rouge de Theatre.

This is positively the best, giving a natural and lifelike glow, never injures the skin, is today considered by the theatrical profession the only safe and satisfactory rouge, and used by them almost exclusively owing to the fine distributive qualities which it possesses so that it can never be noticed or detected.

No. 8E1137 Price, per box.......... **12c**

If by mail, postage extra, per box, 6 cents.

Liquid Rouge.

A harmless liquid preparation for giving color to the cheeks and lips, making them a perfectly natural, pretty color.

No. 8E1140 Price, per bottle........ **15c**

If by mail, postage extra, per bottle, 10c

La Dore's Rubyline.

Rubyline is a refined and harmless rouge prepared in the form of a cream for tinting the cheeks, lips and fingers, leaves a perfectly natural stain or glow and can never be detected. The majority of ladies prefer rouge in this form, as it is put up in a very convenient manner and easily applied.

No. 8E1141 Price, per box........................ **18c**

If by mail, postage extra, 5 cents.

Camphor Cold Cream.

Retail price.............................. **25c**
Our price, each **$0.16**
Our price, per dozen **1.50**

A SALVE OF REMARKABLE HEALING QUALITIES. Of great value when the skin is chapped from cold; it will heal up the cracks and make the skin soft and smooth again, also it cannot be excelled as a soothing and healing application to burns, and dressing for abrasions of the skin, pimples, boils, etc.

No. 8E1145 Price per dozen, **$1.50**; each **16c**

If by mail, postage extra, per box, 6 cents.

HAIR PREPARATIONS.

Danderof.

The Great Scalp Cleaner and Tonic. Permanently cures dandruff, eczema, of the head, itching, hair falling out, humors, and all troubles of the scalp and hair. Will positively clear the scalp from dandruff and render it healthy, promoting the growth of the hair. It is recommended to ladies who desire long, glossy hair. It keeps the hair soft and glossy; prevents baldness; makes the hair grow stronger.

No. 8E1150 Price, per bottle.... **34c**

Unmailable on account weight.

Hair Elixir.

A beautiful dressing for the hair making it soft and glossy; prevents i[t] from splitting and falling out. Cure[s] dandruff and makes the hair grow. **Our Hair Elixir is used and recom**mended by every professional hai[r] dresser in large cities. It is th[e] only safe hair preserver known, an[d] should be used especially for pro[-]tecting and promoting a fine growt[h] of hair.

No. 8E1151 Price, per bottle, 8 ounces............................. **45c**

Unmailable on account of weight.

Eau De Quinine Hair Tonic.

Excellent preparation for strengthening and dressing the hair; much used in Europe by the ladies of the best society. We have the **genuine, imported by ourselves from France,** where it has gained a much deserved reputation **as a valuable hair dressing and tonic. The genuine Eau de Quinine is recognized the world over as a stimulant** to the hair nerves and roots, a strengthener and builder where the natural strength and growth of the hair has become impaired.

No. 8E1152 Price, 8-ounce bottles, **35c**; 4-ounce bottles................ **22c**

If by mail, postage and tube extra, small, 16 cents; large, unmailable on account of weight.

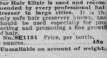

Barbers' Egg Shampoo

This shampoo is the highest grade of sham**poo preparations used by the first class ba**r**bers in the large cities, and is very popular** every part of the country. **As a gentleman** shampoo it is unequaled, **makes clean a**n**d healthy hair, removes itching of the scalp, a**n**d is guaranteed not to contain,** like most oth**er egg shampoos, any alkali,** which leaves th**e hair harsh and dry.** Our barbers' hair shampoo renders the hair soft, smooth and glossy.

No. 8E1156 Price, 8-oz. round shampoo bottle.......................... **25c**

Unmailable on account of weight.

Imperial Shampoo.

A preparation put up especially for ladies' use, thoroughly antiseptic, and supplied in liquid form, making a soft and copious lather, free from alkalies and any injurious substances whatever. **It stimulates the scalp and leaves the hair soft and luxuriant,** and should be used once or twice a month freely. The Imperial Shampoo represents the highest art of shampoo preparations and is put up in handsome eight-ounce sprinkler top bottles, making it very convenient for use. The genuine Imperial Shampoo is never sold for less than $1.00 per bottle.

No. 8E1159 Price, 8-ounce sprinkler top bottle ......(**Unmailable.**)....... **32c**

LATEST DESIGNS in ROCKERS at CHALLENGE PRICES.

AT $1.75 TO $11.15 we offer a wonderful variety of wood seat, cobbler seat and upholstered seat rockers, all new, up to date designs, a better variety, more reliable and high grade rockers than has ever before been offered by any dealer. Note the astonishing value, the big bargain we offer in our $3.95 rocker illustrated below.

This Extra Large Massive Selected Quarter Sawed Solid Oak Beautifully Carved Rocker

THE LEADER OF OUR ROCKER LINE, guaranteed absolutely high grade, offered under our binding guarantee for quality. We guarantee that you cannot buy a rocker of this size and quality from any retail dealer for less than double our price, from any other catalogue house for less than $6.00.

NOTE THE ILLUSTRATION CAREFULLY. Observe the massiveness, solidity, the handsome heavy turned spindles, the extra large comfortable arms, seat and high back, beautiful heavy carvings and decorations, the beautiful gloss finish, note the elegance of this chair throughout, consider our price of $3.95, and then look around in your local furniture stores, look in any other catalogue published and see if you can match it.

FROM THIS LARGE ILLUSTRATION, engraved direct from a photograph of the chair, you can get a little idea of its appearance. It is one of the most wonderful bargains in rockers ever offered. Made of extra selected quarter sawed oak, most carefully made, thoroughly well put together, not flimsy in any particular, will never get loose or shaky like many cheap chairs where quality is sacrificed. Has an extra large very comfortable form fitting deep and wide veneered roll seat, ornamented in front with deep carved scrolls and moulding. Has a high back with one large shaped top panel, one smaller lower panel connected by 11 solid turned spindles. High wide arms connected with the seat on each side by 5 solid turned spindles. Deeply embossed and strong continuous front posts running from the arm to the rockers. Back or under part of chair is turned from extra selected solid oak, each piece fitted perfectly into the other, every joint absolutely solid, plugged, screwed, glued and cemented, every piece and part showing the most careful and skillful workmanship, producing the strongest and best chair that can possibly be constructed, such a chair as has never before been offered outside of the very finest furniture stores. Weight, 30 pounds.

$3.95 IS OUR SPECIAL PRICE for this handsome rocker, a price that is based on the cost of material and labor with a very small profit added. $3.95 is just a few cents above manufacturing cost. When you buy this chair every penny that you send us of the $3.95, outside a very few cents for our profit, goes into material and labor, and as a result we give you in this chair more value for your money than you can possibly get elsewhere.

DON'T BE MISLED. Don't be deceived by a catchy low price that may be offered by some one else. Don't think that if you see a picture and a low price in some other catalogue that you can duplicate the value we here offer you. Unfortunately pictures look very much alike, and other houses in their attempts to meet our prices will lower the quality. This is something we never do. We never sacrifice quality in any degree in order to make a low price. We guarantee that you cannot equal the value we furnish, and that no rocker that looks like ours in a picture in any other catalogue at anything like our $3.95 price will compare with this chair in any way. This we guarantee. If you doubt it let us send you this chair to examine. Order it, enclose our price, order from any other dealer or mail order house at the same time any chair that you think equals this at the same or a lower price, get them both for comparison side by side and if for the same price you do not find our chair better in every way, a much higher quality of goods, or if you do not find that our chair represents really $1.00 to $3.00 more in actual value you will not be under any obligation to keep our chair, we will expect you to return it to us at our expense, and we will promptly return all your money including what you paid for freight charges. If you question our ability to furnish you in this as well as all other lines better goods for less money than you can get elsewhere we are willing to stand or fall by a side by side comparison.

WE CHALLENGE ANY DEALER in Chicago, your own home or elsewhere to furnish this same high quality, solid oak rocker at anything like our $3.95 price.

THOUGH THE ILLUSTRATION WILL GIVE YOU SOME IDEA of the appearance of this chair it must be seen and examined, compared with other rockers to really appreciate the value we offer. It is impossible by means of this plain illustration to give you any real idea of the beauty of the carving, the thorough workmanship throughout, the excellence of the material used, the massiveness, the beautiful glossy gold finish, which brings out in full the beauty of the grain effect of the quarter sawed oak.

LET US SEND YOU THIS CHAIR for we know you will be delighted with it. You will say that you never saw its equal at the price, everyone will admire it, and when they learn the price will admit that it is certainly a big bargain. Don't forget that when you send us your order for this chair, or any other goods, you not only save money, but you will be getting a PROFIT SHARING CERTIFICATE, very valuable, and can soon share in the profits of this business.

$3.95

No. 1E297
OUR SPECIAL ROCKER,
Weight, 30 pounds.
PRICE.......... **$3.95**

$1.75

No. 1E296 Our special cobbler seat rocker. Made of thoroughly seasoned oak, rich golden finish. High arms, high back, with solid posts securely braced, making a comfortable, durable rocker. Spindles are all turned and panels ornamented with a neat design in carving. Weight, 15 pounds. Price.. $1.75

$1.78

No. 1E299 Ladies' sewing rocker. Made of seasoned oak, golden finish. High back, wide shaped seat, covered with best quality cane. Back posts and legs are securely braced to seat, making it extra strong and durable. Spindles and panels are ornamented as shown in illustration. Weight, 15 pounds. Price.... $1.78

$2.05

No. 1E300 Ladies' or gents' cane seat rocker, wide seat, high back and bent arms. Substantial and comfortable, and presenting a pleasing appearance. Spindles are all nicely turned and carvings are neat and attractive. Finished in golden oak. Shipping weight, 18 pounds.
Price............ $2.05

$2.10

No. 1E301 Ladies' veneered saddle seat sewing rocker. Made of oak, golden gloss finish. Medium height back, quarter sawed panels and flat spindles with neat carvings. Back strongly braced making a strong and comfortable rocker.
Price............ $2. 0

$1.95

An artistic high arm and high back rocker, with fancy embossed cobbler seat. Made of quarter sawed oak, golden gloss and birch imitation, mahogany finish. Strongly constructed throughout and ornamented in artistic style.
No. 1E311 Golden oak. Price........ $1.95
No. 1E312 Mahogany finish. Price $1.99

$2.10

No. 1E314 A comfortable and roomy rocker, made of selected elm, golden finish. Wide saddle seat, high back, with broad panels, deeply embossed. Arms supported by three fancy spindles. For comfort it cannot be excelled. Weight, 18 pounds.
Price.......... $2.10

$2.15

No. 1E315 The best and cheapest veneered wood seat rocker ever offered. This rocker is made of golden elm. Top panel is richly carved and connected with lower panel by ten turned spindles. Has wide seat and high back, insuring an easy and comfortable seat. Weight, 20 pounds.
Price............**$2.15**

$2.25

No. 1E315½ Old style Boston rocker, made of elm in golden oak or mahogany finish. Full roll deep seat, high back and arms nicely striped and ornamented. Strong and durable and very comfortable. We are offering this at an exceedingly low price. Weight, 20 pounds.
Golden elm......**$2.25**
Mahogany finish, 2.30

$2.38

No. 1E316 This large cobbler seat rocker is made of quarter sawed oak, golden finish, and is an exceptional bargain at the price offered. High arms, high banister back, neat designs of carving. Rocker is solidly constructed throughout of very best material, cannot be beat for comfort and style. Shipping weight, 20 lbs.
Price............**$2.38**

$2.45

No. 1E317 Beautiful parlor rocker, made of golden oak with imitation leather seat and tufted top panel. Has a high back, wide roomy seat and high arms. Back is supported by five flat spindles, which is the very latest style of construction. Very comfortable and stylish in appearance. Shipping weight, 20 pounds.
Price. **$2.45**

$2.55

No. 1E318 A veneered and roll shaped seat rocker. Made of golden elm. Handsomely carved panels. Arms are exceptionally well braced. Seat is made of specially selected veneering, broad and comfortable. Weight, 18 pounds.
Price..........**$2.55**

$2.45

No. 1E326 A very attractive and serviceable sewing or nursing rocker, made of solid quartered oak with nicely embossed back panel supported by fancy turned and wel braced posts. It is beautifully upholstered or both seat and back with fancy velour. Weight 15 pounds.
Price. **$2.45**

$2.80

No. 1E328 This rocker is made of selected oak, golden gloss finish, or birch, imitation mahogany finish. High back, high arms, spring seat covered with best quality green or red colored velour. Seat and back well braced, making a strong and serviceable as well as ornamental rocker. Weight, 18 pounds. Golden oak....**$2.80**
Mahogany finish.........**2.85**

$2.85

No. 1E329 This is a large, roomy rocker, with a shaped, veneered roll seat. Made of selected rock elm, golden finish. High arms and high back with seven fancy turned spindles in back and four spindles supporting each arm. Top panel is shaped and neatly carved. Weight, 17 pounds.
Price.............**$2.85**

$2.95

The Farmer's Friend.

A high back, wide seat, comfortable rocker. Has heavy steam bent arms and slat spindles. Fancy carvings, as shown in illustration. Weight, 24 pounds.
No. 1E330 Price, wood seat.....................**$2.95**
No. 1E331 Price, cane seat.....................**$3.35**
No. 1E332 Price, leather seat.....................**$4.10**

$2.95

No. 1E338 Our high back cobbler seat rocker. Made of oak, golden finished with cobbler seat, has wide top panel deeply carved, spindles and posts all handsomely turned. Arms are reinforced by iron rods firmly connected by two fancy turned spindles, making it very strong and durable. Weight, 22 pounds.
Price.............**$2.95**

$2.98

No. 1E342 Handsome veneered seat rocker. Made of golden oak, gloss finish with deeply carved lower panel and banister. High back and arms and saddle seat make it easy and comfortable. The veneering used in these seats is carefully selected and guaranteed by the manufacturers. Weight, 2 pounds. Price.......**$2.98**

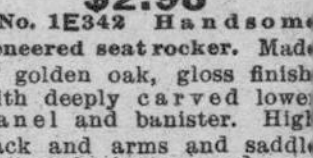

$3.10

No. 1E343 This handsome rocker is made of oak, quarter sawed and beautiful golden finish. Deeply embossed panels and seats, high arms and saddle shaped seat. Three slats in back and three spindles under each arm, forming a perfect brace; making an altogether strong and comfortable rocker. Weight, 20 pounds.
Price.....................**$3.10**

$3.25

No. 1E348 An entirely new design. Made of quarter sawed oak, golden gloss finish. High back with two cross panels deeply embossed, reinforced with five flat spindles. Has high arms strongly braced and shaped, veneered seat. Best construction throughout, making a durable and comfortable rocker. Weight, 20 pounds.
Price.................**$3.25**

$3.45

No. 1E354 This handsome upholstered rocker is made of oak, quarter sawed golden finish or birch, imitation mahogany, highly polished. Has high back with fancy turned spindles, shaped arms and swell front. Spring seat covered in best quality of green or red velour. Strong and very comfortable. Weight, 20 lbs.
Quarter sawed oak...**$3.45**
Birch, imitation mahogany.....................3.50

$3.65

No. 1E356 A handsome roll seat, wide arm, high back rocker, made of oak. Panels and seat quarter sawed, finished golden. Rocker is well constructed, put together with bolts and screws. Wide back panel and apron front neatly carved. Very comfortable. Shipping weight, 25 pounds.
Price, golden finish...**$3.65**

$3.75

No. 1E358 This latest design in a saddle shaped solid wood seat rocker is made of thoroughly seasoned oak golden finish. Has high arms and high back. Spindles in back are flat and arms shaped Richly ornamented with deep carving. Built for strength as well as comfort. Weight 30 pounds. Price.....**$3.75**

$3.55

No. 1E360 Upholstered Rocker. Made of selected oak, or in birch, mahogany finish. It has a high back with a heavy hand carved panel on top, neatly curved arms, fancy shaped spindles and posts. The back and seat are upholstered in a choice quality of velour, ornamented with silk tassels. New in design and elegant in color and finish. Weight, 23 pounds.

Price, golden oak............**$3.55**
Price, mahogany finish .. **3.65**

$3.65

No. 1E364 This is one of our latest designs made of quarter sawed oak, golden gloss finish. High back with beautifully embossed panels and wide seats. High arms and embossed front posts. Deep roll veneered seat. Strongly constructed and very comfortable. Weight, 25 pounds.

Price.......................**$3.65**

$3.85

No. 1E365 Our special platform swing rocker with wide and deep roll seat. High arms, high back, two back panels and seat made of quarter sawed oak, finished golden. A good serviceable rocker that will be an ornament to any room. Shipping weight, 30 pounds.

Price.......................**$3.85**

$3.85

Upholstered high back rocker, made of oak, glossy golden, or birch, mahogany finish. Wide top slat with neat carving, fancy turned back posts, shaped arms, well braced by iron rods and three heavy spindles. Fully upholstered both seat and back with best velour and ornamented with silk tassels. Weight, 23 pounds.

No. 1E368 Price, golden oak........................**$3.85**
No. 1E369 Price, birch, mahogany finish.............. **3.90**

$3.95

No. 1E373 This handsome rocker is one of the best values we have to offer. It is made of quarter sawed oak, golden gloss finish. High back with three wide panels, top panel deeply embossed. High arms with posts ornamented. Deep shaped seat, strongly constructed and comfortable. Weight, 25 pounds.

Price.......................**$3.95**

$4.45

No. 1E377 A beautiful design in a large arm rocker. It is made of the choicest quality of fine grained quarter sawed golden oak with a double curved roll seat. The construction and finish are the very best that skilled workmen can produce. Hand carving on front of roll seat. Broad, shapely panel in back and five spindles under each arm. Shipping weight, 30 pounds.

Price, golden oak, wood seat.........................**$4.45**

$4.65

No. 1E378 A comfortable ornamental rocker, made of quarter sawed oak with veneered full roll seat. High arms and high back. Beautifully carved back panel and turned posts and spindles. Strongly constructed throughout. Arms and front posts connected with bolts and screws. Finished golden. Shipping weight, 35 pounds.

Price......................**$4.65**

$4.75

No. 1E385 Roll seat rocker. Made of quarter sawed and polished oak. Panels, hand carved, shaped arms and carved arm posts, roll on seat beaded and carved. The material in this rocker is especially selected, and it is constructed with special view to comfort and durability. Weight, 35 pounds.

Price......................**$4.75**

$5.20

Patent Rocker.

No. 1E387 A large, comfortable rocker, made of solid quarter sawed golden oak throughout. The seat and back are veneered with the choicest quarter sawed stock. The arms are reinforced by five spindles and heavy hand carved posts. The new style platform base is the strongest possible construction, giving comfort and ease. It has a double curved roll seat. Shipping weight, 30 lbs.

Price.....................**$5.20**

$5.35

No. 1E389 This rocker is exceptional value, made of quarter sawed oak, golden finish, or birch, imitation mahogany finish, hand polished. High arms beautifully shaped with panels in back rounded and carved. Comfortable spring seat covered with best grade of colored velour. Strongly constructed throughout. It meets all the requirements for strength, comfort and beauty. Weight, 30 pounds. Shipped direct from factory in Central New York or Chicago.

Price, quarter sawed oak. **$5.35**
Price, imitation mahogany.............................**$5.40**

$5.75

No. 1E392 This large parlor or library rocker is made of quarter sawed golden oak, or birch, mahogany finish, highly polished. Seat is 19x23 inches and upholstered in very best and latest pattern of velour. Back is 28 inches high, with top panel deeply carved and set with a number of turned spindles. Shipping weight, 40 pounds.

Price, golden oak.....**$5.75**
Price, mahogany finish **5.80**

$5.95

No. 1E394 This handsome wood seat rocker is the very latest design, made of quarter sawed oak, golden finish and highly polished. The material and workmanship on this rocker is first class in every particular. The seat, which is extra large, is 21 inches deep and the back is 27 inches high, making a model that insures comfort. Shipping weight, 35 pounds.

Price, golden oak......**$5.95**

$6.10

No. 1E396 An odd design in parlor rocker with solid wood seat, solid panel back neatly carved, made of quarter sawed oak, golden finish, or birch, imitation mahogany, highly polished. Back is 22 inches high and seat measures 20x22 inches, arm of medium height, making a combination that cannot be excelled for comfort and appearance. Shipping weight, 30 pounds.

Price, golden oak.....**$6.15**
Price, mahogany finish **6.10**

$6.15

No. 1E397 Special McClain rocker made of selected quarter sawed oak. Polished and rubbed. Finished in golden color. Wide paneled back. High arms and deep roll seat. Base is strongly constructed and patent metal swing is nickel plated. Very comfortable and a handsome ornament for library or parlor. Weight, 35 pounds.

Price....................**$6.15**

$6.20

No. 1E401 This handsome rocker is made of quarter sawed golden oak or birch, mahogany finish, highly polished. Seat is wide and deep, back high and upholstered in best quality velour. **This rocker is solid, substantial and attractive in appearance, an ornament for either library or parlor. Shipping weight,** 35 pounds.

Price, golden oak....**$6.25**
Price, mahogany finish..........**6.20**

$6.25

No. 1E403 This McKinley rocker is the handsomest design of this style that has ever been offered. Seat, back and arms made of quarter sawed oak. Spindles, posts and front handsomely carved in rich designs, all hand polished, golden finish. Big, roomy and comfortable. Shipping weight, 30 pounds.
Price.................. $6.25

$6.35

No. 1E403 Parlor and library rocker with upholstered seat and back, made of quarter sawed golden oak or birch, imitation mahogany finish, highly polished. Has extra wide seat and high back upholstered in best quality of velour. A massive, substantial chair. Material and workmanship of the very best. Shipping weight, 40 pounds.
Price, golden oak..... $6.45
Price, mahogany finish, 6.35

$6.85

No. 1E405 This is a solid wood seat rocker of exceptional beauty and entirely new design, made of quarter sawed oak, golden finish, or birch, imitation mahogany, highly polished. Roomy and comfortable seat, measures 19x22 inches and back 24 inches high. Carvings are deep and of artistic designs. Frame is extra heavy and presents a massive appearance. Shp'g wgt, 40 lbs.
Price, golden oak..... $6.95
Imitation mahogany.. 6.85

$7.35

No. 1E407 Extra large platform rocker. Seat upholstered in best quality of velour. Frame is made of quarter sawed oak, finished golden and highly polished. The back is handsomely carved and is 27 inches high. Seat extra large, measures 23x 25 inches, fitted with best steel tempered springs. For comfort and elegance cannot be equaled. Shipping weight, 50 pounds.
Price.................. $7.35

$8.25

No. 1E409 This massive parlor or library rocker is one of the handsomest designs that we have ever offered. It is made of quarter sawed oak or birch, mahogany finish, highly polished. Choice of seats upholstered in best quality of velour or **imitation Spanish leather.** High back with rich carving and the seat is extra large. Shipping weight 45 pounds.
Price, golden oak..... $8.35
Price, mahogany finish 8.25

$8.95

No. 1E410 High back substantial parlor or library rocker. Made of selected quarter sawed oak, highly polished. Has a spring seat upholstered in best quality of genuine leather, wide back panels, curved arms and front posts. Very substantial and comfortable. Will be an ornament to any room. Weight, 30 pounds. Shipped direct from factory in Ohio or from Chicago.
Price, in golden oak only.................. $8.95

$9.85

No. 1E412 The latest out in library or parlor rocker. Made of polished quarter sawed oak, golden finish, with full spring seat covered with best genuine leather, wide back of quarter sawed and polished oak, neatly carved, square posts and shaped arms. Strongly constructed throughout, making it an elegant and durable rocker. Shipping weight, 25 pounds.
Price, quarter sawed oak only.................. $9.85

$9.10

No. 1E414 Large parlor or library rocker. Frame made of selected quarter sawed and polished oak, golden finish. Seat and back upholstered in best grade of imitation Spanish leather. Wide roomy spring seat and high back, bent arms and posts with corners all rounded. Construction of the very best, making a high class serviceable rocker at a very low price. Weight, 30 pounds. Shipped from factory in Central New York or from Chicago.
Price, in oak only.......... $9.10

$10.45

No. 1E416 Beautiful parlor rocker. Made of quarter sawed oak, golden finish, highly polished, upholstered in best genuine leather. Wide spring seat, upholstered back, biscuit tufted. Arms and posts gracefully shaped, making a combination of comfort and elegance that cannot be excelled. The very best material used throughout, insuring strength and durability. Shipping weight, 25 pounds.
Price, oak only $10.45

$11.15

No. 1E418 Our leather seat McKinley rocker, elegant in design. Made of quarter sawed oak, golden finish and hand polished. Spring seat upholstered in best grade genuine leather. Out out broad back panel, heavy posts and heavy side spindles, extending from arms to rocker, adding to strength of construction. For comfort and durability it cannot be beat. Shipping weight, 35 pounds.
Price, genuine leather seat.................. $11.15

$4.95

No. 1E422 This Roman chair is made of selected material, in either quarter sawed oak, golden finish, or birch, imitation mahogany finish, hand polished. Very popular as an odd piece, and comfortable to sit on, the seat and arms having just the required dip to make it satisfactory. Our price is about one-half the regular retail price. Shipped direct from factory in Central Ohio. Shipping weight, 15 pounds.
Price, oak.................. $4.95
Price, mahogany.................. 5.10

$6.15

No. 1E426 Our very newest design Roman chair, made in either oak, golden finish, or imitation mahogany finish and hand polished. Has curved seat and arms. Back beautifully carved and supported by turned spindles. Posts and side pieces beaded. Chair is solidly constructed and will make a comfortable and ornamental piece for parlor. Shipped direct from factory in Central Ohio. Shipping weight, 20 pounds.
Price, oak.................. $6.15
Price, mahogany.. .. .. 6.25

$6.95

No. 1E428 This exceptionally handsome Roman chair is made of oak, quarter sawed, golden finish, or birch, imitation mohogany finish, and highly polished. Material specially selected and strongly constructed. Has neat carvings on back and panels, arms are bent and seat curved, resting on solid wood bases. For a medium priced chair it cannot be equaled for comfort and beauty. Shipped direct from factory in Central Ohio. Shipping weight, 29 pounds. Price, oak.................. $6.95
Price, mahogany.................. 7.10

$9.65

No. 1E430 Our masterpiece in a Roman chair. The latest design made in quarter sawed oak or imitation mahogany, highly polished. Material and workmanship of the very best. Back is extra heavy, with deep carving. Arms bent, seat curved, and resting on handsome French shaped legs. The whole piece is solid, substantial and comfortable. Shipped direct from factory in Central Ohio Shipping weight, 30 pounds.
Price, quartered oak.......... $9.65
Price, mahogany.................. 9.75

No. 1E906 This Sideboard is made of thoroughly air seasoned and kiln dried oak. High gloss, golden finish. The base has a 22x44-inch double top. It has two top drawers with serpentine fronts, one lined for silverware, a large linen drawer and cupboard with double doors below. Fitted with locks, cast brass handles and best quality casters. Mirror is best quality French bevel plate, size, 18x28 inches. The roomy top shelf is supported by neatly curved standards. Compare this sideboard with those sold by others at $18.00 to $20.00 and it will be found a wonderful bargain. Shipped direct from factory in Central Indiana. Shipping weight, 175 lbs. Price.....**$10.95**

No. 1E914 This Sideboard is made of thoroughly seasoned oak, high gloss golden finish. Base has a shaped double top, size 21x44 inches, in a perfect imitation of quarter sawed oak grain. One of the top drawers is lined for silverware. Entire front is richly figured, quarter sawed oak, hand carved claw feet. Mirror is best quality French bevel plate, size 16x28 inches. Broad top shelf supported by handsome curved standards. Decorated with finely executed hand carvings. Fitted with locks, cast brass handles and best quality casters. Thoroughly well made throughout. Compare this sideboard with those offered by others at $20.00 to $25.00. Shipped direct from factory in Western Pennsylvania or Northern Indiana. Shipping weight about 175 lbs Price..........**$12.85**

No. 1E915 This Sideboard is made of thoroughly seasoned and kiln dried oak in a golden finish, highly polished. Base has a 22x45-inch top, shaped to correspond to the double serpentine curved fronts of the drawers. One of the top drawers lined for silverware. Note the shaped French legs with hand carved claw feet. Has full paneled ends and back. Mirror best quality French bevel plate, size, 18x30 inches. The massive Colonial style standards supporting the broad top shelf have hand carved claw feet to match the base. Carvings hand made and finely executed. Thoroughly well made in every detail of construction. Shipped direct from factory in Southern Ohio. Shipping weight, about 175 pounds. Price.........**$14.45**

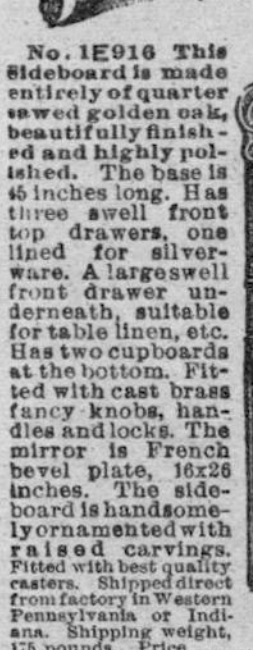

No. 1E916 This Sideboard is made entirely of quarter sawed golden oak, beautifully finished and highly polished. The base is 45 inches long. Has three swell front top drawers, one lined for silverware. A large swell front drawer underneath, suitable for table linen, etc. Has two cupboards at the bottom. Fitted with cast brass fancy knobs, handles and locks. The mirror is French bevel plate, 16x26 inches. The sideboard is handsomely ornamented with raised carvings. Fitted with best quality casters. Shipped direct from factory in Western Pennsylvania or Indiana. Shipping weight, 175 pounds. Price..........**$14.95**

OUR SIDEBOARDS ARE CAREFULLY PACKED TO INSURE SAFE DELIVERY AND SHIPPED DIRECT FROM FACTORY.

No. 1E917 This Sideboard is made of solid oak with a perfect imitation of quartered oak grain in a beautiful golden finish, polished. It has double top, size, 22x47 inches. One of the top drawers lined for silverware. All drawers have shaped fronts. Note the massive standards with cross banded veneering decorated with hand carved lion heads. Mirror best quality of French bevel plate, 18x36 inches. Fitted with locks, cast brass handles and best quality of casters. Thoroughly well made in every detail of construction and finish. Shipped direct from factory near Grand Rapids, Mich. Shipping weight, about 175 pounds. Price..............................**$15.45**

No. 1E920 This Sideboard is made from carefully selected oak in a fine golden finish. The base is 22 inches wide by 48 inches long. It has two spacious cupboards, one large linen drawer and two full swell front top drawers, one of which is lined for silverware. The mirror is best quality French beveled plate, size, 18x36 inches. The elaborate, ornamental and finely executed hand carvings, the massive posts and handsome design make this sideboard very attractive. Fitted with best quality casters. Shipped direct from factory in Southern Indiana, or Pennsylvania, according to location of customer, thereby insuring lowest freight rates. Shipping weight, 175 pounds. Price..............................**$15.65**

No. 1E922 This Sideboard is made of thoroughly seasoned quarter sawed oak golden finish, highly polished. Base has a shaped double top, size 24x46 inches, two top drawers, large linen drawer and spacious cupboard. Drawers have swell fronts. One top drawer lined for silverware. Note the massive corner posts with hand carved claw feet. Mirror is best quality French bevel plate, size 16x28 inches. Spacious top shelf supported by shapely designed standards with hand carved claw feet. All carvings are hand made, smooth cut and finely executed. Cabinet construction high grade throughout. Fitted with locks, cast brass handles and best quality casters. Shipped direct from factory in Pennsylvania or Northern Indiana. Shipping weight, about 175 pounds. Price..............**$15.95**

No. 1E923 This handsome Sideboard is made of specially selected, thoroughly seasoned, quarter sawed oak, golden finish, highly polished. Base has 24x48 inch top, three full swell front center drawers, one of which is lined for silverware, either side of which are spacious closets. Below is a large linen drawer. Supported by curved legs with hand carved claw feet. Mirror is best quality French bevel plate, size 18x36 inches. Broad top shelf supported by shapely veneered standards with hand carved claw feet to match the base. Fitted with locks, keys and best quality cast brass handles and casters. Shipped direct from factory in Southern Ohio. Shipping weight, about 175 pounds. Price..............................**$16.45**

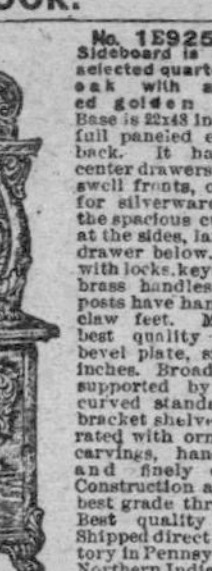

No. 1E925 This Sideboard is made of selected quarter sawed oak with a polished golden finish. Base is 22x48 inches, has full paneled ends and back. It has three center drawers with full swell fronts, one lined for silverware. Note the spacious cupboards at the sides, large linen drawer below. Fitted with locks, keys and cast brass handles. Front posts have hand carved claw feet. Mirror is best quality French bevel plate, size 18x32 inches. Broad top shelf supported by shapely curved standards and bracket shelves. Decorated with ornamented carvings, hand made and finely executed. Construction and finish best grade throughout. Best quality casters. Shipped direct from factory in Pennsylvania or Northern Indiana. Shipping weight, about 175 lbs. Price. **$16.95**

No. 1E926 This Sideboard is made of thoroughly air seasoned and kiln dried solid oak, with highly figured quarter sawed oak front. Popular golden finish. Has a 22x48-inch double top, shaped to correspond with the serpentine curved front of the drawers. One upper drawer is lined for silverware. Lower part of base contains linen drawer and spacious cupboard with double doors. Best quality French bevel plate mirror, 18x32 inches. Carvings throughout are finely executed. Has best quality casters and cast brass knobs and handles. An exceptionally handsome and well made sideboard at a very low price. Shipped direct from our factory in Northern Indiana or Pennsylvania, according to location of customer, thereby insuring lowest freight rates. Shipping weight, 200 pounds. Price..........**$17.25**

No. 1E927 This handsome Colonial design Sideboard is made of thoroughly seasoned, highly figured, quarter sawed golden oak, highly polished. The base is 22x48 inches. The top drawers have rounded fronts, one lined for silverware. Note the massive front corner posts with handsomely figured veneered fronts and hand carved claw feet. The mirror is best quality French bevel plate, size, 18x32 inches. The broad top shelf has box rim supported by massive standards with claw feet to match the base. The crown and base decorated with fine smooth cut hand made carvings. Fitted with locks, cast brass handles and best quality casters. Cabinet work strictly high grade in every detail. Carefully packed to insure safe delivery and shipped direct from factory in Pennsylvania or Northern Indiana. Shipping weight, about 175 pounds. Price..............**$17.35**

No. 1E928 This Sideboard is made of quartered oak, finished golden, rubbed and highly polished. It is 48 inches long. Has two full swell top drawers, one lined for silverware. Has roomy swell front drawer directly underneath, and two large closets below, with swell front doors, solid panel ends. The mirror is French bevel plate, 18x32 inches. The ornamentations are finely executed hand carvings. Strictly high grade throughout. Fitted with best quality cast brass knobs, handles and casters. Shipped direct from our factory in Western Pennsylvania or Indiana, thereby insuring lowest freight rates. Shipping weight, 200 lbs. Price. **$17.45**

No. 1E932 This Sideboard is made of solid golden oak, high gloss finish. The base is 23 inches wide and 46 inches long. Has two full, swell top drawers, one of which is lined for silverware, a roomy drawer and two cupboards below. Has 18x30-inch French bevel plate mirror. Ornamented with heavy hand carvings. Fitted with best quality cast brass handles and casters. Carefully packed and shipped direct from factory in Wisconsin or Pennsylvania, according to location of customer, thereby insuring lowest possible freight charges. Shipping weight, 185 pounds.
Price......**$17.85**

No. 1E948 This Sideboard is made of golden oak, highly figured quartered oak front, rubbed and polished, and is 48 inches long and 22 inches wide. Has two upper swell front drawers, one lined for silverware, and the lower drawer is serpentine in shape, large and roomy. Below this are two cupboards. Top has French bevel plate mirror, 18x36 inches. The handles are solid brass. Best quality casters. Shipped direct from our factory near Grand Rapids, Mich. Shipping weight, 200 lbs.
Price.....**$19.45**

No. 1E955 This Sideboard is made of choice selected quarter sawed oak, highly polished, in a rich, golden finish. It is 4 feet long 2 feet wide. Has two serpentine swell front top drawers, the right hand one lined and divided for silver. Large linen drawers at bottom underneath two large closets. Best brass trimmings. The mirror is the best French bevel plate; size, 18x40 inches. Note the massive roll on top and highly ornamental hand carvings and claw feet. Shipped direct from our factory near Grand Rapids, Michigan. Shipping weight, 225 pounds.
Price......**$25.45**

No. 1E940 This Handsome Sideboard is an entirely new design. Made of solid oak throughout with full quartered oak front. Popular golden hand rubbed polished finish. The base is 4 feet long and 2 feet wide. Has three small top drawers, the middle one lined for silverware. Large linen drawer and double cupboard below. The mirror is the best French bevel plate, size 18x36 inches. Richly ornamented with hand carvings and trimmed with best cast brass knobs, handles and casters. In every respect a strictly high grade sideboard. Retail stores ask $35.00 for this article. Shipped direct from our factory near Grand Rapids, Mich. Shipping weight, 200 pounds.
Price.....**$18.85**

No. 1E952 This Sideboard is made throughout of the choicest selected, highly figured quartered oak, golden finish, highly polished. Base is 22 inches wide and 50 inches long. Has two top drawers, one lined for silverware, one large linen drawer, all full swell front. A spacious cupboard below. Ornamented with genuine hand carvings, and French beveled plate mirror, size, 18x40 inches. Handles are best quality of cast brass. Best quality casters. This sideboard retails in stores at $45.00. Shipped direct from our factory in Pennsylvania. Shipping weight, 200 pounds.
Price.....**$20.85**

No. 1E958 This Sideboard is made almost entirely of thoroughly air seasoned and kiln dried quarter sawed oak, highly polished. It has a 24x50-inch top, shaped to correspond with the serpentine curved front of the drawers. Note the massive front corner posts veneered with selected, highly figured, quartered oak; the broad top shelf supported by massive standards to correspond with the front corner posts. Mirror, best quality of French bevel plate, size 20x36 inches. Best quality of cast brass handles, locks and casters. Construction strictly high grade throughout. Shipped direct from factory near Grand Rapids, Mich. Shipping weight, about 225 pounds.
Price.........**$26.35**

No. 1E943 This exceptionally attractive high grade Sideboard is made of figured, quarter sawed golden oak, highly polished. Base has a 23x46-inch double top and inclosed mouse and dustproof bottom. Drawers are fitted with special guides, locks and best cast brass handles. Note the massive front corner posts with hand made claw feet and roll below cupboard. Mirror is the best quality French bevel plate, size, 18x30 inches. Spacious top shelf supported by double Corinthian columns, below which are bracket shelves resting on standards with claw feet, all hand carved. Crown is decorated with smooth, finely cut hand made carving. Cabinet construction is strictly high grade. This sideboard should be compared with those sold in retail stores at $35.00 to $40.00. Shipped direct from factory in Central Wisconsin. Shipping weight, about 200 lbs. Price.....**$19.25**

No. 1E953 This Massive Colonial Design Sideboard is made of highly figured quarter sawed oak, golden finish, polished. Base is 24x50 inches and has full swell front supported by heavy hand carved claw feet. Top drawer in center lined for silverware. Top section has highly ornamental crown decorated with smooth cut hand made carvings and heavy veneered roll. Broad top shelf supported by massive curved standards resting on bracket shelves above claw feet. Mirror best quality French bevel plate, size 18x40 inches. The beautiful wood, high grade construction and finish combined with attractiveness of design make this sideboard wonderful value at the price we ask. Shipped direct from factory in Pennsylvania. Shipping weight, about 200 lbs.
Price.....**$23.65**

No. 1E965 This Sideboard is made of thoroughly seasoned, highly figured, quarter sawed oak, plane polished. Base has 24x48-inch double top and enclosed mouse and dustproof bottom. Drawers fitted with special guides, locks and cast brass handles. Note the massive round corner posts, heavy roll on the bottom and the hand carved claw feet. Mirror is best quality French bevel plate, size 18x36 inches. Broad top shelf supported by massive Corinthian columns attached to bracket shelves. The highly ornamental carvings are hand made. Cabinet construction strictly high grade throughout. Shipped direct from factory in Central Wisconsin. Shipping weight, about 225 pounds.
Price...**$27.45**

No. 1E966 This Massive Colonial Style Sideboard is made throughout of specially selected, richly figured, quarter sawed, thoroughly seasoned golden oak, highly polished. The base has a 24x54-inch double top. Below is a large linen drawer with serpentine curved front and roomy cupboard, the doors decorated with hand carved dragons' heads; extra large mirror is best quality French bevel plate; size, 18x40 inches. The broad top shelf is supported by massive curved columns, resting on bracket shelves, supported by hand carved claw feet. Fitted with best quality locks, cast brass handles and casters. Cabinet construction strictly high grade in every detail. This sideboard to be fully appreciated must be seen and compared with those offered by others at $50.00 to $60.00. Shipped direct from factory in Pennsylvania. Shipping weight, about 250 pounds Price.................................**$29.75**

No. 1E966½ This Massive Colonial Design Sideboard is made throughout of the best selected, richly figured quarter sawed oak, golden finish, highly polished. Base is 25x50 inches. Has enclosed mouse and dustproof bottom. Top drawers have rounded fronts, one lined for silverware. Below the large linen drawer a spacious cupboard. Fitted with special drawer guides, locks, cast brass handles and best quality casters. Massive front corner posts with highly figured veneered fronts and heavy hand carved claw feet. Top has a roomy cupboard with leaded glass doors. Mirror is best quality French bevel plate, size 24x36 inches. This sideboard should be compared with those offered elsewhere at $50.00 to $60.00. Shipped direct from our factory in Central Wisconsin. Shipping weight, about 300 pounds.
Price.................................**$32.85**

No. 1E967 Massive Colonial Style Sideboard. Made of richly figured quarter sawed golden oak, highly polished. The beautiful arched canopy top has a large French bevel plate mirror; size, 20x30 inches. The china closets on each side have French bevel mirrors; size, 12x18 inches, also inside glass panels and doors. Base has a double top; size, 25x50 inches. It has inclosed mouse and dustproof bottom. Drawers are fitted with special drawer guides, best quality locks, cast brass handles. One top drawer lined for silverware. Best quality casters. Decorated with smooth, finely executed hand made carvings. Perfect in every detail of construction and finish. This sideboard cannot be purchased in retail stores for less than $50.00 to $60.00. Shipped direct from factory in Central Wisconsin. Shipping weight, about 300 pounds.
Price.................................**$35.75**

$9.85 BUFFETS $19.45

AT $9.85 TO $19.45 WE SHOW HANDSOME HIGH GRADE BUFFETS. ALL EXCEPTIONAL VALUES.

Comparison of our Buffets will show every article lower in price than the same quality of Buffet can be purchased elsewhere.

$9.85

No. 1E1001 This Buffet Sideboard is made of thoroughly air seasoned, highly figured, quarter sawed oak, golden finish, highly polished. Height, 52 inches. Base has a double top, size, 18x40 inches. It has two top drawers, one of which is lined for silverware, below which is a large linen drawer and a spacious shelf. Mirror is best quality French bevel plate, size, 8x36 inches. Fitted with locks, best quality cast brass handles and casters. Strictly first class in construction throughout. A useful addition to the dining room. Shipped direct from factory in Pennsylvania or Indiana. Shipping weight, about 100 pounds. Price..........$9.85

No. 1E1003 This Strikingly Attractive New Design Buffet Sideboard is made of thoroughly seasoned, highly figured, quarter sawed oak, golden finish, rubbed and polished. Height, 52 inches. Base has a double top, size 22x40 inches, shaped to correspond with the serpentine curved front. Solid panel ends. One of the top drawers lined for silverware. Note the large linen drawer and roomy shelf below. Mirror best quality French bevel plate, size, 8x36 inches. Fitted with locks, best quality brass handles and casters. Cabinet construction and finish high grade throughout. This buffet sideboard cannot be purchased in retail stores for less than $16.00 to $18.00. Shipped direct from factory in Pennsylvania or Indiana. Shipping weight, about 100 pounds. Price..........$11.85

$11.85

$12.95

No. 1E1009 This Buffet Sideboard is made of thoroughly seasoned oak with a highly polished golden finish. Height, 59 inches. The double top, size, 22x42 inches, has rounded corners and edges. It has a serpentine curved front made of highly figured quarter sawed oak. Top center drawer lined for silverware. Note the spacious cupboards and large linen drawer at the bottom. The handsome French curved legs have hand carved claw feet. Mirror is best quality beveled French plate, size, 18x36 inches, enclosed with a massive rounded frame decorated with finely executed hand carvings. Doors and drawers perfect fitting. Best quality cast brass trimmings and casters. Securely packed and shipped direct from factory in Southern Ohio. Shipping weight, about 125 pounds. Price........$12.95

No. 1E1012 This Combination Buffet China Cabinet is made of highly figured quarter sawed oak, in a golden polished finish. Height, 4 feet 4 inches; width, 3 feet 4 inches; depth, 16 inches. The china compartments in the ends each have two shelves and full swell bent glass doors, size, 14x24 inches. It has two drawers and a spacious cupboard, fitted with lock, keys and best cast brass handles. Top ornamented with a shapely mirror of the best quality French bevel plate, size, 8x30 inches; supported by shapely curved legs. Thoroughly well made and a wonderful bargain at our price. Shipped direct from factory in Southern Indiana. Shipping weight, about 150 pounds. Price $13.85

DON'T FORGET OUR PROFIT SHARING DEPARTMENT.

No. 1E1015 This Buffet Sideboard is made of selected quarter sawed oak, golden polished finish. Height, 65 inches. The base is 23 inches wide by 48 inches long, and has one large linen drawer, two spacious cupboards and two full swell top drawers, one of which is lined for silverware. The mirror in the top is the best quality French bevel plate, size, 14x36 inches. A high grade article in every detail of construction and finish. Shipped direct from factory in Northern Indiana or Pennsylvania, thereby insuring lowest freight charges. Shipping weight, 175 pounds. Price, quarter sawed oak..........$14.45

No. 1E1018 This illustration shows a new and very attractive design in a combination Buffet Sideboard and China Cabinet. The wood is highly figured quarter sawed golden oak, polished finish. Height, 55 inches; length, 44 inches. Base has two top drawers for silverware, etc., and a large linen drawer at the bottom between which is a spacious china cabinet with beautiful leaded glass doors. Mirror is the best quality French bevel plate, size, 10x38 inches. The carvings are genuine hand made. Fitted with locks, keys, cast brass handles and best quality casters. Original in design, high grade in wood, construction and finish. Shipped direct from factory in Northern Illinois. Shipping weight, about 150 pounds. Price...$14.75

$14.75

$15.95

No. 1E1020 This Buffet Sideboard and China Cabinet is exceptionally attractive in design. Made of highly figured quarter sawed oak, golden finish, polished. Height, 52 inches; length, 36 inches; depth, 16 inches. Has large drawer for linen, below which are three roomy drawers each side of which is a spacious compartment for china or silverware. Note the handsome designed leaded glass panels in doors and shapely French shaped legs. Mirror best quality French bevel plate, size, 12x34 inches. Ornamental bracket shelves each side mirror. Fitted with locks, keys and best quality cast brass handles and casters. Strictly high grade in material, construction and finish. Shipped direct from factory in Northern Indiana. Shipping weight, about 140 pounds Price..$15.95

No. 1E1021 This Buffet Sideboard cannot be fully appreciated until seen. Height, 65 inches. The wood is highly figured quarter sawed golden oak, polished. Base is 45 x22 inches and contains two top small drawers, one lined for silverware, below which is a roomy cupboard with double doors, supported with shaped French leg with hand carved claw feet, fitted with best quality French bevel plate mirror, size 12x36 inches, with a roomy shelf above it. Cabinet construction, wood and finish the highest grade. Shipped direct from factory in Northern Indiana. Shipping weight, about 175 pounds. Price...$17.65

$17.65

$17.85

No. 1E1024 This Buffet Sideboard is made of quarter sawed golden oak, polished. Height, 65 inches. Base has a 22x44-inch top with round edges and corners, two top drawers with swell fronts, one of which is lined for silverware. Below is a large linen drawer and a roomy cupboard with double doors. Fitted with special guides, locks, keys and cast brass handles. Best quality casters. Supported by French curved legs with claw feet, inclosed mouse and dustproof bottom. Best quality French bevel plate mirror, size 14x36 inches. The top shelf is supported by shapely curved standards with claw feet. Ornamented with deeply cut carvings on the top and base. Shipped direct from factory in Central Wisconsin. Shipping weight, about 160 pounds. Price, $17.85

No. 1E1027 New Design Buffet Sideboard is made of highly figured quarter sawed oak, hand polished, golden finish. Height, 63 inches. The top is 43 inches long. The fine French beveled plate mirror in top section is 10x30 inches. The base contains two drawers, one of them lined for silverware, and two closets. The shapely hand carved posts and claw feet, strictly high grade construction and beautiful finish makes this a very attractive and useful article. Shipped direct from factory near Grand Rapids, Michigan. Shipping weight, 175 pounds. Price, quarter sawed oak..........$18.35

$18.35

$18.95

No. 1E1031 Of choice quarter sawed oak, golden polished finish. Height, 66 inches. Base is supported by double curved French legs with hand carved claws. Two cupboards, two swell front center drawers and two curved top drawers fill the base, which is 23 inches wide by 48 inches long. One top drawer is lined for silverware. Top is fitted with a genuine French plate mirror, 14x36 inches. Shipped from factory in Northern Indiana or Pennsylvania, thereby insuring lowest freight charges. Shipping weight, 175 pounds. Price..$18.95

No. 1E1033 Buffet China Cabinet is high grade construction and finish. Made of quarter sawed oak, golden finish, highly polished. Height, 54 inches; width, 40 inches. Swell bent glass ends and front. Roomy drawer for linen or silverware. Note the shaped front legs with genuine hand carved claw feet. Mirror is best quality French bevel plate, size, 8x30 inches. Fitted with locks, keys, cast brass handles and best quality casters. You should compare this buffet china cabinet with those offered by others at $25.00 to $30.00 to fully appreciate the wonderful value. Shipped direct from factory in Chicago. Shipping weight, about 150 pounds. Price, quarter sawed oak..........$19.45

No. 1E1042 This Combination Sideboard and China Closet is made of highly figured quarter sawed oak in a golden finish. Height, 67 inches; width, 46 inches. The china compartment has four grooved shelves, a double thick glass end and door. It has two roomy drawers, below which is a spacious cupboard with double doors. Mirror is best quality French bevel plate; size, 14x20 inches. A broad and convenient shelf extends entire length of top. Ornamented with genuine hand carvings. Fitted with locks, keys and best quality cast brass handles. Thoroughly well made in every detail of construction and finish. Sells in retail stores for $25.00. Carefully packed to insure safe delivery and shipped direct from factory near Chicago. Shipping weight, about 175 pounds. Price **$19.45**

No. 1E1045 This Combination Sideboard and China Closet is a useful and ornamental addition to the dining room. Made of highly figured quarter sawed golden oak, highly polished. Height, 70 inches; length, 46 inches. The china cabinet has four adjustable grooved shelves, a double thick glass end and a full swell front glass door. It has two roomy drawers. The top one has a curved front and is lined for silverware. Below the drawers is a spacious cupboard with double doors. The mirror is the best quality French bevel plate, size, 14x20 inches. It has a broad top shelf. Decorated with finely executed hand carvings. Fitted with locks, keys and best quality cast brass handles. Strictly high grade in construction and finish. Shipped direct from factory near Chicago. Shipping weight, about 175 pounds. Price .... **$21.[illegible]5**

No. 1E1046 This Handsome Combination Sideboard and China Closet is made of specially selected, highly figured quarter sawed golden oak, highly polished. It is supported by hand carved French curved claw feet. China compartment has four grooved shelves, double thick glass end and full swell bent glass door with a top panel of highly ornamental genuine leaded glass. It has two large drawers, the top one of which has a curved front and is lined for silverware. Below drawers is a roomy cupboard with double doors. It is 72 inches high, 50 inches wide. Mirror is best quality French bevel plate, size, 18x22 inches. It has a broad top shelf supported on the right hand corner by a beautiful column. Decorated with genuine hand carvings. Fitted with locks, keys and best quality cast brass handles. Carefully packed and shipped direct from factory near Chicago. Shipping weight, about 800 pounds. Price **$25.85**

FREIGHT CHARGES.

In order to save handling expense and reduce the freight charges to the lowest possible amount, we have provided for shipment of almost every article of furniture which we offer direct from the factory to our customers. The immense quantity of each article we sell enables us to make favorable contracts with factories in the East, South and West, and we ship from factory nearest to our customers. Always bear in mind that you pay the freight whether you buy of us or your local dealer, as your local dealer must figure the freight charges he pays in fixing his selling price. The freight charges by our method of shipment will amount to very little as compared to what you save in price when purchasing from us.

Remember also you share in our profit when you buy from us, as fully explained on the last pages of this book.

CHINA CABINETS.

We ship our China Cabinets direct from factory near Chicago, or in Eastern Pennsylvania, most convenient to home of customer, thereby insuring lowest possible freight charge.

Our Leader.

No. 1E1070 This Handsome China Cabinet is made of thoroughly seasoned and kiln dried quarter sawed oak in a golden finish. It is 64 inches high, 36 inches wide and 14 inches deep. Fitted with four grooved shelves. It has double thick bent glass ends and large glass door. Thoroughly well made in every detail. Ornamental in design, beautiful in finish. It must be seen to be fully appreciated. Shipped direct from factory in Southern Ohio or Eastern Pennsylvania. Shipping weight, 150 pounds. Price **$8.50**

No. 1E1074 This China Cabinet is the most wonderful value ever offered. Made of thoroughly air seasoned and kiln dried quarter sawed oak in a beautiful golden finish, 70 inches high, 39 inches wide, supported by French shaped legs. It has hand carved top, finished back, grooved shelves, double thick glass ends. Mirror in top shelf best quality French plate, size 10x30 inches. Construction strictly first class. Best quality French plate mirror furnished for back of any shelf at $2.25 per shelf. Complete with casters. Shipped direct from factory in Chicago or Eastern Pennsylvania. Shipping weight, 175 pounds. Price, without mirror........ **$10.95**

Price, as illustrated **12.95**

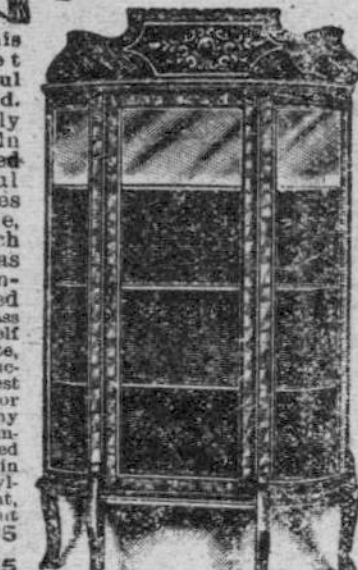

No. 1E1078 This China Cabinet has full swell double thick bent glass ends and front. The wood is thoroughly air seasoned and kiln dried, specially selected, highly figured quarter sawed oak, polished golden finish. Height, 67 inches; width, 36 inches; depth, 16 inches. Mirror on top, 6x18 inches; mirror on back of top shelf, 9x30 inches, both best quality French plate. Finished back, double grooved shelves. Best quality French plate mirror for back of any shelf, $1.45 per shelf. Handsome in design, high grade in construction, beautiful in wood and finish. Shipped direct from factory in Central Indiana or Eastern Pennsylvania. Shipping weight, 175 pounds.

Price, mirror in top decoration only........ **$11.50**

Price, as illustrated **12.95**

No. 1E1082 This China Cabinet is made of selected quarter sawed golden oak, thoroughly air seasoned and kiln dried. It is 69 inches high, 41 inches wide, fitted with best quality double thick bent glass ends. Mirror in top decoration 26x6 inches, mirror in top shelf 10x36 inches, both best quality of French plate. Grooved shelves, finished back. French plate mirrors furnished for back of any shelf at $2.25 per shelf. Shipped direct from factory in Chicago or Eastern Pennsylvania. Shipping weight, 175 pounds.

Price, without mirrors........ **$12.35**

Price, with mirror in top ornament only........ **$13.45**

Price, as illustrated........ **$15.45**

No. 1E1086 This handsome China Cabinet is made of thoroughly air seasoned and kiln dried highly figured, quarter sawed oak, golden finish, highly polished. It is 40 inches wide, 72 inches high, 14 inches deep. Full swell bent glass ends and front with top panels made of best quality leaded glass. Grooved shelves with rounded corners and finished back. Mirror in top decoration, size 8x18 inches; best quality French plate. Note the ornamental bracket shelves on top. French plate mirrors furnished for the back of any shelf, $2.25 extra. Strictly high grade throughout. Shipped direct from factory in Chicago or Eastern Pennsylvania. Shipping weight, about 175 pounds.

Price, without leaded glass........ **$14.75**

Price, as illustrated **$16.95**

No. 1E1090 For beauty of design, high quality of finish and construction this China Cabinet cannot be excelled. Made of specially selected quarter sawed oak, golden finish, highly polished. It has full swell double thick glass ends, grooved shelves, hand carved claw feet. The ornamental hand carved canopy top has French beveled mirror, 8x36 inches. Height, 73 inches; width, 45 inches. French plate mirrors furnished for back of any shelf at $2.25 per shelf. Shipped direct from factory in Chicago or Eastern Pennsylvania. Shipping weight, 190 pounds.

Price, mirror in top decoration only....**$18.95**

Price, mirrors as illustrated........ **$20.45**

No. 1E1094 This China Cabinet must be seen to be fully appreciated. Made of specially selected, thoroughly seasoned, highly figured quarter sawed oak, golden finish, highly polished. It is 43 inches wide, 70 inches high, 15 inches deep. Note the beautiful columns surmounted with hand carved dragon heads on each side of swell front door and the beautiful leaded glass panels in door and bent glass ends. Fitted with grooved shelves with rounded edges. Double paneled finished back. French plate mirrors for back of any shelf, $2.25 per shelf. High grade in every detail of wood, construction and finish. Sells in retail stores at $28.00 to $30.00. Shipped direct from factory in Chicago or Eastern Pennsylvania. Shipping weight, about 175 pounds.

Price, without leaded glass........ **$20.65**

Price, as illustrated........ **$23.25**

No. 1E1098 This handsome China Cabinet is made of the choicest quarter sawed golden oak, piano polished; 79 inches high, 47 inches wide. The best quality French bevel mirror, 8x22 inches, in genuine hand carved canopy top decoration. It has massive round posts, heavy hand carved claw feet, grooved shelves and full swell double thick glass ends. French plate mirrors furnished for back of any shelf at $2.25 per shelf. Shipped direct from factory in Chicago or Eastern Pennsylvania. Shipping weight, 225 pounds.

Price, mirror in top decoration only........ **$24.85**

Price, mirrors as illustrated:...**$26.95**

OUR CHINA CABINETS ARE SECURELY PACKED AND WE GUARANTEE SAFE DELIVERY.

WONDERFUL VALUES IN REVOLVING BOOKCASES.

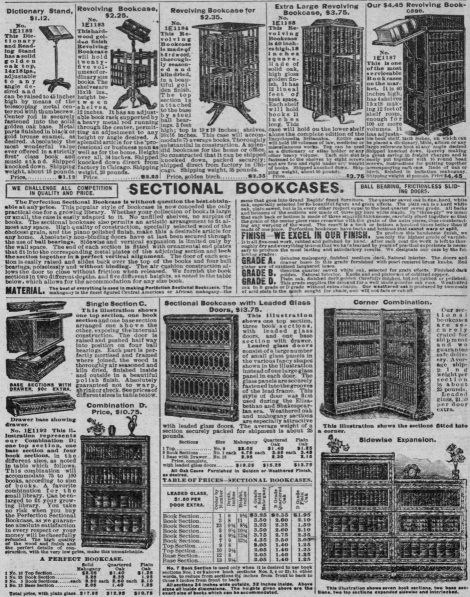

Dictionary Stand, $1.12.

No. 1E1182 This Dictionary and Reading Stand has a solid golden oak top, 14x18 ins., adjustable to any angle desired and can be raised to 45 inches high by means of the telescoping metal center rod with thumbscrew. Center rod is securely fastened into the solid golden oak base. Metal parts finished in black or gold bronze enamel, as desired. Absolutely the most wonderful value ever offered in a strictly first-class book and music stand. Shipped knocked down. Shipping weight, about 15 pounds.
Price............ $1.12

Revolving Bookcase, $2.25.

No. 1E1183 This hardwood golden finish Revolving Bookcase will hold twenty-five volumes of ordinary size books. The shelves are 15x15 ins., height between shelves, 12 inches. It has an adjustable book rack supported by a heavy metal rod running through the center, permitting an adjustment to any height or angle desired. A splendid article for the professional or business man as well as for the home. Height over all, 34 inches. Shipped knocked down direct from factory in Chicago. Shipping weight, 20 pounds.
Price $2.25

Revolving Bookcase for $2.35.

No. 1E1184 This Revolving Bookcase is made of hardwood, thoroughly seasoned and kiln dried, in a beautiful golden finish. The top section is attached to the base by steel ball bearings. 3 feet high; top is 19x19 inches; shelves, 16x16 inches. This case will accommodate 75 average books. Thoroughly substantial in construction. A splendid bookcase for the home or office. So constructed that it can be shipped knocked down, packed securely; shipped direct from factory in Chicago. Shipping weight, 35 pounds.
Price, golden birch........... $2.35

Extra Large Revolving Bookcase, $3.75.

No. 1E1185 This Revolving Bookcase is 40 inches high, 18 inches square. Made of solid oak, high gloss golden finish. It has 12 lineal feet of book space. Each shelf will hold books 11 inches long. This case will hold on the lower shelf alone the complete edition of the Encyclopedia Britannica. Entire case will hold 100 volumes of law, medicine or miscellaneous works. Top can be used as a dictionary or atlas holder or any other heavy volume. Each side slat is fastened to the shelves by eight screws and are firm and rigid under any weight of books. Shipped knocked down. Shipping weight, about 50 pounds.
Price.............................. $3.75

Our $4.45 Revolving Bookcase.

No. 1E1187 This is one of the most serviceable Bookcases on the market. It is 40 inches high, has 4 shelves 15x18 making 12 feet of shelf room, enough for 100 or more volumes. It has adjustable book shelf, 14x15 inches, on which can be placed a dictionary, bible, album or any large reference book at any angle desired Shipped knocked down, thereby making a great saving in freight charges and is easily put together with 16 round head screws, instructions for putting together accompanying each case. Made of oak or birch, finished in imitation mahogany. Shipping weight 40 pounds. Price $4.45

WE CHALLENGE ALL COMPETITION IN QUALITY AND PRICE.

SECTIONAL BOOKCASES.

BALL BEARING, FRICTIONLESS SLIDING DOORS.

The Perfection Sectional Bookcase is without question the best obtainable at any price. This popular style of bookcase is now conceded the only practical one for a growing library. Whether your collection of books is large or small, the case is easily adapted to it. No unfilled shelves, no surplus of books. The sectional bookcase also permits an artistic arrangement to fit almost any space. High quality of construction, specially selected wood of the choicest grain, and the piano polished finish, make this a desirable article for any home. Absolutely non-binding doors have at last been secured through the use of **ball bearings.** Sidewise and vertical expansion is limited only by the wall space. The end of each section is fitted with ornamental end plates that fit into the corresponding metal plates of the adjoining section and **lock the section together in a perfect vertical alignment.** The door of each section is easily raised and slides back over the top of the books and four ball bearings, noiselessly and **without binding.** The air cushion construction allows the door to close without friction when released. We furnish the book sections in two different depths, and five different heights, as noted in the table below, which allows for the accommodation for any size book.

MATERIAL. **The best of everything is used in making Perfection Sectional Bookcases.** The mahogany is the finest figured Central American or African mahogany—the same that goes into Grand Rapids' finest furniture. The quarter sawed oak is fine, hard, white oak, especially selected for its beautiful figure and grain effects. The plain oak is a hard white oak, plain sawed, but is in every other respect equal to the best quarter sawed grade. All backs and bottoms of the sections are made of three-ply hard white maple. By "three-ply" we mean that each back or bottom is made of three separate thicknesses, carefully glued together so that the grain of the center piece runs crosswise with the grain of the outer pieces, thus counteracting any warping of the wood. The result is a back or bottom a hundred times better than if made of one piece. Perfection bookcases have backs and bottoms that **cannot warp or split.**

FINISH—WE EXCEL IN OUR FINISH. To produce this handsome finish, we use only the highest grade of varnish. It is all five-coat work, rubbed and polished by hand. After each coat the work is left to thoroughly dry and everything is done that we have learned by years of practical experience is necessary to produce the most lasting and satisfactory results. We designate our case by the following grades:

GRADE A. Genuine mahogany, finished medium dark. Natural interior. The doors and drawer bases in this grade furnished with pearl centered brass knobs. End plates are of oxidized lacquered brass.

GRADE B. Genuine quarter sawed white oak, selected for grain effects. Finished dark golden. Natural interior. Knobs and end plates are of oxidized copper.

GRADE D. Plain oak, finished dark golden. Carefully finished, but not rubbed or polished. This grade supplies the demand for a well made genuine oak case. Weathered oak in B grade or D grade without extra charge. **Our weathered oak** is produced by two coats of acid stain in the much sought for shade, and will not fade or rub off.

Single Section C.

BASE SECTIONS WITH DRAWER, 90c EXTRA.

Drawer base showing drawer.

This illustration shows one top section, one book section and one base section arranged one above the other, exposing the internal construction. The door is raised and pushed half way into position on four ball bearings. Each part is perfectly mortised and framed where joined, the wood is thoroughly air seasoned and kiln dried, finished inside and outside in a beautiful polish finish. Absolutely guaranteed not to warp, shrink or check. See prices of different sizes in table below.

Combination D. Price, $10.75.

No. 1E1192 This illustration represents our Combination D; one top section, one base section and four book sections, in the different sizes, as noted in table which follows. This combination will accommodate 75 to 100 books, according to size of books. A favorite combination for the small library. Can be enlarged to fit your growing library. You take no risk when you buy the Perfection Sectional Bookcase, as we guarantee absolute satisfaction in every respect or your money will be cheerfully refunded. **The high quality of the wood and finish and the perfect details of construction, with the very low price, make this unmatchable.**

A PERFECT BOOKCASE.

	Solid Mahogany	Quartered Oak	Plain Oak
1 No. 10 Top Section............	$2.05	$1.40	$1.25
1 No. 23 Book Section............	3.25	2.35	1.95
3 No. 3 Book Sections......each	3.50 each	2.60 each	2.10
1 No. 13 Base Section............	2.05	1.40	1.25
Total price, with plain glass..	$17.85	$12.95	$10.75

Sectional Bookcase with Leaded Glass Doors, $13.75.

This illustration shows one top section, three book sections, with leaded glass doors, and one base section with drawer. **Leaded glass doors** consist of a large number of small glass panels in the various fancy shapes shown in the illustration instead of one large glass panel in each door. The glass panels are securely fastened into the grooves of the lead frame. This style of door was first used during the Elizabethan and Shakespearian era. Weathered oak and mahogany sections are especially attractive with leaded glass doors. The average weight of a section securely packed for shipment is about 25 pounds.

Sections	Size	Mahogany	Quartered Oak	Plain Oak
1 Top..................	No. 9	$2.05	$1.40	$1.25
3 Book Sections	No. 1 each	4.75 each	3.85 each	3.45
1 Base with Drawer..	No. 12	2.95	2.30	2.15
Price, complete, with leaded glass doors...		$19.25	$15.25	$13.75

All Oak Cases Furnished in Golden or Weathered Finish, as desired.

TABLE OF PRICES—SECTIONAL BOOKCASES.

LEADED GLASS, $1.50 PER DOOR EXTRA.	Order by Number	Depth, inches	Height, inches	A Grade Solid Mahogany	B Grade Quartered Oak	D Grade Plain Oak
Book Section.....	1	8	9½	$3.25	$2.35	$1.95
Book Section.....	2	8	11	3.50	2.60	2.10
Book Section.....	23	9½	8½	3.25	2.35	1.59
Book Section.....	3	9½	10¼	3.50	2.60	2.10
Book Section.....	4	9½	12¼	3.75	2.75	2.35
Book Section.....	7	9	12⅛	4.35	3.50	3.05
Top Section.......	9	8		2.05	1.40	1.25
Top Section.......	10	9½		2.05	1.40	1.25
Base Section......	12	8		2.05	1.40	1.25
Base Section......	13	9½		2.05	1.40	1.25

No. 7 Book Section is used only when it is desired to use book sections Nos. 1 or 2 above book sections Nos. 3, 4 or 23; in other words, to reduce from sections 9½ inches from front to back to those 8 inches from front to back.

All sections 34 inches wide outside, 32 inches inside. Above sizes all inside dimensions. The heights given above are the exact size of books which can be accommodated.

Corner Combination.

Our sectional bookcases are securely crated for shipment and we guarantee safe delivery. Average shipping weight per section is about 25 pounds. Leaded glass, $1.50 per door extra.

This illustration shows the sections fitted into a corner.

Sidewise Expansion.

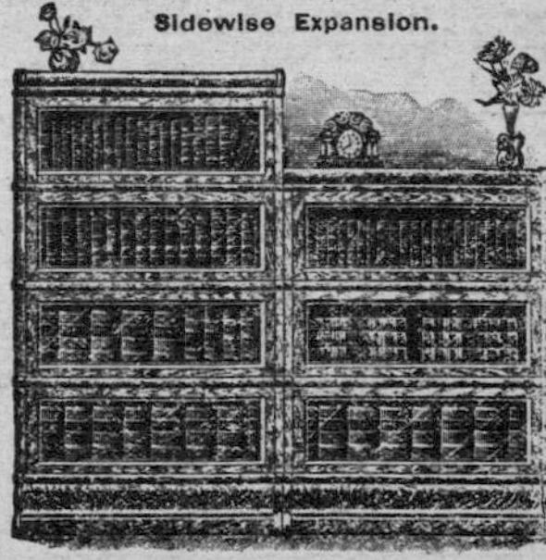

This illustration shows seven book sections, two base sections, two top sections expanded sidewise and interlocked.

WONDERFUL REDUCTION OF PRICES IN HIGH GRADE PARLOR TABLES.

$2.85

No. 1E1196 Adjustable table, made with heavy malleable iron base and wood top, 18x24 inches, which can be tilted to any angle and adjusted to any height. Metal part finished in black or bronze enamel or oxidized copper with golden oak polished top. Adapted for reading, lunches, cards and sewing, as well as the most perfect bedside table ever devised. Be sure to state finish desired. Shipping weight 26 pounds.

Price, black enamel $2.85
Price, bronze enamel 3.25
Price, oxidized copper 4.75

Folding Table.

No. 1E1198 This folding table is made of wavy grained birch in a fine golden finish. The legs are hinged securely to the top, and when open are held in place with a strong flexible brace which extends entirely across the top. Size of top, 24x31 inches. Retails regularly at $2.25. Adapted for lunch, sewing, writing, card parties, etc. Shipping weight, 20 pounds.

Price, golden birch $1.15

No. 1E1199 This folding table is 26 inches long, 32 inches wide. The top is covered with the best quality of green baize cloth or chase leather, as desired. A removable rim attached by screws permits the detaching of the covering for cleaning. The legs are securely framed to a heavy stretcher which is fastened to the top by strong hinges. The metal folding brace is substantial in construction and perfect in operation. A general utility table. Shipping weight, about 20 pounds.

Price, green baize top $2.35
Price, chase leather top 2.45

56c

No. 1E1200 This pretty parlor stand is an exceptionally useful piece of furniture, suitable for lamp or ornament. Made of oak, finished golden. Is 29 inches high with 12-inch top. Shipped knocked down, thereby greatly reducing the freight charges. Can be easily put together with screws, which are provided. Shipping weight, 15 pounds.

Price 56c

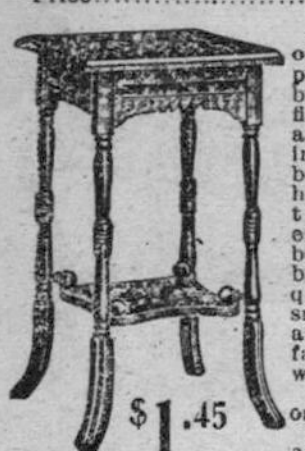

This parlor table is made of solid oak, in a hand polished golden finish, or in birch, mahogany polished finish. It is 32 inches high, and has a top 17x17 inches. The heavy, full boxed top is supported by handsome turned legs. Extra well constructed in every detail. It combines beauty, strength and durability, a combination of qualities hard to find in small parlor tables. Crated and shipped direct from our factory in Chicago. Shipping weight, 25 pounds.

No. 1E1201 Price, golden oak $1.45
No. 1E1203 Price, mahogany finish $1.40

This parlor table is made of solid oak, golden finish. Top is 24x24 inches. Has roomy lower shelf securely fastened to the neatly turned legs. Strictly first class in construction and finish. Shipped direct from Chicago. Shipping weight, 25 pounds.

No. 1E1204 Price, as illustrated $1.15
No. 1E1205 Price, with glass balls and brass claw feet .. $1.45

TABLES ON THIS PAGE, EXCEPT Nos. 1E1201 AND 1E1203 ARE SHIPPED KNOCKED DOWN TO INSURE LOWEST FREIGHT RATES.

Our Leader. A Genuine Quartered Oak Table for $1.20.

No. 1E1208 The best value ever offered in a parlor table at so low a price. Made of quarter sawed oak golden finish. Top, 24 x 24 inches. Broad, shapely lower shelf, smoothly turned, fancy designed legs securely fastened into the top. A table that sells in retail stores for $2.25 to $2.50. Shipping weight, 30 pounds.

	Oak
Price, as illustrated	$1.20

$1.95

No. 1E1209

This parlor table is made of quarter sawed golden oak or birch, imitation mahogany, golden finish, highly polished. The top is 24x24 inches with rounded edges and beautifully embossed rim. The shapely turned legs are firmly attached to the top, strengthened by the spacious and neatly designed lower shelf. Shipping weight, 35 pounds.

	Quartered Oak	Mahogany Finish
Price, brass claw feet...	$1.95	$1.90
Price, wood feet..........	1.65	1.60

$2.25

No. 1E1216 This parlor table has a 24x24-inch shaped top, as shown in the illustration. Made of highly figured quartered golden oak or fine grain birch, finished imitation mahog'ny. Highly polished. Has neat beaded moulding underneath which is screwed to the top, thereby preventing it from warping; shaped lower shelf. Has turned legs with wood feet or brass feet with glass balls. This table sells in furniture stores at $3.50. Shipping weight, 25 pounds.

	Oak	Mahogany Finish
Price, brass claw feet.....	$2.25	$2.20
Price, wood feet..........	1.85	1.80

No. 1E1217 Handsome in design, substantial in construction, beautiful in finish, this parlor table must be seen to be fully appreciated. It is made of selected quarter sawed oak, golden finish or in birch imitation of mahogany, polished. It has a double curved edge top, size, 24 x 24 inches, with embossed rim securely fastened with screws to prevent warping. Has French curved legs and full shaped lower shelf. Shipping weight, 30 pounds.

	Oak	Mahogany Finish
Price..........	$2.00	$1.95

No. 1E1218 This parlor table has a round top 24 inches in diameter with full boxed rim. It is made of highly figured quarter sawed oak, golden finish or birch, in a perfect imitation mahogany finish, highly polished. The roomy shaped lower shelf is supported by neatly turned legs. Strictly high grade in construction; attractive in design and finish. Shipping weight 35 pounds.

	Quartered Oak	Mahogany Finish
Price, brass claw feet	$2.50	$2.45
Price, wood feet	2.15	2.10

No. 1E1222 This is one of the choicest patterns in a parlor table ever designed. The shapely curved 24x24-inch top, ornamented by broad shaped rim richly hand carved in a highly artistic manner. The spacious lower shelf is securely fastened to heavy rope shaped legs. We furnish it in specially selected quarter sawed oak, golden finish, or in choice grained birch in perfect imitation of mahogany, highly polished. Shipping weight, 35 pounds.

	Oak	Mahogany
Price, brass claw feet........	$2.75	$2.70
Price, wood feet..............	2.40	2.35

No. 1E1224 The wood in this parlor table is selected quarter sawed golden oak or birch finished in perfect imitation of mahogany, highly polished. It has a 24x24-inch top with curved rounded edges and a carved box rim. The shapely French legs are securely fastened to the top with patent bolt construction. Compare this table with those sold by others at $4.50 to $5.00. Shipping weight, 35 pounds.

	Quartered Oak	Mahogany Finish
Price..................	$2.65	$2.60

$3.15

No. 1E1225 Another new and handsome design in a parlor table. Has 24x24-inch fancy shaped top, supported by broad rim designed to correspond with top. Has smoothly turned and fluted legs; broad shapely lower shelf. The wood is highly figured quarter sawed golden oak, or birch in imitation mahogany, highly polished finish. High grade in construction in every detail. A table that is sure to please. Shipping weight, 35 pounds.

	Quartered Oak	Mahogany Finish
Price, brass claw feet..	$3.15	$3.10
Price, wood feet........	2.80	2.75

No. 1E1228 You cannot fully appreciate the wonderful value we offer in this parlor table until seen. The wood is highly figured quarter sawed golden oak or birch, imitation of mahogany, highly polished. Note the serpentine curved top, size, 24x24 inches, with boxed rim and the beautiful feather design hand carvings on the legs. A spacious and shapely lower shelf is firmly framed into the legs. Shipping weight, 35 pounds.

	Quartered Oak	Mahogany Finish
Price, brass claw feet....	$3.30	$3.25
Price, wood feet..........	2.95	2.90

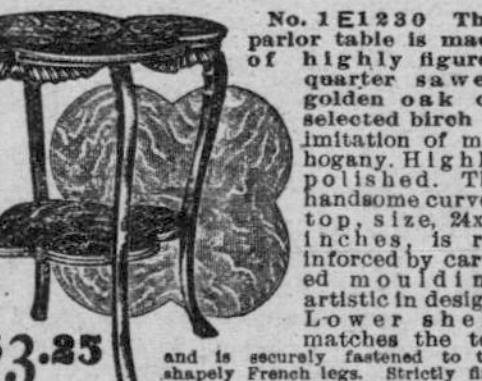

No. 1E1230 This parlor table is made of highly figured quarter sawed golden oak or selected birch in imitation of mahogany. Highly polished. The handsome curved top, size, 24x24 inches, is reinforced by carved moulding artistic in design. Lower shelf matches the top and is securely fastened to the shapely French legs. Strictly first class in every detail. Shipping weight, 35 pounds.

	Quartered Oak	Mahogany Finish
Price.	$3.25	$3.20

$3.45

No. 1E1238 This parlor table should be compared with tables sold in retail stores for $5.00 to $6.00. The top is 24x24 inches and has neatly rounded edges. The wood is highly figured quarter sawed oak in a beautiful finish, or birch in a perfect imitation of mahogany, highly polished. It has an ornamental hand carved boxed rim, handsome French shaped legs and a broad lower shelf. Construction and finish strictly high grade. An exceptionally fine table. Shipped direct from factory in Western New York or Chicago. Shipping weight, 38 pounds.

	Quartered Oak	Mahogany Finish
Price	$3.45	$3.40

$3.75

No. 1E1239 This is an unusually handsome parlor table. Has round top, which is 24 inches in diameter, rounded edges and full boxed rim. The fancy carved French shaped legs are firmly fastened to the top; the neatly shaped lower shelf adds strength and convenience to this beautiful table. The wood is quarter sawed golden oak or birch with a perfect imitation mahogany finish, both highly polished. Wonderful value at our price. Shipped direct from our factory in Western New York or Chicago. Shipping weight, 45 pounds.

	Quartered Oak	Imitation Mahogany
Price	$3.75	$3.65

$4.25

No. 1E1240 This parlor table is graceful in design, substantial in construction, beautiful in wood and finish. Has handsome 24x24-inch curved top with rounded edges and full boxed rim. The full French curved hand carved legs are firmly attached to the top and given additional stability by the spacious and shapely lower shelf. The wood is highly figured quarter sawed golden oak or birch, mahogany finish, highly polished. Wonderful value at our price. Shipping weight, 35 pounds.

	Quarter Sawed Oak	Mahog. Finish
Price	$4.25	$4.15

$4.85

No. 1E1242 This is without question one of the best values in a parlor table ever offered. It is made of beautiful flaky grained quarter sawed oak, or selected wavy grained birch, mahogany finish, highly polished. Brass claw feet holding large glass balls 4 inches in diameter. Heavy, full box curved frame top and broad lower shelf. Size of top, 26x26 inches. Strictly high grade. Carefully crated to insure safe delivery. Shipped direct from factory in Western New York, western orders from Chicago. Shipping weight, 50 pounds.

	Oak	Mahogany
Price, brass claw feet	$4.85	$4.80
Price, wood feet	3.95	3.90

$4.90

No. 1E1242½ This parlor table is made of thoroughly seasoned, highly figured, quarter sawed oak, golden finish, polished. Top is 27x27 inches and has rounded edges and handsome curved boxed rim. Note the large turned and fluted legs with brass claw feet holding large glass balls 4 inches thick. Strictly first class in construction and finish. Compare this table with those offered in retail stores at double our price. Shipping weight, about 50 pounds.

Price, quarter sawed oak $4.90

$4.95

No. 1E1243½ This is, without doubt, one of the handsomest parlor tables we have ever been able to furnish and a big bargain. Made of beautifully figured quartered golden oak or selected birch, in a beautiful mahogany finish, highly polished. It is 29 inches high, 24x24-inch top. Hand carving, and legs of of artistic design. Roomy lower shelf, a strictly high grade piece of furniture. Carefully crated to insure safe delivery. Shipping weight, about 50 lbs.

	Quartered Oak	Mahogany Finish
Price	$4.95	$4.90

$5.45

No. 1E1244 For beauty of design, high quality of wood and finish, this handsome parlor table is without question one of the best values ever offered by any dealer. The wood is specially selected, highly figured quarter sawed oak in a beautiful golden finish or genuine mahogany, piano polished finish. It has a serpentine swell shaped full boxed top, size, 20x26 inches, genuine French shaped legs and spacious lower shelf. It combines artistic beauty with strength and durability. Shipped direct from factory in Western New York or Chicago. Shipping weight, 40 pounds.

	Quartered Oak	Genuine Mahogany
Price	$5.45	$6.25

$5.50

No. 1E1244½ This massive parlor table is made of thoroughly air seasoned and kiln dried highly figured quarter sawed oak in a beautiful golden finish, or selected birch, mahogany finish, highly polished. The top, which is 28x28 inches, has a heavy full boxed edge with finely executed deep embossed rim. The massive, shapely and smooth turned legs are securely fastened to the top by our patent bolt construction and braced with a solid shaped shelf and are fitted with extra large glass ball brass claw feet. This table sells for $8.00 to $9.00 in retail stores. Shipped K. D. from factory in Western New York or Chicago, according to location of customer. Shipping weight, 55 pounds.

	Oak	Mahogany Finish
Price, brass claw feet	$5.50	$5.45
Price, wood feet	4.55	4.50

$6.25

No. 1E1245 This massive parlor table has a shapely double curved top, size, 28x28 inches, reinforced beneath with heavy moulding. The legs ornamented with finely executed feather design hand carvings and fitted with extra large glass ball brass claw feet and a broad shaped lower shelf. Made in highly figured quartered oak or birch, imitation mahogany. Shipped knocked down, to insure lowest freight rate. Shipped direct from factory in Western New York or Chicago, according to location of customer. Shipping weight, 55 pounds.

	Quartered Oak	Mahogany Finish
Price	$6.25	$6.20

$6.45

No. 1E1246 This round table is made of highly figured quarter sawed oak or birch imitation of mahogany, highly polished. Top is 30 inches in diameter, with rounded edges and shapely moulding beneath. Legs are massive and hand carved in feathered design. Fitted with extra large glass ball brass claw feet. Spacious lower shelf. Shipped knocked down to insure lowest freight rate. Shipped direct from factory in Western New York or Chicago, according to location of customer. Shipping weight, 65 pounds.

	Quartered Oak	Mahogany Finish
Price	$6.45	$6.40

$7.35

No. 1E1246½ This massive parlor table is made of thoroughly seasoned, highly figured, quarter sawed oak, highly polished. Extra large top, 30 inches in diameter. Has rounded edges and wide, shaped, boxed rim. Note the massive pedestal, smoothly turned and fluted, supporting the top. Handsome shaped legs securely framed into the pedestal. Construction high grade. A table that sells in retail stores at $10.00 to $12.00. Shipped direct from factory in Chicago. Shipping weight, about 50 pounds.

Price, quarter sawed oak $7.35

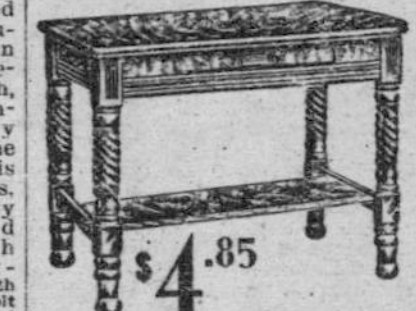

$9.85

No. 1E1247 This magnificent Colonial Style Parlor and Library Table is made in highly figured quarter sawed oak in a golden finish, or birch with genuine mahogany top, rim and shell, piano polished. The top is 36 inches in diameter with neatly rounded edges and full boxed rim. The massive curved legs have heavy hand carved claw feet. The broad and shapely lower shelf has veneered edges. High grade in material, construction and finish. A table for a lifetime. Shipped direct from factory in Western New York or Chicago, according to location of customer. Shipping weight, 65 pounds.

	Quartered Oak	Genuine Mahogany
Price	$9.85	$10.95

$4.85

No. 1E1248 A very choice design in a solid golden oak library or sitting room table. The hand turned rope shaped legs, the roomy lower shelf, the hand polished finish and strictly high grade construction, make this table the greatest value ever offered at so low a price. The top is 2 feet by 3 feet. The spacious drawer has a hand carved pull. Don't be misled by the extremely low price quoted. Shipped from factory in Chicago. Shipping weight, 50 pounds.

Price $4.85

$5.75

No. 1E1250 This library or parlor table is made of selected highly figured quarter sawed golden oak, or in birch imitation of mahogany, highly polished. The top is 24x36 inches, containing a roomy drawer fitted with cast brass knobs. The shapely French legs are securely framed into the heavy boxed rim. Has a spacious lower shelf. Strictly high grade in construction. Shipped direct from our factory in Western New York or Chicago, according to location of customer. Shipping weight, 60 pounds.

	Quartered Oak	Mahogany Finish
Price	$5.75	$5.70

$6.75

No. 1E1251 This Library Table is made of quarter sawed oak, golden finish, polished. Has a 26x40-inch top with rounded edges and corners and roomy drawer with lock and cast brass handles. Note the shapely hand turned and fluted legs, three inches in diameter. Best quality casters. Cabinet construction strictly high grade throughout. Compare this table with those offered in retail stores at $10.00 to $12.00. Shipped from factory in Northern Indiana. Shipping weight, about 75 pounds.

Price $6.75

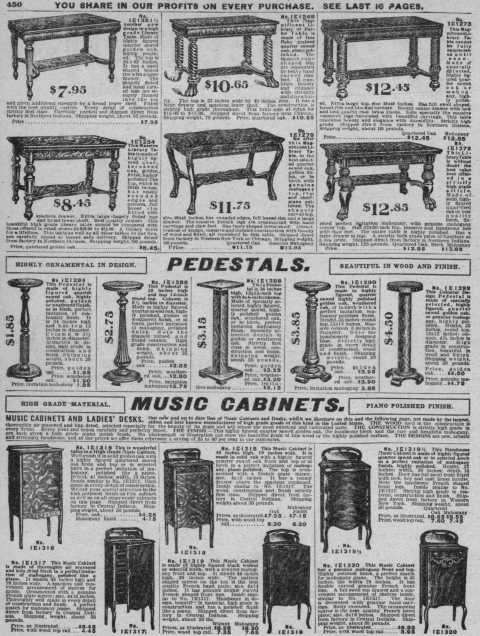

No. 1E1251½ Another new design in a high grade Library Table. Made of highly figured quarter sawed golden oak, highly polished. The top is 26 x 42 inches. It has a swell shaped boxed rim with a large drawer. The shapely fluted and hand turned legs are securely framed into the top and given additional strength by a broad lower shelf. Fitted with the best quality casters. Every detail of construction strictly first class. Carefully packed and shipped direct from factory in Northern Indiana. Shipping weight, about 85 pounds.
Price $7.95

No. 1E1268 This Magnificent Library or Parlor Table is made of fine flaky grained quarter sawed oak, piano polished. The massive rope shaped legs are supported by heavy band carved claw feet. It combines beauty and elegance with strength and durability. The top is 27 inches wide by 40 inches long. It has a large drawer and spacious lower shelf. The construction is strictly high grade throughout. This table sells at retail for $15.00 to $18.00. Shipped direct from factory near Chicago. Shipping weight, 70 pounds. Price, quartered oak...$10.65

No. 1E1273 This Magnificent Library Table cannot be fully appreciated until seen. Made of specially selected, highly figured quarter sawed oak or mahogany, highly polished. Extra large top, size 28x48 inches. Has full swell shaped, boxed rim and blocked corners. Roomy center drawer with lock and best quality cast brass knobs. Note specially the massive veneered legs decorated with beautiful carvings. This table combines beauty and elegance with durability. Strictly high grade. Shipped direct from factory in Northern Indiana. Shipping weight, about 125 pounds.

	Quartered Oak	Mahogany
Price	$12.45	$12.55

No. 1E1254 This Massive Library Table is made of highly figured quarter sawed oak, golden finish, highly polished. The top, which is 28x45 inches, has neatly rounded edges and corners, full boxed rim fitted with spacious drawer. Extra large shapely fluted legs and broad lower shelf. Best quality casters. This beautiful high grade library table should be compared with those offered in retail stores at $12.00 to $14.00. A library table for a lifetime. This table as well as all other tables in our line, are carefully crated to insure safe delivery. Shipped direct from factory in Northern Indiana. Shipping weight, 200 pounds.
Price, quartered golden oak $8.45

No. 1E1270 We offer this Magnificent Library Table, in the best selected quarter sawed oak, golden finish, or in birch with genuine mahogany top, rim and shelf piano polished. The shapely curved top, size, 28x48 inches, has rounded edges, full boxed rim and a large drawer. The massive French legs are ornamented with hand carvings and claw feet. Has fancy shaped lower shelf. Attractiveness of design, massive and durable construction with beauty of wood and finish, all combined in this table. Shipped direct from factory in Western New York or Chicago. Shipping weight, 100 pounds.

	Quartered Oak	Genuine Mahogany
Price	$11.75	$12.95

No. 1E1275 This Library Table is without doubt the best value ever offered in a strictly high grade article. Made of solid, highly figured quartered oak or best quality birch, finished perfect imitation mahogany, with genuine mahogany veneer top. Has 32x50-inch top, massive and handsome legs with claw feet. The entire table is highly polished. Has a large drawer in top. A strictly high grade piece of furniture at a low price. Shipped direct from factory in Northern Indiana. Shipping weight, 125 pounds.

	Quartered Oak	Birch Mahogany
Price	$12.95	$12.85

HIGHLY ORNAMENTAL IN DESIGN.

PEDESTALS.

BEAUTIFUL IN WOOD AND FINISH.

No 1E1284 This Pedestal is made of highly figured quarter sawed oak, highly polished, golden or weathered finish, or in birch, perfect imitation of mahogany finish. It is 34 inches high and has top 12 inches in diameter. Column is 3½ inches in diameter. Attractive in design, high grade in construction and finish. Shipping weight, about 20 pounds.
Price, golden oak $1.95
Price, weathered oak $1.90
Price, imitation mahogany 1.85

No. 1E1286 This Pedestal is 35 inches high and has 14-inch round top. Column is 5½ inches in diameter. Made in highly figured quarter sawed oak, highly polished, golden or weathered finish, or in birch, perfect imitation of mahogany, polished finish. Note the shapely turned and fluted column. High grade construction and finish. Shipping weight, about 25 pounds.
Price, golden oak $2.85
Price, weathered oak.... $2.80
Price, imitation mahogany $2.75

No. 1E1288 This Pedestal is 36 inches high, 12x12-inch top with 4x4-inch column. Made of specially selected, highly figured, quarter sawed, highly polished golden oak, weathered oak, or in birch, perfect imitation mahogany finish. Specially attractive design in golden or weathered oak. Strictly first class in wood, construction and finish. Shipping weight, about 25 pounds.
Price, golden oak... $3.25
Price, weathered oak, $3.20
Price, imitation mahogany $3.15

No. 1E1290 This Pedestal is made in highly figured, quarter sawed highly polished golden oak, weathered oak, or in birch with a perfect imitation mahogany polished finish. Height, 35 inches; round top, 13x13 inches. Massive column 6 inches in diameter. Note the handsomely designed base. Strictly high grade in every detail of construction, wood and finish. Shipping weight, about 30 pounds.
Price, golden oak..... $3.95
Price, weathered oak.. $3.90
Price, imitation mahogany 3.85

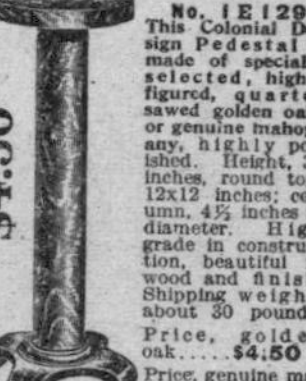

No. 1E1292 This Colonial Design Pedestal is made of specially selected, highly figured, quarter sawed golden oak, or genuine mahogany, highly polished. Height, 35 inches, round top, 12x12 inches; column, 4½ inches in diameter. High grade in construction, beautiful in wood and finish. Shipping weight, about 30 pounds.
Price, golden oak..... $4.50
Price, genuine mahogany.. $4.75

HIGH GRADE MATERIAL.

MUSIC CABINETS.

PIANO POLISHED FINISH.

MUSIC CABINETS AND LADIES' DESKS. Our new and up to date line of Music Cabinets and Desks, which we illustrate on this and the following page, are made by the largest, oldest and best known manufacturer of high grade goods of this kind in the United States. THE WOOD used in the construction is thoroughly air seasoned and kiln dried, selected especially for the beauty of its grain and will please the most exacting and cultivated taste. THE CONSTRUCTION is strictly high grade in every detail. Every joint and tenon carefully and perfectly fitted. THE FINISH.—This highly figured quarter sawed golden oak, the handsome birch and the rare and beautiful mahogany, are each given a high grade piano polish finish. No photograph or illustration can show the beautiful grain of this wood or the highly polished surface. THE DESIGNS are new, artistic and strikingly handsome, and at the prices we offer them represent a saving of 35 to 40 per cent to our customers.

No. 1E1316

No. 1E1316 This is wonderful value in a High Grade Music Cabinet. We furnish it in solid golden oak with a highly figured quartered sawed oak front and top or in selected birch in a perfect imitation of mahogany, polished like a piano. Height, 41 inches; width, 19 inches. Inside similar to No. 1E1317. High grade in every detail of construction. We call your special attention to the high polished finish on this cabinet as well as on all other music cabinets on this page. Shipped direct from factory in Central Indiana. Shipping weight, about 50 pounds.
Price, oak.................. $4.25
Mahogany finish 4.15

No. 1E1318

No. 1E1318 This Music Cabinet is 45 inches high, 19 inches wide. It is made in solid oak with a highly figured quarter sawed oak front and top or in birch in a perfect imitation of mahogany, piano polished. The top is ornamented with a French plate mirror, size, 4x16 inches. It has a roomy drawer above the spacious cupboard. Inside similar to No. 1E1317. The wood, construction and finish strictly first class. Shipped direct from factory in Central Indiana. Shipping weight about 50 pounds.

	Oak	Mahogany Finish
Prices, as illustrated	$7.25	$7.15
Price, with wood top rail	6.30	6.20

No. 1E1319½

No. 1E1319½ This Handsome Music Cabinet is made of highly figured quarter sawed oak or in selected birch in a perfect imitation of mahogany finish, highly polished. Height, 37 inches; width, 20 inches; depth, 16 inches. Door has full swell front fitted with lock, key and cast brass handle. Note the handsome French shaped front legs. Inside similar to No. 1E1317. Strictly high grade in material, construction and finish. Shipped direct from factory in Western New York. Shipping weight, about 50 pounds.

	Quartered Oak	Mahogany
Price, as illustrated	$8.65	$8.55
Price, wood top rail	7.60	7.45

No. 1E1317

No. 1E1317 This Music Cabinet is made of thoroughly air seasoned and kiln dried birch in a perfect imitation of mahogany, polished like a piano. It stands 43 inches high and 19 inches wide. A spacious and convenient arrangement of shelves for music. Ornamented with a genuine French plate mirror; size, 4x16 inches. Thoroughly well made in every detail of construction and finish. A perfect match for mahogany piano. Shipped direct from factory in Central Indiana. Shipping, weight, about 50 pounds.
Price, as illustrated........ $5.45
Price, with wood top rail... 4.45

No. 1E1319

No. 1E1319 This Music Cabinet is made of highly figured black walnut or selected birch, with a genuine mahogany front and top. It stands 44 inches high, 20 inches wide. The pattern shaped mirror on the top is the best quality French band plate; size, 6x14 inches. It has genuine double curved French shaped front legs. Inside similar to No. 1E1317. Handsome in design, beautiful in material, high grade in construction and has a polished finish like a piano. Shipped direct from factory in Central Indiana. Shipping weight, about 50 lbs.

	Walnut	Mahogany
Prices, as illustrated	$8.25	$8.30
Price, wood top rail	7.35	7.65

No. 1E1320

No. 1E1320 This Music Cabinet has a genuine mahogany front and top. Highly polished finish, a perfect match for mahogany piano. The height is 45 inches, the width 19 inches. It has double curved genuine French front legs. A full swell top drawer and a convenient arrangement of shelves inside, similar to No. 1E1317. The door is decorated with genuine hand carvings, finely executed. The ornamental mirror is the best quality French bevel plate; size, 6x16 inches. Shipped direct from factory in Central Indiana. Shipping weight, about 50 pounds.
Price, as illustrated.......... $9.85
Price, with wood top rail..... 8.95

$5.35 DRESSERS $21.50

AT $5.35 TO $21.50 WE OFFER WONDERFUL VALUES IN 1906 DRESSERS.

HANDSOME IN DESIGN, FIRST CLASS CONSTRUCTION AND FINISH, AT A BIG SAVING IN PRICE.

THESE DRESSERS **which we offer this season are made by the largest and most reliable manufacturers in the country.** The designs are all new and up to date, they are shipped direct from the factory, enabling us to make the lowest price possible, based on the actual cost to manufacture with but our one small percentage of profit added. Almost every style of dresser made is illustrated on the following pages but we call your attention to the fact that we can furnish dressers from almost any of our large and handsome line of bedroom suites. The value we give you and the immense saving will only be fully appreciated when you compare these dressers with those offered by others at prices 30 to 40 per cent higher than we ask.

THE WOOD **used in the construction of our dressers is thoroughly air seasoned and kiln dried** before being put through the factory, it is carefully selected, special attention being given to the high quality of the grain.

THE CONSTRUCTION **of our dressers is strictly high grade throughout,** the drawers all dovetailed, the panels built of transverse layers of 3-ply stock, the post and crossbars mortised and framed in the most perfect manner. In fact, every part and piece is thoroughly well made and fitted, the best that modern machinery and skilled workmanship can produce. All the drawers move easily. The bevel plate glass mirrors we use in our dressers are the very best obtainable. We use none of the cheap domestic plate. Every dresser is fully trimmed and castered and absolutely guaranteed in every detail of construction. **The very best quality of material is used in the finishing of our dressers.** The hardwood, oil, the glue and the varnish are the highest grade obtainable. Experienced and skilled workmen only are employed in the factory which makes these goods. The color is a beautiful golden which brings out the handsome grain of the wood.

ABOUT FACTORY SHIPMENTS. **In order to reduce our selling price to the lowest possible point,** we reserve the right to ship direct from our factory, thereby eliminating the freight charges from the factory to Chicago, cartage and handling in the warehouse and the additional liability of damage to the goods, all of which adds to the cost but does not improve the quality. We give you the benefit of every penny saved in this way by adding only our one small margin of profit to the actual cost of the goods at the factory.

FACTORY INSPECTION. **Thoroughly experienced and competent inspectors, men who are expert cabinet makers and finishers,** are employed at each of our factories who carefully inspect every article. Every detail of the construction and finish is rigidly examined before the article is packed for shipment. Each article, after being thoroughly inspected as to **material, construction and finish,** is securely wrapped, burlapped or crated, whichever style of packing is best suited to the style of article, in order to insure safe delivery at destination in the same perfect condition. We guarantee safe delivery.

PROMPT SHIPMENT. **At each of our factories we have prepared immense warehouse room.** The goods are made up, carefully finished, inspected and placed in a perfectly dry and thoroughly ventilated storage room, ample time being given for the finish to thoroughly set, dry and harden before being packed for shipment. We are thus enabled to make shipment within a few days after receiving your order.

QUALITY AND PRICE GUARANTEE. **We guarantee every article in this catalogue to be lower in price than the same quality of goods can be bought elsewhere.** If any other house meets or cuts our prices on any article they do it at the expense of quality. If you do not find this is so by comparing the goods, or if you ever buy anything from us that is not lower in price than the same quality of goods can be bought from any other house, you are especially requested to return our goods at our expense and get your money back at once.

OUR GREAT VOLUME OF BUSINESS **enables us to contract with the best furniture factories located in all parts of the United States,** all of these factories frequently making the same article for us, so that customers living in the vicinity of the factory will have very much less freight to pay than would otherwise be possible. We call particular attention to the location of our factories and the point from which the goods are shipped.

ABOUT FREIGHT CHARGES. **The freight charges on a dresser amounts to next to nothing as compared to what you will save in price.** The freight on an average dresser or chiffonier for a distance of about 500 miles will amount to 75 cents to $1.25. Don't let the item of freight charges prevent you from ordering, for we positively guarantee that after you have paid all the freight charges you will find that you have saved considerable money by sending your order to us.

WE GUARANTEE OUR QUALITY BETTER AND OUR PRICES LOWER THAN THE SAME DRESSERS CAN BE BOUGHT ELSEWHERE.

FREE CLOTHING FREE WATCHES, JEWELRY, ETC.

Your share in our profit. See the free articles you get for your profitsharing certificates. We share our profit with you.

OUR $6.25 DRESSER.

A HIGH CLASS PIECE OF FURNITURE. THE WONDER OF THE FURNITURE WORLD.

$6.25 **for this handsome dresser, made of choice selected oak in a beautiful golden finish.** Undoubtedly the most wonderful value in a strictly first class dresser that has ever been offered by any dealer. The base is 40 inches long by 19 inches wide and contains four roomy drawers. The mirror is the best quality of genuine hand polished French bevel plate; size, 18x20 inches. The frame which incloses the mirror is decorated with ornamental and finely executed genuine hand carvings. The drawers are all dovetailed and are fitted carefully to avoid binding or friction. The frame of this dresser is mortised and joined together in the best manner possible. The durability and construction we guarantee to be equal to any dresser made. The wood used in the construction of this dresser is specially selected from fine grained oak, thoroughly air seasoned and kiln dried and guaranteed not to warp, shrink or check. The finish is strictly high grade, special attention being given to the color to bring out the grain of the wood most effectively. The contract for a large quantity of these dressers enables us to offer them at a very low price, a price below what your retail dealer can buy them for in car lots.

No. 1E1800 Price, $6.25

WE EXPECT **to sell 5,000 of these dressers this season at $6.25.** We believe this page displaying this dresser and the low price of $6.25 will sell 5,000 of these dressers during the ensuing year. If it does we are well repaid in spite of the narrow margin of a few cents profit on each dresser. It will mean 5,000 well satisfied, enthusiastic customers, 5,000 people who will admit to themselves and most likely tell their friends that we certainly sell reliable goods below any kind of competition and that our descriptions and representations can be depended on. These customers will recommend us to their neighbors, when they want to buy other merchandise they will look in our catalogue and see what our price is before buying from some one else. In this way our trade grows and grows, one sale means another, one pleased customer is the means of getting another, and in return for this generous response on the part of our customers, we on our part are going to give them the benefit of every advantage we possess in buying and selling goods and always make our prices as low as possible, which will mean below all others.

No. 1E1800 DRESSER. Shipped direct from factory in Western New York, Southern Indiana or North Carolina, thereby insuring lowest freight charges. Shipping weight, 100 pounds. Price........ **$6.25**

NOTE—We show our lower priced dressers on the next page.

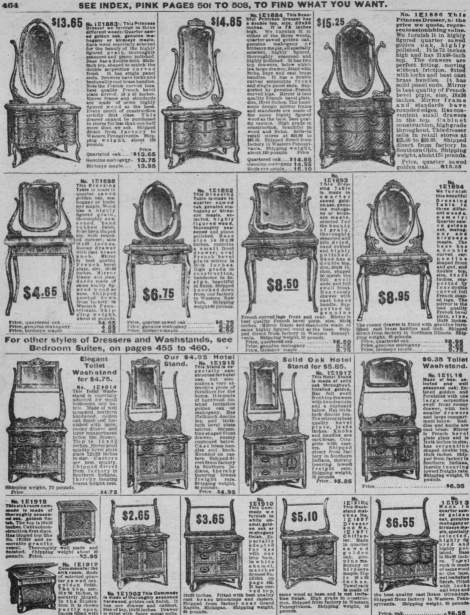

$13.65

No. 1E1883½ This Princess Dresser we furnish in three different woods: Quarter sawed golden oak, genuine mahogany or birdseye maple. Each wood especially selected for the beauty of the highly figured grain, thoroughly seasoned and piano polished. Base has a double deck 20x34-inch top, shaped to match the double serpentine curved front. It has single panel ends. Drawers have locks and best quality cast brass handles. Note the French curved legs. Best quality French bevel plate mirror, 18 x 40 inches. Mirror frame and standards are made of same highly figured wood as the base. Every detail of construction strictly first class. This dresser cannot be purchased in stores for less than one-half more than we ask. Shipped direct from factory in Western Pennsylvania. Shipping weight, about 125 pounds.

	Price
Quartered oak	$13.65
Genuine mahogany	13.75
Birdseye maple	13.95

$14.85

No. 1E1884 This beautiful Princess Dresser has a double top, size, 20x38 inches. It is 78 inches high. We furnish it in either of the three woods, quarter sawed golden oak, genuine mahogany or birdseye maple, all specially selected, highly figured, thoroughly seasoned and highly polished. It has two top drawers, below which is a large drawer, fitted with locks, keys and cast brass handles. It has a double curved serpentine front and single panel ends. Supported by genuine French curved legs. Mirror is best quality French bevel plate, size, 18x40 inches. The handsome design mirror frame and standards are made of the same highly figured wood as the base. Best quality casters. High grade in construction, beautiful in wood and finish. Sells in retail stores at $22.00 to $25.00. Shipped direct from factory in Western Pennsylvania. Shipping weight, about 125 pounds.

	Price
Quartered oak	$14.85
Genuine mahogany	14.95
Birds eye maple	15.10

$15.25

No. 1E1886 This Princess Dresser, at the price we quote, represents astonishing value. We furnish it in highly figured quarter sawed golden oak, highly polished. It is 73 inches high and has 21x38-inch top. The drawers are perfect fitting, moving without friction, fitted with locks and best cast brass handles. It has solid panel ends. Mirror is best quality of French bevel plate, size, 18x36 inches. Mirror frame and standards have rounded edges. Has convenient small drawers in the top. Cabinet construction, high grade throughout. This dresser sells in retail stores at $25.00 to $30.00. Shipped direct from factory in Southern Ohio. Shipping weight, about 125 pounds.

Price, quarter sawed golden oak.....$15.25

No. 1E1888 This Dressing Table is made in quarter sawed golden oak, mahogany or birdseye maple. Wood has a highly figured grain, thoroughly seasoned, hand rubbed finish. Base has a shaped top with rounded corners, size 18x28 inches. Roomy drawer with cast brass knob. Mirror is best quality French bevel plate, size, 16x20 inches. Mirror frame and standards made of same highly figured wood as base. Shipped knocked down from factory in Western Pennsylvania. Shipping weight, about 40 pounds.

Price, quartered oak	$4.65
Price, genuine mahogany	4.85
Price, birdseye maple	4.95

$6.75

No. 1E1892 This Dressing Table is made in quarter sawed oak, genuine mahogany or birdseye maple, selected, highly figured wood, thoroughly seasoned and piano polished. Base size is 18x29 inches, contains a small front drawer; oval French bevel plate mirror is 16x24 inches. High grade in construction, handsome in design, beautiful in finish. Shipped knocked down from our factory in Western New York. Shipping weight 60 pounds.

Price, quarter sawed oak	$6.75
Price, genuine mahogany	6.85
Price, birdseye maple	6.95

For other styles of Dressers and Washstands, see Bedroom Suites, on pages 455 to 460.

$8.50

No. 1E1893 This Dressing Table is made in quarter sawed golden oak, genuine mahogany or birdseye maple, selected for the beauty of grain, thoroughly seasoned and kiln dried, hand rubbed and highly polished. Base has a double top, size, 20x34 inches, shaped to match the full swell ends and full swell front. Has roomy drawer with cast brass handle. Supported by genuine French curved legs front and rear. Mirror is best quality French bevel plate, size, 20x24 inches. Mirror frame and standards made of same highly figured wood as the base. Shipped direct from factory in Western Pennsylvania. Shipping weight, 50 pounds.

Price, quartered oak	$8.50
Price, genuine mahogany	8.65
Price, birdseye maple	8.75

No. 1E1894 We furnish this beautiful Dressing Table in three different woods, namely; Quarter sawed golden oak, mahogany and birdseye maple. The base has a double curved serpentine shaped front and end, and double top, size, 20x30 inches, supported by four double curved full French shaped legs. The mirror is the best quality French bevel plate, size, 16x28 inches. The roomy drawer is fitted with genuine burnished cast brass handles and lock. Shipped direct from factory in Northern Illinois. Shipping weight, 65 pounds.

Price, quartered oak	$8.95
Price, genuine mahogany	9.65
Price, birdseye maple	9.75

Elegant Toilet Washstand for $4.75.

No. 1E1914 This Toilet Washstand is especially adapted for small bedrooms and hotels. Made of well seasoned northern hardwood, golden oak finish and furnished with large, roomy drawer and large compartment below the drawer. Top is 18x32 inches. Mirror good quality bevel plate glass 12x20 inches in size. Casters are best quality. Shipped direct from factory in Southern Indiana, thereby insuring lowest freight rate. Shipping weight, 70 pounds.

Price.....$4.75

Our $4.95 Hotel Stand.

No. 1E1915 This Stand is especially constructed for hotel use, but also makes a very attractive piece of furniture for the home. It is made of hardwood finished imitation golden oak or mahogany. Has 17x33-inch double top and 14x24-inch bevel plate mirror. Serpentine shaped front drawer, roomy cupboard below. Cast brass handles and knob. Mounted on casters. Shipped direct from factory in Southern Indiana, thereby insuring lowest freight rate. Shipping weight, 60 pounds.

Price...$4.95

Solid Oak Hotel Stand for $5.85.

No. 1E1917 This Hotel Stand is made of solid oak throughout, finished golden. Has full swell front top drawers with two drawers and a cupboard below. Has 18x24-inch double top. The mirror is best quality bevel plate, 14x24 inches. Knobs and handles are cast brass. Complete with casters. Shipped direct from factory in Southern Indiana, thereby insuring lowest freight rate. Shipping weight, 75 pounds.

Price.. $5.85

$6.35 Toilet Washstand.

No. 1E1916 Made of best selected and well seasoned oak; finished golden and furnished with one large serpentine swell front roomy drawer, with two smaller drawers and large compartment below. Handles and knobs are cast brass. Mirror is French bevel plate glass and is 14x24 inches in size; has serpentine shaped double top, 18x34 inches. Shipped from factory in Southern Indiana, thereby insuring lowest freight rate. Shipping weight, 70 pounds.

Price.....$6.35

No. 1E1918 This sickroom commode is made of thoroughly seasoned oak, golden finish. The top is 16x16 inches. Cabinet construction first class. Has hinged top like No. 1E1919 and removable granite vessel. Thoroughly well made and finished. Shipping weight about 20 pounds. Price.....$3.95

No. 1E1919 Commode for the sick room. Made of selected quarter sawed oak, golden finish. The top, size, 16x16 inches, is securely hinged. In the illustration it is shown partly open. Inside fitted with removable granite vessel. No sick room can afford to be without one of these commodes. Shipping weight, about 20 pounds. Price.....$4.85

No. 1E1902 This Commode is made of thoroughly seasoned hardwood, golden oak finish. It has one drawer and cabinet. Size of top, 18x32 inches. Drawer is fitted with fancy metal pulls. Shipped direct from factory in Southern Indiana, thereby insuring lowest freight rate. Weight, 50 lbs. Price...$2.65

No. 1E1910 This Commode we furnish in white enamel, golden oak or mahogany finish. Especially adapted for use with our iron beds, in white enamel, matches dresser No. 1E1824 on page 462. It has curved top, 18x33 inches. Fitted with best quality cast brass trimmings and casters. Shipped from factory near Grand Rapids, Michigan. Shipping weight, 65 pounds.

Price, oak finish	$3.65
Price, mahogany finish	3.60
Price, white enamel finish	4.45

No. 1E1910½ This Washstand matches No. 1E1857 Dresser and No. 1E1971 Chiffonier. Made in quarter sawed golden oak, genuine mahogany or birdseye maple. Top is 18x28 inches. Towel rack is made of same wood as base, and is not imitation finish. High grade in construction. Shipped from factory in Western Pennsylvania. Shipping weight, 50 pounds.

Price, oak	$5.10
Price, mahogany	5.25
Price, birdseye maple	5.35

$6.55

No. 1E1913 Made in quarter sawed golden oak, genuine mahogany or birdseye maple, specially selected, highly figured and highly polished. Base is 20x30 inches. Towel rack is made of same wood as the base, not imitation finish. Fitted with locks and keys and the best quality cast brass trimmings. Shipped from factory in Western Pennsylvania. Shipping weight, 65 pounds.

Price, oak	$6.55
Price, mahogany	6.75
Price, birdseye maple	6.85

$1.39 IRON BEDS $12.85

AT $1.39 TO $12.85 We offer you FINER IRON BEDS than were ever before shown. Newest Designs, First Class Material, Construction and Finish. WONDERFUL VALUES.

We Challenge the World on QUALITY and PRICE. A Lower Price than Ours MEANS A POORER QUALITY.

THEY ARE INDESTRUCTIBLE AND WILL NEVER WEAR OUT.

THE METAL USED **in the construction of our beds is strictly high grade throughout.** No rusty scrap iron or corroded refused metals. The highest and be t quality of malleable iron, rolled Bessemer steel and drawn brass tubing.

THE CONSTRUCTION **of our metal beds is the best that modern machinery, science and skilled workmanship can possibly produce.** Every part and parcel is carefully modeled, framed and joined. The joints and chills carefully rounded and smoothed. The rails are made of Bessemer steel in angle shape and will not bend or break. Great care is taken in the fitting of the tongue and grooves by which the rail is fastened to the head and foot end. They stand firm and will support any weight of persons.

THE FINISH **of our iron beds, we guarantee the best that can be made.** The enamel which is used for the several coatings is the highest grade obtainable. Each coat after being carefully and thoroughly applied is baked in a large oven heated to a very high degree of temperature, then thoroughly smoothed and polished. This produces a finish that is impervious to water and all our iron beds can be cleaned of finger marks or other soiling by washing with soap and water.

THE BRASS TRIMMING **which is used in the ornamentation and construction of our metal beds is of the highest quality of drawn brass tubing,** highly polished and burnished, coated with the best quality of French lacquer, which absolutely preserves the polish and prevents tarnishing. Lacquer is to brass what varnish is to wood, it preserves the material.

COLOR BEDS. **We furnish all our iron beds in white enamel unless ordered otherwise.** Under the especial description of each bed it specifically states whether furnished in single solid color or in combination colors. Many designs of beds are much more attractive in **single solid color only** and for that reason we furnish certain patterns in single solid color only. When beds are ordered in colors, shipment will be made direct from factory near Chicago and from three days to one week's time is required before shipment can be made.

HOW TO ORDER. **When ordering a metal bed, be careful to state the width wanted, also the color, otherwise white will be shipped.** We illustrate our beds made up with bolster mattress and covering, but the price quoted is for the bed only. Springs, mattresses and pillows are illustrated and described on pages that follow.

$7.95 FOR THIS IRON BED, SPRING AND MATTRESS.

PART OF OUR PROFIT IS YOURS

You get it, as shown on the last pages. You get a Profit Sharing Certificate with every order.

AT $7.95 **we offer you this handsome design high grade, massive iron bed complete with best quality steel springs and a strictly first class mattress.** The bed is one of our special 3-piece combination beds which have no side rails. The long bar of the spring forms the side rail of the bed. One of the finest methods of construction known and offered exclusively by us. This method makes it possible to pack and ship the bed at less expense. We offer this combination outfit to show what it is possible for us to produce in a strictly high grade bed, spring and mattress at an extremely low price, which is offered only as a sample of the wonderful values we a e giving in our entire bed line. Height of the head end of the bed, 56 inches; foot end, 44 inches. The corner posts are 1 5 16 inches in diameter and are mounted with massive, smooth cast ornamental chills. The top rod and filling rods are ⅜ inch thick. These dimensions make an unusually substantial and massive bed. Finished throughout in best quality white enamel, thoroughly baked and hardened. The **spring frame** is made of high carbon steel angle bars, 1¼ inches wide. The fabric is made of best quality heavy tinned wire interwoven and interlaced in what is called hairpin style, making it absolutely non-sagging and noiseless. The fabric is fastened to the steel frame at each end by 15 high carbon steel spiral springs. This spring combines the greatest comfort and lasting qualities it is possible to obtain. The mattress is the finest of its kind and that skill and our knowledge of mattress construction could enable us to produce. A combination mattress never before offered, suitable for use in any climate. The filling is made of white basswood excelsior, thoroughly screened and freed from all impurities. This forms the inner filling only. One side is covered w th a thick layer of the best quality sanitary sea moss, which is not excelled for its hygienic and comfort giving qualities. The other side of the mattress is covered with thick layers of elastic felt of good quality. This makes the mattress suitable for cold or warm weather and furnishes a firm or soft bed as may be desired. The ticking is extra quality heavy twill, closely stitched and full bound. The mattress is made in the very latest and most up to date manner. Diamond tufted with leather tufts, and we place it in competition with mattresses sold throughout the country at $6.00 to $7.00.

No. 1E2395

Iron Bed, High Grade Spring and Mattress.. $7.95

No. 1E2395	Price complete. Bed, Spring and Mattress (Shipping wt., about 150 lbs.)..	**$7.95**
Full size only.	Price, Iron Bed and Spring..........(Shipping wt., about 110 lbs.).........	**4.65**
Full size only.	Price, Mattress only..................(Shipping wt., about 50 lbs.).........	**3.45**

NOTE—WE SHOW ON THE NEXT PAGE OUR LOWER PRICED IRON BEDS.

Special Iron Crib With Drop Sides, $4.25.

No. 1E2396 **This Child's Iron Bed is made of the best quality malleable iron and high carbon steel.** Height of head end, 42½ inches; height of foot end, 37½ inches. Corner posts are ⅞ inch thick. Filling rods between posts, ⅜ inch thick. Finished in white enamel or in any color desired. It has hinged drop sides. Fitted with a strong woven wire spring. Shipped knocked down. Furnished in two sizes. Shipping weight, 105 pounds.

Size, 2 ft. 6 in. by 4 ft. 6 in. Price.....**$4.25**
Size, 3 feet by 5 feet. Price........... **4.55**

Our $4.65 all Iron Crib, Drop Sides.

No. 1E2398 **This Child's Iron Bed is in white enamel, or any color desired.** Height, head end, 45½ inches; height, foot, 40½ inches. Corner posts, ½ inch. Filling rods, ⅜ inch thick. Made of best quality malleable iron and high carbon steel. Fitted with high grade woven wire spring. It has hinged drop sides. Sells in retail stores at $7.00 to $8.00. Shipped knocked down. Furnished in two sizes. Shipping weight, 115 pounds.

Size, 2 ft. 6 in. by 4 ft. 6 in. Price......**$4.65**
Size, 3 feet by 5 feet. Price........... **4.95**

Our Massive $5.25 Iron Crib With Drop Sides.

No. 1E2400 **This Child's Iron Crib has corner posts 11-16 inches thick;** filling rods, ⅜ inch thick. Height, head end, 39 inches. Finished in white enamel or any other color desired. Fitted with best quality woven wire spring and casters. It has hinged drop sides; best quality malleable iron and high carbon steel used in the bed. Compare the bed with those for sale in retail stores at $8.00 to $10.00. Shipped knocked down. Furnished in two sizes. Shipping weight, 125 pounds.

Size, 2 ft. 6 in. by 4 ft. 6 in. Price......**$5.25**
Size, 3 feet by 5 feet. Price........... **5.85**

Extra High Side Iron Crib, $5.45.

No. 1E2402 **This Child's Iron Bed is 4 feet 6 inches long and 2 feet 6 inches wide.** The main posts and top rods are 1 inch thick and the filling rods 5-16 inch thick. The head and foot are 48 inches high and sides 22 inches high, and the rods are 3¼ inches apart so that the child cannot stick its head through, climb over, fall out or otherwise harm itself. One side can be lowered. Fitted with woven wire springs and best quality casters. Finished in white enamel or any color desired. Be sure to state color desired, otherwise white will be furnished. Shipped knocked down, well crated. Shipping weight, 125 pounds.

Size, 2 ft. 6 in. by 4 ft. 6 in. Price...**$5.45**
Size, 3 feet by 5 feet. Price.......... **5.98**

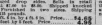

Wonderful Value, $1.39.

No. 1E2404 This Iron Bed is made of the best quality malleable iron and high carbon steel. Height, head end, 48 inches; height, foot end, 38 inches; corner posts, ¾ inch thick; filling rods, ⅜ inch thick; finished in baked white enamel. Wonderful value at our price. Furnished in 3 foot, 3 foot 6 inch, 4 foot and 4 foot 6 inch widths. Shipping weight, 55 pounds.
Price, all sizes....................$1.39

$1.89

No. 1E2405 This Iron Bed has corner posts ⅞ inch diameter. Tops and filling rods, ⅜ inch thick. Height, head, 53 inches, foot, 41 inches. Finished in white enamel or any solid color, with gilt chills. Best quality casters. Furnished in 3 foot, 3 foot 6 inch, 4 foot or 4 foot 6 inch widths. Shipping weight, about 60 pounds. **Be sure to state color desired.**
Price, any solid color, with gilt chills....................$1.89

$2.43

No. 1E2407 This Iron Bed has corner posts ⅞ inch and filling rods ⅜ inch in diameter. Height, head, 54 inches. Height, foot, 44 inches. Finished in white enamel or any solid color. Best quality casters. We furnish it in 3 foot, 3 foot 6 inch, 4 foot and 4 foot 6 inch widths. Weight, about 60 pounds. **Be sure to state color desired.** Price, any solid color....................$2.43

$2.99

No. 1E2410½ This Iron Bed is made of malleable iron with steel filling rods, side and cross rails. Corner posts, 1 1-16 inches thick. Filling rods, ⅜ inch thick. Height of head end, 48 inches. We furnish the bed in 3 foot, 3 foot 6 inch and 4 foot 6 inch widths. White or any solid color, enameled finish. A strong, substantial and new design. Shipping weight, 80 pounds.
Price, any solid color....................$2.99

$3.48

No. 1E2414 This brass trimmed Iron Bed has corner posts 1⅛ inches thick. Top rods, ⅜ inch in diameter. Iron filling rods, 5-16 inch in diameter. Brass center rod in head and foot 15 inches long, ⅜ inch thick. Height, head, 56 inches; foot, 43 inches. Finished in white enamel or any solid color, with gilt chills. Made in 3 foot 6 inch, 4 foot or 4 foot 6 inch widths. Shipping weight, about 100 pounds. **Be sure to state color desired.**
Price, any solid color with gilt chills....................$3.48

$3.69

No. 1E2412 This Bed is made of high grade malleable iron with solid steel filling rods, side and end rails. Corner posts, size 1$\frac{1}{16}$ inches, have large brass knobs and vases. Filling rods ⅜ inch thick. Ornamented with large, fancy chills. Finished in baked white enamel or any solid color. 4-foot 6-inch width only. Best quality casters. Retail stores ask $6.00 to $7.00 for this bed. Shipping weight, about 80 pounds. Price, any solid color....................$3.69

$3.87

No. 1E2418 This Iron Bed has continuous pillars made of 1 1-16 inch iron tubes. Is 60 inches high at the head and 41 inches at the foot. The scrolls are 5-16-inch iron, the bottom rods are ⅜ inch. Finished in best quality baked white enamel. Ornamented with massive fancy gold decorated chills. Complete with best quality casters. Furnished in four widths: 3 feet, 3 foot 6 inch, 4 foot and 4 foot 6 inch. Be sure to state width desired. Shipping weight, 100 pounds. Price, any solid color, with gilt chills....................$3.87

$3.93

No. 1E2420 This Handsome Iron Bed is made of high grade malleable iron with solid steel filling rods and side rails. Height of head end, 60 inches. Posts and top rods are 1$\frac{1}{16}$ inches in diameter. Filling rods, ⅜ inch in diameter. Finished in best quality baked white or any solid color enamel, with gold decorations on chills. Made in 4 foot 6 inch width only. Shipped direct from factory in Central Indiana or Chicago. Shipping weight, 95 pounds.
Price, any solid color, with gilt chills....................$3.93

Our $3.98 Brass Trimmed Iron Bed.
With Seven Rods in Head and Foot.

$3.98

No. 1E2424 Made of the best malleable iron, with steel side rails, end rails and filling rods. Baked white enamel finish, or any solid color, with gilt chills; 1$\frac{1}{16}$-inch pillars; ⅜-inch filling rods and ⅝-inch **brass top rail on both head and foot.** Height of head, 58 inches; height of foot, 42 inches. Has brass spindles and top mounts and four brass vases. Fitted with best casters. Is made in the following widths: 3 foot, 3 foot 6 inch, 4 foot, 4 foot 6 inch. Weight, 90 pounds. Price, any solid color....................$3.98

$4.10

No. 1E2425 This Iron Bed has heavy posts 1⅛ inches thick. Top rods, ⅜ inch and filling rods ⅜ inch in diameter. The heavy smooth cast chills have gilt decorations. Finished in white enamel or any solid color, with gilt chills. Best quality casters. Made in 4 foot 6 inch width only. Wonderful value. Shipping weight, about 90 pounds. **Be sure and state color desired.** Price, any solid color, with gilt chills....................$4.10

$4.25

No. 1E2429 Head is 57 inches high; 45 inches at the foot; made of malleable iron, with solid steel side rails, end rails and filling rods, best baked white enamel finish, or any solid color. Posts, 1$\frac{1}{16}$ inches; filling rods, $\frac{5}{16}$ inch and ⅜ inch. Has brass knobs, vases and rosettes and full extension foot end. Fitted with set of best casters. This bed is made in the following widths: 3 foot 6 inch and 4 foot 6 inch. Shipping weight, 100 pounds.
Price, any solid color....................$4.25

$4.41

No. 1E2434 This Iron Bed is exceptional value. Corner posts made of steel tubing, 1$\frac{1}{16}$ inches in diameter. Top rods, ⅜ inch in diameter. Scroll filling rods, ⅜ inch in diameter. Height, head, 68 inches; height, foot, 50 inches. Finished in white enamel or any solid color. Massive smooth cast chills have gilt decorations. Made in 3 foot, 3 foot 6 inch, 4 foot and 4 foot 6 inch widths. Fitted with best quality casters. Shipping weight, about 110 pounds. Price, any solid color, with gilt chills $4.41

Combination Three-Piece Bed, $4.65

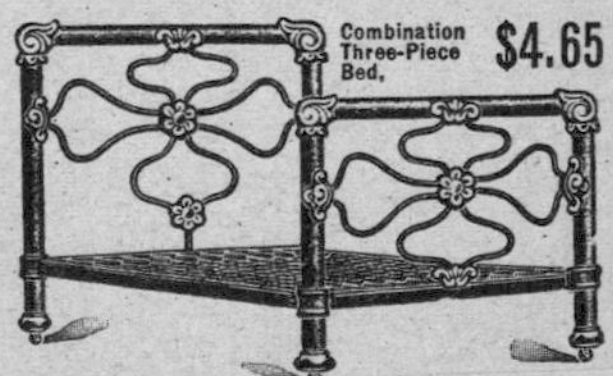

No. 1E2436 This Bed consists of head, foot and high grade spring. When put together are the same as regulation iron beds, but can be furnished at much less money than the iron bed with separate wire spring, on account of the saving of the side rails. The posts are made of ⅞-inch continuous iron tubing. Filling rods are ⅜ and $\frac{5}{16}$ inch, designed with a view of adding to the strength of the bed. Fitted with our high grade spring with hair pin fabr[illegible] with steel coil spring at the ends. Shipping weigh[illegible] about 100 pounds. Price, 3-foot 6-inch bed...$4.55
Price, 4-foot 6-inch bed....................4.65

ANY IRON BED ON THIS OR THE PAGE FOLLOWING

except Nos. 1E2438, 1E2440, 1E2442, 1E2444 and 1E2445, we furnish in the following combination of colors with gilt decorated chills: Maroon and white, pea green and white, pink and white, olive green and white, light blue and white, dark blue and white, emerald green and white, light blue and ivory white. In ordering be sure to state color desired, otherwise we ship white. When finished in a combination of colors, the posts and top rods are finished in the first color mentioned above and the filling rods in white.

$4.73

No. 1E2438 Compare this iron bed with those offered by others at $7.00 to $8.00. Height, head, 61 inches; height, foot, 43 inches. Corner posts are 1 1-16 inches in diameter and made of steel tubing. The handsomely interlaced filling rods are 3/8 inch in diameter. Finished in baked white enamel or any solid color. Massive smooth cast chills have gilt decorations. Furnished in 3 foot 6 inch, 4 foot and 4 foot 6 inch widths. Best quality casters. Shipping weight, about 100 pounds.

Price, any solid color, with gilt chills........................$4.73

COMBINATION 3-PIECE ...BED... $4.79

No. 1E2440 This Bed is composed of three parts only, head, foot and high grade spring, and has no side rails. The saving of the side rails makes the price of the bed much lower than one of the same grade with separate springs, and furthermore makes it possible to pack and ship the bed at less expense. The posts are 1 1/16-inch iron, mounted with four brass vases. The filling rods are 3/8 and 5/16 inch. Fitted with our hair pin fabric metal spring, exceptionally comfortable and guaranteed not to sag. Complete with casters. Shipping weight, 100 pounds.

Price, 3-foot 6-inch bed..............................$4.79
Price, 4-foot 6-inch bed, any solid color...... 4.89

$5.10

No. 1E2442 New design, four poster Iron Bed. Height, head end, 61 inches. Corner posts made of drawn steel tubing 1 inch in diameter. Vertical and cross filling rod 3/8 inch in diameter. Finished in any color baked enamel. Massive smooth cast chills have gilt decorations. Made in 4 foot 6 inch size only. A strikingly handsome bed at an astonishingly low price. Shipping weight, about 100 pounds.

Price, any solid color, with gilt chills........................$5.10

$5.25

No. 1E2444 Head is 72 inches high, foot 59 inches high. The pillars are 1 1-16 inches in diameter, surmounted by handsome brass caps and vases; the spindles, cross rods and ornamental iron work 5-16 inch in diameter, ornamented with brass tips and rosettes. The extended foot rail adds to its already handsome appearance. We furnish this bed 4 feet 6 inches wide by 6 feet long, finished white enamel or any solid color. Complete with set of best casters. Shipping weight, 110 lbs.

Price, any solid color....................................$5.25

Our Combination Three-Piece Bed.

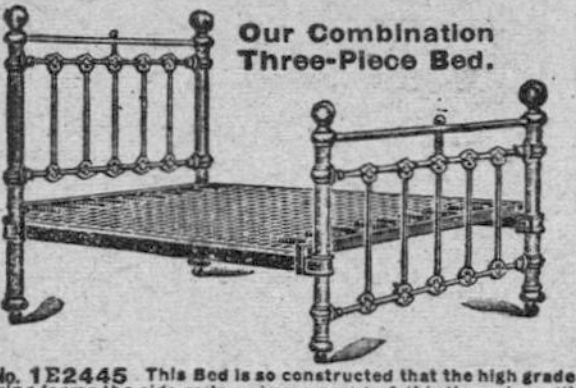

No. 1E2445 This Bed is so constructed that the high grade spring forms the side rails and on account of this the price will be found much lower than our regular iron bed of same grade with wire spring. This bed is exceptionally strong, having 1 1-16-inch posts and surmounted by handsome brass vases, and has 1/2-inch brass top rails. We furnish it only in baked white or any solid color enamel finish. Fitted with our hair pin fabric metal spring, exceptionally comfortable and guaranteed not to sag. Complete with set of best casters. Shipping weight, 100 pounds.

Price, 3-foot 6-inch bed....................................$5.40
Price, 4-foot 5-inch bed, any solid color.................. 5.45

$5.60

No. 1E2448 This bed is made with bow foot; the head is 63 inches high and the foot 48 inches high. The pillars are 1 1-16 inches, the brass vases 1 3/8 inches. It has brass top mounts 3/8 inch, and brass top rails, two brass rosettes. The iron top rod and scrolls are 3/8 inch and all other rods 5-16 inch. This is an exceptionally handsome bed, the brass top rail being especially ornamental as well as durable. Especially attractive, finished in dead black or white enamel or in our combination of pink and white with gilt chills. Fitted with best quality casters. Made in 4 foot or in 4 foot 6 inch widths only. Shipping weight, 88 pounds. **Be sure to state color and width desired.**

Price, any solid color with gilt chills........................$5.60
Price, two colors with gilt chills.............................. 5.90

$5.65

No. 1E2452 Artistic Colonial Iron Bed. This pattern was designed to strongly appeal to lovers of the colonial style, and is offered at an extremely low price. The head end is 61 1/2 inches high and the foot end 47 1/2 inches; has 1 1-16-inch posts, 3/8-inch fillings and 7/8-inch circular tubes. Particular attention is called to the handsome chill work on this bed, which is decidedly artistic and renders the bed an ornament to any room. This bed is unusually attractive in our combination colors of pea green and white with gilt decorated chills. Made in 3 1/2 foot and 4 1/2 foot widths. Fitted with best quality casters. **Be sure to state size and color desired.** Shipping weight, 136 pounds.

Price, any solid color with gilt chills........................$5.65
Price, two colors with gilt chills.............................. 5.95

$5.95

No. 1E2454 An exceptionally attractive Iron Bed. Corner posts and top rails, 1 1-16 inches in diameter. Bottom rods, 7/8 inches, and other filling rods, 3/8-inch thick. Note the massive oval design castings in head and foot board. The large, smooth, gilt decorated chills add to the beauty of this handsome bed. Height, head end, 62 inches; foot end, 45 inches. This bed is very attractive in dead black or pink and white, with gilt chills. Made in 4 foot 6 inch width only. Shipping weight, about 150 pounds. Price, any solid color, with gilt chills.......$5.95

Price, two colors, with gilt chills.............................. 6.25

$6.95

No. 1E2456 An Unusually Handsome Brass Trimmed Bed. 65 inches high at head, 47 inches at foot. Has 1 1-16-inch corner posts and top rods, 7/8-inch bent tube, 3/8-inch filling rods. Handsome 5/8-inch brass spindles with husks in center of head and foot end. Finished in either white, or any solid color enamel with gilt chills or in our combination colors of light blue and white with gilt chills. Made in 3 foot 6 inch and 4 foot 6 inch widths. Best quality casters. Shipping weight, 130 pounds. **Be sure to state width and color desired.** Price, any solid color, with gilt chills..........$6.95

Price, two colors, with gilt chills.............................. 7.25

$6.98

No. 1E2459 This massive new design Iron Bed should be compared with those offered by others at almost double the price we ask. Height, head, 66 inches; foot, 46 inches. Posts, 1 3/8 inches diameter; top rods, 1 1/8 inches diameter. The handsome scroll design filling rods, 3/8 inch in diameter. Center spindle in center head, and foot is 30 inches long, 5/8 inch thick. Finished in any solid color with gilt chills. Specially attractive finished in light blue and ivory white with gilt chills. Best quality casters. Made in 4 foot 6 inch width only. Shipping weight, about 175 pounds. **Be sure to state color desired.**

Price, any solid color, with gilt chills........................$6.98
Price, two colors, with gilt chills.............................. 7.28

$7.35

No. 1E2460 Brass Trimmed Iron Bed. Strikingly handsome design. The posts are made of 1 1-16-inch iron. Top rods are 7/8-inch with 5/8-inch brass spindles and husks. The filling rods are 3/8 inch thick. Unusually handsome and ornamental chills. Height of head, 71 inches; height of foot, 52 inches. Attractive design, any solid color enamel, as well as in combination colors of maroon and white with gilt chills. Best quality of casters. Made in 4 foot or 4 foot 6 inch widths. Shipping weight, 140 pounds. **Be sure to state width and color desired.**

Price, any solid color with gilt chills........................$7.35
Price, two colors with gilt chills.............................. 7.65

$7.65

No. 1E2461 This Iron Bed is made of the best quality malleable iron corner posts and solid steel filling rods. Posts and top rods are 1 5-16 inches thick, filling rods 5/8 inch thick. Height of head end, 64 inches; height of foot end, 45 inches. Furnished in white, or any solid color enamel or combination colors, with gilt decorated chills. Especially handsome, finished in emerald green, with gilt decorated chills. Made in 4 foot 6 inch width only. Best quality casters. **Be sure to state color desired.** Shipping weight, 185 pounds.

Price, any solid color and gilt chills........................$7.65
Price, two colors and gilt chills.............................. 7.95

$7.95

No. 1E2464 This Iron Bed should be compared with what other dealers offer at $12.00 to $15.00, and it will be found handsomer in design, better made, better finished. It is 60 inches high, has massive posts made of 1 5-16-inch iron with full $\frac{5}{8}$-inch filling rods. Top scroll is 1 1-16-inch steel tubing. Center rods in head and foot are made of $\frac{5}{8}$-inch brass with gothic design husks and fancy brass rod ends. This bed is especially attractive in olive green and white, or in maroon and white with gilt chills. Made in 4-foot 6-inch width only. Best quality casters. **Be sure to state color desired.** Shipping weight, 160 pounds.

Price, any solid color and gilt chills........................$7.95
Price, two colors and gilt chills........................ 8.25

$9.65

No. 1E2476 This Massive Iron Bed is a very striking and artistic design, and should only be compared with beds that are sold elsewhere at $15.00 to $18.00. It is 62 inches high, has 1 5-16-inch posts and full $\frac{5}{8}$-inch filling rods, 1 1-16-inch steel top rods, with large $2\frac{1}{4}$-inch brass knobs. The center rods are $\frac{5}{8}$-inch brass with gothic design husks and fancy brass rod ends. We recommend our combination of maroon and white enamel with gilt chills for this massive and exceptionally handsome bed. Fitted with best quality casters. Made in 4-foot 6-inch width only. Shipping weight, 165 pounds. **Be sure to state color desired.** Price, any solid color with gilt chills.... $9.65

Price, two colors with gilt chills........................ 9.95

$11.95

No. 1E2478 This Bed is one of the handsomest and most substantial combination iron and brass beds on the market. It has massive continuous pillars, made of 1 5-16-inch iron. Bottom rods are $\frac{7}{8}$ inch. Has 14 vertical rods made of $\frac{5}{8}$-inch brass tubing, with brass husks 4 inches long. Height of head, $61\frac{1}{2}$ inches; foot, $47\frac{1}{2}$ inches. The chills are extra large, feet massive and ornamental. This bed is especially attractive in dead black or in white with gilt chills. Made in 3 foot 6 inch, 4-foot, or 4-foot 6-inch widths. Fitted with best quality casters. Shipping weight, 185 pounds. **Be sure to state color desired.**

Price, any solid color with gilt chills..................$11.95
Price, two colors with gilt chills........................ 12.25

$8.68

No. 1E2468 This Massive Iron Bed is exceptionally attractive in design. Height, head, 67 inches; foot, 48 inches. Extra heavy posts and top rods are $1\frac{3}{8}$ inches in diameter. The handsome scroll design filling rods are $\frac{3}{8}$ inch in diameter. Brass balls on ends of scroll rods, $\frac{3}{4}$ inch in diameter. Note the massive smooth cast chills and feet. This bed is especially attractive in dead black with gilt chills or in a combination of pea green and white with gilt chills. Fitted with best quality casters. Made in 4-foot 6-inch width only. Shipping weight, about 175 pounds. **Be sure to state color desired.**

Price, any solid color with gilt chills........................$8.68
Price, two colors with gilt chills........................ 8.98

$10.45

No. 1E2479 This Iron Bed is a massive and strikingly handsome design. Head end, 64 inches high. Posts and top rods 1 5-16 inches thick. Extra heavy and highly ornamental chills attach the heavy filling rods to the top rods and posts. Corner posts mounted with finely executed dragons' heads. This bed is strikingly attractive, finished in our combination colors of maroon and white with gilt decorated chills. Made in 4-foot 6-inch width only. Fitted with best quality casters. Shipping weight, 210 pounds. **Be sure to state color desired.**

Price, any solid color with gilt chills........................$10.45
Price, two colors with gilt chills........................ 10.75

$12.85

No. 1E2480 This Beautiful Iron Bed cannot be fully appreciated until seen and compared with beds offered in retail stores at $20.00 to $25.00. Height, head, 69 inches; foot, 47 inches. Posts and top rods, $1\frac{3}{8}$ inches thick. Iron filling rods $\frac{3}{8}$ inch in diameter. Heavy smooth cast chills with gilt decorations. Artistic brass scroll spindles in head and foot are $\frac{5}{8}$ inch thick. Scrolls have brass ball tips $\frac{3}{8}$ inch in diameter. Finished in any solid color with gilt chills or in two colors with gilt chills as desired. Best quality casters. Made in 4-foot 6-inch size only. Shipping weight, about 190 pounds. **Be sure to state color desired.**

Price, any solid color with gilt chills $12.85
Price, two colors with gilt chills.................. 13.15

RARE VALUES IN BRASS BEDS.

$14.95

No. 1E2484 This Brass Bed has continuous posts 1 inch thick, $\frac{5}{8}$ inch filling rods, all ornamented with large brass husks. Height of head, 67 inches. New and attractive design. The best quality brass, highly polished. Wonderful value at our price. Furnished in $3\frac{1}{2}$ feet, 4 feet and 4 feet 6 inch widths. Shipping weight, 125 pounds.

Price, any size $14.95

$17.95

No. 1E2486 A Superb Brass Bed, made of the finest materials and guaranteed to wear and hold its finish for a lifetime. The pillars are 1 inch, knobs 2 inches, top and bottom rails, $\frac{5}{8}$ inch; head is 56 inches high and the swell end footboard is 40 inches high. An unusually fine bed for little money. Furnished 3 feet, 3 feet 6 inches, 4 feet or 4 feet 6 inches in width. Weight, full size, packed, 109 pounds. Price............$17.95

$21.95

No. 1E2492 This Beautiful Brass Bed is so constructed that the heavy $1\frac{1}{2}$-inch posts are merged into the top rails on head and foot end and made doubly strong by the addition of heavy ornamented brass castings at the corners. Filling rods between the posts are $\frac{5}{8}$ inch in diameter and fastened to the crossrails by genuine cast brass T ball castings. Height of head end, 60 inches. Foot end, 39 inches. Furnished in 3 feet, 3 feet 6 inches, 4 feet and 4 feet 6 inches width. Best quality brass tubing. Shipping weight, about 185 pounds. Price ..$21.95

$16.45

No. 1E2485 This Massive Brass Bed has heavy corner posts, $1\frac{1}{2}$ inches in diameter. Made of best quality brass tubing. Height, head, 64 inches; foot, 43 inches. Top rods, $\frac{3}{4}$ inch thick and other rods $\frac{5}{8}$ inch in diameter. The extra large brass balls on top of corner posts, 3 inches in diameter. Note the ornamental husks in center of posts and vertical rods of post ends. Made in 3-foot, 3-foot 6-inch, 4-foot, and 4-foot 6-inch widths. Best quality casters. Perfect in every detail of construction. Shipping weight about 190 pounds. Price, all sizes.... $16.45

$19.85

No. 1E2488 This Handsome Brass Bed has massive posts 2 inches in diameter. The filling between the posts is $\frac{5}{8}$-inch stock, the cathedral knobs on top of posts, 3 inches in diameter. Head is 64 inches high. Foot end 44 inches high. Furnished 3 feet, 3 feet 6 inches, 4 feet and 4 feet 6 inches in width. Our brass beds are made of the best quality of brass tubing, that will not dent or bend. Burnished with the highest grade of genuine French lacquer. This quality of bed retails at $35.00 to $40.00 in stores. Shipping weight, 190 pounds. Price, any size, $19.85

$23.75

No. 1E2496 This Beautiful Brass Bed has massive corner posts, 2 inches in diameter. Height, head, 64 inches; foot 43 inches. Top and bottom rods between posts $\frac{3}{4}$ inch in diameter. Vertical and scroll rods $\frac{5}{8}$ inch in diameter. Extra large knobs on corner posts $3\frac{1}{4}$ inches in diameter. This bed is made of the best quality brass tubing highly burnished. Note the heavy brass mountings on posts and filling rods. Made in 3-foot 6-inch and 4-foot 6-inch widths only. Fitted with best quality casters. Shipping weight, 200 pounds. Price.........$23.75

OUR BRASS BEDS ARE HIGHLY POLISHED AND PRESERVED FROM TARNISHING BY THE BEST QUALITY FRENCH LACQUER.

SANITARY STEEL COUCHES, DAVENPORTS and FOLDING BEDS

OUR SANITARY STEEL COUCHES, Davenports and Folding Beds illustrated below are the newest and best designs in this class of goods. They have been given a well recognized supremacy by reason of their many superior, practical and commendable new features. Absolutely clean, sanitary, light in weight, but strong, durable and comfortable. Adapted for use in every home.

THE FRAME WORK is made of the best quality high carbon Bessemer steel; guaranteed not to bend or break. The rods, bars, posts and rails are securely welded or riveted in such manner as to give the maximum of strength and lasting qualities.

THE SPRING WORK consists of a special fabric, made extra heavy and possesses remarkable sleep inducing qualities. It is absolutely noiseless. The special construction positively eliminates the annoying squeak common to other springs used in articles of this kind.

THE FINISH. We use the best quality gold bronze, or dead black enamel, as desired, on these sanitary steel couches, davenports and folding beds. Unless otherwise ordered we ship gold bronze finish.

THE WONDERFUL UTILITY of all these articles will be readily recognized. Each can be quickly converted into a full sized bed for use at night. The davenports and couches can be suitably draped in a highly artistic manner and are all that can be desired in comfort and durability.

ELASTIC FELT MATTRESS used on our sanitary steel folding beds and couches, is the same quality of material and made in the same manner as our elastic felt mattress, illustrated and described on page 476. It is made thinner in order to conform to the shape of the couch or sofa when opening or closing.

Illustration showing bed closed. Height, 44 inches. Depth, 20 inches.

Showing bed open.

The line shown represents three of the most desirable patterns, being safe, sanitary, light, comfortable, durable and at popular prices.

This style bed is built of light material throughout, thoroughly braced, supplied with woven wire fabric, which in turn is supported with National spring fabric across and lengthwise of the bed, making a strong and durable combination and absolutely prevents sagging. This bed, in its improved form, we guarantee to give perfect satisfaction to the purchaser. In its closed form the bed takes up very little space in the room. Light and easily handled. The finish will be in gold bronze with white enamel finished top. We claim this bed, in its recently improved form, to be the best made and best appearing low priced bed on the market. For mattresses to fit these beds, see page 476.

No. 1E2502 Size, 3 feet 6 inches by 6 feet 2 inches; weight, 55 pounds. Price.......................................**$5.50**

No. 1E2503 Size, 4 feet by 6 feet 2 inches; weight, 60 pounds. Price.......................................**5.95**

Illustration showing bed closed.

Showing bed open.

No. 1E2510

This Steel Folding Bed is made with a fine woven wire fabric supported with fifteen of the best tempered coil springs, making it impossible for the fabric to sag. The top is fitted with brass hooks ready to attach the curtains so that lower portion may be covered in the day time. The top of the bed is stationary and so arranged that when bed is opened it forms head piece. The foot piece folds under the top of the bed and in that position holds the mattress in place when bed is closed. There are no weights of any kind used in the bed, so it is impossible for it to close up when sleeping in same; at the same time it is so made that a child can operate it. Height when closed, 50 inches; depth, 24 inches; length, open, 6 feet 2 inches. Finished in bronze colors. Shipping weight, 125 pounds.

Price, 4-foot bed, without curtains..**$9.75**

Illustration showing bed closed.

No. 1E2381

This Metal Folding Bed combines neatness, lightness, comfort and cleanliness. It is made entirely of steel, except the top. Dimensions, closed, height, 45 inches, depth, 24 inches. Dimensions, open for use, length, 6 feet 2 inches, width, 4 feet. Fitted with the celebrated National spring. Front ornamented with large medallion of stamped steel. Top can be draped and ornamented with bric-a-brac, making an attractive article of furniture for the home. See page 476 for mattresses to fit this bed. Shipping weight, 80 pounds.

Price, with mirror top.......................**$10.50**

Price, with plain top, **9.25**

Showing bed open.

Heavy Cretonne Curtains for Iron Folding Beds, 90 Cents.

No. 1E2530 In the illustrations we show our Folding Bed Couch, either used as a couch when the sides are dropped and covered with a couch cover, or when opened, to be used as a very comfortable, large size bed. **This couch is made of all steel,** making it practically vermin proof, and at the same time strong and durable. It is so constructed that the sides may be lowered and, covered with a mattress and

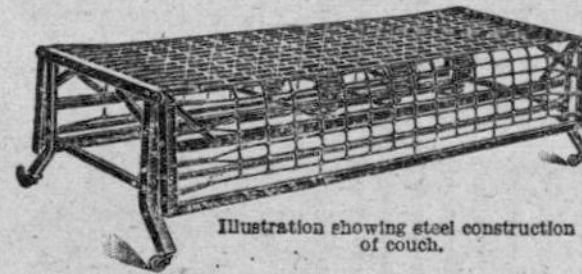

Illustration showing steel construction of couch.

couch cover, it then makes a very handsome and comfortable couch, just as shown in the illustration. The sides may be raised with ease and the folded couch becomes a very comfortable and extra large size bed. It is convenient, takes up little room, is comfortable and attractive. The size of the couch when the sides are dropped down is **74 inches long by 26 inches wide.** The size of the double bed when

Illustration showing couch when bolster and cover are used.

opened out to its full extent is **74 inches long by 50 inches wide.** Finished in gold bronze, complete with casters. Shipping weight, 70 pounds.

We quote below prices on mattress and bolster for this style of couch. By referring to our Dry Goods Department you will find a very complete line of draperies, suitable for a cover, which can be furnished at a very small price.

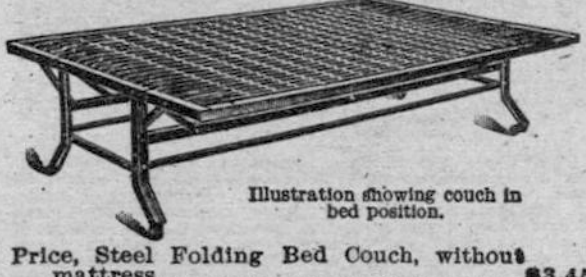

Illustration showing couch in bed position.

Price, Steel Folding Bed Couch, without mattress.......................................**$3.45**

Elastic Felt Mattress, with denim covering.. **2.75**

Elastic Felt Bolster, with figured denim covering....................... **1.15**

No. 1E2532 This Folding Sanitary Steel Davenport Sofa Bed is 74 inches long; width open for use as a bed, 50 inches. Height, back above seat, 17 inches; width seat, 21 inches. Posts, arms and legs are one solid piece of drawn tubing, 1 1-16 inches in diameter. Side rails, end rails and connecting

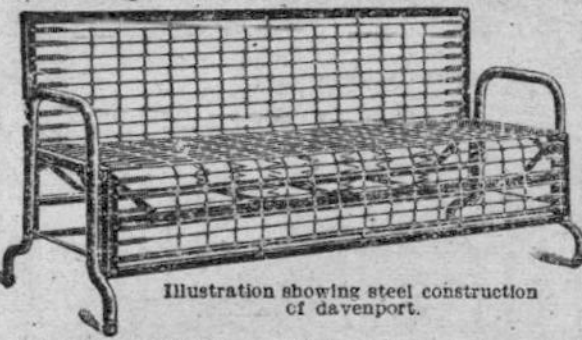

Illustration showing steel construction of davenport.

rods are made of heavy, high carbon steel securely welded or riveted together, making a frame very strong and rigid. Back and front wing are raised and lowered by a simple ratchet attachment a child can operate. The new hair pin double fabric is made of the best quality heavy tinned wire inter-

Illustration showing steel davenport with elastic felt mattress with ruffle.

woven and interlaced in such manner as to be absolutely non-sagging and noiseless. The fabric is fastened at each end by twenty-seven high carbon steel spiral springs. Finished in gold bronze or dead black enamel, as desired. Gold bronze will be shipped un-

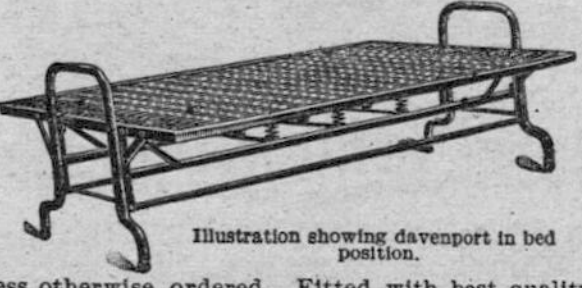

Illustration showing davenport in bed position.

less otherwise ordered. Fitted with best quality casters. Simplicity of construction, attractiveness of design and wonderful strength and durability are combined in this article. Shipping weight, 72 pounds.

Price, Sanitary Steel Davenport, without mattress.......................................**$5.45**

Elastic Felt Mattress, with figured denim cover. **3.35**

No. 1E2534 This Beautiful Sanitary Steel Davenport and Bed Couch is 72 inches long, 21 inches wide, as illustrated, and 48 inches wide opened for use as a bed, as shown in the illustration below. The arms, posts and legs are made of 1¼-inch drawn tubing. The end bars, side rails and cross

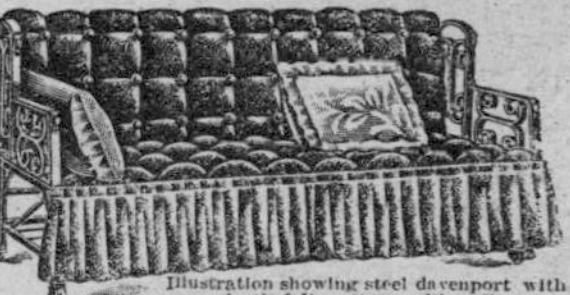

Illustration showing steel davenport with elastic felt mattress with ruffle.

bars are made of heavy high carbon Bessemer steel, securely welded or riveted together. To form a bed the back automatically drops down, the seat slides forward, the arms remaining stationary, forming the head and foot of the bed. The special hair pin fabric used in the spring is very closely woven and attached at the ends to the frame by forty-two high

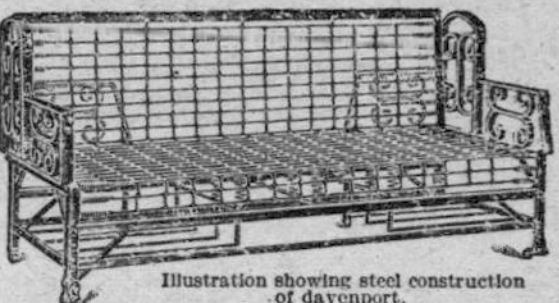

Illustration showing steel construction of davenport.

carbon steel spiral springs, making an absolutely noiseless and perfectly comfortable bed that will not sag or stretch out of shape. Note the bed clothes holders under seat for storing bed clothing.

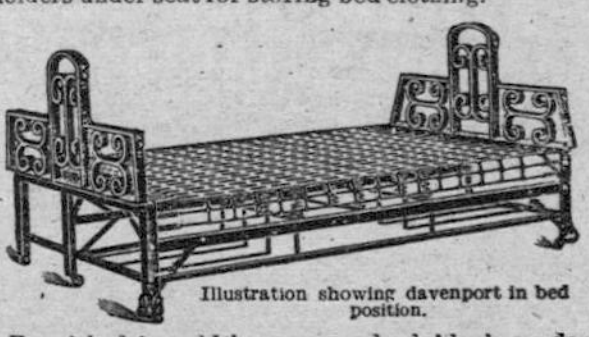

Illustration showing davenport in bed position.

Furnished in gold bronze or dead black as desired. We ship gold bronze unless otherwise ordered. Shipping weight about 90 pounds.

Price, Sanitary Steel Sofa, without mattress.**$7.35**

Price, Elastic Felt Mattress, with figured denim cover............................ **3.35**

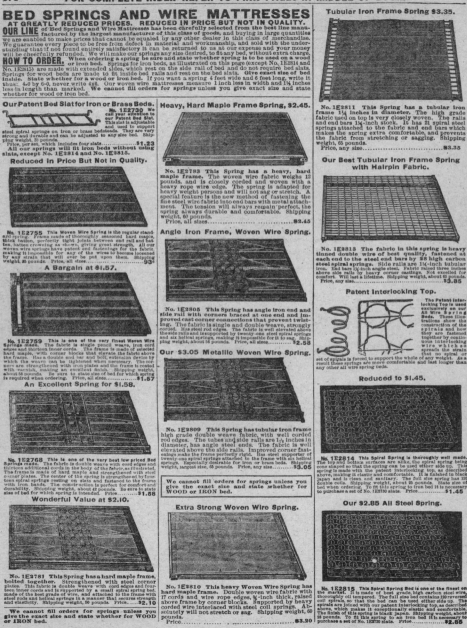

BED SPRINGS AND WIRE MATTRESSES

AT GREATLY REDUCED PRICES. REDUCED IN PRICE BUT NOT IN QUALITY.

OUR LINE of Bed Springs and Wire Mattresses has been carefully selected from the best line manufactured by the largest manufacturer of this class of goods, and buying in large quantities we are enabled to make prices that cannot be equaled by any other dealer in this class of merchandise. We guarantee every piece to be free from defect in material and workmanship, and sold with the understanding that if not found entirely satisfactory it can be returned to us at our expense and your money will be cheerfully refunded. We will make our springs any size desired, to fit any bed, without extra charge.

HOW TO ORDER. When ordering a spring be sure and state whether spring is to be used on a wood or iron bed. Springs for iron beds, as illustrated on this page (except No. 1E2814 and No. 1E2815) are made with extended sides, which rest on the side rail of bed and do not require bed slats. Springs for wood beds are made to fit inside bed rails and rest on the bed slats. **Give exact size of bed inside. State whether for a wood or iron bed.** If you want a spring 4 feet wide and 6 feet long, write it thus: 4-0 by 6-0, never write 4x6. Our woven wire mattresses measure 1 inch less in width and 1¼ inches less in length than marked. **We cannot fill orders for springs unless you give exact size and state whether for wood or iron bed.**

Our Patent Bed Slat for Iron or Brass Beds.

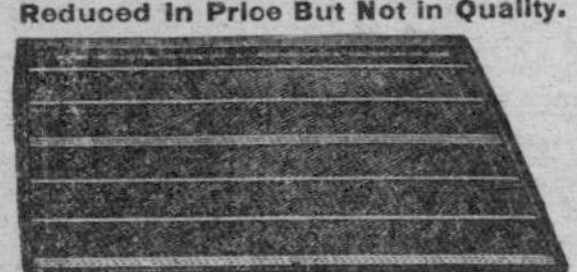

No. 1E2730 We call your attention to our Patent Bed Slat. This slat is adjustable and used to support steel spiral springs on iron or brass bedsteads. They are very strong and durable and can be adjusted to any size bed. Shipping weight, 35 pounds.
Price, per set, which includes four slats....................$1.23

All our springs will fit iron beds without using slats, except No. 1E2814 and No. 1E2815.

Reduced in Price But Not in Quality.

No. 1E2755 This Woven Wire Spring is the regular standard spring. Frame made of thoroughly seasoned hard maple, thick batten, perfectly tight joints between end rail and batten, batten crowning as shown, giving great strength. All our woven wire springs have patent end fastenings for the fabric, making it impossible for any of the wires to become loosened by any strain that will ever be put upon them. Shipping weight, 25 pounds. Price, all sizes....................93c

A Bargain at $1.57.

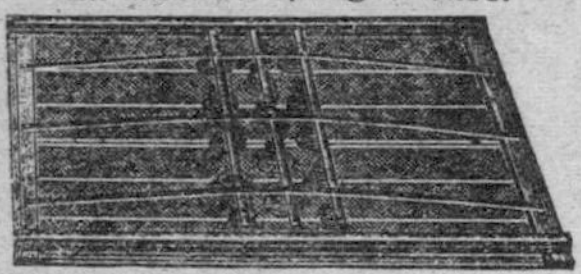

No. 1E2759 This is one of the very finest Woven Wire Springs made. The fabric is single pencil weave, iron cord edges and thirteen inner cords. The frame is made of selected hard maple, with corner blocks that elevate the fabric above the frame. Has a double end bar and bolt, extension device by which the weave can be tightened when necessary. The corners are strengthened with iron plates and the frame is coated with varnish, making an excellent finish. Shipping weight, about 58 pounds. Be sure to state size of bed for which spring is required when ordering. Price, all sizes....................$1.57

An Excellent Spring for $1.58.

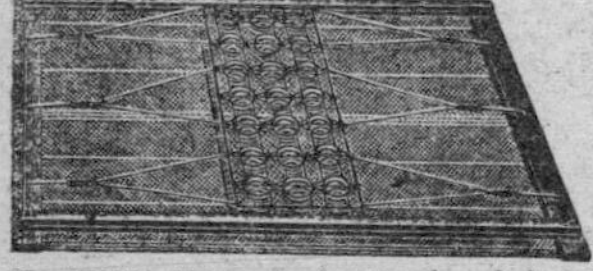

No. 1E2768 This is one of the very best low priced Bed Springs made. The fabric is double weave with cord edges and thirteen additional cords in the body of the fabric, as illustrated. The frame is made of hard maple and strengthened with steel corner plates. The center of the spring is strengthened by fourteen spiral springs resting on slats and fastened to the frame with iron bands. The construction is perfect for comfort and durability. Shipping weight, about 42 pounds. Be sure to state size of bed for which spring is intended. Price..........$1.58

Wonderful Value at $2.10.

No. 1E2781 This Spring has a hard maple frame, bolted together. Strengthened with steel corner plates. This fabric is double weave with cord edges and fourteen inner cords and is supported by a small spiral spring bed, made of the best grade of wire, and attached to the frame with steel rods and helical springs in a manner that secures strength and elasticity. Shipping weight, 50 pounds. Price......$2.10

We cannot fill orders for springs unless you give the exact size and state whether for WOOD or IRON bed.

Heavy, Hard Maple Frame Spring, $2.45.

No. 1E2783 This Spring has a heavy, hard maple frame. The woven wire fabric weighs 12 pounds, and is closely corded and woven with a heavy rope wire edge. The spring is adapted for heavy weight persons and will not sag or stretch. A special feature is the new method of fastening the fine steel wire fabric into end bars with metal attachment. The tension will always remain perfect, the spring always durable and comfortable. Shipping weight, 60 pounds.
Price, all sizes....................$2.45

Angle Iron Frame, Woven Wire Spring.

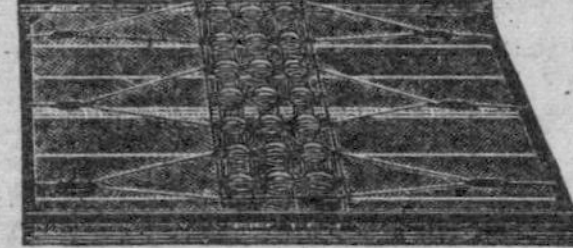

No. 1E2805 This Spring has angle iron end and side rail with corners braced at one end and improved cast corner connections that prevent twisting. The fabric is single and double weave, strongly corded. Has steel rod edges. The fabric is well elevated above the side rails and is supported by twenty-one steel spiral springs and six helical springs, making it impossible for it to sag. Shipping weight, about 56 pounds. Price, all sizes............$2.58

Our $3.05 Metallic Woven Wire Spring.

No. 1E2809 This Spring has tubular iron frame high grade double weave fabric, with well corded rod edges. The tubes and side rails are $1\frac{1}{16}$ inches in diameter, has angle steel ends. The fabric is well elevated above the side rails. Improved corner fastenings make the frame perfectly rigid. Has steel supporter of twenty-one spiral springs attached to the frame with six helical springs. Especially desirable for iron or brass beds. Shipping weight, largest size, 65 pounds. Price, any size..........$3.05

We cannot fill orders for springs unless you give the exact size and state whether for WOOD or IRON bed.

Extra Strong Woven Wire Spring.

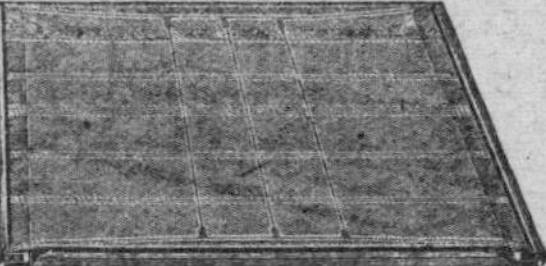

No. 1E2810 This heavy Woven Wire Spring has hard maple frame. Double woven wire fabric with 17 cords and wire rope edges, ⅜-inch thick, raised above frame by corner blocks. Supported by heavy corded wire interlaced with steel coil springs. Absolutely will not stretch or sag. Shipping weight, 60 pounds.
Price....................$3.20

Tubular Iron Frame Spring $3.35.

No. 1E2811 This Spring has a tubular iron frame 1¼ inches in diameter. The high grade fabric used on top is very closely woven. The rails and end bars 1¼-inch stock. It has 21 spiral steel springs attached to the fabric and end bars which makes the spring extra comfortable, and prevents the fabric from stretching or sagging. Shipping weight, 65 pounds.
Price, any size....................$3.35

Our Best Tubular Iron Frame Spring with Hairpin Fabric.

No. 1E2813 The fabric in this spring is heavy tinned double wire of best quality, fastened at each end to the steel end bars by 28 high carbon steel spiral springs. Side rails are 1¼-inch tubular iron. End bars 1¼-inch angle steel. Fabric raised three inches above side rails by heavy corner castings. Not excelled for comfort. Will last a lifetime. Shipping weight, about 65 pounds.
Price, any size....................$3.85

Patent Interlocking Top.

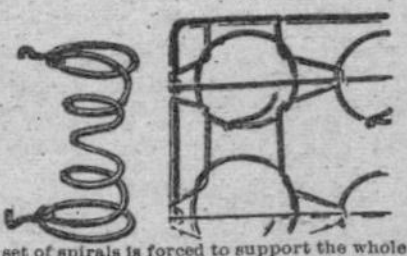

The Patent Interlocking Top is used exclusively on our All Wire Spring Beds. These illustrations show the construction of the spirals and how they are fastened together by continuous interlocking wire which so spreads the strain that no spiral or set of spirals is forced to support the whole of any weight. As a result these springs are more comfortable and last longer than any other all wire spring beds.

Reduced to $1.45.

No. 1E2814 This Spiral Spring is thoroughly well made. The top and bottom surfaces are alike, the spiral spring being cone shaped so that the spring can be used either side up. This spring is made with the patent interlocking top, as described above, making it elastic and comfortable. It is finished in black japan and is clean and sanitary. The full size spring has 120 double coils. Shipping weight, about 25 pounds. State size of bed when ordering. To fit this spring to iron bed it is necessary to purchase a set of No. 1E2730 slats. Price..............$1.45

Our $2.85 All Steel Spring.

No. 1E2815 This Spiral Spring Bed is one of the finest on the market. It is made of best grade, high carbon steel wire, thoroughly oil tempered. The full size bed contains 120 reversed coil spirals, so that the bed can be used either side up. The spirals are joined with our patent interlocking top, as described above, which makes it exceptionally elastic and comfortable. The finish of this spring is black japan. Shipping weight, about 28 pounds. To fit this spring to an iron bed it is necessary to purchase a set of No. 1E2730 slats. Price....................$2.85

Our $3.45 All Steel Spring.

No. 1E2822 The special features of this Spring are the rigid base, unusual strength and extreme lightness in weight. The base is constructed with 12 steel bars joined together by three rows of steel braces. The top of the bed is composed of 120 highly tempered spiral springs bound together with our patent interlocking top, as illustrated and described above. The rigid base makes it impossible for the bed to get out of shape, and together with our interlocking top makes the most perfect spring bed ever placed on the market. **No slats are required with this spring when used on iron beds,** and only three slats when used on wood beds. Finished in black japan, which is exceptionally clean and sanitary. In ordering, be sure to state kind and size of bed for which you wish to use the spring. Shipping weight, about 47 pounds. Price.......... ....**$3.45**

A Strictly First Class Spring, $3.70.

No. 1E2823 This spring has tubular iron frame, 1 5-16 inches in diameter. The close "pencil" weave fabric is elevated four inches above side rails by heavy corner castings, making the entire surface of the spring extra soft and comfortable. Fabric has a heavy rope edge and a heavy coiled wire support, containing 18 highly tempered Bessemer steel springs, suspended by six steel coil springs attached to the end bars. Strictly first class spring, especially adapted for use on iron or brass beds. Guaranteed not to sag. Shipping weight, about 75 pounds. Price.. ....**$3.70**

IN ORDERING, BE SURE TO STATE SIZE AND WHETHER FOR WOOD OR IRON BED.

Double Deck Spring.

No. 1E2824 This is called a double deck spring because the spiral springs are about one-third longer than the ordinary single deck spring, which gives the bed greater elasticity, consequently makes it the most comfortable bed on the market. There are 117 of these deep, highly tempered springs used and the edge springs rest on a steel bar directly over the side rail of the bed. All springs are securely attached to a rigid steel frame and steel slats. The entire spring is handsomely finished in black japan. Made for either iron or wood bed. Shipping weight, about 75 pounds.

Price, as illustrated..............................**$6.25**
Price, without steel frame for wood bed ... **4.75**

WOOD BEDS.

WE QUOTE PRICES SEPARATELY ON WOOD BEDS IN THE BEDROOM SUITES. SEE PAGES 455 TO 460.

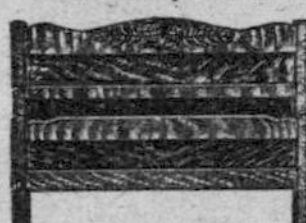

No. 1E2850.

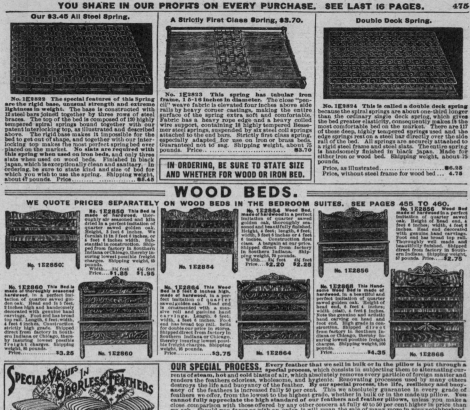

No. 1E2850 This Bed is made of hardwood, thoroughly air seasoned and kiln dried in a perfect imitation of quarter sawed golden oak. Height, 3 feet 6 inches. We furnish it in 3 feet 6 inches, or 4 feet 6 inches width. Substantial in construction. Shipped from factory in Southern Indiana or Chicago, thereby insuring lowest possible freight charges. Shipping weight, 65 pounds.

Width....	3½ feet	4½ feet
Price....	**$1.85**	**$1.95**

No. 1E2854

No. 1E2854 Wood Bed, made of hardwood in a perfect imitation of quarter sawed golden oak, thoroughly seasoned and beautifully finished. Height, 4 feet; length, 6 feet; width, 3 feet 6 inches or 4 feet 6 inches. Construction first class. A bargain at our price. Shipped direct from factory in Southern Indiana. Shipping weight, 70 pounds.

Width....	3½ feet	4½ feet
Price....	**$2.20**	**$2.25**

No. 1E2856

No. 1E2856 Wood Bed made of hardwood in a perfect imitation of quarter sawed oak. Height of head end, 4 feet 6 inches; width, 4 feet 6 inches. Head end decorated with genuine hand carvings. Foot end has broad top rail. Thoroughly well made and beautifully finished. Shipped direct from factory in Southern Indiana. Shipping weight, 57 pounds. Price.....**$2.75**

No. 1E2860 This Bed is made of thoroughly seasoned hardwood, in a perfect imitation of quarter sawed golden oak. Head end is 5 feet, 2 inches high and handsomely decorated with genuine hand carvings. Foot end has broad top rail. Length, 6 feet, width, 4 feet 6 inches. Construction strictly high grade. Shipped direct from factory in Southern Indiana or Chicago, thereby insuring lowest possible freight charges. Shipping weight, 85 pounds.
Price..................**$3.25**

No. 1E2860

No. 1E2864 This Wood Bed is 5 feet 8 inches high, made of hardwood, in a perfect imitation of quarter sawed golden oak. Head end is ornamented with a massive roll and genuine hand carvings. Length, 6 feet; width, 4 feet 6 inches. Foot end has broad top rail. Sells for double our price in stores. Shipped direct from factory in Southern Indiana or Chicago, thereby insuring lowest possible freight charges. Shipping weight, 95 pounds.
Price..................**$3.75**

No. 1E2864

No. 1E2868 This Handsome Wood Bed is made of hardwood, in a beautiful and perfect imitation of quarter sawed golden oak. Height of head end, 6 feet 4 inches; width (slat), 4 feet 6 inches. Note the genuine and artistic hand carving on head and foot end. High grade in construction. Shipped direct from factory in Southern Indiana or Chicago, thereby insuring lowest possible freight charges. Shipping weight, 100 pounds.
Price..................**$4.35**

No. 1E2868

SPECIAL VALUES IN ODORLESS FEATHERS

Feathers when taken from the fowl contain considerable quantities of oil and animal matter. If this is not entirely removed the decomposition which takes place renders the feathers foul smelling and unsanitary.

OUR SPECIAL PROCESS. Every feather that we sell in bulk or in the pillow is put through a special process, which consists in subjecting them to alternating currents **of steam, hot and cold blasts** of air, which absolutely removes every particle of foreign matter and renders the feathers odorless, wholesome, and hygienic. Renovating processes used by many others destroys the life and buoyancy of the feather. **By our special process, the life, resiliency and buoyancy** of the feathers is increased fully 50 per cent. This we absolutely guarantee in every grade of feathers we offer, from the lowest to the highest grade, whether in bulk or in the made up pillow. **You cannot fully appreciate the high standard of our feathers and feather pillows,** unless you make a close comparison with those offered by any other concern at fully 40 to 50 per cent higher in price than we ask. Should you favor us with an order, it will mean the sale of many more in your neighborhood.

OUR PILLOWS. The ticking which we use on our pillows is the very best quality of heavy sateen or Amoskeag twill ticking. We furnish them in a variety of sizes and weights. We especially recommend the 2½, 3 and 3½ pound weights. Each pillow is thoroughly filled and rounded out and will retain its life and buoyancy for years.

Steam Cured Feathers.

No. 1E2954 Grade C3. A very satisfactory graded mixture of duck and small selected turkey feathers and turkey down, absolutely odorless, steam dressed and air blast cured by our special process.
Price, per pound..................................**33c**

No. 1E2956 Grade C2. A mixture of duck feathers, duck down and turkey down. Specially selected, steam dressed, air blast cured by our special process. Odorless and sanitary. A good combination.
Price, per pound..................................**42c**

No. 1E2958 Grade C1. A mixture of pure, prime, live geese feathers with the best quality of specially selected choice duck feathers, free from coarse quills, cured by our special process. Sanitary, odorless and very resilient. Excellent value.
Price, per pound..................................**49c**

No. 1E2960 Grade B3. Pure prime live geese feathers, blended with especially selected choice duck feathers, equal parts. Cold air blast cured, steam dried by our special process. Always satisfactory.
Price, per pound..................................**56c**

No. 1E2962 Grade B2. Pure prime live geese feathers with a slight mixture of choice, specially selected duck feathers. Thoroughly cured by our special process. Exceptionally satisfactory.
Price, per pound..................................**64c**

No. 1E2964 Grade B1. Pure prime live geese feathers. Steam dressed, air blast cured by our special process. Odorless, wholesome and sanitary. Very buoyant. Price, per pound....................**75c**

No. 1E2968 Grade A2. The best quality of extra specially selected pure prime live geese feathers with down. Steam dressed and cured by our special process. Odorless, hygienic and wholesome. A very fine article. Price, per pound.........................**80c**

No. 1E2970 Grade A1. The very choicest pure white live geese feathers. Specially selected with the natural quantity of down retained. Specially cured by our steam and air blast process. Absolutely the best quality. Price, per pound...**88c**

Down.

No. 1E2982 A high grade and special mixture of live goose and live duck down. A thoroughly satisfactory and strictly pure quality. Very resilient and comfort giving. Thoroughly cured by our special process. Price, per pound...............................**60c**

No. 1E2988 The best grade of gray goose down. Pure and strictly high quality. Thoroughly cured by our special process of steam dressing and air blast.
Price, per pound.,..................................**85c**

Pillows.

No. 1E3002 Special Brand. Extra specially selected prime white live geese feathers with extra quantity of down. Cured by our special process. The highest and best grade of feather pillows, best quality of sateen ticking.

Size	21x27	23x28	24x29	26x30	27x31
Weight, each	2 lbs.	2½ lbs.	3 lbs.	3½ lbs.	4 lbs.
Price, each..	**$1.60**	**$2.05**	**$2.40**	**$2.80**	**$3.20**

No. 1E3003 Princess Brand. Extra quality of pure white live geese feathers, with natural quantity of down. Steam dressed, air blast cured by our special process. Best sateen ticking.

Size...	21x27	23x28	24x29	26x30	27x31
Weight, each	2 lbs.	2½ lbs.	3 lbs.	3½ lbs.	4 lbs.
Price, each .	**$1.44**	**$1.80**	**$2.16**	**$2.52**	**$2.88**

No. 1E3005 Our Reliable Brand. Selected, pure white, special steam dressed and blast cured prime live geese feathers. A fine quality, very soft and downy, strictly pure and high grade, best sateen ticking.

Size....	20x27	22x27	23x29	24x29	26x31
Weight, each .	2 lbs.	2½ lbs.	3 lbs.	3½ lbs.	4 lbs.
Price, each....	**$1.21**	**$1.50**	**$1.82**	**$2.12**	**$2.42**

No. 1E3007 Our Famous Brand. Best quality of choice, live, white geese feathers, mixed with the best quality of specially selected choice down, live duck feathers, equal quantities of each. Best sateen ticking. A very fine pillow.

Size..........	20x26	21x27	22x29	24x30	25x30
Weight, each	2 lbs.	2½ lbs.	3 lbs.	3½ lbs.	4 lbs.
Price, each..	**98c**	**$1.22**	**$1.46**	**$1.70**	**$1.95**

No. 1E3008 Our Peerless Brand. A very good quality of mixed geese and duck feathers, special steam dressed and blast cured. Absolutely odorless, wholesome and hygienic. A very satisfactory article, best sateen ticking.

Size..........	19x26	20x27	22x27	24x28	25x30
Weight, each	2 lbs.	2½ lbs.	3 lbs.	3½ lbs.	4 lbs.
Price, each..	**74c**	**93c**	**$1.12**	**$1.30**	**$1.49**

No. 1E3012 Our Lily Brand. A good quality of duck feathers mixed with turkey down, special process steam dressed and blast cured, odorless, sanitary, free from coarse quills and very comfortable, best sateen ticking.

Size....	20x26	21x27	22x28
Weight, per pillow..........	3 lbs.	3½ lbs.	4 lbs.
Price, per pillow............	**65c**	**75c**	**84c**

No. 1E3014 Our Crown Brand. A very satisfactory quality of duck feathers, mixed with turkey down and small turkey feathers, cured by our special process, steam dressed and air blast, odorless, sanitary and wholesome.

Size..	19x26	21x27	22x28
Weight, per pillow...	3 lbs.	3½ lbs.	4 lbs.
Price, per pillow........,...	**45c**	**52c**	**61c**

Down Cushions.

No. 1E3022 Java Brand. Made of imported Japanese silk floss, non-absorbent, verminproof, very resilient and elastic, odorless and hygienic. An ideal sofa cushion. Muslin covered.

Size...........	16x16	18x18	20x20	22x22	24x24	26x26
Price, each...	**21c**	**26c**	**35c**	**47c**	**59c**	**70c**

No. 1E3024 Leader Brand. Filled wit' a mixture of duck and turkey down, steam dressed, air blast .red, odorless and sanitary. Muslin covered.

Size..........	16x16	18x18	20x20	22x22	24x24	26x26
Price, each...	**25c**	**32c**	**45c**	**58c**	**68c**	**95c**

$5.95 ELASTIC FELT MATTRESSES $9.95

GENUINE WHITMORE RED CROSS BRAND

None genuine without this trade mark.

ONE-THIRD OF OUR LIVES IS SPENT IN BED.

A good mattress makes a good bed. Why not have the best mattress money can buy? Our **Dreamland AA Grade Mattress** is the best elastic felt mattress in the world regardless of make, name or price. We invite comparison of the goods.

$9.95 BUYS THE BEST Genuine Whitmore Elastic Felt Mattress in the world for the largest size bed, 4 feet 6 inches in width by 6 feet 3 inches in length. Smaller sizes and different qualities at still lower prices, according to the price list below.

SIXTY NIGHTS' FREE TRIAL.

SAMPLES FREE.

As there are many inferior grades of so called elastic felt mattresses on the market we will, upon request, send postpaid and free of all charges, samples of the ticking and felt used in the Whitmore Sanitary Elastic Felt Mattress, and by comparison you will find them better and cheaper, quality for quality, than any other make.

WE MAKE FOUR GRADES of elastic felt mattresses, the difference in price being due to the relative cost of the felt and ticking, but all four grades possess all of the essential qualities of the best elastic mattresses made, such as softness, resiliency, etc.

DESCRIPTION OF THE GENUINE WHITMORE SANITARY ELASTIC FELT MATTRESS.

The latest, most modern development of mattress making today. Made entirely from cotton, but it is the original and wonderful method of treating this cotton that results in its superior qualities. The cotton used is absolutely pure, and throughout the manipulation and treatment of this cotton extreme care is observed to preserve this original purity and keep the material free from every contaminating influence. The cotton is treated by special process of air, dry heat and steam to properly cure, clean and prepare the fibres for successive handling. The carefully prepared material is then thoroughly worked and beaten into loose, flaky sheets, and these sheets are slowly and evenly drawn and spun so that the fibres are stretched to their utmost tension and are then run over felting machines similar to the rotary printing presses, by which twin sheets are formed, one over the other, the fibres of which unite and interlace and join into a perfect single sheet. Before the sheets go over these machines they go through a certain action which naturally curls and curves the fibres, and in the end we have the wonderfully elastic, beautiful, light, airy, interlacing fibrous sheets which eventually form the filling of our genuine felt mattresses.

SANITARY, VERMIN PROOF, NON-ABSORBENT, WILL NOT MAT, NEVER GET LUMPY, NEVER REQUIRE REMAKING.

READ OUR CHALLENGE OFFER.

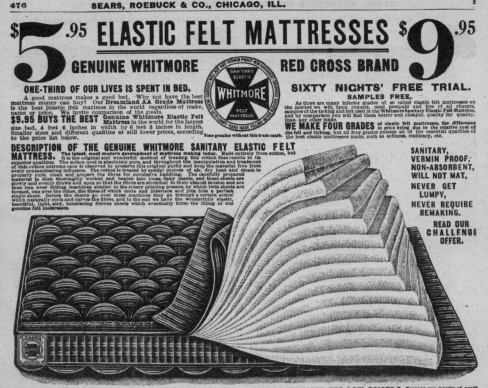

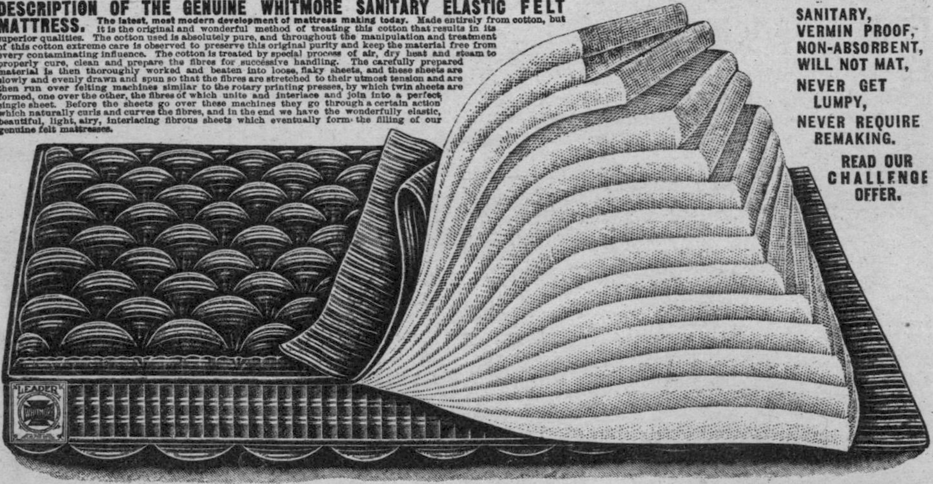

THESE SHEETS ARE BUILT UP IN LAYERS, carefully fitted into the ticking, and, unlike the **ordinary hair mattress, the elastic felt mattress is not stuffed,** but is made just as you would make and pack a box. The felt sheets are laid one upon another very carefully until the required thickness is obtained and then compressed to a fraction of the original thickness, and in this way the whole mass is interlaced into one sheet of uniform thickness throughout, which is then enclosed in a tick entirely by hand. The pattern of the ticking is carefully matched, the softness is evenly distributed, every square inch possesses the same resiliency and it is impossible for the elastic felt mattress to bunch up, to mat down, to shift or fill in any way. The tufting also is very accurate. The tufts are the same distance apart and of the same tension. The stitching and boxing of border is carefully done. There is no mattress that will compare in thorough workmanship and in the splendid results obtained by this care and skill with the **Genuine Whitmore Sanitary Elastic Felt Mattress.**

IT IS THE IDEAL BED. Absolutely clean and sanitary, germproof, verminproof, non-absorbent, as far in advance of the ordinary mattress as the electric light surpasses the tallow candle. You will never know what comfort is until you try an elastic mattress. You will never realize what a real night's rest means until you sleep on an elastic felt mattress.

ABOUT THE FREIGHT CHARGES. We do not quote this mattress "freight prepaid." If we did, we would have to make higher prices, so as to cover freight charges to the most distant points, and the customer living 250 miles away would be helping to pay the freight to the customer living 350 to 1,000 miles away. You must pay the freight, but it is a very small matter. The mattress weighs, packed for shipment, about 50 pounds, and the freight for 100 to 300 miles will be about 25c to 50c; 500 miles, about 65c; greater or less distances in proportion; so you see the freight charges amount to practically nothing as compared with what you save in price by buying from us.

HOW DO WE MAKE THE LOW PRICES? Because our margin of profit is very small; because we ask you only enough money to cover the actual cost of material and only our one narrow profit added; because we sell this splendid article on the same small profit basis as we ask for all of our merchandise; because you are not paying us in each mattress about $5.00 to cover newspaper and magazine advertising expense; because our volume of sales is very large, our expenses of doing business very small and we can accept a smaller profit than any other dealer could afford.

OUR CHALLENGE OFFER. If you are thinking of buying a mattress let us induce you to place your order with us for one of the Genuine Whitmore Sanitary Elastic Felt Mattresses; we want you to select the **Dreamland AA grade,** purely in your own interest, for the greater and lasting satisfaction it will give you over any other make or style. **You be the judge. THIS IS OUR OFFER:** Send us your order, enclose our price; if you desire, send your order at the same time for any other mattress advertised by others, compare them both carefully, note the material, construction, finish, etc., try both mattresses and if, after comparison, test and trial, you do not find our mattress the equal if not the superior, then you are under no obligation; return our mattress at our expense and we will promptly return your money, including transportation charges. Use our mattress for two months, give it sixty nights' trial, and if you decide it is not as splendid as we led you to expect, just return the mattress to us and we will return your money and pay the freight charges both ways. **Remember, also, you get your valuable Profit Sharing Certificate when you order.**

WE CALL SPECIAL ATTENTION TO THE WEIGHT OF OUR MATTRESSES.

Full sizes weigh 45 pounds unpacked. Smaller sizes in proportion. **All weights guaranteed.** We could sell our mattresses at lower prices by reducing the weight, but the lighter weight mattresses would not prove satisfactory.

IN ORDERING MATTRESSES, STATE EXACT LENGTH AND WIDTH OF THE BED AND STATE IF TO BE MADE IN ONE OR TWO PIECES. MATTRESSES MADE IN TWO PARTS, 35 CENTS EXTRA.

No. 1E3137 C Grade Whitmore Elastic Felt Leader Mattress. This mattress is made of light brown felt or yellow colored felt, known as unbleached stock. It is covered with a fair grade of ticking, is full bound, leather tufted and stitched. We guarantee this mattress to be the same grade sold by other dealers at from $6.00 to $8.00, but we do not recommend it. Our grades A and B, at the slight difference in price, are worth more than double, and our AA grade Dreamland at $9.95 is guaranteed to be the finest elastic felt mattress in the world **regardless of name, make or price**.

No. 1E3138 B Grade Elastic Felt Reliance Mattress. This mattress is made of a good grade of felt, generally known as unbleached stock. It is covered with a very good grade of ticking, is full bound, leather tufted and stitched. Standard 4-inch border.

No. 1E3140 A Grade Elastic Felt Our Sanitary Mattress. This mattress is made of all pure white felt, covered with an excellent grade of satin finished ticking, full tufted with cotton tufts, bound and stitched in a most skillful manner, standard 4-inch border. The mattress should be compared with elastic felt mattresses offered generally throughout the country at from $10.00 to $15.00.

No. 1E3142 AA Grade Elastic Felt Dreamland Mattress. Our Dreamland Elastic Felt Mattress is without doubt the finest mattress of its kind in the world. This mattress should be compared only with very best elastic felt mattresses offered by other dealers and manufacturers at from $15.00 up and by close comparison, it will be found to be equal if not superior to any mattress made, regardless of name, make or price. It contains only the very finest grade of elastic felt made from long staple, pure white cotton and covered with the best grade of satin finished ticking, tufted top with heavy cotton tufts, stitched sides, full bound with heavy twill binding, standard 4-inch border and made throughout by the most skilled workmen according to the highest art of mattress construction.

	For Full Size Bed, 4 ft. 6 in. wide by 6 ft. long.	For Bed 4 ft. wide by 6 ft. long.	For Bed 3 ft. 6 in. wide by 6 ft. long.	For Beds 3 ft. wide by 6 ft. long and 2 ft. 6 in. wide by 6 ft. long.	For Folding Bed	For Crib, Child's Bed, 3 ft. wide by 5 ft. long.	For Crib, Child's Bed, 2 ft. 6 in. wide by 4 ft. 6 in. long.
ACTUAL WEIGHT OF MATTRESSES, UNPACKED, POUNDS	45	40	35	30	30	16	12
No. 1E3137	$5.95	$5.75	$5.45	$5.10	$4.80	$3.65	$2.75
No. 1E3138	6.95	6.65	6.15	5.65	4.95	3.95	2.95
No. 1E3140	8.95	8.75	7.95	7.35	6.85	5.15	3.85
No. 1E3142	9.95	9.75	9.45	8.95	8.35	6.45	4.85

All mattresses are carefully packed in heavy paper and new burlap, and safe delivery guaranteed.

Our Leader at $3.50.

No. 1E3408

No. 1E3408 At $3.50 we offer a couch that is better made, better finished and handsomer in appearance than any couch offered by other dealers at from $5.00 to $7.00. While it is without doubt the most wonderful value ever offered at such a low price, and we guarantee it to give excellent service, we especially recommend our couches, ranging from $7.00 up, which are made with our all steel spring construction. This couch is full size, 72 inches long and 26 inches wide. The frame is golden oak, embossed and made of hardwood, finished in imitation mahogany, as desired. This couch contains a full set of best oil tempered steel springs, drawn from high carbon cold rolled steel, 19 springs in all, securely tied. The upholstering is reliable and the covering is an excellent quality of highly colored velour in the latest patterns. We can furnish red, green or brown. Be sure to state color of upholstering and finish of wood desired, otherwise green covering and golden finished frame will be furnished. Complete with best quality casters. Shipping weight, 70 pounds.

Price, covered in velour.......................................$3.50

Our Special $4.15 Overstuffed Couch.

No. 1E3416

No. 1E3416 As a leader, our all overstuffed tufted couch at $4.15 is without doubt the best couch of its kind in the market. It is 72 inches long, 27 inches wide, and made on a substantial hardwood frame, well braced to insure stability. It contains a full set of the best oil tempered steel springs, drawn from high carbon cold rolled steel, 19 springs in all, securely tied, insuring service as well as comfort. The filling, tufting and upholstering is done in a thoroughly reliable manner. It is ornamented with tasseled fringe and fitted with the best quality casters. The covering is an excellent quality of highly colored velour, guaranteed in quality and of the very latest design. Shipping weight 75 pounds.

Price, covered in velour.......................................$4.15

Our $4.75 Overstuffed Couch.

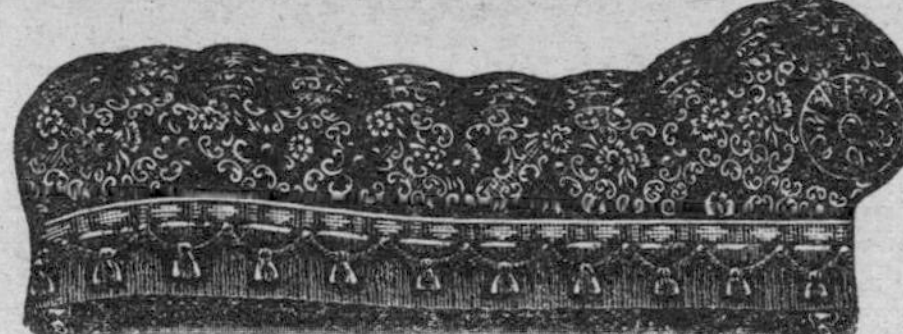

No. 1E3424

No. 1E3424 It is impossible to illustrate the exceptional value which this couch represents. It must be seen to be fully appreciated. The picture gives only a general idea of the style of the couch. It is full size, 74 inches long and 27 inches wide. The frame is built of thoroughly seasoned hardwood, well braced to insure durability. We use a full set of the best quality oil tempered steel springs, drawn from high carbon wire, 24 springs in all, securely tied. The couch comes nicely shaped and tufted and trimmed with good quality fringe. On page 479 we describe the different upholstering materials we can funish. Complete with casters. Shipping weight, 75 pounds.

The number of this couch is No. 1E3424. Always order by number and be sure to state the kind and color of covering desired.

Covering	Figured Velour	Corduroy	Plain Brocaded Velour
Price	$4.75	$4.95	$5.15

Our Fancy Biscuit Tufted Glenham Couch at $5.65.

No. 1E3432

No. 1E3432 This is a very handsome, stylish Couch at an exceedingly low price. It is made at the same factory by the same workmen that make all our other couches and we consider it wonderful value. The frame is made of oak, finished golden, or birch, finished in imitation mahogany, as desired. It is beautifully ornamented with sunken carvings as shown in the illustration. The couch measures 73 inches in length and is 27 inches wide. Has spring edge, seat and head, made with our guaranteed steel spring construction, fully illustrated and described above, with 20 springs in the body and 4 in the head, 24 in all. By the use of this construction the bottom of the couch is left open for air and ventilation. Tow with cotton top is used as filling, which makes the tufts lasting and comfortable. The materials used in covering are fully described on page 479. Complete with best quality casters. Shipping weight, 80 pounds.

The number of this couch is No. 1E3432. Always order by number and be sure to state the kind and color of covering desired.

Covering	Figured Velour	Corduroy	Plain Brocaded Velour
Price	$5.65	$5.85	$6.05

A Handsome Turkish Overstuffed Couch for $6.95.

No. 1E3448

No. 1E3448 For handsome appearance and solid comfort there is not a couch in our entire line that will compare with this one when you consider the remarkable low price at which we are listing it. It is 75 inches long, 30 inches wide and made with eight rows of deep tufts stuffed with a special grade of tow and felted cotton top. The frame is made of hardwood, strongly braced to insure durability. We use our guaranteed indestructible all steel spring construction, as illustrated and described above. The bottom is left open so the inner construction can be plainly seen and which permits of air and ventilation. This couch is made with a full spring edge, an important feature for comfort. The lower part of the couch is trimmed with a handsome overskirt tassel wool fringe. Fitted with best quality casters. On page 479 we describe the quality and color of upholstering materials in which this couch is made. Shipping weight, 75 pounds.

The number of this couch is No. 1E3448. Always order by number and be sure to state the kind and color of covering desired.

Covering	Figured Velour	Corduroy	Plain Brocaded Velour	Fancy Brocaded Plush	Brocaded Verona Plush	Crushed Plush
Price	$6.95	$7.15	$7.35	$7.65	$8.45	$9.55

New Rococo Design Couch, $7.85.

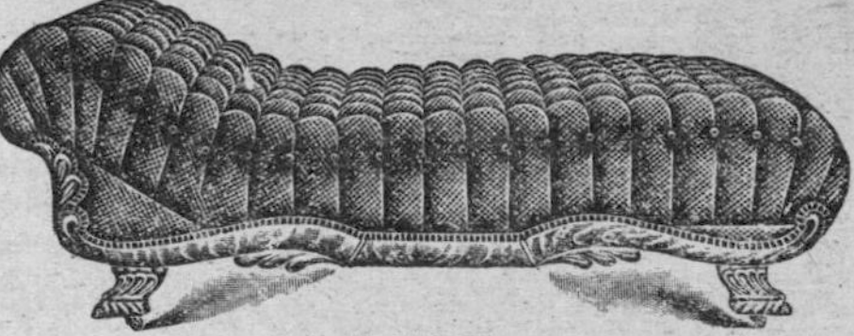

No. 1E3454

No. 1E3454 This couch has an exceptional substantial frame of striking design, handsomely carved claw feet. The design is entirely new and has been especially gotten up for us. The frame throughout is of hardwood, the mouldings, etc., are of select oak, in golden oak finish. This couch is 78 inches long and 30 inches wide, with eight rows of deep hand made tufts put in with all steel tufting buttons, which will not pull off, spring construction is of our guaranteed all steel indestructible spring, has 28 springs in body and 6 in head, 34 in all, with spring edges. Filling is of the very best quality of tow and felted cotton. On page 479 we describe upholstering materials which we can furnish. Complete with casters. Shipping weight, 100 pounds.

The number of this couch is No. 1E3454. Always order by number and be sure to state the kind and color of covering desired.

Covering	Figured Velour	Corduroy	Plain Brocaded Velour	Fancy Brocaded Plush	Brocaded Verona Plush	Crushed Plush
	$7.85	$8.05	$8.25	$8.55	$9.25	$10.45

THE LEGS on all of our couches are detachable, being fastened to the frame by heavy bolts and are easily put on. They are shipped with the legs detached, thereby reducing the freight charges 25 to 40 cents on each couch.

BED COUCHES.

OUR BED COUCHES combine beauty of design, high quality of construction and finish with comfort and durability. They embody all the new ideas in bed couch construction and every one represents the product of years of experience in the manufacture of bed couches. They have been given a well recognized superiority by reason of their many practical and commendable new features. They supply the want of an extra bed where it is impossible to have a regular standing bed, and when not in use as a bed serve equally well as a high grade couch.

THE WOOD used in the construction of our bed couches is thoroughly air seasoned and kiln dried, guaranteed against warping or shrinkage.

WE CALL YOUR SPECIAL ATTENTION to the high grade woven wire spring supported by high carbon steel coil springs on both sides and in the center, used on our bed couches, a feature omitted from bed couches made by other manufacturers. A comfortable, durable spring is essential to a satisfactory bed.

THE WONDERFUL UTILITY of our bed couches will be readily recognized. Each couch can be quickly converted into a bed by unfolding the top section, which is securely hinged to the lower part.

THE LEGS on all our bed couches are detachable, being fastened to the frame by heavy bolts, and are easily put on. They are shipped with the legs detached, thereby reducing the freight charges 25 to 40 cents on each couch.

OUR GUARANTEE. No matter which bed couch you select it will be shipped with the distinct understanding that if not found entirely satisfactory, handsomer in design, higher grade in material, construction and finish, a better couch and a more comfortable and durable bed than you can purchase elsewhere at anywhere near the price we ask, it can be returned to us and we will refund the purchase price together with transportation charges. Our bed couches are shipped direct from factory near Chicago.

Exceptional Value in a Bed Couch, $8.95.

No. 1E3604 This bed couch represents wonderful value. Frame is made of thoroughly seasoned hardwood, veneered with highly figured quarter sawed oak, golden high gloss finish. Decorated with ornamental smooth cut carvings. Has full spring seat. We call your special attention that the bed is fitted with extra quality woven wire mattress, supported by high carbon steel coil springs on both sides and center of bed covered with cotton top mattress attached to the frame, or if desired, with our patent removable mattress, as illustrated and described on this page. Bed open is 72 inches long by 42 inches wide. Couch closed, 24x72 inches. On page 479 we describe the covering used on this couch. Fitted with best quality casters. Shipping weight, 135 pounds.

No. 1E3604

The number of this couch is No. 1E3604. Always order by number and be sure to state the kind and color of covering desired.

Covering	Figured Velour	Corduroy	Plain Brocaded Velour	Fancy Brocaded Plush	Brocaded Verona Plush	Crushed Plush
Price	$8.95	$9.15	$9.35	$9.55	$10.45	$11.40

Same couch fitted with our patent removable mattress, as illustrated and described, $1.00 extra.

Handsome Rococo Bed Couch, $9.25

No. 1E3606 This couch is made in the new rococo design. Frame is oak, finished golden, or birch, finished mahogany, as desired. Has full spring seat, made with six rows of deep tufts. The bed is equipped with an extra quality woven wire mattress, supported with steel coil springs on both sides and center of bed, and covered with good cotton top mattress and extra quality of ticking, or if desired with our patent removable mattress, as illustrated and described on this page. The bed when open is 72 inches long and 50 inches wide, and when closed measures 72 inches in length and 24 inches in width. On page 479 we describe the upholstering materials which we can furnish. Be sure to state finish of frame desired. Fitted with best quality casters. Shipping weight, 130 pounds.

No. 1E3606

The number of this couch is No. 1E3606. Always order by number and be sure to state the kind and color of covering desired.

Covering	Figured Velour	Corduroy	Plain Brocaded Velour	Fancy Brocaded Plush	Brocaded Verona Plush	Crushed Plush
Price	$9.25	$9.45	$9.65	$9.85	$10.75	$11.85

Same couch fitted with our patent removable mattress, as illustrated and described, $1.00 extra.

Victoria Bed Couch, $9.75.

No. 1E3612 This handsome bed couch is of the very latest design. Frame is of oak, golden finish, ornamented with beautiful hand made carvings and claw feet, as shown in illustration. Both sides are alike. It is made with full spring seat and the bed is equipped with extra quality woven wire spring, supported by steel coil springs on both sides and center of bed. Springs are covered with cotton top mattress, good quality of ticking, or if desired with our patent removable mattress as, illustrated and described on this page. The size of bed is 72 inches long and 50 inches wide, when open, and when closed measures 72 inches in length and 24 inches in width. Has six rows small deep biscuit tufts. On page 479 we describe the upholstering material which we can furnish. Complete with casters. Shipping weight, 150 pounds.

No. 1E3612

The number of this couch is No. 1E3612. Always order by number and be sure to state the kind and color of covering desired.

Covering	Figured Velour	Corduroy	Plain Brocaded Velour	Fancy Brocaded Plush	Brocaded Verona Plush	Crushed Plush
Price	$9.75	$9.95	$10.15	$10.35	$11.25	$12.35

Same couch fitted with our patent removable mattress, as illustrated and described, $1.00 extra.

OUR PATENT REMOVABLE MATTRESS

A GOOD MATTRESS MEANS A GOOD BED. This illustration shows our Patent Removable Mattress. Comfort, cleanliness and durability are combined in this bed couch mattress. The wonderful superiority of this mattress over the regular bed couch mattress cannot be fully appreciated until seen, examined and compared with the bed couch mattresses used by other dealers. Made with full bound heavy ticking, guaranteed not to stretch or tear. Filled with new clean white cotton, securely tufted and stitched. This patent removable mattress is attached to the sides of the frame by a very simple device and can be detached for airing with little effort. No bed is absolutely perfect, from a cleanly and hygienic point, unless it can be taken out frequently and given a good airing.

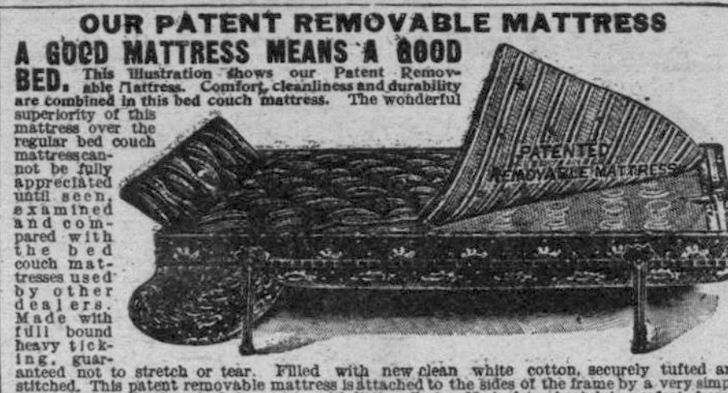

OUR GUARANTEE. If you do not find our Patent Removable Mattress, together with the high grade woven wire spring with steel coil spring supports cleaner, more durable and more comfortable, in fact, worth many times the slight additional cost, you may return this couch bed to us and we will immediately refund your money together with transportation charges. We furnish any bed couch or bed lounge on this page with our Patent Removable Mattress at $1.00 more than prices quoted below.

No. 1E3618 This handsome new design bed couch is 70 inches by 22 inches as illustrated; open as a bed, 72x42 inches. Frame is made of selected northern hardwood, golden oak, high gloss finish. Wood in back is veneered with highly figured quarter sawed oak. This couch is fitted with high grade woven wire spring, supported by steel coil springs on both sides and center of bed, making an extra soft and comfortable bed. Spring is covered with good quality cotton top mattress attached to frame in usual manner, or if desired, with our patent removable mattress, illustrated and described above. Note the handsome claw feet fitted with best quality casters. On page 479 we fully describe the beautiful new designs of high grade coverings used on this couch. Shipping weight, 150 pounds. **The number of this couch is No. 1E3618. Always order by number and be sure to state the kind and color of covering desired.**

No. 1E3618

Covering	Figured Velour	Corduroy	Plain Brocaded Velour	Fancy Brocaded Plush	Brocaded Verona Plush	Crushed Plush
Price	$7.75	$7.95	$8.15	$8.35	$8.65	$8.95

Same couch fitted with our patent removable mattress, illustrated and described, $1.00 extra.

No. 1E3624 This bed lounge is one of the handsomest combination couches in our entire line. It is built on an extra heavy nicely carved and decorated frame made of oak, finished golden. Has heavy claw legs, fitted with best quality casters. It is 70 inches long, 22 inches wide and when open has a bed 72 inches long and 42 inches wide. Full spring seat and full upholstered back. This bed is fitted with woven wire mattress, supported by steel coil springs on both sides and in the center of bed, covered with an excellent cotton top mattress, or if desired, with our patent removable mattress, as illustrated and described above. Good quality ticking. The lounge has full spring seat. Shipping weight, about 150 pounds **The number of this couch is No. 1E3624. Always order by number and be sure to state the kind and color of covering desired.**

No. 1E3624

Covering	Figured Velour	Corduroy	Plain Brocaded Velour	Fancy Brocaded Plush	Brocaded Verona Plush	Crushed Plush
Price	$8.65	$8.85	$9.05	$9.55	$10.05	10 55

Same couch fitted with our patent removable mattress, as illustrated and described, $1.00 extra.

No. 1E3627 This exceptionally attractive new design bed couch is 72 inches by 22 inches as illustrated; 72x42 inches open for use as a bed. Frame is made of selected thoroughly seasoned hardwood, veneered with beautiful flaky quarter sawed oak, high gloss golden finish. Decorated with handsome, smooth, deep cut hand carvings and heavy claw feet. Note especially that this couch is fitted with high grade woven wire springs, supported by steel coil springs on both sides and center, making a very soft and comfortable bed. Spring covered with regular attached cotton top mattress, good quality, or if desired with our patent removable mattress, as illustrated and described above. Good quality ticking. On page 479 we describe the beautiful new patterns in high grade coverings used on this couch. Massive claw feet and best quality casters. Shipping weight, 150 pounds.

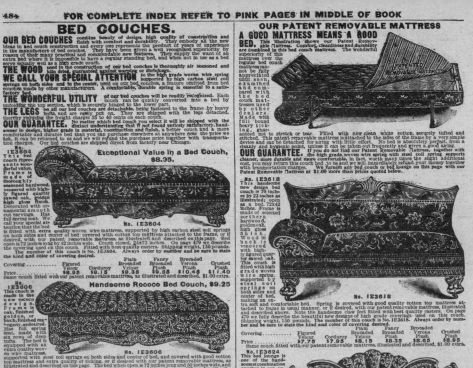

The number of this couch is No. 1E3627. Always order by number and be sure to state the kind and color of covering desired.

Covering	Figured Velour	Corduroy	Plain Brocaded Velour	Fancy Brocaded Plush	Brocaded Verona Plush	Crushed Plush
Price	$9.15	$9.35	$9.55	$10.05	10.45	10.85

Same couch fitted with patent removable mattress, as illustrated and described above, $1.00 extra.

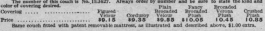

No. 1E3627

The legs on all our bed couches are detachable, being fastened to the frame by heavy bolts and are easily put on. They are shipped with the legs detached, thereby reducing the freight charges 25 to 40 cents on each couch.

... AGITATOR OR RUBBER sets down upon the center post which passes up through the bottom of the tub and adjusts itself ...matically for any quantity of clothes from a few pieces to a tub full. It is built of a clear two-ply lumber with hardwood cleats radiating out from the center on the underside and is provided with perforations to permit the water to pass through it freely. A rustless galvanized cleat, fastened to the agitator by screws, prevents warping and forms the bearing for the center post. It is also provided with two galvanized steel lifting rings for raising it out of the machine. The agitator does not drag the clothes, but gently stirs and turns them, so that every part of them is subjected to the cleansing currents of boiling water which passes through and through them, not once or twice, but hundreds of times, washing them cleaner and better than you could do it by hand and washing a tub full in less time than it would take to wash a single piece on the washboard.

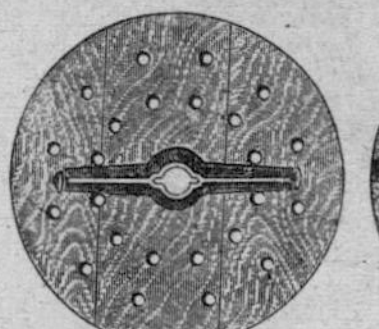

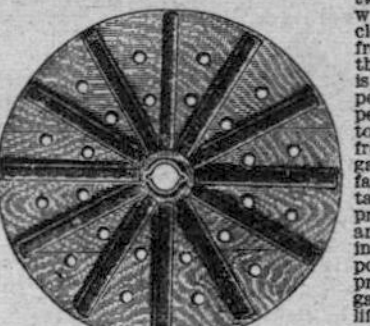

THIS ILLUSTRATION shows you all the gearing there is to the Mississippi. Notice that there are no complicated cog wheels, no heavy fly wheels (the tub itself is the fly wheel), notice the heavy iron brace that strengthens the bottom and prevents the warping and at the same time forms a strong solid foundation for the center post. The powerful crucible steel spring, which is one of the main features of the Mississippi, is also shown. We guarantee it never to break or weaken. This motor spring really does almost all the work of swinging the tub and requires just a little help from you at each swing.

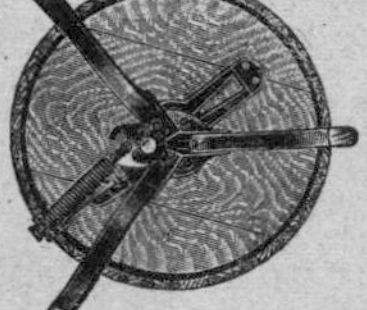

THIS IS THE MOTOR SPRING made of the finest crucible steel and carefully tempered. It is just the right weight and strength to reverse the motion of the tub and bring it back quickly without offering too much resistance to the swing of the operator, it gives the tub its full sweep, but does not permit it to lag. We fully guarantee the quality of these springs and will replace, free of charge, any that show a flaw of any kind or weakness in ten years constant use.

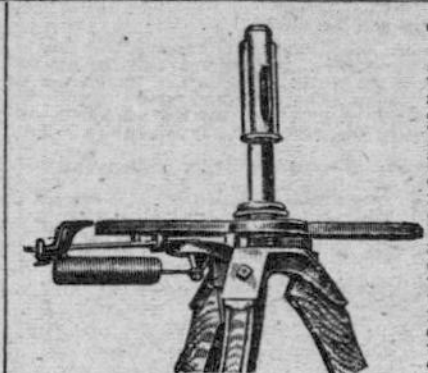

THIS IS A SIDE VIEW of the gearing with the tub removed. At the top is the rustless galvanized center post which extends up inside of the tub and revolves the agitator that sets down over the clothes in the opposite direction to that in which the tub swings. This is one of our exclusive patented features and it is this reverse movement of the agitator in combination with the rotary and oscillating movement of the tub which causes the Mississippi to wash so much cleaner and quicker than any other. The center post is set in motion by a crank shaft just below the cross brace which is fitted with a steel roller bearing operating in a slot in the frame at its outer end, imparting an almost frictionless motion to the post. The heavy steel shaft upon which the tub swings rests on its lower end, which is cone shaped, in a long hardened socket. This shaft runs in oil on its hardened point and is so nearly frictionless that even a touch will start the tub in motion empty or full. The bearing in which it runs is oiltight. It holds the oil and doesn't let it run down onto the floor. You don't have to oil the Mississippi often, once in six months is plenty.

THIS SIMPLE CRANK with its steel roller bearing at the only point where there is any friction, operates in a slot in the frame, giving the reverse movement to the rubber that gently stirs the clothes, so that all parts are washed equally clean. This gentle agitation of the clothes is one of the great reasons why the Mississippi washes so much quicker and cleaner than all other washers of this pattern, which are made with a stationary rubber, which is really no rubber at all.

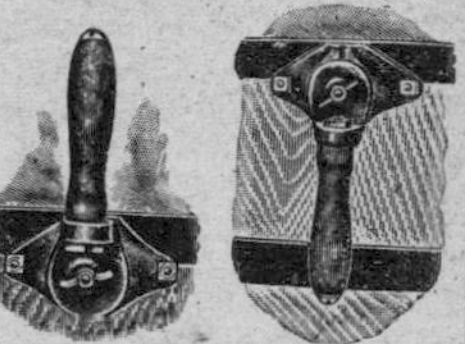

THE OPERATING HANDLE is so arranged that by loosening the thumb nut it may be dropped down out of the way, as shown in this illustration. A groove in the ear which fits a corresponding ridge on the handle holds it perfectly firm and rigid when raised. By locking the tub in a stationary position by means of the brake underneath and dropping the operating handle down out of the way, the Mississippi makes a very handy and convenient kitchen table.

EVERY PART that enters into the construction of the Mississippi Washer must pass a rigid inspection before it is used. The machine is also inspected at various stages of construction and carefully tested before it is finally packed for shipment. Every one is wrapped in heavy paper, strongly crated, leaving our factory in perfect condition and even though it should be shipped to points thousands of miles away it will reach you in the same perfect condition it leaves us, owing to our careful system of packing.

HERE IS WHAT WE GUARANTEE THE MISSISSIPPI WILL DO FOR YOU.

IT WILL WASH ANYTHING

DELICATE LACE CURTAINS, CARPETS, HORSE BLANKETS, RUGS, OR BED CLOTHES AS EASILY AS ORDINARY CLOTHES.

No matter what is in the tub, whether the quantity be small or large, it makes no difference to the easy work of the operator. It is the only washer that cleanses by really forcing the cleansing currents of hot, soapy water through every thread and fibre of the clothes, and by constantly and gently stirring them with an easy rolling motion, so that each part is subjected to a perfect cataract of boiling water, it will wash a big tub of dirty clothes in from five to ten minutes easily, and do it better than it could be done by hand. It does not pull off any buttons nor tear any clothes. It simply washes the dirt out of them quicker and more thoroughly than by any other known system. It is steamtight and watertight No foul, steamy odors to endanger the health of the housewife; no sloppy floors or wet garments. The heat and steam are retained in the tub as they should be, and are not permitted to escape as in open washers or tubs.

ORDER A MISSISSIPPI WASHER TODAY

You will never regret it. It will make washday the easiest of all the week instead of the hardest. The difference will surprise you.

REMEMBER, every machine is sent to you subject to a six months' trial in your own home, which makes you absolutely secure and gives you every opportunity to prove for yourself that everything we say about the Mississippi is absolutely true.

WE GUARANTEE EVERY MACHINE for three years against all defects in material and workmanship, and guarantee that it will reach you safely. The Mississippi has pleased and delighted thousands of others and it will surely satisfy you.

See! The Washing is Finished and the Little Maid Has Done it all Herself. Swinging the Mississippi is so Easy, Even for Little Hands.

No. 23E145 The Mississippi Washer. Price, (Shipping Weight, 65 Pounds) **$5.75**

OUR SUPERBA BALL BEARING Washer $6.50

AT ONLY $6.50

WE OFFER OUR WONDERFUL **SUPERBA BALL BEARING WASHER** as being superior to any washing machine SOLD BY ANYONE AT ANY PRICE.

COMPARED WITH OTHER WASHING MACHINES SOLD AT FROM $10.00 TO $15.00 IT WILL be found to have every real improvement found in every other washer in addition to its great exclusive patented features which put it in a class by itself. No washing machine sold by any other maker has the triple motion, the reverse moving agitator, the combined rotary and oscillating movement of the tub.

These great patented improvements in addition to the other exclusive features of our SUPERBA really make it by far the QUICKEST AND EASIEST WASHER OF ALL.

IT IS EQUIPPED with ball bearings running in tempered steel cones which support the entire weight of the tub and contents. These ball bearings are almost entirely frictionless and our Superba revolves at the slightest touch. A little child can run it just as well as a strong woman and do the washing just as well, no matter whether it is run fast or slow it washes more quickly and perfectly than any other machine.

It is Equipped with Two Powerful Crucible Steel Motor Springs

that do almost all the work of swinging the tub, requiring just a little help from you at each swing. These springs are made from the finest tempered steel and we guarantee that they will NEVER WEAKEN AND NEVER BREAK.

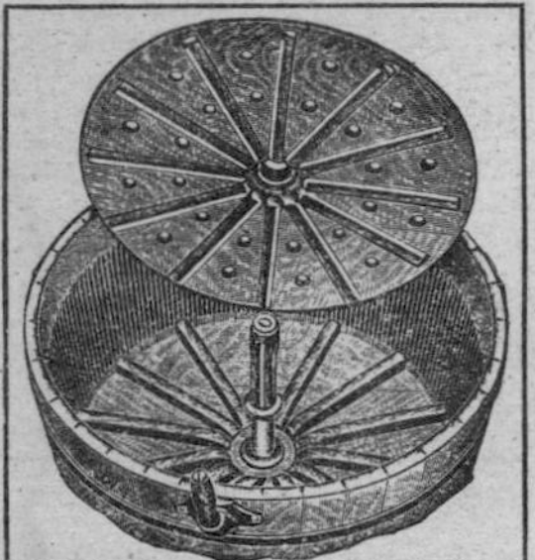

This illustration shows the interior construction. On the bottom of both the tub and rubber are secured hardwood cleats which radiate out from the center.

NOTE THE SIMPLICITY OF THE CONSTRUCTION, as shown in the accompanying illustrations. There are no heavy fly wheels, no complicated gearing in which to catch and mutilate the fingers, nothing to oil or to care for and nothing to get out of order. The tub is carried on a steel pivot and rests on frictionless ball bearings.

Every Superba Washer is sold subject to six months' trial,

during which time you can compare it with washers sold by others at from $10.00 to $15.00. Test it yourself and have your neighbors test it. Put it to any trial you may see fit in order to convince yourself that it is all that we claim it to be.

A WRITTEN THREE-YEAR GUARANTEE AGAINST ALL DEFECTS IN MATERIAL AND WORKMANSHIP IS SENT WITH EVERY ONE,

as explained in full on the previous pages.

REMEMBER, THAT WE POSITIVELY GUARANTEE THAT OUR SUPERBA WASHER WILL WASH ANYTHING AND EVERYTHING CLEANER AND BETTER WITH LESS WEAR AND TEAR THAN ANY MACHINE SOLD BY ANY OTHER CONCERN AND DO IT IN ONE-HALF THE TIME AND WITH ALMOST NO WORK AT ALL. No matter what the other washer may cost, no matter what the maker may claim for it, we are willing to put the Superba along side of it for six months' trial with YOU AS SOLE JUDGE and if at the end of that time you are not convinced that it is

The Strongest, Simplest and Most Thorough WASHING MACHINE you have ever used

you can return it to us and we will refund the purchase price and all the freight charges you have paid.

THE TUB IS MADE FROM THE VERY BEST VIRGINIA CEDAR, one of the most durable woods known, and is corrugated on the inside like a washboard.

THE BOTTOM OF THE RUBBER and the tub are provided with hardwood cleats and the rubber is perforated to permit a free circulation of the hot soapy water. The clothes are thrown into the machine and the rubber set over them. As you swing the tub in one direction the rubber revolves in the opposite direction and gently stirs the clothes so that every thread of them is subjected to the currents of boiling water created by the triple motion of the tub and agitator, again and again, hundreds of times. The centrifugal force generated by the rotary motion of the machine throws the cleansing currents of boiling water to the outside and when the reverse movement occurs it is thrown back to the center on top of the agitator, whence it is drawn down through the holes and forced out through the clothes, carrying all the dirt with it. In five to ten minutes a tubful is washed to snowy cleanliness.

THE SUPERBA WASHER

will wash the hardest and dirtiest clothes to wash, such as mechanics' blouses and overalls and men's working clothes of all kinds, and do it perfectly and without the use of a washboard.

No Other Washer Will Do This

This is the bottom view of the tub, showing the gearing, the twin steel motor springs, the ball bearings and the brake which holds the tub stationary when wringing out the clothes.

No. 23E148 The Superba Washer. Shipping weight, 70 pounds. Price...**$6.50**

The Aurora Washer.

$3.30

No. 23E140 Constructed of the best red southern gum wood, and is stronger, more nicely finished, and larger than any round machine on the market. Supplied with our improved gearing, fully galvanized. Inside of machine is fully corrugated, similar to a washboard, and there are no nails or blocks of any kind on the inside. The machine is made with large end of tub down, allowing plenty of room for water and clothes. The hoops are made of extra heavy galvanized wire, are electrically welded, and are warranted not to break or fall off. Instead of using a square wooden post to work the dolly, we use a square galvanized iron rod making it impossible to tear the most delicate fabric, as the dolly and standard are automatically adjusted to the quantity of clothes contained in the machine. The Aurora closes tight, retaining the heat in the water for a long time, and preventing all odor of foul steam from clothes. This washer can be used on a carpet without soiling it. Large, convenient place for holding the wringer, which need not be moved while using the machine. Shipping weight, 50 pounds. Price..............**$3.30**

The Columbia Rotary Washer.

$5.20

No. 23E144 Columbia Rotary Washer. Easiest and lightest running rotary washer made. Has improved roller bearings, metal parts aluminum coated; no clutches, cams or springs to wear or get out of order. The mechanism is never in the way. Has extra large tub made of perfectly seasoned selected Virginia white cedar fully corrugated like a washboard. Top hoop is flat, middle and bottom hoops are of electric welded galvanized wire, can never come off. It washes the most delicate laces or the heaviest bedding easily, quickly, perfectly. Balance wheel turns in either direction and washes equally well when turned slowly or rapidly. The tub is steam tight as well as water tight, giving out no odor of foul steam, and making no sloppy floors. No other machine combines so many labor saving devices with good workmanship and perfect material. Fully guaranteed, and if not the easiest running machine made, can be returned at our expense and money will be refunded. Weight, 65 pounds.
Price..............**$5.20**

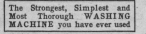

The Revolving Wheel All Metal Steam Washer.

No. 23E149 Having all the latest improvements. Boiler is made of heavy galvanized iron, 21¼x12x10¾ inches, inside measurement. The cylinder is made from heavy tin plate, is 18¾ inches in diameter and 9¾ inches wide. The clothes are placed in this cylinder and washed by the action of the steam. Prints and ginghams can be washed in from five to eight minutes, white flannel in five minutes; red flannel in about one minute; lace curtains in from ten to fifteen minutes. No washboard rubbing is necessary, and clothes will last twice as long. In washing it is not necessary to turn all the while. You turn the cylinder one or two minutes, then go about your other work for a while, then turn the cylinder a minute or two again. You can wash much cleaner in this washer than you can by hand, and the clothes will always keep white and never turn yellow. Does not wear the clothes or pull off the buttons. This machine is made of the best material and should last from five to ten years. Remember, the clothes are not boiled, but cleansed by steam. This is a process which is used by the celebrated French steam cleaning establishments. A heavy tin cover fits closely on the top of this machine, and closely confines the steam. Shipping weight, 30 pounds. Price........$2.80

No. 23E150 All Metal Steam Washer, same as above but provided with bronze faucet on boiler so that water can be drawn off without removing from stove, thus saving all heavy lifting. Price........$3.47

Our Ideal Washer.

No. 23E154 Our Ideal Washer. It does washing equal to any large washing machine, but with greater ease and more rapidity. It washes a tub, pail or boiler full of clothes all at one time, without the usual wear and tear received by all old methods. It forces compressed air, steam and water through the fabric, quickly removing all dirt. It has no equal for dainty fabrics, lace curtains, blankets, woolens, disagreeable cloths, etc. If it does not do all we claim for it, it may be returned and money will be refunded. Made of best tin. Weight, 1½ pounds. Price........$0.39
Price, per dozen........4.40

MRS. POTTS' SAD IRONS.

Set consists of one iron with rounded end, for polishing, weight, 4 pounds; two with regular ends, one weighing 5½ pounds and one 5¾ pounds; one detachable wood handle, always cool, and one iron stand.

No. 2E9345 Mrs. Potts' Sad Irons, in sets of three, with detachable wood handle and iron stand, as described above; finely polished. Price, per set........63c

No. 2E9346 Set of three Mrs. Potts' Sad Irons, as above, finely polished and heavily nickel plated. Price, per set........66c

Sad Iron Handle.

No. 2E9352 Sad Iron Handle. Fits any Mrs. Pott s' pattern sad irons; is all steel and cannot be broken. Asbestos insulated and the coolest handle made. Fits the hand and does not tire the wrist. Nice japanned finish. Price........9c

Sensible Sad Iron

83c

No. 2E9356 Sensible Sad Irons. A handsome outfit, containing three highly nickel plated and polished solid sad irons, ground by perfect machinery, which makes every iron true; and face shaped to make ironing easier than with the old style irons. These solid irons hold the heat longer than the ordinary Mrs. Potts' irons. The handle is the strongest and best made, will not shake, fits the hand perfectly and cannot become accidentally detached. Irons are double pointed and weigh 5, 6 and 7 pounds respectively. Price, per set of three irons, detachable handle and stand, 83c

No. 2E9359 Sensible Sleeve Iron. For laundering shirt waists and children's clothes. Will iron a plait or tuck to the seam. Is nickel plated and polished, with detachable handle. Weight, 4 pounds. Length, 8 inches. Price........29c

No. 2E9375 Old Style Sad Irons, with face finely polished. The 2½-pound is handsomely nickel plated and splendid for laundering shirt waists and other light articles.

Weight, lbs.	2½	5	6	7	8	9
Price	23c	14c	17c	20c	23c	26c

Charcoal Irons.

No. 2E9407 Family Charcoal Irons, with removable top and hardwood handle with shield. Handsomely nickel plated and elegantly finished, with top finished in gold bronze. Is self heating and requires little attention. Uses ordinary charcoal as fuel, is easily regulated to any desired heat and does away with the hot fire on ironing day. Agents charge $2.00 to $2.50 for this iron. Weight, 7 pounds. Price........98c

No. 2E9408 Family Charcoal Iron. Same pattern as above. Plain polished finish. Weight, 6½ pounds. Price........69c

Tailor's Goose.

No. 2E9412 Tailor's Goose, with extra polished face.

Weight, lbs.	12	14	16	18	20	22
Price	48c	56c	64c	72c	80c	88c

CARPET SWEEPERS.

A Carpet Sweeper saves time and money, costs no more than four or five good brooms and will outwear several dozen. Will follow a broom on any carpet and remove more dirt and dust than the broom did and with very much less labor. Does not wear out a carpet as a broom does, and in this way alone will quickly save its cost. Sold under our universal guarantee. If not satisfactory, return it and your money will be refunded.

Acme Carpet Sweeper.

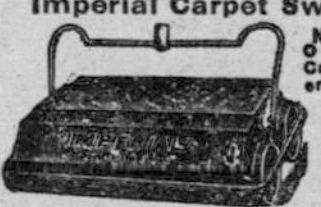

No. 2E9470 The Acme Carpet Sweeper is the best low priced carpet sweeper ever offered. It has broom action, reversible bail, improved dumping device, the new improved braid band, which never comes off, strictly pure bristle brush, handsomely finished case. The metal parts are japanned finish. Weight, boxed 9½ pounds. Price........$1.55

Imperial Carpet Sweeper.

No. 2E9471 Our Imperial Carpet Sweeper contains the famous broom action, and every other feature necessary in a first class sweeper. Made from the best selected cabinet woods in an assortment of attractive finishes. Full nickel plated trimming. Nickel plated on copper, which is the best method known, permits the highest possible finish and will not rust or tarnish. Has the new improved braid band furniture protector encircling the case, patent reversible bail. Wheels outside the case, our everlasting pure bristle brush; pans operate independently by an easy pressure of the finger. Weight, boxed, 9½ pounds. Price........$1.98

Bissell's Grand Rapids, Cyco Bearings.

No. 2E9480 Bissell's Grand Rapids, Cyco Bearings, Carpet Sweeper. The best known and most widely sold carpet sweeper in the world. Contains the famous Bissell broom action, the anti-raveling collector brush ends, the dustproof axle tubes, the new improved Bissell's bail socket, and every other desirable feature necessary in a first class sweeper. Made from the best selected cabinet woods in an assortment of attractive finishes. Has improved braid band furniture protector encircling the case, Bissell's patent reversible bail spring, wheels outside the case, our everlasting pure bristle brush; both pans open at once by an easy pressure of the finger. Fully guaranteed. Weight, boxed, 9½ pounds.
Price, Cyco bearings, japanned metal trimmings........$2.50

Bissell's Sanitary Sweeper.

No. 2E9479 Bissell's Sanitary Sweeper is made by the Bissell Carpet Sweeper Co. of Grand Rapids, Mich., the largest manufacturers of carpet sweepers in the world. It has the renowned Bissell broom action, reversible bail, new improved braid band furniture protector which never comes off, Bissell's reliable new improved spring dumping device, pure bristle sweeping brush, handsomely finished case. All metal parts are nicely japanned. Weight, boxed, 9½ pounds. Price........$1.80

Bissell's Prize, Cyco Bearings, Carpet Sweeper.

$3.00

No. 2E9483 Bissell's Prize Carpet Sweeper, the latest of the Bissell patterns. A sweeper of the highest grade, with one of the handsomest patent case designs. The case is hand polished. The bail, trimmings and iron end pieces are plated with nickel, brass or antique copper, according to the finish of the case. It contains the Bissell broom action, has patent reversible bail, patent bail sockets, the improved braid band furniture protector and our pure bristle wire staple brush, adapted to be easily removed from the sweeper. Its spring dumping device is convenient, opening one pan at a time. Length of case, 14 inches. Its construction throughout is as perfect as care and skill can make it. This is in our opinion the handsomest design and the best finished carpet sweeper made by the Bissell Carpet Sweeper Co. Weight, boxed, 10¼ pounds.
Price, with Cyco bearings........$3.00

SEROCO CARPET SWEEPER, $2.48

THIS IS THE FINEST AND LATEST PRODUCTION IN THE CARPET SWEEPER LINE.

$2.48

THIS ILLUSTRATION which is reproduced from a photograph, shows but the design of the sweeper and gives you no idea of the artistic finish and the beautiful grain of the rare tropical woods used in the case, which are brought out to perfection by the hand rubbed piano polish finish and heightened by the burnished nickel of the metal parts. The case is of the very latest exclusive design and is built up of three-ply veneer and finished in the same manner as the most expensive pianos with three coats of transparent varnish hand rubbed and polished. We furnish our Seroco sweeper in figured mahogany French walnut, birdseye maple, curly birch or silver gray maple, the latest and most popular new finish, which is the same as shown in the illustration. The metal trimmings are first copper plated, then triple nickel plated and polished and will always retain their beautiful luster. Our Seroco sweeper has more specially designed patented features than can be found in any other and these actually double its efficiency, convenience and worth to the user. It is equipped with braid furniture guard, the brush is instantly removable, for cleaning. It has our improved dustproof axle bearing, our rubber brush pulleys, the most perfect ever devised, our improved brush, made of the finest imported Chinese bristles, improved roller bearings, non-tipping attachment and steel handle fastener.

OUR PATENTED ROLLER BEARINGS, shown in the accompanying illustration, are the most notable improvement ever made in the carpet sweeper construction and make the Seroco run far easier than an ordinary sweeper. Our roller bearings have not a single spring or delicate part to wear out or get out of order. Nothing that will ever require attention. They are constructed so that there is absolutely no friction or noise and they never require oiling.

OUR SEROCO SWEEPER will follow the best broom made over any carpet and take out more dust and dirt than the broom did. The pure elastic bristle brush in combination with our great broom action causes it to reach down into the pile of the carpet and draw the dirt out of it, making it look fresh and bright like new, after sweeping. It does not grind the dirt into the carpet to cut and wear the fibre as a broom does. It saves the carpet instead of wearing it out, and this feature alone will soon save its cost.

$2.48, our price for the Seroco sweeper, is wonderfully low. Sweepers of this grade are carried only in the finest retail stores in the larger cities and have never been sold for less than $5.00 and our price represents but a bare margin over the actual cost to build in the largest and best equipped carpet sweeper factory in the United States. It costs you only as much as eight good brooms and will outwear six dozen brooms. It will not only make your carpets last longer and look brighter, but will sweep in one fourth the time of the best broom and with almost no labor at all.

WE FULLY GUARANTEE the Seroco sweeper to give you splendid satisfaction and if you do not find it to be the finest and most perfect sweeper you ever saw and well worth $5.00 you are at liberty to return it to us and we will immediately refund your money. Shipping weight, packed securely in a strong wood box, 10½ pounds.
No. 2E9488 Our special price........$2.48

Pot Chain and Scraper.

No. 2E9510 The Sensible Pot Chain and Scraper is a new and useful article, each ring is double, which makes it very durable. The handle is malleable iron; the blade is steel; the handle and scraper are tinned. Weight, 4 ounces.
Price, per dozen, 85c; each........8c

Can Openers.

No. 2E9535 Sprague Can Opener is without question one of the best can openers in the market. Weight, 5 ounces.
Price, per dozen, 39c; each........4c

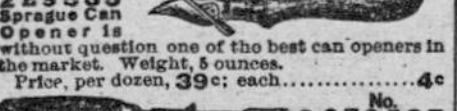

No. 2E9537 Surecut Can Opener. Opens any can, round or square of any size quicker and easier than others. Has tool steel blade and varnished wood handle.
Price........9c

Mincing Knife.

No. 2E9557 Double Mincing Knife. Polished steel blades; enameled handle. Weight, 8 ounces. Price, per dozen, 47c; each..5c

No. 2E9560 Mincing Knife. Cast steel blade, ground sharp; solid malleable iron handle, black enameled which can't split or get loose. Weight, 9 ounces. Price........7c

Fruit Jar Wrench.

No. 2E9595 Fruit Jar Cover Wrench, will not break the cover or can, will not slip or become worthless from long or careless use. It is stamped out of sheet steel and riveted together. It saves jars, rubbers and covers and insures the fruit being properly sealed during the canning season. Weight, 6 oz. Price, per doz., 75c; each.7c

Henis Fruit Press.

No. 2E9610 Henis Fruit and Vegetable Press and Strainer; can be used for a variety of purposes; is especially recommended for mashing potatoes. Potatoes, after being forced through the strainer have a delicious creamy taste that no other method of mashing will impart. It is not necessary to peel the potatoes, as it mashes and removes the skin of boiled potatoes in one operation. Weight, 20 ounces. Price....17c

$22.95 BUYS A $100.00 TYPEWRITER.

FOR ONLY $22.95 WE OFFER THE BURNETT VISIBLE TYPEWRITER guaranteed to be the equal of any standard $100.00 TYPEWRITER on the market. The Burnett is the most modern and up to date typewriter manufactured. It contains more real improvements, more novel and convenient features, is more durable, and better built throughout than any typewriter offered by any other concern at any price. **The Burnett typewriter is an absolute and always visible writer.** The printing point faces the eye of the operator fairly and at the easiest and best position for reading. Every character is in plain sight from the moment it is printed until the page is removed from the machine. The direct hammer blow of the type makes it the most powerful manifolder of any and fifteen or twenty legible carbon copies can be made if desired. It will make perfect and clean cut mimeograph stencils and will turn out copy work exactly resembling original typewriting. It is the speediest machine of any, faster than the fastest operator in the world. The rebound of the typebar after printing is instantaneous, making the piling up of type, a common fault with other machines, unknown. The touch is suprisingly light, even and elastic. The key depression is perfectly even and uniform. The alignment is perfect, permanent and unchanged, regardless of the number of copies made. It is equipped with the Universal Keyboard with one shift, having 42 keys and printing 84 characters. This is the experts' favorite and conceded to be the swiftest keyboard ever devised. The keyboard is the easiest to learn. The Burnett is the simplest, the easiest to understand, the most durable and easiest cleaned of any on the market. In finish and appearance it is equal to the very best. The nickel plated parts are first polished and heavily coppered then nickel plated, making the most durable possible finish. The frame and housings are enameled, hand rubbed and furnace baked, giving them a high glossy black finish, the effectiveness of which is increased by gold stripings. The Burnett is a handsome and fitting addition to the finest office and one which the possessor may well be proud of. We fully guarantee it to be a full size standard machine in every way, equal in durability, in quality and appearance to any $100.00 typewriter made, to be far better in every way than any but the very best and to possess improvements not found in any other machine, which put it in a class by itself, superior to all others.

WE CAN SELL THE BURNETT, **a standard $100.00 typewriter at $22.95,** because of the fact that we have contracted for the entire output of the factory, which is one of the largest and finest in existence, equipped with every modern time saving and labor saving machine necessary to produce **a highest grade typewriter at the lowest possible cost.** We take every machine they can turn out, working to their full capacity every week day in the year at just a small margin over the actual shop cost to build, the actual cost of the material and labor which enters into their construction and to this cost we add only a single small margin of profit. Selling as we do typewriters in connection with thousands of other items and by catalogue only, the expense of printing and distributing the catalogue is divided up among many thousands of articles and is comparatively a small amount on each one so that our selling expense on the Burnett typewriter amounts to but a few cents on each machine. We are satisfied to sell them at a margin of profit which is so small that it would be but a mere incident in the heavy selling expense under the ordinary methods of marketing typewriters. The $100.00 typewriters, on the other hand, are all sold by the old style branch stores and agency system, which has always forced the consumer to pay two to four times the factory cost of the goods and always will. It is a profit piled on profit and expense piled on expense system inaugurated back in the days when a typewriter was a new thing and the demand for it had to be created by personal solicitation and demonstration.

WHEN YOU PAY $100.00 FOR ANY TYPEWRITER YOU DON'T PAY A CENT MORE FOR THE MACHINE ITSELF THAN WE ASK FOR THE BURNETT. THE DIFFERENCE IS ALL PROFIT AND SELLING EXPENSES AND ADDS NOTHING TO THE VALUE OF THE MACHINE AND IS SIMPLY MONEY THROWN AWAY AS FAR AS YOU ARE CONCERNED.

When you buy the Burnett at **$22.95**, all you pay for is the actual cost to build in one of the best equipped factories in the country and a single small margin of profit, nothing more. Nothing for bookkeepers, collectors, rent, taxes, cartage, light, etc., and all the multitude of expenses and profits that add to the selling price of other machines, because we avoid all of these by our simple factory to user selling system which enables us to offer the BURNETT, one of the very best machines, at the heretofore unheard of price of **$22.95**.

ON ONLY $1.00 DEPOSIT.

We will ship the Burnett typewriter to any address on receipt of only $1.00 deposit, to be shipped C. O. D. for the balance, subject to your examination. You can examine it at your railroad depot or express office and if you find it to be just exactly as we represent, pay the balance due to the agent and take up the shipment. It is to your advantage, however, to send cash in full with your order, as by so doing you save some little trouble in the payment of the C. O. D. and also the charge, usually of from 35 to 50 cents, which all express companies make for the collection and return of the money.

60 DAYS' FREE TRIAL ON EVERY BURNETT.

We accept your order for the Burnett Visible Typewriter with the distinct understanding on our part, that whether you mention it in your order or not, it will be shipped to you subject to a full 60 days' trial. Whether you send cash in full with your order or only a dollar deposit on each machine and pay the balance to your express agent you have the privilege of trying it for two full months before finally deciding to keep it. You can compare it with any typewriter on the market selling at any price, even though it be two, three or four times the price paid for the Burnett. Compare it in workmanship and finish, in strength simplicity and durability. Test its speed, touch, action and manifolding power in comparison with other machines, put it to any fair test you may see fit and if after a full 60-day trial in your own office you are not convinced that the Burnett is all we claim it to be and is really a wonderful bargain you are at liberty to box it up and return it to us and we will refund every penny you have paid us and every penny you have paid for transportation charges.

We can afford to make this offer, knowing positively from our own tests that a better all around typewriter than the Burnett is not made. We know that with fair and intelligent usage the Burnett is bound to give perfect satisfaction, that no typewriter, regardless of name or price, is better made, more durable or more perfect in action than the Burnett

We use the Burnett exclusively in our own great establishment in preference to all others. We have found from actual test and use that it is more rapid, stronger and more durable than others and will turn out perfect work day in and day out with less care and attention than any other.

EVERY BURNETT TYPEWRITER GUARANTEED FOR TEN YEARS.

Every Burnett typewriter is accompanied by a ten-year written, binding guarantee, and by the terms of which, as plainly written upon its face, we bind ourselves to replace or repair any part of the machine which may give out through any defect of material or workmanship during that period. This is an absolute guard and protection for the purchaser. Should any part, by chance, contain a hidden flaw or defect it will surely show itself within that time. Every part that enters into the construction of the Burnett typewriter is carefully inspected; they are assembled and adjusted by skilled mechanics and tested by expert operators before packing and while the chance of a defective part is most remote, yet you are fully protected on this point by our ten-year guarantee, the longest and strongest ever given by any typewriter manufacturer.

WE GUARANTEE SAFE DELIVERY ALSO.

Our typewriters are packed in strong, wooden cases and secured in such a manner that it is rarely indeed that one is damaged in transit. Never, unless it receives unusually rough handling or meets with an accident. To protect you from loss in these rare cases we guarantee safe delivery, and should a machine by any chance arrive in a damaged condition we agree to replace or repair it at once entirely free of all expense to you, thus insuring you against any loss in transit.

SOME OF THE BURNETT ADVANTAGES.

The Burnett typewriter was devised by and is built throughout under the direct supervision of a mechanical expert who has given the best part of his life to practical study of typewriter construction. It is a real triumph in writing machine building in the simple ingenuity of its mechanism. Simplicity is the strong point of the Burnett typewriter. In it the desired results are accomplished with fewer and simpler parts than in any other high grade machine. Beside it, the other standard machines look clumsy and complicated, and are clumsy and complicated. Being simple, it is easy to understand and operate. It is less likely to get out of order than other machines. It has fewer bearings and wearing parts. Yet, it contains all the essential points of a high grade writing machine. On it can be accomplished all that can be done on any other machine. It is faster than the fastest operator, it is a strong and perfect manifolder. The bearings are few and simple compared with other machines, yet broad and strong. The touch is quick and elastic and can be regulated to any desired tension. As a billing machine, manifolder, tabulator, stencil cutter, and in every way, it is superior to any machine made.

IT IS THE ONLY PERFECT VISIBLE WRITER.

Any visible typewriter on which the work is in plain sight of the writer as it progresses, is miles in advance of the old style so called "blind" machine, in which the printing point is entirely out of sight on the under side of the platen and in which the platen must be revolved or the carriage lifted up to inspect the work, but there is a big difference in the visible writers. In some the platen is at the extreme rear of the machine and the printing point is hardly visible to the operator at all. In others the printing point is at the extreme top of the platen or at a right angle with the top so that when seen from the natural position of the writer the printed characters are seen at an angle which makes them always difficult to read and frequently impossible when the light is not just right. In the Burnett the printing point is at an angle of 45 degrees from the top of the platen and faces the eye fairly. It is in just the right position to read easily. In just the same position as you would hold a letter or newspaper if you were reading. In other words in just the easiest natural position for reading without straining the eyes.

Every character is in plain sight as soon as printed

View of the printing point. As the type bar leaves the printing point the ribbon drops down, giving an unobstructed view of the work.

This illustration, which is reproduced from a photograph, shows how easy it is to inspect the work as it proceeds, without changing position or straining the eye. In fact, if it did not possess a single feature of merit except that of its absolutely and always visible writing, this feature alone would make it one of the most popular and efficient machines. Few appreciate the wonderful increase in operating speed and consequent saving of time and money obtained by the use of a visible writing machine. The operator of the old style "blind" machine is in the same position as a person groping about in a dark room. He is never certain of anything and his movements are correspondingly slow. It is estimated that from one-fourth to one-third of the operator's time is spent in raising the carriage to look for real or imaginary errors. Then lowering to insert a correction, the mental figuring to find where the correction should be inserted and raising the carriage again to see if it is correctly inserted. Sometimes it is; just as likely is not, necessitating more erasing and more wasting of time. With the Burnett it is different. Every letter is in plain sight as soon as printed and the operator gains in confidence and hence in speed and accuracy. No time is wasted in looking for imaginary errors. Corrections when necessary are quickly and easily made, always in just the right place because it is in plain sight. The visible writing, in combination with the tabular stops, which are placed on the graduated bar at the back of carriage, makes it a splendid billing machine and makes all tabulated work rapid, positive and easy.

This Illustration shows how the writing done with the **BURNETT** is in easy natural view of the Operator.

ACTION AND SPEED.

The action of the Burnett is simple, direct and powerful. There are no corners to turn, no friction, no lost motion, no forcing into position. The moment the key is depressed the type bar is thrust forward and delivers a direct hammer blow. The anviling of the bar at just the moment the impression is made makes the return of the type bar instantaneous. There is no piling up of type, no dragging in the action. The more rapid the operator, the more rapid the action. Its limit of speed has never been reached. The touch is delightfully light and elastic. More work can be done on it in a given time and with less strain and fatigue to the operator than with any other. It is equipped with improved individual key tension by which the tension can be easily adjusted to suit any operator or for any work. The key depression is perfectly uniform on all the keys.

THE ESCAPEMENT AND UNIVERSAL BAR, **on which the speed and action of all typewriters very largely depends,** in the Burnett are operated without any effort whatever on the part of the operator. Every key when depressed, moves the universal bar and in turn operates the escapement, but not until the type bar has almost reached the printing point, when its momentum overcomes the resistance of the universal bar and the escapement is made quickly and positively. The touch of the finger merely lifts the type bar, which offers almost no resistance, instead of lifting the combined weight of type bar and universal bar as in others.

THE KEY LEVERS, TYPE BARS, AND CONNECTIONS are made throughout of the finest **steel.** The keys are of hard black rubber, the character inlaid in white on the surface, the bearings and adjustments are accurate to the thousandth of an inch. The type bar bearing is of a new design, never before used in a typewriter and increases in length with the forward stroke of the bar, making a rigid frictionless bearing which will be unchanged after years of use. The type are of the finest tempered Swedish steel and will print as clearly and distinctly after long usage as when new.

THE ALIGNMENT IS PERFECT AND UNCHANGING. **The type bars lay in a half circle, and as each approaches the printing point it enters a guide plate with an opening just wide enough to permit it to enter without binding, causing each type to print at exactly the same point.** This together with the strong broad type bar bearings make the alignment permanent and unchanged. The type all approaching the common printing point from one direction, the alignment remains unchanged when manifolding, regardless of the number of manifolded copies made.

THE BURNETT IS NEARLY NOISELESS.

In operating the only sound heard is the sharp click of the type striking the platen. All sound of the type bars dropping back into position and of the rebound of the key levers is prevented by felt and leather strips. The inside of the front and rear housings are also felt lined, making it the most noiseless machine made.

IN THE BURNETT WE USE THE UNIVERSAL KEYBOARD

WITH ONE SHIFT.

IT HAS 42 KEYS AND WRITES 84 CHARACTERS **including capitals, small letters, figures, fractions and punctuation marks.** The shift lock and marginal release key are at the right and left hand of the upper bank of keys and the shift and release key at the left end of the lower bank. In the ordinary position, the lower case or small letters are printed. If all capitals are desired, a single pressure of the upper right hand shift key marked "Cap" which locks automatically when depressed, secures them. This in turn is released by touching the lower left shift key which is also depressed when a single or few capitals are desired.

THE UNIVERSAL KEYBOARD **as furnished in the Burnett is the easiest of any to learn and the speediest in operation.** It is small and compact, measuring but 3¾ by 10 inches and all the keys can be reached with little or no movement of the arms. This keyboard is used, with but few exceptions, on all the leading makes of typewriters and anyone can learn to operate the Burnett in a few moments' time.

THE UNIVERSAL KEYBOARD.

The Universal Keyboard as used in the Burnett Typewriter.

MANIFOLDING.

Careful tests have proven the Burnett to be the most powerful manifolder on the market. It will make more and clearer carbon copies at one writing than any other. Ten to fifteen legible copies can be easily made if necessary. The direct hammer blow of the type all coming from one direction not only increases its manifolding power but preserves the perfect alignment regardless of the number of copies made. In making mimeograph stencils the impression of the type is strong and clear cut and mimeograph copies from a Burnett made stencil will look exactly like original typewriting.

LOCKING DEVICE AND RELEASE KEY. **At the end of each line the machine locks automatically, preventing the piling up of type or printing one character over another.** By a slight pressure of the release key on the upper left side of the keyboard, the locking device is released so that several additional characters or a hyphen can be added when desired.

MARGINAL STOPS **are provided on a graduated rack in the rear of the carriage.** These are instantly adjusted to leave any width of margin on both right and left sides of the paper that may be desired. They can be moved to any position on the rack by depressing a small lever and lock automatically wherever placed, giving you any desired width of margin. The bell ringer and locking device are controlled by an independent stop on the left of the rack. The bell will ring and the machine lock at any point it is placed, ending the line positively without other adjustment. Depressing the marginal release key on the left side of the keyboard allows you to print additional matter outside of the marginal line, locking at the end of the line automatically.

SPECIMEN OF WORK. This shows the type style of the Burnett Typewriter.

The Burnett is furnished in Pica type only. This style is shown in the above illustration. It is used almost universally in business correspondence, so much so that there is almost no call for any other.

CARRIAGE AND PLATEN.

The carriage is simple and strong in construction. The moving parts are few and each is positive in action and never fails, there is no guesswork, press the desired lever and its work is accomplished instantly. The carriage travels on anti-friction steel ball bearings running in flat grooves with but two points of contact. Its lightness in combination with its anti-friction bearings make it quickly responsive to a light tension of the operating spring and hence increases its operating speed. **The platen is instantly removed from the machine by slightly depressing the platen hooks on each side of the carriage and raising it from the groove in which it rests.** This is done without disturbing the work in any way, and it can be replaced just as quickly and easily as it is removed, and the typewriting continued at just the point where it was stopped. This valuable improvement is found in no other visible writing machine. It is a great advantage. If, for instance, you are doing manifolding work and making a number of carbon copies and desire to write a telegram, letter or postal, simply remove platen and place another platen in the machine and you can do the necessary writing, remove the second platen and replace it with the original and continue the manifolding work just where you left off. No time is lost in removing the work from the feed roll and replacing it. No matching of copies. No handling of carbons and smutting of work and fingers.

The Platen.

The paper fingers shown on either side of the platen roll are thin, flexible and carefully tempered. They hold the paper firmly and evenly, and by means of the small knobs at their base are easily adjusted to hold paper of any width from a half inch to the full width of the platen roll, and at any part of the roll. Paper of any width, light or heavy in weight, envelopes, postal cards and index cards of any size are grasped with equal facility.

LINE SPACER
LINE SPACING SWITCH
LEFT PAPER FINGER
PLATEN RELEASE LEVER
PLATEN HOOK
LEFT PLATEN TWIRLER
CARRIAGE RELEASE LEVER

Left end of the carriage and platen.

This illustration shows the left end of the carriage with the operating parts indicated. They are all in plain sight, within easy reach and under the direct control of the operator at all times.

THE LINE SPACER. **By the same movement of the hand which returns the carriage to begin a new line,** the line spacer is automatically operated, giving any number of spaces desired from one to five, according to the adjustment of the line spacing switch.

THE LINE SPACING SWITCH **is located just in front of and below the line spacer.** It is adjusted to any desired number of spaces up to five by simply raising the switch and dropping it into the slot desired, when no further adjustment is necessary.

THE PAPER FINGERS. **There are two adjustable paper fingers, the left one being shown in this illustration.** They can be easily regulated to hold paper or cards of any width and are moved by a small pear shaped knob at their base.

THE PLATEN RELEASE LEVER **when thrown forward disengages the ratchet and gives a perfectly free movement of the platen for interlining, filling in ruled blanks, etc.** It is thrown back into its normal position before beginning to write on regular lines again. For ordinary corrections its use is unnecessary, as the platen ratchet is constructed so that platen can be readily turned in either direction by either end twirler independently of the release lever, which is only used when a perfectly free movement of the platen is desired.

THE PLATEN HOOKS **lock the platen into position on the carriage and by simply depressing them the platen can be removed.** The guide rails on the carriage insure the platen going back into place properly and it can be removed and replaced in a moment.

THE PLATEN TWIRLERS **give perfect control of the platen.** By revolving either or both of the platen twirlers the paper is carried from the paper table through the feed rolls into position for writing. It can also be raised or lowered and finally removed from the machine by simply turning either twirler.

THE CARRIAGE RELEASE LEVER **is located just below the left platen twirler.** By drawing it forward the escapement rack is lifted from the ratchet, giving a perfectly free movement of the carriage to the extreme right or left, enabling the operator to easily make a correction or insertion at any point on the line.

The right end of the carriage is shown here with the platen raised out of its position on the carriage. The right paper finger, platen twirler and platen hook perform the same functions as the similar parts at the left end of the carriage.

THE FEED ROLL RELEASE **is pushed backwards when it is desired to release the pressure of the feed rolls upon the platen for the purpose of straightening the paper when in the machine.** This permits the adjustment of the most delicate paper without tearing. The feed roll release is also used when inserting a number of sheets of paper or heavy cards. Before starting to write it is thrown forward into its normal position so that paper will feed straight all the way through.

RIGHT PAPER FINGER
FEED ROLL RELEASE
RIGHT PLATEN TWIRLER
RIBBON WINDER KNOB
PLATEN HOOK

Right end of the carriage with platen slightly raised.

THE RIBBON AND RIBBON MOVEMENT.

The ribbon spools are placed in two dustproof cups at the top of the machine in front, in the easiest and most convenient place to reach. The operation of the machine causes the ribbon to travel slowly from one spool to the other, presenting a new surface to each type, insuring even wear of ribbon and uniform shade in printing. When the ribbon is all wound on to one spool its movement is reversed by moving a small push button on the right of the machine below the ribbon cup. The ribbon can also be readily fed from one spool to the other by revolving the ribbon winder knobs at the top of the cups. The ribbon spools are easily removed and a duplicate pair inserted in a few moments' time when it is desired to change the ribbon. To emphasize a few words or figures by printing them in a different color, simply place a piece of carbon paper of the desired color behind the ribbon guides and it is printed quickly and neatly. The ribbons are easily put on and easily removed. They are used evenly from end to end. The feed is positive and simple, nothing hard to understand or to get out of order.

CLEANING THE TYPE. **The Burnett is the easy to clean typewriter.** The type all lay face upwards in a half circle side by side directly in front of the operator and a few sweeps back and forth of any ordinary type brush cleans them all quickly and completely. No diving down into the heart of the machine, no special attachments or brushes, no cleaning of type one by one, just a few sweeps of the brush on the upturned face of the type and they are all cleaned.

FINISH AND TRIMMINGS.

The Burnett typewriter is built throughout of the finest material that money can buy. All parts are made by fine automatic machinery and adjusted to the thousandth part of an inch. The action and all working parts and bearings are made of the best steel and the frame is of tough gray iron. The body of the machine is enameled with high grade black japan, hand rubbed and baked in ovens at a high temperature, making a smooth glossy and most durable finish. It is tastefully decorated with gold stripings and lettering. All the working parts are first copper plated and then nickel plated and polished. It is beautiful and symmetrical in design and an ornament to the finest office.

OUR NAME DOES NOT APPEAR ON THE MACHINE.

It is simply lettered "Burnett" on the front housing and "Burnett Typewriter Co., Chicago, U. S. A." on the front lower bar. While we would gladly have you show the Burnett typewriter to your friends and business acquaintances and tell them where you got it and what you paid for it, yet the matter rests entirely with you and you may do as you see fit. On our part the transaction is confidential, as our name does not appear on the machine itself, nor on the case in which it is packed.

ANYONE CAN EASILY LEARN TO OPERATE IT.

It has the Universal Keyboard, the easiest of all to learn and the one used in almost all the standard machines, so that if you have been using any other typewriter you can learn to operate the Burnett in a few minutes' time. For the beginner it is the easiest of any to learn. Its working parts are few and simple compared with other machines. Its great visible writing feature prevents all guess work and increases the confidence of the learner wonderfully. The absence of complicated mechanism, the ease of cleaning and changing the ribbon and of performing every other operation that is necessary on a typewriter makes it an ideal machine for the beginner to learn on.

With every machine we send a complete instruction booklet which describes and explains fully the use of all the various parts with diagrams on which every moving part is plainly shown so that anyone can easily and quickly learn to operate the Burnett, even if they have never seen a typewriter in use.

WE CAN ALWAYS FURNISH REPAIRS.

The Burnett is so carefully and strongly constructed that there is little likelihood that repairs will ever be required. Still if by accident or long use any part should break or wear out we can always furnish repairs at about one-half what other typewriter makers charge for similar parts. We do not seek to make a profit on repairs, but charge only enough to cover the cost and handling expense. In case of serious injury to a machine it can be returned to us and we will put it in perfect condition at the lowest possible cost, not more than one-half what other makers ask for similar work.

IT IS THE GREATEST OF ALL MODERN BUSINESS HELPS, **and no business no matter how large or how small can afford to be without it.** Every merchant, manufacturer and professional man, whether doctor, lawyer or minister needs a typewriter and needs it every day. At our wonderfully low price of $22.95 for the Burnett, the best of all typewriters, it is within the reach of all.

IN ORDERING A BURNETT TYPEWRITER, **you can make no mistake. You run no risk. Our sixty days' free trial permits you to put it to every test,** compare it with all other machines and prove to your own satisfaction that it is all that we claim it to be, and if you do not find it so you can return it to us at our expense within that time and we will refund all your money and pay all the transportation charges.

Our ten-year written binding guarantee protects you absolutely against defect in material and workmanship. We guarantee safe delivery and will replace or repair any machine damaged in transit free of charge. We guarantee it to be faster and more accurate than any other machine, to be the most perfect visible writer and to please and satisfy you in every way.

Don't think of buying any typewriter of any make without first giving it a trial and test in comparison with the Burnett.

No. 23E8900 Burnett Visible Typewriter. Shipping weight, 25 pounds. Price........ **$22.95**

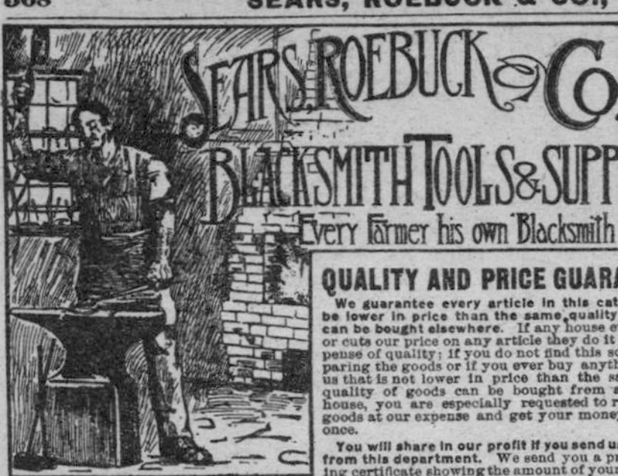

Sears, Roebuck & Co.
Blacksmith Tools & Supplies.
Every Farmer his own Blacksmith.

QUALITY AND PRICE GUARANTEE

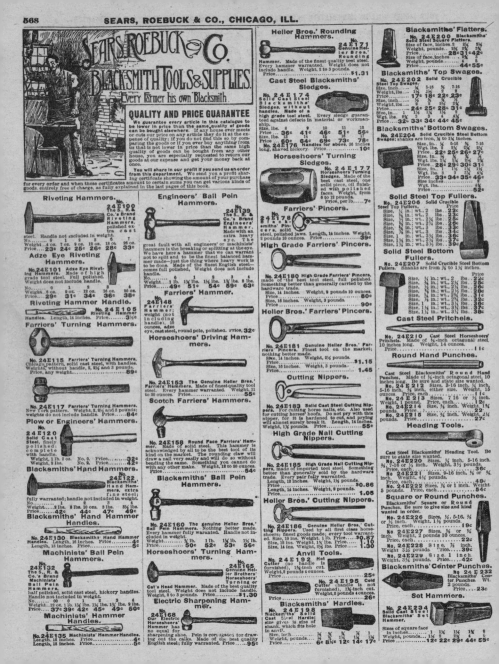

We guarantee every article in this catalogue to be lower in price than the same quality of goods can be bought elsewhere. If any house ever meets or cuts our price on any article they do it at the expense of quality; if you do not find this so by comparing the goods or if you ever buy anything from us that is not lower in price than the same high quality of goods can be bought from any other house, you are especially requested to return our goods at our expense and get your money back at once.

You will share in our profit if you send us an order from this department. We send you a profit sharing certificate showing the amount of your purchase for every order and when these certificates amount to certain sums you can get various kinds of goods, entirely free of charge, as fully explained in the last pages of this book.

Riveting Hammers.

No. 24E100 The S., R. & Co.'s Brand Riveting Hammers, polished extra cast steel. Handle not included in weight.

No.	0	1	2	3	5	7
Weight	4 oz.	7 oz.	9 oz.	12 oz.	18 oz.	26 oz.
Price	23c	24c	25c	26c	28c	33c

Adze Eye Riveting Hammers.

No. 24E101 Adze Eye Riveting Hammers. Made of high grade tool steel. Full polished. Weight does not include handle.

No.	0	1	2	3	4
Weight	6 oz.	9 oz.	12 oz.	16 oz.	20 oz.
Price	29c	31c	34c	36c	38c

Riveting Hammer Handle.

No. 24E105 Riveting Hammer Handles. Length, 14 inches. Price......3½c

Farriers' Turning Hammers.

No. 24E115 Farriers' Turning Hammers, Chicago pattern, solid cast steel, with handles. Weights, without handle, 2, 2½ and 3 pounds. Price, any weight......89c

No. 24E117 Farriers' Turning Hammers, New York pattern. Weight, 2, 2½ and 3 pounds; weights do not include handle. Price......84c

Plow or Engineers' Hammers.

No. 24E120 Solid Cast Steel, finely polished; complete with handle.
Weight, 1 lb. 2 oz. No. 0. Price......32c
Weight, 2 lbs. No. 2. Price......42c

Blacksmiths' Hand Hammers.

No. 24E122 Blacksmiths' Hand Hammers, extra fine steel; fully warranted; handle not included in weight.

No.	1	2	3	4
Weight	2 lbs.	2 lbs. 10 ozs.	3 lbs.	3½ lbs.
Price	42c	44c	47c	49c

Blacksmiths' Hand Hammer Handles.

No. 24E130 Blacksmiths' Hand Hammer Handles. Length, 16 inches. Price......4c
Length, 18 inches. Price......5c

Machinists' Ball Pein Hammers.

No. 24E132 The S., R. & Co.'s Brand Machinists' Ball Pein Hammers, half polished, solid cast steel, hickory handles. Handle not included in weight.

No.	00	0	1	2	3	4
Weight	12 oz.	1 lb.	1¼ lbs.	1½ lbs.	1¾ lbs.	2 lbs.
Price	37c	39c	42c	45c	49c	50c

Machinists' Hammer Handles.

No. 24E135 Machinists' Hammer Handles.
Length, 16 inches. Price......4c
Length, 18 inches. Price......5c

Engineers' Ball Pein Hammers.

No. 24E139 The S., R. & Co.'s Brand Engineers' Hammer. Made with an extra heavy eye. The great fault with all engineers' or machinists' hammers is the breaking or splitting at the eye. We have here a hammer that we can warrant not to split and to be the finest balanced hammer made—just the thing where heavy work is to be done. Made of the finest English steel—comes full polished, Weight does not include handle.

No.	0	1	2	3	4
Weight	1 lb.	1¼ lbs.	1½ lbs.	1¾ lbs.	2 lbs.
Price	49c	51c	54c	59c	63c

Farriers' Hammer.

No. 24E148 Farriers' Hammer; weight (not including handle), 10 ounces, adze eye, cast steel, round pole, polished. Price, 32c

Horseshoers' Driving Hammers.

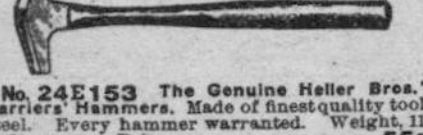

No. 24E153 The Genuine Heller Bros.' Farriers' Hammers. Made of finest quality tool steel. Every hammer warranted. Weight, 11 to 20 ounces. Price......55c

Scotch Farriers' Hammers.

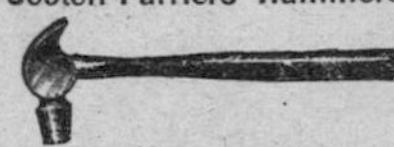

No. 24E158 Round Face Farriers' Hammer. Made of solid steel. This hammer is acknowledged by all to be the best tool of its kind on the market. The rounding claw will draw a nail very easily and will do so without bending the same. Something you cannot do with any other make. Weight, 12 to 20 ounces. Price......54c

Blacksmiths' Ball Pein Hammers.

No. 24E160 The genuine Heller Bros.' Ball Pein Hammers. Nothing better made. Every hammer fully waranted. Handle not included in weight.

Weight	¾ lb.	1 lb.	1¼ lb.	1½ lb.
Price	50c	52c	53c	56c

Horseshoers' Turning Hammers.

No. 24E165 Genuine Heller Brothers' Horseshoers' Turning or Cat's Head Hammer. Made of the best quality tool steel. Weight does not include handle. Weight, 2 to 3 pounds. Price......$1.30

Electric Sharpening Hammer.

No. 24E168 Our Electric Horseshoers' Hammer has no equal for sharpening shoe. Pein is corrugated for drawing out the calks. Made of the best quality English steel; fully warranted. Price......95c

Heller Bros.' Rounding Hammers.

No. 24E171 Genuine Heller Bros.' Rounding Hammer. Made of the finest quality tool steel. Every hammer warranted. Weight does not include handle. Weight, 2 to 3 pounds.
Price......$1.31

Cast Steel Blacksmiths' Sledges.

No. 24E174 Solid Cast Steel Blacksmiths' Sledges, without handles. Made of a high grade tool steel. Every sledge guaranteed against defects in material or workmanship.

Size, lbs.	8	9	10	11	12
Price	36c	41c	46c	51c	56c
Size, lbs.	13	14	15	16	17
Price	60c	64c	69c	73c	78c

No. 24E176 Handles for above, 36 inches long, shaved hickory. Price......10c

Horseshoers' Turning Sledges.

No. 24E177 Horseshoers' Turning Sledges. Made of the best cast steel, one solid piece, oil finished with polished faces. Weight, from 6 to 12 pounds.
Price, per lb......7c

Farriers' Pincers.

No. 24E178 Blacksmiths' Pincers, solid steel, polished jaws. Length, 14 inches. Weight, 2 pounds 10 ounces. Price......39c

High Grade Farriers' Pincers.

No. 24E180 High Grade Farriers' Pincers, made of the best tool steel, full polished. Something better than generally carried by the hardware trade.
Size, 14 inches. Weight, 2 pounds 10 ounces. Price......80c
Size, 16 inches. Weight, 3 pounds. Price......90c

Heller Bros.' Farriers' Pincers.

No. 24E181 Genuine Heller Bros.' Farriers' Pincers. Finest tool on the market; nothing better made.
Size, 14 inches. Weight, 2½ pounds. Price......$1.15
Size, 16 inches. Weight, 3 pounds. Price......1.45

Cutting Nippers.

No. 24E183 Solid Cast Steel Cutting Nippers. For cutting horse nails, etc. Also used for cutting horses' hoofs. Do not pry with this nipper, for it is hardened to cut, and prying will almost surely break it. Length, 14 inches. Weight, 1¾ pounds. Price......55c

High Grade Nail Cutting Nippers.

No. 24E185 High Grade Nail Cutting Nippers, made of imported tool steel. Something better than generally sold by the hardware trade. Every pair fully warranted.
Length, 12 inches. Weight, 1½ pounds. Price......$0.86
Length, 14 inches. Weight, 2 pounds. Price......1.05

Heller Bros.' Cutting Nippers.

No. 24E186 Genuine Heller Bros.' Cutting Nippers. Used by all first class horseshoers; finest goods made; every tool warranted. Size, 10 ins. Weight, 1 lb. Price......$0.87
Size, 12 ins. Weight, 1¾ lbs. Price......1.10
Size, 14 ins. Weight, 2½ lbs. Price......1.30

Anvil Tools.

No. 24E192 Hot Cutter (no handle is furnished), 1⅜-inch cut. Weight, 2 pounds 4 ounces.
Price......25c

No. 24E195 Cold Cutter (handle is not furnished), 1⅜-inch cut. Weight, 2 pounds 4 ounces.
Price......26c

Blacksmiths' Hardies.

No. 24E198 Blacksmiths' Solid Cast Steel Hardie; size given is size of shank, which fits hole in anvil.

Size, inch	½	⅝	¾	⅞	1
Weight, pounds	½	¾	1⅛	1¼	1½
Price	6c	8½c	12c	14c	17c

Blacksmiths' Flatters.

No. 24E200 Blacksmiths' Solid Steel Square Flatters.

Size of face, inches	2	2¼	2½
Weight, pounds	2⅜	2¾	3¾
Price	28c	31c	42c
Size of face, inches	2¾	3	
Weight, pounds	4	5	
Price	44c	55c	

Blacksmiths' Top Swages.

No. 24E202 Solid Crucible Steel Top Swages.

Size, inch		¼	5-16	⅜	7-16
Weight, lbs.		1½	1½	2	2
Price		17c	18c	22c	23c
Size, inch		½	⅝	¾	⅞
Weight, lbs.		2	2	2½	2¾
Price		24c	25c	28c	31c
Size, in.	1	1⅛	1¼	1½	2
Wgt. lbs.	2¾	3	3	4	4½
Price	32c	33c	34c	44c	45c

Blacksmiths' Bottom Swages.

No. 24E204 Solid Crucible Steel Bottom Swages; shanks are iron, ⅞ to 1¼ inches.

Size, in.	¼	5-16	⅜	7-16
Wgt. lbs.	2	2¼	2¼	2¼
Price	22c	25c	26c	27c
Size, in.	½	⅝	¾	⅞
Wgt. lbs.	2¼	2¼	2½	2¾
Price	28c	29c	30c	31c
Size, in.	1	1⅛	1¼	1½
Wgt. lbs.	3	3	3¼	4½
Price	33c	34c	35c	46c
Size inches				2
Wgt. lbs.				4¾
Price				52c

Solid Steel Top Fullers.

No. 24E206 Solid Crucible Steel Top Fullers.

Size	Weight	Price
¼ in.	2 lbs.	22c
⅜ in.	2 lbs.	23c
½ in.	2¼ lbs.	25c
⅝ in.	2¼ lbs.	26c
¾ in.	3 lbs.	33c
⅞ in.	3 lbs.	34c
1 in.	3¼ lbs.	36c
1⅛ in.	3¼ lbs.	37c
1¼ in.	3½ lbs.	39c

Solid Steel Bottom Fullers.

No. 24E207 Solid Crucible Steel Bottom Fullers. Shanks are from ⅞ to 1¼ inches.

Size	Weight	Price
¼ in.	2 lbs.	22c
⅜ in.	2¼ lbs.	25c
½ in.	2¼ lbs.	26c
⅝ in.	2½ lbs.	28c
¾ in.	2¾ lbs.	31c
⅞ in.	2¾ lbs.	32c
1 in.	3¼ lbs.	36c
1⅛ in.	3¼ lbs.	37c
1¼ in.	3¼ lbs.	38c

Cast Steel Pritchels.

No. 24E210 Cast Steel Horseshoers' Pritchels. Made of ⅝-inch octagonal steel, 10 inches long. Weight, 14 ounces.
Price......11c

Round Hand Punches.

Cast Steel Blacksmiths' Round Hand Punches. Made of ⅝-inch octagonal steel, 10 inches long. Be sure and state size wanted.

No. 24E212 Sizes, 3-16 inch, ¼ inch, 5-16 inch, ⅜ inch, either size. Weight, 15 ounces. Price, each......11c

No. 24E213 Sizes, 7-16 or ½ inch. Weight, 1 pound. Price, each......12c

No. 24E214 Size, ⅝ inch. Weight, 1¾ pounds. Price......22c

No. 24E215 Size, ¾ inch. Weight, 2¼ pounds. Price......27c

Heading Tools.

Cast Steel Blacksmiths' Heading Tool. Be sure to state size wanted.

No. 24E220 Sizes, ¼ inch, 5-16 inch, ⅜, 7-16 or ½ inch. Weight, 3½ pounds. Price, each......36c

No. 24E221 Sizes, 9-16 inch, ⅝ or ¾ inch. Weight, 4½ pounds. Price, each......48c

No. 24E222 Sizes, ⅞ or 1 inch. Weight 5 pounds. Price, each......54c

Square or Round Punches.

Blacksmiths' Square or Round Punches. Be sure to give size and kind wanted in order.

No. 24E226 Sizes, ¼, 5-16, ⅜ or ½ inch. Weight, 1¾ pounds. Price, each......19c

No. 24E227 Sizes, ⅝ or ¾ inch. Weight, 2 pounds 10 ounces. Price, each......22c

No. 24E228 Size, ⅞ inch. Weight 3½ pounds. Price......39c

No. 24E229 Size, 1 inch. Weight, 3¾ pounds. Price......42c

Blacksmiths' Center Punches.

No. 24E232 Blacksmiths' Center Punches. Wt. 2 pounds. Price......23c

Set Hammers.

No. 24E234 Solid Cast Steel Blacksmiths' Set Hammer.

Sizes of square face in inches	1	1¼	1½	1¾	2
Weight, pounds	1⅛	2	2¾	4	5
Price	12c	22c	29c	44c	55c

OUR $39.90 SET OF BLACKSMITHS' TOOLS.

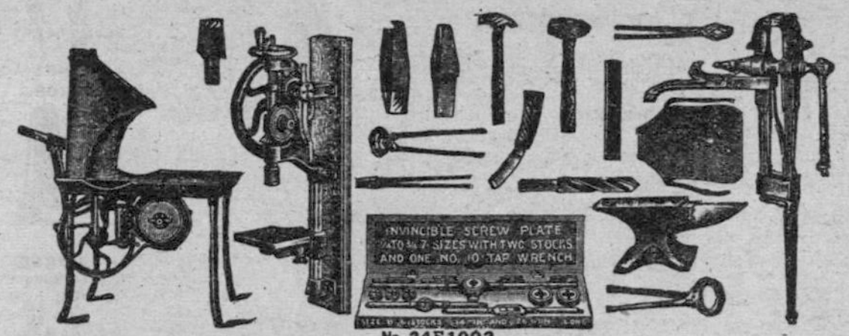

No. 24E1002

THE ANVIL. We furnish our 100-pound American solid wrought anvil with steel face, one of the best anvils made in this or any other country. The body and base are wrought iron; face and horn are steel welded together by an electric process which makes practically one solid piece. We warrant this anvil against defects or being too hard or soft.

CUTTING NIPPERS; are made of a solid piece of steel, no welds, length, 14 inches. **Farriers' Pincers** are the V. & B. brand, made from one solid piece of steel; length, 14 inches. **Flat Lip Tongs** are 22 inches long and are drop forged from one piece of steel; no welds to break. **Bolt Tongs** will hold bolts of iron 5-16 to ½-inch in diameter, are drop forged thus doing away with all welds. **Horse Rasp** is our S., R. & Co.'s make, is double faced, hand cut and is 14 inches long. **Hot Cutter** has a 1⅜-inch cut and weighs 2 pounds 2 ounces. **Cold Cutter** has a 1⅜-inch cut, and weighs 2 pounds 14 ounces.

To accommodate our customers we will allow them to omit any article in this outfit and substitute any article (pertaining to blacksmiths' supplies only) in exchange at our regular catalogue prices for article omitted, also for new article selected.

No. 24E1002 Price for complete outfit as illustrated and described........ **$39.90**

ALL TOOLS ARE A1, the best we carry, and are guaranteed to be made of high grade material of perfect workmanship. We replace any tool found defective, free of charge. A set suitable for any blacksmith shop.

THE FORGE. We furnish a lever forge with a half hood; size of fan, 12 inches; height of forge, 30 inches; size of hearth, 35x23 inches. Weight, 145 pounds. It is the best finished and most perfect motion lever forge made. Will produce a welding heat on 3-inch iron in seven minutes.

THE DRILL. We furnish our No. 10 ball bearing post drill, one of the best drills we carry. The shaft and spindle are made of best grade tool steel. Has our improved third gear. The spindle is supplied with steel balls which add greatly to the running of the drill. Takes drills with ½-inch round shank. Weight, 110 pounds. For full description of this drill see No. 24E812.

THE VISE. We furnish a solid wrought iron vise with steel face and jaws; has machine cut screw; an A1 vise in every respect. Weight, 50 pounds.

THE SCREW PLATE. We furnish our invincible screw plate known to all mechanics as being the most perfect thread cutting tool ever invented. Guaranteed to cut a perfect thread with a single cut. The sizes are ¼, ⅜, ½, ⅝ and ¾-inch; five taps and five pairs of dies. Comes complete in a heavy oak case, as shown in illustration.

THE BLACKSMITHS' APRON. Our regular $1.03 split leather apron, extra large size complete with straps.

Farriers' Knife is the imported IXL Wostenholm. **Hardie** is 1¼-inch and fits the anvil. **Hand Hammer** weighs 3 pounds, is made of best grade tool steel. **Farriers' Hammer** is our S., R. & Co.'s brand, and weighs 1 lb., handle included.

THE DRILLS, of which we furnish eight in number, size ⅛, 3-16, ¼, 5-16, ⅜, ½, ⅝ and ¾ have ½-inch round shank and are made to fit the drill. They are what is called the Morse pattern twist drill and are guaranteed against flaws or defects in workmanship.

OUR $52.95 SPECIAL SET OF BLACKSMITHS' TOOLS.

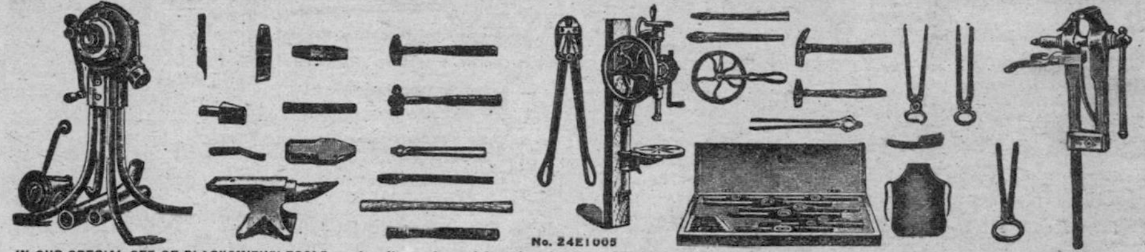

No. 24E1005

IN OUR SPECIAL SET OF BLACKSMITHS' TOOLS we show the most complete up to date outfit sold by anyone. A set that is complete and large enough for any shop. All tools are high grade and the most improved patterns on the market.

THE BLOWER is our Tiger 20th Century, complete with tuyere iron. A blower that will give a blast equal to a 48-inch bellows.

THE DRILL is our large 125-pound drill, one of the best drills we carry. It has a self feed attachment, is double geared, drills to the center of a 15-inch circle, holds round shank drills and will bore up to 1¼-inch hole.

THE VISE is our solid box wrought vise. Weight, 60 pounds.

THE SCREW PLATE is our invincible full mounted plate, each die having a separate holder. Cuts seven sizes, ¼ to ¾-inch. Complete in hardwood case.

THE ANVIL is our American wrought. Weight, 125 pounds.

DRILLS. We furnish ten high grade round shank bits that fit the above drill. Sizes, 3-16, ¼, 5-16, ⅜, 7-16, ½, ⅝, ¾, ⅞ and 1-inch. One hot cutter, size 1⅜ inches; one cold cutter, size 1⅜ inches; one hardie that fits anvil; one pair farriers' tongs, 14-inch; one pair flat tongs, 20-inch; one pair flat tongs 22-inch; one pair bolt tongs, 5-16 to ½-inch; one pair bolt tongs, ½ to ¾ inch; one steel blacksmiths' sledge with handle; one pair Maud S farriers' pincers, 14 inch, solid steel; one pair nail cutting nippers, 12-inch, solid steel; one electric sharpening hammer, weight, 2 or 2½ pounds; one blacksmiths' hand hammer, weight 3 pounds; one farriers' hammer, Cincinnati pattern, weight 14 to 18 ounces; one Keystone adjustable farriers' knife; one Sears, Roebuck & Co. horse rasp, 14 inches long; one large size blacksmiths' apron; one pair high grade hoof parers, 14 inches long; one pair Randall bolt clippers, cuts up to ½-inch bolt, nothing better made; one riveting hammer, all steel, weight, 9 ounces; one all steel toe knife; one tire measuring wheel, all steel, drop forged.

No. 24E1005 Price for complete outfit as illustrated and described.......... **$52.95**

THE ACME FORGES.—PORTABLE LEVER TYPE.

$4.95

The line of Acme Forges, illustrated on this and the following pages, will be found to contain those of suitable capacity for all classes of blacksmith work. A close examination of the several designs will clearly show that each individual machine is particularly adapted to the requirements for which it is recommended. A careful study of all the desirable features of a forge for a given service has been made and the greatest possible number embodied. In the construction of the Acme forges only the best material and workmanship enter. The greatest accuracy is constantly insisted upon in the erection and assembling of the machines, which results in all parts being brought into the closest relation to each other. The most approved methods of securing them are employed. In consequence there is no gradual rattling loose or becoming wabbly after the machines are used for a time. All these deficiencies, common to cheap forges, will be found to be entirely avoided. **NOTICE: To prevent fire pan from cracking always put in a layer of clay before starting fire. This applies to all forges.**

Our $4.95 Portable Forge Leader.

We believe we are headquarters for everything desirable in portable forges. We have made our contracts with several of the very largest and most reliable manufacturers in the country, concerns who are strictly headquarters for the manufacture of the highest grade portable forges on the market. There are many cheap, inferior forges offered, and some of our competitors may even attempt to meet or cut our prices; but when a forge is offered at within 10 or 20 per cent of the price we are able to name, you can depend upon it you are not getting the same grade of work. There is perhaps no more necessary or economic machine on a farm than one of our strictly high grade portable forges. In one year it will save its cost ten times over in time, to say nothing of the saving in blacksmiths' bills.

At $4.95 we offer you a strictly high grade, fully guaranteed forge, which you could not duplicate elsewhere, in a wholesale way, at anywhere near what we ask for it. We are able to get the price so low ($4.95) that every farmer in selecting a forge should order this in preference to a cheaper one. The motion is a very simple device. It has a self acting ratchet; no springs or anything to get out of order. It is made from the very best material. The lever is connected with a segment of gears which speeds the driving wheel up to a very high speed. It requires a very slight movement of the lever to get the strongest blast. Having but three legs, it stands very firmly on an uneven foundation, and is purposely made for the work we claim. Height of forge, 30 inches; hearth, 21 inches in diameter; fan, 8 inches. Weight, 80 pounds. This is the largest forge we ever saw offered at anything like the price, and we would ask you to compare the size of hearth and fan with other forges at about the same price, and draw your own conclusions.

NOTICE **We sell more forges than any other one concern in the U. S. Quality and price have done the business.**

WE WANT **to sell another 5,000 of these $4.95 forges during the coming year,** and with the expectation that we will sell this number, have reduced our price to $4.95. By making our contract on this basis, we were able to get the price down to about the actual cost of material and labor. This forge is accepted by the railroad companies at second class freight rate.

No. 24E1006 Price.. **$4.95**

Our $3.75 Forge.

Remember when you buy a forge from us, all sizes, weights, etc., will correspond with catalogue description. We guarantee weights and sizes to be just as represented or money refunded.

$3.75

NOTICE—There are concerns who advertise a forge similar to this as a great bargain, at a much higher price than we ask for it. While it is a good forge for the money, we show several forges that are equally as low, if not greater bargains than this one. We have a large stock and can make prompt shipments in any quantity.

No. 24E1009 Sears, Roebuck & Co.'s Portable Forge is especially built for farmers' and planters' use or for light repairing. Blacksmiths should buy a larger forge. This lever motion forge has pipe legs. Has 8-inch fan. Stands 30 inches high. Hearth is 18 inches in diameter. Will produce a welding heat on fine iron in five minutes. Compare weight, size of fan, etc., with any other make and you will see this is the cheapest forge for the size sold by anyone. Weight, 65 pounds. Price.... **$3.75**

Our Acme No. 352 Forge.

Only $6.70 for this Splendid Forge.

$6.70

No. 24E1012 This forge is of the same high grade as our No. 24E1009, but with hood entirely closed. The large sliding door in front and smaller door in rear affords convenience in handling long bars. The escape of sparks, fumes and smoke is effectually prevented and this type of forge is particularly adapted to places where combustible material is lying about or where bright metal work is attacked by fumes from the fire. Hearth, 18 inches diameter; fan, 8 inches, height, 30 inches. Weight, 75 pounds. Price.............................. **$6.70**

OUR QUALITY and PRICE GUARANTEE

WE GUARANTEE OUR PRICES for like quality to be lower than any other house in America. In comparing our catalogue with other houses, when another house quotes as low or a lower price than we, we guarantee that you will find a wide difference in quality in our favor. If you send us an order and do not find this difference in quality in our favor in every instance, you can return the goods to us at our expense, and we will immediately return your money.

Acme No. 200 Forge.

We would call your special attention to our No. 200 Acme Forge, inasmuch as we have here the best forge for the money sold by anyone. Notice the make up, size and weight, then compare it with any forge on the market and see if you are not getting 33⅓ per cent more forge for your money than you can get elsewhere. This is a forge of our own design, is made up in quantities of 1,000 forges at a time, which has reduced the cost of manufacture to a minimum. It is large enough for general blacksmithing, and as a forge for the farm or ranch it has no equal. Has a perfect tuyere iron and blast and the size and shape of hearth permits ample room for coal and to lay tools upon. The fan is 12½ inches in diameter; hearth is 36x25 inches, stands 30 inches high, and weighs 180 pounds without crating. Will produce welding heat on 3-inch iron in five minutes.

No. 24E1014 Price, with shield... **$8.75**
No. 24E1015 Price, with half hood, as per illustration, without water tank **$9.95**

If wanted with water tank, as shown in illustration, add 90 cents to above price.

Acme No. 165 Forge.

No. 24E1020 **This forge is heavily and durably built.** The proportions adapt it to general blacksmiths' use up to the heaviest kind of work. It is furnished with the latest type of ball tuyere iron with improved fire pot, combining center and side blast, which is able to stand continuous heavy work without burning out; an improved steel friction clutch is used. This is a high class forge in every detail. Size of hearth, 46x33½ inches; fan, 14½ inches. Height, 30 inches; length over all, 54 inches. Weight, 300 pounds.

Price, with coal box........ **$15.85**
Price, with coal box and water tank **16.65**

Tiger Steel Forge, $11.95.

No. 24E1021 **In this forge we have the only up to date blower on the market. As a rivet forge or to be used in boiler or repair shop it has no equal.** It is provided with the Royal style of blower, which has the flat, straight cut gears, insuring double the life of bevel or worm gears, which combined with steel shafts makes it by far the best forge made by anyone. The gear case is oiltight and dustproof, permitting the gears to run in a bath of oil. We use no belts, clutches or ratchets. The hearth is of sheet steel, making the forge light and neat in appearance. Can be quickly and easily taken apart for transportation, and its extreme lightness and simplicity make it a most desirable move-about forge. The crank turns to right or left as suits operator. Will give a welding heat on 3½-inch iron in about ten minutes. Has 18-inch hearth, 9-inch fan. Height, 30 inches over all. Weight, 70 pounds. Price, .. **$11.95**

Acme Forge No. 300.

This forge is to be used in large blacksmith shops, plow and railroad shops, etc., where heavy work is done and a first class forge is wanted. In this forge we have combined our Tiger blower with a high grade cast forge, which combination makes the best outfit sold by anyone. The fan is extra large and the blast is direct from blower to fire. Easy to operate and equal in volume to any demand required. Size of hearth, 33½x46 inches; diameter of fan, 12 inches; height, 30 inches; length over all, 54 inches. Weight, 275 pounds.

No. 24E1024 Price with either coal or water box **$16.95**
No. 24E1025 Price, with both coal and water box........ **$17.95**

Royal Steel Forge.

Our Royal Steel Forge is designed for boilermakers, bridge builders, quarries, railways, well drillers, or for any outside work where the hood is not needed. Our Famous Royal style of blower, with cut gears fitted in oil tight case, is used for furnishing the blast, the crank of which turns to right or left, affording a blast as steady and strong as a power blower. A welding heat on 4-inch iron can easily be made in about 10 minutes. This blower itself can be revolved half way around and operated by helper without his standing in the way of the smith. This feature every smith will appreciate. Its ease of operation and noiseless mechanism, with no belts, ratchet or clutch, recommend it over others. For shipment or transportation, it is easily and quickly taken apart and all parts packed in its own hearth, which forms a strong shipping case. Size, 30x36 inches; diameter of fan, 10 inches; height, 30 inches. Length over all, 44 inches. Weight, 210 pounds.

No. 24E1027 Price, without water tank........ **$25.00**
No. 24E1027½ Price, with water tank........ **$28.00**

Cast Iron Swage Blocks.

Only 2¾ cents per pound. Made of the best pig iron, used by blacksmiths in shaping iron in different designs.

No. 24E1028 No. 1. Size, 3⅝x10x14. Weight, about 110 pounds. Price, per pound... **2¾c**
No. 24E1029 No. 2. Size, 3⅞x11x15. Weight, about 135 pounds. Price, per pound........ **2¾c**
No. 24E1030 No. 3. Size, 4¼x11x15. Weight, about 155 pounds. Price, per pound........ **2¾c**

Cast Iron Leveling Blocks.

No. 24E1031 Especially intended for plow work. The blocks are made of superior pig iron and are accurately planed on one side. To ascertain the weight, figure 1 pound to 4 cubic inches. Come 1½ to 3 inches thick by 14 to 24 inches wide and 18 to 30 inches long.

Price, per pound........ **2¾c**

Steel Harrow Teeth.

No. 24E1032 **Give length when ordering.**

Size, inches	Wt. per doz. lbs.	Per doz.
½x8	6½	**20c**
½x8½	7	**22c**
½x9	7¼	**23c**
9-16x8½	9	**28c**
9-16x9	9½	**30c**
⅝x8½	11	**32c**
⅝x9	11¼	**33c**
⅝x9½	11½	**34c**
⅝x10	12	**36c**
¾x10	17	**51c**
¾x11	21	**63c**

Lightning Plow Shares.

Lightning Plow Share, fully welded and point finished. Perfected to meet the demand for a fully welded plow share, that can be quickly and easily fitted to the different make of plows, thus saving the hard work of welding on the landside and finishing the point. The Lightning share can be fitted to the angle of more plows than any other welded share in the market. The landside extends at the heel and is long enough to cut to fit any plow. Either right or left hand. Be sure and state kind wanted. Average weight, 13 pounds.

No. 24E1033 Made of crucible cast steel.
Price, 12-inch........ **$1.09**
14-inch........ **1.29**
16-inch........ **1.39**

No. 24E1034 Made of soft center steel.
Price, 12-inch........ **$1.56**
14-inch........ **1.67**
16-inch........ **1.79**

Plow Shares.

They are made of the best soft center and solid crucible cast steel. Perfect shape with an upset edge, and can be easily fitted to any plow. Be sure and state right or left hand. Average weight, 9 pounds.

No. 24E1035 No. 1 Shares. For old ground plows, made from soft center steel.
12-inch. Weight, 7¾ pounds. Price........ **76c**
14-inch. Weight, 8¾ pounds. Price........ **89c**
16-inch. Weight, 9½ pounds. Price........ **99c**

No. 24E1036 No. 2 Shares. For old ground plows, made from crucible steel.
12-inch. Weight, 7 pounds. Price........ **59c**
14-inch. Weight, 8¾ pounds. Price........ **73c**
16-inch. Weight, 9½ pounds. Price........ **77c**

Landside Plates.

No. 24E1037 No. 1 Landside Plates, ready for use, made of soft center steel.
14-inch. Weight, 5¼ pounds. Price........ **55c**
16-inch. Weight, 5¾ pounds. Price........ **60c**

No. 24E1038 No. 2 Landside Plates, ready for use, made of crucible cast steel.
14-inch. Weight, 5¼ pounds. Price........ **45c**
16-inch. Weight, 5¾ pounds. Price........ **47c**

Plow Anvil.

No. 24E298 Plow Anvil, not cast iron, but solid cast steel; oil finished, polished face. Weight, 4 pounds. Price........ **32c**

Blacksmiths' Cones or Mandrels.

No. 24E1040 Made of the best pig iron. No flaws.

Size	H'ght ins.	Diam. at base, inches	Diam. at top, inches	W'ght about lbs.	Price, per lb.
1½	40	10	1	105	3¼c
2	48	12	1	120	3¼c
3	52	14	1	160	3¼c
4	54	16	2	240	3¼c

The above are estimated weights and may vary five pounds more or less. We charge for actual weight.

New Green River Shoeing Vise and Bolt Header.

The vise, which drops open when not in use, forms both sharp and straight calks, the forming die being of tool steel of proper shape. The swaging plate for sharp calks is furnished with a full number of grooves for large and small calks. It can be placed so that the grooves run either way as may be preferred. Size, ⅜, 5-16, ⅜, 7-16, ½, ⅝, ¾ inch. Any length up to 24 inches.

No. 24E1045 Price, complete for shoeing and bolt heading........ **$10.25**
No. 24E1046 Price, for shoeing only (without bolt heading attachment)... **$9.50**

Blacksmiths' Aprons.

No. 24E1050 Split Leather Aprons. Size, 26x34 inches. Price.. **89c**

Horse-shoers' Aprons.

No. 24E1052 Standard Split Leather Aprons. Our own special brand. Size, 28x38 inches. Price.... **$1.02**

No. 24E1054 Pigskin Aprons. Size, 28x38 inches. Price........ **$1.72**

Peace's Spoke Tenoning Machine.

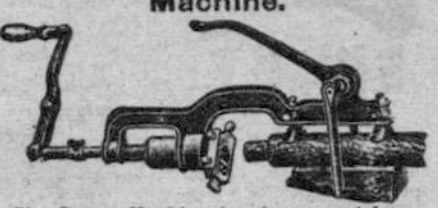

The Peace Machine has been used for last ten years with general satisfaction. made in the most workmanlike manner castings being malleable iron and the a head made extra heavy. The knife starts o[illegible] blank of spokes and centers perfectly. Th[illegible] auger is kept cutting by force of the spr[illegible] Can be used on any size spoke or disc of wh[illegible] and is readily applied without removing fro[illegible] where spokes are driven. Cuts any size fro[illegible] ¾ to 1¾. Weight, 8 pounds.

No. 24E1060 Price, without felloe attachment........ **$7.42**
No. 24E1061 Price, with felloe attachment........ **8.69**

Ideal Shear.

No. 24E1068 **Ideal Shear for Blacksmiths' and Workers in Iron.** The knives are 5 inches long, are double edge and reversible and will therefore do double the work of a single knife. This machine will cut a bar of common iron ¼x2 inches or 3-16x2½ inches or ⅛x5 inches. It is the biggest little machine on the market, weighing less than 100 pounds. Has few parts, is strong, compact and handy. The lowest price machine for its capacity sold by anyone. Price........ **$6.25**
Extra knives. Price, each........ **.30**

Ideal Punch.

No. 24E1069 Ideal Punch, an improvement over all others in its line. The most powerful punch of its size and price ever made. It is not a toy, but a high grade machine. A strong, durable and compact punch with no outlaying parts to get out of order. One die plate and five punches go with each machine. Size punches, ⅛, ¼, 5-16, ⅜ and 7-16 inch. Made of a high grade tool steel. Will punch a ⅜-inch hole in ⅛-inch iron or 7-16-inch in ¼-inch. Will work four inches from edge. Weight, 120 pounds complete.

The Big Little Punch. Price, complete........ **$10.00**

Dole's Hub Boxing Machine.

The old standard Dole's Hub Boxing Machine with **Edwards' Improved Open Feed and Gauge Plate.** The No. 1 machine is suitable for buggy and carriage work and will grasp hubs from 2 to 6 inches in diameter. No. 2 is suitable for buggy, carriage and wagon work, and will grasp hubs from 2 to 12 inches in diameter. The No. 3 is suitable for the heaviest class of wagon work, and will take hubs from 2½ to 15 inches in diameter. Weight, about 25 pounds.

No. 24E1077 No. 1. Price **$16.25**
No. 24E1078 No. 2. Price **18.40**
No. 24E1079 No. 3. Price **19.50**

We furnish with the Nos. 1 and 2 an extra mandrel made lighter at the end, with an extra set of small bits, which makes them suitable for light class of work, for $2.40 extra.

BLACKSMITHS' BELLOWS.

No. 24E1080 **Blacksmiths' Bellows,** standard patterns. We use cowhide leather, prepared especially for our use, and we guarantee it to wear equal to any made. We use whitewood, basswood and pine in the wood work, which is kiln dried, making it perfectly dry, that it may not be affected by the climate. The weight of our bellows is about as follows. They may vary a little, but not much:

Width, inches....	24	26	28
Weight, pounds...	30	35	40
Price........	**$2.51**	**$2.87**	**$3.17**
Width, inches.....	30	32	34
Weight, pounds...	45	50	60
Price........	**$3.26**	**$3.56**	**$4.12**
Width, inches.....	35	38	40
Weight, pounds...	68	78	100
Price........	**$4.61**	**$5.12**	**$5.87**

No. 24E1084 **Extra Long Pattern Bellows.**

Width, inches	34	36	38	40
Weight, pounds	73	87	105	125
Price.....	**$5.37**	**$5.47**	**$6.75**	**$7.35**
Width, inches.	44	46	48	
Weight, pounds	147	200	225	
Price......	**$10.42**	**$12.43**	**$14.35**	

Tuyere Iron.

No. 24E1089 **Single Duck's Nest Tuyere Iron.** Weight, 12 lbs. Price.... **32c**

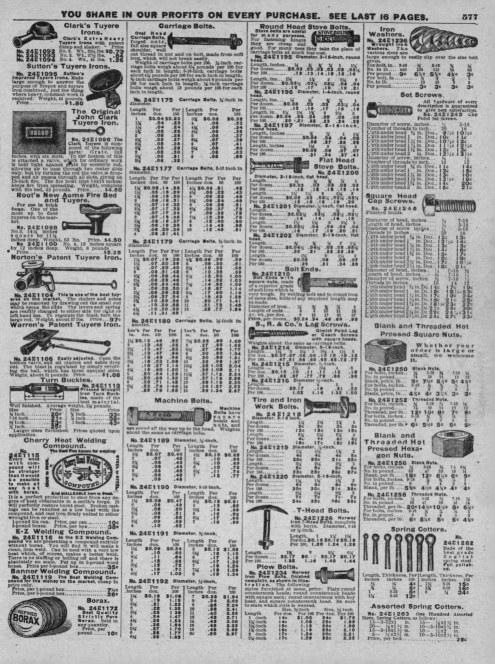

Clark's Tuyere Irons.

Clark's Extra Heavy Tuyere Irons with patent dump and shaker. Price

No.	Size	Weight	Price
No. 24E1092	No. 2.	Wt., 22½ lbs.	$0.73
No. 24E1093	No. 3.	Wt., 27½ lbs.	.84
No. 24E1094	No. 4.	Wt., 45 lbs.	1.26

Sutton's Tuyere Irons.

No. 24E1095 Sutton's Improved Tuyere Irons. Made large enough to answer the purpose of firepot and tuyere iron combined, just the thing where heavy, constant work is required. Weight, 44 pounds. Price........ ....$1.80

The Original John Clark Tuyere Iron.

No. 24E1096 The Clark Tuyere is composed of the following parts: Grate, 3x8 inches, with six slots. To the bottom of this is attached a valve, which for ordinary work is held tight against grate by eccentric rod, allowing air to pass through two center slots only, but by turning the rod the valve is dropped and air passes through all slots, giving an 18-inch fire. The fire bowl (size 14x18 inches) keeps fire from spreading. Weight, complete with fire bed, 45 pounds. Price......$4.60

Root's New Acme Fire Bed and Tuyere.

For use in brick forge. One of the most up to date tuyeres on the market.

No. 24E1098 No. 3. 14¼ inches square by 11½ inches deep. Weight, 63 lbs. Price, $4.50

No 24E1100 No. 4. 18 inches square by 12 inches deep. Weight, 8 pounds. Price......................$5.25

Norton's Patent Tuyere Iron.

No. 24E1104 This is one of the best tuyeres on the market. The cinders and ashes may be removed by drawing out the small rod which opens the slide. The levers and spring are readily changed to either side for right or left hand use. To regulate the blast, turn the large rod. Weight, about 27 lbs. Price....97c

Warren's Patent Tuyere Iron.

No. 24E1106 Easily adjusted. Open the bottom valve, and all cinders and ashes drop out. The blast is regulated by simply revolving the ball, which has three unequal sides. Weight, about 31 pounds. Price........$1.08

Turn Buckles.

No. 24E1113 Pressed Wrought Iron Turn Buckles, made of the best material. Well finished. Average weight, 2½ pounds.

Size	Price	Size	Price
⅜ inch	20c	¾ inch	33c
7-16 inch	21c	⅞ inch	38c
½ inch	23c	1 inch	43c
⅝ inch	25c		

Larger sizes furnished. Prices quoted upon application.

Cherry Heat Welding Compound.

No. 24E1115 Every weld with compound will be stronger than it would be possible to make at any heat with borax. It is a perfect protection to steel from any degree of heat obtainable in a smith's forge. It will perfectly restore burnt steel. Broken castings can be reunited at a low heat with the compound, and cast iron firmly united to either wrought iron or steel.

1-pound tin can. Price, per can..........10c
5-pound boxes. Price, per box..... ....38c

E-Z Welding Compound.

No. 24E1116 In the E-Z Welding Compound we are presenting a compound entirely without borax. You will find it will make a clean, firm weld. Can be used with a very low heat which, of course, makes a better weld. There is no sluffing or boiling off and there is absolutely no scale. Put up in 5-pound wood boxes. Price per 5-pound box..............35c

Banner Welding Compound.

No. 24E1119 The Best Welding Compound for the money on the market, cheap in price only.

Price, per 1-pound box....................7½c
Price, per 5-pound box....................26c

Borax.

No. 24E1172 Best Quality Strictly Pure Borax. Sold in any quantity. Price, per pound.......10c

Carriage Bolts.

Oval Head Carriage Bolts, forged nuts, full size square shoulder, well cut thread in nut and on bolt, made from soft iron, which will not break easily.

Weight of carriage bolts per 100. ¼-inch carriage bolts weigh about 2½ pounds per 100 for each inch in length; 5-16-inch carriage bolts about 4¼ pounds per 100 for each inch in length; ⅜-inch carriage bolts weigh about 6 pounds per 100 for each inch in length; ½-inch carriage bolts weigh about 13 pounds per 100 for each inch in length.

No. 24E1175 Carriage Bolts, ¼-inch in diameter.

Length inches	Per doz.	Per 100	Length inches	Per doz.	Per 100
1	$0.04	$0.23	3¾	$0.06	$0.32
1¼	.04	.23	4	.06	.33
1½	.04	.24	4¼	.06	.34
1¾	.05	.25	4½	.06	.35
2	.05	.26	5	.06	.37
2¼	.05	.27	5½	.07	.39
2½	.05	.28	6	.07	.41
2¾	..05	.29	6½	.08	.60
3	.05	.30	7	.08	.63
3¼	.05	.31	8	.08	.68
3½	.06	.32			

No. 24E1177 Carriage Bolts, 5-16 inch in diameter.

Length inches	Per doz.	Per 50	Per 100	Length inches	Per doz.	Per 50	Per 100
1¼	$0.05	.14	.28	4¼	$0.08	.21	.42
1½	.05	.15	.29	4½	.08	.22	.43
1¾	.06	.15	.30	5	.09	.23	.46
2	.06	.16	.31	5½	.09	.24	.48
2¼	.07	.16	.32	6	.09	.26	.51
2½	.07	.17	.33	6½	.09	.37	.73
2¾	.07	.17	.34	7	.09	.38	.75
3	.07	.18	.36	7½	.10	.39	.78
3¼	.08	.19	.37	8	.12	.40	.80
3½	.08	.19	.38	9	.14	.43	.85
3¾	.08	.20	.39	10	.15	.46	.91
4	.08	.21	.41				

No. 24E1179 Carriage Bolts, ⅜-inch in diameter.

Length inches	Per doz.	Per 50	Per 100	Length inches	Per doz.	Per 50	Per 100
1¼	$0.07	.19	.38	4¾	$0.09	.30	.59
1½	.07	.20	.39	5	.09	.30	.61
1¾	.07	.20	.40	5½	.10	.33	.65
2	.08	.21	.42	6	.10	.35	.69
2¼	.08	.22	.44	6½	.13	.50	1.00
2½	.08	.23	.46	7	.14	.52	1.03
2¾	.09	.24	.48	7½	.14	.55	1.09
3	.09	.25	.50	8	.15	.57	1.14
3¼	.09	.26	.52	8½	.17	.60	1.19
3½	.09	.27	.54	9	.18	.63	1.25
3¾	.10	.28	.56	10	.20	.71	1.41
4	.10	.29	.58	11	.21	.73	1.45
4¼	.10	.30	.60	12	.22	.77	1.54
4½	.11	.31	.62				

No. 24E1180 Carriage Bolts, ½-inch in ameter.

Len'h in.	Per doz.	Per 50	Per 100	Len'h in.	Per doz.	Per 50	Per 100
1½	$0.13	.46	.92	7½	$0.25	.80	1.60
2	.13	.46	.92	8	.27	.85	1.69
2¼	.13	.47	.93	8½	.27	.89	1.77
2½	.13	.47	.94	9	.30	.92	1.84
3	.18	.49	.98	9½	.30	.96	1.91
3½	.18	.53	1.06	10	.32	.99	1.97
4	.19	.57	1.14	10½	.32	1.02	2.04
4½	.19	.60	1.20	11	.35	1.06	2.11
5	.20	.64	1.28	11½	.37	1.12	2.24
5½	.20	.68	1.35	12	.37	1.13	2.25
6	.23	.71	1.42	13	.38	1.19	2.38
6½	.23	.74	1.48	14	.38	1.27	2.53
7	.25	.78	1.55	15	.39	1.34	2.67

Machine Bolts.

Machine Bolts have square heads and nuts, and are round all the way up to the head. Weights about the same as carriage bolts.

No. 24E1189 Diameter, ¼-inch.

Length inches	Per doz.	Per 100	Length inches	Per doz.	Per 100
1½	$0.07	$0.40	4½	$0.10	$0.65
2	.07	.42	5	.10	.66
2¼	.08	.43	5½	.10	.69
2½	.08	.44	6	.10	.72
3	.08	.45	6½	.11	.74
3½	.08	.46	7	.12	.77
4	.09	.48			

No. 24E1190 Diameter, 5-16 inch.

Length inches	Per doz.	Per 100	Length inches	Per doz.	Per 100
1½	$0.08	$0.47	4½	$0.12	$0.81
2	.08	.49	5	.13	.85
2¼	.08	.50	5½	.14	.89
2½	.08	.51	6	.16	.92
3	.09	.52	6½	.17	.96
3½	.09	.59	7	.18	.99
4	.10	.62			

No. 24E1191 Diameter, ⅜-inch.

Length inches	Per doz.	Per 100	Length inches	Per doz.	Per 100
1½	$0.09	$0.54	5	$0.15	$1.05
2	.10	.60	5½	.16	1.10
2½	.11	.64	6	.17	1.15
3	.12	.68	6½	.17	1.20
3½	.13	.72	7	.18	1.24
4	.16	.74	7½	.18	1.28
4½	.17	1.00	8	.19	1.34

No. 24E1192 Diameter, ½-inch.

Length inches	Per doz.	Per 100	Length inches	Per doz.	Per 100
1½	$0.19	$1.08	7	$0.33	$1.94
2	.19	1.15	8	.34	2.09
2½	.21	1.23	9	.36	2.24
3	.22	1.32	10	.38	2.41
3½	.23	1 38	11	.40	2.56
4	.24	1.47	12	.42	2.71
4½	.25	1.53	14	.43	3.00
5	.26	1.64	16	.45	3.33
5½	.27	1.70	18	.48	3.65
6	.28	1.77	20	.50	3.97
6½	.32	1.85			

Round Head Stove Bolts.

Stove bolts are useful for many purposes. For fastening hinges they are cheap and good. For many uses they take the place of carriage bolts at much less cost.

No. 24E1195 Diameter, 3-16-inch, round head.

Length, inches	½	⅝	¾	⅞	1	1¼
Per dozen	$0.03	.03	.03	.03	.03	.03½
Per 100	.13	.13	.14	.15	.16	.16

Length, ins.	1½	1¾	2	2½	3
Per dozen	$0.03½	.03½	.03½	.04	.04
Per 100	.16	.17	.18	.19	.21

No. 24E1196 Diameter, 1-4-inch, round head.

Length, ins.	½	⅝	¾	⅞	1
Per dozen	$0.03	.03	.03	.03½	.04
Per 100	.15	.16	.17	.18	.19

Length, in.	1¼	1½	1¾	2	2½	3
Per dozen	$0.04	.04	.04	.05	.05	.05
Per 100	.20	.21	.22	.23	.24	.25

No. 24E1197 Diameter, 5-16-inch, round head.

Length, inches	¾	⅞	1	1¼
Per dozen	$0.04	.04	.04	.05
Per 100	.26	.27	.28	.28
Length, inches	1½	2	2½	3
Per dozen	$0.06	.06	.07	.07
Per 100	.31	.34	.37	.41

Flat Head Stove Bolts.

No. 24E1200 Diameter, 3-16-inch, flat head.

Length	½	⅝	¾	⅞	1
Per dozen	$0.03	.03	.03	.03	.03
Per 100	.12	.12	.12	.13	.14
Length	1¼	1½	2	2½	3
Per dozen	$0.03	.03	.03½	.03½	.03½
Per 100	.15	.16	.18	.19	.20

No. 24E1201 Diameter, ¼-inch, flat head.

Length	⅝	¾	⅞	1	
Per dozen	$0.03½	.03½	.03½	.03½	
Per 100	.14	.14	.14	.15	
Length	1¼	1½	2	2½	3
Per dozen	$0.03½	.04	.04	.04	.04
Per 100	.16	.17	.19	.20	.21

No. 24E1202 Diameter, 5-16-inch, flat head.

Length	⅝	¾	⅞	1	1¼
Per dozen	$0.04½	.04½	.05	.05	.05½
Per 100	.20	.21	.22	.23	.26

Length	1½	2	2½	3
Per dozen	$0.05	.06	.06	.07
Per 100	.29	.31	.34	.38

Bolt Ends.

No. 24E1210 Bolt Ends with square nuts, made of a superior grade of soft iron which is very tough. By welding bolt end to round iron of same size, bolts of any required length may be made.

Diameter of iron	½	⅝	¾	⅞	1
Length of ends	8	9	10	11	12
Av. wt., per doz.	6	11	17	25	37
Price, per dozen	$0.24	.34	.46	.69	.98

S., R. & Co.'s Lag Screws.

Gimlet Point Lag or Coach Screws with square heads. Weights about the same as carriage bolts.

No. 24E1214 Diameter, 5-16-inch.

Length	1½	2	2½	3	3½	4	4½	5
Per doz.	$0.07	.07	.08	.08	.10	10	.10	.12
Per 100	.47	.51	.56	.60	.65	.68	.73	.77

No. 24E1215 Diameter, ⅜-inch.

Length	2	2½	3	3½	4	5
Per doz.	$0.10	.10	.11	.11	.12	.16
Per 100	.62	.67	.77	.79	.86	.96

No. 24E1216 Diameter ½-inch.

Length	3	4	5	6
Per dozen	$0.17	.19	.21	.23
Per 100	1.02	1.16	1.32	1.50

Tire and Iron Work Bolts.

No. 24E1218 Diameter, 3-16 inch.

Length	1¼	1½	1¾	2
Per dozen	3c	3c	3c	3c
Per 100	12c	12c	13c	15c
Length	2¼	2½	2¾	3
Per dozen	4c	4c	4c	4c
Per 100	16c	17c	18c	19c

No. 24E1219 Diameter, ¼-inch.

Length	1¼	1½	1¾	2
Per dozen	4c	4c	4c	5c
Per 100	20c	20c	21c	22c
Length	2¼	2½	2¾	3
Per dozen	5c	5c	5c	6c
Per 100	23c	25c	26c	27c

No. 24E1220 Diameter, 5-16-inch.

Length	1¼	1½	1¾	2
Per dozen	6c	6c	6c	6c
Per 100	30c	30c	31c	32c
Length	2¼	2½	2¾	3
Per dozen	7c	7c	7c	7c
Per 100	34c	35c	36c	38c

T-Head Bolts.

No. 24E1226 Norway Iron T-Head Bolts, complete with burrs. Diameter, 3-16 or ¼-inch.

Length,	1	1¼	1½	
Per doz.	$0.16	$0.16	$0.16	
Per 100,	1.20	1.24	1.28	
Length	1¾	2	2¼	2½
Per dozen	$0.17	$0.17	$0.17	$0.17
Per 100	1.32	1.36	1.40	1.44

Plow Bolts.

No. 24E1234 Norway Iron Plow Bolts, finished complete, as shown in illustration. The following styles furnished at same price: Plain round countersunk heads; round countersunk heads with square neck; round countersunk with key head, and square countersunk head. Be sure to state which style is wanted.

Length	Size, ⅜-inch Per doz.	Size, ⅜-inch Per 100	Size, ½-inch Per doz.	Size, ½-inch Per 100
1 -inch	14c	$1.00	24c	$1.75
1¼-inch	14c	1.08	25c	1.89
1½-inch	15c	1.13	26c	1.99
1¾-inch	16c	1.19	28c	2.10
2 -inch	17c	1.24	30c	2.21
2¼-inch	17c	1.29	32c	2.32

Iron Washers.

No. 24E1236 Wrought Iron Washers. The various sizes are large enough to easily slip over the size bolt given.

For bolt, in.	3-16	¼	5-16	⅜	½
No. in lb.	440	139	113	55	20
Per pound	9c	6¾c	5¾c	4¾c	3c
For bolt, in		⅝	¾	⅞	1
No. in lb.		13	10	9	8
Per pound		3c	3c	3c	3c

Set Screws.

All hardware of every description is guaranteed to give best satisfaction.

No. 24E1245 Cup Point Set Screws.

Diameter of screw, inches	¼	5-16
Number of threads to inch	20	18
L'gth under head ¾ in. Doz.	9½c	10½c
L'gth under head 1 in. Doz.	10c	11c
L'gth under head 1¼ in. Doz.	10½c	12c
L'gth under head 1½ in. Doz.	11½c	12½c
L'gth under head 1¾ in. Doz.	12c	13c
L'gth under head 2 in. Doz.	12½c	13½c
Diameter of screw, inches	⅜	½
Number of threads to inch	16	12
L'gth under head ¾ in. Doz.	11c	14c
L'gth under head 1 in. Doz.	12c	15c
L'gth under head 1¼ in Doz.	13c	16c
L'gth under head 1½ in. Doz.	13½c	19c
L'gth under head 1¾ in. Doz.	14c	20c
L'gth under head 2 in. Doz.	15c	21c

Square Head Cap Screws.

No. 24E1246 Finished heads.

Diameter of head, inches	⅜	7-16	
Length of head, inches	¼	5-16	
Diameter of screw inches	¼	5-16	
Threads to inches	20	18	
L'gth under head ¾ in. Doz.	12c	13c	
L'gth under head 1 in. Doz.	12½c	14c	
L'gth under head 1¼ in. Doz.	13c	15c	
L'gth under head 1½ in. Doz.	14c	16c	
L'gth under head 1¾ in. Doz.	15c	17c	
L'gth under head 2 in. Doz.	16c	18c	
L'gth under head 2¼ in. Doz.	17c	18½c	
L'gth under head 2½ in. Doz.	18c	21c	
Diameter of head, inches	½	9-16	⅝
Length of head, inches	⅜	7-16	½
Diameter of screw, inches	⅜	7-16	½
Threads to inches	16	14	12
L'gth under head ¾ in. Dz.	14c	17c	19c
L'gth under head 1 in. Dz.	15c	18½c	23c
L'gth under head 1¼ in. Dz.	17c	19c	24c
L'gth under head 1½ in. Dz.	18c	21c	25c
L'gth under head 1¾ in. Dz.	18½c	23c	27c
L'gth under head 2 in. Dz.	21c	24c	30c
L'gth under head 2¼ in. Dz.	22c	24½c	31c
L'gth under head 2½ in. Dz.	24c	27c	33c

Blank and Threaded Hot Pressed Square Nuts.

Whether your order is large or small, we welcome it.

No. 24E1250 Blank Nuts.

For bolts, inches	¼	5-16	⅜	7-16	½
No. in pound	74	39	21	13	12
Blank, price, lb.	9c	7½c	5¾c	5c	4¾c
For bolts, inches	9-16	⅝	¾	⅞	1
No. in pound	7	6	3	2	2
Blank, price, lb.	4¾c	4c	3¾c	3c	3c

No. 24E1252 Threaded Nuts.

For bolts, inches	¼	5-16	⅜	7-16	½
No. in pound	74	39	21	13	12
Threaded, per lb.	12c	10c	8c	7c	6c
For bolts, inches	9-16	⅝	¾	⅞	1
No. in pound	7	6	3	2	2
Threaded, per lb.	6c	5½c	5c	5c	5c

Blank and Threaded Hot Pressed Hexagon Nuts.

No. 24E1256 Blank Nuts.

For bolts, inches.	¼	5-16	⅜	7-1	6½
No. in pound	88	47	26	16	14
Blank, per lb.	18c	12c	8¼c	6c	5c
For bolts, inches.	9-16	⅝	¾	⅞	1
No. in pound	8	5	4	3	2
Blank, per lb.	5¾c	4½c	4¼c	4c	4c

No. 24E1258 Threaded Nuts.

For bolts, inches.	¼	5-16	⅜	7-16	½
No. in pound	88	47	26	16	14
Threaded, per lb.	20c	14½c	10½c	8c	6¾c
For bolts, inches.	9-16	⅝	¾	⅞	1
No. in pound	8	5	4	3	2
Threaded, per lb.	6c	5¼c	5c	5c	4¾c

Spring Cotters.

No. 24E1262 Made of the best grade English spring steel. **Full polished.**

Length, inches	Thickness, inches	Per 100	Length, inches	Thickness, inches	Per 100
½	⅛	4c	1½	3-16	15c
¾	⅛	6c	1¾	3-16	16c
1	5-32	8c	2	¼	34c
1¼	3-16	13c			

Assorted Spring Cotters.

No. 24E1263 One Hundred Assorted Sizes, Spring Cotters, as follows:

15—3-32x1 in. 15— ⅛x1¼ in.
20— ⅛x1½ in. 10—3-16x1¾ in.
15—3-16x1½ in. 10— ¼x2 in.
5— ¼x2½ in. 10—5-16x2½ in.

Price, per box..........................25c

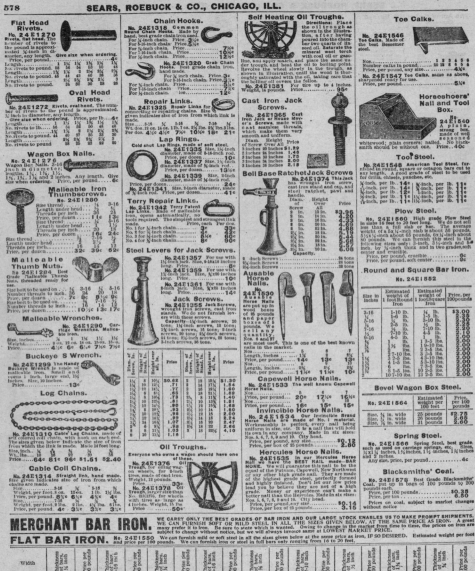

Flat Head Rivets.

No. 24E1270 Rivets, flat head. The number of rivets to the pound is approximated ⅛-inch in diameter, any length. **Give size when ordering.**

Price, per pound.......... 4c

Length	1	1⅛	1¼	1⅜	1½	1⅝
No. rivets to pound	58	56	54	53	50	48
Length	1¾	1⅞	2	2⅛	2¼	2⅜
No. rivets to pound	46	44	42	40	38	36
Length		2½	2⅝	2¾	2⅞	3
No. rivets to pound		34	32	30	28	26

Oval Head Rivets.

No. 24E1272 Rivets, oval head. The number of rivets to the pound is approximated. ⅛-inch in diameter, any length.

Give size when ordering. Price, per lb.... 4c

Length	1	1⅛	1¼	1⅜	1½	1⅝
No. rivets to lb.	56	54	52	50	48	46
Length	1¾	1⅞	2	2⅛	2¼	2⅜
No. rivets to pound	44	40	37	35	33	30
Length		2½	2⅝	2¾	2⅞	3
No. rivets to pound		28	25	23	22	20

Wagon Box Nails.

No. 24E1276 Wagon Box Nails. 3-16 inch in diameter; lengths, 1¼, 1⅜, 1½, 1⅝, 1¾, 1⅞ and 2 inches. Any length. Give size when ordering. Price, per pound..... 6c

Malleable Iron Thumbscrews.

No. 24E1280

Size thread	⅛	3-16
Length under head	½	¾
Threads per inch	36	24
Price, per dozen	11c	13c
Size thread	¼	5-16
Length under head	1	1½
Threads per inch	20	18
Price, per dozen	16c	24c

Size thread	⅜	7-16	½
Length under head	2	2½	3
Threads per inch	16	14	12
Price, per dozen	32c	39c	62c

Malleable Thumb Nuts.

No 24E1284 Best Grade Malleable Thumb Nuts, threaded ready for use.

Size bolt to be used on	⅛	3-16	¼	5-16
Number threads to inch	36	24	20	18
Price, per dozen	7c	8c	8½c	9c
Size bolt to be used on	⅜	7-16	½	
Number threads to inch	16	14	12	
Price, per dozen	10½c	13c	17c	

Malleable Wrenches.

No. 24E1290 Carriage Wrenches. Malleable Iron.

Size, inches	⅞	1	1⅛	1¼	1⅜
Weight	9 oz.	12 oz.	14 oz.	15 oz.	16 oz.
Price	4½c	6c	6½c	7½c	7½c

Buckeye S Wrench.

No. 24E1299 The Handy Buckeye Wrench is made of malleable iron. Small end opens 1 inch, large end, 1⅜ inches. Size, 10 inches.

Price.......... 13c

Log Chains.

No. 24E1310 Cable Log Chains, made of self colored coil chain, with hook on each end. The sizes given below indicate the size of iron from which the link is made. Made 14 feet long.

Size, inch	¼	5-16	⅜	½	⅝
Wt., lbs.	10	16	22	39	58
Price	64c	81c	96c	$1.51	$2.40

Cable Coil Chains.

No. 24E1314 Straight link, hand made. Size given indicates size of iron from which chains are made.

Size	3-16	¼	5-16	⅜
Weight, per foot	8 oz.	12 oz.	1 lb.	1½ lbs.
Price, per pound	8¾c	6¼c	4¾c	4c
Size	7-16	½	⅝	¾
Weight, per foot	2 lbs.	2 lbs.	4½ lbs.	6 lbs.
Price, per pound	4c	3¾c	3¾c	3¾c

Chain Hooks.

No. 24E1318 Common Round Chain Hooks. Made by hand, best grade chain iron used.

For ¼-inch chain. Price.. 3½c
For 5-16-inch chain. Price. 5½c
For ⅜-inch chain. Price.......... 7½c
For 7-16-inch chain. Price.......... 10½c
For ½-inch chain. Price.......... 12½c

No. 24E1320 Grab Chain Hooks. Best grade chain iron, hand made.

For ¼ inch chain. Price. 3c
For 5-16-inch chain. Price, 3¾c
For ⅜-inch chain. Price.......... 5¼c
For 7-16-inch chain Price.......... 7¾c
For ½-inch chain. Price.......... 12c

Repair Links.

No. 24E1325 Repair Links for connecting or repairing chains. Size given indicates size of iron from which link is made.

Size	3-16	¼	5-16	⅜	7-16	½
Wt. doz.	12 oz.	14 oz.	1 lb. 7 oz.	2⅛ lbs.	2¾ lbs.	3 lbs.
Per doz.	4½c	4½c	7½c	10½c	18c	21c

Lap Rings.

Cold shut Lap Rings, made of soft steel.

No. 24E1335 Size, 1½-inch diameter, made of 5-16-inch rod. Price, per dozen.......... 10c

No. 24E1337 Size, 1⅝-inch diameter, made of ⅜-inch rod. Price, per dozen.......... 13½c

No. 24E1339 Size, 2-inch diameter, made of ½-inch rod. Price, per dozen.......... 24c

No. 24E1341 Size, 2-inch diameter, made of ⅝-inch rod. Price, per dozen.......... 41c

Terry Repair Links.

No. 24E1342 Terry Patent Lap Links. Made of malleable iron, opens automatically, no tools required. The simplest and strongest link made.

	Price, each	Per doz.
No. 1 for ¼-inch chain	3c	33c
No. 2 for ⅜-inch chain	4c	42c
No. 3 for ½-inch chain	5½c	60c
No. 4 for ⅝-inch chain	8c	90c

Steel Levers for Jack Screws.

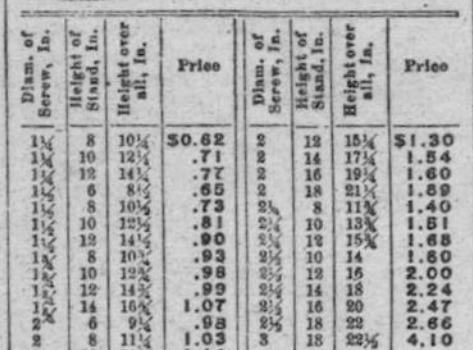

No. 24E1357 For use with 1½-inch jack. Size, 9-16x18 inches long. Price.......... 8c

No. 24E1359 For use with 1¾-inch jack. Size, ⅝x20 inches long. Price.......... 10c

No. 24E1361 For use with 2-inch jack. Size, ¾x22 inches long. Price.......... 14c

Jack Screws.

No. 24E1355 Jack Screws, wrought iron screws, cast iron stands. We do not furnish levers with these screws.

Capacity—1¼-inch screws, 10 tons; 1½-inch screws, 12 tons; 1¾-inch screws, 15 tons; 2-inch screws, 20 tons; 2¼-inch screws, 24 tons; 2½-inch screws, 28 tons; 3-inch screws, 36 tons.

Diam. of Screw, In.	Height of Stand, In.	Height over all, In.	Price	Diam. of Screw, In.	Height of Stand, In.	Height over all, In.	Price
1¼	8	10¼	$0.62	2	12	15¼	$1.30
1¼	10	12¼	.71	2	14	17¼	1.54
1¼	12	14¼	.77	2	16	19¼	1.60
1½	6	8½	.65	2	18	21¼	1.89
1½	8	10½	.73	2¼	8	11¾	1.40
1½	10	12½	.81	2¼	10	13¾	1.51
1½	12	14½	.90	2¼	12	15¾	1.68
1¾	8	10¾	.93	2½	10	14	1.80
1¾	10	12¾	.98	2½	12	16	2.00
1¾	12	14¾	.99	2½	14	18	2.24
1¾	14	16¾	1.07	2½	16	20	2.47
2	6	9¼	.98	2½	18	22	2.66
2	8	11¼	1.03	3	18	22½	4.10
2	10	13¼	1.16				

Oil Troughs.

Everyone who owns a wagon should have one of these.

No. 24E1376 Oil Trough, for oiling wagon wheels, for 2-inch tires, made of cast iron. Weight, 12 pounds. Price.......... 33c

No. 24E1378 Oil Trough, larger size than No. 24E1376, for wheels with tires as large as 4 inches. Weight, 15 lbs. Price.......... 50c

Self Heating Oil Troughs.

Directions: Place the oil trough as shown in the illustration, after having poured into the chamber two quarts of linseed oil. **Saturate the mineral wool torch** with coal oil or gasoline, and apply match, and place the same under trough, and heat the oil to boiling point. Revolve the wheel slowly in the trough, as shown in illustration, until the wood is thoroughly saturated with the oil, taking care that the boiling oil covers the felloe.

No. 24E1381 For tire up to 4 inches. Weight, 14 pounds. Price.......... 95c

Cast Iron Jack Screws.

No. 24E1365 Cast Iron Jack or House Mover's Screws, made with cast seamless threads, which make them very smooth and uniform.

Diam. of Screw	Height Over All	Price
3 inches	20 inches	$1.29
3 inches	24 inches	1.48
3 inches	30 inches	1.75
3 inches	34 inches	2.00
3 inches	36 inches	2.15

Bell Base Ratchet Jack Screws

No. 24E1374 This Jack has wrought iron screw, cast iron stand and cap, and steel ratchet, pawl and handle.

Diam. of Screw	Height Over All	Price
2 in.	12 in.	$3.96
2 in.	14 in.	4.20
2 in.	16 in.	4.33
2 in.	20 in.	4.69
2 in.	22 in.	4.88
2¼ in.	18 in.	5.19
2¼ in.	20 in.	5.44
2¼ in.	22 in.	5.68
2½ in.	18 in.	5.57
2½ in.	20 in.	6.08

Capacity.

2 -inch Screws.......... 24 tons
2¼-inch Screws.......... 28 tons
2½-inch Screws.......... 32 tons

Ausable Horse Nails.

No. 24E1530 Ausable Horse Nails are put up in wood boxes of 25 pounds and paper boxes of 5 pounds. We sell any quantity. Nos. 6 and 7 are most used. This is one of the best known nails in the market.

Nos	5	6	7
Length, inches	1⅞	2	2⅛
Price, per pound	14c	13c	13c
Nos	8	9	10
Length, inches	2⅜	2½	2⅝
Price, per pound	11½c	11½c	10c

Capewell Horse Nails.

No. 24E1533 The well known Capewell Horse Nails.

Nos	5	6	7
Price, per pound	20c	17½c	16½c
Nos	8	9	10
Price, per pound	16c	15c	15c

Invincible Horse Nails.

No. 24E1534 Our Invincible Brand Horse Nails are made of No. 1 material. Workmanship is perfect, every nail being uniform in size, etc. It is a nail that will hold its own in any company. Made in six sizes: Nos. 5, 6, 7, 8, 9 and 10. City head.

Price, per pound, any size.......... $0.12
Price, per box of 25 pounds.......... 2.80

Hercules Horse Nails.

No. 24E1535 In our Hercules Horse Nail we have the **BEST NAIL made—BAR NONE.** We will guarantee this nail to be the equal of the Putnam, Capewell, New Northwest or any other high grade nail. They are made of the highest grade steel, perfectly formed and highly finished. Don't let our low price lead you to believe they are not of a high grade. Money or experience can't make a better nail than the Hercules. Made in six sizes: Nos. 5, 6, 7, 8, 9 and 10. City head.

Price, per pound, any size.......... $0.14
Price, per box of 25 pounds.......... 3.15

Toe Calks.

No. 24E1546 Toe Calks. Made of the best Bessemer steel.

Nos	1	2	3	4	5	6
Number calks in pound	20	12	8	6	5	4

Price, per pound, any size.......... 4¼c

No. 24E1547 Toe Calks, same as above, sharpened ready for use.

Price, per pound.......... 5¼c

Horseshoers' Nail and Tool Box.

No. 24E1540 A plain, strong box, made of well seasoned whitewood; plain corners; nailed. No blacksmith should be without one. Price.. 40c

Tool Steel.

No. 24E1548 American Tool Steel, furnished in round, square or octagon bars cut to any length. A good grade of steel to be used for drills, chisels, punches, etc.

¼-inch, per lb.	14c	⅝-inch, per lb.	11c
5-16-inch, per lb.	14c	¾-inch, per lb.	11c
⅜-inch, per lb.	12c	1-inch, per lb.	11c
½-inch, per lb.	11c	1¼-inch, per lb.	11c
9-16-inch, per lb.	11c	1½-inch, per lb.	11c

Plow Steel.

No. 24E1560 High grade Plow Steel in slabs 16 feet to 20 feet long. We do not sell less than a full slab or bar. The average weight of a 5x¼-inch slab is about 56 pounds, 5½x¼-inch about 65 pounds, 6x¼-inch about 80 pounds. We can furnish this steel in the following sizes only: 3-inch, 3½-inch and 5-inch by ¼-inch thick and in two grades, soft center and crucible.

Price, per pound, crucible.......... 6c
Price, per pound, soft center.......... 8c

Round and Square Bar Iron.

No. 24E1552

Size in inches	Estimated weight of 1 foot Round Iron	Estimated weight of 1 foot Square Iron	Price, per 100 pounds
3-16	1-10 lb.	⅛ lb.	$3.00
¼	1-6 lb.	1-5 lb.	2.35
5-16	¼ lb.	3-10 lb.	2.30
⅜	2-5 lb.	½ lb.	2.25
7-16	½ lb.	7-10 lb.	2.20
½	7-10 lb.	4-5 lb.	2.10
9-16	4-5 lb.	1 lb.	2.00
⅝	1 lb.	1 3-5 lbs.	2.00
¾	1½ lbs.	1 9-10 lbs.	2.00
⅞	2 lbs.	2 3-5 lbs.	2.00
1	2 7-10 lbs.	3 2-5 lbs.	2.00
1⅛	3 2-5 lbs.	4 3-10 lbs.	2.00
1¼	4 1-5 lbs.	5 3-10 lbs.	2.00
1½	6 lbs.	7 3-5 lbs.	2.00
1¾	8 1-5 lbs.	10 2-5 lbs.	2.00
2	10 7-10 lbs.	13 2-5 lbs.	2.00

Bevel Wagon Box Steel.

No. 24E1564	Estimated weight per 100 feet	Price, per 100 pounds
Size, ⅝ in. wide	25 pounds	$2.75
Size, ¾ in. wide	26 pounds	2.65
Size, ⅞ in. wide	31 pounds	2.60

Spring Steel.

No. 24E1566 Spring Steel, best grade such as used on carriage springs, etc. Sizes, ¼x1¼ inches, 1⅜ inches, 1½ inches, 1¾ inches and 2 inches.

Any size, price, per pound.......... 4c

Blacksmiths' Coal.

No. 24E1578 Best Grade Blacksmiths' Coal, put up in bags of 100 pounds to 200 pounds each.

Price, per 100 pounds.......... $0.35
Price, per ton.......... 6.50

Prices on coal, subject to market changes without notice

MERCHANT BAR IRON.

WE CARRY ONLY THE BEST GRADES OF BAR IRON AND OUR LARGE STOCK ENABLES US TO MAKE PROMPT SHIPMENTS. WE CAN FURNISH SOFT OR MILD STEEL IN ALL THE SIZES GIVEN BELOW, AT THE SAME PRICE AS IRON. A great many prefer it to iron. Be sure to state which is wanted. Owing to change in the market from time to time, the prices on iron are subject to change without notice, but we will always invoice same at LOWEST MARKET PRICE.

FLAT BAR IRON.

No. 24E1550 We can furnish mild or soft steel in all the sizes given below at the same price as iron, IF SO DESIRED. Estimated weight per foot and price per 100 pounds. We can furnish iron or steel in full bars only ranging from 16 to 20 feet.

Width	Thickness of bars, ⅛ inch	Price per 100 pounds	Thickness of bars, 3-16 inch	Price per 100 pounds	Thickness of bars, ¼ inch	Price per 100 pounds	Thickness of bars, 5-16 inch	Price per 100 pounds
1 inch	2-5 lb	$2.50	3-5 lb	$2.40	4-5 lb	$2.35	1 lb	$2.35
1⅛ inches	½ lb	2.50	7-10 lb	2.40	1 lb	2.35	1 1-5 lbs	2.35
1¼ inches	½ lb	2.50	4-5 lb	2.40	1 lb	2.35	1 3-10 lbs	2.35
1⅜ inches	2-5 lb	2.50	9-10 lb	2.40	1 1-5 lbs	2.35	1½ lbs	2.35
1½ inches	3-5 lb	2.45	1 lb	2.40	1¼ lbs	2.25	1 3-5 lbs	2.25
1⅝ inches	7-10 lb	2.45	1 lb	2.35	1 2-5 lbs	2.25	1 7-10 lbs	2.25
1¾ inches	¾ lb	2.45	1 1-10 lbs	2.35	1½ lbs	2.25	1 9-10 lbs	2.25
2 inches	4-5 lb	2.45	1¼ lbs	2.35	1 7-10 lbs	2.25	2 1-10 lbs	2.25
2½ inches	1 lb	2.45	1½ lbs	2.35	2 1-10 lbs	2.25	2 7-10 lbs	2.25
3 inches	1¼ lbs	2.45	1 9-10 lbs	2.35	2½ lbs	2.25	3 1-5 lbs	2.25
3½ inches	1½ lbs	2.45	2¼ lbs	2.35	3 lbs	2.25	3 7-10 lbs	2.25
4 inches	1 7-10 lbs	2.45	2½ lbs	2.35	3 2-5 lbs	2.25	4¼ lbs	2.25

Width	Thickness of bars, ⅜ inch	Price per 100 pounds	Thickness of bars, 7-10 inch	Price per 100 pounds	Thickness of bars, ½ inch	Price per 100 pounds	Thickness of bars, 1⅝ inch	Price per 100 pounds	Thickness of bars, ¾ inch	Price per 100 pounds
1 inch	1¼ lbs	$2.15	1½ lbs	$2.15	1¾ lbs	$2.15	2 1-10 lbs	$2.15	2½ lbs	$2.15
1⅛ inches	1 2-5 lbs	2.15	1 7-10 lbs	2.15	2 lbs	2.15	2 3-5 lbs	2.15	2 9-10 lbs	2.15
1¼ inches	1 3-5 lbs	2.15	1 9-10 lbs	2.15	2¼ lbs	2.15	2 7-10 lbs	2.15	3¼ lbs	2.15
1⅜ inches	1 4-5 lbs	2.15	2 lbs	2.15	2½ lbs	2.15	3 lbs	2.15	3½ lbs	2.15
1½ inches	1 9-10 lbs	2.15	2¼ lbs	2.15	2½ lbs	2.15	3 1-5 lbs	2.15	3 2-5 lbs	2.15
1⅝ inches	2 lbs	2.15	2½ lbs	2.15	2¾ lbs	2.15	3½ lbs	2.15	4¼ lbs	2.15
1¾ inches	2¼ lbs	2.15	2⅝ lbs	2.15	3 lbs	2.15	3¾ lbs	2.15	4½ lbs	2.15
2 inches	2½ lbs	2.15	3 lbs	2.15	3½ lbs	2.15	4¼ lbs	2.15	5 1-10 lbs	2.15
2½ inches	3 1-5 lbs	2.15	3¾ lbs	2.15	4¼ lbs	2.15	5 3-10 lbs	2.15	6 2-5 lbs	2.15
3 inches	3 4-5 lbs	2.15	4½ lbs	2.15	5¼ lbs	2.15	6 2-5 lbs	2.15	7 7-10 lbs	2.15
3½ inches	4½ lbs	2.15	5¼ lbs	2.15	6 lbs	2.15	7½ lbs	2.15	9 lbs	2.15
4 inches	5 1-10 lbs	2.15	6 lbs	2.15	6 4-5 lbs	2.15	8½ lbs	2.15	10¼ lbs	2.15

The Acme Knapsack Sprayer.

Concaved to fit the back. All Brass Pump.

No. 24E5505 This machine consists of a tank holding four gallons and a pump made entirely of brass, which cannot corrode or rust. There is a large air chamber placed inside the tank for convenience, which has sufficient capacity to keep up the pressure and continue to discharge the spray for one minute after the operator stops pumping. The lower valve is screwed to bottom of cylinder, hence no trouble to reach the valves. There is a large opening on top for the reception of liquid, with a fine strainer set inside. Four feet of best rubber hose and a brass pipe 15 inches long with a stop cock are furnished with each machine. The nozzle is our combination Vermorel, so highly recommended, and gives universal satisfaction. For vineyards, nurseries, potato, tobacco and cotton fields.

Price, with galvanized tank......**$6.22**
Price, copper tank, with agitator....**9.95**

Acme Jr. Barrel Spraying Pump.

No. 24E5517 Acme Jr. Barrel Spraying Pump. The Acme Jr. has all working parts, which must come in contact with the solutions used, made of brass. The parts made of brass are the upper cylinder, lower cylinder, bucket, valve seat, lower cap, hose connection, strainer, agitator, tip and nozzles. It is furnished with a jet agitator, which keeps the contents of barrel thoroughly mixed.

Furnished complete as shown in illustration with one or two leads of ½-inch hose. Weight, 26 pounds.

Price, complete with one lead of hose.......**$3.90**
Price complete with two leads of hose......**$4.45**

Improved Spray and Force Pump.

No. 24E5518 Improved Spray and Force Pump. It is beyond question the most perfect and effective hand apparatus ever invented for throwing water. It supplies a universal want, for every family needs some kind of a force sprinkler and pump. In variety of service, simplicity of construction and ease of operation, it has no equal. Is always ready for use, not liable to get out of order, and so light and convenient that it can be used easily and effectively by anyone. Made of heavy, bright tin coated with Egyptian lacquer. Weight, 2¾ pounds.
Price......**64c**

Spraying Pump.

No. 24E5520 The construction of the pump requires the pressure on the handle to be all done on the down stroke, the pressure on the cylinder acting as a cushion, and partly forcing the handle up again, thus making it very easy of operation, requiring no foot rest or other device to steady it. The hose can be detached at top of pump and a nozzle attached in its place, either for spraying, sprinkling, or throwing a solid stream. It is also arranged so that a small stream is discharged with great force from the bottom of the pump into the bucket or barrel, serving to thoroughly agitate the mixture at all times when the pump is in use. For washing buggies, windows, etc., it is very useful. Weight, about 5 pounds.
Price......**$1.92**

Acme Portable Cast Force Pump.

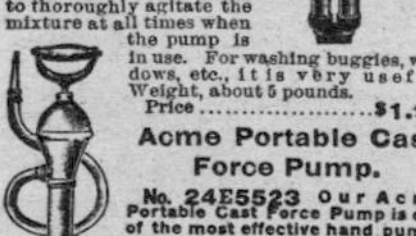

No. 24E5523 Our Acme Portable Cast Force Pump is one of the most effective hand pumps on the market. Is made extra strong; nicely finished. Is adapted for spraying trees, washing windows and wagons, sprinkling lawns, etc. Furnished complete with hose and connections, brass nozzle and sprinkler. Weight, 11¾ pounds. Price........**$4.05**

Acme Fire Extinguisher.

No. 24E5525 A device that every store, factory and residence should be equipped with. Absolute protection against loss by fire can now be assured to property owners at a small cost. The Acme Chemical Fire Extinguisher is the simplest and most powerful machine made. It is made of heavy copper securely riveted and soldered and highly polished. Holds three gallons and throws a stream 40 feet when in action. The solution used contains no acids to destroy fabrics, etc., although it is the most powerful fire extinguisher solution known. Solution for re-charging can be obtained from any druggist for 15 cents. Full directions sent with each machine. Weight, when ready for use, 12 lbs. Price...**$4.98**

Pump Cylinders.

By means of the cylinder water is raised, and unless the cylinder is well made no good results can be obtained. A good cylinder must be bored true and plunger must fit accurately. Valves must be simple and durable. The cost of repairing a cylinder is usually more than its first cost, so it pays to get the best. Our cylinders are the best that skilled workmen can produce and our prices as low as equally well made goods can be sold for. Cylinders 10 inches long have 6-inch stroke and can be used in wells up to 35 feet deep. Cylinders 12 inches long have 6-inch stroke and can be used in wells up to 75 feet deep. Cylinders 14 inches long have 8-inch stroke and can be used in wells up to 150 feet deep. Cylinders 16 inches long have 10-inch stroke and can be used in wells up to 200 feet deep. Cylinders 2 inches in diameter are fitted for 1-inch pipe. Cylinders 3½ inches in diameter are fitted for 1½-inch pipe. Cylinders 4 inches in diameter are fitted for 2-inch pipe. All others fitted for 1¼-inch pipe.

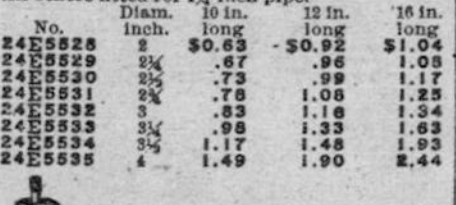

No.	Diam. inch.	10 in. long	12 in. long	16 in. long
24E5528	2	$0.63	$0.92	$1.04
24E5529	2¼	.67	.96	1.05
24E5530	2½	.73	.99	1.17
24E5531	2¾	.78	1.06	1.25
24E5532	3	.83	1.16	1.34
24E5533	3¼	.98	1.33	1.63
24E5534	3½	1.17	1.48	1.93
24E5535	4	1.49	1.90	2.44

Brass Body Cylinders.

Brass Body Cylinders are practically as good as the solid brass, and much cheaper. The barrel is made of a seamless brass tube, and workmanship, stroke and capacity are all same as iron cylinders. 10 and 12-inch cylinders have 6-inch stroke, 14-inch cylinder has 8-inch stroke and 16-inch cylinder has 10-inch stroke.

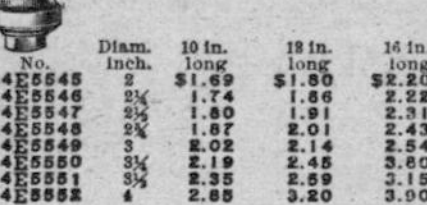

No.	Diam. inch.	10 in. long	12 in. long	16 in. long
24E5545	2	$1.69	$1.80	$2.20
24E5546	2¼	1.74	1.86	2.22
24E5547	2½	1.80	1.91	2.31
24E5548	2¾	1.87	2.01	2.43
24E5549	3	2.02	2.14	2.54
24E5550	3¼	2.19	2.45	3.80
24E5551	3½	2.35	2.59	3.15
24E5552	4	2.85	3.20	3.90

Artesian Well Brass Cylinders.

This illustration represents our all brass cylinder to be used in artesian wells, the shell being made of heavy seamless brass tubing, fitted with hard brass or bronze ball valves and which are supplied with best cupped oak tanned leathers. This cylinder may be placed in open wells and in drilled wells where the pipe or casing is long enough to take the cylinder attachments. They are adapted to work in the deepest well.

NOTE—The plunger and lower valves may be removed through the connecting pipe, which is larger in diameter than the bore of the cylinder, thus making it convenient when repairs are necessary.

No.	Length of Cylinder, Inches	Stroke, Inches	Inside Diameter, Inches	Fitted for Pipe	Price
24E5560	36	16	1⅜	1½-inch	$ 7.50
24E5561	33	16	1¾	2 -inch	9.50
24E5562	43	24	2¼	2½-inch	15.00
24E5563	45	24	2¾	3 -inch	18.00
24E5564	49	24	3¼	3½-inch	25.00
24E5565	51	24	3¾	4 -inch	36.00
24E5566	59	30	4¼	4½-inch	46.00

No.	Size, inches	Fitted Pipe, inches	Stroke, inches	Price, Iron	Price, Brass Lined
24E5570	2 x16	11¼	8	$2.70	$3.50
24E5571	2¼x16	1¼	8	3.00	4.00
24E5572	2½x16	1¼	8	3.35	4.30
24E5573	2 x18	1¼	10	2.90	4.00
24E5574	2¼x18	1¼	10	3.15	4.35
24E5575	2½x18	1¼	10	3.50	4.70
24E5576	2¾x18	1¼	8	4.45	5.40
24E5577	3 x18	1¼	8	5.70	7.00
24E5578	2 x20	1¼	12	3.05	4.35
24E5579	2¼x20	1¼	12	3.35	4.75
24E5580	2½x20	1¼	12	3.70	4.65
24E5581	2¾x20	1¼	10	4.45	5.95
24E5582	3 x20	1¼	10	5.60	8.00

Irrigation Cylinders.

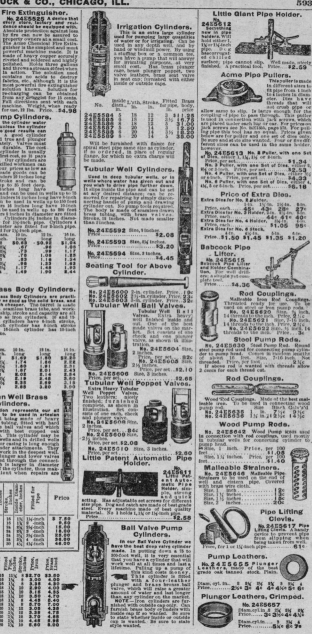

This is an extra large cylinder used for pumping large quantities of water or for irrigating. Can be used in any depth well, and by hand or windmill power. By using a stuffing box or a common tee, you have a pump that will answer for irrigating purposes, at very small cost. Has brass plunger cage, brass plunger poppet, two valve leathers, brass seat valve in seat cap; furnished with either inside or outside caps.

No.	Inside diam., in.	L'gth, in.	Stroke, in.	Fitted for pipe, in.	Brass body, price
24E5584	5	18	12	3	$11.25
24E5585	6	18	12	3½	16.75
24E5586	8	18	12	5	31.00
24E5587	5	20	14	3	12.50
24E5588	6	20	14	3½	18.20
24E5589	8	20	14	5	35.00

Will be furnished with flange for spiral steel pipe same size as cylinder, if so ordered, in place of regular flange, for which no extra charge will be made.

Tubular Well Cylinders.

Used in deep tubular wells, or in wells where water has given out and you wish to drive pipe further down. It slips inside the pipe and can be set at any desired distance; can be removed for repairing by simply disconnecting handle of pump and drawing cylinder out. No pump tools required. The body is made of seamless drawn brass tubing, with brass valves. Stroke, 12 inches. Not made smaller than 2 inches.

No. 24E5592 Size, 2 inches. Price......**$2.08**
No. 24E5593 Size, 2½ inches. Price......**$3.20**
No. 24E5594 Size, 3 inches. Price......**$4.45**

Seating Tool for Above Cylinder.

No. 24E5600 2-in. cylinder. Price..**19c**
No. 24E5602 2½-in. cylinder. Price..**23c**
No. 24E5603 3-in. cylinder. Price..**32c**

Tubular Well Ball Valves.

Tubular Well Ball Valves. Extra heavy; well finished inside and out. One of the best made valves on the market. Set consists of one check and one plunger valve, as shown in illustration.

No. 24E5604 Size, 2 inches. Price, per set....**82c**
No. 24E5605 Size, 2½ inches. Price, per set...**$2.10**
No. 24E5606 Size, 3 inches. Price, per set......**$2.65**

Tubular Well Poppet Valves.

Extra Heavy Tubular Well Poppet Valves. Two leathers; nicely finished; furnished complete, as shown in illustration. Set consists of one each, check and plunger valve.

No. 24E5608 Size, 2 inches. Price, per set...**84c**
No. 24E5609 Size, 2½ inches. Price, per set.**$2.08**
No. 24E5610 Size, 3 inches. Price, per set......**$2.60**

Little Patent Automatic Pipe Holder.

No. 24E5611 Little Patent Automatic Pipe Holder, simple, strong and quick acting. Has adjustable set screws for different size pipe. Dog and catch are made of best grade steel. Every machine made of best quality material. No. 1 holds 1, 1¼ or 1½-inch pipe.
Price......**$2.58**

Ball Valve Pump Cylinders.

In our Ball Valve Cylinder we have the best deep valve cylinder made. In putting down a 75 to 300-foot well, it is very essential that you have a cylinder that will work well at all times and last a lifetime. Pulling up a pump of this kind costs money. This cylinder is fitted with a four-leather plunger and brass bronze ball valve, which will raise a greater amount of water and last longer than any cylinder on the market.

NOTE—Iron cylinders are furnished with outside cap only. Can furnish brass body cylinders with inside cap if so wanted. Be sure to state whether inside or outside cap is wanted. Be sure to state style wanted.

Little Giant Pipe Holder.

No. 24E5612 Something new in pipe holders. Will hold either 1, 1¼ or 1½-inch pipe. Dog has corrugated chilled surface; pipe cannot slip. Well made, nicely finished. A practical tool. Price....**$2.59**

Acme Pipe Pullers.

This puller is made in different sizes to fit pipe from 1 inch to 6 inches in diameter. Dies have threads that will not crush pipe or allow same to slip. Is large enough for the coupling of pipe to pass through. This puller is used in connection with jack screws, which are placed under each lug or car. For prices on jack screws see No. 24E1355, page 578. For pulling pipe this tool has no equal. Prices given below are for puller and one set of dies only. Be sure and state size wanted. Four or five different sizes can be used in the same holder, however.

No. 24E5613 No. 2 Puller, with one Set of Dies, either 1, 1¼, 1½ or 2-inch.
Price, per set.......**$1.34**
No. 3 Puller, with one Set of Dies, either 2, 2½ or 3-inch. Price, per set.......**$2.53**
No. 4 Puller, with one Set of Dies, either 3½ or 4-inch. Price, per set.......**$4.33**
No. 6 Puller, with one Set of Dies, either 4, 4½, 5 or 6-inch. Price, per set.......**$6.18**

Price of Extra Dies.

Extra Dies for No. 2 Holder.

	1-in.	1¼-in.	1½-in.	2-in.
Price, each......	45c	43c	28c	27c

Extra Dies for No. 3 Holder.

	2-in.	2½-in.	3-in.
Price, each......	44c	41c	40c

Extra Dies for No. 4 Holder.

	3½-in.	4-in.
Price, each......	$1.05	95c

Extra Dies for No. 6 Stock.

	4-in.	4½-in.	5-in.	6-in.
Price..	$1.50	$1.45	$1.35	$1.20

Babcock Pipe Lifter.

No. 24E5615 Babcock Pipe Lifter and Holder Combination. For well drillers; a simple yet complete tool.
Price......**$4.36**

Rod Couplings.

Malleable Iron Rod Couplings. Threaded ready for use. To be used on steel or iron pump rods.

No. 24E5620 Size, ⅜ inch, 14 threads to the inch. Price, **2¼c**
No. 24E5621 Size, 7-16 inch, 14 threads to the inch. Price, **2¼c**
No. 24E5622 Size, ½ inch, 14 threads to the inch. Price...**3c**

Steel Pump Rods.

No. 24E5630 Steel Pump Rod. Round steel pump rod used for connecting pump cylinder to pump head. Comes in random lengths of about 16 feet. Size, 7-16 inch. Not threaded. Price, per foot..........**2¼c**

If above rod is wanted with threads allow 2 cents for each thread cut.

Rod Couplings.

Wood Rod Couplings. Made of the best malleable iron. To be used in connecting wood pump rod.

	Size	Black	Galv'z'd
No. 24E5635	1 in.	7½c	9½c
No. 24E5636	1¼ in.	12½c	14½c

Wood Pump Rods.

No. 24E5642 Wood Pump Rods used in connection with rod couplings, used mostly in tubular wells for connecting cylinder to pump head.

Size, 1 inch. Price, per 100 feet......**$1.05**
Size, 1¼ inches. Price, per 100 feet......**$1.40**

Malleable Strainers.

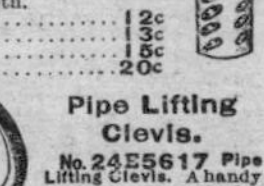

No. 24E5646 Malleable Pipe Strainers to be used on the end of well and cistern pipe. Covered with brass wire cloth.

Size, 1 inch............**12c**
Size, 1¼ inches............**13c**
Size, 1½ inches............**15c**
Size, 2 inches............**20c**

Pipe Lifting Clevis.

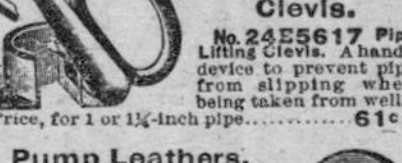

No. 24E5617 Pipe Lifting Clevis. A handy device to prevent pipe from slipping when being taken from well.
Price, for 1 or 1¼-inch pipe..........**61c**

Pump Leathers.

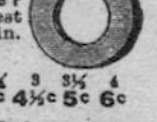

No. 24E5655 Plunger Leathers, made of the best grade oak tanned stock. Plain.

Diam. cyl. in..	2	2¼	2½	2¾	3	3½	4
Price..........	2½c	3c	4c	4c	4½c	5c	6c

Plunger Leathers, Crimped.

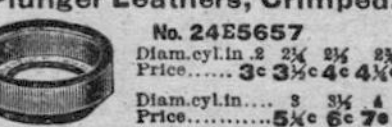

No. 24E5657

Diam. cyl. in.	2	2¼	2½	2¾
Price......	3c	3½c	4c	4½c

Diam. cyl. in....	3	3½	4
Price..........	5½c	6c	7c

Lower Valve Leathers.

No. 24E5659 Our special price 2½c to 6c.

Diam. cyl. inches	2		2¼
Price	2½c		3c
Diam. cyl. inches	2½		2¾
Price	4c		4c
Diam. cyl. inches	3	3½	4
Price	4½c	5c	6c

Water Conductor.

No. 24E5665 This Cast Iron Conductor hangs over and directly under the spout of the pump. The pipe is screwed in at lower outlet on side to conduct water to a tank or trough that may be some distance from the pump.

Price, 1¼ or 1½-inch pipe...22c

Foot Valves.

We recommend that Foot Valve and Strainer should be placed on lower end of pipe in wells more than 15 or 18 feet deep. It makes pump work much easier and the strainer prevents anything from entering the pipe which might clog the valves in cylinder. Made in two sizes.

No. 24E5670 For 1¼-in. pipe. Price...24c
No. 24E5671 For 1½-in. pipe. Price...34c
No. 24E5672 For 2-in. pipe. Price...46c

Drive Well Points.

Drive Well Points are made of wrought iron pipe, galvanized inside and out after the holes are punched. It is covered with a brass gauze, and gauze is covered and protected by a perforated brass jacket. No. 60 gauze is most commonly used. No. 100 gauze is for quicksand. Either flush point for tubular wells or with cast head for driving. Be sure and state which is wanted.

No. 24E5680 Flush Point.
No. 24E5681 Cast Point.

Diam. inches	Length, inches	60 Gauze, Price	100 Gauze, Price
1¼	24	$0.43	$0.92
1¼	30	.55	1.19
1¼	36	.60	1.44
1¼	42	.80	1.64
1½	30	.72	1.42
1½	36	.87	1.72
2	36	1.26	2.26
2	48	1.62	3.02

24E5680 24E5681

Driving Caps.

No. 24E6098 Driving Caps used for driving pipe for drive wells. Made extra heavy, will not crush the thread.

Size, inches	1¼	1½	2
Price	13c	15c	29c

Acme Well Force Pump Packing Heads.

No. 24E5686 Straight Rod Packing Head or Stuffing Box for Windmill and Force Pumps, made of the best grade malleable iron, with brass glands and brass rods. It has ½-inch rod coupling at top and 7-16-inch rod coupling at bottom.

Size for pipe, inch	1	1¼
Price	$1.15	$1.20
Size for pipe, inch	1½	2
Price	$1.21	1.22

Packing Head for Wood Rod.

No. 24E5688 Windmill Force Pump Packing Head for Mill with Wood Rod. Has brass glands, and brass rods, finished complete ready for use.

Size for pipe, inches	Price
1¼	$1.60
1½	1.65
2	1.70

Artesian Well Working Head.

New Deep Well Working Head. Has double guides at sides while the stuffing box below can be used for forcing as well as raising water. Has hinged rod attachment.

No. 24E5689 24-inch stroke.

	Price
For 2 -inch pipe	$ 9.00
For 2½-inch pipe	9.05
For 3 -inch pipe	9.10
For 3½-inch pipe	13.50
For 4 -inch pipe	13.75

Standard Wrought Iron Pipe.

No. 24E5710 Black Iron Pipe.
No. 24E5711 Galvanized Iron Pipe.

Black and Galvanized. For steam, gas and water. When pipe is ordered in full lengths, one coupling is furnished free with each piece. Prices given below are for pipe in random lengths (16 to 20 ft.) Where you specify exact lengths we charge for threads on both ends as per list below. No coupling with pipe cut to exact length. Prices of pipe subject to fluctuations of the market.

Inside Diameter	Pounds per foot	Black, per foot	Galvanized, per foot	Extra threads, per cut
⅛-inch	¼	2c	3c	2c
¼-inch	½	2c	3c	2c
⅜-inch	⅗	2c	3c	2c
½-inch	⅘	2½c	3½c	2c
¾-inch	1 1/10	3c	4½c	2c
1-inch	1⅗	4c	6c	3c
1¼-inch	2⅕	5½c	8c	3c
1½-inch	2⅗	6½c	9½c	4c
2 -inch	3⅗	7¼c	13c	4c
2½-inch	5⅘	14c	21c	8c
3 -inch	7½	18½c	27½c	10c
3½-inch	9	23½c	34½c	12c
4 -inch	10⅘	26½c	38½c	16c
4½-inch	12½	32c	47½c	22c
5 -inch	14½	35c	52½c	24c
6 -inch	18⅘	47c	68½c	32c

Be sure to allow for cost of cutting threads when pipe is ordered cut to exact lengths.

Standard Well Casing.

In random lengths, with threads and couplings, unless otherwise ordered.

No. 24E5712 Black Casing.

Inside Diameter, Inches	Outside Diameter, Inches	Pounds, per foot	Price Black, per foot
2	2¼	2¾	15c
3	3¼	4	25c
3¼	3½	4⅛	26c
3½	3¾	4⅝	27c
4	4¼	6	32c
4½	4¾	7	34c
5	5¼	8	42c
5⅝	6	10⅛	52c
6⅝	7	12¼	63c
8¼	8⅝	15	76c

Iron Pipe Fittings.

We illustrate the fittings that are commonly used, but can furnish any fitting that is made. If you want any fitting not quoted here, you can safely order it from us, allowing sufficient money to pay for it, and we will fill your order promptly; or, if you prefer, write us and we will promptly and cheerfully quote price.

About sizes—Remember that the size of iron pipe is inside measure and that fittings are for pipe of corresponding size. We show below the comparative sizes of iron pipe.

Pipe size, inch	⅛	¼	⅜	½	¾
Outside measure, in.	40/100	54/100	67/100	84/100	1 5/100
Pipe size, inches	1	1¼	1½	2	
Outside measure, inches	1 31/100	1 66/100	1 9/10	2 37/100	

Wrought Iron Couplings.

No. 24E5720 Black.

Pipe, inches	¼	⅜	½	¾	1	1¼	1½	2
Black, each	2c	2¼c	2½c	3¼c	4¼c	5½c	6½c	9¼c

No. 24E5721 Galvanized.

Pipe, inches	¼	⅜	½	¾	1	1¼	1½	2
Galv'd, each	2¼c	2¾c	3¼c	4¼c	6c	8¼c	10¼c	14c

Malleable Elbows.

No. 24E5724 Black.

Pipe, inch	¼	⅜	½	¾	1
Black	2c	2½c	3½c	5½c	7c
Pipe, inches	1¼	1½	2		
Black	8½c	11½c	16½c		

No. 24E5725 Galvanized.

Pipe, inches	¼	⅜	½	¾	1	1¼
Galv'd, each	2½c	3½c	5½c	7½c	11c	13c
Pipe, inches	1½	2				
Galv'd, each	20c	29c				

Street Elbows.

No. 24E5726 Malleable Iron Street Elbows.

Pipe, inches	⅜	½	¾	1	1¼
Black. Price, each	5c	6c	9c	12c	18c

No. 24E5727 Galvanized.

Pipe inches	⅜	½	¾	1	1¼
Galvanized. Each	6c	7c	13c	16c	26c

45 Degrees Malleable Elbows.

No. 24E5728 Black.

Pipe, inch	¼	⅜	½	¾
Black, each	3½c	3½c	4½c	6½c
Pipe, inches	1	1¼	1½	2
Black, each	9½c	12½c	18½c	27c

No. 24E5729 Galvanized.

Pipe, inches	¼	⅜	½	¾	1	1¼	1½	2
Galv'd, each	5c	5½c	7c	8¾c	14c	15½c	29c	38c

Malleable Tees.

No. 24E5732 Black.

Pipe, inch	¼	⅜	½	¾
Price	2½c	3½c	4½c	5½c
Pipe, inches	1	1¼	1½	2
Price	8½	10½	14½c	19½c

No. 24E5733 Galvanized.

Pipe, in.	¼	⅜	½	¾	1	1¼	1½	2
Price	3½c	3¾c	5½c	7c	13c	17c	23½c	34c

Malleable Crosses.

All our fittings are Proctor goods, the highest grade made.

No. 24E5736 Black.

Pipe, inch	¼	⅜	½	¾
Price	3½c	4½c	4½c	7½c
Pipe, in.	1	1¼	1½	2
Price	10½c	13½c	19½c	33c

No. 24E5737 Galvanized.

Pipe, inches	½	¾	1	1¼	1½	2
Price	7c	10c	16c	23c	33c	50c

Malleable Unions.

No. 24E5740 Black.

Pipe inches	¼	⅜	½	¾
Price	6½c	7½c	8½c	9¼c
Pipe inch	1	1¼	1½	2
Price	10½c	14½c	17½c	23c

No. 24E5741 Galvanized.

Pipe inches	¼	⅜	½	¾
Price	8½c	10½c	11½c	12½c
Pipe inches	1	1¼	1½	2
Price	15½c	20½c	26½c	33c

Malleable Reducers.

To reduce one size—size given is big end.

No. 24E5744 Black.

Pipe, inch	¼	⅜	½	¾
Price	2c	2c	2c	3½c
Pipe, inches	1	1¼	1½	2
Price	5½c	7½c	9½c	15½c

No. 24E5745 Galvanized.

Pipe inches	½	¾	1	1¼	1½	2
Price	3½c	5½c	8½c	10½c	14½c	24c

Cast Iron Plugs.

No. 24E5748 Black.

Pipe in.	¼	⅜	½	¾
Price	1½c	1½c	1½c	1½c
Pipe in.	1	1¼	1½	2
Price	2c	2½c	3½c	3½c

No. 24E5749 Galvanized.

Pipe in.	¼	⅜	½	¾	1	1¼	1½	2
Price	2c	2c	2c	2½c	3½c	4½c	5½c	6½c

Bushings.

Reducing one size outside size is given.

No. 24E5752 Black.

Pipe, in.	⅜	½	¾	1	1¼	1½	2
Price	2c	2c	2½c	2½c	2½c	3½c	4½c

No. 24E5753 Galvanized.

Pipe, in.	⅜	½	¾	1	1¼	1½	2
Price	3½c	3½c	4½c	4½c	5½c	7½c	9½c

Lock Nuts.

No. 24E5755

Pipe, in.	¼	⅜	½	¾
Price	2c	2c	2c	2c
Pipe, in.	1	1¼	1½	2
Price	3c	4c	5c	6c

Pipe Caps.

No. 24E5758 Black.

Pipe, inch	¼	⅜	½	¾
Price	2c	2½c	2½c	3½c
Pipe, inches	1	1¼	1½	2
Price	4c	5c	9½c	13c

No. 24E5759 Galvanized.

Pipe, in.	¼	⅜	½	¾	1	1¼	1½	2
Price	2c	2c	3c	3c	4c	7c	11c	16c

Nipples.

State length wanted.

All nipples 6 inches long or over will be charged at price per foot of iron pipe with cost of cutting threads added.

Size ins.	No. 24E5763 Black short, Price	No. 24E5764 Galvanized short, Price	No. 24E5765 Black long, Price	No. 24E5766 Galvanized long Price
¼	1½c	2c	2c	3c
⅜	1½c	2c	2½c	3c
½	1¾c	2c	2¾c	3¼c
¾	2c	2¾c	3c	4c
1	2¾c	3¾c	3½c	5½c
1¼	3¾c	4¾c	4¾c	8c
1½	4c	6c	6½c	9c
2	6c	7c	8½c	10c

Malleable Return Bends, Open Pattern.

No. 24E5769 Black.

Pipe, in.	½	¾	1
Price	5½c	11½c	16c
Pipe, in.	1¼	1½	2
Price	20c	27c	35c

Brass Straightway Double Gate Valves.

No. 24E5788 These Standard Double Disc Gate Valves have brass seats and rising stem, tested to 100 pounds steam pressure. In the construction of these valves the bearing of the wedge being central it acts uniformly on all parts of the disc, consequently it will force the disc to the seats and have an equal bearing on all parts. These valves are used either for steam or water where a full opening (same size of pipe), is required and will allow the water to be drained from pipes in cold weather.

Sizes	½	¾	1	1¼
Price	44c	60c	72c	$1.20
Sizes	1½	2	2½	3
Price	$1.81	$2.58	$4.81	$6.85

Standard Butterfly Valves.

No. 24E5820 All Brass Butterfly Valves, nothing better made.

Size, inches	¾	1	1¼	1½
Price	94c	$1.35	$1.73	$2.00
Size, inches		2	2½	3
Price		$3.30	$4.40	$6.60

Brass Globe Valves.

No. 24E5826

For pipe, inch	¼	⅜
Price	$0.21	$0.23
For pipe, inch	½	¾
Price	.30	.38
For pipe, inch	1	1¼
Price	.54	.75
For pipe, inch	1½	2
Price	1.05	1.59

Brass Angle Valves.

No. 24E5828

For pipe, inch	¼	⅜
Price	$0.21	$0.23
For pipe, inch	½	¾
Price	.30	.38
For pipe, inch	1	1¼
Price	.54	.75
For pipe, inch	1½	2
Price	1.05	1.59

Brass Cross Valves.

No. 24E5830

For pipe, inch	¼	⅜
Price	$0.44	$0.45
For pipe, inch	½	¾
Price	.53	.72
For pipe, inch	1	1¼
Price	.88	1.25
For pipe, inch	1½	2
Price	1.87	2.84

Horizontal Check Valves.

No. 24E5832.

For pipe, in.	¼	⅜
Price	21c	23c
For pipe, in.	½	¾
Price	29c	38c
For pipe, in.	1	1¼
Price	49c	69c
For pipe, in.	1½	2
Price	$0.95	$1.58

Horizontal Check Valve With Drip Cock.

No. 24E5833 Same as No. 24E5832, except it is equiped with Drip cock which enables you to drain any water that might remain in the seat of the valve.

For pipe, inches	½	¾	1
Price	78c	93c	$1.15
For pipe, inches		1¼	1½
Price		$1.48	$1.97

Brass Three-Way Cocks.

No. 24E5834

For pipe, in.	½	¾
Price	$0.75	$0.90
For pipe, in.	1	1¼
Price	1.12	1.72
For pipe, in.	1½	2
Price	2.14	3.30
For pipe, in.	2½	3
Price	6.00	7.00

Steam Cocks.

No. 24E5836 Brass Flat Head Steam Cocks, best quality.

For pipe, in.	¼	⅜
Price	$0.25	$0.30
For pipe, in.	½	¾
Price	.35	.46
For pipe, in.	1	1¼
Price	.69	1.11
For pipe, in.	1½	2
Price	1.45	2.18
For pipe, in.	2½	3
Price	4.59	6.74

Vertical Check Valves.

No. 24E5838 Brass Vertical Check Valves, best quality.

For pipe, in.	¼	⅜
Price	$0.24	$0.25
For pipe, in.	½	¾
Price	.33	.40
For pipe, in.	1	1¼
Price	.61	.80
For pipe, in.	1½	2
Price	1.10	1.78

Swing Check Valves.

No. 24E5840 Brass Swing Check Valve.

Size, in.	½	¾
Price	$0.66	$0.82
Size, in.	1	1¼
Price	1.04	1.27
Size, in.	1½	2
Price	1.65	2.24

Jenkins Bros.' Globe Valves.

No. 24E5850 Nothing better made in the way of a brass valve than Jenkins Bros.' Will last longer and give better satisfaction than any other make. All brass goods bearing the Jenkins brand are fully warranted.

Size, in.	⅛	¼	⅜	½	¾
Price	41c	42c	47c	60c	82c
Size, in.	1	1¼	1½	2	
Price	$1.10	$1.40	$2.05	$3.25	

Jenkins Bros.' Angle Valves.

No. 24E5852

Size, in.	⅛	¼	⅜	½	¾
Price	40c	41c	46c	59c	82c
Size, in.	1	1¼	1½	2	
Price	$1.11	1.42	2.07	3.30	

Jenkins Bros.' Cross Valves.

No. 24E5854

Size, in.	⅜	½	¾	1
Price	80c	90c	$1.02	$1.20
Size, in.	1¼	1½		2
Price	$1.85	$2.35		$3.80

Jenkins Bros.' Angle Check Valves.

No. 24E5856

Size, in.	⅜	½	¾	1
Price	45c	46c	71c	96c
Size, in.	1¼	1½	2	
Price	$1.35	$1.90	$2.85	

Jenkins Bros.' Horizontal Check Valves.

No. 24E5858

Size, in.	⅜	½	¾	1
Price	43c	46c	71c	97c
Size, in.	1¼	1½	2	
Price	$1.34	$1.91	$2.84	

Jenkins Bros.' Vertical Check Valves.

No. 24E5860

Size, in.	⅜	½	¾	1
Price	44c	47c	71c	98c
Size, in.	1¼	1½	2	
Price	$1.35	$1.92	$2.86	

Water Pipe Stops.

No. 24E5870 Brass Rough Stop, lever handle, screwed for iron pipe.

Size, inches	½	¾	1
Price, plain	29c	44c	74c
Size, inches	1¼	1½	2
Price, plain	$1.02	$1.52	$2.85

Check and Waste.

No. 24E5872 All Brass Check and Waste, lever handle, screwed for iron pipe.

Size, inches	½	¾	1	1¼	1½
Price	31c	48c	83c	$1.08	$1.58

Rough Brass Stop, T Handle.

No. 24E5874 Rough Brass Stop, T Handle, screwed for iron pipe.

Size, in.	½	¾
Price	29c	44c
Size, in.	1	1¼
Price	64c	$1.02
Size, in.		1½
Price		$1.51

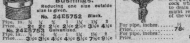

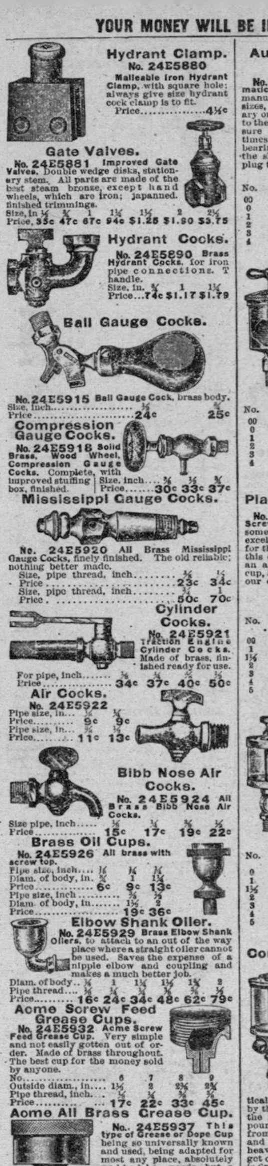

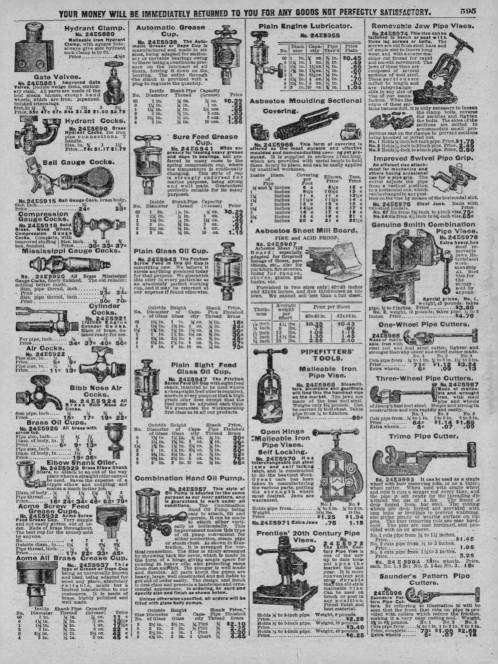

Hydrant Clamp.

No. 24E5880 **Malleable Iron Hydrant Clamp,** with square hole; always give size hydrant cock clamp is to fit.
Price........4½c

Gate Valves.

No. 24E5881 **Improved Gate Valves.** Double wedge disks, stationary stem. All parts are made of the best steam bronze, except hand wheels, which are iron; japanned, finished trimmings.

Size, in.	½	¾	1	1¼	1½	2	2½
Price	35c	47c	67c	94c	$1.25	$1.90	$3.75

Hydrant Cocks.

No. 24E5890 **Brass Hydrant Cocks,** for iron pipe connections. T handle.

Size, in.	¾	1	1¼
Price	74c	$1.17	$1.79

Ball Gauge Cocks.

No. 24E5915 **Ball Gauge Cock,** brass body.

Size, inch	½	¾
Price	24c	25c

Compression Gauge Cocks.

No. 24E5918 **Solid Brass, Wood Wheel, Compression Gauge Cocks.** Complete, with improved stuffing box, finished.

Size, inch	⅜	½	¾
Price	30c	33c	37c

Mississippi Gauge Cocks.

No. 24E5920 All Brass Mississippi Gauge Cocks, finely finished. The old reliable; nothing better made.

Size, pipe thread, inch	⅜	½
Price	23c	34c
Size, pipe thread, inch	¾	1
Price	50c	70c

Cylinder Cocks.

No. 24E5921 **Traction Engine Cylinder Cocks.** Made of brass, finished ready for use.

For pipe, inch	⅛	¼	⅜	½
Price	34c	37c	40c	50c

Air Cocks.

No. 24E5922

Pipe size, in.	⅛	¼
Price	9c	9c
Pipe size, in.	⅜	½
Price	11c	13c

Bibb Nose Air Cocks.

No. 24E5924 **All Brass Bibb Nose Air Cocks.**

Size pipe, inch	⅛	¼	⅜	½
Price	15c	17c	19c	22c

Brass Oil Cups.

No. 24E5926 **All brass with screw top.**

Pipe size, inch	⅛	⅛	⅛
Diam. of body, in.	¾	1	1¼
Price	6c	9c	13c
Pipe size, inch		⅜	½
Diam. of body, in.		1½	2
Price		19c	36c

Elbow Shank Oiler.

No. 24E5929 **Brass Elbow Shank Oilers,** to attach to an out of the way place where a straight oiler cannot be used. Saves the expense of a nipple elbow and coupling and makes a much better job.

Diam. of body	¾	1	1¼	1½	1¾	2
Pipe thread	⅛	¼	¼	⅜	⅜	½
Price	16c	24c	34c	48c	62c	79c

Acme Screw Feed Grease Cups.

No. 24E5932 **Acme Screw Feed Grease Cup.** Very simple and not easily gotten out of order. Made of brass throughout. The best cup for the money sold by anyone.

No.	6	7	8	9
Outside diam., in.	1½	2	2⅜	2¾
Pipe thread, inch	⅛	¼	⅜	⅜
Price	17c	22c	33c	45c

Acme All Brass Grease Cup.

No. 24E5937 **This type of Grease or Dope Cup** being so universally known and used, being adapted for most any place, absolutely reliable, needs but a limited introduction to our customers. It is made of brass, highly polished and well made.

No.	Inside Diameter	Shank Pipe Thread	Capacity (Grease)	Price
00	1 in.	⅛ in.	¼ oz.	11 c
0	1¼ in.	¼ in.	¾ oz.	13½c
1	1½ in.	¼ in.	1 oz.	17½c
2	2 in.	⅜ in.	2 oz.	22 c
3	2½ in.	½ in.	3½ oz.	42 c
4	3 in.	½ in.	5 oz.	45 c

Automatic Grease Cup.

No. 24E5938 **The Automatic Grease or Dope Cup** is manufactured and made in six sizes, being adapted for stationary or movable bearings owing to there being a continuous pressure on the lubricant at all times, forcing it down on the bearing. The outlet through the shank is provided with a plug to regulate the quantity.

No.	Inside Diameter	Shank Pipe Thread	Capacity (Grease)	Price
00	1 in.	⅛ in.	⅛ oz.	$0.39
0	1¼ in.	¼ in.	1 oz.	.52
1	1½ in.	¼ in.	1½ ozs.	.65
2	2 in.	⅜ in.	3 ozs.	.83
3	2½ in.	½ in.	6 ozs.	1.05
4	3 in.	½ in.	10 ozs.	1.56

Sure Feed Grease Cup.

No. 24E5941 **Made expressly for feeding heavy grease and dope to bearings,** and preferred in many cases to the spring compression cup, where the temperature is continually changing. This style of cup is strongly endorsed for marine purposes, being strong and well made. Guaranteed perfectly reliable for its many purposes.

No.	Inside Diameter	Shank Pipe Thread	Capacity (Grease)	Price
00	1 in.	⅛ in.	⅛ oz.	$0.29
0	1¼ in.	¼ in.	1 oz.	.35
1	1½ in.	¼ in.	1½ oz.	.46
2	2 in.	⅜ in.	3 oz.	.57
3	2½ in.	½ in.	6 oz.	.81
4	3 in.	½ in.	10 oz.	1.15

Plain Glass Oil Cup.

No. 24E5943 **The Friction Screw Feed in this Oil Cup is** something new. We believe it excels anything produced today for that purpose. We guarantee this oiler in every particular as an absolutely perfect working cup, and it may be returned at our expense if found otherwise.

No.	Outside Diameter of Glass	Height of Glass	Capacity	Shank Pipe Thread	Price, Finished Brass
00	1⅛ in.	1 in.	⅛ oz.	⅛ in.	18c
1	1½ in.	1⅜ in.	1 oz.	¼ in.	24c
1½	1¾ in.	1⅝ in.	1½ oz.	¼ in.	30c
2	2 in.	1⅞ in.	2½ oz.	⅜ in.	36c
3	2¼ in.	2⅛ in.	4 oz.	⅜ in.	45c
4	2½ in.	2⅜ in.	5 oz.	⅜ in.	57c
5	3 in.	3 in.	10 oz.	½ in.	73c

Plain Sight Feed Glass Oil Cup.

No. 24E5947 **The Friction Screw Feed Oil Cup** with sight feed shank, intended to be used where a cheap sight feed oiler is required, answers every purpose that a high grade oiler does except that the feed must be adjusted each time. We guarantee the workmanship first class as in all our products.

No.	Outside Diameter of Glass	Height of Glass	Capacity	Shank Pipe Thread	Price, Finished Brass
0	1¼ in.	1⅛ in.	⅜ oz.	⅛ in.	30c
1	1½ in.	1⅜ in.	1 oz.	¼ in.	36c
1½	1¾ in.	1⅝ in.	1½ oz.	¼ in.	43c
2	2 in.	1⅞ in.	2½ oz.	⅜ in.	50c
3	2¼ in.	2⅛ in.	4 oz.	⅜ in.	62c
4	2½ in.	2⅜ in.	5 oz.	⅜ in.	76c
5	3 in.	3 in.	10 oz.	½ in.	96c

Combination Hand Oil Pump.

No. 24E5957 **This style of Oil Pump is adapted for the same purpose as our lever pattern, and is guaranteed to work under all conditions.** The Combination Hand Oil Pump being easy to attach, fill and operate, it can be made to attach either vertically or horizontally. This improvement makes this type of oil pump convenient for either connection, steam pipe or steam chest. As shown in illustration, it is arranged for vertical connection. The filler is nicely arranged by throwing back the cover, which is made in the form of a hinge, giving ample space for pouring in heavy oils; also protecting same from dust and dirt. The plunger is well made and durable. All parts about the pump are heavy, large, well constructed and not liable to get out of order easily. The design and finish is first class and presents a handsome and ornamental appearance. **In ordering, be sure and specify size and finish as shown below.**

Unless otherwise specified, all orders will be filled with glass body pumps.

Size No.	Outside Diameter of Glass	Height of Glass	Capacity	Shank Pipe Thread	Price, Finished Brass
3	2½ in.	2⅜ in.	¼ Pint	⅜	$2.10
5	3 in.	3 in.	½ Pint	⅜	2.75
6	3½ in.	4 in.	1 Pint	½	3.30
8	4¼ in.	5 in.	1 Quart	½	4.45

Plain Engine Lubricator.

No. 24E5955

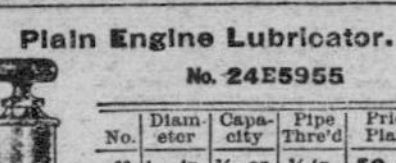

No.	Diameter	Capacity	Pipe Thre'd	Price Plain
00	1 in.	¼ oz.	⅜ in.	$0.45
0	1¼ in.	1 oz.	⅜ in.	.49
1	1½ in.	1¼ oz.	⅜ in.	.56
2	1¾ in.	1½ oz.	½ in.	.60
3	2 in.	2½ oz.	½ in.	.71
4	2¼ in.	4 oz.	½ in.	.70
5	2½ in.	5 oz.	½ in.	.80
6	3 in.	10 oz.	¾ in.	1.04

Asbestos Moulding Sectional Covering.

No. 24E5966 **This form of covering is offered as the most durable and effective moulded and non-conducting covering yet produced.** It is supplied in sections 3 feet long, which are provided with metal bands to hold them firmly in place, and can be easily applied by unskilled workmen.

Inside Diam. of Pipe		Covering per Foot	Elbows, Price	Tees, Price
½ and ¾	inches	8 c	8½c	12 c
1	inches	9½c	10½c	13 c
1¼	inches	11 c	11 c	13½c
1½	inches	11½c	11½c	14 c
2	inches	13 c	13 c	15 c
2½	inches	14½c	15 c	17 c
3	inches	16 c	17 c	19 c
3½	inches	18 c	19 c	21 c
4	inches	20 c	21 c	25½c

Asbestos Sheet Mill Board.

FIRE and ACID PROOF.

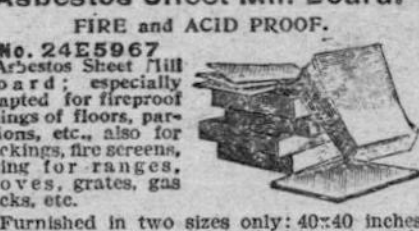

No. 24E5967 Asbestos Sheet Mill Board; especially adapted for fireproof linings of floors, partitions, etc., also for packings, fire screens, lining for ranges, stoves, grates, gas backs, etc.

Furnished in two sizes only: 40x40 inches and 42x44 inches, and five thicknesses as follows. We cannot sell less than a full sheet.

Thickness	Average weight per Sheet	Price per Sheet 40x40 in.	Price per Sheet 42x44 in.
1/16 inch	4¼ lbs.	$0.38	$0.43
⅛ inch	8 lbs.	.72	.80
3/16 inch	12 lbs.	1.08	1.15
¼ inch	14½ lbs.	1.30	1.45
⅜ inch	25 lbs.	2.25	2.40

PIPEFITTERS' TOOLS.

Malleable Iron Pipe Vise.

No. 24E5968 **Steamfitters, plumbers and gasfitters will find this the handiest vise on the market.** The jaws are made of the best tool steel. Weighs only 6½ pounds. Can be carried in tool chest. Takes pipe from ⅛ to 2 inches.
Price........80c

Open Hinge Malleable Iron Pipe Vises. Self Locking.

No. 24E5970 **Has interchangeable cut steel jaws and self locking latch, and is constructed to do the heaviest work. Great care has been taken in manufacturing the various parts, putting the strength where most desired. Jaws are warranted.**

	No. 1	No. 2
Holds pipe from	⅛ to 2 in.	⅛ to 3 in.
Weight	14½ lbs.	18 lbs.
Price	$1.25	$1.94
No. 24E5971 Extra Jaws	.75	1.15

Prentiss' 20th Century Pipe Vises.

No. 24E5972 **The 20th Century Pipe Vise** is one of the new up to date tools put upon the market the last year. It is more convenient and more durable than the old style malleable vise. Can be used on bench or post in any position. Finest finish and best material.

Holds ⅛ to 2-inch pipe. Weight, 8 pounds. Price........$2.28
Holds ⅛ to 3-inch pipe. Weight, 18 pounds. Price........$3.40
Holds ⅛ to 4-inch pipe. Weight, 40 pounds. Price........$6.25

Removable Jaw Pipe Vises.

No. 24E5974 **This vise can be fastened to bench or post with three lag screws or bolts.** The screws are cut from steel bars and of ample size to insure long wear, and with a coarse machine cut thread for rapid and smooth movement. The jaws of these vises are composed of several sections of tool steel. These sections are milled to length and are interchangeable in any size of vise of our manufacture. When the edges of these sections become dull, it is only necessary to loosen the clamp bolts, reverse the sections and tighten the bolts. The sides of the sections are milled to accommodate small projections cast on the clamps to prevent sections being knocked or jarred out.

No. 1 Holds ⅛-inch to 2-inch pipe. Price, $1.75
No. 2 Holds ⅛-inch to 3-inch pipe. Price, 2.45
No. 3 Holds ½-inch to 4-inch pipe. Price, 3.50

Improved Swivel Pipe Grip.

An efficient vise attachment for mechanics and others having occasional use for a pipe grip. The swivel adjusts the pipe from a vertical position to a horizontal one, which can be changed to any position on the vise by means of the horizontal slot.

No. 24E5975 **Steel Jaws.** Made with two-sized holders.

	Price
No. 67 fits from 2½-inch to 4-inch vise,	75c
No. 68 fits from 4½ inch to 5¾-inch vise,	85c

Genuine Smith Combination Pipe Vises.

No. 24E5976 **Extra heavy, has** steel removable jaws. Material and workmanship A1. Best vise for the money sold by anyone.

Special prices. No. 1, weight, 45 pounds; takes pipe, ⅛ to 2 inches. Price........$3.80
No. 2, weight, 72 pounds; takes pipe, ⅛ to 3 inches. Price........$4.70

One-Wheel Pipe Cutters.

No. 24E5985 **Made of malleable iron with** steel rod and tool steel cutter; lighter and stronger than any other one-wheel cutter made.

	No. 1	No. 2	No. 3
Cuts pipe from	⅛ to 1 in.	¾ to 2 in.	1¼ to 3 in.
Price	71c	$1.12	$3.24
Extra wheels	6c	.09	.13

Three-Wheel Pipe Cutters.

No. 24E5987 **Made of malleable and wrought iron, with steel pins and wheels** of Jessop's best tool steel. Simple and strong in construction and cuts rapidly and easily.

	No. 1	No. 2	No. 3
Cuts pipe from	⅛ to 1 in.	1 to 2 in.	2 to 3 in.
Price	84c	$1.14	$1.88
Extra wheels	5c	.07	.09

Trimo Pipe Cutter.

No. 24E5993 It can be used as a single wheel with burr removing rolls, or as a three-wheel cutter. When used with single wheel and rolls it cuts a square end every time, and the pipe is left ready for the threading die without the use of a file. The frame is drop forged from bar steel. The cutting wheels are drop forged and provided with long hubs or bearings to prevent wabbling, also giving plenty of wearing surface on the pins. The burr removing rolls are case hardened. The pins are case hardened, and provided with an oil groove.

No. 1 cuts pipe from ⅛ to 1¼ inches. Price........$1.45
No. 2 cuts pipe from ½ to 2 inches. Price........1.95
No. 3 cuts pipe from 1¼ to 3 inches. Price........3.25

No. 24 E 5994 Extra wheels. Price, each, No. 1, 13c; No. 2, 14c; No. 3, 18c

Saunder's Pattern Pipe Cutters.

No. 24E5996 **Saunders' Pattern Pipe Cutters.** By referring to illustration it will be seen that the front that rubs on pipe is provided with rollers which reduce the friction, making it a very easy cutting tool. Weight, 3¾ to 6¾ pounds.

	No. 1	No. 2	No. 3
Cuts pipe from	⅛ to 1 in.	1 to 2 in.	2 to 3 in.
Price, complete	73c	$1.08	$2.68
Extra wheels	6c	.07	.14

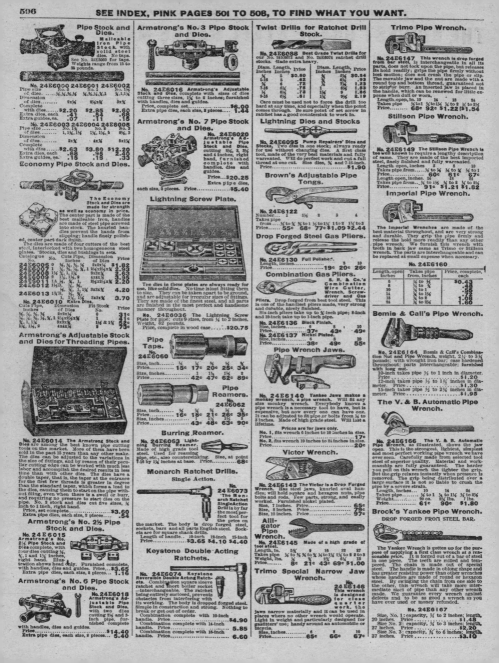

Pipe Stock and Dies.

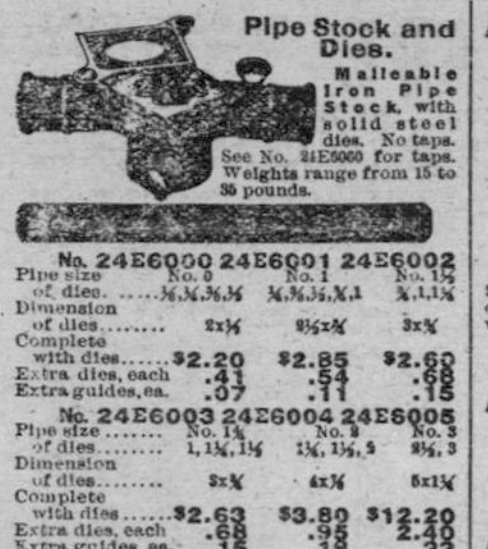

Malleable Iron Pipe Stock, with solid steel dies. No taps. See No. 24E6060 for taps. Weights range from 15 to 35 pounds.

No.	24E6000	24E6001	24E6002
Pipe size	No. 0	No. 1	No. 1½
of dies	⅛,¼,⅜,½	¼,⅜,½,¾,1	¾,1,1¼
Dimension of dies	2x½	2½x⅝	3x¾
Complete with dies	$2.20	$2.85	$2.60
Extra dies, each	.41	.54	.68
Extra guides, ea.	.07	.11	.15

No.	24E6003	24E6004	24E6005
Pipe size	No. 1½	No. 2	No. 3
of dies	1, 1¼, 1½	1¼, 1½, 2	2½, 3
Dimension of dies	3x¾	4x⅞	5x1¼
Complete with dies	$2.63	$3.80	$12.20
Extra dies, each	.68	.95	2.40
Extra guides, ea.	.15	.18	.33

Economy Pipe Stock and Dies.

The Economy Stock and Dies are made for strength as well as economy in price. The center part is made of the best malleable iron, handles are made of steel pipe screwed into stock. The knurled handles prevent the hands from slipping; handle finely polished, center part dark finish.

The dies are made of four cutters of the best steel, interlocked with two homogeneous steel plates. Stocks, dies and bushings in sets.

Catalogue No.	No.	Cuts Pipe, inches	Dimension of Dies	Price
24E6006	0	⅛, ¼, ⅜, ½	2x2x½	$1.82
24E6007	1	⅛, ⅜, ½, ¾, 1	2½x2½x¾	2.93
24E6008	1½	¾, 1, 1¼	3x3x¾	2.63
24E6009	2	1¼, 1½, 2	4x4x⅞	3.95
24E6011	1A	½, ¾, 1,	2½x2½x¾	2.20
24E6012	1½B,	¼, ⅜, ½, ¾, 1, 1¼	3x3x¾	4.20
24E6013	1¾B,	½, ¾, 1, 1¼, 1½	3x3x¾	3.70

No. 24E6010 Extra Dies.

Cuts Pipe, inches	Dimension of Dies	Fit Stock No.	Price
⅛, ¼, ⅜, ½	2x2x½	0	31c
⅛, ¼, ⅜, ½, ¾, 1	2½x2½x¾	1	41c
¾, 1, 1¼	3x3x¾	1½ & 1¾	52c
1¼, 1½, 2	4x4x⅞	2	73c

Armstrong's Adjustable Stock and Dies for Threading Pipes.

No. 24E6014 The Armstrong Stock and Dies are among the best known pipe cutting tools on the market. More of them have been sold in the past 15 years than any other make. The dies can be adjusted to the variations in the size of fittings, and by reason of their peculiar cutting edge can be worked with much less labor and accomplish the desired results in less time than with other dies. The dies have a double taper, that is, the taper at the entrance for the first few threads is greater in degree than the standard taper, which forms a lead to the dies, causing them to start on the pipe without filing, even when there is a swell or burr, and requiring no pressure to start dies on the pipe. No. 2 stock and dies cut five sizes, ¼ inch to 1 inch, right hand.

Price, set complete....................$3.60
Extra pipe dies, each size, 2 pieces.... .54

Armstrong's No. 2½ Pipe Stock and Dies.

No. 24E6015 Armstrong's No. 2½ Pipe Stock and Dies complete, with four dies cutting ½, ¾, 1 and 1¼ inches, right hand. Illustration shows head only. Furnished complete, with handles, dies and guides. Price....$3.65
Extra pipe dies, each size, 2 pieces... 1.16

Armstrong's No. 6 Pipe Stock and Dies.

No. 24E6018 Armstrong's Adjustable Pipe Stock and Dies, with two dies cutting 2½ and 3-inch pipe, furnished complete with handles, dies and guides.
Price....................$14.40
Extra pipe dies, each size, 2 pieces... 5.40

Armstrong's No. 3 Pipe Stock and Dies.

No. 24E6016 Armstrong's Adjustable Stock and Dies, complete with sizes of dies cutting three sizes, 1¼ to 2 inches; furnished with handles, dies and guides.
Price, complete set....................$6.00
Extra pipe dies, each size, 2 pieces.... 1.44

Armstrong's No. 7 Pipe Stock and Dies.

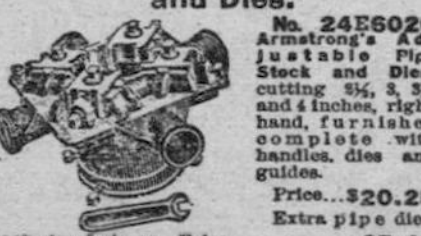

No. 24E6020 Armstrong's Adjustable Pipe Stock and Dies, cutting 2½, 3, 3½ and 4 inches, right hand, furnished complete with handles, dies and guides.
Price...$20.25
Extra pipe dies, each size, 2 pieces. Price....................$5.40

Lightning Screw Plate.

The dies in these plates are always ready for use, like solid dies. No time is lost fitting them to size. They can be taken apart to be ground, and are adjustable for irregular sizes of fittings. They are made of the finest steel, and all parts are finished in the most perfect and handsome manner throughout.

No. 24E6036 The Lightning Screw Plate for pipe; cuts 9 sizes, from ¼ to 2 inches. Weight, 62 pounds.
Price, complete in wood case.......$20.75

Pipe Taps. No. 24E6060

Size, inch	⅛	¼	⅜	½	¾
Price	15c	17c	20c	25c	34c
Size, inches	1	1¼	1½	2	
Price	42c	47c	62c	89c	

Pipe Reamers. No. 24E6062

Size, inch	⅛	¼	⅜	½	¾
Price	16c	18c	21c	26c	35c
Size, inches	1	1¼	1½	2	
Price	43c	48c	63c	90c	

Burring Reamer.

No. 24E6063 Lightning Burring Reamer. Made of high grade tool steel. Used for reaming pipe, etc., also countersinking. Size, at point 1-16 by 1¼ inches at base. Price..........68c

Monarch Ratchet Drills.

Single Action.

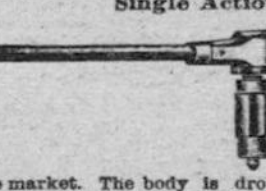

No. 24E6073 The Monarch Ratchet Single Action Drill is by far the most perfect tool for the price on the market. The body is drop forged steel, sockets, bars and all parts English steel. Sockets are for square shank drills.

Length of handle..	10-inch	12-inch	15-inch
Price	$3.65	$4.10	$4.40

Keystone Double Acting Ratchets.

No. 24E6074 Keystone Reversible Double Acting Ratchets. Combination square sleeve ratchet and short boiler socket—interchangeable. The ratchet being entirely enclosed, prevents obstacles from interfering with its working. The body is dropped forged steel. Simple in construction and strong. Nothing to break or get out of order.

Combination complete with 10-inch handle. Price....................$4.90
Combination complete with 14-inch handle. Price.................... 5.85
Combination complete with 16-inch handle. Price.................... 6.60

Twist Drills for Ratchet Drill Stock.

No. 24E6088 Best Grade Twist Drills for our No. 24E6073 and No. 24E6074 ratchet drill stocks. Made extra heavy.

Diam. Inches	Length, Inches	Price	Diam. Inches	Length, Inches	Price
¼	5	$0.60	⅝	5½	$0.84
5-16	5	.62	¾	6½	.93
⅜	6	.72	⅞	7½	1.23
7-16	6¼	.75	1	8½	1.53
½	6½	.78	1⅛	9	1.86
9-16	6½	.81	1¼	9½	2.19

Care must be used not to force the drill too hard at any time, and especially when the point comes through. Be sure point of set screw in ratchet has a good countersink to work in.

Lightning Dies and Stocks

No. 24E6095 Pump Repairers' Dies and Stocks, Two dies in one stock; always ready for use without changing dies. A first class tool, made of the very best materials and fully warranted. Will do perfect work and cut a full thread at one cut. Size dies, ⅜ and 7-16-inch.
Price....................$1.90

Brown's Adjustable Pipe Tongs.

No. 24E6122

Number	1	1½	2	3	4
Takes pipe from	⅛ to ¾	⅜ to 1	½ to 1¼	1 to 2	1¼ to 3
Price	55c	68c	77c	$1.09	$2.44

Drop Forged Steel Gas Pliers.

No. 24E6130 Full Polished.

Length, inches	6	8	10
Price	19c	20c	26c

Combination Gas Pliers.

S. R. & Co.'s Combination Wire Cutter, Wrench, Screwdriver and Gas Pliers. Drop forged from best tool steel. This is one of the handiest pliers made, very strong and durable, nicely finished.

Six-inch pliers take up to ⅜-inch pipe; 8-inch and 10-inch take up to 1-inch pipe.

No. 24E6136 Black Finish.

Size, inches	6	8	10
Price	37c	43c	49c

No. 24E6137 Nickel Plated.

Size, inches	6	8	10
Price	38c	49c	55c

Pipe Wrench Jaws.

No. 24E6140 Yankee Jaws makes a monkey wrench, a pipe wrench. Will fit any size monkey wrench. Everybody knows a pipe wrench is a necessary tool to have, but is expensive, but now every one can have one. It can be adjusted to fit pipe or bolts from ⅛ to 3 inches. Made of high grade steel. Will last a lifetime.

Prices are for jaws only.

No. 1, fits wrench 6 inches to 10 inches in size.
Price....................17c
No. 2, fits wrench 10 inches to 24 inches in size.
Price....................20c

Victor Wrench.

No. 24E6143 The Victor is a Drop Forged Wrench. Has steel jaws, knurled oval handles; will hold square and hexagon nuts, pipe bolts and rods. Few parts, strong, and easily worked. Furnished nickel plated.

Size, 7 inches. Price.................... 65c
Size, 8 inches. Price.................... 79c
Size, 10 inches. Price.................... 97c

Alligator Pipe Wrench.

No. 24E6145 Made of a high grade of tool steel.

Length, in.	5¾	9	15	22	27
Takes pipe	⅛ to ⅜	⅜ to ¾	½ to 1¼	1¼ to 2	2 to 3
Weight, lbs.	¼	¾	2¼	6¼	13
Price	8c	21c	43c	69c	$1.00

Trimo Special Narrow Jaw Wrench.

No. 24E6146 This wrench is designed for close quarter work, the jaws narrow materially and it can be used in places where no other wrench would operate. Light in weight and particularly designed for gasfitters' use; handy around an automobile or bicycle.

Size, inches	6	8	10
Price	65c	66c	67c

Trimo Pipe Wrench.

No. 24E6147 This wrench is drop forged from bar steel, is interchangeable in all its parts, does not lock upon the pipe, but releases its hold readily; grips the pipe firmly without lost motion; does not crush the pipe or slip. The movable jaw and the nut are made with a round top and bottom thread, guaranteed not to strip or burr. An inserted jaw is placed in the handle, which can be renewed for little expense when dull or worn.

Length, open, in.	10	14	18	24
Takes pipe	⅛ to 1	⅛ to 1½	⅛ to 2	½ to 2½
Price	68c	92c	$1.22	$1.84

Stillson Pipe Wrench.

No. 24E6149 The Stillson Pipe Wrench is too well known to require a lengthy description of same. They are made of the best imported steel, finely finished and fully warranted.

Length open, inches	6	8	10
Takes pipe from	⅛ to ½	⅛ to ¾	⅛ to 1
Price	60c	61c	67c
Length open, inches	14	18	24
Takes pipe from	⅛ to 1½	⅛ to 2	⅛ to 2½
Price	91c	$1.21	$1.82

Imperial Pipe Wrench.

The Imperial Wrenches are made of the best material throughout, and are very strong and durable. They grip the pipe firmly and release the hold more readily than any other pipe wrench. We furnish this wrench with teeth in back jaw same as Trimo or Stillson wrench. The parts are interchangeable and can be replaced at small expense when necessary.

No. 24E6160

Length, open inches	Takes pipe from, inches	Price, complete, each
6	⅛ to ½	$0.43
8	⅛ to ¾	.48
10	⅛ to 1	.55
14	¼ to 1½	.72
18	¼ to 2	1.08
24	¼ to 2½	1.60

Bemis & Call's Pipe Wrench.

No. 24E6164 Bemis & Call's Combination Nut and Pipe Wrench, weight, 2¼ to 3½ pounds; with wrought iron bar; case hardened throughout; parts interchangeable; furnished with long nut.

10-inch takes pipe ½ to 1 inch in diameter.
Price....................$1.20
12-inch takes pipe ½ to 1¼ inches in diameter. Price....................$1.30
15-inch takes pipe ½ to 2¼ inches in diameter. Price....................$1.95

The V. & B. Automatic Pipe Wrench.

No. 24E6166 The V. & B. Automatic Pipe Wrench, as illustrated, shows the jaw open. This is the strongest, lightest, simplest and most perfect working pipe wrench we have ever seen. Carefully made from selected tool steel of superior quality. Material and workmanship are fully guaranteed. The harder you pull on this wrench the tighter the grip. But the grip relaxes instantly when pressure is removed. The grip being distributed over a large surface it is not so liable to crush the pipe by a severe strain.

Length, inches	10	14	18
Takes pipe	⅛ to 1	⅛ to 1¼	½ to 2½
Weight	20 oz.	2¼ lbs.	7 lbs.
Price	61c	90c	$1.80

Brock's Yankee Pipe Wrench.

DROP FORGED FROM STEEL BAR.

The Yankee Wrench is gotten up for the purpose of supplying a first class wrench at a reasonable price. It is forged out of a bar of steel in one piece. The teeth are milled and tempered. The chain is made out of special steel. The handle is made in oblong shape and has greater resisting power than other wrenches whose handles are made of round or hexagon steel. By swinging the chain from one side to the other, this wrench will take more intermediate sizes of pipe than any other wrench made. We guarantee every wrench against defects and to be as good a wrench as you have ever used or money refunded.

No. 24E6167

Size, No. 1: capacity, ¼ to 2 inches; length, 20 inches. Price....................$1.48
Size No. 2: capacity, ¼ to 3 inches; length, 27 inches. Price....................$2.20
Size No. 3: capacity, ¾ to 6 inches; length, 37 inches. Price....................$3.10

THE HIGHEST GRADE STEEL RANGE MADE

For HARD COAL, SOFT COAL OR WOOD.

THIS IS OUR ACME TRIUMPH BLUE POLISHED STEEL RANGE, nickel trimmed, complete with high shelf and warming closet. EQUIPPED WITH THE FAMOUS PEQUABUCK OVEN THERMOMETER, THE BEST EVER BUILT, the exact same stoves as the Acme Triumphs illustrated and described on the two preceding pages, the only difference being in the equipment. You will note this stove has no reservoir, but is otherwise complete with high warming closet.

IT IS A SIX-HOLE, HIGH CLOSET RANGE, made from the highest grade polished blue steel plate made. A heavier plate than is used by other makers. Mounted on a handsome rococo base, beautifully nickel trimmed throughout, with nickel bands, brackets, doors, frame, corners, medallions, dampers, ornamentations, etc. It combines every high grade feature of every other high grade steel range, with the defects of none; asbestos lined, reinforced, braced and strengthened, will outwear two ordinary steel ranges, most economic in the consumption of fuel, even in the distribution of heat, a perfect baker, easy to operate, easy to handle. Every stove covered by our written binding guarantee. At the prices named, we furnish this range in the sizes and dimensions below. Prices do not include pipe or cooking utensils. For cooking utensils see pages 517 to 534. For our $1.00 to $5.00 C. O. D. subject to examination offer see page 716. Strongly crated and delivered on cars at our foundry in Newark, Ohio.

Price List of the Acme Triumph Six-Hole Polished Steel Plate Range, Without Reservoir, With High Closet.

Catalogue Number	Range No.	Size of Lids	Size of Oven, Inches	Size of Main Top, Inches	Size of End Shelf, Inches	Height to Main Top, Inches	Length of Fire Box for Wood, Inches	Size of Pipe to Fit Collar, Inches	Shipping Weight, Pounds	Price, with High Closet
22E35	8-16	No. 8	16x21x14	35x29	7½x21½	30½	26½	7	420	$24.37
22E36	8-18	No. 8	18x21x14	37x29	7½x21½	30½	26½	7	435	25.95
22E37	8-20	No. 8	20x21x14	39x29	7½x21½	30½	26½	7	440	28.08
22E38	9-18	No. 9	18x21x14	37x29	7½x21½	30½	26½	7	435	26.20
22E39	9-20	No. 9	20x21x14	39x29	7½x21½	30½	26½	7	440	28.33

Water Fronts for Acme Triumph Ranges. Each...... $2.50

Do not mistake water fronts for water reservoirs. If extension water reservoirs are wanted, see the preceding pages, showing catalogue Nos. 22E20 to 22E34.

A good, sensitive, quick working Oven Thermometer adds much to the comfort and convenience of those who do the baking. It measures heat just as the clock measures time; tells you when your oven has reached the degree of heat desired, and makes GOOD BAKING EASY TO THE INEXPERIENCED

WE CAN ALWAYS FURNISH REPAIRS FOR ACMES. SEE PAGE 721 ABOUT STOVE REPAIRS.

THE HIGHEST GRADE STEEL RANGE MADE FOR $22.43.

For Hard Coal, Soft Coal and Wood.

THIS IS OUR ACME TRIUMPH SIX-HOLE BLUE POLISHED STEEL RANGE, with full nickel trimming, nickel bands, rococo base, high back and shelf, exactly as illustrated, the same steel ran , as shown on this and the other two preceding pages. This illustrates the range without the reservoir, without the warming closet, but with the high back and shelf in the style that we furnish, all complete at from $22.43 to $26.40, according to style. GUARANTEED THE HIGHEST GRADE MADE.

We will be pleased to accept your order for this range or any one of our Acme Triumph Ranges, to be sent to you with the understanding and agreement that you can give the range 30 days' trial in your own home, during which time you can put it to every test, compare it with ranges sold by others at nearly double the price, and if you do not find it perfectly satisfactory in every way, the equal of any range made, regardless of price, if you do not find you have made a big saving in cost, you can return the range to us at our expense and we will immediately return your money, together with any freight charges paid by you.

REMEMBER the range is ready to set up. There is nothing to do but put in the pipe and then a fire. It burns hard coal, soft coal, wood or coke, burns anything that can be burnt in any stove, suitable for all countries, all conditions, all kinds of work. Made of blue polished steel, extra thick, the heaviest steel plate used by any maker; handsome nickel trimmings and mountings throughout, handsome heavy rococo base. We guarantee to always be prepared to furnish you repairs and parts promptly and at actual factory cost. We guarantee the stove to reach you in perfect condition. It will only take a day or two for your order to reach us and then a day or two for the stove to reach you. If you send us your order you will get the stove in just a few days. You will have very little freight to pay, 50 cents to $1.00 carries one of these stoves several hundred miles.

AT THE PRICES NAMED we furnish this range in the sizes and dimensions below. Prices do not include pipe or cooking utensils. For cooking utensils see pages 517 to 534. See page 716 for our liberal $1.00 to $5.00 C. O. D. subject to examination offer. Strongly crated and delivered on cars at our foundry at Newark, Ohio.

Price List of the Acme Triumph Six-Hole Polished Steel Plate Range, without Reservoir, with High Shelf.

Catalogue Number	Range Number	Size of Lids	Size of Oven, Inches	Size of Main Top, Inches	Size of End Shelf, Inches	Height to Main Top, Inches	Length of Fire Box for Wood, Inches	Size of Pipe to Fit Collar, Inches	Shipping Weight, Pounds	Price, with High Shelf
22E40	8-16	No. 8	16x21x14	35x29	7½x21½	30½	26½	7	400	$22.43
22E41	8-18	No. 8	18x21x14	37x29	7½x21½	30½	26½	7	415	24.01
22E42	8-20	No. 8	20x21x14	38x29	7½x21½	30½	26½	7	420	26.15
22E43	9-18	No. 9	18x21x14	37x29	7½x21½	30½	26½	7	415	24.26
22E44	9-20	No. 9	20x21x14	39x29	7½x21½	30½	26½	7	420	26.40

Water Fronts for Acme Triumphs, each.......................... $2.50

Do not mistake water fronts for water reservoirs. If extension water reservoirs are wanted, see the preceding pages, showing catalogue Nos. 22E20 to 22E34. See page 716 about hot water fronts.

THE HIGHEST GRADE STEEL RANGE MADE IN THE SQUARE STYLE

For HARD COAL, SOFT COAL or WOOD.

THIS IS THE ACME TRIUMPH STEEL RANGE, the exact same range as shown in the two illustrations above and in the two pages preceding, but as illustrated hereon and offered at $19.88 to $23.85, according to size as listed below, it comes in the square style without reservoir and without high shelf or warming closet, and in this particular style it is especially popular in towns and cities where they have a city water system, and where the city water systems are in use we are then asked to fit in this stove a water front. This we do when requested, at $2.50 extra.

THIS IS OUR REGULAR ACME TRIUMPH blue polished steel, nickel trimmed and nickel finished, asbestos lined, six-hole, rococo cast base steel range, made to burn hard coal, soft coal or wood; put out under our binding guarantee, and sent to any address anywhere on receipt of price, with the privilege of using it 30 days, during which time you can put it to every test, and if you are not satisfied you have gotten a better range than you could possibly buy elsewhere and at a big saving in cost to you, you can return it to us at our expense, and we will immediately return your money, together with any freight charges paid by you.

DON'T THINK IT WILL TAKE TOO LONG to get the stove. We will ship it the day we receive your order, for we always carry a big stock on hand. It will reach you in just a few days, you will have very little freight charges to pay. Stoves are taken by the railroad companies at a low freight rate (third class) and the freight will amount to from 50 cents to $2.50 for from 100 to 1,000 miles. Greater or less distances in proportion. The freight amounts to next to nothing compared with the amount of money we save you.

UNDERSTAND, we guarantee the stove to reach you in perfect order, guarantee it against breakage, and we bargain and agree to always furnish repairs in the years to come. We send you a book that makes it very simple for you to select any repair or part at any time, even ten years after you buy the stove.

REMEMBER, it comes practically ready for use, but a few minutes' work to put on the top lids, put up the stovepipe and start your fire. It requires no expert, no experience, you take no chance, and remember, with every stove, we issue our written binding guarantee, the strongest guarantee given with any stove made, by the terms and conditions of which if any piece or part gives out by reason of defect in material or workmanship we will repair or replace it free of charge.

Price List of the Acme Triumph Six-Hole Polished Steel Plate Range Without Reservoir. Strongly crated and delivered on the cars at our foundry in Newark, Ohio.

Catalogue Number	Range Number	Size of Lids	Size of Oven, Inches	Size of Main Top, Inches	Size of End Shelf, Inches	Height to Main Top, Inches	Length of Fire Box for Wood, Inches	Size of Pipe to Fit Collar, Inches	Shipping Weight, Pounds	Price
22E45	8-16	No. 8	16x21x14	35x29	7½x21½	30½	26½	7	350	$19.88
22E46	8-18	No. 8	18x21x14	37x29	7½x21½	30½	26½	7	365	21.47
22E47	8-20	No. 8	20x21x14	39x29	7½x21½	30½	26½	7	370	23.60
22E48	9-18	No. 9	18x21x14	37x29	7½x21½	30½	26½	7	365	21.72
22E49	9-20	No. 9	20x21x14	39x29	7½x21½	30½	26½	7	370	23.85

A Perfect Beauty.

Sears, Roebuck & Co., Chicago, Ill. New Philadelphia, Ohio.

Gentlemen:—I am perfectly satisfied with the range, and think it a perfect beauty. Owing to the prices they ask for ranges here I am sure I saved at least $15.00 by buying of you. Very truly yours,

W. J ADDLEMAN.

Water Fronts for Acme Triumphs, each.......................... $2.50

Do not mistake water fronts for water reservoirs. If extension water reservoirs are wanted, see the preceding pages, showing catalogue Nos. 22E20 to 22E34.

THE BEST BLACK ENAMELED STEEL RANGE MADE, $25.07

FOR HARD COAL, SOFT COAL OR WOOD.

THIS IS OUR ACME REGAL black enameled, nickel trimmed steel range with complete equipment, exactly as illustrated, including our famous Pequabuck thermometer, rustproof cast iron reservoir casing with porcelain lined water tank, high warming closet, duplex grate, full equipment throughout, which we furnish at from $25.07 to $29.04, according to size as per list below, which we put out under our binding guarantee as in every way the highest grade black enameled, nickel trimmed steel range on the market.

THIS RANGE is made of heavier steel than goes into any other steel range on the market. We have equipped our factory with special steel working machinery that we might cut, punch, shape, bend, draw and in other ways handle a much heavier steel plate than is handled in any other steel range factory in America, and all this is done with a view of furnishing our customers a stronger, more lasting, more economical fuel consuming, better baking and easier regulating style range than is made by any other maker.

DIFFERENT FROM ALL OTHER MAKES, this stove is asbestos lined throughout. The asbestos being fireproof and a nonconductor controls the heat, adds greatly to the life of the stove, adds wonderfully to its baking possibilities, makes it easy to control and makes it an economical fuel consumer.

THE ACME REGAL as illustrated hereon is furnished in five different sizes as listed below, is made of the highest grade material throughout; main top, covers and centers are made from cast plate from Birmingham iron, is furnished with one graduated lid and five solid covers, heavily nickel plated throughout, nickel bands in front and around warming closet, nickel bracket shelves, corners, doors, medallions and trimmings, richly nickel plated and handsomely decorated oven door frame, the most beautifully nickel trimmed steel range on the market, the heaviest steel plate ever used on a range; all asbestos lined throughout, a range that will be practically as good as new after the ordinary range is worn out. Understand, this stove burns anything, hard coal, soft coal, coke or wood.

THIS ILLUSTRATION shows the stove with complete equipment, rustproof cast iron reservoir casing deep porcelain lined reservoir, high shelf, bracket and warming closet, all complete. We also furnish the exact same stove in five other styles of equipment, as shown on the next two pages following. The stoves, however, are exactly alike, the only difference being in the equipment, and you will note we furnish this stove in various sizes at from $17.55 upwards, as shown on the next two following pages. If you order a steel range we advise by all means that you select one of the highest grade, either this, our **Acme Regal** or **Acme Triumph.** They are heavy steel plate stoves, stoves that are so much heaver, so much stronger, so much more lasting so much more economic in the consumption of fuel, so much more even in the distribution of heat, so much better bakers and can be handled so much more easily than any other steel ranges made. **PRICES DO NOT INCLUDE PIPE OR COOKING UTENSILS.** **FOR COOKING UTENSILS SEE PAGES 517 TO 534.**

We furnish this stove exactly as illustrated in the different sizes at the following prices:

Price List of the ACME REGAL 6-HOLE STEEL RANGE with Porcelain Lined Reservoir and High Closet. Strongly crated and delivered on the cars at our foundry in Newark, Ohio.

Catalogue Number	Range No.	Size of Lids	Size of Oven, Inches	Main Top, Including Reservoir	Height to Main Top, Inches	Length of Fire Box for Wood	Size of Pipe to Fit Collar	Shipping Weight	PRICE
22E50	8-16	No. 8	16x21x14	46x29	30½	26½ in.	7 in.	470 lbs.	$25.07
22E51	8-18	No. 8	18x21x14	48x29	30½	26½ in.	7 in.	485 lbs.	26.66
22E52	8-20	No. 8	20x21x14	50x29	30½	26½ in.	7 in.	490 lbs.	28.79
22E53	9-18	No. 9	18x21x14	48x29	30½	26½ in.	7 in.	485 lbs.	26.91
22E54	9-20	No. 9	20x21x14	50x29	30½	26½ in.	7 in.	490 lbs.	29.04

ENTIRELY SATISFIED. SAVED $15.00.

Sears, Roebuck & Co., Chicago, Ill. St. Johns, Ohio.

Gentlemen:—The Acme Regal Range which I purchased of you is giving entire satisfaction. It is a splendid baker, burns nicely, and takes very little fuel; in fact it is as good as ranges costing from $10.00 to $15.00 more at the retail dealers.

Wishing you success, I remain, Respectfully, LOUIS B. DOBIE.

THE HIGHEST GRADE BLACK ENAMELED STEEL RANGE MADE.

THIS IS THE ACME REGAL HIGH SHELF AND RESERVOIR STEEL RANGE, FOR HARD COAL, SOFT COAL OR WOOD. Put out under our guarantee as the HEAVIEST STEEL PLATE, strongest, handsomest, best made, best finished and most lasting black enameled, nickel trimmed steel range made in any foundry in America.

SEND US YOUR ORDER AT THE SPECIAL PRICES NAMED, we will send the stove to you with the understanding and agreement, first, that it must reach you in perfect condition, and if any piece or part is broken, cracked, or in any way damaged, we will replace or repair it free of charge, send you a new stove or return you your money as you may direct. You can give the stove 30 days' trial in your own home, during which time you can put it to every test, compare it with stoves that sell generally at double the price, and if you are not convinced that you have gotten the best black enameled, nickel trimmed steel range on the market and at a big saving in cost to you, you can return the stove to us at our expense, and we will immediately return your money together with any freight charges paid by you. See page 716, showing how strongly we crate our stoves.

50 CENTS TO $1.50 will carry this range from one hundred to five hundred miles from the foundry according to distance. Greater or lesser distances in proportion. We guarantee it to reach you in perfect order, we will furnish you any repairs or parts you may want in the years to come, and in shipping the stove we will mail you a little book which tells you just how to order any piece or part. It will only take you a few days to get the stove. We carry them in stock ready to ship the day your order is received, and a day or two will carry this stove to you hundreds of miles away.

YOU TAKE NO RISK in ordering this steel range from us, for if you do not find it the best steel range made, the strongest, most lasting, most satisfactory steel range you ever used, you can return it to us at our expense and get your money back. Every range is covered by our written, binding guarantee, covering every piece and part that enters into the stove.

YOU WILL SHARE IN THE PROFITS of our business if you send us your order for this or any other range. Part of the money you send us will come back to you in the shape of profit, as is fully explained in the last pages of this book.

IF YOU WANT A STEEL RANGE we especially urge that you select one of our Acme Regal steel ranges or our blue polished Acme Triumph, the highest grade steel ranges made. We recommend these ranges in preference to our Acme Renown or Acme Hummer, for the Acme Regal and Acme Triumph have the heaviest steel plate and are the strongest and highest grade steel ranges made. No such high grade steel range work goes out of any other foundry in America.

WE HAVE EQUIPPED OUR FOUNDRY at Newark, Ohio, with every facility for making the highest grade steel ranges on the market. We have had built for us special heavy steel working machinery that we might draw, bend, shape, cut, punch and in a general way handle a heavier steel plate than is used in other range foundries. Our nickeling plant is built with a view of putting on a much heavier nickel plate on the nickel work. Ours, so far as we know, is the only steel range plant that has a department for asbestos lining, and all steel ranges are given a heavy asbestos lining. Every part is cut, shaped and made true to gauge, insuring a perfect fit, and in this way we get a stronger, handsomer, more lasting, more economical fuel consuming, a better baking and an altogether higher grade range than is made in any other foundry.

ASK YOUR NEIGHBORS who have bought stoves from us how we have pleased them and how much money we have saved them. Don't buy a range or stove of any kind until you first give us the opportunity of placing one of our ranges or stoves in your home on our 30 days' trial plan. Don't think the freight charges will be too much, don't think you will be delayed in getting the stove, don't think you will have any trouble in setting it up and working it, don't think there will be any trouble about getting repairs in the years to come. We guarantee you against all this, and after you have given the stove 30 days' trial if you are not perfectly satisfied with it, send it back at our expense, and we will immediately return your money; but in selecting a steel range we especially urge that you take either one of our Acme Regals or Acme Triumphs.

$23.32 to $27.29 IN ANY OF THE FOLLOWING SIZES AS LISTED BELOW. Prices do not include pipe or cooking utensils. For cooking utensils see pages 517 to 534.

SEE PAGE 716 FOR OUR LIBERAL $1.00 TO $5.00 C. O. D. SUBJECT TO EXAMINATION OFFER.

PRICE LIST OF THE ACME REGAL SIX-HOLE STEEL RANGE WITH PORCELAIN LINED RESERVOIR AND HIGH SHELF. Strongly crated and delivered on board cars at our foundry in Newark, O.

Catalogue Number	Range No.	Size of Lids	Size of Oven, Inches	Main Top Including Reservoir	Height to Main Top	Fire Box for Wood	Pipe Collar	Shipping Weight, Lbs.	Price
22E55	8-16	No. 8	16x21x14	46x29	30½	26½	7 in.	450	$23.32
22E56	8-18	No. 8	18x21x14	48x29	30½	26½	7 in.	465	24.91
22E57	8-20	No. 8	20x21x14	50x29	30½	26½	7 in.	470	27.04
22E58	9-18	No. 9	18x21x14	48x29	30½	26½	7 in.	465	25.16
22E59	9-20	No. 9	20x21x14	50x29	30½	26½	7 in.	470	27.29

THIS IS THE REGULAR STYLE SIX-HOLE STEEL RANGE. Equipped with our famous Pequabuck thermometer, rustproof cast iron reservoir casing and porcelain lined water reservoir. The main top, covers and centers are made from the finest cast stove plate, the entire body from the very best cold rolled heavy steel plate, a heavier steel plate than is used in any other steel range made; nickel bands, corners, oven door frame, doors, brackets, shelves, medallions, dampers, trimmings, etc. It combines every high grade feature of every other high grade steel range made, with the defects of none. Burns hard coal, soft coal, coke or wood. Comes ready to put on the loose parts and stove pipe and start the fire, exactly the same range as is shown on preceding page in the large illustration, the only difference being that this range has the high shelf instead of the warming closet.

OUR SPECIAL PRICES OF $23.32 TO $27.29 barely covers the cost of material and labor in our own foundry, with but our one small percentage of profit added.

SAVED $20.00.

Huntsville, Kan.

Sears, Roebuck & Co.,
Chicago, Ill.

Dear Sirs:—Will say we are more than pleased with the Acme Regal. It reached us in perfect order and am highly pleased with it. It is all that it is represented to be. I just saved about $20.00 on the stove. If I had bought here I would have had to pay about $45.00 for the same stove. I ordered a stove for my brother-in-law, and they say as I do about the stove. I remain, yours respectfully,
JOHN WITHRODER.

$23.32 TO $27.29

THE HEAVY PLATE ACME REGAL WITHOUT HIGH SHELF.

THIS IS THE SIX-HOLE COAL OR WOOD BURNING ACME REGAL STEEL RANGE, the exact same range as shown in the illustration above and in the large full page illustration on preceding page, excepting it is without high shelf or warming closet, but complete with deep porcelain lined reservoir, exactly as shown in the illustration.

THIS IS A REGULAR SIX-HOLE STOVE, equipped with our famous Pequabuck thermometer, rustproof cast iron reservoir casing and porcelain lined water tank; made to burn hard coal, soft coal, coke or wood, made in the five different sizes as listed below, made with deep porcelain lined reservoir with the fullest equipment of nickel trimming, nickel bands, nickel corners, nickel frames, doors, medallions, bolts, hinges, etc., everything the highest grade, everything the best, one of the handsomest stoves on the market, a steel range that will out wear two ordinary steel ranges; heavier steel plate than is used on any other steel range made, more bracing, back lining, staying, bolting, etc., asbestos lining throughout, a range embodying every good feature of every other high grade range made, with the defects of none, such a range as you can get from no other house, a range built in our own foundry at Newark, Ohio, the largest foundry in the world, and offered to you at the actual cost to us, the cost of material and labor, with but our one small percentage of profit added.

EVERY RANGE bears the name "Acme Regal, Newark Stove Works, Chicago." Our name does not appear on any stove. This makes it possible for stove dealers to order stoves from us to sell again. They can add whatever profit they like and their customer need not know from whom they bought or how much they paid for the stove or the profit they are asking. We have a large trade among big stove dealers as well as consumers, for the price we name is lower than any dealer can buy elsewhere in carload lots.

A VISIT TO OUR STOVE FOUNDRY at Newark, Ohio, a picture which appears on the introductory page, will convince any stove buyer or stove maker that we are in a position to make better stoves at a lower cost than any other maker in America. More than two thousand people are employed in this stove foundry. We have our own railroad yards, electric conveyers, an endless amount of polishing, nickeling, finishing, steel drawing, shaping, cutting and punching machinery, etc., a vastly greater variety of labor saving and high quality making machinery than will be found in any other foundry. The raw material, such as pig iron, steel, nickel, etc., is bought in so much larger quantities than other makers can buy that it gives us a great advantage in cost. Much of the work that others do by hand we do by machinery. Every facility is introduced to reduce the labor and improve quality, and you, the buyer, get every benefit, for we offer you this stove at the actual cost to produce, the cost to us in our own foundry at Newark, Ohio, with but our one small percentage of profit added.

YOU TAKE NO RISK IN ORDERING A STEEL RANGE FROM US. Don't hesitate a moment on the question of freight charges, delay, ability to set up and operate or future repairs, for we guarantee you absolutely against any possible disappointment in this direction. We have a large stock of these stoves on hand and can ship your order the day it is received. It will only take a few days for your order to reach us and the stove to reach you. We guarantee it to reach you in perfect condition. We send with every stove a written binding guarantee. The stove is ready to set up and use and anyone can set the stove up in a few minutes, put in the pipe and you are ready for the fire. You will find it will operate perfectly, you will find it will use less fuel than other stoves, bake better, be handsomer in appearance and last longer than any other steel range made.

ABOUT REPAIRS. We will send you a little booklet that will tell you just how, in the years to come, you can order from us any piece or part, which we guarantee we will furnish you when wanted at actual factory cost, a mere fraction of what others charge for parts and repairs.

YOU WILL FIND THE FREIGHT CHARGES will amount to next to nothing compared with what you will save in cost. This stove can be shipped to almost any point in Ohio, Pennsylvania, New York, New England, Virginias, Illinois, Michigan, Indiana, Iowa or Wisconsin for from 25 cents to $2.50. Greater distances in proportion. If you order this stove from us and do not get it promptly and in perfect order, and do not find that you have saved more than ten times the freight charges you can return it to us at our expense, and we will immediately return your money.

WE BUILD CHEAPER STEEL RANGES (Refer to the Acme Hummer and Acme Renown) but they are built of lighter steel plate, they are made lighter throughout, and while they will give first class satisfaction, will outlast many ranges that are made and sold by others at double the price, we especially urge in ordering a steel range that you order the best steel range possible to build, either the black enameled nickel trimmed Acme Regal in this or one of the other styles, or the blue polished steel Acme Triumph, for in these ranges you get the best that money can buy.

DON'T OVERLOOK OUR CUSTOMERS' PROFIT SHARING PLAN. Remember, if you send us an order for a range, part of your money will come back to you in the shape of your share of the profit in our business, as fully explained in the last pages of this catalogue. We have a system by which our customers share liberally in our profits, and all this is made plain in the last pages of this book. If you are thinking of buying a stove of any kind, if you have looked at the stove in your home market, have learned their prices, delay just a few days and send us your order for one of our ranges or other stoves on our 30 days' trial plan. Set each stove up in your home, try them out thoroughly, and if we don't give you a much better stove at a much lower price than you can buy elsewhere, send it back to us and get your money back. You take no risk, you have everything to gain, for if we don't please you and save you money we don't want you to keep our stove; if we do please you and save you money you cannot afford to buy a stove of another make.

OUR SPECIAL PRICES $21.43 TO $26.39 for sizes listed below. Prices do not include pipe or cooking utensils. For cooking utensils, see pages 517 to 534. See page 716 for our liberal $1.00 to $5.00 C. O. D. Subject to Examination Offer.

PRICE LIST of the ACME REGAL SIX-HOLE STEEL RANGE with PORCELAIN LINED RESERVOIR. Strongly crated and delivered on board cars at our foundry in Newark, Ohio.

Catalogue Number	Range No.	Size of Lids	Size of Oven, Inches	Main Top Including Reservoir	Height to Main Top	Fire Box for Wood	Pipe Collar	Shipping Weight, Lbs.	Price
22E60	8-16	No. 8	16x21x14	46x29	30½	26½	7 in.	400	$21.43
22E61	8-18	No. 8	18x21x14	48x29	30½	26½	7 in.	415	23.02
22E62	8-20	No. 8	20x21x14	50x29	30½	26½	7 in.	420	25.14
22E63	9-18	No. 9	18x21x14	48x29	30½	26½	7 in.	415	23.27
22E64	9-20	No. 9	20x21x14	50x29	30½	26½	7 in.	420	26.39

STOVE REPAIRS. PLEASE NOTICE.—We can always furnish repairs for Acmes. In ordering repairs for stoves, it is very important to give your purchase invoice number or the most complete and explicit information possible. By strictly adhering to the following rules, a great deal of annoyance, expense and delay may be averted. 1st. State whether stove is for coal only, for wood only, or a combined wood and coal burning construction. 2d. If cook stove or range, say if square top or with reservoir. 3d. The back of the stove is at the pipe collar. Stand facing the hearth on a cook stove or facing the oven door of a range. 4th. Give full number, shown on outside of main top. In many instances the same size of griddle holes are placed on different stove bodies, namely, 7-18, 8-18, 8-20, 9-20, etc., and the single No. 7, 8 or 9 in this instance would be no indication of the correct size of the stove. 5th. Be particular to furnish all dates of patents. 6th. When legs are desired, say if stove is supplied with legs only or on leg base. 7th. Give name of stove in full.

A strict observance of these directions will be mutually advantageous.

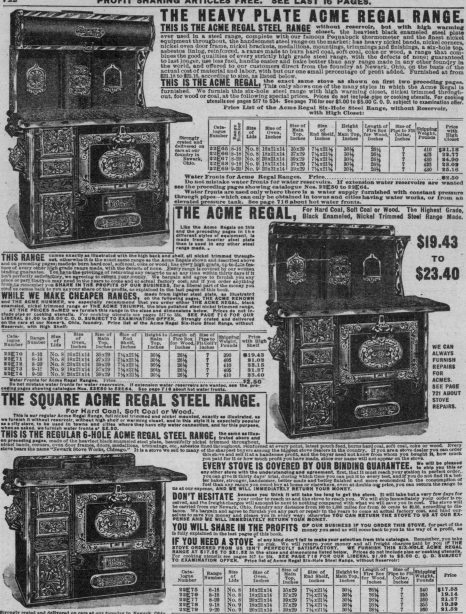

THE HEAVY PLATE ACME REGAL RANGE.

THIS IS THE ACME REGAL STEEL RANGE without reservoir, but with high warming closet, the heaviest black enameled steel plate ever used in a steel range, complete with our famous Pequabuck thermometer and the finest nickel equipment throughout, the handsomest steel range on the market; has heavy nickel bands, nickel corners, nickel oven door frame, nickel brackets, medallions, mountings, trimmings and finishings, a six-hole top, asbestos lining, reinforced, a range made to burn hard coal, soft coal, coke or wood, a range that combines the good qualities of every strictly high grade steel range, with the defects of none; guaranteed to last longer, use less fuel, handle easier and bake better than any range made in any other foundry in the world, and offered to our customers direct from the foundry at Newark, Ohio, on the basis of the actual cost of material and labor, with but our one small percentage of profit added. Furnished at from $21.18 to $25.16, according to size, as listed below.

THIS IS THE ACME REGAL, the exact same stove as shown on first two preceding pages. This only shows one of the many styles in which the Acme Regal is furnished. We furnish this six-hole steel range with high warming closet, nickel trimmed throughout, for wood or coal, at the following special prices. Prices do not include pipe or cooking utensils. For cooking utensils see pages 517 to 534. See page 716 for our $1.00 to $5.00 C. O. D. subject to examination offer.

Price List of the Acme Regal Six-Hole Steel Range, without Reservoir, with High Closet:

Strongly crated and delivered on cars at our foundry in Newark, Ohio.

Catalogue Number	Range Number	Size of Lids	Size of Oven, Inches	Size of Main Top, Inches	Size of End Shelf, Inches	Height to Main Top, Inches	Length of Fire Box for Wood, Inches	Size of Pipe to Fit Collar, Inches	Shipping Weight, Pounds	Price with High Closet
22E65	8-16	No. 8	16x21x14	35x29	7½x21½	30½	26½	7	410	$21.18
22E66	8-18	No. 8	18x21x14	37x29	7½x21½	30½	26½	7	425	22.77
22E67	8-20	No. 8	20x21x14	39x29	7½x21½	30½	26½	7	430	24.90
22E68	9-18	No. 9	18x21x14	37x29	7½x21½	30½	26½	7	425	23.02
22E69	9-20	No. 9	20x21x14	39x29	7½x21½	30½	26½	7	430	25.16

Water Fronts for Acme Regal Ranges. Price..............................$2.50

Do not mistake water fronts for water reservoirs. If extension water reservoirs are wanted see the preceding pages showing catalogue Nos. 22E50 to 22E64.

Water fronts are used only where there is a water supply furnished with constant pressure through pipes—which can only be obtained in towns and cities having water works, or from an elevated pressure tank. See page 716 about hot water fronts.

THE ACME REGAL, For Hard Coal, Soft Coal or Wood. The Highest Grade, Black Enameled, Nickel Trimmed Steel Range Made.

Like the Acme Regals on this and the preceding pages in the different styles of equipment, is made from heavier steel plate than is used in any other steel range made.

$19.43 TO $23.40

WE CAN ALWAYS FURNISH REPAIRS FOR ACMES. SEE PAGE 721 ABOUT STOVE REPAIRS.

THIS RANGE comes exactly as illustrated with the high back and shelf, all nickel trimmed throughout, otherwise it is the exact same range as the Acme Regals shown and described above and on preceding pages; made to burn hard coal, soft coal, coke or wood; has every high grade, up to date feature of every other high grade range made, with the defects of none. Every range is covered by our written binding guarantee. You have the privilege of returning any range to us at any time within thirty days if it isn't perfectly satisfactory, we agreeing to return your money. We bargain and agree to furnish you any piece or part that you may need in the years to come and at actual factory cost; and if you order anything from us remember you SHARE IN THE PROFITS OF OUR BUSINESS, for a liberal part of the money you send us comes back to you as your share of the profits, as explained in the last pages of this book.

WHILE WE MAKE CHEAPER RANGES, made from lighter steel plate, as illustrated on the following pages, THE ACME RENOWN and THE ACME HUMMER, we especially recommend that you order either THE ACME REGAL, black enameled, nickel trimmed range or THE ACME TRIUMPH, the blue polished steel nickel trimmed range.

AT THE PRICES NAMED we furnish this range in the sizes and dimensions below. Prices do not include pipe or cooking utensils. For cooking utensils see pages 517 to 534. SEE PAGE 716 FOR OUR LIBERAL $1.00 to $5.00 C. O. D. SUBJECT TO EXAMINATION OFFER. Strongly crated and delivered on the cars at our Newark, Ohio, foundry. Price list of the Acme Regal Six-Hole Steel Range, without Reservoir, with High Shelf:

Catalogue Number	Range Number	Size of Lids	Size of Oven, Inches	Size of Main Top, Inches	Size of End Shelf, Inches	Height to Main Top, Inches	Length of Fire Box for Wood, Inches	Size of Pipe to Fit Coll'r Inches	Shipping Weight, Pounds	Price with High Shelf
22E70	8-16	No. 8	16x21x14	35x29	7½x21½	30½	26½	7	390	$19.43
22E71	8-18	No. 8	18x21x14	37x29	7½x21½	30½	26½	7	405	21.02
22E72	8-20	No. 8	20x21x14	39x29	7½x21½	30½	26½	7	410	23.15
22E73	9-18	No. 9	18x21x14	37x29	7½x21½	30½	26½	7	405	21.27
22E74	9-20	No. 9	20x21x14	39x29	7½x21½	30½	26½	7	410	23.40

Water Fronts for Acme Regal Ranges. Price..............................$2.50

Do not mistake water fronts for water reservoirs. If extension water reservoirs are wanted, see the preceding pages showing catalogue Nos. 22E50 to 22E64. See page 716 about hot water fronts.

THE SQUARE ACME REGAL STEEL RANGE.

For Hard Coal, Soft Coal or Wood.

This is our regular Acme Regal Range, full nickel trimmed and nickel mounted, exactly as illustrated, as we furnish it without reservoir, without high shelf or warming closet, and in this style it is especially popular as a city stove, to be used in towns and cities where they have city water connection, and for this purpose, when so asked, we furnish water fronts at $2.50.

THIS IS THE REGULAR 6-HOLE ACME REGAL STEEL RANGE, the same as illustrated above and on preceding pages, made of the heaviest black enameled steel plate, beautifully nickel trimmed throughout, nickel bands, corners, oven door frames, doors, medallions, trimmings, etc., asbestos lined throughout, reinforced at every point, latest pouch feed, burns hard coal, soft coal, coke or wood. Every stove bears the name "Newark Stove Works, Chicago." It is a stove we sell to many of the sharpest buyers among the biggest stove dealers in the country. If you are a stove dealer you can order this stove and sell it at a handsome profit, and the buyer need not know from whom you bought it, how much you paid for it or how much profit you have made, since our name will not appear on the stove.

EVERY STOVE IS COVERED BY OUR BINDING GUARANTEE. We will be pleased to ship you this or any other stove with the understanding and agreement, first, that it must reach your station in perfect order, you can give it thirty days' trial, during which time you can put it to every test, and if you do not find it a better baker, stronger, handsomer, better made and better finished and more economical in the consumption of fuel than any range you could buy at home or elsewhere, even at double our price, you can return the range to us at our expense, AND WE WILL IMMEDIATELY RETURN YOUR MONEY.

DON'T HESITATE because you think it will take too long to get the stove. It will take but a very few days for your order to reach us and the stove to reach you. We will ship immediately your order is received, and the freight charges will amount to next to nothing compared with what we will save you in cost. The stove will be carried from our Newark, Ohio, foundry any distance from 100 to 1,000 miles for from 50 cents to $2.50, according to distance. We bargain and agree to furnish you any part or repair in the years to come at actual factory cost, and bind ourselves to save you money and please you in every way; otherwise YOU CAN RETURN THE STOVE TO US AT OUR EXPENSE AND WE WILL IMMEDIATELY RETURN YOUR MONEY.

YOU WILL SHARE IN THE PROFITS OF OUR BUSINESS IF YOU ORDER THIS STOVE, for part of the money you send us will come back to you in the way of a profit, as is fully explained in the last pages of this book.

IF YOU NEED A STOVE of any kind don't fail to make your selection from this catalogue. Remember, you take no risk. We will return your money and all freight charges paid by you IF THE STOVE ORDERED FROM US ISN'T PERFECTLY SATISFACTORY. WE FURNISH THIS SIX-HOLE ACME REGAL RANGE AT $17.55 TO $21.52 in the sizes and dimensions listed below. Prices do not include pipe or cooking utensils. For cooking utensils see pages 517 to 534. SEE PAGE 716 FOR OUR LIBERAL $1.00 to $5.00 C. O. D. SUBJECT TO EXAMINATION OFFER. Price list of Acme Regal Six-Hole Steel Range, without Reservoir:

Catalogue Number	Range Number	Size of Lids	Size of Oven, Inches	Size of Main Top, Inches	Size of End Shelf, Inches	Height to Main Top, Inches	Length of Fire Box for Wood, Inches	Size of Pipe to Fit Collar, Inches	Shipping Weight, Pounds	Price
22E75	8-16	No. 8	16x21x14	35x29	7½x21½	30½	26½	7	340	$17.55
22E76	8-18	No. 8	18x21x14	37x29	7½x21½	30½	26½	7	355	19.14
22E77	8-20	No. 8	20x21x14	39x29	7½x21½	30½	26½	7	360	21.27
22E78	9-18	No. 9	18x21x14	37x29	7½x21½	30½	26½	7	355	19.39
22E79	9-20	No. 9	20x21x14	39x29	7½x21½	30½	26½	7	360	21.52

Strongly crated and delivered on cars at our foundry in Newark, Ohio.

Water Fronts for Acme Regal Ranges. Price..............................$2.50

Do not mistake water fronts for water reservoirs. If extension water reservoirs are wanted, see the preceding pages showing catalogue Nos. 22E50 to 22E64.

Water fronts are used only where there is a water supply furnished with a constant pressure through pipes, which can only be obtained in towns and cities having water works, or from an elevated pressure tank. See page 716 about water fronts.

BLACK AND WHITE TWILLED COTTON WORK SHIRTS, 38c

THE KIND YOU PAY 50 CENTS FOR ELSEWHERE.

You may find work shirts quoted by others at 38 cents, but ours are FAR SUPERIOR in quality. This we guarantee. If you doubt it do this: Order our shirts at 38 cents and at the same time order the shirts others price at 38 cents and if you don't find ours very much better, MADE FROM A HEAVIER DRILL, better made, longer, cut wider across the shoulders, bigger yoke, better reinforced, more generous in every proportion, then you can return ours and get your money back. If you are in doubt send for all the shirts and send back the poorer kind; keep the best value. We can stand the comparison because we give the best value.

If by mail, postage extra, each, 15 cents.

No. 34E373 Heavy Black and White Drill, White Figures. Sizes, 14½ to 17. Price, each.........$0.38 Per dozen.......... 4.25

No. 34E374 Heavy Black Drill, Fancy Colored Stripes Sizes 14½ to 17. Price, each.........$0.38 Per dozen.......... 4.25

No. 34E378 Heavy Black and White Drill, White Stripes. Sizes, 14½ to 17, extra sizes, 17½ to 19. Price, each.........$0.38 Per dozen.......... 4.25

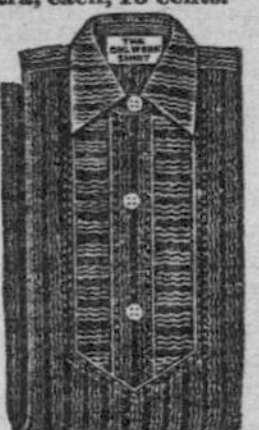

No. 34E380 Heavy Black and White Drill, Corded Front, White Stripes. Sizes, 14½ to 17. Price, each.........$0.38 Per dozen.......... 4.25

No. 34E381 Heavy Black and White Drill, Double Front and Back, White Figures. Sizes, 14½ to 17. Price, each.........$0.38 Per dozen.......... 4.25

No. 34E383 Heavy Black and White Drill, Double Front and Back, White Stripes. Sizes, 14½ to 17. Price, each.........$0.38 Per dozen.......... 4.25

COLORED COTTON WORK SHIRTS, EACH, 38 CENTS; PER DOZEN, $4.25

No. 34E358 Heavy Cheviot, Fancy Striped. Sizes, 14½ to 17. Price, each.........$0.38 Per dozen.......... 4.25

No. 34E359 Heavy Cheviot, Fancy Plaids. Sizes, 14½ to 17. Price, each.........$0.38 Per dozen.......... 4.25

No. 34E360 Heavy Cheviot, Tan Colored only, Fancy Colored Stripes. Sizes, 14½ to 17. Price, each.........$0.38 Per dozen.......... 4.25

No. 34E372 Heavy Twill, Plain Black only. Sizes, 14½ to 17. Price, each.........$0.38 Per dozen.......... 4.25

No. 34E363 Heavy Chambray, Plain Blue only. Sizes, 14½ to 17. Price, each.........$0.38 Per dozen.......... 4.25

No. 34E304 Plain Tan Colored Twill. Sizes, 14½ to 17. Price, each.........$0.38 Per dozen.......... 4.25

Cotton Work Shirts, Each, 38 Cents.

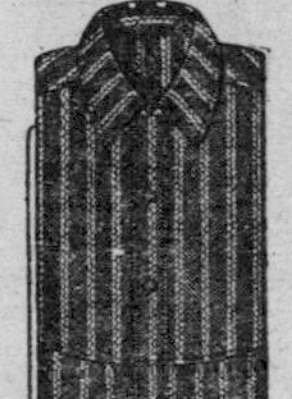

No. 34E367 Heavy Cheviot, Double Front and Back, Fancy Stripes. Sizes, 14½ to 17. Price, each.........$0.38 Per dozen.......... 4.25

No. 34E369 Heavy Cheviot, Military Style, Fancy Stripes. Sizes, 14½ to 17. Price, each.........$0.38 Per dozen.......... 4.25

EXTRA HEAVY COTTON WORK SHIRTS.

No. 34E401 Falcon Twill, Colored Stripes. Sizes, 14½ to 17. Price, each.........$0.45 Per dozen.......... 5.25

No. 34E400 Plain Black Moleskin, Fleece Lined. Sizes, 14½ to 17. Price, each.........$0.55 Per dozen.......... 6.00

No. 34E402 Buckskin Color Moleskin, Fleece Lined. Sizes, 14½ to 17. Price, each.........$0.49 Per dozen.......... 5.60

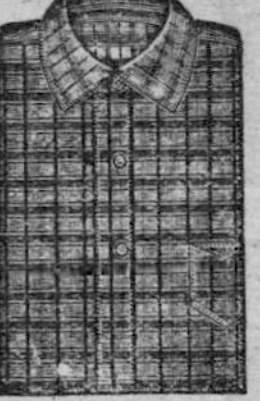

No. 34E405 Cotton Cassimere, Colored Stripes or Plaids. Sizes, 14½ to 17. Price, each.........$0.45 Per dozen.......... 5.25

Firemen's or Teamsters' Blue Cotton Shirts.

No. 34E391 Fireman's or Teamsters' Cotton Blue Twill. Sizes, 14½ to 17. Price, each.......$0.95 Per dozen.......... 11.00

WHAT SIZE DO YOU WEAR?

REMEMBER If you fail to state SIZE we cannot fill your order.

MEN'S FAST BLACK SATEEN SHIRTS.

No. 34E393 Heavy Plain Black Sateen. Sizes, 14½ to 17. Price, each.........$0.39 Per dozen.......... 4.25

No. 34E395 Our Leader, Extra Heavy Sateen. Sizes, 14½ to 17. Price, each.........$0.75 Per dozen.......... 8.50

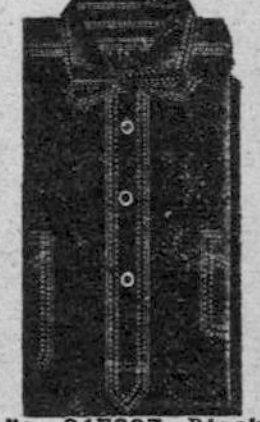

No. 34E397 Black Sateen, White Stitched. Sizes, 14½ to 17. Price, each.........$1.00 Per dozen.......... 11.75

No. 34E398 White Stitched, Fancy Black Figured Sateen. Sizes, 14½ to 17. Price, each.....$1.00 Per dozen.......... 11.75

IF BY MAIL, POSTAGE EXTRA, EACH, 15 CENTS.

Our Great 69c Leaders.

No. 34E410 Mens' Fine Silk Striped Madras Shirts. Our new button down collar; necktie to match. One pocket, and cut large in the body. The color designs in these are pleasing to those desiring quiet effects. Made in stripes, blue, pink and black, etc. Sizes, 14½, 15, 15½, 16, 16½ and 17. Price, each $0.69
Per dozen 8.00
If by mail, postage extra, each, 10c.

No. 34E412 Men's Fine Silk Striped Madras Cloth Shirts. Made with yoke back, large full body and flowir 'end tie to m' ch. One poc') on left side eautiful stripes, in which blue and white or black and white are the predominating colors. Sizes, 14½, 15, 15½, 16, 16½ and 17. Each..$0.69
Per doz. 8.00
If by mail, postage extra, each, 10c.

Men's Fancy Colored Mercerized Silk Shirts, $1.35.

No. 34E414 Men's Fancy Colored Mercerized Silk Shirts. Made of a fine quality mercerized madras cloth. Double stitched throughout with silk, pearl buttons, one pocket and soft cuffs attached. Has the appearance of an all silk shirt and will wear better. Fancy colors such as blue, brown or gray. Sizes, 14½, 15, 15½, 16, 16½ and 17.
Price, per dozen..$15.25; each..$1.35
If by mail, postage extra, each, 10c.

Men's Plain Colored "Soiesette" Shirts, $1.15.

No. 34E416 Men's Plain Colored Soiesette Shirts, made of a fine quality mercerized cotton fabric, has the appearance of an all silk shirt and will wear better. Double stitched throughout, pearl buttons, one pocket, and soft cuffs attached. Plain colors only, cream white or tan. Sizes, 14½, 15, 15½, 16, 16½ and 17. Price, each..$ 1.15
Per dozen 13.50
If by mail, postage extra, each, 10c.

Men's Plain Colored Pongee Shirts, 80 Cents.

No. 34E418 Men's Plain Colored Cotton Pongee Shirts. Double stitched throughout with silk, yoke back, faced sleeves, pearl buttons, soft cuffs attached and one pocket. Plain colors only, tan or cream white. Sizes, 14½, 15, 15½, 16, 16½ and 17. Each..$0.80
Dozen... 9.00
If by mail, postage extra, each, 10 cents.

Men's Plain White or Tan Colored Mercerized Madras Shirts, $1.45.

No. 34E420 Men's Plain Colored Mercerized Madras Shirts, made of a heavy madras cloth. Double stitched throughout with silk, yoke back, faced sleeves, pearl buttons, one pocket, and soft cuffs attached. Colors are plain tan or white. Sizes, 14½, 15, 15½, 16, 16½ and 17.
Price, ea. $1.45
Per doz. 16.50
If by mail, postage extra, each, 12c.

Men's Plain Colored Mercerized Corded Madras Shirts, $1.45.

No. 34E422 Men's Plain Colored Mercerized Silk Shirts, made of a fine quality corded madras cloth. The cords are slightly raised, running about ⅛ inch apart. Silk stitched throughout, pearl buttons, one pocket, and soft cuffs attached. Plain colors only, cream white or tan. Sizes, 14½, 15, 15½, 16, 16½ and 17.
Each..... $1.45
Per dozen $16.50
If by mail, postage extra, each, 10c.

Men's Plain Colored Silk Shirts, $1.65.

No. 34E424 Men's Fine Silk Shirts. Made from cloth about 75 per cent pure silk. The finest workmanship, double stitched throughout with silk, pearl buttons, one pocket, and soft cuffs attached. Plain colors only. Tan, cream white, blue or gray. Sizes, 14½, 15, 15½, 16, 16½ and 17. Each, $ 1.65
Per dozen 18.75
If by mail, postage extra, each, 10c.

Fancy Silk Shirts, $1.65.

No. 34E426 Men's Fine Silk Shirts. Made from cloth about 75 per cent pure silk. The finest workmanship, stitched with silk, and has every improvement known to the trade. Double stitched silk, two pockets, and soft cuffs attached. A large variety of new and stylish patterns of modest and delicate colorings. Sizes, 14½, 15, 15½, 16, 16½ and 17.
Price $1.65
If by mail, postage extra, each, 10c.

Fine Silk Shirts, $1.85.

No. 34E428 Men's Fine Silk Shirts Made from c' ' about 75 per cent pure silk. The finest workmanship, double stitched with silk, yoke back, pearl buttons, faced sleeves, one pocket, and soft cuffs attached. Plain tan colored only with small silk figures of the same color. Sizes, 14½, 15, 15½, 16, 16½ and 17. Price, each ..... $ 1.85
Per dozen 21.00
If by mail, postage extra, each, 10c.

White Mohair Shirts, $1.50.

No. 34E430 Men's Fine White Mohair Shirts, light weight, made of fine, close texture mohair, superior quality, fine soft cloth, one pocket, faced sleeves, felled seams, soft cuffs attached and pearl buttons down the front. Color, white only. Sizes, 14½, 15, 15½, 16, 16½ and 17.
Price... $1.50
If by mail, postage extra, each, 10c.

MEN'S NIGHTSHIRTS.

SPECIAL NOTE—Men's Nightshirts are not made in half sizes.

Muslin Nightshirts, 45 Cents.

No. 34E606 Men's Muslin Fancy Front Nightshirt. With collar. Sizes, 14, 15, 16, 17 and 18.
Price, each. $0.45
Per dozen.. 5.25

Very Fine Muslin Nightshirts, 75c.

No. 34E612 Men's Fancy Front Muslin Nightshirts. With collar. Sizes, 14, 15, 16, 17 and 18.
Price, each..... $0.75
Per dozen..... 9.00

Plain White Nightshirts.

No. 34E614 Men's Plain White Muslin Nightshirts. With collar. Sizes, 14, 15, 16, 17, 18 and 19.
Price 75c
If by mail, postage extra, 14 cents.

No. 34E615 Men's Extra Fine Muslin French Neck Nightshirts; fancy trimmed, without a collar. Sizes, 14, 15, 16, 17 and 18. Price.. $0.75
Per dozen 9.00
If by mail, postage extra, 14 cents.

No. 34E618 Men's Extra Fine Muslin French Neck Nightshirts; embroidered, without a collar. Sizes, 14, 15, 16, 17 and 18. Price..... 95c
If by mail, postage extra, 14 cents.

Men's French Flannelette Nightshirts.

No. 34E620 Men's Good Quality Flannelette or Domet Nightshirts. Sizes, 14, 15, 16, 17 and 18.
Price $0.39
Per dozen..... 4.25
If by mail, postage extra, each, 16 cents.

No. 34E626 Men's Extra Fine French Flannelette Cloth Nightshirts. Sizes, 14, 15, 16, 17 and 18.
Price..... 75c
If by mail, postage extra, 18 cents.

No. 34E628 Men's Extra Heavy Flannel Nightshirts. Sizes, 15, 16, 17 and 18.
Price. 95c
If by mail, postage extra, 19 cents.

Men's Blue Flannel Overshirts.

Sizes, 14½, 15, 15½, 16, 16½ and 17.

Single Breasted.

No. 34E535 Mixed 79c
No. 34E540 Pure Wool... $1.70
No. 34E541 California... $1.95

Double Breasted, with large pearl buttons.

No. 34E544 Union Flannel.. 95c
No. 34E550 All Wool $1.75
No. 34E552 California.... $1.95
No. 34E556 Fireman's $2 25

If by mail, postage extra, each, 22 cents.

Men's Colored Flannel Shirts.

Winter Weight. Sizes, 14½, 15, 15½, 16, 16½ and 17. Colors, tan, gray, brown or dark mixed.

No. 34E560 Mixed 80c
No. 34E566 Very Soft $1.65
No. 34E568 Medium Heavy. Price.. $1.75
No. 34E569 Heavy .. $1.95
No. 34E570 Very Fine $2.20
No. 34E572 Extra Fine $2.70
No. 34E573 Fancy Plaited Front. Price.... 85c
No. 34E575 Fancy Silk Embroidered Front. Price.. $1.45

If by mail, postage extra, each, 20 cents.

Men's Winter Fancy Flannel Shirts.

Sizes, 14½, 15, 15½, 16, 16½ and 17. Assorted Colors.

No. 34E577 Twill 40c
No. 34E578 Union Twill.. 60c
No. 34E580 Cassimere 95c
No. 34E581 Heavy $1.45
No. 34E582 Heavy and Fine. Price.. $1.95
No. 34E583 Without Collars. Price 59c
No. 34E584 Without Collars. Price..... $1.45
No. 34E586 Buffalo Flannel. Price.... $1.20
No. 34E587 Buffalo Flannel. Price.... $1.95

Postage extra, 19c.

Men's Heavy Jersey Overshirts, Fleece Lined.

Sizes, 14½, 15, 15½, 16, 16½ and 17. Single Breasted.

No. 34E588 Plain Blue.. 38c
No. 34E589 Plain Blue.. 55c
No. 34E591 All wool 78c

Double Breasted.

No. 34E596 Heavy..... 48c
No. 34E599 Extra Heavy, 93c

Postage extra, 25c.

Men's Heavy Corduroy Shirts.

No. 34E585 Heavy Light Gray Corduroy Shirts. Open all the way down.. $2.20

MEN'S SWEATERS

Sizes, 34 to 44 inches breast measure. Plain colors only.

No. 34E804 Three-quarters Wool. Black, navy or maroon 75c
No. 34E806 Nearly All Wool. Black, navy or maroon 95c
No. 34E808 Fine Domestic Wool. Black, navy or cardinal $1.45
No. 34E812 Fine Australian Yarn. Black, cardinal, navy or white..... $1.95
No. 34E816 Heavy Australian Wool. Black, navy, cardinal, royal or white.. $2.65
No. 34E818 Shaker All Wool Sweater. Navy or tan $3.65
No. 34E822 Heavy Shaker Worsted Hunting Sweater, with two large pockets knit on front. Tan only $3.20

If by mail, postage extra, each, 24 cents.

MEN'S CARDIGAN OR KNIT JACKETS.

Sizes, 34 to 42 inches Breast Measure. Single Breasted, Two Pockets.

No. 34E1862 Cotton worsted. Black only. Price $0.95
No. 34E1863 Wool worsted. Black or brown. Price $1.65
No. 34E1864 Fine worsted. Black or brown. Price $1.95
No. 34E1865 Very fine worsted. Black or brown. Price $2.90
No. 34E1866 Fancy knit raised stripe effect. Black only. Price..... $1.95

Double Breasted, Pearl Buttons.

No. 34E1867 Fine worsted. Black or brown. Price $1.95
No. 34E1868 Very fine. Black or brown. Price..... $2.95

If by mail, postage extra, each, 24 cents.

MEN'S STOCKINET OR JERSEY KNIT COATS.

Sizes, 36 to 44 inches Breast Measure.

Single Breasted. Price
No. 34E1870 Black only....... $1.95

Double Breasted.
No. 34E1871 Black only....... 2.20
No. 34E1872 Black only. ..... 3.[illegible]
No. 34E1873 Black only. ..... 3.[illegible]
No. 34E1874 Gray only. ..... 3.[illegible]

If by mail, postage extra, each, 38 cents.

BOYS' SHIRTS.

Boys' Laundered White Shirts.

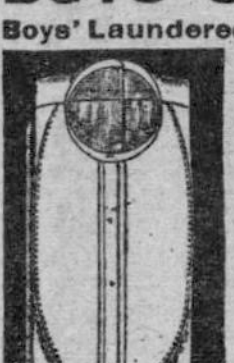

No. 34E664 An Extra Fine Quality Boys' Laundered White Shirt, made from specially selected muslin with all linen bosom. Thoroughly well made and reinforced. Fine dress finish; open back. Sizes, 12, 12½, 13, 13½ and 14.
Price........65c
If by mail, postage extra, 10 cents.

BOYS' COLORED SHIRTS.

Boys' All Colored Percale Shirts, 43c.

No. 34E670 Boys' or Youths' All Colored Percale Shirts, with medium bosom, laundered, open back only; made of good quality percale, in large variety of stripes, plaids, blue, pink, red, etc. Sizes, 12, 12½, 13, 13½ and 14. What size do you wear?
Price, each...$0.43
Per dozen... 4.75
Postage extra, 10c.

Boys' Fancy Negligee Shirts.

35c Three for $1.00. 35c

No. 34E675 Boys' Regular Negligee Shirts. In a variety of colors. We consider this the best value for the money that we have ever quoted in a boy's shirt. We advise ordering at once, as at our extremely low price of 35 cents each, or three for $1.00, they are sure to be sold out quickly. Pearl buttons, double stitched. Sizes, 12, 12½, 13, 13½ and 14. Price, each.......$0.35
3 for.......... 1.00
If by mail, postage, extra, each, 10c.

Boys' New Novelty Summer Shirts, 50 Cents.

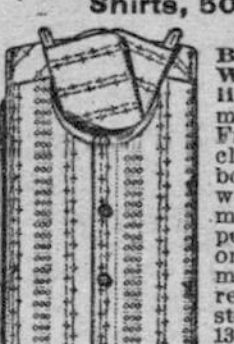

No. 34E677 Boys' Fancy Open Work Bosom Negligee Shirts. Body made of a new French percale cloth, fancy striped body, with open work bosom to match. Yoke back, pearl buttons and one pair of cuffs to match. Colors, red, blue or black stripes. Sizes, 12½, 13, 13½ and 14.
Price, each.$0.50
Per dozen.. 5.50
If by mail, postage extra, each, 10c.

Boys' Negligee Shirts, 38c.

No. 34E678 Made of French Percale, with two collars and one pair of cuffs to match. The designs are in stripes on solid background, such as blue, tan or black and white. Do not forget size. Sizes, 12, 12½, 13, 13½ and 14.
Price, each.$0.38
Per dozen.. 4.25
If by mail, postage extra, 10 cents.

Boys' Fancy Silk Bosom Negligee Shirts, 50 cents.

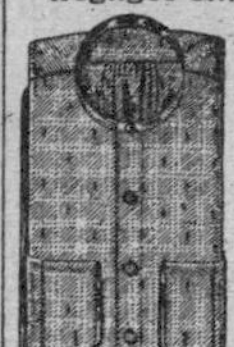

No. 34E680 Boys' Fancy Silk Bosom Shirts. The body is made of a fine percale with a fancy silk bosom to match. Solid colors such as blue, tan and gray, with contrasting colored stripes and figures. Sizes, 12½, 13, 13½ and 14.
Price, each $0.50
Per dozen.. 5.50
Postage extra, each, 10 cents.

Boys' Plain Tan Colored Pongee Shirts, 75 Cents.

No. 34E681 Boys' Negligee Style Pongee Shirts, made of a light weight cloth. Double stitched throughout, yoke back, faced sleeves, pearl buttons and soft cuffs attached. Plain tan color only. Sizes, 12½, 13, 13½, and 14.
Price, each.$0.75
Per dozen.. 8.50
Postage extra, each, 10c.

Boys' Laundered Negligee Shirts, 35 Cents.

No. 34E682 Boys' Laundered Negligee Shirts. Made from fancy colored French percale, with attached turn down collar and cuffs, white ground with colorings of black, blue, etc. Sizes, 12½, 13, 13½ and 14.
Price, ea.$0.35
Per doz... 3.90
Postage extra, each, 10 cents.

Boys' Soft or Negligee Shirts Not Starched, 38 Cents.

No. 34E684 Boys' Good quality Sateen Shirts, fast colors in light colored stripes. Yoke back, pearl buttons, shaped shoulders, extension neckband, felled seams, and double stitched. Sizes, 12, 12½, 13, 13½ and 14.
Price, each $0.38
Per dozen.... 4.25
If by mail, postage extra, each, 10 cents.

Boys' Soft Shirts, 35c.

No. 34E686 Boys' Soft Shirts, made of fine madras. Double stitched throughout, shaped shoulders and extension neckband, one pocket, large assortment of stripes of all colors. Sizes, 12½, 13, 13½ and 14.
Price, each.$0.35
Per dozen.. 3.90
If by mail, postage extra, each, 10c.

Boys' Soft Shirts, 38 Cents.

No. 34E688 Boys' Light Weight Twill Kiki Cloth Shirts. A good, strong, durable cloth that will stand wear. Pearl buttons, double stitched, one pocket, cuffs attached. Plain tan color only. Sizes, 12½, 13, 13½ and 14.
Price, each..$0.38
Per dozen.... 4.25
If by mail, postage extra, each, 10c.

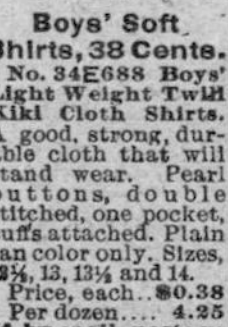

DON'T FAIL TO STATE SIZE WHEN ORDERING.

Boys' Plain Tan Colored Pongee Shirts, 75 Cents.

No. 34E690 Boys' Plain Colored Cotton Pongee Shirts. Double stitched throughout, yoke back, pearl buttons, one pocket and soft cuffs attached. Plain tan color only. Sizes, 12½, 13, 13½ and 14.
Price, per dozen, $8.50; each....75c
If by mail, postage extra, each 10c.

Boys' Flannelette Overshirts at 38 Cents.

No. 34E702 Boys' Fancy Striped Flannelette Overshirts. Soft and fine, extra well made; assorted light and medium colors, good weight. Sizes, 12, 12½, 13, 13½ and 14.
Price, each...$0.38
Per dozen ... 4.25
If by mail, postage extra, each, 7c.

Boys' Black Sateen Overshirts 38c.

No. 34E706 Boys' Fast Black Sateen Overshirts. Finely made and finished, one pocket, yoke back and double stitched. Sizes, 12½, 13, 13½ and 14.
Each.....$0.38
Per dozen 4.25
If by mail, postage extra, each, 6 cents.

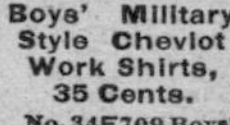

Boys' Military Style Cheviot Work Shirts, 35 Cents.

No. 34E709 Boys' Cheviot Work Shirts, made in the new military style, reinforced front, as shown in illustration. Double stitched throughout, two pockets. Fancy colored stripes. Sizes, 12½, 13, 13½ and 14.
Price, per dozen, $3.90; each....35c
If by mail, postage extra, each, 10c.

Good Value at 35 Cents.

No. 34E710 Boys' Black and White Stripes, Twilled Cotton Overshirts, made in first class manner. A good strong working shirt. Sizes, 12½, 13, 13½ and 14.
Price, each, $0.35
Per dozen.. 3.90
If by mail, postage extra, each, 10c.

Boys' Fancy Stripe Chambray Work Shirts, 35c.

No. 34E711 Boys' Chambray Work Shirts, made of a very heavy chambray with fancy colored stripes. Yoke back, extension neckband, and double stitched. Sizes, 12½, 13, 13½ and 14.
Each........$0.35
Per dozen.. 3.90
If by mail, postage extra, each, 10c.

Boys' Woven Chambray Overshirts, 35 Cents.

No. 34E712 Boys' Plain Blue Woven Chambray Overshirts. One of the best fast color cloths that will stand repeated washing and hard wear. Sizes, 12½, 13, 13½ and 14.
Each......$0.35
Per dozen 3.90
If by mail, postage extra, each 10c

Boys' Plain Tan Colored Cotton Work Shirts, 35 Cents.

No. 34E713 Boys' Twilled Cotton Work Shirts. Tan color with three rows of red stitching on front plait and pocket. Sizes, 12½, 13, 13½ and 14.
Price, each.$0.35
Per dozen.. 3.90
If by mail, postage extra, each, 10c.

BOYS' NIGHTSHIRTS.

Boys' Muslin Nightshirts.

No. 34E780 Boys' Muslin Nightshirts. Full size and length. Sizes, 12, 13 and 14.
Price 45c
If by mail, postage extra, 10 cents.

Boys' Flannelette Nightshirts.

No. 34E790 Heavy Domet Flannel. Size 12, 13 and 14. Each, $0.35
Price, per doz.. 3.90
No. 34E792 Extra Heavy Flannel. Sizes 12, 13 and 14.
Price, each.......59c
If by mail postage extra, each, 14 cents.

Boys' Flannel Shirts.

Sizes, 12½ to 14.
No. 34E720 Plain colored 75c
No. 34E721 Plain colored, fancy front..........80c
No. 34E722 Single breasted, blue flannel........75c
No. 34E726 Double breasted, blue flannel 80c
No. 34E732 Blue Jersey Shirts. Price..........37c
If by mail, postage extra, each, 15 cents.

BOYS' SWEATERS.

Plain colors only. Sizes, 24 to 34 inches.
No. 34E864 All Wool. Black, cardinal, blue or navy......75c
No. 34E865 Fine Worsted. Navy, black, royal or cardinal. Price.....95c
No. 34E866 Australian Wool. Cardinal, navy, black or white. Price, $1.45
Postage extra, each, 14 cents.

LADIES' SWEATERS.

Sizes, 32 to 40 ins. Plain colors only.
No. 34E894 All Wool. Button on shoulder. White, black, royal or scarlet........95c
No. 34E895 All Wool. Stripe weave. Button down the front. White, black, royal or scarlet.....$1.35
No. 34E896 All Worsted, zigzag weave, pearl buttons down the front. White, black, royal or scarlet. Price, $1.48
No. 34E897 Extra Fine Wool, fancy, weave, pearl buttons down the front. White, black, royal or scarlet..$1.95
If by mail, postage extra, each, 15 cents.

MEN'S LINEN COLLARS, 10 CENTS

Our collars at 10 cents are 4-ply pure linen and warranted to be such. They are equal to any collars retailing at 15 cents each.
DO NOT FAIL TO STATE SIZE FOR COLLARS.
If by mail, postage on collars extra, per dozen, 15 cents; each, 2 cents.

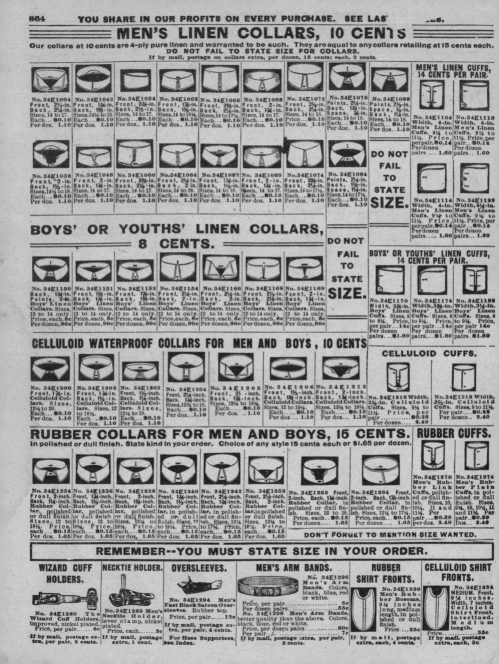

No. 34E1004 Front, 2½-in. Back, 2¼-in. Sizes, 14 to 17. Each... $0.10 Per doz. 1.10

No. 34E1042 Front, 1¾-in. Back, 1⅝-in. Sizes, 14½ to 19. Each... $0.10 Per doz. 1.10

No. 34E1054 Front, 2⅜-in. Back, 2⅜-in. Sizes, 14 to 17. Each... $0.10 Per doz.. 1.10

No. 34E1062 Front, 1⅞-in. Back, 1½-in. Sizes, 14 to 18½. Each... $0.10 Per doz.. 1.10

No. 34E1066 Front, 2⅝-in. Back, 2¼-in. Sizes, 14 to 17½. Each... $0.10 Per doz. 1.10

No. 34E1068 Front, 2-in. Back, 1¾-in. Sizes, 14 to 17. Each... $0.10 Per doz. 1.10

No. 34E1072 Front, 2½-in. Back, 2¼-in. Sizes, 14 to 18. Price... $0.10 Per doz. 1.10

No. 34E1076 Points, 2¼-in. Back, 1¾-in. Space, ¾-in. Sizes, 14 to 18. Each... $0.10 Per doz. 1.10

No. 34E1088 Points, 2½-in. Space, ½-in. Back, 1¼-in. Sizes, 14 to 18. Each... $0.10 Per doz... 1.10

No. 34E1038 Front, 2-in. Back, 1½-in. Sizes, 14½ to 18. Each... $0.10 Per doz. 1.10

No. 34E1048 Front, 2-in. Back, 1¾-in. Sizes, 14 to 17. Each... $0.10 Per doz. 1.10

No. 34E1060 Front, 2⅝-in. Back, 2½-in. Sizes, 14 to 17. Each... $0.10 Per doz. 1.10

No. 34E1064 Front, 2¼ in. Back, 2 in. Sizes, 14 to 18. Each... $0.10 Per doz. 1.10

No. 34E1067 Front, 1¾-in. Back, 1½-in. Sizes, 14 to 18. Each... $0.10 Per doz. 1.10

No. 34E1069 Front, 2-in. Back, 1¾-in. Sizes, 14 to 17. Each... $0.10 Per doz. 1.10

No. 34E1074 Front, 2⅝-in. Back, 2¼-in. Sizes, 14 to 17½. Each... $0.10 Per doz. 1.10

No. 34E1084 Points, 2¼-in. Back, 1⅛-in. Space, 1¼-in. Sizes, 14 to 17½. Each... $0.10 Per doz. 1.10

DO NOT FAIL TO STATE SIZE.

MEN'S LINEN CUFFS, 14 CENTS PER PAIR.

No. 34E1104 Width, 4-in. Men's Linen Cuffs. 9½ to 11½. Price, per pair, $0.14 Per dozen pairs ... 1.60

No. 34E1110 Width, 4-in. Men's Linen Cuffs. 9½ to 11½. Price, per pair.. $0.14 Per dozen pairs.. 1.60

No. 34E1114 Width, 4-in. Men's Linen Cuffs. 9½ to 11½. Price, per pair, $0.14 Per dozen pairs..... 1.60

No. 34E1128 Width, 4¼-in. Men's Linen Cuffs. 9½ to 11½. Price, per pair... $0.14 Per dozen pairs... 1.60

BOYS' OR YOUTHS' LINEN COLLARS, 8 CENTS.

No. 34E1150 Back, 1¾-in. Points, 2-in. Boys' Linen Collars. Sizes, 12 to 14 only. Price, each, 8c Per dozen, 90c

No. 34E1151 Front, 1⅝-in. Back, 1⅜-in. Boys' Linen Collars. Sizes. 12 to 14 only. Price, each, 8c Per dozen, 90c

No. 34E1152 Front, 1⅞-in. Back, 1⅝-in. Boys' Linen Collars. Sizes, 12 to 14 only. Price, each, 8c Per dozen, 90c

No. 34E1154 Front, 2¼-in. Back, 2-in. Boys' Linen Collars. Sizes, 12 to 14 only. Price, each, 8c Per dozen, 90c

No. 34E1166 Front, 2¼-in. Back, 2-in. Boys' Linen Collars. Sizes, 12 to 14 only. Price, each, 8c Per dozen, 90c

No. 34E1168 Front, 2½-in. Back, 2⅛-in. Boys' Linen Collars. Sizes, 12 to 14 only. Price, each, 8c Per dozen, 90c

No. 34E1169 Front, 2-in. Back, 1¾-in. Boys' Linen Collars. Sizes, 12 to 14 only. Price, each, 8c Per dozen, 90c

DO NOT FAIL TO STATE SIZE.

BOYS' OR YOUTHS' LINEN CUFFS, 14 CENTS PER PAIR.

No. 34E1170 Width, 3⅜-in. Boys' Linen Cuffs. Sizes, 8 to 9½. Price, per pair...14c Per dozen pairs. ..$1.60

No. 34E1174 Width, 3⅝-in. Boys' Linen Cuffs. Sizes, 8 to 9½. Price, per pair...14c Per dozen pairs....$1.60

No. 34E1189 Width, 3¼-in. Boys' Linen Cuffs. Sizes, 8 to 9½. Price, per pair 14c Per dozen pairs. $1.60

CELLULOID WATERPROOF COLLARS FOR MEN AND BOYS, 10 CENTS

No. 34E1200 Front, 1⅞-in. Celluloid Collars. Sizes, 12½ to 20. Each... $0.10 Per doz. 1.10

No. 34E1202 Front, 1¾-in. Back, 1½-in. Celluloid Collars. Sizes, 12 to 18½. Each ..$0.10 Per doz. 1.10

No. 34E1203 Front, 1½-inch. Back, 1¼-inch. Celluloid Collars. Sizes, 12½ to 18. Each... $0.10 Per doz. 1.10

No. 34E1204 Front, 2¼-inch. Back, 1¾-inch. Sizes, 12½ to 18. Each... $0.10 Per doz...1.10

No. 34E1205 Front, 2½-inch. Back, 1⅞-inch. Sizes, 12½ to 18½. Each..... $0.10 Per doz. ..1.10

No. 34E1206 Front, 1½-inch. Back, 1⅝-inch. Celluloid Collars. Sizes, 12 to 19½. Each..... $0.10 Per doz... 1.10

No. 34E1212 Front, 2-inch. Back, 1¾-inch. Celluloid Collars. Sizes, 13½ to 18½. Each..... $0.10 Per doz... 1.10

CELLULOID CUFFS.

No. 34E1216 Width, 3½-in. Celluloid Cuffs. Sizes, 9½ to 11½. Price, per pair ....$0.22 Per dozen.... 2.40

No. 34E1218 Width, 3½-in. Celluloid Cuffs. Sizes, 9 to 11½. Per pair... $0.22 Per dozen.. 2.40

RUBBER COLLARS FOR MEN AND BOYS, 15 CENTS.

In polished or dull finish. State kind in your order. Choice of any style 15 cents each or $1.65 per dozen.

No. 34E1234 Front, 2-inch. Back, 1¼-inch. Rubber Collar, polished or dull finish. Sizes, 12 to 18½. Price, each... $0.15 Per doz. 1.65

No. 34E1236 Front, 1¾-inch. Back, 1½-inch. Rubber Collar, polished or dull finish. Sizes, 12 to 18½. Price, each.... $0.15 Per doz. 1.65

No. 34E1238 Front, 2-inch. Back, 1⅝-inch. Rubber Collar, polished or dull finish. Sizes, 12½ to 18½. Price, each.... $0.15 Per doz. 1.65

No. 34E1240 Front, 1¾-inch. Back, 1½-inch. Rubber Collar, in polished or dull finish. Sizes, 12 to 18½. Price, each.... $0.15 Per doz. 1.65

No. 34E1242 Front, 2¼-inch. Back, 1¾-inch. Rubber Collar, in polished or dull finish. Sizes, 13¼ to 17½. Price, each.... $0.15 Per doz. 1.65

No. 34E1252 Front, 2¼-inch. Back, 2-inch. Rubber Collar, in polished or dull finish. Sizes, 13½ to 17½. Price, each.... $0.15 Per doz. 1.65

No. 34E1262 Front, 2-inch. Back, 1¾-inch. Rubber Collar, in polished or dull finish. Sizes, 12 to 18. Price, each.. $0.15 Per dozen.... 1.65

No. 34E1264 Front, 2-inch. Back, 1⅞-inch. Rubber Collar, in polished or dull finish. Sizes, 13½ to 17½. Price, each.. $0.15 Per dozen.... 1.65

RUBBER CUFFS.

No. 34E1270 Men's Rubber Link Cuffs, polished or dull finish. Sizes, 10, 10½, 11 and 11½. Per pair ....$0.30 per doz. 3.40

No. 34E1274 Men's Rubber Plain Cuffs, in polished or dull finish. Sizes, 9½, 10, 10½, 11 and 11½. Per pair.. $0.30 Doz... 3.40

DON'T FORGET TO MENTION SIZE WANTED.

REMEMBER--YOU MUST STATE SIZE IN YOUR ORDER.

WIZARD CUFF HOLDERS.

No. 34E1280 The Wizard Cuff Holders, improved, nickel plated. Price, per pair..........6c

If by mail, postage extra, per pair, 2 cents.

NECKTIE HOLDER.

No. 34E1288 Men's Necktie Holder, lever clamp, nickel plated. Price, each.......2c

If by mail, postage extra, 1 cent.

OVERSLEEVES.

No. 34E1294 Men's Fast Black Sateen Oversleeves. Rubber top. Price, per pair.......13c

If by mail, postage extra, per pair, 4 cents.

For Hose Supporters, see Index.

MEN'S ARM BANDS.

No. 34E1296 Men's Arm Bands. Colors, black, blue, red or white.
Price, per pair......................5c
Per dozen pairs......................55c

No. 34E1298 Men's Arm Bands, better quality than the above. Colors, black, blue, red or white.
Price, per dozen pairs..............80c
Per pair 7c

If by mail, postage extra, per pair, 2 cents.

RUBBER SHIRT FRONTS.

No. 34E1230 Men's Rubber Bosoms, 9¾ inches long, medium length, in polished or dull finish. Price ...35c

If by mail, postage extra, each, 4 cents.

CELLULOID SHIRT FRONTS.

No. 34E1224 MEDIUM. Front, 9¼ inches. Width, 7 inches. Celluloid Shirt Front, interlined. Medium length. Price...............35c

If by mail, postage extra, each, 3c.

MEN'S HIGH GRADE FANCY COLORED SILK NECKWEAR.

For 10c we sell you silk bows that others ask 20c for. For 19c we sell neckwear that everyone else charges 35c or more. Our 29c neckties are the same kind you pay elsewhere 45c or more.

——ALWAYS STATE COLOR YOU PREFER AND ORDER BY NUMBER.——

THE ILLUSTRATIONS SHOW THE STYLES ONLY. WE FURNISH THEM IN A BIG VARIETY OF PATTERNS AND COLORINGS. ALL THE VERY LATEST AND MOST UP TO DATE.

If by mail, postage extra, on all neckwear, each, 2 cents.

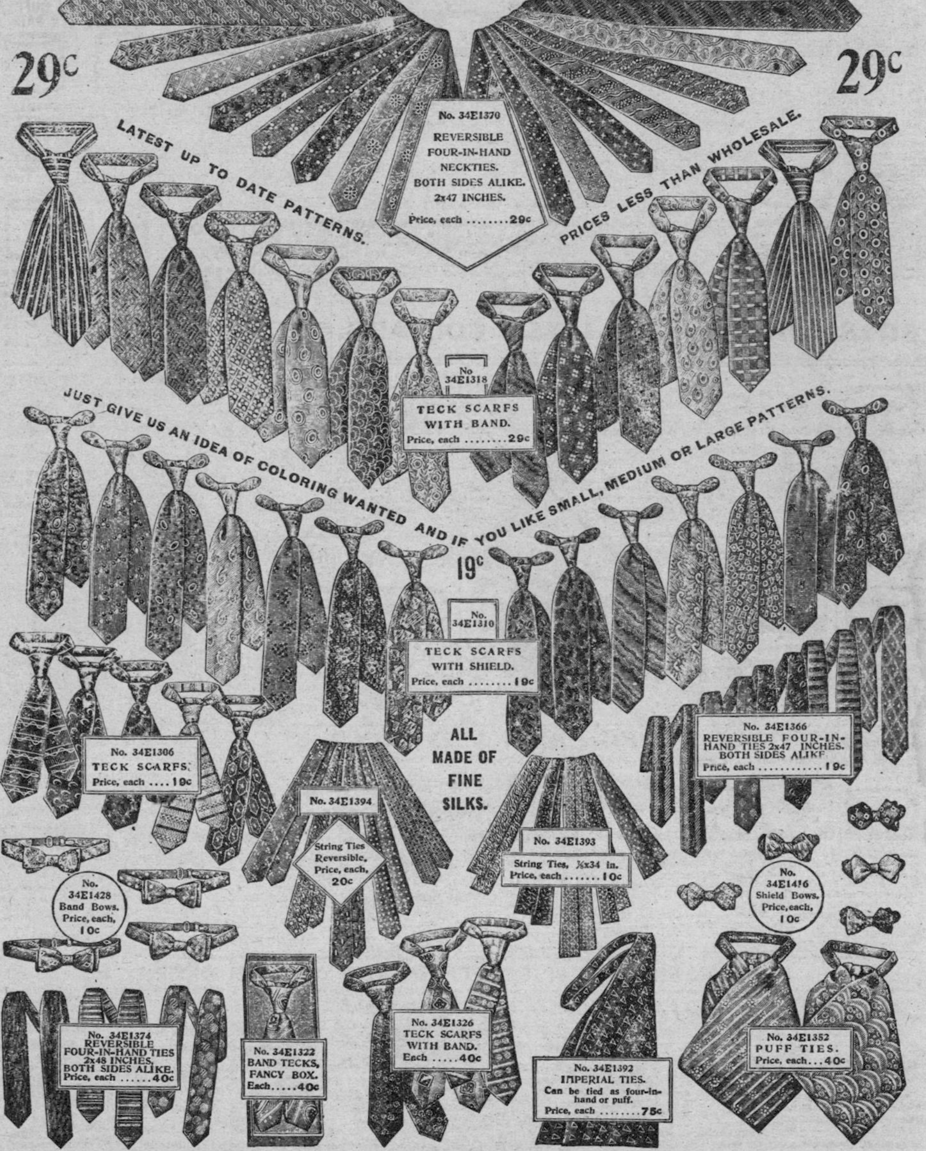

MEN'S PLAIN BLACK SILK OR SATIN NECKWEAR.

Made of the best and highest grade silk or satin, in the newest shapes, fine linings, and best grade of workmanship.
If by mail, postage extra, each, 2 cents.

Teck Ties.
Black Silk or Satin.
Different qualities according to price.

No. 34E1332 Price, 25c
No. 34E1334 Price, 40c
No. 34E1336 Price, 75c

Puff Ties.
Plain Black Silk or Satin.

No. 34E1344
Price........40c

Four-in-Hands.
Plain Black Silk or Satin.

No. 34E1376
Price........40c

Men's Silk String Ties.
Plain Black Silk.

No. 34E1396
Price..........................25c

Plain Black Silk Folded Tie.

No. 34E1398
Price..........................20c

Band Bows.
Plain Black Silk or Satin.

No. 34E1440
Price..............15c

No. 34E1444
Price..............25c

Shield Bows.
Plain Black Silk or Satin.

No. 34E1400
Price........10c

No. 34E1404
Price........19c

MEN'S COTTON SUMMER NECKWEAR.

Colored Madras Band Bows.

No. 34E1466
Price..........................5c

Colored Madras Shield Bows.

No. 34E1474
Price..........................5c

White Lawn Band Bows.

No. 34E1484
Price....................4c

No. 34E1488
Price....................10c

No. 34E1490
Price....................19c

PROFIT SHARING ARTICLES FREE.
See last 16 pages.

Embroidered White Lawn Band Bows.

No. 34E1494
Price....................8c

No. 34E1496
Price....................15c

White Lawn Shield Bows.

No. 34E1500
Price....................3c

White Lawn String Ties.

No. 34E1508 Price, per dozen....10c
No. 34E1510 Price, per dozen....15c
No. 34E1512 Price, per dozen....25c

Colored Percale String Ties.

No. 34E1518 Price, per dozen....10c
No. 34E1522 Price, per dozen....18c

Colored Madras String Ties.

No. 34E1528 Price, per dozen.....40c
No. 34E1530 Price, per dozen.....65c

No. 34E1566 Men's Plain, Colored Mercerized Madras Four-in-hands, 2¼x50 inches. Colors, white, black, navy, wine, blue, lavender or tan. Price........20c

No. 34E1570 Men's Plain, Colored Mercerized Madras Teck Ties. Colors, white, black, navy, wine, blue, lavender or tan. Price.....18c

SILK WINDSOR TIES.

Plaids.

No. 34E1574
Price......20c

Blue Polka Dots.
No. 34E1576
Price......20c

Plain colors, black, white, navy, yellow or red.

No. 34E1578
Price......20c

Children's Fancy Colored Silk Plaid Bows.

No. 34E1582
Price..............25c

BOYS' FINE SILK NECKWEAR.

Made of the finest silks, and comes in a large variety of fancy colors, in stripes, figures and Persian designs. Made a special size for boys, in the shapes as shown in illustrations.

PLEASE STATE COLOR DESIRED.

Silk Tecks.

34E1586
Price, 17c

Silk Four-in-Hands.

34E1588
Price, 17c

Silk Shield Tecks.

34E1590
Price, 19c

String Ties.
No. 34E1592
Price......10c

Silk Band Bows.
No. 34E1594
Price.....10c

Silk Shield Bows
No. 34E1598
Price......10c

ORDER BY NUMBER.

MEN'S AND BOYS' LEATHER BELTS.

Always Give Waist Measure When ordering Belts. If by mail, postage extra, each, 7 cents.

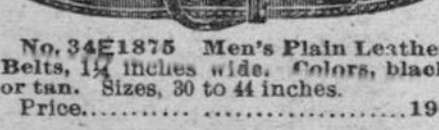

No. 34E1875 Men's Plain Leather Belts, 1½ inches wide. Colors, black or tan. Sizes, 30 to 44 inches.
Price..........................19c

No. 34E1883 Men's Extra Wide, Plain Leather Belts, 2¼ inches wide. Colors, black or tan. Sizes, 30 to 44 inches. Price..............29c

No. 34E1891 Men's Turkish Morocco Leather Belts, braided, 1½ inches wide. Color, brown only. Sizes, 30 to 42 inches. Price..................75c

No. 34E1877 Men's Grain Leather Belts, 1¼ inches wide. Large metal eyelets. Color, orange only. Sizes, 30 to 42 inches. Price..............22c

No. 34E1885 Men's Braided Imitation Morocco Leather Belts, 1¼ inches wide. Colors, black or tan. Sizes, 30 to 42 inches. Price..............35c

No. 34E1893 Men's Lined Calfskin Leather Belts, 1¼ inches wide. Colors, black or buckskin tan. Sizes, 30 to 42 inches. Price..............75c

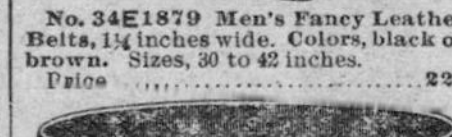

No. 34E1879 Men's Fancy Leather Belts, 1¼ inches wide. Colors, black or brown. Sizes, 30 to 42 inches.
Price..........................22c

No. 34E1887 Men's Calfskin Leather Belts, 1¼ inches wide. Colors, black or brown. Sizes, 30 to 42 inches. Price..35c

No. 34E1881 Men's English Calf Leather Belts, 1¼ inches wide. Colors, black or tan. Sizes, 30 to 42 inches.
Price..........................35c

No. 34E1889 Men's Patent Leather Belts, 1¼ inches wide. Color, black only. Sizes, 30 to 42 inches. Price..35c

BOYS' BELTS.

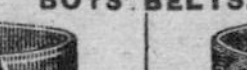

No. 34E1895 Boys' Leather Belts, 1 inch wide. Color, tan only. Sizes, 24 to 30 inches.
Price..........................15c

No. 34E1897 Boys' Grain Leather Belts, 1 inch wide. Colors, black or brown. Sizes, 24 to 30 inches.
Price..........................25c

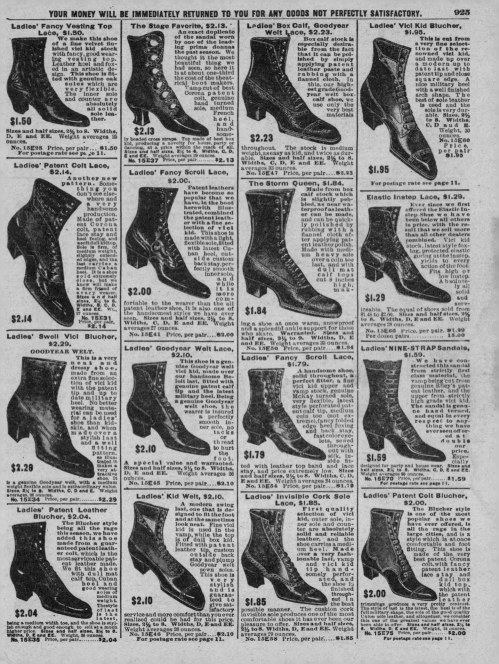

Ladies' Fancy Vesting Top Lace, $1.50.

We make this shoe of a fine velvet finished vici kid stock with fancy, good wearing vesting top. Leather heel and foxed in an artistic design. This shoe is fitted with genuine oak soles which are very flexible. The inner sole and counter are absolutely all solid sole leather.

$1.50

Sizes and half sizes, 2½ to 8. Widths, D, E and EE. Weight averages 25 ounces.

No. 15E28 Price, per pair.... $1.50

For postage rate see page 11.

Ladies' Patent Colt Lace, $2.14.

Another new pattern. Something you don't see elsewhere and a very handsome production. Made of patent Corona colt, patent lace stay and heel foxing, and a soft dull kid top. Sole is firm, of medium weight, slightly extended edges, and the last carries a medium Cuban heel. It is a shoe sold extremely close, but we know will make a firm friend of every wearer. Sizes and half sizes, 2½ to 8. Widths, B, C, D, E and EE. Wt., 27 ounces.

$2.14

No. 15E31 Price, per pair, $2.14

Ladies' Swell Vici Blucher, $2.29.

GOODYEAR WELT.

This is a very neat and dressy shoe, made from an extra fine selection of vici kid with the patent tip and up to date military heel. No better wearing material can be used for a ladies' shoe than kidskin, and when made over a stylish last and a well fitting pattern, as illustrated it makes a very attractive shoe. It is a genuine Goodyear welt, with a medium weight flexible sole and is extraordinary value. Sizes, 2½ to 8. Widths, C, D and E. Weight averages 28 ounces.

$2.29

No. 15E34 Price, per pair..........$2.29

Ladies' Patent Leather Blucher, $2.04.

The Blucher style being all the rage this season, we have added this shoe made from a guaranteed patent leather colt, which is the most serviceable patent leather made. We fit this shoe with dull mat calf top, Cuban heel and good wearing soles of medium weight. The style of last is the latest, being a medium width toe, and the shoe is stylish enough and good enough to sell at a much higher price. Sizes and half sizes, 2½ to 8. Widths, D, E and EE. Weight, 28 ounces.

$2.04

No. 15E35 Price, per pair..........$2.04

The Stage Favorite, $2.13.

An exact duplicate of the sandal worn by one of the leading prima donnas the past season. We thought it the most beautiful thing we had seen, so here it is at about one-third the cost of the theatrical boot makers. Vamp cut of best Corona patent colt, genuine hand turned sole, medium French heel, and handsomely beaded cross straps. Top made of best box kid, producing a novelty for house, party or dancing, at a price within the reach of all. Sizes and half sizes, 2½ to 8. Widths, C, D, E and EE. Weight averages 19 ounces.

$2.13

No. 15E37 Price, per pair.........$2.13

Ladies' Fancy Scroll Lace, $2.00.

Patent leathers have become so popular that we have, in the boot herewith illustrated, combined the patent leather with a fine selection of vici kid. This shoe is made with a light, flexible sole, fitted with latest Cuban heel, outside custom back stay, perfectly smooth inner sole, and while it is more comfortable to the wearer than the all patent leather shoe, it is also one of the handsomest styles we have ever seen. Sizes and half sizes, 2½ to 8. Widths, C, D, E and EE. Weight averages 27 ounces.

$2.00

No. 15E41 Price, per pair....$2.00

Ladies' Goodyear Welt Lace, $2.10.

This shoe is a genuine Goodyear welt vici kid, made over our handsome Beloit last, fitted with genuine patent calf tip and the latest military heel. Being a genuine Goodyear welt shoe, the wearer is insured a perfectly smooth inner sole, no tacks or thread to hurt the foot. A special value and warranted. Sizes and half sizes, 2½ to 8. Widths, D, E and EE. Weight averages 26 ounces.

$2.10

No. 15E45 Price, per pair....$2.10

Ladies' Kid Welt, $2.10.

A modern swing last, one that is designed to fit the foot and at the same time look neat. Fine vici kid is used in the vamp, while the top is of dull box kid. Fitted with patent leather tip, custom outside back stay and plump Goodyear welt sewn soles. This shoe is very stylish and is guaranteed to give satisfactory service and more comfort than you ever realized could be had for this price. Sizes, 2½ to 8. Widths, D, E and EE. Weight averages 26 ounces.

$2.10

No. 15E46 Price, per pair....$2.10

For postage rate see page 11.

Ladies' Box Calf, Goodyear Welt Lace, $2.23.

Box calf stock is especially desirable from the fact that it can be polished by simply applying patent leather paste and rubbing with a flannel cloth. In this, our high-est grade Goodyear welt box calf shoe, we use only the very best materials throughout. The stock is medium weight, as easy as kid, and twice as durable. Sizes and half sizes, 2½ to 8. Widths, C, D, E and EE. Weight averages 33 ounces.

$2.23

No. 15E47 Price, per pair....$2.23

The Storm Queen, $1.84.

Made from box calf stock which is slightly pebbled, as near waterproof as leather can be made, and can be quickly polished by rubbing with a flannel cloth after applying patent leather polish. Made with medium heavy sole over a coin toe last, and with dull mat calf tops cut 8 inches high, making a shoe at once warm, snowproof and a splendid ankle support for those who skate. Warranted. Sizes and half sizes, 2½ to 9. Widths, D, E and EE. Weight averages 33 ounces.

$1.84

No. 15E50 Price, per pair....$1.84

Ladies' Fancy Scroll Lace, $1.79.

A handsome shoe, solid throughout, a perfect fitter, a fine vici kid upper and vamp stock, genuine McKay turned sole, very flexible, latest style perforated patent calf tip, medium coin toe (not extreme), fancy folded edge heel foxing and back stay, fast color eyelets, sewed throughout with silk, inside fitted with leather top band and lace stay, and price extremely low. Sizes and half sizes, 2½ to 8. Widths, C, D, E and EE. Weight averages 24 ounces.

$1.79

No. 15E54 Price, per pair....$1.79

Ladies' Invisible Cork Sole Lace, $1.85.

First quality selection of vici kid, outer sole, inner sole and counter are absolutely solid and reliable leather, and the shoe carries a medium heel. Made over a very fashionable last, vamp and vici kid tip handsomely perforated, and the shoe is finished throughout in the best possible manner. The cushion cork invisible sole produces one of the most comfortable shoes it has ever been our pleasure to offer. Sizes and half sizes, 2½ to 8. Widths, D, E and EE. Weight averages 29 ounces.

$1.85

No. 15E58 Price, per pair....$1.85

Ladies' Vici Kid Blucher, $1.95.

This is cut from a very fine selection of the renowned vici kid, and made up over a modern up to date last with patent tip and close square edge. A nice military heel with a well finished arch shape. The best of sole leather is used and the sole is very durable. Sizes, 2½ to 8. Widths, C, D and E. Weight, 30 ounces.

No. 15E60 Price, per pair $1.95

$1.95

For postage rate see page 11.

Elastic Instep Lace, $1.29.

Ever since we first offered the Elastic Instep Shoe we have been below all others in price, with the result that we sell more than all other dealers combined. Vici kid stock, latest style foxing, protected elastic goring at the instep, yields to every action of the foot. Fits high or low instep. Absolutely all solid and serviceable. The equal of shoes sold from $1.48 to $2.00. Sizes and half sizes, 2½ to 8. Widths, D, E and EE. Weight averages 28 ounces.

$1.29

No. 15E66 Price, per pair. $1.29
Per dozen pairs.............. 15.00

Ladies' NINE-STRAP Sandals, $1.59.

We have constructed this sandal from strictly first class material, the vamp being cut from genuine Riley's patent leather, and the upper from strictly high grade vici kid. The sandal is genuine hand turned, and equal in every respect to anything we have ever seen offered at double our price. Especially designed for party and house wear. Sizes and half sizes, 2½ to 8. Widths, C, D, E and EE. Weight averages 20 ounces.

$1.59

No. 15E70 Price, per pair........$1.59

For postage rate see page 11.

Ladies' Patent Colt Blucher, $2.00.

The Blucher style is one of the most popular shoes we have ever offered, is all the rage in the large cities, and is a style which is at once comfortable and foot fitting. This shoe is made of the very best patent Corona colt, with fancy patent leather lace stay and dull box kid top, which with the patent leather trimmings produces a very pretty contrast. The style of last is the latest, the heel is of the full military shape, the sole of the good quality Union sole leather, and altogether, we consider this one of the greatest values we have ever been able to offer. Sizes and half sizes, 2½ to 8. Widths, D, E and EE. Weight, 24 ounces.

$2.00

No. 15E75 Price, per pair........$2.00

For postage rate see page 11.

DON'T FAIL TO GIVE SIZE AND WIDTH WHEN YOU ORDER

Ladies' Fancy Blucher, $2.06.

$2.06

A shoe built for those who prefer the soft vici kid vamp, which gives so much comfort, and still want a dressy shoe. Made with light flexible sole, patent leather tip, patent lace stay and heel foxing, dull mat calf top, latest Blucher pattern and medium Cuban heel. All the style usually found in the $3.00 kind, and a solid serviceable shoe. Sizes and half sizes, 2½ to 8. Widths, C, D, E and EE. Weight, 25 ounces.

No. 15E77 Price, per pair....$2.06

The Latest Style Common Sense Lace, $1.89.

$1.89

We make this shoe from a fine soft vici kid, over a handsome round toe common sense last and with straight perforated patent leather tip. The soles are cut from good oak sole leather flexible as a hand turn and much more durable than those usually found on a shoe at this price. The back stay is of the very latest pattern, making it absolutely ripproof, and to add all the comfort possible we fit the shoe with the very latest style low heel, which is the most comfortable made. Sizes and half sizes, 2½ to 9. Widths, D, E and EE. Weight averages 29 ounces.

No. 15E79 Price, per pair....$1.89

For postage rates see page 11.

Ladies' Patent Colt, $1.42.

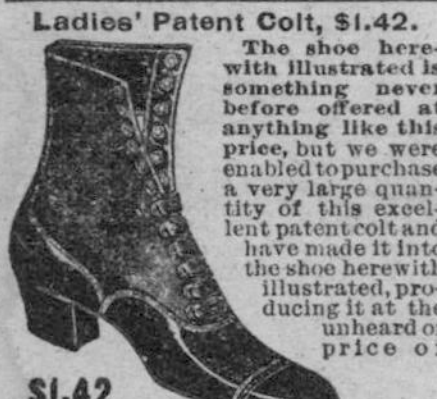

$1.42

The shoe herewith illustrated is something never before offered at anything like this price, but we were enabled to purchase a very large quantity of this excellent patent colt and have made it into the shoe herewith illustrated, producing it at the unheard of price of $1.42. The style of last is the medium round toe. The shoe is fitted with mat calf top, the latest style heel, flexible sole, custom outside back stay, and is reliable. Sizes and half sizes, 2½ to 8. Widths, D, E and EE. Weight averages 26 ounces.

No. 15E82 Price, per pair...$ 1.42
Per dozen pairs................ 16.50

For postage rate see page 11.

Ladies' Low Heeled Shoes, $1.79.

$1.79

This shoe is made from genuine vici kid, on a medium coin toe last, with medium weight sewn sole, slightly extended edges, and the low heel so comfortable and so much in demand. This is one of the best shoes we quote in the low heel style, is made in a thoroughly first class factory, absolutely all solid counter and inner sole, will give excellent satisfaction, at the same time being very dressy. Sizes and half sizes, 2½ to 7. Widths, full. Weight averages 30 ounces.

No. 15E84 Price, per pair....$1.79

Ladies' Dongola Lace, Suitable for Street Wear, $1.69.

$1.69

This shoe is made of good quality vici kid stock, made over the latest Newark last; patent tip. Outer and inner sole and counter are absolutely solid and reliable leather. The vamp is high cut in a new and handsome arched instep pattern. The heel is a medium height. It is especially desirable for street wear. Sizes, 2½ to 8. Widths, D, E and EE. Weight, 30 ounces.

No. 15E86 Price, per pair...$1.69

Ladies' Box Calf Blucher, $1.50.

$1.50

Nothing more durable, more comfortable or better looking for general wear than box calf. This shoe is made over a comfortable fitting last, medium soles, medium heels, late style blucher pattern, long outside back stay and will give splendid service. It is exceptional value. Sizes and half sizes, 2½ to 8. Widths, D, E and EE. Weight, 25 ounces.

No. 15E88 Price, per pair...$ 1.50
Per dozen pairs................ 16.50

Ladies' Vici Kid Lace, $1.50.

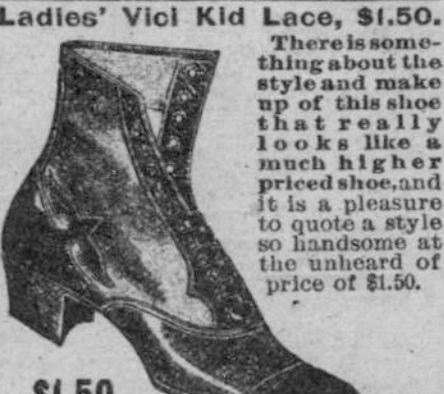

$1.50

There is something about the style and make up of this shoe that really looks like a much higher priced shoe, and it is a pleasure to quote a style so handsome at the unheard of price of $1.50.

This shoe is made over a coin toe last, fitted with patent tip, military heel and flexible soles, which are cut from a very good quality of Union leather. The vamps are of good vici kid, the top being a dull box kid, splendidly trimmed throughout. Sizes and half sizes, 2½ to 8. Widths, D, E and EE. Weight averages 25 ounces.

No. 15E91 Price, per pair...$ 1.50
Per dozen pairs................ 16.50

For postage rate see page 11.

Ladies' Leather Lined Lace, $1.63.

LEATHER LINED

$1.63

Vici kid soft finished medium sole, slightly extended, medium heel, patent leather tip and an absolutely all solid western made shoe. Perforated vamp and heel foxing, full leather lined to the toe, producing a warm, comfortable and dressy shoe unequaled for wear at a similar price. Sizes, 2½ to 8. Widths, D, E and EE. Weight, 26 oz.

No. 15E93 Price, per pair... $1.63
Per dozen pairs................ 18.00

Ladies' Patent Button, $1.50.

$1.50

This shoe is cut from a fine chrome patent stock, and the upper from a special selection of dull kid, and is of the style that ordinarily goes into a $3.00 shoe. Nice high military heel and in every way an up to date shoe. Sizes, 2½ to 8. Widths C, D and E. Weight, 30 ounces.

No. 15E94 Price, per pair...$1.50

Ladies' Patent Leather Blucher, $1.50.

$1.50

Unheard of at anything like the price, but producing just such shoes makes our enormous business possible. Good patent leather vamps and foxing, dull calf tops, medium heel, the new swing last, slightly extended soles stitched all around, and guaranteed counter and inner sole. A world beater for the price and very dressy. Sizes and half sizes, 2½ to 8. Widths, D, E and EE. Weight, 26 ozs.

No. 15E95 Price, per pair.......$ 1.50
Per dozen pairs..................... 16.50

Ladies' Kid Blucher, $1.43.

$1.43

No wholesaler or manufacturer would furnish it to you cheaper. No retailer can excel it under $2.00. Soft vici kid vamp, dull mat calf top, patent tip, medium heel and slightly extended sole. A very handsome Blucher cut shoe, foot fitting and as durable as it is handsome. Sizes and half sizes, 2½ to 8. Widths, D, E and EE. Weight, 26 ounces.

No. 15E96 Price, per pair...$ 1.43
Per dozen pairs................ 16.00

Ladies' Genuine Box Calf Leather Lined Lace, $1.55.

$1.55

This shoe is made of box calfskin; the soles are of extra quality leather and are very serviceable. The seams are stitched with a double row of stitching which is practically ripproof. Carries a full back stay, medium heel, and is lined throughout with leather. While this shoe is built with the intention of being one of the best wearing shoes that we carry, it is, at the same time, a neat appearing shoe. Sizes, 2½ to 8. Widths, D, E and EE. Average weight about 30 ounces.

No. 15E97 Price, per pair...$ 1.55
Per dozen pairs................ 16.80

Ladies' Spring Heel Lace, $1.50

$1.50

Ladies' spring heel shoes to fit well should be made over lasts made especially for spring heels, and we wish to call special attention to the fact that these, our $1.50 shoes are made over our own lasts, made by us with the one desire to produce, at a price within the reach of all, a shoe which would tread square and fit the foot in the same manner as the very best shoe made. This shoe is cut from a good plump dongola kid, bright finish and serviceable. The last is the popular coin, which is the very latest style, is round and about the width of a half dollar across the toe. The tip is of the newest design and cut from imported patent leather. The bottoms are cut from fine Union sole leather, sewed by the McKay process, very flexible and durable. Sizes, 2½ to 8. Widths, D, E and EE. Weight, 24 ounces.

No. 15E99 Price, per pair, $ 1.50
Per dozen pairs.............. 16.20

Ladies' Vici Kid Lace, $1.50.

$1.50

Made of good soft vici kid stock over a medium broad toe last, with patent leather tips, slightly perforated vamp and sensible heel. The soles are medium heavy, fair stitched edges, so that the shoe really looks like a Goodyear welt. Counter and inner sole are solid sole leather, and the shoe is built for service. Sizes and half sizes, 2½ to 8. Widths, D, E and EE. Weight, 29 ozs.

No. 15E101 Price, per pair, $ 1.50
Per dozen pairs.............. 16.20

Ladies' Kid Lace, $1.35.

$1.35

Many of our customers have been surprised to buy a shoe for so little money and still get excellent wear. The service which this shoe gives does not surprise us from the fact that we cut a good selection of chrome kid, use a splendid sole leather and have it made by shoe makers who have a reputation for turning out wear resisting shoes. The style of last is a medium coin, kid tip and lace stay, and it is a desirable shoe for the money. Sizes and half sizes, 2½ to 8. Widths, D, E and EE. Weight averages 29 ounces.

No. 15E103 Price, per pair. $ 1.35
Per dozen pairs.............. 15.00

For postage rate see page 11.

Ladies' Kid Congress Comfort Shoe, $1.56.

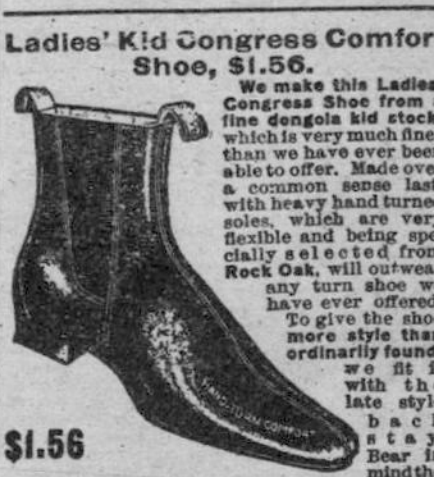

$1.56

We make this Ladies' Congress Shoe from a fine dongola kid stock, which is very much finer than we have ever been able to offer. Made over a common sense last, with heavy hand turned soles, which are very flexible and being specially selected from Rock Oak, will outwear any turn shoe we have ever offered. To give the shoe more style than ordinarily found, we fit it with the late style back stay. Bear in mind the fact that the materials are all specially selected, and quality the aim, rather than price. Extraordinary value. Sizes and half sizes, 2½ to 9. Widths, EE. Weight averages 29 ounces.

No. 15E105 Price, per pair.....$1.56
Per dozen pairs..................... 16.80

Ladies' Box Calf Lace, $1.48.

We make this shoe over the St. Louis common sense last, with low, sensible heel, absolutely solid sole leather counter and inner sole, and suitable for hard wear. The shoe is made in the same factory as our higher grade shoes, hence fits better and shows a good deal more style than is usually found in this kind of a shoe. Sizes and half sizes, 3 to 8. Full widths.

$1.48

Weight averages 28 ounces.
No. 15E107 Price, per pair.....$ 1.48
Per dozen pairs.......... 16.50

Ladies' Patent Colt Blucher, $1.50.

This is the first time we have ever been able to offer Ladies' Patent Colt Blucher made over a stylish up to date last for $1.50 per pair. This shoe is made in a factory that makes good shoes, therefore the pattern, style and fitting qualities are absolutely correct. The vamp and heel foxing are of excellent quality patent colt, the top is of dull mat calf, cut in the Blucher style which is all the rage this season. This shoe carries a medium weight slightly extended sole and a medium height Cuban heel. This shoe has the appearance of a high priced shoe and will give satisfactory wear. Sizes and half sizes, 2½ to 8. Widths, D, E and EE. Weight, averages 28 ozs.

$1.50

No. 15E110 Price, per pair......$ 1.50
Per dozen pairs.......... 16.20

Ladies' Vici Kid Lace, $1.39.

This boot is made over the fashionable Rochester last, with patent leather tip, medium weight, imitation welt sole, and suitable for dress or street wear. The stock is a velvet finished vici kid, and mat calf top. Counter and inner sole are of one piece of sole leather and the shoe is very serviceable. Sizes and half sizes, 2½ to 8. Widths, D, E and EE. Weight, 28 ounces.

$1.39

No. 15E111 Price, per pair.......$1.39
Per dozen pairs.......... 15.60

Women's Box Calf Lace, $1.50.

Made from a fine chrome box calfskin, with medium heavy sole over the coin toe last. The shoe has a genuine box calf top, and is an ideal shoe for general wear. Looks just as well as any $3.00 shoe, and as to the wear, we guarantee it. Sizes and half sizes, 2½ to 8. Widths, D, E and EE. Weight averages 38 ounces.

$1.50

No. 15E114 Price, per pair.....$ 1.50
Per dozen pairs.......... 16.80

Old Ladies' Comfort Shoe.

Made from fine vici kid, over a common sense last, with medium weight hand turned soles. We have added to it the new style back stay, which gives the shoe a better appearance, and to those who want a first class shoe we want to say that this one is far better than any we have ever offered. Each and every pair guaranteed to be the most comfortable and best fitting shoe on the market at any price, and the specially selected rock oak soles insure double the wear ordinarily found at this price. Sizes and half sizes, 2½ to 9. Widths, C, D, E and EE. Weight averages 25 ounces.

$1.56

No. 15E117 Price, per pair.....$ 1.56
Per dozen pairs.......... 16.80

Women's Patent Leather Lace, $1.23.

A style, grace of outline, and stock unheard of at anything like this price. Patent leather vamp with fancy stitched imitation tip, dongola top, long back stay and figured velvet inlaid lace stay. The shoe is fitted with Cuban heel, light imitation turned sole, reliable counter and inner sole and will give good service. Sizes and half sizes, 2½ to 8. Widths, D, E and EE. Weight, 28 ozs.

$1.23

No. 15E119 Price, per pair.....$ 1.23
Per dozen pairs.......... 14.00

Ladies' Dongola Blucher.

This Ladies' Blucher Shoe is the only one we have ever seen offered at anywhere near our price. Made from a fair selection of dongola stock, fitted with patent tip, outside back stay, and soles of good quality. Those who wish a shoe of this price will receive extraordinary value. Sizes and half sizes, 2½ to 8. Widths, D, E and EE. Weight, 28 ounces.

$1.39

No. 15E122 Price, per pair $1.39
Dozen prs. $15.60

Ladies' Patent Foxed Lace.

Ladies' vici kid lace, made with patent leather tip and heel foxing, Cuban heel, fancy perforated vamp, and light flexible sole. This shoe is fitted with guaranteed counter and inner sole, and has a style not usually found at this price. Sizes and half sizes, 2½ to 8.

$1.29

Widths, D, E and EE. Weight, 28 ozs.
No. 15E125 Price, per pair..$ 1.29
Per dozen pairs.......... 14.00

Grand Leader Lace, $1.29.

Made from a special selection of genuine dongola kid, over the beautiful Rochester round toe last with patent leather tip. We have this shoe made with solid one-piece sole leather counter and inner sole, flexible machine sewed inner sole, and we actually believe it better than those usually sold at $1.75 by the retail stores. Sizes and half sizes, 2½ to 8. Widths, D, E and EE. Weight averages 28 ounces.

$1.29

No. 15E132 Price, per pair....$ 1.29
Per dozen pairs.......... 14.00

Ladies' Everyday Shoe, $1.39.

Genuine chrome kangaroo calf. Quite plump, has a slightly pebbled surface, and will give splendid service. The shoe is made over a handsome mannish last, cut with half seamless vamp, and fitted with the latest English back stay. The soles are fairly plump in weight. Sizes and half sizes, 2½ to 8. Widths, D, E and EE. Weight averages about 32 ounces.

$1.39

No. 15E136 Price, per pair........$1.39
Per dozen pairs.......... 16.00

Ladies' Velvet Stay Kid Lace, Scroll Design, $1.29.

The design is pretty, the shoe is built by first class workmen, will give a great deal of service, as the kid stock is firm, the counter and insole reliable, and we are enabled to offer it to you at the unheard of price of $1.29. Sizes and half sizes, 2½ to 8. Widths, D, E and EE. Weight averages 23 ounces.

$1.29

No. 15E138 Price, per pair.....$ 1.29
Per dozen pairs.......... 14.00

Ladies' Heavy Kangaroo Grain, $1.15.

This shoe is made from kangaroo grain leather, sometimes quoted as kangaroo calf. It is one of the strongest leathers made, yet soft and pliable. This shoe is made for those desiring a shoe for hard, heavy wear. Heavy soles, guaranteed counter and insole, and an exceptional value for the price quoted. Sizes and half sizes, 2½ to 8. Widths, full. Weight averages 33 ounces.

ALL SOLID

$1.15

No. 15E141 Price, per pair.........$1.15
Per dozen pairs.......... 12.60

Ladies' Kangaroo Calf, Warranted, $1.49.

Kangaroo calf, we emphasize calf because it is the best wearing leather made, and so many firms quote this stock and substitute the kangaroo grain, like we use in our No. 15E141 shoe at $1.15. This shoe is built for service, best upper stock, best sole, insole and counter we can buy. Seamless pattern (no rip), standard screw fastened, and absolutely built on honor. Sizes and half sizes, 2½ to 8. Widths, full. Weight averages 32 ounces.

SEAMLESS

$1.49

No. 15E145 Price per pair......$ 1.49
Per dozen pairs.......... 16.00

Ladies' Kid Blucher, $1.09.

More stylish than any $1.50 shoe we ever saw. Rather sell you a better shoe, but this is the usual $1.25 to $1.50 kind. Genuine kid stock, firm good wearing sole, patent tip and guaranteed leather counter and insole. Sizes, 2½ to 8. Widths, full. Weight, 25 ozs.

$1.09

No. 15E157 Price, per pair....$1.09
Per dozen pairs.......... 12.00

Ladies' Kangaroo Grain Lace Shoe, $1.15.

Ladies' Kangaroo Grain, Lace. A soft stock which will turn water and wear like iron. Broad plain toe, and all solid leather, heavy sole, and made especially for hard, heavy wear. Sizes, 3 to 9; no half sizes. Full widths. Weight averages 30 ounces.

$1.15

No. 15E163 Price, per pair.....$ 1.15
Per dozen pairs.......... 12.60

Old Ladies' Vici Lace with Rubber Heels, $1.20.

This shoe is cut from a medium weight vici kid of a fine quality and made over a comfortable common sense last, with a nice, flexible sole and rubber heel, the most comfortable shoe made for those with tender feet. Sizes, 4 to 9. Full widths only. Weight, 28 ounces.

RUBBER HEEL

No. 15E166 Price, per pair.$1.20

Old Ladies' Kid Lace Shoe, $1.05.

Old Ladies' Kid Lace Shoe, cut from a good plump dongola kid, and made over a broad, common sense last, which insures the wearer solid comfort. This shoe carries a good plump sole; is a genuine hand turn and low, broad heel. Sizes, 3 to 8. Full widths. Weight averages 24 ounces.

$1.05

No. 15E167 Price, per pair.$ 1.05
Per dozen pairs.......... 12.00

Ladies' Rubber Heel Nullifiers, $1.00

Made of a nice medium weight vici kid, patent tip and with a rubber heel. This makes it a sort of a combination shoe, for either an indoor slipper or an outdoor shoe. It has an extra plump turned sole which, while giving good satisfaction as a wearer, is soft and easy to the foot. Sizes, 2½ to 8. Full widths only. Weight, 24 ounces.

RUBBER HEEL

No. 15E168 Price, per pair.$1.00

Ladies' Dongola Leader, $1.05.

We prefer to sell better shoes, but for those who buy a shoe at from $1.25 to $1.50, we add this one. Genuine dongola stock, two-piece leather inner sole, counter guaranteed to outwear the shoe and good, firm outer sole. A shoe generally retailed from $1.25 to $1.50. Sizes and half sizes, 2½ to 8. Widths, full. Weight, 28 ounces.

$1.05

No. 15E169 Price, per pair.$1.05
Per dozen pairs.......... 12.00

Ladies' Silver Gray and Patent Oxford, $1.95.

This is absolutely a most exclusive style, made with large white enameled eyelets, over a most fashionable high grade, good fitting last, and by skilled labor who make nothing but the extreme high grades of ladies' footwear. The materials used in this shoe are specially selected, and the quarters are protected on the back seam by a patent leather stay. Sizes, 2½ to 7. Widths, B, C, D and E. Weight, 20 ounces.

$1.95

No. 15E170 Price, per pair.$1.95

Ladies' Wing Tip Oxford, $2.25.

$2.25

A very stylish and up to date ladies' walking shoe, Blucher pattern, cut from a fine selection of patent coltskin and a top of dull mat calf. A genuine Goodyear welt, but made up light, yet serviceable as a summer shoe. The whole design of this shoe, including the last over which it is made, is one of our very latest productions, and we know it cannot be beaten anywhere for less than 50 cents to 75 cents per pair more than we quote it at. **Sizes, 2½ to 8. Widths, B, C, D and E.** Weight, 25 ounces.

No. 15E171 Price, per pair . $2.25

Ladies' Patent Corona Colt Blucher Oxford, $2.00.

$2.00

This shoe is cut from the very best selection of this famous patent leather—is made over a medium round toe last, with perforated tip and fitted with the latest full military heel. The Blucher pattern is one of the handsomest we have and is especially attractive when fitted with the dull mat calf top which is used in this shoe. The lace stay and heel foxing are slightly perforated, the shoe carries fast color eyelets, is genuine Goodyear welt sewn, producing flexibility and a perfectly smooth inner sole. **Sizes and half sizes, 2½ to 8. Widths, C, D, E and EE.** Weight averages 26 ounces.

No. 15E172 Price, per pair........$2.00

Ladies' Goodyear Welt Patent Leather Oxford, $1.75.

$1.75

Made from a splendid quality of patent leather, over a medium round toe last, with perforated tip and dull mat kid top. This shoe is genuine Goodyear welt sewn, carries the latest full Cuban heel, is trimmed throughout in the very best manner, and to those who wish a snappy, foot fitting, shape retaining Oxford at a medium price, we recommend it. **Sizes and half sizes, 2½ to 8. Widths, C, D, E and EE.** Weight averages 26 ounces.

No. 15E173 Price, per pair........$1.75

Gunmetal Gibson Tie, $1.95.

$1.95

This is a very swell low shoe, cut from a fine light selection of Gunmetal calfskin, and made over a handsome last with high Cuban heel, and extra well finished arch shank. This is a specially neat summer dressy low shoe, and the gunmetal calf will be very popular. **Sizes, 2½ to 7. Widths, C, D and E.** Weight, 18 ounces.

No. 15E174 Price, per pair..$1.95

Ladies' Patent Colt Oxford, $1.50.

$1.50

We know that the Oxford herewith illustrated would sell at much higher prices in retail shoe stores, but our policy is to make the price as low as possible. This Oxford is made from a good quality of genuine corona patent colt, over a handsome narrow round toe last; it is fitted with dull mat calf top, latest style heel foxing, flexible sole and serviceable. **Sizes and half sizes, 2½ to 8. Widths, C, D, E and EE.** Weight averages 25 ounces.

No. 15E175 Price, per pair.......$1.50

Ladies' Dress Oxford, Reduced to $1.50.

$1.50

Fine vici kid vamp, patent leather tip and quarter, and dull box kid top. This shoe is made with flexible hand turned sole, and being hand lasted and made in our best factory, will fit the foot and hold its shape much better than the lower priced goods usually sold in Oxfords. This shoe carries a medium concave heel, slightly perforated quarter, and as a whole is a handsome, genteel shoe for street or dress wear. **Sizes and half sizes, 2½ to 8. Widths, C, D, E and EE.** Weight averages 19 ounces.

No. 15E179 Price, per pair........$1.50

Ladies' Lizard Top Cleopatra Tie, $1.85.

$1.85

A most stylish and dressy slipper, with a genuine lizard top. Beaded vamp and very pretty worked perforations. Made of fine vici kid, over a turned last with full Cuban heel and ribbon ties. The best sandal we carry and an excellent value. **Sizes, 2½ to 8. Widths, B, C, D and E.** Weight, 16 ounces.

No. 15E180 Price, per pair...$1.85

Patent Colt Ribbon Tie, $1.53.

$1.53

Another new style, destined to be all the rage this season, is the ribbon tie herewith illustrated. Made with Corona patent colt vamp and heel foxing, fashionable Blucher pattern and dull mat calf top, fitted with large eyelets and ribbon tie. The sole is of medium weight, fair stitched, cut of first class leather, and to those wishing the latest style, a good, serviceable, foot fitting low shoe, and at an unheard of price, we recommend it. **Sizes, 2½ to 8. Widths, D, E and EE.** Weight, averages 23 ounces.

No. 15E181 Price, per pair...$1.53

Ladies' New Colonial Ties, $1.54.

$1.54

The latest style in Colonial Oxfords, is the one herewith illustrated, showing the fancy fleur de lis pattern, and a black bow at the instep. This shoe is made from a very fine selection of vici kid, light weight, flexible soles, is fitted with medium heel, and we consider it one of the most fashionable low shoes we have ever offered. **Sizes and half sizes, 2½ to 8. Widths, C, D, E and EE.** Weight averages 18 ounces.

No. 15E183 Price, per pair..$1.54

Ladies' Patent Leather Sandal Oxford, $1.39.

$1.39

We consider the Oxford herewith illustrated one of the handsomest ever offered in a medium priced shoe. Made with good patent leather vamp, bright dongola quarter, with fancy open work lace stay and medium opera heel; a beautiful shoe for dress or party wear. **Sizes and half sizes, 2½ to 8. Widths, C, D, E and EE.** Weight averages 20 ounces.

No. 15E187 Price, per pair........$1.39

Ladies' Fancy Inlaid Oxford, $1.35.

$1.35

Ladies' Genuine Dongola Oxford, made over a medium round toe last, with patent tip, and fitted with a full military heel. Soles are cut from good quality sole leather, are flexible, and the quarter is a beautiful design, showing the effect of open work, at the same time being inlaid with silver leather. This is one of the most beautiful low shoes we have ever offered, and at the price quoted, is a rare value. **Sizes and half sizes, 2½ to 8. Widths, D, E and EE.** Weight averages 19 ounces.

No. 15E193 Price, per pair...$1.35

Ladies' Turned Vici Kid Blucher, $1.52.

$1.52

Ladies' Vici Kid Blucher, fine velvet finished stock, with patent colt tip, heel foxing and lace stay, producing a handsome panel effect, the top being a dull mat calf. Fitted with fine oak hand turned sole, medium height Cuban heel, trimmed in the best manner throughout, and besides being an exclusive style, is a value you cannot duplicate elsewhere. **Sizes and half sizes, 2½ to 8. Widths, C, D and EE.** Weight averages 18 ounces.

No. 15E194 Price, per pair...$1.52

Ladies' Kid Blucher, $1.54.

$1.54

A fine mellow vici kid vamp and perforated foxing, with dull mat calf top, patent leather tip and lace stay. Fitted with half double sole, black fair stitched, producing the effect of a Goodyear welt, medium Cuban heel and solid leather throughout. Built for style and fitting qualities, with the wearing points always in mind. **Sizes and half sizes, 2½ to 8. Widths, D, E and EE.** Weight averages 22 ounces.

No. 15E211 Price, per pair...$1.54

Latest Style Button Princess, $1.29.

$1.29

We have made this front gore slipper from fine vici kid over a medium round toe last, with patent tip and medium heel. To increase the beauty of the shoe, we have made it with clasp buttons, although with the elastic goring over the instep it is not absolutely necessary that the buttons be used. **Sizes and half sizes, 2½ to 8. Widths, D, E and EE.** Weight averages 21 ounces.

No. 15E219 Price, per pair........$1.29

For postage rate, see page 11.

Ladies' Four-Strap Black Kid Beaded Sandal, $1.37.

$1.37

We have designed this slipper for those who wish a strictly up to date dress shoe, made of fine quality of kid, handsomely lined, straps and edge neatly bound. Genuine hand turned sole, making it very light weight and especially suitable for party wear. Fancy beaded jet ornament on straps. **Sizes and half sizes, 2½ to 8. Widths, C, D, E and EE.** Weight averages 21 ounces.

No. 15E221 Price, per pair...... $1.37

Ladies' Ribbon Tie Sandal, $1.38.

$1.38

Brand new in every particular is the sandal herewith illustrated. Fine vici kid, genuine hand turned sole, open work effect on vamp, which shows a handsome lace backing. Fitted with Cuban heel, large silk ribbon tie, kid stock lining and good in quality as it is original in design. **Sizes, 2½ to 8. Widths, C, D, E and EE.** Weight averages 17 ounces.

No. 15E223 Price, per pair. $1.38

Ladies' All Patent Leather Sandal, $1.28.

$1.28

While this sandal is intended for dress wear, a great many are being used for street wear this season. The soles are hand turned and very flexible military heel, reliable patent colt stock, and a value unequaled. **Sizes and half sizes, 2½ to 8. Widths, D and E.** Average weight, 21 ounces.

No. 15E225 Price, per pair. $1.28

Ladies' Ultra Stylish Strap and Bow Slipper, $1.35.

$1.35

This is one of the very latest additions to the line of ladies' fine footwear, and the regular bow of light flimsy material is replaced by one of patent leather, which will retain its shape as long as the shoe lasts. For a nice dress or party slipper this cannot be beaten, and it is made in a factory where nothing but high grade goods are produced. Turned sole and Cuban heel. **Sizes, 2½ to 8. Widths, C, D and E.** Weight averages 19 ounces.

No. 15E228 Price, per pair. $1.35

Ladies' Half Congress, $1.37.

$1.37

Desirable features of this handsome half Congress Shoe: It can be worn in the house or on the street, it can be put on or taken off quickly, no shoe laces to break, no button hook to be used. The best goring is used and the shoe is made of choice vici kid over a neat coin toe last with diamond patent leather tip. The soles are strictly hand turned. **Sizes and half sizes, 2½ to 8. Widths, C, D, E and EE.** Weight about 22 ounces.

No. 15E231 Price, per pair. $1.37

Ladies' Sandal Oxford, $1.19.

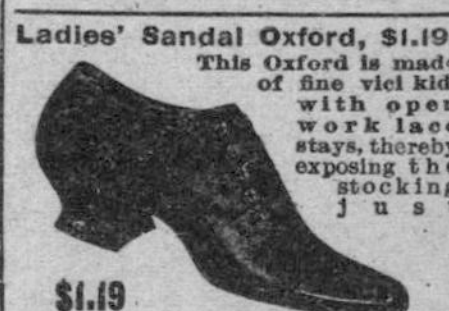

$1.19

This Oxford is made of fine vici kid, with open work lace stays, thereby exposing the stocking just enough to produce one of the daintiest effects yet seen in a summer Oxford. The soles are cut from the very best of leather and flexible. **Sizes and half sizes, 2½ to 8. Widths, D, E and EE.** Weight averages 21 ounces.

No. 15E234 Price, per pair..$1.19